BIODIVERSITY
IN THE BRAZILIAN AMAZON

BIODIVERSITY
IN THE BRAZILIAN AMAZON

BIODIVERSITY
IN THE BRAZILIAN AMAZON

ASSESSMENT AND PRIORITY ACTIONS FOR CONSERVATION,
SUSTAINABLE USE AND BENEFIT SHARING

Editors
Adalberto Veríssimo Imazon
Adriana Moreira Ipam
Donald Sawyer ISPN
Iza dos Santos GTA
Luiz Paulo Pinto CI

Associate Editor
Tony Gross

General Coordination
João Paulo Ribeiro Capobianco

Co-publishers

INSTITUTO
SOCIOAMBIENTAL
www.socioambiental.org

Estação Liberdade

Assessment and Identification of Priority Actions for the Conservation, Sustainable Use and Benefit Sharing of the Biodiversity of the Brazilian Amazon

PROBIO – Conservation and Sustainable Use of the Brazilian Biological Diversity Project

MINISTÉRIO DO MEIO AMBIENTE

BRASIL UM PAÍS DE TODOS GOVERNO FEDERAL

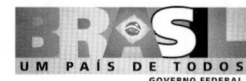

Coordinating consortium
Instituto Socioambiental – ISA (General Coordination)
João Paulo R. Capobianco, Adriana Ramos and Geraldo Andrello
Instituto do Homem e Meio Ambiente da Amazônia – Imazon
Adalberto Veríssimo and Eugênio Arima
Instituto de Pesquisa Ambiental da Amazônia – Ipam
Adriana Moreira and Paulo Moutinho
Grupo de Trabalho Amazônico – GTA
Iza dos Santos
Conservation International do Brasil
Luiz Paulo Pinto and Roberto Cavalcanti
Instituto Sociedade, População e Natureza – ISPN
Donald Sawyer and Maurício Pontes

Thematic consultants
Invertebrates: William Leslie Overal
Aquatic Biota: Ronaldo B. Barthem
Amphibians: Claudia Azevedo-Ramos and Ulisses Galatti
Reptiles: Richard C. Vogt, Gláucia Moreira and Ana Cristina de Oliveira Cordeiro Duarte
Birds: David C. Oren
Mammals: Maria Nazareth F. Da Silva, Anthony B. Rylands and James I. Patton
Plants: Bruce W. Nelson and Alexandre A. de Oliveira
Traditional Peoples: Antonio Carlos Diegues, Beto Ricardo, Geraldo Andrello, José Heder Benatti, Juliana Santilli, Manuela Carneiro da Cunha, Márcia Nunes and Mauro Almeida
Conservation Areas: Fany Ricardo, João Paulo R. Capobianco and Leandro V. Ferreira
Indigenous Lands: Fany Ricardo and Márcio Santilli
Ecological functions of forest ecosystems: Paulo Moutinho and Daniel Nepstad
Socioeconomic aspects: Adalberto Veríssimo, André Guimarães, Donald Sawyer, Eugênio Arima, Eirivelthon Lima, Marky Brito and Maurício Pontes

Advisory Committee
Inpa · Museu Paraense Emílio Goeldi · Embrapa · UFPa · Sociedade Civil Mamirauá · Fase · Aimex · CNA · CNS · Coiab · Fetagri-PA · MMA · Ibama · Sectan/PA · OEMA do Amapá · Coordenadoria de Saneamento e Meio Ambiente de Santarém · Prefeitura Municipal de Xapuri

Ministry of the Environment Team
João Paulo Ribeiro Capobianco (Biodiversity and Forestry Secretary)
Paulo Yoshio Kageyama (Director of the National Program for Biodiversity Conservation)

Conservation and Sustainable Use of the Brazilian Biological Diversity Project - Probio Team
Daniela América Suarez de Oliveira (Manager), Arles Eduardo Noga, Carlos Alberto Benfica Alvarez, Cilúlia Maria Maury, Danilo Pisani de Souza, Edileide Pereira da Silva, Gisele da Silva, Júlio César Roma, Karina Moraes Gontijo Pereira, Kátia Geórgia Costa Gonçalves, Márcia Maria Noura Paes, Marinez Lemos Costa, Rita de Cássia Cerqueira Conde, Ronaldo Brandão dos Santos, Rosângela Guilherme de Abreu and Sérgio Luiz Pessoa

Instituto Socioambiental Team
Geoprocessing Lab of the Instituto Socioambiental:
Alicia Rolla (cartographic coordination and production); Cícero Cardoso Augusto (cartographic engineer/SIG analyst); Edna Amorim dos Santos (cartographer); Rosimeire Rurico Sacó (data editor); Viviane Mazin (geographer)
Data processing: Rodolfo Marincek Neto and Alexandre Malfatti
Documentation: Ângela Galvão, Leila Maria Monteiro da Silva and Luiz Adriano dos Santos
Consultant: Marcos Rosa (geographer)
Graphic production: Vera Feitosa
Press Officers: Maura Campanili and Marco A. Gonçalves
Macapa Workshop Organization: Lia Assumpção and Marussia Whately
Administrative Support: ISA Administration Team

CEFORH Team - Centro de Formação e Desenvolvimento de Recursos Humanos do Governo do Estado do Amapá (Center for Human Resource Training and Development of the State of Amapá)(support to the Macapá Workshop):
Rita de Cássia Lima Andréa (general coordination)
Adriana Cláudia Dias Lacerda, Álvaro Ataíde Ramalho de Oliveira, Celeste Maria Barros Campos Soares, Eunice Corrêa dos Santos, Lúcio Nascimento Batista, Maria da Conceição Guedes Capiberibe, Maria do Socorro Alberto Furtado, Maria Izabel de Albuquerque Cambraia, Olanise Ferreira dos Santos, Robson Palmerin Costa and Sônia Maria da Silva Mont'Alverne Canto

Support
Banco Mundial • Comissão Européia • Centro de Formação e Desenvolvimento de Recursos Humanos do Estado do Amapá (CEFORH) • Conselho Nacional de Desenvolvimento Científico e Tecnológico (CNPq) • Financiadora de Estudos e Projetos do Ministério da Ciência e Tecnologia (Finep) • Governo do Estado do Amapá • GEF • ICCO • Norwegian Rainforest Foundation • USAid • World Wildlife Fund (WWF)

World Bank · EUROPEAN COMISSION · ICCO
CNPq Conselho Nacional de Desenvolvimento Científico e Tecnológico · USAID · GOVERNO DO AMAPÁ PARTICIPAÇÃO E CIDADANIA
FINEP FINANCIADORA DE ESTUDOS E PROJETOS MINISTÉRIO DA CIÊNCIA E TECNOLOGIA · NORWEGIAN RAINFOREST FOUNDATION · CEFORH CENTRO DE FORMAÇÃO E DESENVOLVIMENTO DE RECURSOS HUMANOS GOVERNO DO ESTADO DO AMAPÁ
GEF · WWF

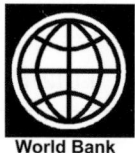

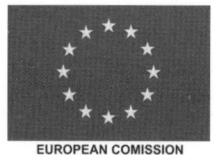

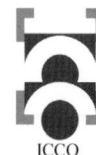

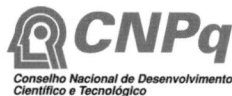

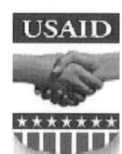

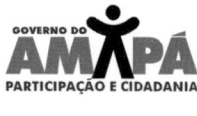

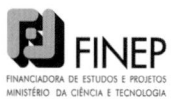

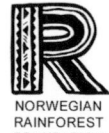

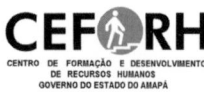

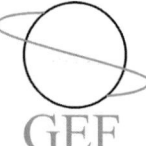

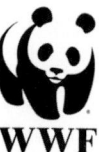

Authors

Adalberto Veríssimo   Adriana Martini   Alexandre A. de Oliveira
Ana Cristina de Oliveira Cordeiro Duarte   André Guimarães   Anthony B. Rylands
Antonio Carlos Diegues   Beto Ricardo   Bruce W. Nelson   Christopher Uhl   Claudia Azevedo-Ramos
Daniel Nepstad   David C. Oren   Donald Sawyer   Edmar Moretti   Eirivelthon Lima   Eugênio Arima
Fany Ricardo   Garo Batmanian   Geraldo Andrello   Gláucia Maciel Moreira   James L. Patton
João Paulo R. Capobianco   José Heder Benatti   José Maria Cardoso da Silva   Juliana Santilli
Júlio Falcomer   Laure Emperaire   Leandro V. Ferreira   Luís Fernando S. N. de Sá
Manuela Carneiro da Cunha   Márcia Nunes   Márcio Santilli   Maria Iolita Bampi
Maria Nazareth F. da Silva   Marky Brito   Maurício Pontes Monteiro   Mauro W. B. Almeida
Moacyr B. Arruda   Nelson de Araújo Rosa   Paulo Moutinho   Richard C. Vogt   Robert Buschbacher
Ronaldo B. Barthem   Rosa Lemos de Sá   Ulisses Galatti   William L. Overal

Photographers

Araquém Alcântara   Beto Ricardo   Michel Pellanders   Paulo Santos   Pedro Martinelli

This work is co-published by the Instituto Socioambiental and Editora Estação Liberdade.

Instituto Socioambiental (ISA)

ISA is a non-profit organization, recognized as an OSCIP (Civil Society Organization Working in the Public Interest), established on 22 April 1994 by highly qualified people with extensive experience in defending social and environmental rights.

With headquarters in São Paulo and branches in Brasília (Federal District) and São Gabriel da Cachoeira (state of Amazonas) and local offices for pilot projects, ISA's goals are to defend social property and rights, both collective and dispersed, relating to the environment, the cultural heritage, human rights and peoples' rights. ISA carries out research and studies and sets up projects and programs that promote environmental sustainability and acknowledge Brazil's cultural and biological diversity.

To learn more about ISA visit www.socioambiental.org

Board of Directors
Neide Esterci (chairperson), Enrique Svirsky (vice-chairperson), Beto Ricardo, Carlos Frederico Marés de Souza Filho, Laymert Garcia dos Santos, Márcio Santilli, Nilto Tatto, Sérgio Mauro [Sema] Santos Filho

General Secretary
Sérgio Leitão

Executive Secretary
Nilto Tatto

Coordinators
Alicia Rolla, André Villas-Bôas, Angela Galvão, Beto Ricardo, Carlos Macedo, Fany Ricardo, Márcio Santilli, Maria Inês Zanchetta, Marina Kahn, Marussia Whately and Rodolfo Marincek Neto

Institutional support
ICCO, NCA, European Commission

INSTITUTO SOCIOAMBIENTAL
www.socioambiental.org

São Paulo
Av. Higienópolis, 901
01238-001 São Paulo - SP - Brazil
tel: +55 (11) 3660-7949
fax: +55 (11) 3660-7941
isa@socioambiental.org

Brasília
SCLN 210, bloco C, sala 112
70862-530 Brasília - DF - Brazil
tel: +55 (61) 349-5114
fax: +55 (61) 274-7608
isadf@socioambiental.org

São Gabriel da Cachoeira
Rua Projetada, 70 - Centro
Caixa Postal 21
96750-000 São Gabriel da Cachoeira - AM - Brazil
tel: +55 (97) 471-2193
fax: +55 (97) 471-1156
isarionegro@uol.com.br

ACKNOWLEDGEMENTS

The co-publishers wish to reiterate their thanks to Araquém Alcântara, Pedro Martinelli, Michel Pellanders, Paulo Santos and Beto Ricardo, who kindly ceded the photos included in this work.

Editora Estação Liberdade (EEL)

Publishing Director: Angel Bojadsen
Commercial Director: Edilberto Fernando Verza

EDITORA ESTAÇÃO LIBERDADE
www.estacaoliberdade.com.br

Rua Dona Elisa, 116
01155-030 São Paulo - SP - Brazil
tel: 55 11 3661-2881
fax: 55 11 3825-4239
e-mail: editora@estacaoliberdade.com.br

General Coordination: João Paulo R. Capobianco (ISA)
Publishers: Angel Bojadsen (EEL) and Edilberto Fernando Verza (EEL)
Associate editor for the English edition: Tony Gross
Translators: Anthony Sean Cleaver, Julie Malzoni, Peter Schavier and Amabile Maria Bonturi
Design: Edilberto Fernando Verza and Pedro Barros (EEL)
Photographic lay-out: Natanael Longo de Oliveira
Desktop publishing: Pedro Barros (EEL)
Cover photos: Michel Pellanders; *back cover photo:* Pedro Martinelli (see complete photographic credits on page 534)
Maps: ISA Geoprocessing Lab
Image scanning: Labtec

Printed in Brazil by LIS Gráfica Editora

CIP-Brasil. Catalogação na Fonte
Sindicato Nacional dos Editores de Livros, RJ.

B512

    Biodiversity in the Brazilian Amazon : asssessment and priority actions for conservation, sustainable use and benefit sharing / editors, Adalberto Veríssimo... [et al.] ; associate editor, Tony Gross ; general coordination, João Paulo Ribeiro Capobianco ; [translated by Tony Gross... et al.]. – São Paulo : Estação Liberdade : Instituto Socioambiental, 2004.

    Translation of: *Biodiversidade na Amazônia brasileira*
    Includes bibliographical references
    ISBN 85-7448-093-2   (Estação Liberdade)
    ISBN 85-85994-28-2   (Instituto Socioambiental)

    1. Biodiversity conservation - Amazon River Region. 2. Conservation of natural resources - Amazon River Region. 3. Sustainable development - Amazon River Region. I. Veríssimo, Adalberto, 1965-. II. Capobianco, João Paulo Ribeiro, 1957-. III. Instituto Socioambiental.

04-1480   CDD 333.951209811
                               CDU 330.15(811)

Contents

- 12 Glossary
- 15 Introduction
- 17 Photographic essay
- 49 Conservation area categories
- 51 Thematic documents 1
  Biodiversity and the ecological functions of ecosystems
  - 52 The importance of invertebrates for the conservation of Amazonian biodiversity
    William L. Overal
  - 62 Aquatic biota
    Ronaldo B. Barthem
  - 80 Technical report on the amphibian diversity of the Brazilian Amazon
    Claudia Azevedo-Ramos and Ulisses Galatti
  - 90 Reptile biodiversity of the Amazon Forest biome and priority action for its conservation
    Richard C. Vogt, Gláucia Maciel Moreira and Ana Cristina de Oliveira Cordeiro Duarte
  - 97 The biogeography and conservation of birds in the Amazon region
    David C. Oren
  - 109 Biogeography and conservation of mammals in the Brazilian Amazon Forest
    Maria Nazareth F. da Silva, Anthony B. Rylands and James L. Patton
  - 131 Quantitative floristic inventory and conservation status of vegetation types in the Brazilian Amazon
    Bruce W. Nelson and Alexandre A. de Oliveira
  - 175 The ecological functions of forest ecosystems: implications for the conservation and use of Amazonian biodiversity
    Paulo Moutinho and Daniel Nepstad

- 181 Thematic documents 2
  Sociodiversity and traditional knowledge
  - 182 Traditional populations and environmental conservation
    Manuela Carneiro da Cunha and Mauro W. B. Almeida
  - 192 Contemporary native sociodiversity in Brazil and biodiversity in the Amazon
    Beto Ricardo
  - 203 Traditional populations and biodiversity in Amazonia: a GIS-based bibliographical survey
    Antonio Carlos Diegues, Geraldo Andrello and Márcia Nunes
  - 224 Elements for a discussion on the conservation of agrobiodiversity: the example of manioc (*Manihot esculenta* Crantz) in the Brazilian Amazon
    Laure Emperaire
  - 234 Biodiversity and traditional knowledge
    Juliana Santilli

245 Thematic documents 3
Conservation areas and indigenous lands

- 246 Conservation areas in Legal Amazonia
  Fany Ricardo and João Paulo R. Capobianco
- 251 Indigenous lands in Legal Amazonia
  Fany Ricardo
- 259 Overlapping federal and state conservation areas, indigenous lands, military areas, and prospecting reserves in Legal Amazonia
  Fany Ricardo
- 262 Representativity of conservation areas and indigenous lands in relation to the vegetation types of Legal Amazonia
  João Paulo R. Capobianco
- 266 Identifying priority areas for biodiversity conservation by means of the representativity of conservation areas and vegetation types in the ecoregions of Brazilian Amazonia
  Leandro V. Ferreira, Rosa Lemos de Sá, Robert Buschbacher, Garo Batmanian, José Maria Cardoso da Silva, Moacyr B. Arruda, Edmar Moretti, Luís Fernando S. N. de Sá, Júlio Falcomer and Maria Iolita Bampi
- 285 Incidence of mining applications and titles in federal and state conservation areas in Legal Amazonia
  Fany Ricardo
- 288 Indigenous natural resources reserves
  Márcio Santilli
- 291 Forms of access to land and the conservation of the Amazon forest: a legal analysis of the regularization of the lands of quilombolas and rubber tappers
  José Heder Benatti
- 298 Human presence in conservation areas: a scientific, legal or political impasse?
  José Heder Benatti

305 Thematic documents 4
Socioeconomic and anthropogenic pressures

- 306 An analysis of the demography, socioeconomics and anthropogenic pressures in the Legal Amazon region
  Maurício Pontes Monteiro and Donald Sawyer
- 318 Amazon integration and development corridors – projects and plans
  Marky Brito
- 324 Overview of land use in Amazonia: timber, agriculture and livestock
  Adalberto Veríssimo, Eugênio Arima and Eirivelthon Lima
- 335 Tree species potentially threatened by logging activities in Amazonia
  Adriana Martini, Nelson de Araújo Rosa and Christopher Uhl
- 345 Business opportunities in Amazonia: sustainable alternatives
  André Guimarães

349 Brazilian Legal Amazonia
Thematic Maps

- 350 Base map
- 352 Hydrographic system
- 354 Vegetation
- 356 Ecoregions

- 358 Special use areas
- 360 Soybean, maize and rice cultivation; total population; livestock; and population density
- 362 Mining licenses
- 364 Anthropogenic pressure index
- 366 Disturbed areas
- 368 Deforestation patterns
- 370 Water balance
- 372 Fire risk
- 374 Satellite monitoring of forest fires
- 376 Land settlement projects
- 378 Logging activity and development corridors
- 380 Traditional knowledge

383 Macapá Workshop
Priority areas for the biodiversity of the Brazilian Amazon

- 384 Methodology
- 387 Overall assessment of the results
- 404 Keys to priority area levels
- 405 Priority areas for conservation, sustainable use and benefit sharing by region of the Brazilian Amazon
  - 410 *Araguaia / Tocantins / Maranhão region*
  - 414 *Solimões / Amazonas floodplains region*
  - 418 *Upper Xingu / Tapajós / Rondônia / Mato Grosso region*
  - 424 *Guiana shield region*
  - 427 *Lower Xingu / Tajapós / Madeira region*
  - 433 *Rio Negro / Rio Branco region*
  - 438 *Juruá / Purus / Acre region*
- 443 Priority areas for conservation, sustainable use and benefit sharing by thematic working group
  - 450 *Birds*
  - 460 *Aquatic biota*
  - 465 *Mammals*
  - 470 *Invertebrates*
  - 473 *Plants*
  - 479 *Reptiles and amphibians*
  - 485 *Conservation areas*
  - 491 *Environmental goods and services*
  - 496 *New economic opportunities*
  - 505 *Tratidional populations and indigenous peoples*
  - 509 *Anthropogenic pressure*
  - 516 *Development corridors*
- 520 General recommendations
  - 520 *WG1 - Strict protection conservation areas*
  - 521 *WG2 - Economic use of altered areas*
  - 522 *WG3 - Indigenous lands*
  - 523 *WG4 - Sustainable use conservation areas and traditional populations*
  - 523 *WG5 - Research on biological and cultural diversity*
  - 525 *WG6 - Anthropogenic pressures and development corridors*
- 527 Bibliography
- 529 List of participants in the Macapá Workshop

534 Photographic credits

Glossary

Glossary of acronyms and terms

ABA	Associação Brasileira de Antropologia (Brazilian Anthropological Association)
ACIRNE	Associação das Comunidades Indígenas do Rio Negro (Association of Indigenous Communities of the Rio Negro)
Agrotec	Centro de Tecnologia Agro-ecológica de Pequenos Agricultores (Center for Agro-environmental Technology for Small Farmers)
Ahimor	Administração das Hidrovias da Amazônia Oriental (Eastern Amazonia Waterways Management Board)
Ahitar	Administração da Hidrovia Tocantins-Araguaia (Tocantins-Araguaia Waterway Management Board)
aipim	see macaxeira
Amazônia Legal	see Legal Amazonia
AMNH	American Museum of Natural History, New York
ANEEL	Agência Nacional de Energia Elétrica (National Electricity Agency)
APA	Área de Proteção Ambiental (Environmental Protection Area)
ARIE	Área de Relevante Interesse Ecológico (Area of special ecological importance)
área protegida	Protected area
Arqmo	Associação das Comunidades Remanescentes de Quilombo do Município de Oriximiná (Association of Communities Descendents of Quilombos of the Municipality of Oriximiná, Pará)
babaçu	The babassu palm (*Orbignya martiana* and *O. oleifera*)
babaçueiro(a)	Babaçu nut collector
BASA	Banco da Amazônia S.A. (Bank of Amazonia)
BNDES	Banco Nacional de Desenvolvimento Econômico e Social (National Bank for Economic and Social Development)
BRG	Bureau des Ressources Génétiques (Genetic Resources Board), France
caatinga	The semi-arid region of northeastern Brazil
caboclo	Of mixed European and indigenous descent
CAF	Corporación Andina de Fomento (Andean development Corporation)
caiçara	Member of a traditional coastal community of Rio de Janeiro, São Paulo and Paraná states
campina	Amazon grasslands
campinarana	Amazon grasslands on sandy soil
capoeira	Secondary growth on previously cleared land
castanheira (do Pará)	Brazil nut tree (*Bertholletia excelsa*)
castanheiro(a)	Brazil nut collector
cativo	Captive, in thrall (i.e. seringueiro subject to a boss), cf. liberto
CBD	Convention on Biological Diversity
CBH	Circumference at breast height
CEAPAC	Centro de Apoio aos Projetos de Ação Comunitária (Center for Support to Community Action Projects)
Cedenpa	Centro de Defesa e Estudo do Negro no Pará (Center for the Study and Defense of Black People in Pará)
CEDI	Centro Ecumênico de Documentação e Informação (Ecumenical Documentation and Information Center)
CENAQUA	Centro Nacional de Quelônios da Amazônia (National Amazonian Chelonia Center)
CEPLAC	Comissão Executiva do Plano da Lavoura Cacaueira (Cocoa Cultivation Planning Agency)
cerrado	Savanna
CGPG	Conselho de Gestão do Patrimônio Genético (Council for the Management of Genetic Assets)
CI	Conservation International
CIMI	Conselho Indigenista Missionário (Indian Missionary Council)
CNB	Conselho Nacional da Borracha (National Rubber Council)
CNBB	Conferência Nacional dos Bispos do Brasil (National Conference of Bishops of Brazil)
CNPMF	Centro Nacional de Pesquia de Mandioca e Fruticultura da Embrapa em Cruz das Almas (Bahia) (Embrapa National Center for Research on Manioc and Fruit Crops in Cruz das Almas, Bahia)
CNPq	Conselho Nacional de Desenvolvimento Científico e Tecnológico (National Council for Scientific and Technological Development)
CNPT	Centro Nacional de Desenvolvimento Sustentado das Populações Tradicionais (National Center for the Sustainable Development of Traditional Populations)
CNRS	Centre national de la recherche scientifique (National Center for Scientific Research), France
CNS	Conselho Nacional dos Seringueiros (National Council of Rubber-Tappers)
COBRAPHI	Comissão Brasileira para Programas Hidrológicas Internacionais (Brazilian Committee for International Hydrological Programs)
COICA	Confederação das Organizações Indígenas da Bacia Amazônica (Confederation of Indigenous Organizations of the Amazon Basin)
CONAGE	Coordenação Nacional de Geólogos (National Association of Geologists)
CONAIE	Confederación de Nacionalidades Indígenas del Ecuador (Confederation of Indigenous Nations of Ecuador)
CONAMA	Conselho Nacional do Meio Ambiente (National Environmental Council)
CONTAG	Confederação Nacional dos Trabalhadores na Agricultura (National Confederation of Agricultural Workers)
CPAA	Centro de Pesquisa Agroflorestal da Amazonia/Embrapa (Embrapa Agroforestry Research Center of Amazonia, Manaus)
CPATU	Centro de Pesquisa Agropecuária do Trópico Humido/Embrapa (Embrapa Agricultural Research Center of the Humid Tropics)
CPRM	Companhia de Pesquisas de Recursos Minerais (Company for Mineral Resource Research)
CPT	Pastoral Land Commission (of the CNBB)
CRI	Cartório de Registro de Imóveis (local land registry)
CTA	Centro dos Trabalhadores da Amazônia (Amazon Workers Center)
DCA	Decorrelated Correspondence Analysis
DBH	Diameter at breast height
DER	Departamento de Estradas de Rodagem (State Highway Department)
Direct use conservation area	Under the SNUC legislation, conservation areas whose purpose is to harmonize nature conservation and the sustainable use of elements of their natural resources (i.e. sustainable use areas)
DNAEE	Departamento Nacional de Águas e Energia Elétrica (National Water and Electricity Agency) abolished in 1996 with the creation of ANEEL
DNER	Departamento Nacional de Estradas de Rodagem (National Highways Agency)
DNPM	Departamento Nacional de Produção Mineral (National Mineral Production Agency)
DOCEGEO	Rio Doce Geologia e Mineração (Rio Doce Geology and Mining Company)
DOU	Diário Oficial da União (official federal gazette)
Ecoporé	Ação Ecológica Vale do Guaporé (Guaporé Valley Ecological Action)
Ecuarunari	Confederación de Pueblos de la Nacionalidad Kichwa del Ecuador (Federation of Peoples of the Quichua Nationality of Ecuador)
Edelca	Electrificación del Caroni C. A. (Caroni Electricity Company of Venezuela)
EIA	Environmental Impact Assessment
Eletrobrás	Centrais Elétricas Brasileiras (National Electricity Board of Brazil)

Eletronorte	Centrais Elétricas do Norte do Brasil (Northern Brazil Electricity Board)	**INPE**	Instituto Nacional de Pesquisas Espaciais (National Space Research Institute)
EMBRAPA	Empresa Brasileira de Pesquisa Agropecuária (Brazilian Agricultural Research Company)	**IPAM**	Instituto de Pesquisa Ambiental da Amazônia (Institute for Amazonian Environmental Research, Belém)
empate	'Obstruction', tactic used by seringueiros to prevent clearing of forest	**IPEA**	Instituto de Pesquisa Econômica Aplicada (Institute for Applied Economic Research)
Esalq	Escola Superior de Agronomia Luiz de Queiroz (Luiz de Queiroz Advanced School of Agronomy), São Paulo	**IPHAN**	Instituto do Patrimônio Histórico e Artístico Nacional (National Historical and Artistic Heritage Institute)
ESEC	Estação Ecológica (Ecological Station)	**IRD**	L'Institut de recherche pour le développement (Institute of Research for Development), France
Estrada	Circuit of rubber trees tapped by a seringueiro		
FAO	Food and Agriculture Organization of the United Nations	**ISA**	Instituto Socioambiental
FAPESP	Fundação de Amparo à Pesquisa do Estado de São Paulo (State of São Paulo Research Foundation)	**ISPN**	Instituto Sociedade, População e Natureza
		Iterpa	Instituto de Terras do Pará (State Land Agency of Pará)
fazenda	Farm, ranch, large estate	**IUCN**	World Conservation Union
Fema	Fundação Estadual do Meio Ambiente (State Environment Foundation)	**jangadeiro**	Member of a raft fishing community of northeastern Brazil
Fenocin	Federación Nacional de Organizaciones Campesinas, Indígenas y Negras del Ecuador (National Federation of Peasant, Indigenous and Black Organizations of Ecuador)	**Legal Amazonia**	*see below*
		liberto	Free, seringueiro working on his/her own account, cf. 'cativo'
		LPG	Liquefied petroleum gas
Ferronorte	Ferrovias Norte Brasil SA (North Brazil Railroad)	**macaxeira**	'Sweet' or 'tame' manioc, i.e. non-poisonous variety that can be eaten without processing to remove toxins
Fetagri	Federação dos Trabalhadores na Agricultura no Estado do Pará (Federation of Agricultural Workers in the State of Pará)	**mandioca**	Manioc, cassava (Manihot esculenta Crantz)
FFT	Fundação Floresta Tropical (Tropical Forest Foundation)	**MEB**	Movimento de Educação de Base (Grassroots Education Movement)
FIV	Family Importance Value	**MMA**	Ministério do Meio Ambiente (Ministry of the Environment)
FJP	Fundação João Pinheiro (João Pinheiro Foundation)	**MN**	Museu Nacional (National Museum, Rio de Janeiro)
FLONA	Floresta Nacional (National Forest)	**MPEG**	Museu Paraense Emílio Goeldi (Emílio Goeldi Museum of Pará, Belém)
FMNH	Field Museum of Natural History, Chicago		
FNO	Fundo Constitucional de Financiamento do Norte (Constitutional Financial Fund for the North)	**MPF**	Ministério Público Federal (Federal Prosecution Service)
		MPO	Ministério do Planejamento e Orçamento (Ministry of Planning and Budgets)
Foirn	Federação das Organizações Indígenas do Rio Negro (Federation of Indigenous Organizations of the Rio Negro)	**MST**	Movimento dos Trabalhadores Rurais Sem Terra (Movement of Landless Rural Workers)
Funai	Fundação Nacional do Índio (Federal Indian Affairs Agency)	**MZUSP**	Museu Zoológico da Universidade de São Paulo (Zoological Museum of the University of São Paulo)
GIS	Geographic Information System		
GPD	Grupo de Desenvolvimento e Preservação (Development and Conservation Group)	**NAEA**	Núcleo de Alto Estudos da Amazônia (Institute of Advanced Studies of Amazonia, Belém)
GTA	Grupo de Trabalho Amazônico (Amazon Working Group)	**Nafta**	North American Free Trade Agreement
HDI	Human Development Index	**NGO**	Non-governmental organization
IAN	Instituto Agronômico do Norte (Northern Institute of Agronomy)	**Nupaub**	Núcleo de Apoio à Pesquisa sobre Populações Humanas e Áreas Úmidas Brasileiras - USP (Support Unit for Research on Human Populations and Wetlands in Brazil, University of São Paulo)
IBAMA	Instituto Brasileira do Meio Ambiente e dos Recursos Naturais Renováveis (Brazilian Institute for the Environment and Renewable Natural Resources)		
		ODA	Overseas Development Administration, UK (now Department for International Development)
IBDF	Instituto Brasileiro de Desenvolvimento Florestal (Brazilian Institute for Forestry Development). Merged with other federal agencies in 1989 to form IBAMA	**OIT**	*see* ILO
		Paraná	Secondary channel (of river)
IBGE	Instituto Brasileiro de Geografia e Estatística (Brazilian Geographical and Statistical Institute)	**PARNA**	Parque Nacional (National Park)
		PDBFF	Projeto Dinâmico Biológica de Fragmentos Florestais (Biological Dynamics of Forest Fragments Project)
igapó	Forests seasonally flooded by black water		
igarapé	Stream, channel	**PGR**	Procuradoria-Geral da República (Office of the Federal Prosecutor-General)
ILO	International Labour Organization (United Nations)		
Imazon	Instituto do Homem e Meio Ambiente da Amazônia	**Planafloro**	Plano Agropecuário e Florestal de Rondônia (Rondonia Natural Resource Management Project)
INCRA	Instituto Nacional de Colonização e Reforma Agrária (National Institute for Colonization and Agrarian Reform)		
		PNMA	Política Nacional do Meio Ambiente (National Environment Policy)
Indecopi	Instituto Nacional de la Defensa de la Competencia y de la Protección de la Propriedad Intelectual (National Institute for the Defense of Competition and Protection of Intellectual Property, Peru)	**PNRH**	Política Nacional de Recursos Hídricos (National Water Resources Policy)
		PNUD	Programa das Nações Unidas para o Desenvolvimento (United Nations Development Programme, UNDP)
Indigenista	A FUNAI or NGO specialist working directly with indigenous communities	**PPG-7**	Programa Piloto para a Proteção das Florestas Tropicais do Brasil (Pilot Program to Conserve the Brazilian Rain Forests) (of the G-7 countries)
Indirect use conservation area	Under the SNUC legislation, conservation areas whose purpose is the protection of nature and where only indirect use of their natural resources is allowed (i.e. strict protection areas)		
		praieiro	Member of a seashore community of the coast of Pará
INPA	Instituto Nacional de Pesquisas da Amazônia (National Amazon Research Institute, Manaus)		

Probem	Programa Brasileiro de Ecologia Molecular para o Uso Sustentável da Biodiversidade da Amazônia (Brazilian Program of Molecular Ecology for the Sustainable Use of the Biodiversity of Amazonia)	**SNUC**	Sistema Nacional de Unidades de Conservação (National Conservation Area System)
		sororoca	*Stromanthe stromanthoides* (Marantaceae)
		SPI	Serviço de Proteção aos Índios (Indian Protection Service)
Probio	Projeto de Conservação e Utilização da Diversidade Biológica Brasileira (Conservation and Sustainable Use of Brazilian Biological Diversity Project)	**SPU**	Serviço de Patrimônio da União (the registry of federal assets)
		SPVEA	Superintendência do Plano de Valorização Econômica da Amazônia (Agency for the Amazon Economic Growth Plan)
Prodeagro	Projeto de Desenvolvimento Agroambiental do Estado de Mato Grosso (Mato Grosso Agro-Environmental Development Project)	**STR**	Sindicato de Trabalhadores Rurais (Rural Workers Union)
		SUDAM	Superintendência do Desenvolvimento da Amazônia (Amazon Development Agency)
Prodes	Projeto de Estimativa de Deflorestamento da Amazônia (Estimating Deforestation in Amazonia Project), INPE	**SUDEPE**	Superintendência do Desenvolvimento da Pesca (Federal fisheries development agency incorporated in 1989 into Ibama (qv.))
Pronabio	Programa Nacional da Diversidade Biológica (National Program for Biological Diversity)	**SUDHEVEA**	Superintendência do Desenvolvimento da Borracha (Rubber Development Board)
PSDB	Partido da Social Democracia Brasileira (Brazilian Social Democracy Party)	**tepuí**	Inselberg, isolated mountain top
		terra firme	Dense non-alluvial rain forest (literally 'firm ground').
PT	Partido dos Trabalhadores (Workers' Party)	**TFF**	Tropical Forest Foundation
quilombo	Community originating from a settlement of fugitive slaves established prior to the abolition of slavery in 1888	**TI**	Terra Indígena (Indigenous Land)
		TRIPs	Agreement on Trade-Related Intellectual Property Rights (of the World Trade Organization)
quilombola	Member of a quilombo	**UDR**	União Democrática Ruralista (national organization of landowners and agribusiness interests)
RadamBrasil	Projeto Radar da Amazônia (Amazonian Radar Project): survey and mapping of natural resources in Brazil - soil, geology, geomorphology, vegetation and land use - by use of radar. Project carried out by the Brazilian government in the 1970s and 1980s. Also known as Projeto Radam.	**UFPA**	Universidade Federal do Pará (Federal University of Pará)
		UFRGS	Universidade Federal do Rio Grande do Sul (Federal University of Rio Grande do Sul)
		UNDP	United Nations Development Programme
		UNEP	United Nations Environment Programme
REBIO	Reserva Biológica (Biological Reserve)	**UNI**	União das Nações Indígenas (Union of Indigenous Nations)
RESEX	Reserva Extrativista (Extractive Reserve)	**Unicamp**	Universidade Estadual de Campinas (State University of Campinas)
Reserva garimpeira	Prospecting reserve	**UC**	Unidade de Conservação (Conservation area)
ribeirinho	Member of a traditional riparian community, especially in Amazonia	**USAID**	United States Agency for International Development
		USNH	National Museum of Natural History, Smithsonian Institute, Washington DC
RIRN	Reserva Indígena de Recursos Naturais (Indigenous Natural Resources Reserve)	**USP**	Universidade de São Paulo (University of São Paulo)
Sagri	Secretaria de Agricultura (Department of Agriculture of the State of Pará)	**várzea**	Floodplain, seasonally inundated by muddy water
		WHRC	Woods Hole Research Center
SBPC	Sociedade Brasileira pelo Progresso da Ciência (Brazilian Society for the Advancement of Science)	**WWF**	World Wide Fund for Nature
		ZFM	Zona Franca de Manaus (Manaus Free Zone)
Sectam	Secretaria de Ciência, Tecnologia, e Meio Ambiente do Estado do Pará (Department of Science, Technology, and the Environment of the State of Pará)		
Secult	Secretaria Executiva de Cultura (Department of Culture of the State of Pará)		
SEINF	Secretaria de Estado de Infra-Estrutura (Department of Infrastructure of the State of Amazonas)		
seringal	Rubber estate		
seringueira	Rubber tree (*Hevea brasiliensis*)		
seringueiro(a)	Rubber tapper		
sitiante	Owner of a 'sítio' (small farm or ranch)		
SIV	Specific Importance Value		

Amazônia Legal (Legal Amazonia) covers the states of Acre, Amazonas, Amapá, Mato Grosso, Pará, Rondônia, Roraima, together with Maranhão west of the 44th meridian and Tocantins north of the 13th parallel (virtually the entire state). (A tiny portion of the state of Goiás north of the 13th parallel is also technically located in Legal Amazonia).

Abbreviations of Brazilian states

AC	**Acre**	PB	Paraiba
AL	Alagoas	PE	Pernambuco
AM	**Amazonas**	PI	Piauí
AP	**Amapá**	PR	Paraná
BA	Bahia	RJ	Rio de Janeiro
CE	Ceará	RN	Rio Grande do Norte
DF	Distrito Federal	**RO**	**Rondônia**
ES	Espírito Santo	**RR**	**Roraima**
GO	Goiás	RS	Rio Grande do Sul
MA	**Maranhão**	SC	Santa Catarina
MG	Minas Gerais	SE	Sergipe
MS	Mato Grosso do Sul	SP	São Paulo
MT	**Mato Grosso**	**TO**	**Tocantins**
PA	**Pará**		

States in bold are located within Legal Amazonia

Introduction

João Paulo R. Capobianco
General project coordinator

Brazil currently possesses around 3.6 million square kilometers of forests, making it number three, behind Russia and Canada, in the list of countries with the greatest area of dense forests. However for tropical forests, Brazil is the country with the most extensive coverage – three times that of the Democratic Republic of the Congo, the country with the next most extensive coverage (UNEP 2001).

The great majority of Brazilian tropical forests are concentrated in the Amazon region, now that the Atlantic Forest has been reduced to around 100,000 square kilometers or less than eight percent of its original extent. Of the more than six million square kilometers that is estimated to be the current extent of the Amazon forest in South America, no less than sixty percent is to be found in Brazilian territory.

As far as biodiversity goes, the Brazilian figures are equally impressive. The country holds the world's highest levels of animal and plant richness – somewhere between ten and twenty percent of the 1.5 million species so far recorded. These include around 55,000 species of seed plants (around 22% of the global total), 502 species of mammals, 1,677 bird species, 600 amphibian species and 2,657 fish species. These represent, respectively, 10.8%, 17.2%, 15% and 10.7% of the global species totals (Joly and Bicudo 1998). Bearing in mind the fact that the greater part of the world's biodiversity remains unstudied, and that the developed countries are way out in front as regards biological inventories, it is expected that future research in Brazil – and especially in Amazonia – will significantly increase the country's place in the rankings, which are now based on currently-available figures.

In addition to its biological diversity, the Amazon contains amazing cultural diversity. It is home to around 170 indigenous peoples with a population of approximately 180,000 individuals, 357 communities of descendants of escaped slaves, and thousands of communities of rubber tappers, brazil nut collectors, riverbank dwellers, babassu nut gatherers and others.

The Amazon also plays an important role in the environmental stability of the planet. It fixes more than a hundred trillion tons of carbon. Its vegetation releases about seven trillion tons of water a year into the atmosphere through evapotranspiration, and its rivers account for about twenty percent of all the freshwater released into the oceans from all the world's rivers.

The turn of the new century finds this remarkable set of socio-environmental assets with their original characteristics still relatively well preserved. In today's wired world it is still possible in Amazonia to find at least fifty isolated indigenous communities with no regular contact with the outside world.

However, at the national and international levels, twenty-first century Amazonia is much more than a symbolic cultural icon for its natural and cultural importance or its importance for the ecological equilibrium of the planet. It is a scientific and technological frontier in an era characterized by the advance of biotechnology and genetic engineering. Its potential in these fields is enormous. Brazil's first national report to the Convention on Biological Diversity (MMA 1998) states that biological diversity is critically important at the economic level and that, for example, the agroindustrial sector, which derives direct benefits from genetic resources, accounts for around forty percent of Brazil's gross domestic product. The growing global market for the products of biotechnology is in turn worth between 470 and 780 billion dollars a year (Arnt 2001) and its future growth requires the active components and genetic codes found in natura. This is a field in which the irony of history has brought together both ends of the string of time: at one end, the most advanced laboratories that science can develop and, at the other, the knowledge of traditional populations that allows the identification of the active components hidden within the complexities of tropical ecosystems.

The future of the Amazon will however not be decided just by its socio-environmental importance nor by its potential. The threats of degradation are proceeding at accelerating rates. Official figures on deforestation in the region from Brazil's National Space Research Institute show that rates are both extremely high and increasing. Already around 570,000 square kilometers of forest have been lost in the region, an area equivalent to the size of France, and the average for the seven years from 1993 was 17,600 square kilometers a year (Inpe 2001). If such rates persist, the amount that will be lost over a period of thirty years will be greater than that over the previous five hundred years.

The true picture may however be even more serious. The official figures only refer to areas where the forest cover has been completely removed by clear cutting. The degradation that results from other forms of logging or burning is not calculated (Krug 2001). If we add the 11,730 square kilometers of forest destroyed in the fires in the state of Roraima in 1998 (Shimabukuro et al. 2000) and the 15,000 square kilometers in the region which, it is estimated, suffer each year the impacts of the selective logging of high-value timber, the total for the forest area degraded in 1998 jumps from the 17,383 square kilometers calculated by the National Space Research Institute to 44,113 square kilometers; in other words, more than double.

In addition, and unless environmental zoning measures are adopted, the expanding cultivation of soybean in savanna and forest areas of the Amazon represents another threat. In the period between 1997 and 2000, soybean production in the state of Rôndonia shot up from 4,500 tons to 45,000 tons, a nine hundred percent increase.

It was in this context of opportunities and threats, when the need to develop a strategic plan for the Amazon region could no longer be postponed, that the project 'Assessment and Identification of Priority Actions for the Conservation, Sustainable Use and Sharing of the Benefits of the Biodiversity of the Brazilian Amazon' was conceived.

The initiative included a set of projects and regional consultation workshops organized by the Ministry of the Environment, through the National Program for Biological Diversity, in fulfillment of Brazil's commitments under the Convention on Biological Diversity, opened for signature during the Earth Summit in Rio de Janeiro in 1992, and as a contribution to the preparation of Brazil's national biodiversity strategy.

The aim was to carry out an assessment of the biodiversity of the Amazon forest biome, using the Legal Amazon region as the unit of analysis, and to identify the environmental, social and economic factors affecting its conservation, its use and the sharing of the benefits resulting from such use.

Two sizeable challenges needed to be addressed. The first was to collect and to render capable of an integrated analysis the greatest possible volume of the available information on the Legal Amazon region. The second was to identify the greatest number of specialists who could share their different fields of expertise and together identify by consensus the critical areas and the priorities for action to conserve, sustainably use and share the benefits of the region's biodiversity.

It took approximately a year and a half to locate, organize and standardize the information on Amazonia scattered throughout dozens of public bodies and private institutions. Once the information base was brought together, more than two hundred researchers and specialists volunteered their time and met in the city of Macapá from 20 to 25 September 1999 in order to carry out the tasks proposed.

The result was the identification and description of 385 priority areas for biodiversity in Amazonia. To the biological data for each of these there was added information on, amongst other things, economic activities, development programs, demographic data, rates of deforestation and susceptibility to fire. In this way it was possible to assess the level of stability of each area and to identify priority action on the basis of short, medium and long term scenarios.

The results of the project were disseminated immediately after the Macapá Workshop, in a simplified format on the project's own website (www.socioambiental.org/website/bio/index.htm) and in full by means of the CD-ROM presented to the Ministry of the Environment and the organizations making up the coordinating consortium. Since then some important advances have been made. The priority areas identified were fully incorporated into the proposal for the expansion of protected areas in the Amazon submitted by the Brazilian government to the Global Environment Facility (GEF). The program of the Ministry of the Environment to expand and consolidate the network of national and state forests benefited from the information arising out of the project. Finally, calling attention to the possible impacts on the priority areas identified by the Macapá Workshop that could arise from the Program of National Integration and Development Corridors (better known as Avança Brasil) led to the decision of the federal government to undertake a strategic environmental assessment, something that will greatly assist to improve the proposals.

We now hope that further disseminating the results of the project through the present publication will lead to new ways and opportunities for Brazilian public to assist in the conservation, sustainable use and sharing of the benefits of the biodiversity of the Brazilian Amazon.

December 2001

Note to the English edition

Biodiversity in the Brazilian Amazon was originally published in Portuguese in December 2001. In 2003 it won the Prêmio Jabuti [the Turtle Prize] both in the Natural and Health Sciences category and as the Non-fiction Book of the Year. The Prêmio Jabuti is Brazil's foremost book award, organized annually by the Câmara Brasileira do Livro since 1959.

The texts and GIS data were originally prepared for the Macapá Workshop held in September 1999. The data were revised in January 2000, with the exceptions noted in the chapters below where data were again revised in October 2001 or April 2004. Given the scope of the undertaking and the resources that would have been required, the editors have not attempted to revise all these data for the English language edition.

This publication therefore represents a unique synthesis of the status of scientific knowledge of the biodiversity of the Brazilian Amazon and an analysis of policy options as they stood at the turn of the new millennium.

The publication of the English edition comes at a moment when the future of the Amazon region is still uncertain. There are simultaneously encouraging and worrying signs. Biodiversity loss continues; the pressures from unsustainable forms of biodiversity use continue to be high and in some areas are greater than ever; conflicts persist over rights to land and to the biological resources they contain; and the resources available for the scientific research and the implementation of the conservation measures that this book identifies are still inadequate. On the other hand, new legal and policy instruments are being developed; inter-sectoral approaches to harmonizing economic development and environmental protection in the region are emerging at federal and state levels; and opinion polls show that Amazonia and biodiversity loss are matters that continue to concern the Brazilian public.

In publishing this book in English, the editors hope to have provided a valuable and authoritative guide to readers outside Brazil on the richness and complexities both of the biological diversity of the Brazilian Amazon region and of the policy debates on its conservation, sustainable use and the equitable sharing of the benefits arising from utilization of the genetic resources it contains.

April 2004

26

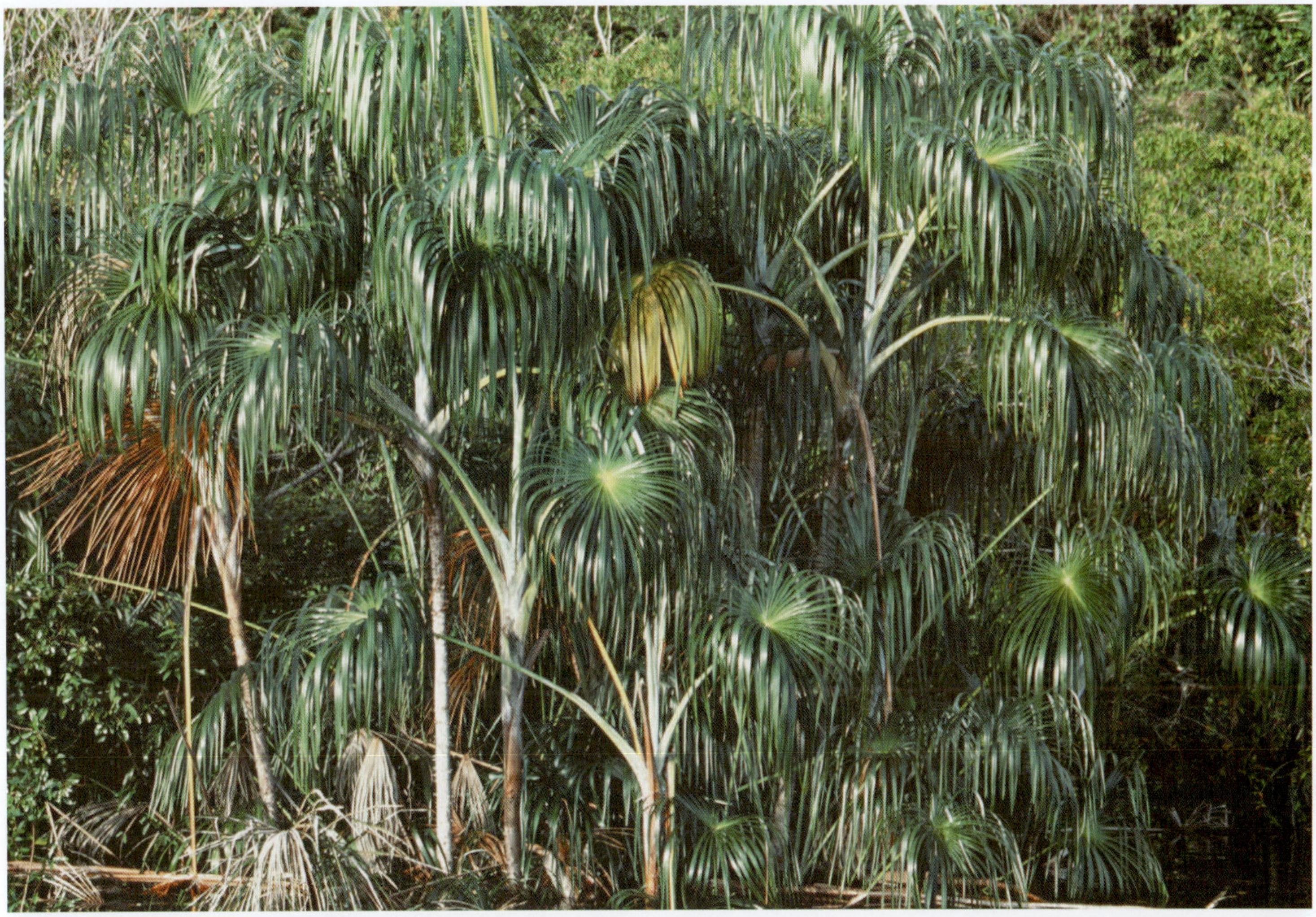

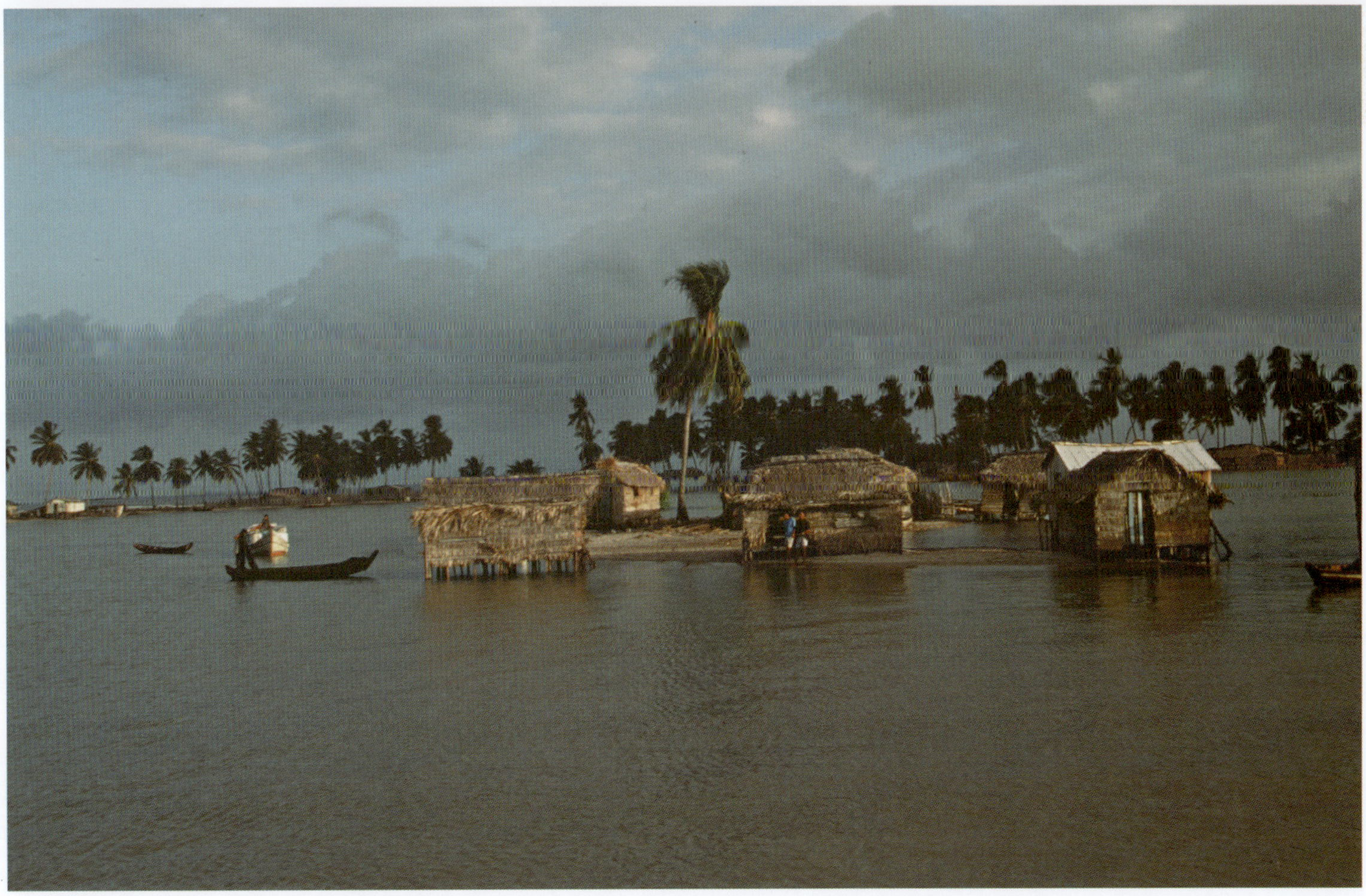

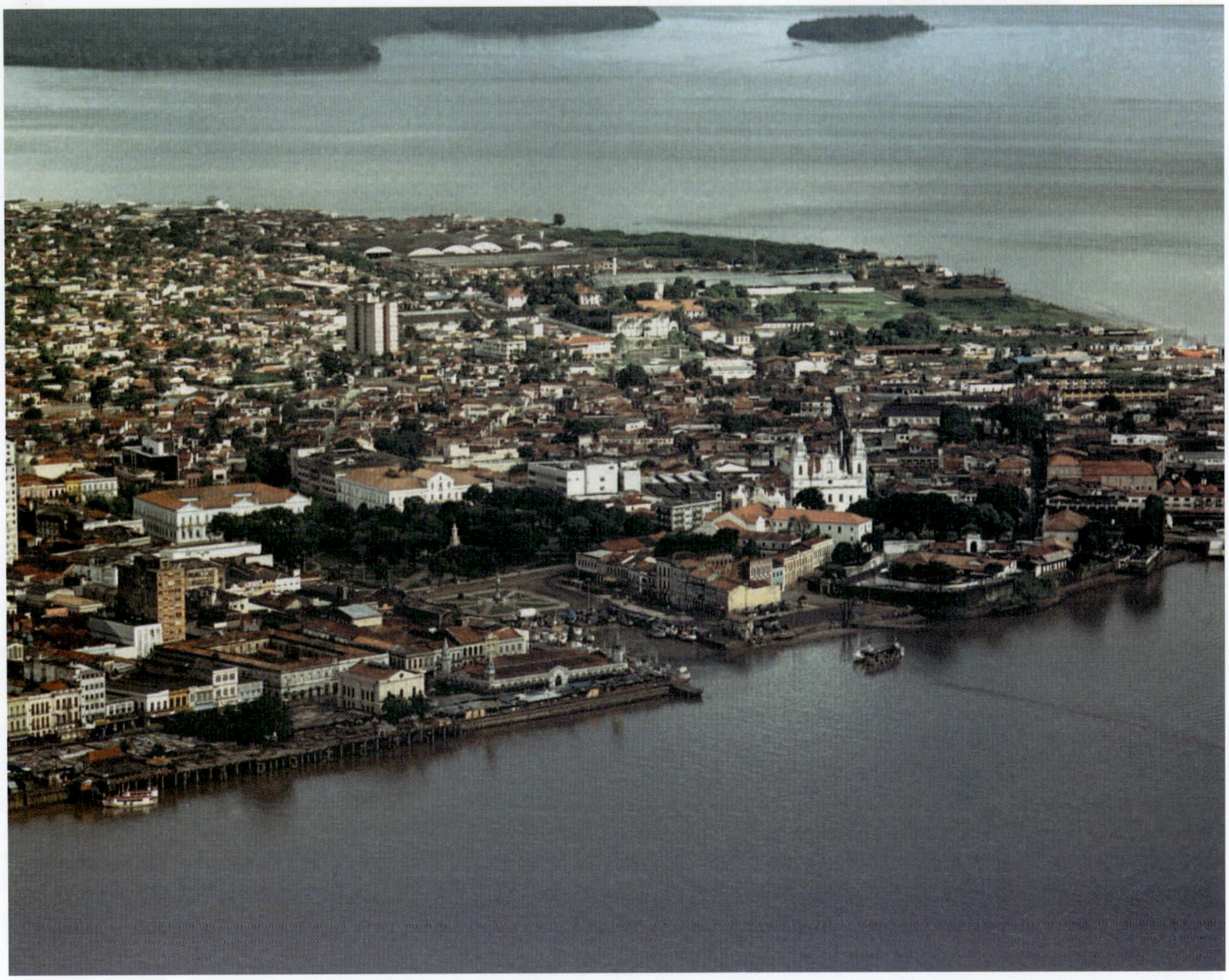

38

39

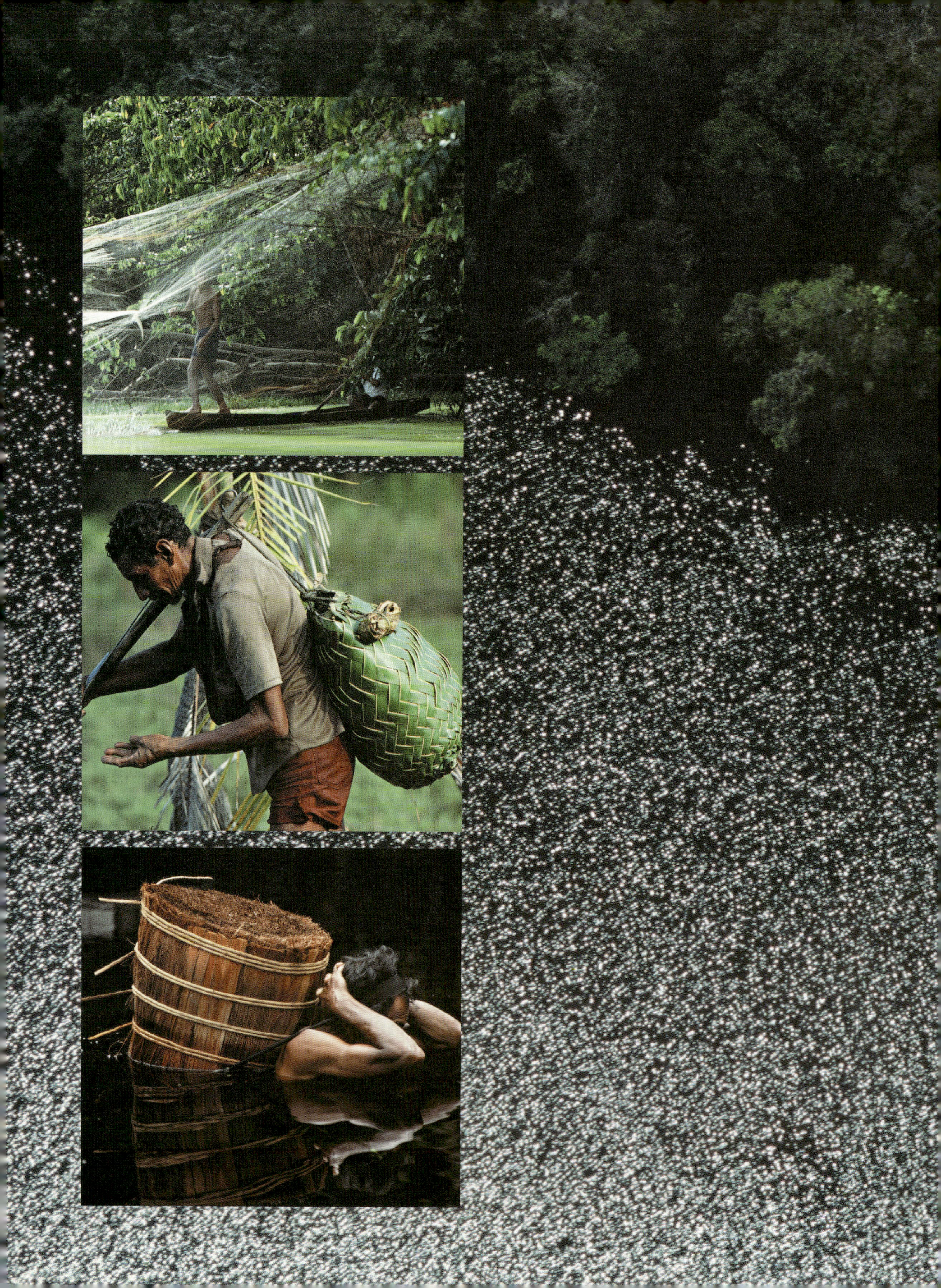

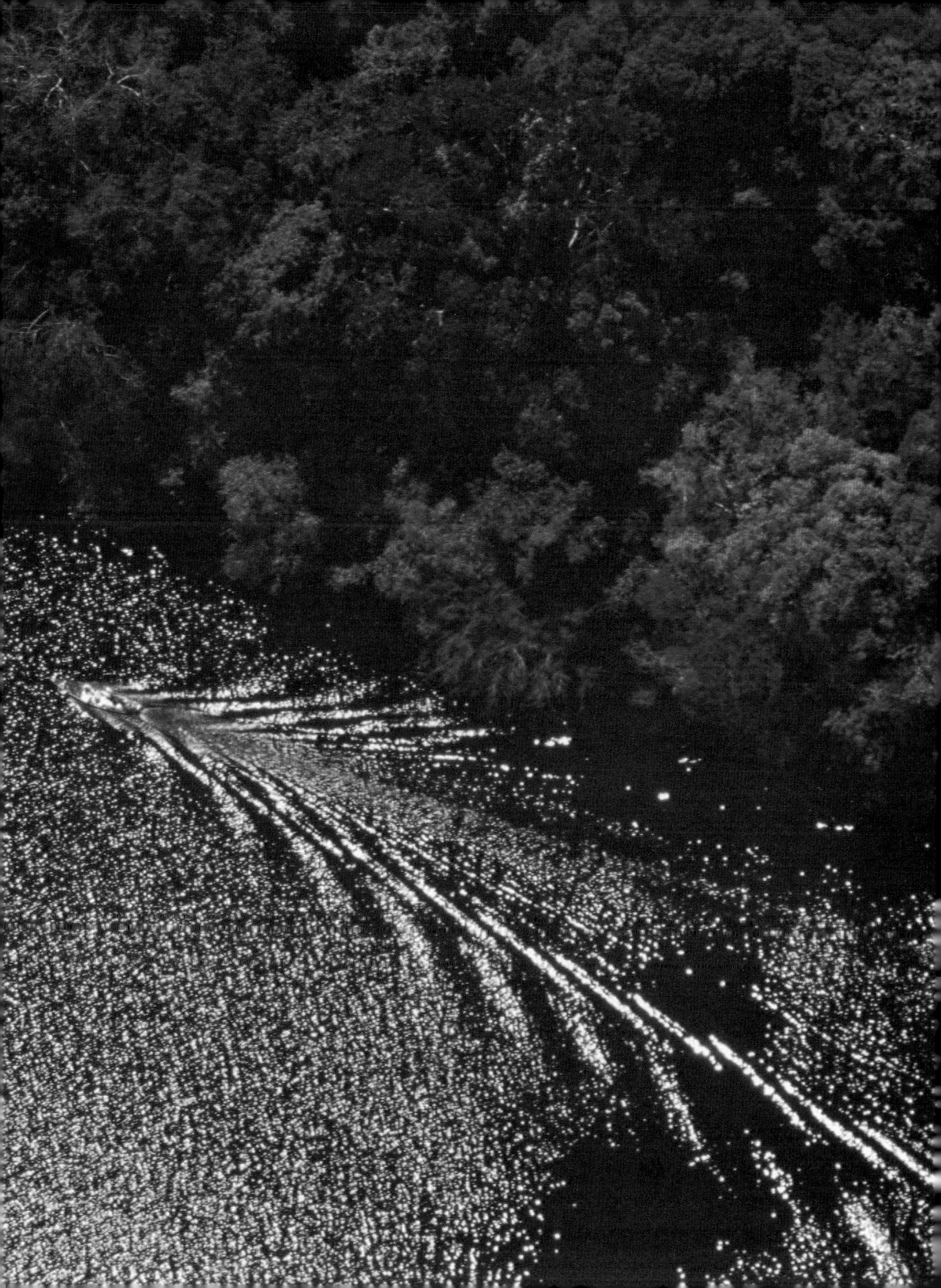

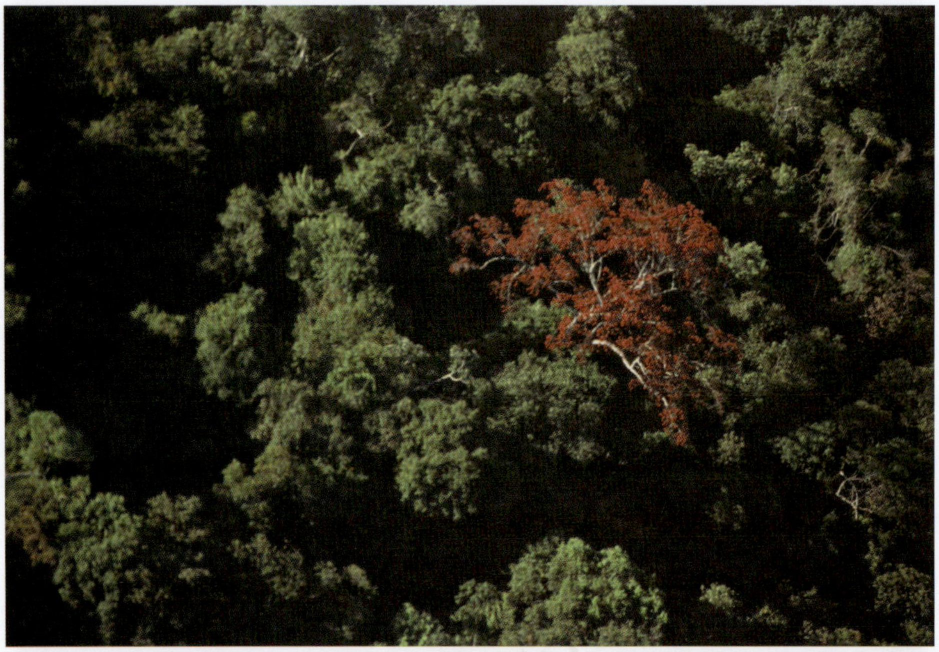

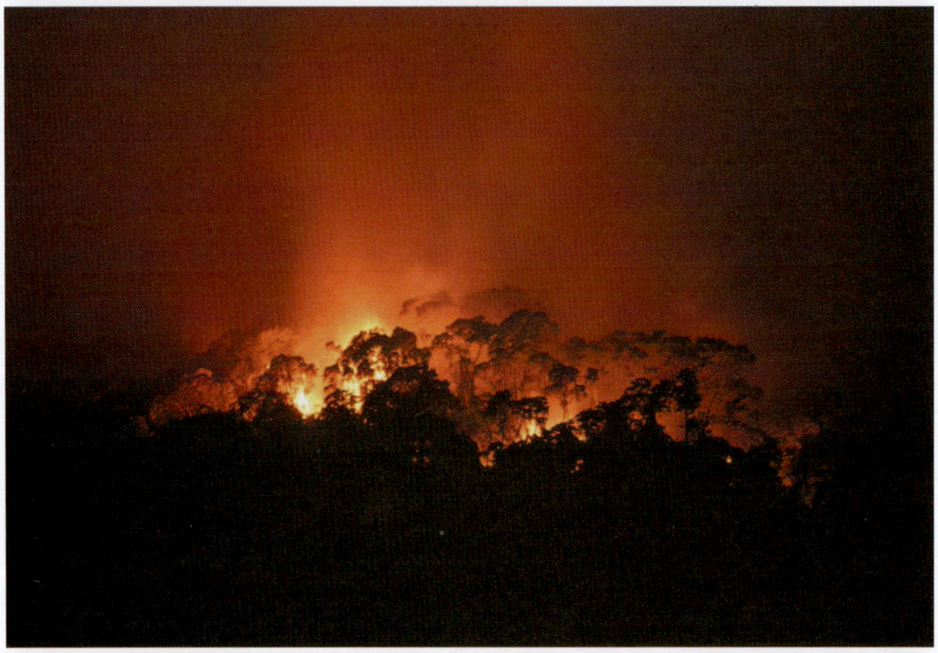

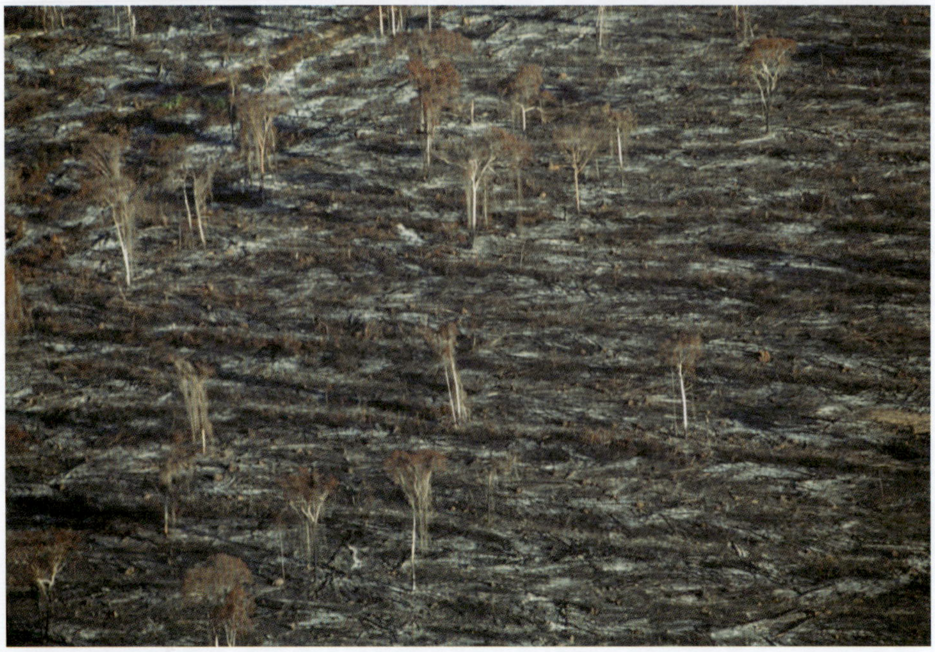

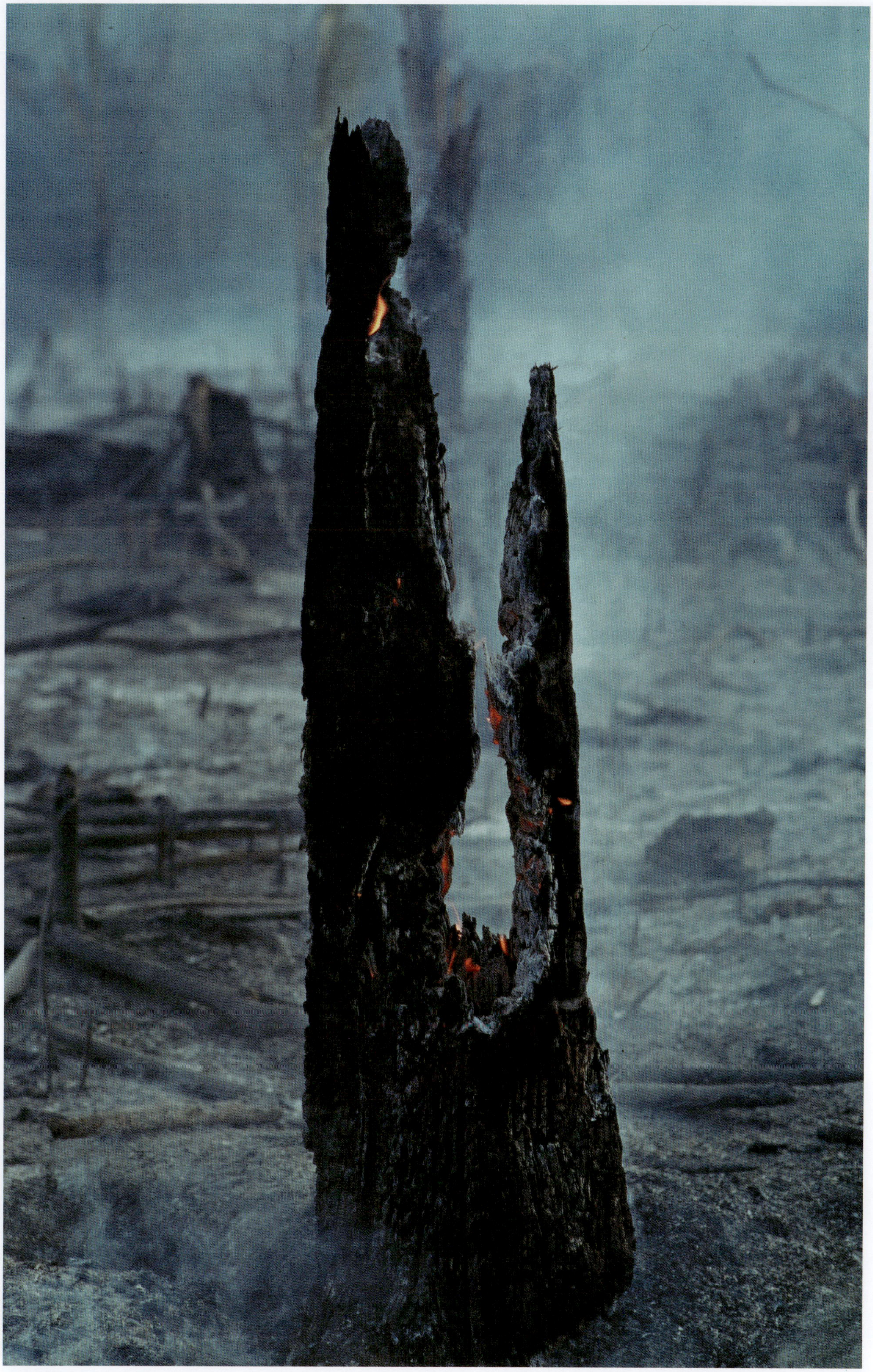

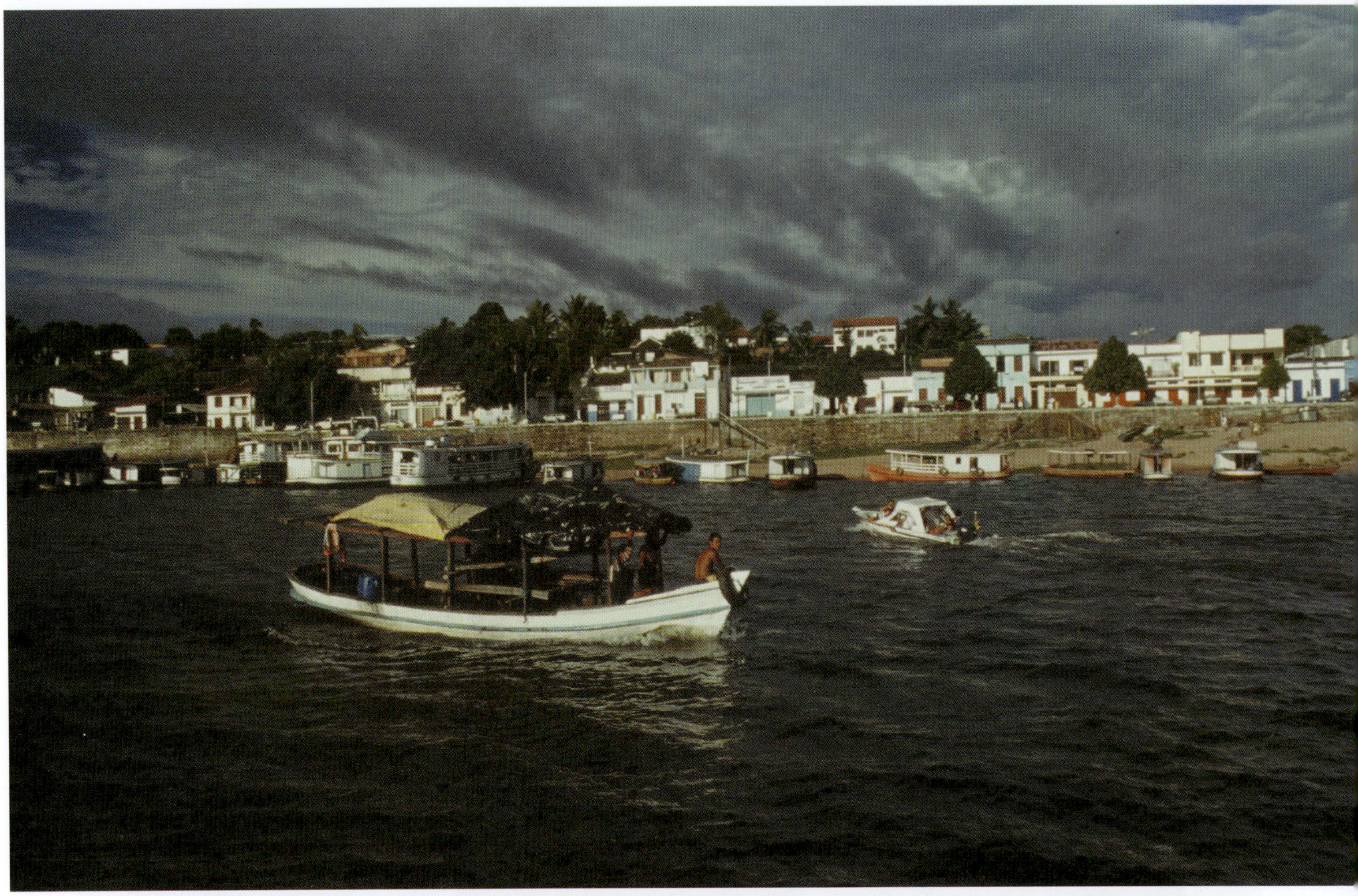

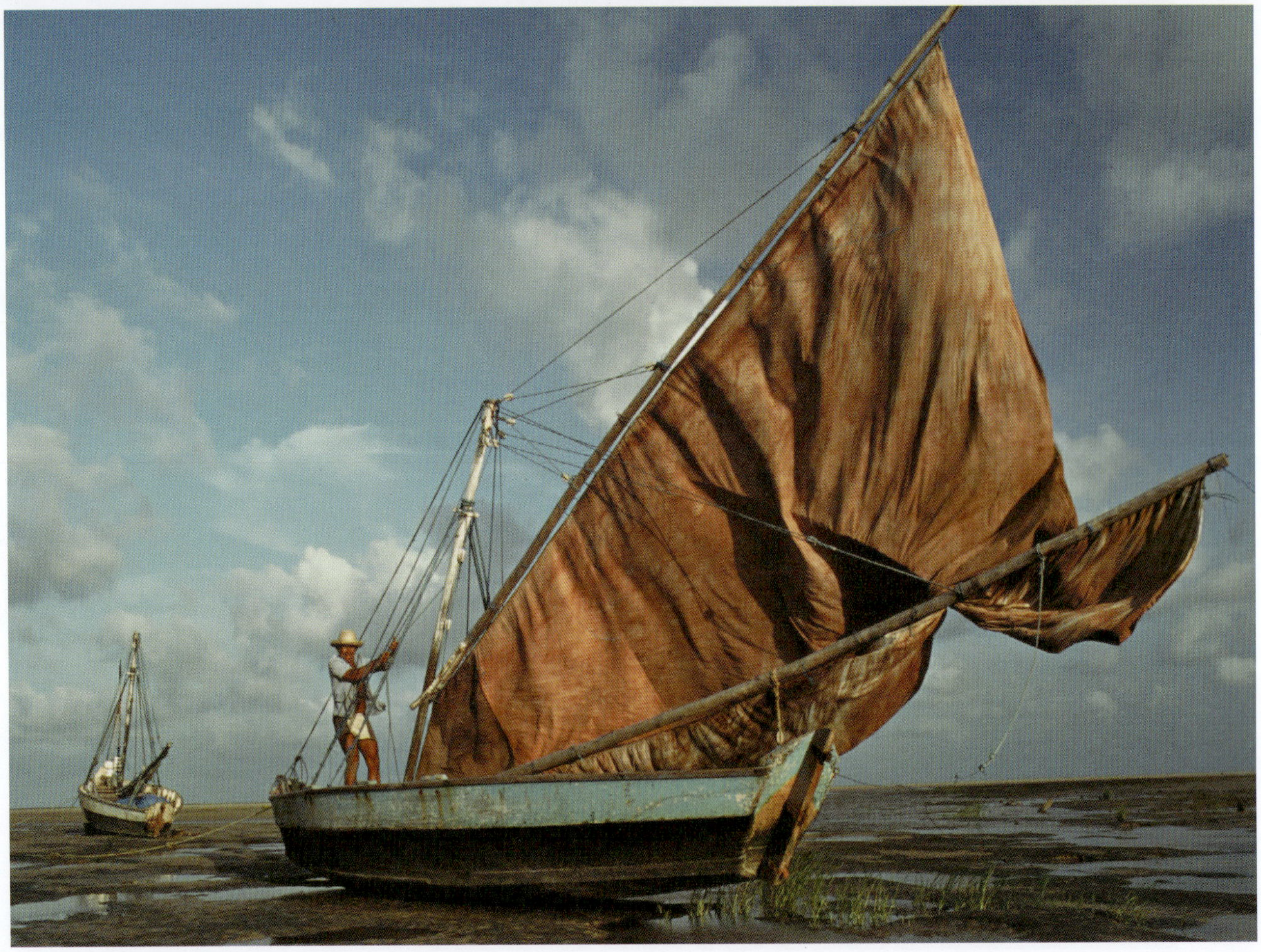

45

46

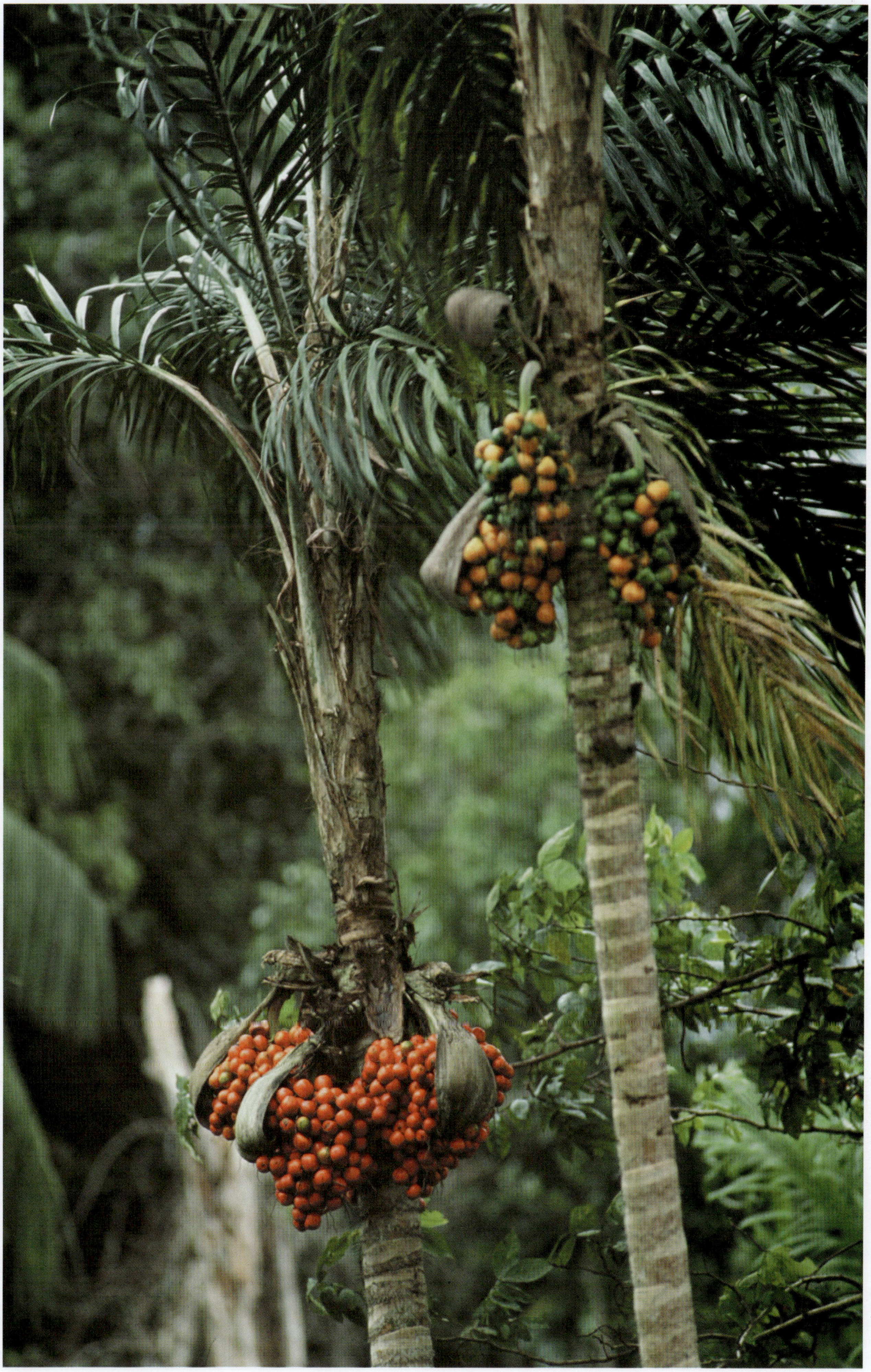

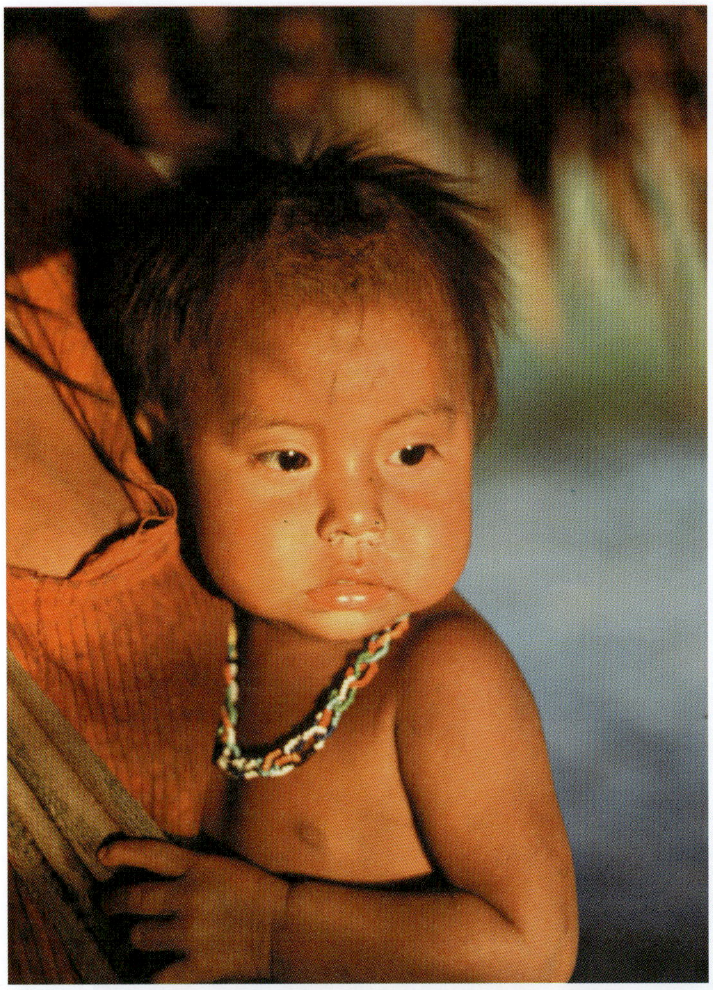

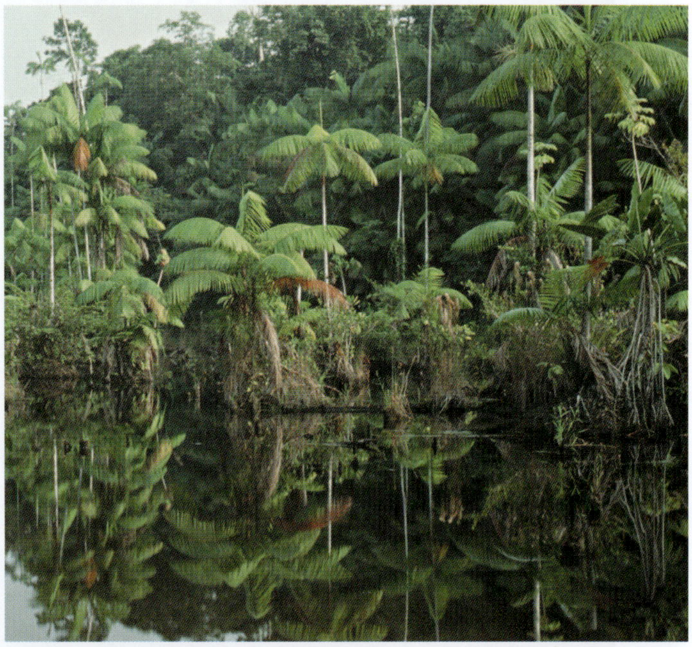

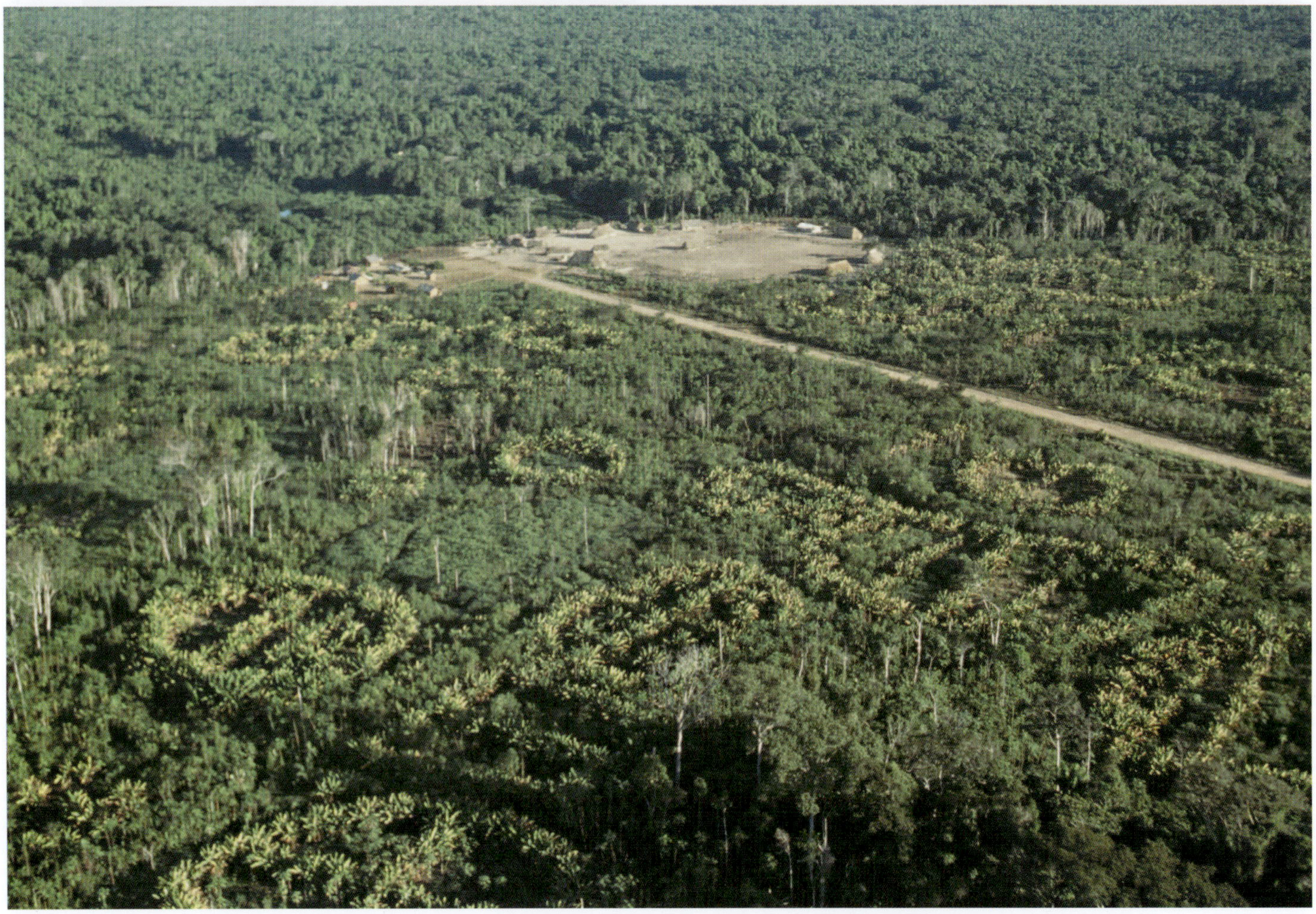

Conservation area categories

The categories of conservation areas (Unidades de Conservação – UCs) used throughout this book are the official categories established under federal legislation by Law 9.985 of July 2000 which instituted the Sistema Nacional de Unidades de Conservação – SNUC (National System of Conservation Areas).

Conservation areas that make up the SNUC fall into two groups:

- **Strict protection areas** (unidades de proteção integral), also referred to as *indirect use conservation areas* (unidades de conservação de uso indireto), whose purpose is the protection of nature and where only indirect use of their natural resources is allowed; and

- **Sustainable use areas** (unidades de uso sustentável), also referred to as *direct use conservation areas* (unidades de conservação de uso direto), whose purpose is to harmonise nature conservation and the sustainable use of elements of their natural resources.

Strict protection areas comprise the follow categories:

Ecological Station (Estação Ecológica – Esec)
PURPOSE   Preservation of nature and scientific studies
OWNERSHIP Public
ACCESS   No public access, except for educational purposes in accordance with the management plan; scientific research with prior permission

Biological Reserve (Reserva Biológica – Rebio)
PURPOSE   Complete preservation of the biota and other natural attributes existing within its borders
OWNERSHIP Public
ACCESS   No public access, except for educational purposes in accordance with the management plan; scientific research with prior permission

National Park (Parque Nacional – Parna)
PURPOSE   Preservation of natural ecosystems of special ecological importance and scenic beauty, scientific research, environmental education, recreation and ecological tourism
OWNERSHIP Public
ACCESS   Public access in accordance with the management plan; scientific research with prior permission
OTHER   When established by states or municipalities, to be called respectively State Park (Parque Estadual) and Municipal Nature Park (Parque Natural Municipal)

Natural Monument (Monumento Natural)
PURPOSE   Preservation of natural sites that are rare, unusual or of great scenic beauty
OWNERSHIP Can be privately owned provided the land and natural resource use of the owner(s) is compatible with the purposes of the conservation area
ACCESS   Public access in accordance with the management plan

Wildlife Refuge (Refúgio de Vida Silvestre)
PURPOSE   Protection of natural environments to ensure the existence or reproduction of species or communities of local flora and of resident or migratory fauna
OWNERSHIP Can be privately owned provided the land and natural resource use of the owner(s) is compatible with the purposes of the conservation area
ACCESS   Public access in accordance with the management plan; scientific research with prior permission

---

Sustainable use areas comprise the follow categories:

Environmental Protection Area (Área de Proteção Ambiental – APA)
CHARACTERISTICS Large area with a certain degree of human occupation, containing abiotic, biotic, esthetic or cultural attributes especially important for the quality of life of the human population
PURPOSE   To protect the biological diversity, regulate human occupation and ensure sustainability of the natural resource use
OWNERSHIP   Public or private
ACCESS   Public lands: Public access and scientific research in accordance with management authority by-laws; Private lands: in accordance with conditions set by the owner(s)
MANAGEMENT   Council: presided by the management authority and comprising public bodies, civil society organizations and residents

continues

Area of Special Ecological Importance (Área de Relevante Interesse Ecológico – Arie)
CHARACTERISTICS Small area with little or no human occupation, containing unusual natural characteristics or rare examples of regional biota
PURPOSE Maintenance of natural ecosystems of regional or local importance and regulation of permitted use to ensure compatibility with nature conservation purposes
OWNERSHIP Public or private

National Forest (Floresta Nacional – Flona)
CHARACTERISTICS Area of predominantly native forest cover
PURPOSE Sustainable multiple uses of forest resources and scientific research
OWNERSHIP Public; continued occupation by traditional communities present prior to creation of National Forest
ACCESS Public access in accordance with the management plan; scientific research with prior permission permitted and encouraged
MANAGEMENT Consultative Council: presided by management authority and comprising public bodies, civil society organizations and, where present, resident traditional communities
OTHER When established by states or municipalities, to be called respectively State Forest (Floresta Estudual) and Municipal Forest (Floresta Municipal)

Extractive Reserve (Reserva Extrativista – Resex)
CHARACTERISTICS Area used by traditional populations whose subsistence is based principally on extractive activities
PURPOSE To protect the way of life and culture of these populations and ensure the sustainable use of natural resources
OWNERSHIP Public; with use concession to the traditional extractive population
ACCESS Public access permitted, provided this is compatible with local interests and in accordance with the management plan; scientific research with prior permission permitted and encouraged
MANAGEMENT Deliberative Council: presided by the management authority and comprising public bodies, civil society organizations and resident traditional communities; the Deliberative Council approves the management plan
OTHER Mining and hunting (amateur or professional) prohibited; commercial logging only permitted on a sustainable basis, in special circumstances, and as a complement to other activities

Fauna Reserve (Reserva de Fauna)
CHARACTERISTICS Area of animal populations of native species, terrestrial or aquatic, resident or migratory
PURPOSE Technical and scientific study of sustainable economic management of faunistic resources
OWNERSHIP Public
ACCESS Public access in accordance with management authority by-laws
OTHER Hunting (amateur or professional) prohibited

Sustainable Development Reserve (Reserva de Desenvolvimento Sustentável)
CHARACTERISTICS Natural area inhabited by traditional populations whose livelihoods are based on sustainable systems of natural resource use, developed over generations and adapted to local ecological conditions, and which play a key role in nature conservation and maintaining biological diversity
PURPOSE Nature preservation; improvement of the quality of life and use of natural resources of traditional populations; respect, preserve and enhance the knowledge and environmental management practices of these populations
OWNERSHIP Public
MANAGEMENT Deliberative Council: presided by the management authority and comprising public bodies, civil society organizations and resident traditional communities; the Deliberative Council approves the management plan; the management plan will define zones of strict protection , of sustainable use, buffer zones and ecological corridors

Private Natural Heritage Reserve (Reserva Particular do Patrimônio Natural – RPPN)
PURPOSE Private area, registered in perpetuity, for the conservation of biological diversity
OWNERSHIP Private
MANAGEMENT Public bodies belonging to the SNUC will provide the owner(s) with scientific and technical guidance for the preparation of a management plan

Areas occupied by indigenous communities – *Indigenous Lands* (Terras Indígenas) and *Indigenous Parks* (Parques Indígenas) – fall under separate legislation and procedures. Full details can be found in the section 'Conservation areas and indigenous lands'. A new category – Indigenous Natural Resources Reserve (Reserva Indígena de Recursos Naturais or RIRN) – has been proposed; see the chapter 'Indigenous natural resources reserves' in the section Thematic documents 3, p. 288.

Thematic documents 1

Biodiversity and the ecological functions of ecosystems

The importance of invertebrates for the conservation of Amazonian biodiversity

William L. Overal

Abstract

Although the diversity of many invertebrate groups finds its highest levels in Amazonia, the use of invertebrates to define conservation priorities for the region raises many problems: incomplete faunistic studies, variation in sampling techniques and levels, lack of specialist taxonomists, lack of databases bringing together the information in existing collections in museums and research institutes, and the often confused state of invertebrate taxonomy. Among all invertebrate groups, only the butterflies can provide solid criteria for identifying biodiversity conservation areas in Amazonia. Other groups which may have the potential to help define conservation areas and actions are: ants, bees, social wasps, some beetle families, termites, mites of the Oribatidae family, worms, soil-dwelling arthropods, dragonflies, freshwater shrimps, and other aquatic groups. They have been chosen for their species richness, local abundance in different ecosystems, or their ecological importance. Their ability to act as indications of total biodiversity or to contribute to the maintenance of ecosystem functions can be considered as high. Priority areas for biodiversity conservation should include not only areas of high biodiversity, but also those that harbor rare or endangered species, as well as those which have already been studied or from where different species have been collected for taxonomic purposes (type locations). Areas of sharp relief or comprising unique ecosystems should also receive priority. Proposals are made to increase the level of protection of a number of Amazonian habitats.

The problem

The current problem is to determine how to preserve the biota of Amazonia on the basis of information obtained through the study of invertebrates.

This is not a simple matter. As the reader may already know, invertebrates constitute more than 95% of all animal species, comprising twenty to thirty phyla. Estimates of the numbers of species arrive at almost astronomical figures. At the same time more than 70% of Amazonian invertebrates have not yet been scientifically named and, given current surveying and identification rates, this situation will continue for a long time to come.

Notwithstanding their importance for the maintenance of ecosystem functions and human well-being, invertebrates are ignored (not to say disliked), and research funds are scarce compared to those for vertebrates. Although they dominate Amazonia in terms of numbers of species, of individuals, and of biomass, invertebrates are not yet given priority in the preparation of biodiversity conservation projects and are rarely considered as crucial elements of the biodiversity to be conserved. Invertebrates stand out by the services they provide in recycling nutrients. Soil-dwelling animals in particular perform various functions, such as the decomposition of detritus, natural pest control, plant pollination, seed dispersal and germination, turning over soils, transmission of diseases to humans and other vertebrates, and constituting food for vertebrates.

Invertebrates need to be treated differently from vertebrates. Normally it is the relative or absolute number of species that determines the setting of priorities for biodiversity conservation areas; however, this information is not available for invertebrates, nor is there any definitive data on species richness for the majority of areas under study. Even for well studied groups, such as butterflies, the data are scarce, especially for a region with such species richness. For this and other reasons to be explained below, the criteria to be applied for the conservation of invertebrates need to take other parameters into account, such as the use of species as indicators of biodiversity (surrogates), the maintenance of ecosystem functioning (environmental quality), species with public appeal (butterflies, dragonflies), keystone species, and rare species isolated by evolutionary processes (relict species). On the other hand, invertebrates (like vertebrates) do not exist in isolation and can only be conserved as integral parts of functioning ecosystems.

The nature of the available data

Invertebrate studies

The tradition that guides studies on these animals makes it difficult to use these species for biodiversity conservation. With only a few exceptions, research on invertebrates in the Amazon has been carried out by nonresidents, people usually working in isolation on one or more taxonomic groups. The collections they use are located outside the region, in a wide range of places around the globe, in museums and universities in southern Brazil, in Europe and in North America. The occurrence of an invertebrate species in Amazonia generally goes unpublished, even when previously unknown, since publishers and the naturalists themselves look down on such notes as trivial. (The data, for instance, on a third of all mollusk species in South America are limited to their original collection). There is thus an immense repository of data on the occurrence and geographical distribution of Amazonian invertebrates in museums and collections, in filing cabinets and in registration books.

During the course of a lifetime, a researcher might master the taxonomy of a few thousand species of invertebrates at most, a number well below current needs for a faunistic survey of these animals. There is no guarantee that, with the death or retirement of this researcher, anyone else will continue the work. Amazonia, and Brazil generally, lack expert taxonomists able to identify invertebrates in general, or even the most important species from an economic point of view (pests, disease vectors, pollinator species, biological control agents, etc.). We should not hold previous generations of researchers responsible for the lack of information currently needed. Suffice it to say that society has now woken up to the work of naturalists and taxonomists, and is asking where and how to conserve species. Previously, however, such questions did not inform the traditions of invertebrate studies.

Taxonomy

Discussing biological diversity without being able to name the species is an almost metaphysical problem. It is common to say that modern biology began with the Linnaean system of nomenclature. Previously there had been no way to index and retain information on organisms as there was no system of labeling species. Linking nomenclature to phylogeny increased our ability to extrapolate on the basis of species classified as belonging to the same group. In addition, biogeography has become a science.

With this in mind one might wonder why the taxonomy of a large number of invertebrate groups in South America, especially in Amazonia, is still at a stage that does not enable its use by laypeople or by biologists not experts on these groups. This situation of neglect of invertebrates has arisen, in part, as a result of the great number of different species, the reduced size of some groups, taxonomic problems (especially regarding species differentiation in highly diversified groups), little collecting activity in the majority of habitats, and the lack of funds for taxonomic studies of invertebrates.

Surveys of invertebrate fauna

Despite the numerical and functional importance of invertebrates, the biogeographical basis of invertebrate fauna is still scarcely addressed in inventories of tropical biodiversity. The distribution of invertebrates is far less understood than that of vertebrates, and the information available is less systematized and virtually inaccessible to the general public.

Invertebrates, and insects in general, are enormously diversified in Amazonia (Adis 1990; Erwin 1982, 1983a, 1983b, 1988; May 1988, Stork 1988, Wilson 1987). For instance, the number of insect species is estimated at almost 30 million, with the highest level of diversification found in tropical forest canopies (Perry 1991). The conservation of insect biodiversity, which includes pollinator species, seed dispersing species, species serving a few plants as 'bodyguards' and as biological pest control agents, is necessary for the functioning of tropical rain forest ecosystems (Janzen 1987). Nevertheless, the insects of Amazonia remain little known.

Additional, more complete surveys of the invertebrates of this region are required. Basic information that might help to manage the fauna, such as which species are found in specific areas in the Amazon, and what their geographical and ecological distribution areas are, is nonexistent. The few institutions in the region with the mandate to carry out such studies and to house systematic collections do not have the necessary human, material, bibliographical, or financial resources for the task. The postgraduate courses in organic biology, both in and outside the Amazon region, focus on the formation of field ecologists and biologists, thus contributing to the lack of taxonomic specialists whose task it is to give names to plants and animals.

Sampling methods are in need of standardization so that different locations can be compared. The simple collecting of specimens, although necessary, must be supplemented by long-term studies. Incomplete collections are those that contain only the most common species and fail to secure those rarer species that could provide more precise information on the areas under study.

In general, collecting efforts in the Amazon region have been weak, hindered by difficulties of access or lack of incentives. We are unable either to confirm the nonexistence of invertebrate species in large areas or to provide lists of species (even for the most common groups) to municipalities or conservation managers. As a result of the swift advance of agricultural activities in the region, and the accelerated degradation of landscapes due to anthropogenic activities, we can neither confirm nor predict which species of invertebrates are threatened with (or are on the way to) extinction.

As is well known, Amazonia is not a homogeneous region but a mosaic of different habitats with differentiated faunas. Igapó (seasonally flooded forest), várzea (flood plains), terra firme, campina (open grassland), savannas, mangrove swamps, and marshland are only a few of the habitats that constitute the region. A faunistic inventory will need to include studies on these different communities and ecosystems.

International collaboration will be necessary in order to overcome the lack of specialists and to prepare a new generation of taxonomists. It will be particularly necessary for students to spend time in the large European and North American museums, in order to be able to take over the responsibility for surveying Amazonian fauna. There is no alternative other than visiting these relics of a colonial era when the biodiversity of the Amazon region was the object of curiosity and envy for the elites of other countries.

Criteria for the selection of invertebrate groups

Even with international support and a new generation of researchers trained for and dedicated to the mission of surveying the invertebrate fauna of the Amazon, it will still be necessary to decide which groups should be given priority for collecting, study and mapping. On the one hand we could argue that it's impossible to do everything at the same time. On the other hand we have to recognize that there is no homogeneity among invertebrate groups: some of them are more important in terms of the information they are likely to provide in the shortest possible time.

For instance, priority should be given to invertebrate species with economic value. We might, for example, select pollinators of cultivated or gathered plants, biological pest control agents, species that are important in the diet of humans and domestic or farm animals, or species which transmit diseases.

Species of critical importance for ecosystem functioning should also be prioritized, such as crustaceans that make up zooplankton, termites and mites with a roles in recycling organic materials, other decomposers, micro predators and parasitoids that are important in maintaining the natural balance, and species that serve as food for other animals.

Attention should also be paid to invertebrate species which form distinct communities, generally restricted to threatened enclaves such as Amazonian caatinga (scrub savanna), campinarana (wooded grasslands), terra firme and floodplain lakes, tepuís (inselbergs), mangrove swamps, rocky plains, and caves.

Some invertebrate groups are biological indicators of environmental quality and also merit priority treatment, such as Chironomidae (Diptera) and Ephemeridae (Ephemeroptera) larvae and aquatic protozoa in igapó areas, recognized as indicators of water quality.

Groups of species can be useful for estimating the entire biological diversity of an area. Invertebrate groups that have been suggested as surrogates include butterflies, spiders and Oribatidae mites. All could be indicators of overall species richness within communities.

Taxonomists and evolutionary biologists have drawn attention to those invertebrate groups that could reflect phylogenetic diversity, especially in the case of small old groups of distinct and terminal evolutionary lineage, as is the case of relict groups such as Ricinulei (Arachnida) and Onychophora.

Nor should we forget those invertebrate species studied *in situ* and which exemplify biological principles, such as the butterflies of the subfamilies Heliconiinae and Ithomiinae, which form complexes of Batesian mimicry in the Amazon.

There are also those with cultural, esthetical, and historical value, for instance, the beautiful butterflies of the region, species relevant to the mythology of indigenous peoples, species used in traditional medicine, and others which inspire feelings of beauty.

We can begin the list by thinking of invertebrate species which are endangered at the local (extirpation) or global (extinction) levels. Given that they cannot be manufactured in laboratories, every effort must be made to prevent species loss. After all, each one of them represents a living experiment of millions of years, genes we do not want to lose, and the possibility of finding new biological resources. Rare species are not always endangered: rarity itself is a form of defense, preventing extermination through predation or disease. Endemic species whose geographic distribution is restricted to small areas are not always endangered, but may often be considered vulnerable to ecological changes in their habitats.

Criteria for the selection of areas and ecosystems

As we have seen, identification of priority areas and ecosystems is needed. Not all locations have the same numbers, or even the same species, of invertebrates. Selection by area must take into account the biology of the target organisms of the conservation action. It is not always the case that a marginal area, however large it may be, is appropriate for species conservation.

As a first step we should think of the so-called 'hot spots', areas of the greatest biodiversity where the number of species in general or of keystone species is highest. For Amazonian invertebrates, however, this type of information is only available (in incomplete form) for butterflies.

Next we have areas of high endemism, where the invertebrate fauna is comprised of characteristic species that are not present at other locations. These might be areas of high relief for the region, such as Pico da Neblina, Monte Roraima, and the Serra dos Carajás, or forest enclaves such campina, Amazonian caatinga and campinarana.

Representative interfluvial areas and headwaters of Amazonian rivers would be important for biodiversity conservation, as well as land corridors between biodiversity conservation areas.

From a practical point of view one must recognize the importance of those areas already established as conservation areas or which are in some way protected or recognized as conservation areas. Many of these are multiple use areas, in other words they can simultaneously serve as areas of biological or archeological conservation, extractive reserves or indigenous reserves.

Neither should we neglect those areas where traditional biological studies have been carried out, and which have provided museum collections with specimens of animals and other organisms. Taxonomists consider certain places to have a special value as type-locations (the site where the species holotype was collected, for example).

Key invertebrate groups

Which are the invertebrate groups that might provide data to solve the problem of choosing priority actions and areas for biodiversity conservation in the Amazon region? In the short and medium term there are few, in spite of the broad diversity of invertebrates as a whole. Butterflies, social insects (ants, bees, hornets, and termites), groups of the soil mesofauna (Oribatidae mites, worms, myriapods, and others), beetles, dragonflies, fresh water shrimps, and few aquatic insects (Ephemeridae and Diptera) suggest themselves. In the following section we present a summary of each key group.

Butterflies

Butterfly studies in the Amazon have not yet come of age despite the remarkable endeavors of generations of naturalists, entomologists, predecessors, and colleagues who have bequeathed us valuable information on the most diverse butterfly fauna on earth. Despite its species richness, the butterfly fauna of Amazonia has been poorly studied: less than a dozen locations have been investigated in depth to establish relatively complete fauna listings. At the same time, the incomplete taxonomy of the butterfly families Riodinidae, Lycaenidae, and Hesperiidae has hindered work on these groups and put off researchers who could have used these families for faunistic and ecological studies.

The locations listed in Table 1 are the only sites in the Amazon where butterflies have been collected in depth, and which allow some comparisons to be made. Cacaulândia in Rondônia, Alto Rio Juruá in Acre, and Pakitza in the National Park of Manu in Peru possess the richest butterfly fauna in the world. Other Amazonian locations host 1,200 species. Specimens have been collected in only a few of these, which results in a general low level of information on butterflies in the Amazon, although still greater than for the majority of other groups discussed below.

Moreover, the studies listed in Table 1 are based mainly on fewer than 1,000 hours of collection or observation time per researcher. This is due to the fact that the studies were carried out by peripatetic specialists, and not by local residents of the sampled areas. The exception is Trinidad, where only scientists and their students, rather than amateur naturalists, contributed to the final list of species. It is necessary to increase the range of data of these surveys by collecting throughout the different seasons of the year, increasing the number of collection hours per researcher, and varying the capture methods. Negative data, in other words the apparent nonexistence of a species in a determined community, cannot be accepted as long the sampling methods lack standardized capture and observation techniques, involving months and years of accumulated experience in fauna collection and study. For now we have some essential data, obtained through great sacrifice by dedicated scientists, but this data does not yet allow us to answer the more intriguing or useful questions in the areas of biogeography, evolution and ecology.

Currently there are approximately 7,500 known butterfly species in the world, with 3,300 of these in Brazil and 1,800 in the Amazon (Legg 1978; Shields 1989; Brown 1996). Wallace (1853, 1854) and Bates (1861, 1862, 1863, 1864) were the first to study the Lepidoptera fauna. Reverend Moss, whilst residing in Belém, (1919, 1933, 1949) contributed greatly to the knowledge of butterflies in the Amazon. During the 1940s, Alois Strympl (1949) increased the butterfly collection of the Goeldi Museum, particularly the genus *Agrias*, but, unfortunately, none of these specimens remain in the collection.

Otero (1972) and Otero & Marigo (1990, 1992) publicized the Lepidoptera fauna in well-illustrated popular books. At present the leading researchers on Amazonian butterflies are K. S. Brown Jr., O. H. H. Mielke, and M. Casagrande. Other specialists such as G. Lamas, T. C. Emmel, G. T. Austin, R. Robbins, and D. Harvey, all of them listed in the bibliography, promise to make the Amazonian butterfly fauna even more accessible to biological study at this turn of the century.

Sample size is very important when it comes to identifying areas with the richest butterfly fauna. A single collection carried out by the author and four assistants during a three-week period in 1998 at the Ferreira Penna Scientific Station, the Goeldi Museum reserve in the Caxiuanã national forest, resulted in more than 90 species of the families Pieridae, Papilionidae, and Nymphalidae. It is likely that, with just a few more collections, Caxiuanã could be considered an area rich in butterfly species, solely as a result of reasonably prolonged research. This demonstrates the danger of looking for 'hot spots': the search may artificially create what it sets out to find.

Nevertheless, these areas of western Amazonia covered by butterfly studies should be included among the priority areas for biodiversity conservation.

Ants

Because of their ecological prevalence and extremely high diversity in Amazonia, ants represent a key group of animals in the different forest ecosystems. They constitute almost a third of the entire animal biomass found in Amazon forest canopies (Fittkau & Klinge 1973; Adis et al. 1984), and total more than 3,000 Amazonian species (W. L. Overal, estimate based on unpublished data). Ants are important for their interaction with the vegetation (Huxley & Cutler 1991; Vasconcelos 1988, 1990;

TABLE 1 - LOCATIONS OF BUTTERFLY FAUNA SURVEYS IN THE AMAZON AND ADJACENT AREAS (DATA ACCORDING TO BROWN 1999 AND OTHER SOURCES)

Country	Location	Total number of butterflies species	Species of Nymphalidae (%)	Species of Ithominae (%)	Sources
Trinidad	whole island	652	145 (22)	17 (2.6)	Barcant 1970
Venezuela	Táchira, rio Frio	1,200	320 (27)	60 (5.0)	Nield 1997, Manrique in Brown 1999
Guyana	Caiene	1,232	330 (27)	46 (3.7)	Brevignon in Brown 1999
Colombia	Meta, rio Negro	1,200	300 (25)	60 (5.0)	Schmidt-Mumm in Brown 1999
	Alto Rio Putumayo	500	138 (28)	24 (4.8)	Salazar 1995
	Mocoa-Orito	1,020	279 (27)	59 (5.8)	Salazar 1995
Ecuador	Napo, Limoncocha	1,200	320 (27)	54 (4.5)	Drummond in Brown 1999
	Tungura, Topo/Zuñag	1,200	350 (29)	80 (6.7)	Velástegui in Brown 1999
Peru	Loreto, Alto Rio Napo	870	239 (27)	52 (6.0)	Lamas et al. 1996
	Junin, Mina Pichita	1,200	340 (28)	80 (6.7)	Brown 1999
	Madre Diós, Pakitza	1,307	396 (26)	62 (4.8)	Robbins et al. 1996
	Madre Diós, Tambopata	1,234	337 (27)	42 (3.4)	Lamas in Brown 1999
Brazil	Roraima, ilha de Maracá	530	147 (28)	11 (2.1)	Mielke & Casagrande 1992
	Pará, Belém, Utinga (forest reserve)	800	220 (28)	24 (3.0)	Bates, Moss & Museu Goeldi in Brown 1999
	Amazonas, Manaus, PDBFF	660	181 (28)	20 (3.1)	Brown & Hutchings 1997
	Pará, serra dos Carajás	720	198 (28)	33 (4.6)	Otero & Marigo 1992, Brown 1999
	Amazonas, Humaitá	800	220 (28)	27 (3.4)	Brown 1999
	Acre, Alto Rio Juruá	1,536	467 (26)	80 (4.7)	Brown 1999
	Rondônia, Cacaulândia	1,730	416 (24)	64 (4.1)	Austin in Brown 1999
	Acre, Xapuri	1,200	330 (28)	50 (4.2)	Brown 1999
	Rondônia, Riozinho	1,000	280 (28)	40 (4.0)	Brown 1999
	Rondônia, Colorado	1,200	340 (28)	50 (4.2)	Brown 1999

Benson 1985; Fowler 1993; Patrizia et al. 1991), as well as with other animals and the soil (Banner 1900). Vasconcelos (1990) estimated that more than 5% of Amazonian biomass could consist of red fire ants. In spite of their extreme importance for the region, their geographical and ecological distribution, and the structure of their communities have not yet been studied. By and large, systematic collection and identification efforts have not been made.

So far only eight studies containing surveys of local ant fauna in the Amazon have been published (Verhaagh 1991; Cover Et Al. 1990; Wilson 1987; Kempf 1970; Andrade Neto 1987; Benson & Harada 1988; Jaffe 1989). This is mainly due to taxonomic and collecting difficulties. In addition, the results obtained so far are not comparable because of differences in sampling methods (baits (Benson & Harada 1988; Andrade Neto 1987), insecticides (Wilson 1987), general collection (Cover et al. 1990; Kempf 1970)), collection efforts or duration, different ecosystems (flooded forest (Majer & Delabie 1994)) or not (Kempf 1970, 1961), inselberg (Jaffe et al. 1989), capoeiras, etc.), and other factors. In his thesis, recently completed at the Federal University of Pará and the Emílio Goeldi Museum of Pará, S. Ketelhut (1999) lists 134 species of 42 genera found in a forest region in Paragominas, Pará. Collection was carried out in an area of less than one square kilometer, using only a few pitfall traps, which still permitted an extrapolation of more than 200 expected species. Ants continue to be an important yet unknown component of Amazonian biodiversity. Table 2 summarizes some of the data on the rich variety of species in neotropical ant communities.

Collecting experience in the Amazon (W. L. Overal, field data) suggests that ants constitute a highly diversified group in the region, and that the list of species in terra firme rain forests could easily include up to 400 species, corresponding to one fifth of all the species to be found in the Amazon region. (2,358 ant species have already been described for the neotropical region (Bolton 1995)). Although there may be broad 'alpha' diversity, it is possible to find the same species in separate locations in the region or in diverse habitats. This is due to the 'opportunistic' nature of ants, which are generally omnivorous and able to colonize different types of vegetation and to adapt through 'social homeostasis' (changes to the colonies' internal microclimates). Thus we can say that a comparatively lower 'beta' diversity of ants in the region is likely.

The effect of army ants (subfamily Ecitoninae) on animals of the leaf litter mesofauna can be very specific and lead to a situation of permanent subclimax in these communities (Franks & Bossart 1983). Harper's thesis (1988) describes the studies on these animals in Manaus, especially their relation to birds which depend on them.

Competitive interaction among ant species is interpreted by some authors (Leston 1973) as giving rise to small-scale dislocation and competitive exclusion. The resulting pattern of nest distribution in a location is referred to as the ant 'mosaic'. This idea has not been fully demonstrated in practice, and the only research carried out in the neotropical region lacks sufficient data to demonstrate this 'mosaic' (Leston 1978).

Studies based on microclimatic variation in order to explain the nonrandom distribution of nests and ant colonies have so far been more successful (Levings 1998).

Books (Hölldobler & Wilson 1990; Bolton 1994) and articles (for example, Brandão 1991; Mackay & Vinson 1989) have been recently published which allow for identification of ants up to the level of genera. The Department of Zoology of the Goeldi

TABLE 2 - COMPOSITION OF ANT COMMUNITIES IN NEOTROPICAL FORESTS BASED ON DIFFERENT STUDIES AND METHODOLOGIES (ADAPTED FROM KETHELHUT 1999)

Location	no. of genera	no. of species	Methodology used	Sources
OTHER COUNTRIES				
Panama	49	127	Bait, Berlese	Levings 1983
Costa Rica	42	135	*Pitfall*, Winkler	Olson 1991
BRAZIL				
Atlantic Forest, 5 reserves	36	118	Various	Majer 1990
Ilha do Cardoso, São Paulo	35	76	Baits, *pitfall*	Fowler & Pesquero 1996
Manaus, Amazonas	49	307	Various	Benson & Harada 1988
Manaus, Amazonas	60	227	*Pitfall*, leaf litter, soil	Vasconcelos & Delabie 1999
Manaus, Amazonas	21	100	Canopy spraying	Harada & Adis 1997
Trombetas, Pará	52	206	Various	Majer 1996
Caxiuanã, Pará	40	126	Various	Overal, Harada, Mascarenhas 1997
Paragominas, Pará	32	96	*Pitfall*	Moutinho 1998
Paragominas, Pará	42	134	*Pitfall*	Ketelhut 1999

Museum holds relevant myrmecological literature and a systematic ant collection of the neotropical region, and is able to offer sufficient support for the laboratory work foreseen in this project.

Unfortunately, the studies so far carried out on the ant fauna of the Amazon do not identify the areas of highest biodiversity which could assist to focus biodiversity conservation efforts. The few areas under consideration represent a good start and should be taken into account for future in depth studies.

Bees

There are more than 30,000 known bee species worldwide, with more than 7,000 in South America, and more than 4,000 in Brazil (O'Toole & Raw 1991). The Amazon region reveals a range of 2,500 to 3,000 species.

The native bees of the Amazon are taxonomically well studied and several researchers have specialized in this group. Research in Brazil on pollination is up to date and undertaken by a number of research centers in Amazonia and in southern Brazil. The bee groups that might be able to help with issues related to biological conservation in the Amazon are euglossine bees, Meliponidae (stingless bees) and others, such as Xylocopidae and Anthophorinae.

The pollination of plants by bees is especially common in the forested areas of Amazonia, where the wind is blocked off and the distance between two individuals of the same tree species can reach up to hundreds of meters. Janzen and others discovered that euglossine bees fly kilometers to get back to their nests, suggesting a wider range than previously assumed. Forests and bees have a very specific relationship.

The breeding of native bees for honey is a widespread activity among traditional populations of the region. Of more than

80 species of Meliponidae bees, around 20 are bred by locals. This activity seems to be in decline, lacking both incentives and the systematization of data, as pointed out by P. Nogueira-Neto in his recent book (1997).

In spite of their importance, bees are not yet reliable indicators of areas of high biodiversity or endemism, as the studies are still geographically ad hoc and of brief duration. Data to address problems of zoogeography and diversity patterns of bees are not available. Even studies on pollination are rudimentary and scarce, especially in the case of high trees where inflorescence occurs dozens of meters above the ground.

It is assumed that the diversity of bees mirrors that of plants given the close relationship between them. It is possible to collect bees using bait, essences for euglossines, and honey or sugar for Meliponidae. Bees appear while the higher plants remain untouched. There is thus an opportunity to be explored for using these insects for rapid area assessments.

Hornets

Since the publication of O. W. Richards' book (1978), the rich social wasp fauna in South America has attracted more and more attention. There is currently research in progress on their taxonomy and zoogeography, as well as their behavior and ecological role. It is to be expected that a group of more than 220 species in the Amazon will become a research tool for biodiversity conservation issues. Ad hoc research indicates faunas with a varying number of species: 88 (Belém), 63 (Serrá dos Carajás), and 43 (Caxiuanã national forest).

Beetles

The families Cicindelidae, Carabidae, Cerambycidae, Chrysomelidae, and Scarabaeidae (scarab beetles) are the beetle groups most frequently cited as indicators of biodiversity. The order Coleoptera is highly diversified, with more than 250,000 described species and potentially millions more to be identified. However, research carried out so far does not allow for comparisons between areas or predictions. The potential of this group remains in reserve for the future, when standardized methods will provide better guidance for the collection and sampling of species. Many beetle groups such as Chrysomelidae and Cerambycidae are herbivores and their diversity patterns will be related to those of plants.

Termites

Termites constitute almost half the biomass of all soil-dwelling invertebrates. With thousands of species, they do not form a particularly diversified group, although they have an essential ecological role in Amazonia, that of recycling organic materials, particularly lignin and cellulose. There are good collections in Brazil and the Amazon region. There is a recent catalogue (Araújo 1977), and the group has been the subject of various revisions and updates

One of these studies, of major importance to Brazil and carried out by Mathews (1977), examined termite fauna in an area of transition from savanna to forest in the state of Mato Grosso. In a total area of less than 20 square kilometers, Mathews found 99 species belonging to four termite families, including two new genera and 26 new species. Since then, further regional studies in the Amazon have been carried out by Bandeira, Harada, Constantino, Mill, Martinus, and others.

Once again, there is no common methodology among the different studies, nor are there significant sample sizes. Only a few locations were examined and none of the studies was longer than a few months, not enough to follow changes in community formation throughout the annual cycle. Biochemical data on termites indicate that they could be important for nitrogen fixation, but initial research on this by Bandeira & Bradley has not been followed up.

As a consequence, termites cannot be used to suggest priority conservation areas in the Amazon. However, it is believed that within a short period of time this group could become a useful tool for estimating biodiversity and determining ecosystem health.

Spiders

There are currently more than 500 known Amazonian spider species in Brazil. However, this number ought to be at least four times higher, approximately 2,500. Panama, which is geographically far smaller but better explored in terms of spider fauna, has 1,260 species (Nentwig 1993); at least half of them could also exist in the Amazon, especially because of the lack of barriers for the immature forms, which are dispersed by wind (ballooning). The locations in the Amazon that are always cited by the classical literature on spiders are Belém and Manaus, but there are also more recent studies carried out in the Ducke reserve (close to Manaus) and in Caxiuanã.

The Spider Biodiversity Project was conducted in 1991 and 1996 with the participation of Dr. Ludwig Beck, Dr. Hubert Höfer, Dr. Thierry R. Gasnier, Dr. Antônio D. Brescovit, Rosamary Silva Vieira, and Alexandre Bonaldo. The main area of study was the Adolfo Ducke Forest Reserve, located 25 km north of Manaus, an area of approximately 10,000 hectares composed of dense terra firme primary forest on poor soil dating back to the tertiary era. Collections and experiments were carried out in an area approximately 3 x 5 kilometers, mainly on a plateau. The vegetation consists of 'stricto sensu terra firme forest'. There are only slight temperature variations in the region around Manaus. The average temperature is 27.9 °C in the warmest month (September) and 25.8 °C in the coolest month (February). The mean annual precipitation in the reserve is 2,480 mm; the wettest months are January and May, the driest are July and November.

During the first year of this project (1991) an inventory of the area's arachnid fauna was compiled based on a variety of manual (entomological umbrella, square leaf litter samples) and automatic (pitfall trap, soil and trunk trap, canopy fogging) collection methods. The researchers studied the spider community's structure (assemblage), abundance, species richness, distribution over layers, seasonality, etc. Hypotheses about the factors influencing diversity were formulated and tested throughout the following years, based on field observation, focused collection and experiments.

(More than 450 morpho-species were identified from these collections, and the list of spiders from the Ducke reserve amounts to 472 species, including some identifications and/or descriptions added by other authors.) At the beginning of the study approximately 30% of the species had not been described (at least >130 spp). Later on many of them were described by specialists who participated in the project or by other arachnologists provided with access to the material. The Ducke reserve is the type-location of 31 species. The 472 species are made up of 53 families and 260 genera (according to Platnick 1994). The families with the highest number of species are Salticidae (116), Araneida (80), and Theridiidae (58). Surprisingly rich are Corinnidae with 37 species, Ctenidae with 17, and Mygalomorphae with 22 species from 10 families. Genera with many species are *Micrathena* (16), *Dipoena* (13), *Alpaida* (12), *Corinna* (10), *Lyssomanes* (9), and *Argyrodes* (9 species).

The main ecological results are: the abundance of spiders in the Ducke reserve appears low compared with that of other forest areas, whether in the tropics (inundated forest areas in the region around Manaus), or in temperate zones (Germany, United States). The density of spiders on the ground decreased throughout these studies regardless of time and spatial variations, possibly due to the frequent presence of raiding army ants (*Eciton burchelli* and *Labidus preadaptar*). An independent study (R. Vieira's master's degree thesis) showed that these two species benefit considerably from some spiders (above all the nomadic *Ctenus*) as prey and, consequently, might influence the population numbers of these species and the local guild of nomadic spiders as a whole on the ground.

The high diversity of predators (ants, myriapods, wasps, toads, lizards, and birds) seems to have created a predatory pressure on spiders which has led to a multiplicity of cryptic forms and behaviors. These low occurrences might explain the coexistence of various similar species within the same habitat (T. Gasnier studied four *Ctenus* species for his Ph.D thesis). Taking such predation into account, those structures and characteristics of the habitats that provide refuge can be seen as important. The relationship between spider density and the quantity of leaf litter on the ground has been shown through a series of field experiments.

In Caxiuanã, Martins & Lise (1997) found more than 100 species in a single collection, which indicates how easy it is to collect spiders and to create a biodiversity hot spot by focused efforts. Likewise a single spider collection in the Mamirauá reserve resulted in more than 100 species.

Coddington has proposed that spiders be considered an indicator group of total biodiversity. There are projects in progress in the Amazon that incorporate his methodology. The potential, however, remains an issue for the future: at present spiders cannot provide guidance for the selection of conservation areas or actions in Amazonia.

Oribatidae mites

Oribatidae mites are an important group of soil mesofauna, and on the basis of collections in Amazonia, appear to represent a significant proportion of the animal biomass. They play an important role as decomposers of organic material. Their taxonomy, although very specialized, does not hinder their study. The majority of studies employ the concept of morpho-species and identification up to the level of genera, based on Balogh's guide books (1972, 1982). Unfortunately, frequently found immature forms cannot be identified as species, and sometimes not even as genera.

In general, Oribatidae collections (leaf litter and soil using a Berlese funnel) in the Amazon result in 20 to 50 species per area, and the fauna is highly diverse between locations. The potential of this group to supply information on total biodiversity and ecosystem conditions is high. However, we cannot use studies that have not yet been carried out. It is another group for the future.

Worms

With the death of Dr. Gilberto Righi, in 1998, Brazil lost a great man, an expert in worm taxonomy, zoogeography and biology. Righi not only contributed to identifying large worm collections from all parts of Brazil, but also to the training of new specialists.

More than 45 species from Mato Grosso and Rondônia are known (Righi 1990). At least another 35 have been identified from collections carried out in Pará, the Serra dos Carajás, and the Rio Tocantins valley. All in all the worm fauna in the Amazon may add up to more than 100 species. Their importance, however, is not in their numbers, but in their role in turning over soil. Future studies will certainly confirm the importance of this key group in identifying conservation areas and in the maintenance of ecosystem functions.

Other soil arthropods

Myriapods, especially Diplopoda, form another diversified group; however, their taxonomy does not allow them to be used as a reference for biodiversity conservation. It is estimated that the Amazon region holds more than 3,000 species of Diplopoda, but only 200 have been described. Centipedes (Chilopoda) comprise a smaller number of species which may show greater geographical distribution.

Collembola is another important group of soil-dwelling animals. There are currently ongoing fauna and taxonomy studies which might help to confirm Collembola as a key group for the evaluation of total biodiversity and ecosystem status. There are approximately 80 Collembola species in the Amazon region. They are one of the dominant groups of the soil mesofauna. Oliveira and Macambira are two researchers dedicated to Collembola studies and who carry out research on their communities in Amazonia. The taxonomy still requires the assistance of specialists for species identification.

Another group requiring long-term studies and intensive collections is the group of pseudoscorpions. Adis and Mahnert (1990) cite a fauna in Manaus which contains 26 genera and 60 species, several with specified habitats: in forest areas which are flooded or not, by black or white water. Although the group has the potential to provide information, their taxonomy is still complicated for nonspecialists. More than 120 species can be found in the Amazon region (Adis, manuscript).

Dragonflies

Dragonflies (Odonata) constitute a group of numerous species, easy to observe and collect, with updated taxonomy and active specialists. Brazilian collections in museums and research institutes permit identification. There is great potential for the use of dragonflies in identifying and monitoring conservation areas in the Amazon region.

Aquatic insects

Ephemerids are not numerous, and some rivers or rivulets may present apparent monocultures or only a few species. Nevertheless, the group is frequently cited as a potential indicator of the changed states of watercourses. It is often suggested that ephemerids be used to monitor water pollution levels in mining projects, especially where there is waste. Collecting chrysalises would be recommended, even when the current taxonomy is based on adults. Breeding projects in laboratories might help to fill this information gap.

Aquatic Diptera

Due to their low tolerance to lack of oxygen in water, Chironomidae larvae are used as indicators of river pollution, especially when caused by industries or the use of chemical fertilizers in agriculture. Related research work in the Amazon on Chironomidae has not occurred yet, but research on Simuliidae indicates that the quality of a habitat, measured in terms of oxygenation and water purity, may influence the density and composition of gnat larvae.

Fresh water shrimps

Given their importance for human consumption and their role as a keystone species for aquatic communities in Amazonia, the fresh water shrimp species (mostly belonging to the genus *Macrobrachium*) deserve attention as indicators of ecosystem functioning. The total number of species is less than 50, but in the Amazon estuary these produce thousands of tons of protein per annum, which support rural and urban populations of the region. The species are important components of the aquatic food chain and are also found in the stomach content of fish in many parts of the Amazon.

The taxonomy of the group allows species identification, and revision work is currently in progress. As they are easy to collect, shrimps should become a key group for research on aquatic systems. For the time being we have to wait for basic studies on the biology and niches of different species.

Other aquatic groups

Bivalves (Molusca: Bivalva) in Amazonia appear to inhabit only white water rivers and streams, and are not found in black waters. Their ecological role in the region is not well understood, neither is their tolerance to environmental changes. Protozoa (Thecamoebae Protozoa, Rhizopoda) from rivulets close to Manaus have been suggested by I. Walker (1982) as indicators of water quality.

Proposals

Given that the data on invertebrates, especially insects, does not allow the selection of areas for the conservation of the biodiversity of these animals, the choice of areas should be based on plant diversity (assuming that the majority of insects, for example, can be associated to plant species) and on the distribution of different ecosystems.

Major emphasis must be given to the protection of habitats, above all to the safeguarding of locations which are known to be home to rich invertebrate faunas. In order to conserve biological diversity it is essential to maintain areas that are at present protected by means of management plans and to encourage environmental education activities. In addition, in order to conserve invertebrate fauna, the original vegetation of privately owned land should be maintained, avoiding deforestation or fire.

It is proposed that igapós in Amazonia be considered for biodiversity conservation areas. Igapós are forests seasonally flooded by black water. They comprise less than 1% of the entire area of the region and are of no use for agriculture. As it is an environment subject to periodical flooding, the invertebrates living there have developed a series of ecological strategies and morphological adaptations (Adis 1988). Many species normally considered to be members of soil groups migrate vertically towards the forest canopies. The only places where such ecosystems are protected are the Anavilhanas and Jaú national parks. The proposal is to prohibit landscape changes in igapó areas, which occur mainly through logging.

It is proposed to consider the Amazonian floodplain forests as sites for the creation of new conservation areas. They comprise around 2% of the total area of the region, but are where human occupation has been most intense, and the exploitation of natural resources most predatory. Logging activities in the floodplains threaten the habitats of many invertebrates which have adapted to flooding and are therefore restricted to living in these areas. Up to now only a few conservation areas include floodplain habitats; the most important being the Mamirauá reserve. As regards the creation of new conservation areas, it is proposed to give priority to floodplain sites at the mouth of the Rio Madeira and in the Amazon estuary. There is, for example, no conservation area on the Ilha de Marajó.

It is proposed that enclave areas such as the grasslands (campinas) of the Rio Negro and the rocky plains of central Amazonia be considered for conservation areas. Again, there are no data that can confirm the presumed high levels of endemism in these areas, but the soil and microclimate characteristics suggest that the fauna must be quite diverse, and therefore a possible target for conservation action.

It is proposed that Amazonian caves be considered for conservation areas. The fauna in the caves of the region is quite distinct, occasionally resembling that of the Andes. The caves of the Rio Xingu valley were investigated in 1986 and 1987 by students of the Federal University of Pará, who collected many species which at the time had not yet been recorded for that region. The caves of the Chapada dos Guimarães and the Serra dos Carajás also contain insect and other arthropod fauna which are quite different from those found in rainforests. For this reason caves need greater legal protection against depredation and vandalism.

Environmental education campaigns will be necessary to inform the public about the importance of invertebrates and to stress their importance for biodiversity conservation planning for Amazonia.

Our current knowledge of Amazonian invertebrates is insufficient to allow for effective management or to ensure conservation. Therefore it is vital to acquire better knowledge of these species and the ecosystems in which they can be found, and this in turn requires more in depth collecting and study. In addition to individual research projects in existing conservation areas, it is proposed that a federal Amazon biological survey service be created with the mandate to compile an inventory of the region's biota, establish major collections, and support to systematic studies on the geographical distribution of species and on conservation biology, in cooperation with museums and other national research centers. The collections must be preserved, classified taxonomically, and kept in adequate museum facilities that are accessible to the scientific community. The establishment of this biological survey service is essential to stimulate and focus research efforts, and to make best use of the time that is left before many invertebrate species are lost forever. Scientific biodiversity issues can only be addressed and resolved by means of large collections of organisms, which is why the creation of a national biological survey service in Amazonia is proposed.

Bibliography

ADIS, J. Thirty Million Arthropod Species: too Many or too Few? *J. Trop. Ecol.* n. 6, p. 115-8, 1990.

ADIS, J.; V. MAHNERT. On the Species Composition of Pseudoscorpiones (Arachnida) from Amazonian Dryland and Inundation Forests in Brazil. *Rev. Suisse Zool.*, v. 97, n. 1, p. 49-53, 1990.

ADIS, J. et al. Arthropods from the Canopy of Inundated and Terra Firme Forests Near Manaus, Brazil, with Critical Considerations on the Pyrethrum Fogging Technique. *Stud. Neotrop. Fauna Environm*, v. 19, n. 4, p. 223-236, 1984.

ANDRADE NETO, H. G. Taxa de exploração de iscas por formigas em uma floresta de terra firme na Amazônia oriental. *Bol. Mus. Paraense Emílio Goeldi, sér. Zool*, n. 3, p. 219-234, 1987.

ARAÚJO, R. L. *Catálogo dos isoptera do Novo Mundo*. Rio de Janeiro: Academia Brasileira de Ciências, 1977.

BALOGH, J. *The Oribatid Genera of the World*. Budapest: Akademiai Kiado, 1972.

_____. *The Oribatid Genera of the World*, 2nd ed. Budapest: Akademiai Kiado, 1982.

BATES, H. W. Contributions to an Insect Fauna of the Amazon Valley. Lepidoptera: Papilionidae. *J. Ent.*, n. 1, p. 218-245, 1861.

_____. Contributions to an Insect Fauna of the Amazon Valley. Lepidoptera: Heliconidae. *Trans. Linn. Soc. Lond*, n. 23, p. 495-566, 1862.

_____. *The Naturalist on the Amazon River*. London: J. Murray, 1863.

_____. Contributions to an Insect Fauna of the Amazon Valley. Lepidoptera: Nymphalidae. *J. Ent.*, n. 2, p. 175-213, 1864.

BENSON, W. W. Amazon Ant Plants. In: PRANCE, G. T.; LOVEJOY, T. E. *Amazonia: Key Environments*. London: Pergammon, p. 239-265, 1985.

BENSON, W. W.; HARADA, A. Y. Local Diversity of Tropical and Temperate Ant Faunas (Hymenoptera, Formicidae). *Acta Amazonica*, v. 18, n. 3/4, p. 275-289, 1988 [1989].

BOLTON, B. *Identification Guide to the Ant Genera of the World*. Cambridge (Mass.): Harvard University Press, 1994.

_____. A Taxonomic and Zoogeographical Census of the Extant ant Taxa (Hymenoptera: Formicidae). *J. Nat. Hist.*, n. 29, p. 1037-1056, 1995.

BRANDÃO, C. R. F. Adendos ao catálogo abreviado das formigas da região Neotropical (Hymenoptera: Formicidae). *Rev. Brasil. Entomol.*, n. 35, p. 319-412, 1991.

BROWN Jr., K. S. Diversity of Brazilian Lepidoptera: History of Study, Methods for Measurement, and Use ss Indicator for Genetic, Specific and System Richness. In: BICUDO, C. E. M.; MENEZES, N. *Biodiversity in Brazil: A First Approach*. São Paulo: CNPq, 1996. p. 221-254.

_____. Diversidade biológica na Bacia Amazônica: distribuição, fontes, multiplicação, conservação, utilização e manutenção por populações tradicionais. Mérida (Venezuela): M. Monastério, 1999.

COVER, S. P. et al. The Ant Community of a Tropical Lowland Rainforest Site in Peruvian Amazonia. In: VEERESH, G. K. et. al. *Social Insects and the Environment. Proceedings of the 11th International Congress of IUSSI, 1990*. New Delhi: Oxford & IBH Publishing Co., p. 699-700, 1990.

ERWIN, T. L. Tropical Forests: Their Richness in Coleoptera and Other Arthropod Species. *Coleopt. Bull.*, n. 36, p. 74-75, 1982.

_____. Beetles and Other Insects of Tropical Forest Canopies at Manaus, Brazil, Sampled by Insecticidal Fogging. In: SUTTON, S. L. at al. *Tropical Rain Forest: Ecology and Management*. Oxford: Blackwell, 1983. p. 59-75.

_____. Tropical Forest Canopies: the Last Biotic Frontier. *Bull. Ent. Soc. Amer.*, n. 29, p. 14-19, 1983.

_____. The Tropical Forest Canopy: the Heart of Biotic Diversity. In: WILSON, E. O. *Biodiversity*. Washington: National Academy Press, 1988.

FITTKAU, E. A.; KLINGE, H.. The Biomass and Trophic Structure of the Central Amazonian Rain Forest Ecosystem. *Biotropica*, n. 5, p. 2-14, 1973.

FOWLER, H. G. Herbivory and Assemblage Structure of Myrmecophytous Understory Plants and their Associated Ants in the Central Amazon. *Insect. Soc*, v. 40, n. 1, p. 137-145, 1993.

FRANKS, N. R.; BOSSERT, W. H. The Influence of Swarm Raiding Army Ants on the Patchiness and Diversity of a Tropical Leaf Litter Ant Community. In: SUTTON, S. L., *Tropical rain forest: ecology and management. Special Publication of the British Ecological Societ*, n. 2. Oxford: Blackwell, 1983. p. 151-163.

HARPER, L. H. The Conservation of Ant-Following Birds in Central Amazonian Forest Fragments. *Biology Department*. Albany: State University of New York at Albany, p. 226, 1988.

HUXLEY, C.; CUTLER, D. F. *Ant-plant Interactions*. London: Oxford University Press, 1991.

JAFFE, K. et al. Mirmecofauna de los tepuyes Marahuaka y Huachamakare (Territorio Federal Amazonas, Venezuela). *Acta Terramaris*, n. 1, p. 33-37, 1989.

JANZEN, D. H. Insect Diversity of a Costa Rican Dry Forest: Why Keep It and How? *Biol. J. Linn. Soc. Lond*, n. 30, p. 343-356, 1987.

KEMPF, W. W. A Survey of the Ants of the Soil Fauna in Surinam. *Studia Ent.*, n. s., n. 4, p. 481-524, 1961.

_____. Levantamento das formigas da mata amazônica nos arredores de Belém, Pará, Brasil. *Studia Ent.*, n. s., n. 13, p. 321-344, 1970.

KETELHUT, S. *Formigas numa floresta da Amazônia Oriental*. Tese (Ph.D. in Zoology). Belém, Universidade Federal do Pará e Museu Paraense Emílio Goeldi, 1999.

LEGG, G. A Note on the Diversity of World Lepidoptera. *Biol. J. Linn. Soc. Lond*, n. 10, p. 343-347, 1978.

LESTON, D. The Ant Mosaic: Tropical Tree Crops and the Limiting of Pests and Diseases. *PANS (Pest Artic. News Summ.)*, n. 19, p. 311-341, 1973.

LESTON, D. A Neotropical Ant Mosaic. *Ann. Entomol. Soc. Amer*, n. 71, p. 649-653, 1978.

MACKAY, W. P.; VINSON, S. B. A Guide to Species Identification of New World Ants (Hymenoptera: Formicidae). *Sociobiology*, n. 16, p. 3-47, 1989.

MAJER, J. D.; DELABIE, J. H. C. Comparison of the Ant Communities of Annually Inundated and Terra Firme Forests at Trombetas in the Brazilian Amazon. *Insect. Soc*, n. 41, p. 343-359, 1994.

MARTINS, M. B.; LISE, A.. As aranhas. In.: LISBOA, P. L. B. *Caxiuanã*. Belém: Museu Paraense Emílio Goeldi, 1997. p. 381-388.

MATHEWS, A. G. A. *Studies on Termites from the Mato Grosso State, Brazil*. Rio de Janeiro: Academia Brasileira de Ciências, 1977.

MAY, R. M. How Many Species Are There on Earth? *Science*, n. 241, p. 1441-1449, 1988.

MOSS, A. M. The *Papilios* of Pará. *Novit. Zool*, n. 26, p. 295-319, 1919.

_____. Some Generalizations on *Adelpha*, a Neotropical Genus of Nymphalid Butterflies of the Group Limenitidi. *Nov. Zool*, n. 39, p. 12-20, 1933.

_____. Biological Notes on Some Hesperiidae of Pará and the Amazon. *Acta Zool. Lilloana, Tucumán*, v. 2, n. 3, p. 27-79, 1949.

NENTWIG, W. *Spiders of Panama: Biogeography, Investigation, Phenology, Check List, Key and Bibliography of a Tropical Spider Fauna*. Gainesville (Florida): Sandhill Crane Press, 1993.

NOGUEIRA NETO, P. *Vida e criação de abelhas indígenas sem ferrão*. Sao Paulo: Ed. Nogueirapis, 1997.

OTERO, L. S. *Insetos brasileiros e seu meio*. Tokyo: Koyo Shoin Co., 1972.

OTERO, L. S.; MARIGO, L. C. *Borboletas: beleza e comportamento das espécies*. Rio de Janeiro: Marigo Comunicação Visual, 1990.

_____. *Borboletas de Carajás. Butterflies of Carajás*. Rio de Janeiro: Companhia Vale do Rio Doce, 1992.

O'TOOLE, C.; RAW, A.. *Bees of the World*. New York & Oxford: Facts on File, 1991.

PATRIZIA, L. et al. Distribution of Extrafloral Nectaries in Different Vegetation Types in Amazonian Brazil. *Flora*, n. 185, p. 33-38, 1991.

PERRY, D. *A vida na copa da floresta*. São Paulo: Interação, 1991.

PLATNICK, N. I. *Advances in Spider Taxonomy 1988-1991, with Synonymies and Transfers 1940-1980*. New York: New York Entomological Society, 1994.

RICHARDS, O. W. *The Social Wasps of the Americas Excluding the Vespinae*. London: British Museum (Natural History), 1978.

RIGHI, G. *Oligochaeta de Rondônia*. Brasília: CNPq, 1990.

SCHIELDS, O. World Numbers of Butterflies. *J. Lepid. Soc*, n. 43, p. 178-183, 1989.

STORK, N. E. Insect Diversity: Facts, Fiction and Speculation. *Biol. J. Linn. Soc. Lond*, n. 35, p. 321-337, 1988.

STRYMPL, A. Vinte e seis anos caçando *agrias* na Amazônia. *Bol. Mus. Paraense Emílio Goeldi*, n. 10, p. 185-209, 1949.

VASCONCELOS, H. L. Distribution of Atta (*Hymenoptera: Formicidae*) in Terra Firme Rain Forest of Central Amazonia: Density, Species Composition and Preliminary Results on Effects of Forest Fragmentation. *Acta Amazonia*, n. 18, p. 309-315, 1988.

_____. Foraging Activity of Two Species of Leaf-Cutting Ants (*Atta*) in a Primary Rain Forest of the Central Amazon. *Insect Soc*, n. 37, p. 131-146, 1990.

VERHAAGH, M. Clearing a Tropical Rain Forest: Effects on the Ant Fauna. In.: ERDELEN, W, et al. *Tropical Ecosystems: Systems Characteristics, Utilization Patterns, and Conservation Issues*. Margraf Scientific Books, p. 59-68, 1991.

WALKER, I. The Benthic Litter-Dwelling Macrofauna of the Amazonian Forest Stream Taruma-Mirim: Patterns of Colonization and their Implications for Community Stability. *Hydrobiologia*, v. 291, n. 2, p. 75-92, 1994.

WALLACE, A. R. *A Narrative of Travels on the Amazon and Rio Negro, with an Account of the Native Tribes and Observations on the Climate, Geology, and Natural History of the Amazon Valley*. London: Reeve & Co, 1853.

_____. On the Habits of Butterflies of the Amazon Valley. *Trans. Ent. Soc. Lond*, v. 2, n. 2, p. 253-264, 1854.

WILSON, E. O. The Arboreal Ant Fauna of Peruvian Amazon Forests: a First Assessment. *Biotropica*, n. 19, p. 245-251, 1987.

AQUATIC BIOTA

Ronaldo B. Barthem *Museu Paraense Emílio Goeldi; Ministério da Ciência e Tecnologia*

INTRODUCTION

Aquatic environments, marine and inland, are home to a large diversity of life from different kingdoms, from algae and bacteria, macrophytes and arthropods (crustaceans and insects) to vertebrates. Despite containing fewer species than terrestrial environments (May 1988), aquatic environments encompass a greater diversity of phyla (Ray 1988). Their biodiversity is still little known, and may be comparable to terrestrial biodiversity (Ryman et al. 1995)

The need to conserve aquatic biodiversity has become more apparent in the last two or three decades. The loss of genetic resources, habitats and ecosystems, together with species extinction and other issues have led to discussion in scientific journals such as *Conservation Biology* and *Biological Conservation* and by organizations dedicated to the principles of biological conservation, such as the World Conservation Union (IUCN), the World Resources Institute (WRI) and the World Wide Fund for Nature (WWF) (Ryman et al. 1995). The need for conservation is borne out by the present status of aquatic biodiversity, which is very precarious, reveals astonishingly high rates of loss, and is aggravated by an almost complete failure to manage aquatic resource use (Philipp et al. 1995).

The state of the world's aquatic habitats is not good (Armantrout 1995) and efforts to conserve aquatic systems lag far behind those devoted to terrestrial systems (Ryman et al. 1995). Some of the difficulties of protecting aquatic habitats arise from the fact that they differ from terrestrial habitats in the following ways: (i) aquatic habitats are continuous, like the atmosphere, and many are international, which facilitates environmental damage, such as the spread of pollutants, and makes effective control difficult; (ii) terrestrial species are more attractive than aquatic species which, besides being less visible, are usually exploited by traditional fishing-programs aimed at protecting pandas, for instance, tend to be better supported than those for controlling shark fishing; (iii) fish species, especially freshwater species, display a greater genetic diversity within their populations compared to terrestrial vertebrates, and are also more influenced by environmental changes and more prone to human-induced genetic alterations (Ryman et al. 1995).

Of the fauna inhabiting aquatic environments, fish represent more than half the world's known vertebrate species with 24,618 fish species as against 23,550 other vertebrate species (Nelson 1994). Fish are widely distributed all over the world (Moyle and Cech 1982) and are of high economic importance, with natural populations exploited by fishing in both marine and inland aquatic environments (Pitcher and Hart 1996). Given that this taxonomic group is more widely known than any other group inhabiting the aquatic environment, this paper will focus on the assessment and establishment of priority actions for the conservation and sustainable use of fish in the Amazonian biome.

METHODOLOGY

Priority actions for the conservation and sustainable use of fish from the Amazonian biome are hampered by the lack of knowledge of the taxonomic make-up and distribution patterns of Amazonian ichthyofauna, without which it is impossible for researchers to identify endangered areas, determine priority areas for biodiversity conservation, and detect future alterations in the composition of the fauna (Menezes 1996). Given this, this paper avoids seeking actions that would need to be based upon indicators such as endemism and species richness. The premise is therefore that, if the mechanisms that control aquatic ecosystems are conserved, the chances that the aquatic biodiversity will also be conserved will be high. The paper will thus focus mainly on factors that determine, in the most integrated way, how the aquatic system currently functions.

What then are these factors, or rather, what is threatening this system?. This paper presents a review of our knowledge of the aquatic environment of Amazonia and its annual cycles, and of fish diversity and its response to the annual environmental changes. It also presents the various types of use of the aquatic resource and the main threats posed to fish and to the environment as a whole. It then discusses a set of suggested priority actions for the conservation of the aquatic system of the Amazonian biome.

THE ENVIRONMENT

The size of the Amazon basin and its environmental heterogeneity are factors of crucial importance for the maintenance of its high level of diversity. The basin's characteristics and its landscape are macro aspects to be considered within the aquatic system. The floodplain, on the other hand, is an environment of specific importance for the aquatic communities occupying a large portion of the Amazon basin. Finally, the annual cycle is basically determined by the hydrological cycle, which controls biological cycles and determines the composition of both the fauna and flora along the river.

The basin

The drainage area of the Amazon river, together with that of the Tocantins, totals 6,869,000 km² (Cobraphi 1984), which is equivalent to about one and a half times the size of the second largest basin in the world, the Congo river basin in Africa (Marlier 1973), and about one third of the total area of South America. The discharge of the Amazon river reaches levels in excess of 6,700 km³ per year (Cobraphi 1984), which is nearly five times as much as the Congo river, whose discharge ranks second in the world, and is 20% of all the freshwater poured into the planet's oceans by all rivers (Milliman and Meade 1983). Although the Tocantins is generally considered a tributary of the Amazon, it is actually a different basin, since the mouths of these rivers are partially separated by the Ilha de Marajó. For the purposes of this paper, the Amazon basin is defined as the drainage areas of the Amazon and Tocantins rivers.

Nine countries are home to the Amazon forest and seven of them, Brazil, Bolivia, Peru, Colombia, Ecuador, Venezuela and Guiana, are drained by the Amazon-Tocantins basin (Table 1). The geographic distribution of these two rivers is as follows: 68% of their area is in Brazil, 11% in Peru, 10% in Bolivia, 6% in Colombia, 2% in Ecuador. The remaining 3% is located in Venezuela and Guiana. The Amazon basin occupies half the total area of Brazil, Peru and Bolivia together, and the Amazon forest encompasses almost three quarters of the territories of Guiana and Suriname. This gives a measure of the importance of this region to the member countries of the Treaty for Amazon Cooperation.

The longest stretch of the Amazon river rises over 5,000 meters above sea level in the Yarupa glaciers in the Peruvian Andes and flows for some 5,890 kilometers before reaching the sea (Barbosa 1962, Salati et al.1983). During its descent, this river changes names seven times and receives thousands of tributaries, many of which are over 2,000 kilometers long. The Amazon is first called the Apurimac and descends 800 kilometers through the Peruvian Andes before it reaches the Mantaro, where its name changes to the Ene. The Ene flows a little less than 150 kilometers before it joins the Perene. From here onward it is called the Tombo for the next 150 kilometers until it joins the Urubamba to form the Ucayali. It then flows for 1,500 kilometers until it meets the Marañon. From this point to its mouth, the river is flanked on both sides by a continuous floodplain. After joining the Marañon, the river is known as the Amazonas, a name that it keeps until it meets the Javari at the border with Brazil, at which point it becomes known as the Solimões. At this point it has descended 2,969 kilometers through Peruvian and Colombian territory. In Brazil, the main river keeps the name Solimões until it reaches the Rio Negro, where it once again becomes known as the Amazonas. It flows for a total of 2,921 kilometers through Brazilian territory. The main tributaries of the Amazon basin are the Urubamba, Pachitea, Pacaya, Tapiuche, Marañon, Nanay, Napo, Javair, Putumayo-Içá, Jutái, Juruá, Caquetá-Japurá, Purus, Negro, Madeira, Trombetas, Tapajós and Xingu (Barthem et al. 1995).

The landscape

The Amazon landscape is basically shaped by three geological structures: the Andean cordillera to the west, the crystalline Guiana shields to the north and Brazilian shields to the south, and the sedimentary basin in the center. The Andean cordillera was formed by the westward movement of the South American tectonic plate as it separated from Africa at the end of the Mesozoic era, over 70 million years ago. The landscape extends over almost the entire western side of the continent, forming a row of mountains and volcanoes which separates the eastern and the western basins and comprises the highest elevations in the Americas, including its highest point Mount Aconcágua. The Andean cordillera is divided into the northern, central, and southern Andes, and the Amazon basin drains the eastern slopes of the northern and central Andes (Barthem et al. 1995). Due to very high precipitation levels in the region, an average 2,127 mm/year and as much as 8,000 mm/year on the slopes of the Andes, the process of erosion is intense, and the heavy minerals leached into the water system make a substantial contribution to the sedimentation on the bed of the Amazon river (Landim et al. 1983). The amount of sediment carried into the Atlantic Ocean is around 0.82 to 0.93 x 10³ million tons/year (Meade et al. 1979), which represents the world's third highest discharge of sediments from a river, after the Ganges (India and Pakistan) and the Yellow River (China) (Milliman and Meade 1983).

The crystalline shields are geological formations molded in the Pre-Cambrian period from granite and gneiss with heights predominantly above 200 meters (Salati et al. 1983). The most prominent elevations are found in the north, on the Imeri, Tapirapecó, Parima, Pacaraima, Acarai and Tumucumaque ranges. Elevations to the south are lower, such as those of the Pacaás Novos, Parecis, Apiacá, Cachimbo, Seringa and Carajás ranges (Brazilian Institute of Geography and Statistics – IBGE 1977).

The sedimentary Amazon basin amounts to some 2 x 10⁶ km² and was formed during the Cenozoic era by sediments brought down from the crystalline shields and the Andes, which were deposited on the river and lake floors during the Tertiary and Quaternary periods. The surface is for the most part level, with a slope of around 20 mm/km, which accounts for the complex system of meanders and the low altitude of cities far from the mouth of the river, such as Manaus (40 m above the sea level and 1,287 kilometers upstream), Tabatinga or Letícia (65 m above sea level and 2,920 kilometers upstream), and Iquitos (107 m

TABLE 1 - Drainage area of the Amazon Basin and Forest					
	A	B	C	D	E
Country	Amazon Basin (x 1,000 km²)	Amazon Forest (x 1,000 km²)	Country area (x 1,000 km²)	A/C %	B/C %
Brazil	4,657	5,003	8,512	54	59
Peru	770	770	1,285	60	60
Bolivia	724	724	1,099	66	66
Colombia	399	399	1,139	35	35
Ecuador	133	133	284	47	47
Venezuela	56	56	912	6	6
Guiana	*	160	215	*	74
Suriname	*	125	164	*	76
French Guiana	*	*	544	*	*
Total	6,869	7,085	14,154		

* No data available.

above sea level and 3,400 kilometers upstream) (Salati et al. 1983).

The three geological structures are fundamentally important for the chemical quality of the water, as well as for the variety and growth rate of fish, as the drainage area has a decisive impact on the chemical composition of Amazonian rivers. Current classification of water types follows the geological structures and identifies three types: white, clear, and black waters (Sioli 1967, 1975; Sioli and Klinge 1965).

White water rivers are those which contain large amounts of suspended material and, as a consequence, present high levels of turbidity with a visibility of around 20 cm. They rise on the slopes of the Andes, and include the Amazonas, Napo, Marañon, Tigre, Juruá, Purus and Madeira rivers. Water conductivity is high, usually above 60 micromho/cm, and the pH is close to neutral (6.5 to 7) due to the presence of diluted carbon which serves as a buffer. A direct relationship between sediment load and river level can be observed in these rivers (Guerra et al. 1990, Schmidt 1982, Meade et al. 1979).

Clear water rivers have very transparent water, with visibility reaching down to a depth of 5 meters, as in the case of the Tapajós, Xingu and Trombetas rivers. They rise on the crystalline Guiana and Brazilian shields, whose soils are heavily eroded with little or almost nothing left to be carried away by the water. Consequently, these rivers are chemically pure with very low conductivity (6 to 50 micromho/cm and an almost neutral pH, 5 to 6).

Black water rivers such as the Negro and Urubu, contain high concentrations of humic acids in colloidal form, which accounts for their dark color and low pH (4 to 5.5). They rise on the shields and in the sedimentary basin, draining areas of low vegetation on the sandy soils of the campina grasslands. (Here organic material is unable to fully decompose and the porosity of the soil allows the humic acid colloids to be carried away by the river.) The water is chemically purer than that of the clear water rivers with conductivity of up to 8 micromho/cm.

The floodplain

The basins of the main rivers in South America, namely the Amazon, Orinoco, Magdalena, Paraná-Paraguay and São Francisco rivers, share a number of physiographic characteristics, such as large areas of poorly drained plains and heavy seasonal rains, which contribute to the formation of extensive floodplains (Klinge et al. 1990). This environment, defined as an aquatic-terrestrial transition zone (ATTZ) or seasonally flooded area ('an area periodically flooded by the lateral overflowing of rivers and lakes and/or by direct precipitation or by underground water sources, forming as a result an environment with specific physical and chemical characteristics which trigger adaptive morphological, anatomical, physiological, phenotypic and/or ethological responses in the biota, shaping the community structure') has a critical influence on the composition and productivity of the fish of the Amazon river basin (Junk et al. 1989).

Such areas may be flooded by rivers overflowing, by local rains and by tidal effects. Junk and Furch (1993) define the types of flooded areas in Amazonia as: 1) areas in which flooding is caused by rivers overflowing, stretching from Pucallpa in Peru to close to the mouth of the Amazon and whose width varies along the length of the river; 2) forests periodically flooded by rainfall, in poorly drained areas of the Rio Negro; 3) savannas periodically flooded by rainfall on the upper stretches of the Branco, Araguaia, Xingu, and Madeira rivers; and 4) coastal areas flooded by the tides.

Estimates for the total inundated area are still preliminary, in view of the differences in the methods and scales employed. The total flooded area was estimated by Bayley and Petrere (1989) to be 180,360 km^2, or 2.6% of the area of the basin. The floodplain in the Peruvian Amazon region was estimated to be 62,100 km^2 by Salo et al. (1986) and the active flooded area was estimated by Bayley (1981) to be 41,600 km^2. The system formed by the confluence of the Beni, Madre de Dios, Mamoré and Itenez rivers comprises about 145 rivers and 37 lakes (Arteaga 1991), and the Itenez contains a flooded area of 100,000 to 150,000 km^2 (Lauzanne et al. 1990). The confluence of the Solimões, Japurá, Jutaí and Içá rivers in Brazil has a flooded area of 49,530 km^2 and, in the lower Amazon at the confluence of the Amazon, Madeira, Tapajós and Xingu rivers, estimates are that the flooded area is somewhere around 37,000 km^2 (Bayley and Petrere 1989).

The floodplain contains areas with special characteristics, which can be classified as igapó, várzea lake, flooded grasslands, gallery forests, lakes formed on alluvial islands, ox-bow lakes, secondary channels (*paraná*) and main channels (Sioli 1975). These areas are of extreme importance for fish, which are distributed in different habitats according to their characteristics.

The hydrological cycle

Seasonality in the Amazon basin is characterized by rainfall and by alterations in river levels. Rainfall within the basin is not uniform, neither in relation to the time of year nor in respect of different locations. Rainfall is contingent on the position of the sun during the year and, as the Amazon basin extends into both hemispheres, two distinct periods of heavy rain occur: one in the southern summer, when heavy rains cause the overflowing of the southern rivers, and another in the northern summer, when overflowing occurs on the headwaters of the northern rivers (IBGE 1977). Seasonal variations in rainfall cause fluctuations in water levels, which vary according to the time of year and the location. The usual annual fluctuation pattern is unimodal, although it tends to be bimodal in some regions of the Andes (Marlier 1973). The average annual water level fluctuation also varies from place to place. In Manaus, the average is around 10 meters; in Parantins, 5 meters; and in Iquitos, 7 meters (IBGE 1977).

The hydrological cycle of the river fluctuates in phases, which flood marginal areas and can be considered as the main force influencing the biota (Junk et al. 1989). Overflow occurs when the volume of water increases to such an extent that the channel is insufficient to contain the flow. The extent of flooding in Amazonia appears to be closely linked to the El Niño phenomenon, as the driest periods in Amazonia correspond to climatic anomalies in the tropical Pacific (Richey et al. 1989).

THE FAUNA

Diversity of fish fauna

Fish inhabiting inland aquatic environments can be of two types: euryhaline and strictly fresh water fish. Euryhaline fish are marine species capable of swimming into rivers and lakes, such as the bull shark *Carcharhinus leucas* and the largetooth sawfish *Pristis perotteti*, and their conservation is not fundamentally associated with inland waters. On the other hand, strictly freshwater fish species are physically limited to hydrographic basins, and these are the areas that need to be considered for the conservation and management of this fish fauna.

Among the zoogeographical regions for freshwater fish, the Neotropical region is the world's richest in terms of species and yet the least known (Moyle and Cech 1982). The number of fish species in South America remains unknown, with the greatest fish diversity concentrated in Amazonia (Menezes 1996). Roberts (1972) estimates that the number of fish species present in the Amazon basin is greater than that found in all the other basins in the world. Böhlke et al. (1978) consider that the present knowledge of the South American ichthyofauna is comparable to that of the United States and Canada a century ago and that at least 40% of the fish species in South America have not yet been described, which would increase the number of known fish species from 1,300 to over 1,800. Menezes (1996) estimates that there are around 3,000 fish species in South America. The composition of the Amazon ichthyofauna is based mainly on the species of the superorder Ostariophysi, which comprises about 85% of Amazon species, 43% of which belong to the order Characiformes, 39% in the order Siluriformes and 3% in the Gymnotiformes. The remaining species belong to 14 other families from different orders (Lowe-McConnell 1987). Appendix 1 shows a list of commercial Amazonian species and their popular names based on Barthem et al. (1995).

The distribution of Amazonian ichthyofauna diversity among the different regions is still difficult to assess as very few papers on the field have been published on diversity in different parts of the Amazon basin. The Colombian Amazon is said to be home to over 500 fish species, of which 241 have been listed for the Caquetá-Japurá basin (Castro and Arboleda 1988). Ortega and Vari (1986) have listed 736 species for Peru, 85% of which relating to the Amazon portion of the country. Ovchynnyk (1971) describes 276 fish species for Ecuador, and Barriga (1991) increases this figure to 708 species, distributed among 307 genera and 61 families of freshwater fish. Lauzane and Loubens (1985) report 280 species on the Mamoré and Bustamante (1991) reports 473 species on the Napo, both in Bolivia.

The Brazilian Amazon comprises 68% of the drainage area of the Amazon basin and diversity assessment studies have been carried out on a sub-regional basis. Goulding et al. (1988) have identified at least 450 fish species in the Rio Negro, but believe this number could exceed 700 if the various biotypes were to be properly sampled. Santos (1986/87) has found over 260 species in the Jamari, Machado, Guaporé, and Mamoré rivers in the state of Rondônia. Bayley (1982) found over 220 fish species in the Solimões floodplain near Manaus. Santos et al. (1984) have inventoried over 300 species on the lower Tocantins alone. Ferreira et al. (1998) list more than 130 species of commercial fish in the floodplains around Santarém. Many of these species are widely distributed, such as the migratory *tambaqui* (Araújo-Lima and Goulding 1998) and the large catfish. Other species have a limited distribution; they are confined to particular regions as a result of environmental barriers or of the chemical characteristics of the water. *Symphysodon discus*, for instance, is confined to clear waters, while *S. aequifasciata* is confined to white waters (Junk 1997).

The high diversity of fish in the Neotropical region, in particular the Amazon basin, can be explained by various factors, such as the age and size of the drainage system; high environmental heterogeneity, which favors a wide diversity of niches; and the history of rivers being captured from neighboring basins over geological time, resulting in the interchange of fauna. These are some of the causes of high indices of both alpha and beta diversity (Lowe-McConnell 1987). However we know that the numbers shown above underestimate the real picture, as finding new species is still very common and there are numerous groups whose description merits greater attention. One example that illustrates the backward state of knowledge of Amazonian ichthyofauna is the case of the recently described *Merodontotus tigrinum*, a species of large Pimelodidae (Siluriformes), which, although unknown to science, was already well known to local fishermen (Britski 1981). It is not difficult to suppose that there must be very high levels of endemism in the headwaters of the basin (Menezes 1996) and that future revisions may lead to the separation of species currently considered as single species, including some that are extremely common, such as the giant catfish, *Brachyplatystoma filamentosum*.

Biological productivity

The trophic chain of large water bodies usually starts with phytoplankton, as is the case in the oceans. However, the phytoplankton productivity of Amazonian rivers is usually low. White water rivers, which usually exhibit high concentrations of nutrients, are also very turbid with a very narrow euphotic zone. Turbulence caused by the current of these rivers prevents the phytoplankton from being exposed to sunlight for the necessary minimum period of time and thus restricts its growth. In areas with slower water flow, where sediment decantation occurs, the surface is usually shaded with aquatic macrophytes and by the flooded forest, which, again, restricts the growth of phytoplankton. On the other hand, clear water and black water rivers, which feature a more diverse euphotic fauna, have a low concentration of nutrients, and this constitutes unfavorable conditions for primary productivity (Junk 1980). The areas in which the production of phytoplankton is important consist of the floodplain lakes, when decantation of turbid waters occurs (Fisher 1979), and of the mouth bays of clear water rivers, which have a wide euphotic zone, despite the scarcity of nutrients (Schimidt 1980).

Areas which are periodically flooded by white water, known as várzea or floodplain, constitute the main trophic source supporting the aquatic biota in the Amazon basin. These extend along areas the Amazon from Pucallpa in Peru to its mouth. The floodplain is a source of fruit, seeds, leaves, terrestrial arthropods and other foods that feed fish. The trophic network is extremely complex as a result both of the diversity of food that enters the aquatic system and of the diversity of the ichthyofauna and the broad feeding spectrum represented by each species (Lowe-McConnell 1987; Goulding 1979, 1980; Bayley 1982; Junk et al. 1989).

Allochthonous material washed into the aquatic system supports a fish biomass that is harvested for human consumption. In the Peruvian Amazon, the ichthyomass of lentic environments was estimated by two methods: total removal using rotenone, and acoustically. Values obtained using rotenone ranged from 67.1 to 150.7 kg/ha for white waters and 31.4 to 147.6 kg/ha for black waters. The acoustic method gave values ranging from 160.3 to 939 kg/ha (Guerra et al. 1990). Bayley (1982) estimated values of 7 to 144 kg/ha for fish production in the Solimões floodplain near Manaus, using finemeshed nets. Predators form a considerable part of the fish biomass with some species reaching lengths of up to 2 meters, such as *Brachyplatystoma filamentosum* and *Arapaima gigas* (Barthem and Goulding 1997).

The biological cycle

Species are adapted to store energy in their bodies in the form of fat whenever food availability is high, and to spawn whenever an environmental change is favorable to the survival of offspring. There is a tendency for Amazonian fish species to spawn once a year, during the period of rising water levels when eggs and larvae can be carried away to flooded areas, which offer food and shelter. Other species, such as Cichlidae and Sciaenidae, spawn several times a year. In either case, the rains and the hydrological cycle serve to synchronize this endogenous physiological rhythm (Schwassmann 1978).

Migrations

Amazonian fishing is based on the exploitation of three major fish groups, classified according to their migratory and reproductive patterns: fish that migrate over long distances, fish with patterns of limited migration, and fish that move between different aquatic habitats, although migration is not necessary for the completion of their biological cycles (Barthem et al. 1997).

Species migrating extensively are those that cover long stretches of the main channel and are strongly linked to the estuary. The species belonging to this group are the piramutaba (*Brachyplatystoma vaillantii*) and the dourada (*B. flavicans*). Their reproductive cycle is still unknown, but recent data on these species suggest they cover almost the entire channel, from the mouth to the upper reaches, using the estuary for reproduction and the upper Amazon as spawning ground (Barthem and Goulding 1997).

Species with a limited migration pattern are those that use the main channel to move upstream from one floodplain or tributary to another floodplain or tributary. Species that normally show this migration pattern belong to the order Characiformes, for example the tambaqui (*Colossoma macropomum*), pacu (*Mylossoma spp*), jaraqui (*Semaprochilodus spp*) and curimatã (*Prochilodus nigricans*). On the basis of the migration patterns of the jaraqui (Ribeiro and Petrere 1990) and the tambaqui (Goulding 1979), three types of migratory movements have been defined: trophic, reproductive, and dispersive. During the flood season, these species remain in the flooded areas feeding on forest products. As soon as the river begins to fall, they begin dispersive migration, which occurs during the dry season and on the main river, always in an upstream direction. The shoals then stop moving and wait for the beginning of the rainy season and for waters to rise. When this happens, the shoals of reproducing fish move to the spawning grounds; this is the reproductive migration. Following spawning, the shoals move to flooded areas; undertaking trophic migration.

Species that do not need to migrate to complete their biological cycle are those typical of the floodplain, such as the pirarucu (*Arapaima gigas*), aruanã (*Osteoglossum bicirhosum*), tucunaré (*Cichla spp*), acará (*Cichlidae* in general) and pescada (*Plagioscion spp*). These species have either annual or biannual reproductive cycles and do not need to migrate to complete them.

THE USE OF HYDRIC AND HYDROBIOLOGICAL RESOURCES

Fishing

Fishing in Amazonia consists of capture for consumption, for sport or for the ornamental trade.

Fishing for consumption

Fishing for consumption is one of the most traditional economic activities in Amazonia and has provided the basis for urban development in a region that until recently lacked domestic animal production for flood supply. Figures on total fish capture for human consumption for the whole Amazon basin were obtained by Bayley and Petrere (1989) on the basis of recorded commercial landings, figures from other regions of the world with comparable conditions, and on *per capita* fish consumption in the region. The authors estimated production to be 200,000 tons a year, representing 20 to 25% of the total yield from both marine and fresh water sources in Brazil (Dias Neto and Mesquita 1988).

It is estimated that fishing in Amazonia generates at least US$ 100 million a year in the regional markets, with no federal or state subsidies involved. This estimate is based on a total catch in excess of 200,000 tons and on the price of fish being around US$ 0.50 per kilo. This market provides direct employment for 200,000 workers (Fischer et al. 1992), and is the main source of animal protein for the population of Amazonia (Shrimpton and Giugliano 1979, Jesus et al. 1991). Fishing sustains related formal and informal economic activities, such as the maintenance and repair of nets and engines, ice making, boat building and other trades. It also supports the river transportation network of Amazonia by creating demand for infrastructure services, such as shipyards, mechanics and ports which service its fleet of small and medium-sized boats. Moreover, fishing boats are often used as passenger or cargo boats, or vice-versa as a part of the non-fishing fleet depends at any given time on fishing.

Export of fish takes place through cold storage plants licensed by the Brazilian ministry of health. Fish exports were most important for the balance of trade of the Amazonian states during the 1970s and 1980s and the early 1990s. The state of Pará exported more than US$ 12 million worth of piramutaba in 1986, and the state of Amazonas exported about US$ 1.5 million worth of the same species in 1993. Exports from Pará, mainly shrimp and piramutaba, began in the 1970s and are now worth between US$ 35 and US$ 45 million a year. In the period between 1975 and 1984 fish represented about 10% of the state's total exports of US$ 444,914,000 and was its fifth most important export. With the production and export of iron ore from the Projeto Carajás, total exports from Pará rose to an average of US$ 1,156,628,000, and fish exports came to represent only about 3% of total exports. With current decreases in the production of piramutaba and shrimp, fishing's share has been further reduced.

The ornamental fish trade

Capture of ornamental fish constitutes an important source of revenue for the region. Exports generate around US$ 2 million a year and support around ten thousand jobs (Chao 1993). The state of Amazonas is mainly responsible for these exports, accounting for 90% of the total, with the state of Pará accounting for the remainder. Ornamental fishing started in 1959 in Benjamin Constant on Brazil's border with Peru, and later spread throughout the state of Amazonas. Exports of ornamental fish in Manaus peaked in 1979 when 20 million fish were exported. This figure dropped to less than 13 million in 1982 and 1983, and hovered around the 17 million mark in the late 1980s. Exports were worth about US$ 600,000 for the state in 1982 and US$ 1.5 million in 1993 (Barthem et al. 1995).

Ornamental fishery represents a viable economic option in various areas of the Amazon where there are few other means of subsistence. The low yield of fish for consumption on the Rio Negro is well known, however it is here that ornamental fish capture is most developed. The river is the principle source of fish for export and employs 60 to 75% of those engaged in this activity in the state (Chao 1993). A few cities in the region have given up other activities in order to engage in the ornamental fish trade. Barcelos, on the Rio Negro, has ceased timber production and is now known as the 'ornamental fish capital'. Gold miners from Altamira on the Xingu turned to ornamental fishing when the gold ran out. The former prospectors dive with their same rudimentary air pumps, previously used for dragging the river bottoms in search of gold, to fish by hand small Loricariidae or Calichthyidae. Species of these families shelter among rocks and in the deepest stretches rapids, which makes this type of fishery very dangerous (Jaime R. Carvalho Jr., director of the Centro Jovem de Aquarismo, Belém, Pará, personal communication).

Sport fishing

Sport fishery is an activity with a high development potential. However, growth has been very modest and there are no available statistics on which to assess its economic importance.

Hydroelectric plants

Nearly 91% of the electric energy generated in Brazil come from hydroelectric plants. The Amazon and Tocantins basins represent an estimated hydroelectric potential of between 61,700 and 65,700 MW and the latter is being considered as a possible source for energy transmission to the northeastern and southeastern Brazil (DNAEE 1984). The main hydroelectric plant built in the region is the Tucuruí power station on the Tocantins, with an estimated potential of 8,125 MW and a reservoir of 2,430 km^2. Next come the Balbina power station, on the Uatumã near Manaus, and the Samuel on the Jamari, a tributary of the Madeira. These two plants have a capacity of 250 and 216 MW and reservoirs of 2,360 and 579 km^2, respectively. Finally, there are the smaller plants: the Coaracy-Nunes on the Araguari in Amapá and the Curuá-Una on the river of the same name in Pará; these have a capacity of 40 and 30 MW and reservoirs of 23 and 37 km^2, respectively (Mello 1993). As energy consumption in Brazil is increasingly dependent on the hydroelectric sector, its contribution has increased from 16% in 1970 to 39% in 1997.

Although major projects for the construction of hydroelectric construction are currently on hold due to the lack of federal funds, the region's rivers remain a resource to be exploited by the country as a whole.

River transportation

Amazonian rivers are navigable along much of their length, some twenty five thousand kilometers of waterways, making river transportation the most obvious means of transportation in the region. Foreign cargo ships regularly sail up the Amazon to supply cities such as Iquitos in Peru and Letícia in Colombia. Recent federal government projects aimed at fostering sustainable economic development (the 'Brasil em Ação' Program) have budgeted for an investment of R$ 246.4 million in developing navigable waterways on the Tocantins and Madeira rivers. These projects would reduce the cost of transporting grains grown in southern Amazonia and enable the creation of a multimodal transport corridor by the dredging, removal of obstacles and signaling of the waterway (1,516 kilometers); paving the BR-153 highway from São Geraldo to Marabá (156 kilometers); and completing construction of the Imperatriz–Estreito railway link in Maranhão (120 kilometers).

The state of Pará has two waterway projects: the Marajó and the Tapajós waterways. The Marajó waterway is intended to improve navigation between Belém and Macapá. Previous studies sought to do this by crossing the Arari lake, whereas the current plan foresees connecting the Atuá and Anajás rivers through excavation, dredging, straightening and widening the rivers.

The main goal of the Tapajós waterway project is to consolidate regional infrastructure in order to turn the state of Mato Grosso and part of the western central region of Brazil into a global granary. The lower Tapajós is navigable for 345 kilometers upstream from its mouth to near the vicinity of São Luís. Further upstream between São Luís and Buburé, there are 28 kilometers of waterfalls, and upstream from these, near the mouth of the Jamanxim, there is a 170-kilometer stretch that offers reasonable conditions for navigation. The next stretch, approximately 50 kilometers, consists of a straight stretch of difficult conditions with a number of rapids leading up to the Mangabalzinho waterfall. The next 147 kilometers, which include the city of Jacareacanga, offer reasonable navigation as far as the Chacorão waterfall. Upstream from the Chacorão rapids to the mouth of the Teles Pires, there is a stretch of approximately 111 kilometers with rocky outcrops. The final stretch, as far as the Rasteira waterfalls and which is about 192 kilometers long, does not permit satisfactory navigation. The project aims to make the 1,043 kilometers from the mouth of the river to the Rasteira waterfalls navigable by canal building, obstacle removing and building a lock between São Luís and Buburé, and removing obstacles and dredging between Buburé and the Rasteira falls.

Agriculture and livestock raising

White water floodplains are of great interest to farmers because of the fertility of their soils, which favors high productivity cultivation of crops on the higher lands, such as maize (2.5 to 4.65 tons/ha), rice (3.2 to 4.5 tons/ha), manioc (15 to 20 tons/ha), bananas (1,100 bunches/ha) and fibrous plants such as jute (2 to 3 tons/ha). An association of terra firme pastures with the natural low floodplains or with deforested higher floodplain areas allows for extensive and very productive cattle and water buffalo raising. Mediterranean buffaloes weigh between 372 and 402 kilos at two years (Teixeira e Cardoso 1991). Goulding and Ferreira (1996) estimated livestock production in Amazonia to be around 22,000 tons a year or US$ 44 million/year. This productivity makes ranching very attractive to local farmers who have increasingly been treating the floodplain as an important site for local livestock production.

Logging on the floodplain

Logging in Amazonia is an economically important activity, not just for the region, but for the country as a whole. Logging is concentrated in the states of Pará, Rondônia and Mato Grosso, and involves around 25,000 producers. The main timber species of the floodplains are virola (*Virola surinamensis*), sumaúma (*Ceiba petrandra*) and açacu (*Hura crepitans*) among others. In the Marajó archipelago, virola is the main source of raw material for the region's plywood industries (Homma 1998).

MAIN THREATS TO THE ICHTHYOFAUNA

Threatened species

The main species of freshwater fish that appear on the IUCN (World Conservation Union) Red List of Threatened Species (http://www.redlist.org) inhabit the more densely populated regions of Brazil, such as the southeast, south and mid-western regions (Table 2). No reliable data are available on threatened fish species in the Brazilian Amazon, nor on disappearances or extinctions. We know however that over-fishing and environmental change, such as deforestation along river banks, mining in the river channel, or damming have frequently led to the local reduction or even disappearance of some species.

Two fish species in the Amazon have been classified as 'Data Deficient' by the IUCN. One of these is the pirarucu (*Arapaima gigas*) and, although considered a species at risk of extinction as a result of human activities, its populations have so far survived the pressure of fishing activities in significantly changed environments, such as the lakes on the Ilha de Marajó and on the lower Amazon. The other, *Phreatobius cisternatum*, inhabits the water table of an extensive region at the mouth of the Amazon. There are no available data on the extent of its distribution, nor whether it is threatened in any way. Clearly in urban areas and areas of dredging for land reclamation, where subsoil impacts are more evident, survival of this species may be affected. On the other hand, there is as yet no evidence that the impact of deforestation on the water table is affecting the survival of this species. Nevertheless, should the species turn out to be widely distributed throughout the Amazon basin, it is unlikely to be under threat of extinction.

The introduction of exotic species

The introduction of exotic species in Amazonia has occurred through the escape of fish from breeding tanks belonging to fish farmers or government agencies. The introduction of species from other continents, such as carps and tilapias, as well as from other basins, as is the case of the pacu-caranha (*Piaractus mesopotamicus*) and the curimatã-pacu (*Prochilodus margravii*) may pose a threat to the equilibrium of the ichthyological fauna (Guimarães 1993). However, none of these species has yet been found in the natural habitat, which suggests that their populations have not yet managed to establish themselves in the basin.

TABLE 2 - THREATENED FRESHWATER FISH SPECIES IN BRAZIL			
Arapaimidae	*Arapaima gigas*	DD	Amazonia
Characidae	*Catabasis acuminatus*	DD	Paraná-Paraguai
	Stygichthys typhlops	DD	Minas Gerais
Aplocheleidae	*Cynolebias boitonei*	VU	Distrito Federal
	Cynolebias constanciae	VU B1+2ac+3bd	Rio de Janeiro
	Cynolebias marmoratus	VU B1+2ac+3bd	Rio de Janeiro
	Cynolebias minimus	VU B1+2ac+3bd	Rio de Janeiro
	Cynolebias opalescens	VU B1+2ac+3bd	Rio de Janeiro
	Cynolebias splendens	VU B1+2ac+3bd	Rio de Janeiro
Pimelodidae	*Caecorhamdella brasilensis*	DD	Paraná-Paraguai
	Pimelodella kronei	DD	São Paulo
	Phreatobius cisternatum	DD	Amazonia

VU = Vulnerable. A taxon is vulnerable when it faces high risk of extinction in the wild in the near future, in accordance with the following criteria:
B) Extent area of occurrence estimated to be less than 20,000 km², with the following characteristics:
1) Severely fragmented or known to exist at no more than 10 locations;
2) Continuing decline in any of the following: (a) extent of occurrence, (b) occupancy, (c) area, extent and/or quality of habitat, (d) number of locations or subpopulations;
3) Extreme fluctuations in any of the following: (a) extent of occurence, (b) area of occupancy, (c) number of locations or subpopulations, (d) number of mature individuals.
DD = Data deficient. A taxon is Data Deficient when there is inadequate informations to make a direct, or indirect, assessment of its risk of extinction, based on its distribution and/or population status.

Fishing

Despite its socioeconomic importance, fishing in Brazilian inland waters has been neglected by government agencies. Consequently, no policy for the management of renewable fish resources in inland waters has been established, despite the need for such policy to guide management plans for fish stocks (Barthem 1995; Barthem et al. 1995; Isaac and Barthem 1995), and to resolve the conflicts involving different groups of fishermen and riparian communities that have been occurring since the 1970s.

Legislation on freshwater fishing in Brazil dates back to 1912, was followed by the enactment of the Fishing Code (Código de Pesca) of 1938, and was revised with the creation of the federal agency for fishery development SUDEPE (Superintendência do Desenvolvimento da Pesca) established by Law no. 10 of October 11, 1962 and by Decree-Law no. 221 of 1967 (Fischer et al. 1992). The current legislation is based on Decree-Laws 221 and 7670 of 1988, which govern all Brazil's inland waters, its territorial sea, contiguous zone and continental shelf, and the high-sea zones (Isaac et al. 1993). Decree-Law 221 is very comprehensive, providing for the protection and support of fishing in general and contains provisions (i) prohibiting fishing with explosives in areas where it could affect shipping and within 500 meters of sewage outlets, (ii) requiring SUDEPE to provide a list of species requiring protection in respect of minimum capture size and closed seasons, to regulate and control fishing equipment, and to regulate the import and export of species, and (iii) defining three categories of fishers: commercial, sports, and scientific. Zoning of fishing areas appears to be a means of avoiding conflicts between different groups of fishers. In the estuary, SUDEPE's regulation 007/1976 prohibits industrial fishing south of 00°05' N and west of 48°00' W, in order to minimize the conflicts existing between the industrial and artisan fleets. Regulation 200/1990 divided the Grande de Monte Alegre lake into two parts, one for commercial fishing and the other for subsistence fishing by riparian communities. The problem with establishing fishing zones is how to prevent fishers from using the unauthorized areas. In all these cases, there are no geographical landmarks to assist the identification of the body of water in question, nor there are sufficient human resources for enforcement. The establishment of a closed season has only been attempted in the case of the pirarucu (*Arapaima gigas*). Regulation 480/1991 prohibits fishing for pirarucu during the six months from December 1 to May 31 (Isaac et al. 1993).

Nevertheless, the current legal apparatus for managing fisheries in Amazonia does not appear to be effective when it comes to controlling overexploitation of a particular fish resource. A few years ago, Barthem and Petrere (1995) and Isaac and Ruffino (1996) showed that, respectively, the piramutaba and tambaqui were being overexploited. Despite the availability of this information, very little has so far been done to address this issue.

Fishing with poisons

The use of poisons is most commonly found among indigenous communities living along small rivers or where fish are scarce, rather than in commercial fishery. The use of timbó (a fish poison extracted from the barbasco vine *Tephrosia toxicofera*) by the Desana indians of the of Rio Negro is an example of this type of fishing on tributaries of the Amazon River where fish for consumption are scarce (Ribeiro 1992). Inhabitants of the Solimões-Amazonas floodplain who do not have the necessary equipment or skills for fishing use the sap of the açacu tree (*Hura crepitans*, Euphorbiaceae) to poison floodplain fish. This method is not popular among the local fishermen as the açacu sap causes eye irritation and nausea (Barthem et al. 1995).

Agriculture and livestock raising

One of the first significant impacts on the Amazon floodplain arose as a result of the jute industry. In order to meet the high demand for sacking for coffee exports, the Brazilian government invested heavily in the cultivation of fiber crops. Jute, whose cultivation arose on the banks of the Ganges and Brahmaputra rivers in Asia, was successfully introduced onto the Amazon floodplain and experienced its first boom following Japanese investments in 1937. The heyday came in 1952 as Brazil achieved self-sufficiency in jute production, and decline set in after 1970 (Homma 1998). Following this decline, the resulting deforested areas on both the high and low floodplains were used as pasture during the dry season for cattle and water buffalo. The area of most significant deforestation is the lower Amazon, where ranchers and jute farmers have been operating for many decades (MacGrath et al. 1994). The impact of ranching on the floodplains is evidenced by the destruction of aquatic macrophytes caused both by grazing and by trampling by livestock, with serious consequences for the aquatic biodiversity (Goulding et al. 1996).

Deforestation of headwater areas has a predictably negative impact on aquatic biodiversity. It changes the habitat structure, affects the water retention capacity of soils and the physicochemical properties of water, silts up riverbeds and causes a reduction in surface runoff (Silva and Silva 1993). In addition, improper use of pesticides poses a threat to the aquatic communities of the river systems close to crop growing areas. The headwaters of the Araguaia-Tocantins and Guamá rivers are the most affected by agricultural development in southeastern Amazonia, as the forest is more susceptible to fires and their soils more prone to drying out during the dry season (Nepstad et al. 1998).

Coca growing and the manufacture of cocaine

Coca (*Erythroxylon coca* var. *coca*, *E. coca* var. *ipadu*, *E. novogranatense* var. *truxillense* and *E. novogranatense* var. *novogranotense*) is an Amazon plant widely known for the illegal trade in its product – cocaine. The impact of coca farming on the aquatic environment occurs not only as a result of the clearing of forest areas for crop growing, as previously mentioned, but also as a result of the process of refining. The use of millions of liters of kerosene, sulfuric acid, lime, acetone and toluene to refine coca paste has a devastating impact on the aquatic communities inhabiting the streams that drain coca-growing areas (Barthem et al. 1996).

Mining

Mining began to play an important role in the Amazon economy in the 1960s, with the beginning of mining for manganese in Serra do Navio (Amapá), cassiterite in Rondônia, and gold in the Tapajós region. This intensified in the 1970s, when the Brazilian government invested in surveys and prospection through the Amazonian Radar Project (Projeto Radar da Amazônia – RADAM), the Company for Mineral Resource Research (Companhia de Pesquisas de Recursos Minerais – CPRM), and the Rio Doce Geology and Mining company (Rio Doce Geologia e Mineração – DOCEGEO) (Dall'Agnol 1995). The 1980s were marked by a decline in cassiterite production in Rondônia and the start of bauxite mining on the Trombetas, manganese in Marabá, cassiterite in the state of Amazonas, iron and manganese in Carajás, and china clay in the state of Amapá (Dall'Agnol 1995).

Gold prospecting was also an important phenomenon in the 1980s, as gold fever spread from the Tapajós basin and Serra Pelada in southern Pará into vast regions of the state of Rondônia, northern Mato Grosso and finally Roraima (Dall'Agnol 1995). The toxic potential of mercury is controlled by its interaction with particulate material, organic or inorganic, whose chemistry is extremely complex and little known. One of the compounds resulting from this complex chemistry is methyl mercury (CH_3Hg^+), a highly toxic form of mercury. Concern with mercury contamination arises from the possibility that there may be a continual process of methyl mercury production in the water whereby its fixation by living organisms introduces it into the food chain, where it will be biomagnified. In this manner, methyl mercury fixation could trigger a slow and uncontrollable process of poisoning the whole system.

The greatest impact of mining activities, especially gold prospecting, on Amazonian biota is perhaps less related to contamination by heavy metals and has more to do with the complete degradation of mining locations. Gold prospecting completely alters the riverbeds and increases the sediment load carried off by the current. As a result, there are marked downstream changes, both in terms of the physical chemistry of the water and of the type of sediments deposited on the riverbed. This type of impact is more evident in small tributaries – areas where the chances of finding new and endemic species are high, as is the case of the Jamanxim river, a tributary of the Trombetas river.

Oil

Commercial oil extraction in the Brazilian Amazon is basically restricted to the region of the Urucu, a tributary of the Coari. Oil is extracted in terra firme areas and pumped to the margins of the Tefé. The oil was originally transported by small barges down the narrow and winding Tefé river to the Solimões. Once it reached the Solimões it was pumped into larger vessels and taken to the refinery at Manaus. Barge movements on the Tefé damaged its vegetation as barges scraped the riverbanks and knocked down trees as they were being maneuvered. With the completion in 1998 of the 280-kilometer pipeline connecting Urucu to Coari, barges were replaced by other means of transport and the impact on the riverside vegetation reverted to that caused by normal shipping. A 420-kilometer long gas pipeline connecting Coari to Manaus and 500-kilometer long pipeline from Urucu to Porto Velho have been built to supply gas to thermoelectric power stations. The impacts of these pipelines, which cross large rivers such as the Solimões and various small rivers, have not yet been assessed. Nothing is so far known about oil pollution in the Solimões-Amazonas system (Barthem 1995).

Waterways

Dikes and small canals have been built on poorly drained sites in various regions of Amazonia. These have been well documented in the Ilha de Marajó and lower Amazon regions, where farmers have sought to manage the floodplain as a means of improving production and transport to market.

The first large-scale waterways are yet to be built. This will take place in two completely distinct environments: the poorly drained areas of the Ilha de Marajó and the rapids of the Tapajós. In both cases, river channels will be straightened and dredged in order to make navigation easier. The impact on the poorly drained areas of the Ilha de Marajó will be felt with the improvement of drainage, which will cause the interior of the island to dry out more quickly. The construction of the Tapajós waterway may cause the extinction, along its route, of a type of habitat essential to a community that lives on the rapids of this river. The pacu (*Utiaritichthys sennaebragai*), originally described on the basis of four samples collected above the Utiarity rapids on the Papagaio river, a tributary of the Tapajós (Gosline 1951), is an example of one such species inhabiting the rapids and feeding on the aquatic plants of the Podostemaceae family that grow on the rocks.

Hydroelectric plants

Damming rivers to generate electricity represents one of the most significant impacts on the aquatic biota, both upstream and downstream of the dam. The Tucuruí hydroelectric plant has been one of the best studied dams in Amazonia, both before and after closure of its sluices. The observed impacts downstream were of high fish mortality once the turbines entered into operation and, in the following years, of a decrease in diversity, alteration in species composition, and reduction in total biomass. Upstream a total change in the ecosystem, previously rapids and now an immense lake, was observed with a decrease in diversity, few dominant species, and fluctuations in total biomass, which increased in some years and decreased in others (Merona et al. 1987; Leite and Bittencourt 1991). Species that undertake long migrations, such as piramutaba and dourada, became practically extinct upstream.

Urban pollution

Population growth in Amazonia is often analyzed from the perspective of the expansion of the agricultural frontier by a peasantry expelled from older agricultural areas. However, population growth has taken place principally in the context of urbanization, in conditions of poor basic sanitation and which results in serious consequences for both the environment and the population (Becker 1995). The impacts of this type of pollution, involving both domestic and industrial waste, have not yet been assessed for the environment as a whole, although its imediate consequences can be seen in the small rivers draining urban areas (Silva and Silva 1993).

Priority areas for conservation

The situation of the aquatic system of the Amazonian biome is less worrying than that of other major river basins (Arthington and Welcomme 1995). Understanding gained from managing other basins both in Brazil and in other countries can help reconcile the economic development of the region's natural resources with the conservation of its biodiversity. Three aspects need to be given equal treatment in order to achieve this goal: (i) knowledge of the region's biodiversity; (ii) legislation appropriate to the particular needs of the region; and (ii) international agreements to conserve the overall integrity of the basin.

Biodiversity: inventories and ecology

Alpha diversity – the number of species in a community – in the Amazon basin is undoubtedly high and results from diversification of a variety of ecological niches (Lowe-McConnell 1987) However, our limited taxonomic knowledge of the fish fauna as a whole hampers an adequate assessment of the beta diversity, which increases as species occur in different environmental gradients across the basin. If, on the one hand, species living on the banks of the main channel basin show great mobility and occupy large portions of the river, on the other, the fauna of the clear water or black water tributaries may be isolated by environmental characteristics, although the aquatic environment is continuous. Such isolation may account for the occurrence of endemic species mainly in headwaters (Menzes 1996, Junk 1997).

Key species (endemic or rare) for defining priority areas for conservation

The use of key species, whether endemic or rare, to define priority areas for conservation is hampered both by poor knowledge of their taxonomic composition and of their distribution patterns (Menezes 1996). The lack of good collections for the region as a whole makes it difficult to identify areas of endemism. Britsky and Figueiredo (1972) demonstrated this situation by presenting the case of *Tetranematichthys quadrifilis*, a species described by Kner in 1857 on the basis of a single sample from the Guaporé river. A few other samples were only recently collected on the upper Rio Negro, on the Japurá, near the city of Belém, and on the Tocantins. The species is rare in all places from which it was sampled; however, proper collecting showed that it is widely distributed and therefore could not be considered a key species for conservation in any of the areas in which it occurred, contrary to what had previously been thought. Even in places well frequented by the local population, new fish species still continue to be reported. Investigation carried out on the bed of the Amazonas – the area of the heaviest traffic of the country's largest river fleet – by Dr. John G. Lundberg of the University of Arizona, in cooperation with the National Council for Scientific and Technological Development (Conselho Nacional de Desenvolvimento Científico e Tecnológico – CNPq), found several species that were new to science (Menezes 1996). The Amazonian species on the IUCN Red List of Threatened Species cannot be considered key species for defining priority areas for conservation given the wide distribution of one (*Arapaima gigas*) and our restricted knowledge of the other (*Phreatobius cisternatum*).

Migratory species for defining ecosystem integrity

Barthem et al. (1997) classify commercial Amazonian fish species as long-distance migratory, migratory, or sedentary. Migratory fish species use more than one habitat to complete their biological cycle. Tambaqui and jaraqui, for instance, use flooded areas as feeding grounds, migrate along the main channel during the low water season, and use particular habitats, such as the confluence of white water with black or clear water rivers, for spawning (Ribeiro and Petrere 1990; Goulding 1979, 1980 and 1988; Araújo-Lima and Goulding 1998). The long-distance migrators, piramutaba and dourada, use the estuary for growth or feeding, thousands of kilometers of the Solimões-Amazonas and its tributaries as feeding or wintering areas, and still unknown upstream stretches of white water rivers for reproduction (Barthem and Goulding 1997).

These species define for themselves the dimensions of the ecosystems that need to be considered for their management. Coincidently, migratory fishes are the species of greatest importance for consumption fishing, which suggests that management of their habitats should be treated in an integrated way. Conservation of upstream and downstream stretches may be less important than the impact caused by a dam, by over-fishing in the estuary, or by pollution in the spawning areas, for instance. Although the biological cycle of migratory species is not completely known, the concept of integrating protection into the ecosystem needs to be considered when addressing conservation of aquatic biodiversity. This concept involves those countries that share the Amazon region, since some are home to different habitats essential for the survival of these species.

Key environments for defining priority areas for conservation

Environments such as the rapids and small streams of the crystalline Guiana or Brazilian shields, the main river channels and the different types of flooded areas (river overflows, forest and savannas seasonally flooded by rainfall, and coastal areas flooded by high tides) are not only home to endemic species but also sustain a large fish biomass exploited by both commercial and subsistence fisheries. Such environments could be considered as key environments, which would help define priority areas for conservation. One way to categorize these environments would be to consider the different sub-basins of the Amazon basin, the landscapes defined by the geological past, and the different types of flooded areas.

The Amazon floodplain

One of the most important environments of the Amazon basin is its floodplain, an area flooded through river overflow. This environment is home to many endemic species from various taxonomic groups and supports a large biomass with several species of fish regularly exploited by both commercial and subsistence fisheries. A few species are endemic in certain stretches of the river. That is the case of the White Bald-Headed Uacari monkey (*Cacajao calvus calvus*), a species which helped guide the demarcation of the Mamirauá Sustainable Development Reserve. This is the only floodplain protected area in the Brazilian Amazon, covering the confluence of the Japurá and Solimões rivers – one of the largest floodplain areas of Amazonia. This exemple needs to be replicated in other floodplain areas in central Amazonia, on the lower Amazon and in tidally-flooded coastal areas.

White water floodplains are relatively well conserved upstream of the mouth of the Purus, where there is no large-scale deforestation by ranching or agriculture. The Purus floodplains from Lábrea to its mouth, and those of the Juruá from Eirunepé to its mouth, are extensive areas of extreme importance for fish supplies to Manaus and should be conserved on account both of the subsistence needs of the local economy and of the maintenance of the floodplain ecosystem. The same is the case for the floodplains at the confluence of the Içá and the Jutaí with the Solimões.

The floodplains of the Solimões-Amazon downstream of the Purus, are not so well conserved, principally in the vicinity of Santarém. An extensive area of floodplain in the area disputed by the states of Amazonas and Pará, at the confluence of the Nhamundá with the Amazonas, would be a good choice for a protected area in view of its fairly good conservation status.

The floodplains of the lower Amazon, between the mouths of the Tapajós and the Xingu, exhibit a distinct type of environment, where flooding is caused by both high tides and river overflow. Despite being situated between the two largest cities of Amazonia, little is known about this environment. On the other hand, the fact that it is a marshy area means that little development has taken place in the area.

The logging industry and small farmers have heavily exploited the floodplain, a forest area between the mouth of the Xingu and the mangrove forests. Despite this, it is still fairly well conserved in the region of the Breves channels and the inner Amazon delta (including the Gurupá, Mexiana, and Caviana islands), where no large-scale farming activities have occurred. The conservation of this region depends mainly on the management of its logging and heart of palm extraction activities.

Rainfall flooded plains are very typical of the interiors of the large islands of the mouth of the Amazon and in coastal Amapá and Pará. This is the most threatened environment of the entire Amazon basin as a result of the length of human occupation, which has led to the construction of dams and canals throughout this period, and of the potential for expansion of ranching and agriculture. This region comprises extensive cattle and water buffalo ranches, and may become an area of rice farming now that the Brazilian Agriculture Research Company (Empresa Brasileira de Pesquisa Agropecuária – Embrapa) has bred a variety specifically suited to the Marajó region. Conservation of this habitat could be achieved through the establishment of private reserves to exploit its ecotourism potential.

The beaches of white, clear and black water rivers are all important environments for the reproduction of chelonians. Government agencies, such as the Brazilian Institute for the Environment and Renewable Natural Resources (Instituto Brasileiro do Meio Ambiente e dos Recursos Naturais Renováveis – Ibama), are already engaged in the protection of turtles, whose meat and eggs are still over-harvested. Attempts to permit turtle breeding have been made both by governmental and private enterprises, but the ease of capture during their reproduction period and the continued existence of an illegal black market mean that their conservation will always be under threat. The most efficient way of protecting turtles would be to persuade people to abandon the habit of eating them. Although this may be hard to imagine, the urbanization of Amazonia is in fact changing the habits of those generations growing up in cities and who increasingly purchase their food in stores that can be easily inspected, such as supermarkets. Restrictions on the sale of turtles and measures to protect the beaches during the hatching season continue to be the best way to protect these species.

The Guiana Shield: Rio Negro

Various rivers drain the Guiana shields, and the largest of these is the Rio Negro sub-basin. A few flooded areas in this basin stand out, such as the Anavilhanas archipelago and the un-named archipelago located between the Rio Branco and the Padauani and Demini rivers (Goulding et al. 1988), which are flooded by overflow from the Negro. An ecological station already protects the former, but the latter is still in need of protection.

A similar environment is that formed by forest periodically flooded by intensive rainfall and which occurs in vast unbroken areas, both along the banks of the Negro and the Branco rivers and on the headwaters of their tributaries. These habitats are still well conserved and no large-scale ranching or agricultural activities appear to be taking place.

The savannas of the Rio Branco seasonally flooded by rainfall are an environment that favors both ranching and rice growing. In addition, the region is prone to fires during the dry season. Given this, more attention should be paid to its conservation, particularly since the state of Roraima will experience an increase in development activities once it is linked to the Caribbean by the BR-174 highway. Rapids and headwaters are areas subject to more severe impacts, such as those caused by prospecting activities. Their conservation depends on the enforcement of environmental legislation, which is difficult given that prospecting is widespread throughout the region.

The Guiana Shield: the Trombetas, Jari, Araguari and other rivers

The drainage areas for most of these rivers are located on the Guiana shields, which is characterized by rapids and headwaters of small rivers. Large development projects are taking place in these basins, such as bauxite extraction on the Trombetas, china clay extraction and paper production on the Jari, and manganese extraction on the Araguari. Conservation of this region depends on the enforcement of environmental legislation, which is made easier by the concentration of these projects in smaller areas. In addition, the Araguari is dammed by one of the oldest hydroelectric plants in Amazonia, the Coaraci-Nunes power station, which was built without any environmental impact study being carried out.

The Central Brazilian Shield: the Tocantins

The Tocantins basin is one of the most seriously affected in the entire Amazon Basin. Two large hydroelectric plants have been: the Tucuruí plant on the lower Tocantins, and the Lajeado plant on the upper Tocantins. In addition, its headwaters have suffered the effects of farming and ranching activities, which are widespread throughout southern Pará and the north of the state of Tocantins, and by past and present prospecting activities.

The Central Brazilian Shield: the Xingu

The ichthyofauna of the Xingu river downstream of the Altamira falls is totally distinct from the upstream fauna. Little is yet known about the fauna and ecology of this system, in which most of the impacts of prospecting, farming and ranching activities have been felt in its headwaters. Plans still exist for the construction of a hydroelectric dam above the town of Altamira. These plans were brought to a halt by intense resistance on the part of the region's indigenous people, who organized protests against this enterprise. Despite intense public opposition, there is a growing demand for electricity in the country and this region is one of the best options for the construction of hydroelectric power stations (Mello 1993). Either way, research is needed in this region to better understand its ichthyofauna and to assess the possible impacts of hydroelectric plants or other activities.

The Central Brazilian Shield: the Tapajós

Of all the rivers draining the Brazilian shield, the Tapajós is the one most heavily affected by prospecting, both in its headwaters and by dredging of the main channel. Unfortunately the state of knowledge of this river's ichthyofauna and of the ecology of this drainage system is still precarious and data on the impact of these activities in the area are still unavailable. There is a proposal for the construction of another waterway around a stretch of rapids and whose impact has not yet been assessed due to the same lack of knowledge of the local fauna.

The Central Brazilian Shield: the tributaries of the Madeira

The headwaters of the Madeira rise on the slopes of the Andes, but its tributaries drain the Central Brazilian shield. The main impacts are caused by: (i) prospecting, involving dredging of the main channel of the sub-basin; (ii) construction of the Samuel hydroelectric dam on the Jamari; and (iii) intense ranching and farming in its headwaters. Little is known about the fauna and ecology of these tributaries, and studies have focused on the habitat formed by the Madeira and the areas close to its tributaries. The problem of mercury contamination in the area is well known, while the impact of dredging on the migration of large catfish species on the Madeira has not yet been properly assessed.

The Andean Slopes: the Amazonas, Madeira, Purus, Juruá and Japurá rivers

The watersheds of the white water rivers barely fall within Brazilian territory. Their protection therefore implies agreements with neighboring countries, as in the recent case between Peru and Ecuador.

Workshop 90 – Biological Priorities for the Conservation of Amazonia

The ichthyology team which identified priority areas for conservation in Amazonia at the 'Workshop 90 – Biological Priorities for the Conservation of the Amazon', held in January 1990 in Manaus, considered bio-ecological endemism, diversity and spectrum to be the basic criteria for selecting conservation areas.

The main indicator groups would be endemic species of a few families and subfamilies, such as Cichlidae, Potamotrygonidae, Acestrorhynchidae, Serrasalminae, Rivulidae, Lebiasinidae, Loricariidae, Curimatidae and Cynopotaminae. These criteria permitted the definition of twelve priority regions for conservation: basins with distinct geological pasts, such as the rivers that drain the Guiana and Central Brazilian shields and those draining the Andean foothills (regions 3, 4, 5, 6, 7, 9, 10 e 11); and the areas of sedimentary plains dominated by flooded areas, such as the estuarine coast and the white water floodplains, which are areas of great importance for fishing (regions 1, 8 and 12). The Bragantina region (region 2) was considered to be an intermediate region since its drainage area is neither part of the Central Brazilian shield nor can it be considered part of the Amazon plain.

Legislation

Legal instruments for the protection of this biodiversity are, to a large extent, already established under existing legislation. However, enforcement depends not only on acquiring greater knowledge in order to better justify proposed protection, but also on the organization of federal, state, and municipal government agencies and of society as a whole, such that these fully comply with protection measures.

The Law on Waters (Law 9433/1997 – the Lei das Águas) is a recent and up to date instrument that establishes the basis for overall water management. Unfortunately, this law was drafted with a greater focus on the situation in northeastern Brazil (water scarcity) and the southern and southeastern regions (excessive pollution) than on the situation in Amazonia (Kelman 1998). On the other hand, threats to the ichthyofauna are in large part covered by current legislation and by the National Water Resources Policy (Política Nacional de Recursos Hídricos) of the Ministry of the Environment (MMA) (Appendix 2). The ministry is responsible for management of activities relating to fishing, introductions of exotic species, and the use of floodplains and headwaters for farming and ranching. The Federal Police (Polícia Federal) is already heavily engaged in combating drug trafficking in the Brazilian Amazon. The environmental legislation already covers the impacts caused by mining and oil extraction. The construction of waterways and hydroelectric plants entails large-scale investments, and projects are subject to highly restrictive environmental regulations (Kelman 1998)

In view of the multiple uses of water and hydro-biological resources and of the continuous nature of this environment across the entire basin, initiatives for protecting the aquatic biota invariably involve negotiations with the different economic sectors involved, such as the fishing, farming and ranching, logging, energy and mining sectors. This tends to spread efforts across various fronts, jeopardizing integrated action on the part of the different conservation projects.

International agreements

The Amazon Co-operation Treaty was signed on July 3, 1978 by the countries that share the Amazon region: Bolivia, Brazil, Colombia, Ecuador, Guiana, Peru, Suriname, and Venezuela. The 'Lima Declaration' signed on December 5, 1995, by the foreign ministers of the treaty signatory countries, states that these countries 'have initiated an important and unprecedented process of agreement and cooperation, contributing to the sustainable development of their respective Amazonian territories and to the improvement of the living standards of their populations'. This declaration contains the terms of agreement with respect to water and hydro-biological resources and to biological diversity (Appendix 3). The treaty signatory countries agree to endorse the principles of the Convention on Biological Diversity and principles concerning the proper use of water and hydrobiological resources. Ways to implement management actions and biodiversity conservation of Amazonia thus depend mainly upon the action and political will of these countries, given that international diplomatic instruments are already in place.

Conclusion

The criteria based on key-species adopted by the ichthyology team at the 'Workshop 90 – Biological Priorities for the Conservation of Amazonia' – led to the identification of regions that, in general, coincide with those identified using key-environment criteria.

A study of migratory species shows that conservation action and biodiversity management require joint action, involving all the countries sharing the Amazon basin.

The advantage of working with key-environments can be seen in the ease of devising protection mechanisms for a defined area, such as the creation of reserves or the enforcement of environmental legislation. These actions are harder to implement when their basis is sparse information on the distribution and biology of a sub-set of key-species. On the other hand, the efficacy of such conservation efforts will only be validated when we have better information on the taxonomy, distribution, and ecology of Amazonian biodiversity.

Therefore, priority actions for the conservation and sustainable use of the biological diversity of the aquatic system of the Brazilian Amazon biome must concentrate on:

1: Research on the taxonomy, biogeography, biology, and ecology of species endemic to certain regions and of migratory species;

2: Actions to protect and manage key environments:

(i) Flooded areas of the Amazon plain (floodplain and igapós); involving legal mechanisms already in place such as fishing and logging management, restrictions on granting licenses for farming and ranching, establishment of protected floodplain areas, such as the Mamirauá Sustainable Reserve (Ayres et al. 1997). This last is an example that should be followed by both state and private landowners, not just to conserve the biodiversity of areas subject to flooding along the sedimentary plains, but also to ensure the continuity of economic activities of vital importance to the region, such as fishing and ecotourism.

(ii) Flooded areas, rapids and headwaters of the Guiana shields (the Negro, Trombetas, Jari, Araguari and other rivers):

these currently suffer the impacts of prospecting and of large-scale projects. Prospecting is difficult to control since it is widespread and often clandestine. On the other hand, companies engaged in large-scale development projects can play an active role in the conservation of the basins where they are located as this is an opportunity to improve their public image.

(iii) Flooded areas, rapids and headwaters of the Brazilian shield, comprising the Tocantins, Xingu, Tapajós and Madeira rivers. The headwaters and rapids of the rivers that drain the Brazilian shield are those suffering the greatest impacts. The basin of the Tocantins runs the highest risk, followed by the basins of the Madeira and the Tapajós. Enforcement of existing legislation could be enough to contain the majority of the impacts. The protection of these areas should be addressed with a view to protecting not only biodiversity and water sources, but also protecting against soil erosion. In addition, greater efforts should be devoted to both taxonomic and ecological studies in order to assess the degree of damage such impacts are causing to these basins and their biodiversity.

(iv) Andean foothills (the Amazonas, Madeira, Purus, Juruá and Japurá rivers): protection and management of this region involves international agreements among the countries sharing the Amazon basin. The management of fishing for migratory catfish species is an example of the conservation and sustainable use of a resource shared by the signatories of the Amazon Co-operation Treaty.

Bibliography

ARAÚJO-LIMA; GOULDING, M. So Fruitful a Fish: Ecology, Conservation, and Aquaculture of the Amazon's Tambaqui. In: *Biology and Resource Management in the Tropics Series.* New York: Columbia Univ. Press, 1998.

ARMANTROUT, N. B. Condition of the World's Aquatic Habitats. In: ARMANTROUT, N. B. (Org.). *Condition of the World's Aquatic Habitats. Proceedings of the World Fisheries Congress, Theme 1.* New Delhi: Oxford & IBH Publishing, 1995. p. 1-9.

ARTEAGA, F. *Informe sobre las pesquerías en la Cuenca Amazônica de Bolivia.* La Paz: Centro de Desarrollo Pesquero, 1991.

ARTHINGTON, A, H. A.; WELCOMME, R. L. The Condition of Large River Systems of the World. In: ARMANTROUT, N. B. (Ed.). *Condition of the World's Aquatic Habitats. Proceedings of the World Fisheries Congress, Theme 1.* New Delhi: Oxford & IBH Publishing, 1995. p. 44-75.

AYRES, J. M. et al. Mamirauá: The Conservation of Amazonian Flooded Forests. In: CLARIDGE, G. F.; O'CALLAGHAN, B. (Eds.). *Community Involvement in Wetland Management: Lessons from the Field. Incorporating the Proceedings of Workshop 3: Wetlands, Local People and Development, of the International,* Conference on Wetlands and Development held in Kuala Lumpur, Malaysia, 9-13 oct. 1995. Kuala Lumpur: Wetlands International, 1997.

BARBOSA, R. P. Rios brasileiros com mais de 500 km de extensão, *Rev. Brasil. Geogr*, v. 24, n. 1, p. 126-134, 1962.

BARRIGA, R. *Peces de agua dulce.* Ecuador: 1991.

BARTHEM, R. B. Developmental of Commercial Fisheries in the Amazon Basin and Consequences for Fish Stocks and Subsistence Fishing. In: CLÜSENER-GODT, M.; SACHS, I. (Eds.). *Brazilian Perspectives on Sustainable Development of Amazon Region.* Man & the Biosphere Series. Unesco and The Parthenon Publishing Group, 1995. p. 175-204.

BARTHEM, R. B.; GOULDING, M. The Catfish Connection: Ecology, Migration, and Conservation of Amazon Predators. In: *Biology and Resource Management in the Tropics Series.* New York: Columbia Univ. Press, 1997.

BARTHEM, R. B.; PETRERE Jr., M. Fisheries and Population Dynamics of *Brachyplatystoma vaillantii* (*Pimelodidae*) in the Amazon Estuary. In: ARMANTROUT, N. B. (Ed.). *Condition of the World's Aquatic Habitat. Proceeding of the World Fisheries Congress, Theme 1.* New Delhi: Oxford & IBH Publishing, 1995. p. 329-340.

BARTHEM, R. B.; GUERRA, H.; VALDERRAMA, M. *Diagnóstico de los recursos hidrobiológicos de la Amazonia.* Tratado de Cooperación Amazónica-Secretaria Pro Tempore, 22, 1995.

BARTHEM, R. B. et al. A pesca na Amazônia: problemas e perspectivas para o seu manejo. In: VALLADARES-PADUA, C.; BODMER, R.; CULLEN Jr., L. (Eds). *Manejo e conservação da vida silvestre no Brasil.* MCT-CNPq, Sociedade Civil Mamirauá, 1997.

BAYLEY, P. Características de inundación en los ríos y áreas de captación en la Amazonia peruana: una interpretación basada en imágenes LANDSAT e informes de ONERN, *IMARPE*, report, n. 81, 1981. p. 245-303.

BAYLEY, P. B. *Central Amazon Fish Populations: Biomass, Production and Some Dynamic Characteristics.* Doctoral Thesis (PhD). Canada: Dalhousie University, 1982.

BAYLEY, P. B.; PETRERE Jr., M. Amazon Fisheries: Assessment Methods, Current Status, and Management Options. In: DODGE, P. (Ed.). *Proceedings of the International Large River Symposium.* Can. Spec. Publ. Fish. Aquat. Sci., 1989. p. 385-398.

BECKER, B. Undoing Myths: The Amazon, an Urbanized Forest Pages. In: CLÜSENER-GODT, M.; SACHS, I. (Eds.). *Brazilian Perspectives on Sustainable Development of the Amazon Region.* Man & the Biosphere Series. Unesco and The Parthenon Publishing Group, 1995. p. 53-90.

BÖHLKE, J. E.; WEITZMAN, S. H.; MENEZES, N. A. Estado atual da sistemática dos peixes de água doce da América do Sul, *Acta Amazonica,* v. 8, n. 4, 1978. p. 657-677.

BRITSKI, E. A. Sobre um novo gênero e espécie de *Sorubiminae* da Amazônia (*Pisces, Siluriformes*), *Papéis avulsos de zoologia,* v. 34, n. 7, 1981. p. 109-114.

BRITSKI, E. A.; FIGUEIREDO, J. L. Peixes brasileiros que necessitam de proteção. In: *Espécies da fauna brasileira ameaçadas de extinção.* Rio de Janeiro: Academia Brasileira de Ciências, 1972. p. 159-163.

BUSTAMANTE, W. *Informe del Ecuador en la 'Consulta de expertos sobre la planificación de la ordenación de los recursos vivos acuáticos de la Cuenca Amazónica'.* Lima: 1991.

CASTRO, D. *Los peces del río Putumayo, sector Puerto Leguízamo.* Mocoa: CAP, 1990.

CASTRO, D.; ARBOLEDA, A. Lista preliminar de peces del río Caquetá, *Boletín biología marina,* Universidad Jorge T. Lozano, v. 8, p. 7-14, 1988.

CHAO, N. L. Conservation of Rio Negro's Ornamental Fishes, *Tropical Fish Hobbyist,* p. 99-114, january 1993.

COPRAPHI. Hidrologia e climatologia na região amazônica brasileira. Informação disponível e atividades em desenvolvimento. SEMINÁRIO INTERNACIONAL DE HIDROLOGIA E CLIMATOLOGIA DA AMAZÔNIA, Manaus, July 23 to 27, 1984.

DALL'AGNOL, R. Mining without Destruction?: Problems and Prospects for the Garimpos and Major Mining Projects. In: CLÜSENER-GODT, M.; SACHS, I. (Eds.). *Brazilian Perspectives on Sustainable Development of the Amazon Region.* Man and the Biosphere Series. Unesco and The Parthenon Publishing Group, 1995. p. 205-236.

DAY, J. A.; DAVIES, B. R. The Amazon River System. In: DAVIES, R; WALKER, K. F. (Eds.). *The Ecology of River Systems.* Dordrecht (Netherlands): Dr. W. Junk Publishers, 1986. p. 289-318.

DIAS NETO, J.; MESQUITA, J. X. Potencialidade e exploração dos recursos pesqueiros do Brasil, *Ciência e Cultura,* v. 40, n. 5, p. 427-441, 1988.

DNAEE. *Ação do DNAEE na área de recursos hídricos:* Região Norte. Ministério de Minas e Energia, Departamento Nacional de Águas e Energia Elétrica, Divisão de Controle de Recursos Hídricos, 1984.

FERREIRA, E., ZUANO, J. A. S.; SANTOS, G. M dos. *Peixes comerciais do Médio Amazonas:* Região de Santarém, Pará. Brasília: Ibama, 1998.

FISCHER, C. F. A., CHAGAS, A. L. das G. A.; DORNELLES, L. D. C. *Pesca de águas interiores.* Col. Meio Ambiente, série Estudos: Pesca. Brasília: Ibama, 1992.

FISHER, T. R. Plankton and Primary Production in Aquatic Systems of the Central Amazon Basin, *Comp. Biochem. Physiol.*, n. 62, p. 31-38, 1979.

GOSLINE, W. A. Notes on the Characid Fishes of the Subfamily *Serrasalminae*. In: *Proceedings of the California Academy of Sciences*, 27, 1951. p. 17-64.

GOULDING, M. *Ecologia da pesca do rio Madeira*. Belém: INPA/CNPq, 1979.

_____. *The Fishes and the Forest: Explorations in Amazonian Natural History*. Berkeley: University of California Press, 1980.

_____. Ecology and Management of Migratory Food Fishes of the Amazon Basin. In: ALMEIDA, F.; PRINGLE, C. M. (Eds.). *Tropical Rainforests, Diversity and Conservation*. San Francisco: California Academy of Sciences, 1988. p. 71-85.

GOULDING, M.; SMITH, N.; MAHAR, D. J. *Floods of Fortune: Ecology & Economy along the Amazon*. New York: Columbia Univ. Press, 1996.

GUERRA, H. et al. La pesquería en el Amazonas peruano, *Interciencia*, v. 15, n. 6, p. 469-475, 1990.

GUERRA, H.; MONTREUIL, V.; VILLACORTA, M. Avances del programa de evaluación de recursos pesqueros en la Amazonía peruana, *COPESCAL*, Colombia, p. 73-115, 1981.

GUIMARÃES, S. F. Algumas diretrizes para o desenvolvimento da pesca e da aquacultura na Amazônia brasileira. In: FERREIRA, E. J. G. et al. (Eds.). *Bases científicas para estratégia de preservação e desenvolvimento da Amazônia*, v. 2. Manaus: INPA, 1993.

HOMMA, A. K. *Amazônia*: meio ambiente e desenvolvimento agrícola. Belém: Embrapa-Cpatu, 1998.

IBGE. *Geografia do Brasil*: Região Norte. FIBGE, diretoria técnica, Geografia do Brasil. Rio de Janeiro: 1977.

ISAAC, V. J.; BARTHEM, R. B. Os recursos pesqueiros da Amazônia brasileira, *Bol. Mus. Paraense Emílio Goeldi*, v. 11, n. 2, p. 151-194, 1995.

ISAAC, V. J.; RUFFINO, M. Population Dynamics of Tambaqui *Colossoma macropomum* Cuvier 1818, in the Lower Amazon, Brazil, *Fisheries Management*, v. 3, n. 4, p. 315-333, 1996.

ISAAC, V. J.; ROCHA, V. L. C.; MOTA, S. Algumas considerações sobre a legislação da 'piracema' e outras restrições da pesca da região do Médio Amazonas. In: FURTADO, L; MELLO, A. F.; LEITÃO, W. (Eds.). *Povos das águas: realidade e perspectiva da Amazônia*. Belém: MPEG/UFPA, 1993. p. 187-211.

JESUS, R. S. de et al. Técnicas para conservação de pescado na Amazônia. In: VAL, A. L.; FIGLIULO, R.; FELDBERG, E. (Orgs.). *Bases científicas para estratégia de preservação e desenvolvimento da Amazônia*, v. 1. Manaus: INPA, 1991.

JUNK, W. J. Áreas inundáveis: um desafio para a limnologia, *Acta Amazônica*, v. 10, n. 4, p. 775-795, 1980.

_____. The Central Amazon Floodplain: Ecology of a Pulsing System. In: *Ecological Studies*, v. 126. Berlin: Springer Verlag, 1997.

JUNK, W. J.; FURCH, K. A General Review of Tropical South American Floodplains, *Wetlands Ecology and Management*, v. 2, n. 4, p. 231-238, 1993.

JUNK, W.; BAYLEY, P. B.; SPARKS, R. E. The Flood Pulse Concept in River-Floodplain Systems. In: DODGE, D. P. (Ed.). *Proceedings of the International Large River Symposium Can. Spec. Publ. Fish. Aquat. Sci.*, 106, 1989. p. 110-127.

KELMAN, J. *Gestão integrada de recursos hídricos*, unpublished. 1998.

KLINGE, H.; JUNK, W. J.; REVILLA, C. J. Status and Distribution of Forested Wetlands in Tropical South America, *For. Ecol. Manage.*, n. 33/34, p. 81-101, 1990.

LANDIM, P. M. B. et al. Minerais pesados provenientes de areais do leito do rio Amazonas, *Acta Amazônica*, v. 13, n. 1, p. 51-72, 1983.

LAUZANE, L.; LOUBENS, G. Peces del río Mamoré. In: *Orstom-Cordebeni-UTB*. Paris: L'orstom, 1985.

LAUZANE, L.; LOUBENS, G.; LEGUENNEC, B. Pesca y biología pesquera en el Mamore Medio (Región de Trinidad, Bolivia), *Interciência*, v. 15, n. 6, p. 452-460, 1990.

LEITE, R de A. N.; BITTENCOURT, M. M. Impacto das hidrelétricas sobre a ictiofauna da Amazônia: o exemplo de Tucuruí. In: *Bases científicas para estratégia de preservação e desenvolvimento da Amazônia: fatos e perspectivas*, vol. 1. In: VAL, A. L.; FIGLIULO, R.; FELDBERG, E. (Eds.). Manaus: INPA, 1991. p. 85-104.

LOWE-MCCONNELL, R. H. *Ecological Studies in Tropical Fish Communities*. Cambridge University Press: 1987.

MACGRATH, D. G.; CASTRO F. de; FITEMMA, C. Reservas de lago e o manejo comunitário da pesca no Baixo Amazonas: uma avaliação preliminar. In: D'INCAO, M. A.; SILVEIRA, I. M. (Eds.). *A Amazônia e a crise da modernização*. Belém: Museu Paraense Emílio Goeldi, 1994. p. 389-402.

MARLIER, G. Limnology of the Congo and Amazon Rivers. In: MEGGERS, B. J.; AYENSI, E. S.; DUCKWORTH, W. B. (Eds.). *Tropical Forests Ecosystem in Africa and South America. A Comparative Review*. Washington: Smithsonian Inst. Pres., 1973.

MAY, R. M. How Many Species are there on Earth?, *Science*, n. 241, p. 1441-1449, 1988.

MEADE, R. H. et al. Sediments Loads in Amazon River, *Nature*, v. 278, n. 8, p. 162-164, 1979.

MELLO, J. A. S. N de. Hidrelétricas na Amazônia e o meio ambiente. In: FERREIRA, E. J. G. et al. (Eds.). *Bases científicas para estratégia de preservação e desenvolvimento da Amazônia*, v. 2. Manaus: INPA, 1993. p. 11-16.

MENEZES, N. A. Methods for Assessing Freshwater Fish Diversity. In: BICUDO, M.; MENEZES, N. A. (Eds.). *Biodiversity in Brazil:* a First Aproach. Proceedings of the Workshop Methods for the Assessment of Biodiversity in Plants and Animals held at Campos do Jordão, Brazil, 26-30 May 1996. p. 289-296.

MERONA, B. de; CARVALHO, J. L. de; BITTENCOURT, M. M. Les Effets de la fermeture du barrage de Tucurui (Brésil) sur l'ichtyofaune en aval, *Rev. Hydrobiol. Trop.*, v. 20, n. 1, p. 73-84, 1987.

MILLIMAN, J. D.; MEADE, R. H. World-wide Delivery of River Sediment to the Oceans, *The Journal of Geology*, v. 91, n. 1, p. 1-21, 1983.

MOYLE, P. B.; CECH Jr., J. J. *Fishes:* An Introduction to Ichthyology. Prentice-Hall, 1982.

NELSON, J. S. *Fishes of the World*, 3th ed. New York: John Wiley & Sons, 1994.

NEPSTAD, D. et al. Forest Fire Prediction and Prevention in the Brazilian Amazon, *Conservation Biology*, v. 12, n. 5, p. 951-953, 1988.

ORTEGA, A. H.; VARI, R. Annotated Checklist of Fresh Water Fishes of Peru, *Smithsonian Contributions of Zoology*, n. 437, 1986.

OVCHYNNYK, M. Peces de agua dulce del Ecuador. In: *Monograph Series Nr. 1. Latin American Studies Center*. East Lansing: Michigan St. Univ., 1971.

PHILIPP, D. P. et al. Protection of Aquatic Biodiversity: Will We Meet the Challenge?. In: PHILIPP, D. P. et al. (Eds.). *Protection of Aquatic Biodiversity. Proceedings of the World Fisheries Congress, Theme 3*. New Delhi: Oxford & IBH Publishing, 1995. p. 1-10.

PITCHER, T. J.; HART, P. J. B. *Fisheries Ecology*. Champan and Hall, 1996.

RAY, G. C. Ecological Diversity in Coastal Zones and Oceans. In: WILSON, E. O.; PETER, F. M. (Eds.). *Biodiversity*. Washington: National Academic Press, 1988. p. 36-50.

RIBEIRO, B. G. Cestos e outras técnicas de pesca dos índios Desúna. In: ENCONTRO DE CIÊNCIAS SOCIAIS E O MAR NO BRASIL, 4: 1990. *Anais*. São Paulo: PPCAUB-USP, 1992

RIBEIRO, M. C. L. B.; PETRERE Jr., M. Fisheries Ecology and Management of the Jaraqui (*Semaprochilodus taeniurus, S. insignis*) in the Central Amazonia, *Regulated Rivers & Management*, 5, 1990. p. 195-215.

RICHEY, J. E.; NOBRE, C.; DESER, C. Amazon River Discharge and Climate Variability: 1903 to 1985, *Science*, n. 246, p. 101-103, 1989.

ROBERTS, T. R. Ecology of Fish in the Amazon and Congo Basins, *Bulletin of the Museum of Comparative Zoology*, n.143, p. 117-147, 1972.

RYMAN, N.; UTTER, F.; LAIKRE, L. Protection of Aquatic Biodiversity. In: PHILIPP, D. P. et al. (Eds.). *Protection of Aquatic Biodiversity. Proceedings of the World Fisheries Congress, Theme 3*. New Delhi: Oxford & IBH Publishing, 1995. p. 11-35.

SALATI, E. et al. *Amazônia: desenvolvimento, integração e ecologia*. São Paulo: Brasiliense, CNPq, 1983.

SALO, J. et al. River Dynamics and the Diversity of Amazon Lowland Forest, *Nature*, n. 322, p. 254-258, 1986.

SANTOS, M. dos. Composição dos pescados e situação da pesca no Estado de Rondônia, *Acta Amazonica*, n. 16/17, p. 43-48, 1986/87.

SANTOS, M. dos; JEGU, M.; MERONA, B. Catálogo de peixes comerciais do baixo rio Tocantins. In: *Projeto Tucuruí*. Manaus: Eletronorte/CNPq/INPA, 1984.

SCHMIDT, G. W. Primary Production of Phytoplankton in Three Types of Amazonian Waters. Some Investigations on the Phytoplankton and its Primary Productivity in the Clear Water of the Lower Rio Tapajós, Pará (Brazil), *Amazoniana*, v. 7, n. 3, p. 335-348, 1982.

SCHWASSMANN. H. O. Times of Annual Spawning and Reproductive Strategies in Amazonian Fishes. In: THORPE, E. J. (Ed.). *Rhythmic Activity of Fishes*. London: Academic Press, 1978. p. 187-200.

SERRÃO, E. A. Possibilidades para o desenvolvimento agropecuário e florestal sustentado na Amazônia. In: ARAGÓN, L. E. (Ed.) *Desenvolvimento sustentável nos trópicos úmidos,* tomo II. Belém: Unamaz/UFPA, 1992. p. 435-460.

SHRIMPTON, R.; GIUGLIANO, R. Consumo de alimentos e alguns nutrientes em Manaus. 1973-4, *Acta Amazonica,* v. 9, n. 1, p. 117-141, 1979.

SILVA, E. N. S.; SILVA, C. P. D. Expansão de Manaus como exemplo do processo de extinção dos igarapés. In: FERREIRA, E. J. G. et al. (Ed.). *Bases científicas para estratégia de preservação e desenvolvimento da Amazônia,* v. 2. Manaus: INPA, 1993.

SIOLI, H. Studies in Amazonian Waters. In: *Atas do Simpósio sobre a Biota Amazônica,* v. 3, Limnologia. 1967. p. 9-50.

_____. Amazon Tributaries and Drainage Basins. In: HASLER, A. D. (Ed.). *Coupling of Land and Water Systems.* Berlin: Springer Verlag, 1975. p. 199-213.

SIOLI, H.; KLINGE, H. Sobre águas e solo da Amazônia brasileira, *Boletim geográfico,* n. 185, p. 195-205, 1965.

TEIXEIRA, M. F. N.; CARDOSO, A. *Várzeas da Amazônia:* caracterização e uso na produção agrícola. Belém: FCAP, Serviço de documentação e informação, 1991.

Appendix 1

List of principle fish species captured for consumption or for ornamental trade and their common names according to country				
Family	Scientific name	Colombian Amazonia	Peruvian Amazonia	Brazilian Amazonia
Anostomidae	*Abramites hypelonotus*	abramite		
	Abramites sp	abramite	abramite	abramite
	Anostomus anostomus	anostomus		
	Leporinus fasciatus	omima		aracu
	Leporinus friderici	omima		aracu-flamengo
	Leporinus sp	omima, cheo	lisa	aracu
	Schysodon sp	omima, cheo, lisa	lisa	aracu-comum
Arapaimidae	*Arapaima gigas*	pirarucu, paiche	paiche	pirarucu
	Bunocephalus coracoideus	catalina		banjo
	Bunocephalus spp	banjo cat		
Auchenipetridae	*Auchenipterichthys thoracatus*	zamora cunchi		
	Parauchenipterus galiatus	novia cunchi		
Callichthyidae	*Brochis splendens*	cory green cat		
	Corydoras agassizi	cory agassizi		
	Corydoras arcuatus	cory aruatus		
	Corydoras elegans	cory elegans		
	Corydoras hastatus	cory hastatus		
	Corydoras julii	cory julii		
	Corydoras melanistus	cory melanistius		
	Corydoras punctatus	cory puntatus		
	Corydoras rabauti	cory rabauti		
	Corydoras sp	cory San Juan		
	Corydoras sp	cory orange cat		
	Corydoras spp	corredora		coridora
	Dianema urostriata	porthol rayado		
	Dyanema longibarbis	porthol corriente		
	Hoplosternum sp		shiruí	tamoatá
Characidae	*Acestrorhynchus spp*	cachorro		
	Aphyocharax sp	cola roja, ararí	cola roja	anostomus
	Apistograma agassizi	apistograma		agassizi
	Boehkea fredcochui	tetra azul		
	Brycon spp	sabalo	sábalo cola roja	matrinchã
	Chalceus ssp			
	Characidium fasciatus	characidium		
	Colossoma macropomum	gamitana, gambitana, cachama	gamitana	tambaqui, ruelo
	Hemigramus ocellifer			
	Hemigramus pulcher	hemigramus		
	Hemigramus sp	rodostromus		
	Hemigramus spp	brillante		torpedinho, olho-de-fogo
	Hypessobrycon erythostigma	bleeding heart		
	Hyphessobrycon bentoni	rosaceus		

continues

Family	Scientific name	Colombian Amazonia	Peruvian Amazonia	Brazilian Amazonia
Characidae	*Hyphessobrycon inessi*	neón		
	Hyphessobrycon loretoensis	tetra loreto		
	Hyphessobrycon sp	black ulrey		
	Hyphessobrycon sp	roberty tetra		
	Metynnis hypsauchen	metynnis		
	Metynnis sp	moneda	palometa	pacu
	Moenchausia oligolopis	moenkhausia		
	Moenchausia lepidura	argentino tetra		
	Myles rubripinis	red hook	palometa	pacu
	Mylossoma spp	palometas	palometa	pacu
	Paracheirodon axelrodi	cardenal		cardinal
	Paracheirodon innesi	néon tetra		
	Piaractus brachypomus	paco	paco	pirapitinga
	Prianobrama filigera	boodfin amazon		
	Serrasalmus nattereri		panã, piraña	piranha-caju
	Serrasalmus rhombeus		panã, piraña	piranha-preta
	Serrasalmus spp	piranha		
	Thayeria obliqua	oblicua		
	Triportheus angulatus		sardina	sardinha-chata
	Triportheus elongatus		sardina	sardinha-comprida
	Triportheus rotundatus	catalina		
Chilodontidae	*Chilodus punctatus*	chilodus		
	Chilodus sp	chilodos	chilodos	
Cichlidae	*Aequidens spp*	aequidens moroni		
	Apistogramma agazzizi	apistograma		
	Astronotus ocellatus	oscar	acarahuazú	acará-açu
	Cichla spp	tucunare	tucunaré	tucunaré
	Cichlassoma severum	falso disco		acará
	Cichlassoma temporale		bufurqui	
Cichlidae	*Crenicichla spp*	añashúa		
	Geophagus spp	mojarra		acará-rói-rói
	Heros severum	severum		
	Mesonauta festivus	festivum		
	Pterophyllum escalare	escalar		
	Pterophyllum scalare	scalare		
	Satanoperca jurupari	jurupari		
	Satanopercha jurupari	mojarra	bufurqui	acará
	Symphysodon aequifasciatum	disco		disco
Clupeidae	*Pellona castelnaeana*		sardina	apapá-amarelo
	Pellona flavipinnis			apapá-branco
Ctenoluciidae	*Boulengerella maculata*	beedle fish		
	Boulengerella spp	agujón		peixe-agulha
Curimatidae	*Curimata spp*		ractacara	branquinha
	Curimatella alburna	chillón		branquinha
	Potamorhina latior		yahurachi	
	Psectrogaster amazonica		yahurachi	
Cynodontidae	*Hydrolycus scomberoides*	payara, dentón real		peixe-cachorro
	Raphiodon vulpinus	machete	chambira	peixe-cachorro
Doradidae	*Acanthodora spp*	dora		ronca-ronca
	Agamyxis pectinifrons	rafael spotted		
	Amblydoras hancockii	spinosissimus		
	Hassar spp	bufeo cunshi		
	Megalodoras irwini	zuntarito hurero		
	Megalodoras sp	sierra, matacaiman		bacu
	Oxidoras niger	sierra, matacaiman	turushuqui	cuiú-cuiú, cujuba
	Oxydoras niger	oxidoras niger		
	Platydoras costatus	rafael stripped		
Electrophoridae	*Electrophorus electricus*	temblon		poraquê
	Electrophorus electrius	electric eel		
Erythrinidae	*Hoplias malabaricus*		fasaco	traíra
Gasteropelecidae	*Carnegiella marthae*	hachet marthae		
	Carnegiella spp	estrigata		borboleta

continues

Family	Scientific name	Colombian Amazonia	Peruvian Amazonia	Brazilian Amazonia
Gasteropelecidae	*Carnegiella strigata*	hachet strigata		
	Torococharax stellatus	hachet toracocharax		
Hemiodontidae	*Anodus elongatus*		yulilla	cubiu
	Hemiodus sp			
Hypophthalmidae	*Hypopthalmus sp*	mapara	maparate	mapará
Hypopomidae	*Hypopomus spp*	spotted knife fish		
Lebiasinidae	*Copeina guttata*	copeina gutata		
	Copella spp	copeina auratus		
	Nannostomus spp	lapiz		lápis
	Nannostomus spp	copeina auratus		
	Nannostomus trifasciatus	trifasciatus		
Lepidosirenidae	*Lepidosiren paradoxa*	pez pulmon	lungfish	pirambóia
Loricariidae	*Chaetostomus spp*	xenocara		
	Farlowella spp	farlowella		
	Hypostomos sp	hipostomo		acari-bodó
	Hypostomus sp	plecostomus		
	Loricaria spp	loricaria		acari-cachimbo
	Otocinclus sp	otocinclo		cascudinho, limpa-vidro
	Panaque negrolineatus	cucha royal		
	Pterigoplichthys spp	cucha	carachama	acari-bodó
Nandidae	*Monocirrhus polyacanthus*	pez hoja		peixe-folha
	Monoirrhus polyacanthus	leaf fish		
Osteoglossidae	*Osteoglossum bicirrhossum*	arawana	arahuana	aruanã
Parodontidae	*Apareidon pongoensis*	pongo pongo		
Pimelodidae	*Brachiplatystoma filamentosum*	zúngaro dorado		
	Brachiplatystoma juruense	zúngaro alianza		
	Brachiplatystoma sp	zúngaro saltón		
	Brachyplatystoma filamentosum	pirahiba, lechero, valenton	saltón,	piraíba, filhote
	Brachyplatystoma flavicans	dorado, plateado	dorado	dourada
	Brachyplatystoma juruensi	siete babas		zebra, flamengo
	Brachyplatystoma vaillantii	pirabuton		piramutaba
	Callophysus macropterus	simi, mota		piracatinga
	Callopphysus macropterus	zúngaro mota		
	Duopalatinus sp	cunshi blanco		
	Hemisorubim platyrhinchos	toa		
	Leiarius marmoratus	achara		
	Microglanis sp	bumble bee cat		
	Paltystoma matichthys sturio	zúngaro toa		
	Paulicea lutkeni	peje negro, chontaduro, pacamu	cunchi mama	jaú, pacamão
	Phractocephalus hemiliopterus	pirarara, guacamayo	pez torre	pirarara
	Phratocephalus hemioliopterus	red tailed cat (torre)		
	Pimelodella spp	pimelodella		mandií
	Pimelodus spp	pimelodella común		
	Pimelodus blochii	picalón, nicuro		mandií
	Pimelodus pictus	tigrito		mandií
	Pinirampus pirinampus	long finned rat		
	Platynematichthys notatus	capaz		cara-de-gato
	Platysilurus barbatus	zungarito barbatus		
	Pseudoplatystoma fasciatum	zúngaro doncella		
	Pseudoplatystoma filamentosum	pintado, rayado, pintadillo	doncella	surubim
	Pseudoplatystoma tigrinum	bagre tigre	tigre zúngaro	caparari
	Pseudoplatystoma tigrinus	zúngaro tigre		
	Sorubim lima	shovelnose (shiripira)		
	Sorubimichthys planiceps	cabo de hacha, peje leña		peixe-lenha
	Sorubimichthys planiceps	acha cubo		
	Sorubimichthys planiceps	acha cubo		
Potamotrygonidae	*Potamotrygon spp*	stinger ray	stinger ray	
Prochilodontidae	*Prochilodus nigricans*	bocachico	boquichico	curimatá
	Semaprochilodus amazonensis	yaraquí		

continues

Family	Scientific name	Colombian Amazonia	Peruvian Amazonia	Brazilian Amazonia
Prochilodontidae	*Semaprochilodus spp*	sapuara	yaraquí	jaraqui
Rhamphichthyidae	*Rhamphichthys rostratus*	elephant nose		
Rivulidae	*Pterolevias peruensis*	rivolus peruensi		
	Rivolus spp	rivulus común		
Sciaenidae	*Plagioscion squamossisimus*	curvina	corvina	pescada branca
	Plagioscion surinamensis	curvina, curvinata		pescada cascuda
Soleidae	*Achirus achirus*	sun fish		
Sternopygidae	*Eigenmannia virescens*	cuchillo		sarapó
Sternopygidae	*Eigenmannia sp.*	green knife fish		
	Sternophygus macrurus	ghost knife fish		
Synbranchidae	*Synbranchus marmoratus*	atinga, marbled eel		
Tetraodontidae	*Colomesus osellus*	puffer		
	Colomessus pscitattus	tamborero		baiacu

Appendix 2

The Ministry of the Environment has designated the Secretariat for Water Resources (Secretaria de Recursos Hídricos) to implement the National Water Resources Policy (Política Nacional de Recursos Hídricos) in accordance with its mandate.

MANDATE
Article 10. The mandate of the Secretariat for Water Resources is to implement the National Water Reosurces Policy, to propose regulations, to define strategies, to implement programs and projects, in matters relating to:
I - the integrated management of sustainable multiple uses of water resources;
II - the implementation of the National System for Water Resources;
III - the integration of water resource management and environmental management;
IV - the implementation of the instruments of the National Water Resources Policy, *inter alia* the granting of use rights for water resources under federal jurisdiction, except in the case of authorizations for hydroelectric purposes, and in conformity with overall criteria established by the National Council for Water Resources (Conselho Nacional de Recursos Hídricos).
Single Paragraph: The Secretariat for Water Resources also undertakes the duties of the executive secretariat of the National Council for Water Resources.

Appendix 3

Main features of the Lima Declaration signed on December 5, 1995 by the foreign ministers of the signatory countries of the Amazon Co-operation Treaty.
(i) Promote the use of water resources for environmentally suitable purposes and in accordance with criteria established for their conservation, use, and rational management;
(ii) Emphasize the economic and social importance of Amazonian hydro-biological resources for the subsistence of the region's urban and rural populations and that these resources can serve as the basis for new economic activities at the local, regional, and national levels.

(iii) Affirm the need to develop economic activities sustained by Amazonian hydro-biological resources with a view to meeting the needs of the human population and to increasing the region's economic production.
(iv) Request firm support from agencies for international technical and financial cooperation and from the private sector for the devolopment of aquaculture projects, fisheries management, management of alligator and turtle farming and for the farming of other aquatic and semi-aquatic regional species.
(v) Ratify the principles of the Convention on Biological Diversity which are based on the sovereignty that the states exercise over their biological resources and on the fair and equitable sharing of their benefits, and promote joint discussion under the aegis of the ACT on implementation of the Convention on Biological Diversity.
(vi) Emphasize that biological diversity resources constitute the potential for the development of new economic activities that sustainably use forest and water resources, especially with regard to genetic resources, plants for food and with medicinal properties, food coloring, pesticides, fibers and other uses of importance to the treaty countries;
(vii) Agree upon the need to develop registries of Amazonian genetic resources, to support economic activities based on species of regional flora, fauna and microorganisms, and to establish rules for protecting the intellectual property and other proprietary rights of holders of traditional knowledge and to maximize the social and economic benefits to such communities;
(viii) Establish an institute for research and protection of the genetic resources of the Amazonia, to which end its Pro Tempore Secretariat together with the parties involved shall convene a regional seminar for the preparation of a project to be submitted to the Eighth Ordinary Meeting of the Council for Amazon Cooperation, which will decide upon the headquarters and the starting date for the activities of establishment of the institute.
(ix) Urge agencies for international cooperation, bilateral and multilateral, to continue to provide support to ongoing activities and projects for the sustainable use of biological diversity, as well as to increase technical and financial support for inventories, conservation, monitoring and for the development of new economic activities, especially those involving Amazonian genetic resources, farming of native fish species, captive breeding, research and inventories of food and medicinal plants, and the development of economic projects based on biodiversity and biotechnology.

Technical report on the amphibian diversity of the Brazilian Amazon

Claudia Azevedo-Ramos *Centro de Filosofia e Ciências Humanas, Universidade Federal do Pará*
Ulisses Galatti *Museu Paraense Emílio Goeldi*

Introduction

The purpose of this report is to identify areas for conservation and new areas for inventories of the amphibian fauna of the Brazilian Amazon, as well as to identify both endemic and endangered species. To this end, our concern has been to include as much data on the subject as possible, whether published or unpublished, in order to obtain the most realistic picture of the current state of knowledge of this group.

Method

In defining priority areas for conservation and those areas requiring inventories, we took as a starting point the distribution of amphibian species, the level of species richness, the degree of endemism, and the proximity of a given area to sources of environmental disturbance. Scientific papers, reports, field data available on the Internet, researchers' unpublished lists, and museum data were used to compile findings on the richness and distribution of species in the Amazon. Each data source was classified as follows: 1. long-term inventories: inventories drawn up over a period of more than two months; 2. short-term inventories: inventories drawn up over a period of less than two months; 3. incomplete inventories: inventories drawn up in only a few days or targeting only a few amphibian families. In order to better represent the fauna of a given region, a few inventories had to be arbitrarily divided into subregions whenever the scale they encompassed was too large; this was the case with inventories drawn up for areas along major rivers. Inventories that covered areas in close proximity to one another were combined into one single region; for example, in the case of the island of Maracá and Ajarani in the State of Roraima.

The synonymies between species were checked and updated in accordance with Frost (1993). Undetermined species (identified as *sp* only) were used only for estimating the total number of species for a given locality. Undetermined species were not taken into account for similarity analyses or for estimates of the total number of species in the Brazilian Amazon, since it was impossible to determine whether these species were distinct from those recorded at other localities.

Similarity between two areas was estimated according to Sorensen's index as modified (2C/(A+B), where C is the number of species in common between two localities, A is the total number of species at site A, and B is the total number of species at site B; Krebs, 1989), also termed the biogeographical similarity coefficient by Duellman (1990).

Rainfall data for each site were added in order to determine the relationship between species richness and rainfall. Information on rainfall was either obtained from the scientific papers themselves or estimated on the basis of precipitation data for the period 1961 to 1990 (cf. Inmet/CPET/INPE).

Results

A total of 29 inventoried localities were found for the Brazilian Amazon. However, data from São Félix do Xingu were not included in the analyses because they were not available. Long-term inventories were drawn up in only thirteen (46%) of the total inventoried localities (Table 1).

Anurofauna diversity

A total of 163 species of amphibians was found for the Brazilian Amazon. However, it is important to note that this figure represents a minimum number of species, since neither undetermined species nor description records for isolated species were used for the analyses. The relative importance of undetermined species *vis-à-vis* estimates of the total number of species in a given locality can be seen in Table 2. In a few localities, this number reaches almost 40% of the species collected, which illustrates the present difficulties for taxonomic studies and, consequently, for the assessment of the amphibian diversity of the Amazon. Furthermore, new descriptions may reveal endemism patterns which are still unknown. Because there are few articles which mention levels of endemism, we analyzed those species which were found at only a single site (Table 2).

A total of 38 species were identified as occurring at only one locality. However, most of the species are known from other sites both in the Amazon in general and in other parts of Brazil (Frost, 1985: Duellman, 1993). A comparison of these data to those of Frost (1985) and Duellman (1993) indicates that probably only twelve species (7.4% of the total species in the region) are endemic to the Brazilian Amazon (Table 2). The greater number of species recorded at only one site is likely to be the result of the gaps in Amazonian inventories. Additionally, we have found no references to endangered species in the bibliography consulted.

Bufo marinus, *B. thyponius* (Bufonidae), *Scinax rubra* (Hylidae) and *Adenomera andreae* (Leptodactylidae) were the only species to occur in more than 80% of the sites. *Bufo marinus* was the only species to occur on all sites.

The areas richest in species were Manaus (Amazonas), Carajás (Pará), the Rio Madeira (Amazonas); the Rio Juruá (Amazonas); Costa Marques (Rondônia); Guajará-Mirim (Rondônia) and along the BR-364 highway (Rondônia). Taraquá (Amazonas), Alter do Chão (Pará) and Trombetas/Nhamundá (Pará) were areas where the least diversity was observed. The number of species found in each locality can be seen in Figure 3.

Few areas stand out as having extreme similarities in their fauna, in other words either very high or very low levels of similarity in their fauna (Figure 3). The only locality with more open vegetation assessed (Alter do Chão, near Santarém, Pará) revealed the least diversity in comparison to other forested areas, although it did reveal a unique flora, as indicated by its low degree of similarity with other localities. It is also interesting to note that the average indices of similarity between localities ranged from low to intermediate (an average of 0.40 in a range of 0.30 to 0.47). This implies that conserving the site with the highest degree of similarity with the others would only result in a fraction of the known anurofauna diversity being conserved.

In drawing up conservation area policies for Amazonia, it is important to bear in mind that the greater the distance between two localities, the lower the degree of similarity of the fauna encountered (Figure 1, $F_{76,1}$ = 11.666; P = 0.001).

No significant relationship was found between species richness and rainfall levels for the species inventoried ($F_{13,1}$ = 3.280; P = 0.098), although a positive tendency can be observed in the data (Figure 2).

All the localities (N = 28) were grouped by state in order to determine the number of species by macro-region and the frequency of occurrence of each species at each site in a given state (Table 4). This analysis revealed that the anurofauna varied considerably from locality to locality within the same political unit. Most of the species occurred at only one or two sites. The relevance of these findings lies in the fact that, in order to achieve effective conservation of species, efforts towards this will have to transcend the political borders of each state, as the fauna of any given subregion may be more similar to that of a neighboring state than to that of other subregions within the same state.

Another conclusion to be drawn from these findings is that, depending on the size of a conservation area established within a state, this area will only be representative of a portion of the overall diversity of that particular region.

TABLE 1 - INVENTORIED LOCATIONS IN THE BRAZILIAN AMAZON AND THEIR RESPECTIVE DATA SOURCES. THE INVENTORY TYPE CORRESPONDS TO 1 (LONG-TERM INVENTORIES > 2 MONTHS); 2 (SHORT-TERM < 2 MONTHS); 3 (INCOMPLETE INVENTORIES). THE DATES OF NON-PUBLISHED DATA REFER TO THE YEAR THE INVENTORY WAS DRAWN UP.

State	Localities	Length (~months)	Inventory type	Source
Acre	Porto Walter	2.33	1	Caldwell (unpublished), 1996
Amapá	Champion	1.67	2	Coli (unpublished), 1998
	Serra do Navio	0.67	2	Hoogmoed & Pires (unpublished), 1988
Amazonas	Alto Juruá	4.00	1	Gascon (unpublished), 1991/92; Gascon (1996)
	Alto Purus	0.53	2	Heyer (1977)
	Baixo Juruá	4.00	1	Gascon (unpublished), 1991/92; Gascon (1996)
	Baixo Purus	0.53	2	Heyer (1977)
	Ituxi	2.33	1	Caldwell (unpublished), 1997
	Madeira	0.82	2	Heyer (1977)
	Mamirauá	1.30	2	Hoogmoed & Pires (unpublished), 1994
	Manaus	12.00	1	Zimmerman & Rodrigues (1990); Hero (1990)
	Médio Juruá	4.00	1	Gascon (unpublished), 1991/92; Gascon (1996)
	Médio Purus	0.53	2	Heyer (1977)
	Taraquá	0.33	3	Henzl & Galatti (unpublished), 1996
	Urucu	0.90	2	Gascon & Pereira (1993) Hoogmoed & Pires (unpublished), 1989
Pará	Alter do Chão	0.50	1	Caldwell (unpublished), 1997; Azevedo-Ramos et al. (1999)
	Belém	9.50	1	Crump (1971); Estupiñán & Galatti (forthcoming)
	Carajás	1.00	2	Galatti (unpublished), 1997/98
	Caxiuanã	6.80	1	Ávila-Pires & Hoogmoed (1997); Estupiñán et al. (forthcoming)
	Paragominas	2.33	1	Ramos (unpublished), 1998/99
	Santarém	2.33	1	Caldwell (unpublished), 1995
	Trombenta/Nhamundá	0.50	2	Hoogmoed & Pires (unpublished), 1988
Rondônia	Alto Madeira	0.82	2	Heyer (1977); Moreira et al. (unpublished), 1997
	BR-364	7.40	1	Vanzolini (1986); Moreira et al. (unpublished), 1996/97
	C. Marques	0.63	2	Moreira et al. (unpublished), 1996/97
	Extrema	0.60	2	Moreira et al. (unpublished), 1996/97
	Guajará-Mirim	3.83	1	Moreira et al. (unpublished), 1996/97; Caldwell (unpublished), 1998; U. Galatti (unpublished), 1999
Roraima	Ajanari/Maracá	9.00	1	Martins (1998); Caldwell (unpublished), 1993

TABLE 2 - RELATIVE IMPORTANCE OF THE NUMBER OF UNDETERMINED SPECIES IN RELATION TO TOTAL SPECIES, AND COMPARISON BETWEEN SPECIES OCCURRING IN ONLY ONE LOCATION AND THOSE ENDEMIC SPECIES ACCORDING TO FROST (1985) AND DUELLMAN (1993). FOR ENDEMIC SPECIES, THE LOCATION-TYPES ARE INDICATED IN FOOTNOTES WHERE THESE DO NOT EXACTLY CORRESPOND TO THE INVENTORY LOCALITIES.

Locality	State	Number of undetermined species / Total (%)	Species ocurring only once in the inventories	Endemic species (Frost 1985; Duellman 1993)
Médio Juruá	Amazonas	19/78 (24.36)	1 *Leptodactylus diedrus*	1 *Leptodactylus dantasi* [1]
BR-364	Rondônia	12/68 (17.65)	1 *Leptodactylus podicipinus*	0
Alto Juruá	Acre	13/59 (22.03)	0	0
Guajará-Mirim	Rondônia	11/56 (19.64)	0	
Costa Marques	Rondônia	04/54 (7.41)	0	0
Manaus	Amazonas	01/53 (1.89)	9 *Bufo dapsilis* *Cochranella oyampiensis* *Colostethus stepheni* *Eleutherodactylus okendeni* *Leptodactylus riveroi* *Chiasmocleis hudsoni* *Synapturanus salseri* *Typhlonectes cunhai* *Pipa arrabali*	2 *Colostethus stepheni* [2] *Typhlonectes cunhai*
Urucu	Amazonas	13/51 (25.49)	0	0
Médio/Baixo Madeira	Amazonas	03/51 (5.88)	0	0
Porto Walter	Acre	10/48 (20.83)	4 *Hemiphractus scutatus* *Phyllomedusa atelopoide* *Scinax funerea* *Eleutherodactylus sulcatus*	0
Carajás	Pará	02/47 (4.25)	1 *Epipedobates flavopictus*	0
Alto Madeira	Amazonas	03/46 (6.52)	0	0
Ajarani-Maracá	Roraima	05/45 (11.11)	6 *Allophryne ruthveni* *Dendrobates leucomelas* *Hyla crepitans* *Scinax exigua* *Pleurodema brachyops* *Pseudopaludicula boliviana*	0
Baixo Juruá	Amazonas	07/44 (15.91)	0	0
Ituxi	Amazonas	09/42 (21.43)	0	0
Caxiuanã	Pará	01/41 (2.44)	0	0
Belém	Pará	02/38 (5.26)	2 *Hyla bokermani* *Scinax baumgardneri*	0
Champion	Amapá	05/36 (13.89)	2 *Eleutherodactylus conspicillatus* *Lysapsus laevis*	0
Extrema	Rondônia	07/36 (19.44)	0	0
Santarém	Pará	05/35 (14.28)	2 *Bufo glaberrimus* *Dendrobates castaneoticus*	2 *Dendrobates castaneoticus* *Hyla inframaculata*
Mamirauá	Amazonas	13/33 (39.39)	0	0
Médio Purus	Amazonas	02/33 (6.60)	0	0
Alto Purus	Amazonas	02/31 (6.45)	1 *Hyla pauiniensis*	2 *Hyla pauiniensis* *Hyla xapurensis* [3]
Baixo Purus	Amazonas	00/31 (0.00)	0	1 *Hyla imitator* [4]
Paragominas	Amazonas	01/30 (3.33)	0	0

continues

Localities	State	Number of undetermined species / Total (%)	Species ocurring only once in the inventories	Endemic species (Frost 1985; Duellman 1993)
Serra do Navio	Amapá	02/27 (7.41)	5 *Epipedobates pulchripectus* *Adelophryne gutturosa* *Eleutherodactylus chiastonotus* *Eleutherodactylus gutturalis* *Eleutherodactylus zeucotylus*	2 *Epipedobates pulchripectus* *Hyla dentei*
Trombetas / Nhamundá	Pará	06/25 (24.0)	0	0
Taraquá	Amazonas	05/18 (27.77)	0	2 *Hyla tintinnabulum* [5] *Scinax lindsay* [6]
Alter do Chão	Pará	02/18 (11.11)	0	0

1. Feijó/Acre; 2. Presidente Figueiredo/Amazonas; 3. Xapuri/Acre; 4. Lago Codajás/Amazonas; 5. Rio Uaupés/Amazonas; 6. Rio Uaupés, 3 km Yapina (Colombia), in Taraquá/Amazonas

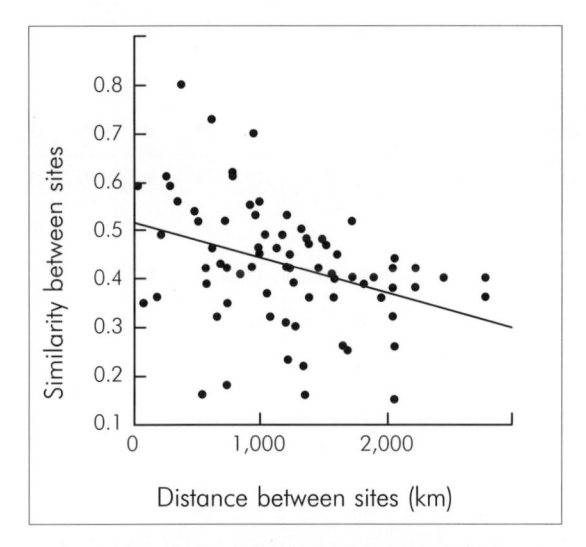

Figure 1. Relationship between indices of species similarity and distance between sites for thirteen localities with long-term inventories.

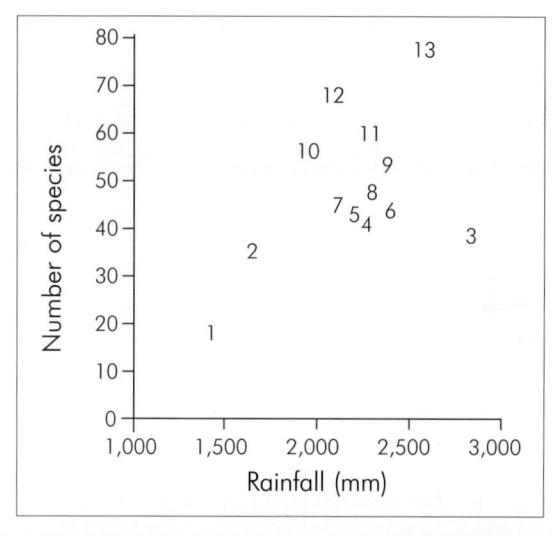

Figure 2. Relationship between the number of amphibian species and rainfall for thirteen sites in the Brazilian Amazon. From top to bottom: 1-Alter do Chão; 2-Santarém; 3-Belém; 4-Caixuanã; 5-Ituxi; 6-Lower Juruá; 7-Roraima; 8-Porto Walter; 9-Manaus; 10-Guajará-Mirim; 11-Upper Juruá; 12-BR; 13-Middle Juruá.

Priority areas for new inventories

Based on Figure 3, we were able to determine which regions have been well inventoried and which areas still need their anurofauna to be sampled. Due to their easy accessibility, most of the inventoried areas in Amazonia are located along major rivers and near highways; there is a need for research programs in the areas between the major rivers.

In southeastern Amazonia, which includes the Tapajós, Xingu, and Tocantins/Araguaia river basins, inventories should, whenever possible, cover the whole latitudinal gradient and reach the southern limit of the region, those areas of ecological tension or transition areas between the biomes of the Amazon and the more open vegetation of central Brazil.

Based on the gaps identified in those areas in which the anurofauna has been inventoried, fifteen areas were identified as priority areas for new inventories, drawn up mainly on the basis of the region's hydrographic system. The rationale behind our selection of these areas was simply the complete lack of knowledge and/or the existence of incomplete data on the anurofauna of these regions.

1. The area between the Madeira and the Tapajós rivers (as far as the southern limit of Amazonia);
2. The Rio Tapajós basin;
3. The area between the Tapajós and the Xingu rivers (as far as southern limit of Amazonia);
4. The Rio Xingu basin;
5. The area between the Xingu and the Tocantins rivers (as far as the southern limit of Amazonia);
6. The hydrographic basin of the Tocantins and Araguaia rivers (up to the southern limits of the Amazon);
7. The Rio Gurupi region, in the northeast of the State of Pará;
8. The Ilha de Marajó;
9. The area between the Branco and the Jari rivers, comprising the basins and micro-basins of the Jatapu, Mapuera, Trombetas, Paru, and Ipitinga rivers;
10. The Rio Negro basin;
11. The area between the Negro and the Solimões rivers and the Rio Japurá region;
12. The area between the Solimões and the Javari rivers and the Rio Juruá;
13. The area between the Juruá and the Purus rivers;
14. The area between the Purus and the Madeira rivers;
15. Both the inner and the southern regions of the Guaporé Biological Reserve, on the Bolivian border.

Conscious that these areas represent a large part of the Amazon for which we have no knowledge of the amphibian fauna, we suggest that future efforts should consider selecting a few

TABLE 3 - TOTAL NUMBER OF SPECIES (IN BOLD) AND NUMBER OF SPECIES COMMON TO TWO LOCALITIES (TOP OF TABLE). NUMBERS IN THE TABLE BELOW REFER TO ESTIMATIONS OF SIMILARITY ACCORDING TO THE SORENSEN INDEX, SHOWING THE EXTREME SIMILARITY VALUES (VERY HIGH OR VERY LOW) BETWEEN AREAS. THE AVERAGE OF THE SIMILARITY VALUES BY LOCALITY IS SHOWN AT THE BOTTOM OF THE TABLE.

	STM	MA	RR	ITU	CH	PW	CJ	AR	PA	BE	CAX	APU	MPU	BPU	MAD	MJU	AJU	BJU	SN	AMA	TRO	EXT	CM	MAM	URU	BR	GUA	ACh
STM	**30**	16	13	16	13	15	20	9	13	14	17	10	12	11	15	18	16	14	11	18	9	14	18	5	20	21	18	8
MA	0.39	**52**	15	18	19	18	27	9	15	17	20	9	13	12	19	25	20	19	12	21	15	19	28	7	25	25	24	10
RR	0.37	0.32	**40**	11	16	10	19	8	14	17	13	7	13	19	14	11	11	7	7	22	9	10	21	7	11	23	18	13
ITU	0.50	0.42	0.30	**33**	12	22	16	7	10	13	17	12	15	14	19	24	24	16	10	18	8	17	18	7	21	24	24	4
CH	0.42	0.46	0.45	0.37	**31**	13	18	7	12	13	14	10	13	12	19	19	13	10	9	16	11	11	19	8	16	19	17	10
PW	0.44	0.40	0.25	0.62	0.38	**38**	17	6	11	15	15	11	15	14	19	27	25	20	8	16	8	17	18	7	22	20	19	4
CJ	0.53	0.56	0.40	0.41	0.47	0.41	**45**	11	19	22	23	12	14	12	19	23	19	17	14	26	11	19	27	10	25	29	23	9
AR	0.42	0.28	0.30	0.18	0.32	0.23	0.32	**13**	3	6	10	6	6	6	7	7	6	6	6	11	7	7	9	6	9	11	9	4
PA	0.44	0.37	0.41	0.32	0.40	0.33	0.51	0.14	**29**	18	18	7	8	8	13	15	11	11	9	15	9	12	18	4	14	14	14	7
BE	0.42	0.39	0.45	0.38	0.39	0.40	0.54	0.24	0.55	**36**	19	8	11	12	15	19	15	13	10	17	8	14	25	8	18	18	13	9
CAX	0.49	0.43	0.32	0.47	0.39	0.38	0.54	0.76	0.52	0.50	**40**	10	13	13	20	20	20	18	8	25	9	17	24	9	19	23	17	10
APU	0.34	0.22	0.35	0.39	0.33	0.33	0.32	0.29	0.28	0.25	0.29	**29**	19	10	18	18	16	7	9	18	8	11	14	12	15	20	15	2
MPU	0.39	0.31	0.37	0.47	0.42	0.48	0.37	0.27	0.26	0.33	0.37	0.63	**31**	19	21	24	18	14	10	16	7	15	19	14	19	21	15	4
BPU	0.36	0.29	0.53	0.44	0.39	0.41	0.32	0.27	0.26	0.36	0.37	0.33	0.61	**31**	24	22	17	15	5	15	6	12	16	11	16	22	13	7
MAD	0.38	0.38	0.32	0.47	0.48	0.44	0.41	0.23	0.36	0.36	0.45	0.47	0.53	0.61	**48**	32	25	20	8	31	11	15	25	12	22	33	20	10
MJU	0.40	0.45	0.22	0.52	0.42	0.56	0.44	0.19	0.34	0.40	0.40	0.41	0.53	0.49	0.60	**59**	42	35	11	23	10	21	30	12	31	32	27	8
AJU	0.42	0.41	0.26	0.61	0.65	0.59	0.13	0.20	0.29	0.36	0.42	0.43	0.47	0.44	0.53	0.80	**46**	29	9	19	7	20	23	8	25	27	25	6
BJU	0.42	0.43	0.18	0.46	0.29	0.53	0.41	0.17	0.33	0.36	0.47	0.21	0.41	0.44	0.47	0.73	0.70	**37**	8	16	7	17	19	7	21	21	17	6
SN	0.40	0.31	0.21	0.55	0.32	0.25	0.40	0.32	0.33	0.33	0.25	0.33	0.36	0.18	0.22	0.26	0.25	0.26	**25**	12	11	8	11	9	17	15	12	4
AMA	0.49	0.44	0.53	0.47	0.43	0.39	0.59	0.39	0.42	0.43	0.60	0.50	0.43	0.40	0.68	0.45	0.43	0.40	0.35	**43**	14	18	28	12	22	33	22	11
TRO	0.37	0.42	0.30	0.31	0.44	0.28	0.34	0.44	0.45	0.29	0.30	0.33	0.28	0.24	0.33	0.25	0.21	0.25	0.50	0.45	**19**	8	10	6	12	12	11	5
EXT	0.47	0.47	0.29	0.55	0.37	0.51	0.51	0.33	0.41	0.43	0.49	0.38	0.50	0.40	0.39	0.48	0.53	0.51	0.30	0.50	0.33	**29**	22	9	22	19	19	6
CM	0.45	0.55	0.47	0.43	0.47	0.40	0.57	0.28	0.46	0.58	0.53	0.35	0.47	0.39	0.51	0.55	0.48	0.44	0.29	0.60	0.58	0.56	**50**	12	24	32	25	12
MAM	0.20	0.19	0.23	0.26	0.31	0.24	0.27	0.36	0.16	0.29	0.30	0.49	0.55	0.43	0.35	0.30	0.24	0.24	0.40	0.38	0.31	0.37	0.34	**20**	10	12	6	3
URU	0.42	0.54	0.27	0.57	0.44	0.56	0.58	0.33	0.40	0.47	0.47	0.43	0.53	0.44	0.49	0.62	0.57	0.54	0.51	0.52	0.40	0.63	0.53	0.33	**41**	29	25	6
BR	0.49	0.46	0.48	0.54	0.44	0.42	0.57	0.64	0.33	0.39	0.48	0.47	0.48	0.50	0.63	0.56	0.53	0.45	0.37	0.67	0.32	0.45	0.60	0.32	0.60	**56**	30	11
GUA	0.48	0.49	0.42	0.61	0.45	0.46	0.51	0.31	0.38	0.32	0.36	0.40	0.39	0.34	0.43	0.52	0.55	0.41	0.34	0.50	0.34	0.51	0.53	0.18	0.58	0.59	**45**	11
ACh	0.35	0.29	0.46	0.16	0.42	0.15	0.29	0.27	0.31	0.35	0.36	0.09	0.17	0.30	0.31	0.21	0.26	0.23	0.19	0.37	0.29	0.27	0.36	0.17	0.21	0.31	0.36	**16**
Average	0.42	0.39	0.35	0.44	0.41	0.40	0.43	0.31	0.36	0.39	0.43	0.36	0.42	0.39	0.42	0.45	0.43	0.40	0.32	0.47	0.34	0.44	0.47	0.30	0.48	0.48	0.43	0.30

sites representative of the diversity of natural environments of each area in order to obtain a representative collection of the diversity of the local fauna. We also suggest that higher priority be given to regions adjacent to the 'arc of deforestation' (the northeastern and southern parts of the State of Pará, the northern part of the State of Mato Grosso, and the northern parts of the states of Rondônia and Acre), since these are subject to intense anthropogenic pressure and rapid degradation of their natural habitats.

Since inventories carried out on an east-west axis have revealed a fauna that is typical of each place studied, rather than sub-samples of richer areas, we strongly recommend that the sampling pattern include localities along this axis in order to obtain a better idea of Amazonian diversity. In addition, the region between the Branco and the Jari rivers should equally be considered a priority area for new inventories given the high degree of endemism found in the neighboring areas of Suriname and of French Guyana, which suggests that a unique fauna is likely to be found in this area.

Priority areas for conservation

Various criteria may be used to determine priority areas for conservation. Among these, land use patterns, areas of anthro-

TABLE 4 - FREQUENCY [ABSOLUTE (%)] WITH WHICH SPECIES OCCUR BY LOCALITIES USED TO REPRESENT EACH STATE

State	Number of localities with examples of the same species								Total species
	1	2	3	4	5	6	7	8	
Amazonas	43 (43)	18 (18)	12 (12)	15 (15)	3 (3)	5 (5)	2 (2)	2 (2)	100
Pará	22 (27)	16 (20)	13 (16)	13 (16)	8 (10)	5 (6)	3 (4)	1 (1)	81
Rondônia	27 (30)	20 (22)	24 (27)	6 (7)	12 (13)				89
Amapá	38 (81)	9 (19)							47
Acre	38 (100)								38
Roraima	45 (100)								45

pogenic pressure, conservation areas and political and regional interests should be included. For purposes of simplification, the areas listed below were chosen solely on the basis of criteria related to the diversity of anurous species (for instance, number and similarity of species; number of unique or endangered species). To assist the identification of priority areas, only two external factors were considered: (1) priority was given to areas with higher anthropogenic pressure, using as indicators ease of access by water and road networks; (2) lower priority was given to areas where conservation areas have already been established.

Our findings show that the fauna from the east to the west of Amazonia is represented by assemblages that are typical of each region, although they retain a degree of similarity with assemblages of other regions. Thus, the diversity of habitats found in different regions of the Amazon must be conserved so that both local faunistic identity and Amazonian diversity as a whole are conserved.

A large number of parks, reserves, and ecological stations have been created in the Amazon. Most states contain a representative number of these conservation areas, although their effective protection is not considered in this study.

Nevertheless, these areas are likely to become isolated through the conversion of forests into other ecosystems due to advancing human occupation, mainly in eastern Amazonia. This isolation may jeopardize the viability of resident populations or, more generally, that of those species which use these areas as a 'springboard' to other areas. We have therefore given priority to areas which permit connections between existing conservation areas and have identified those regions where a shortfall of protected areas exists.

Precise limits were not established for each region since this will depend upon site visits and upon detailed knowledge of the ecosystems characteristic of each region, which is currently unavailable. Rather than attempt this, we have restricted ourselves to recommending relevant areas for future, more detailed studies for the potential creation of conservation areas.

Therefore reference to a particular area does not necessary imply a suggestion to conserve the area as a whole, but rather of that ecosystem diversity and those characteristics of the area that have the potential to ensure the maintenance of the species diversity of Amazonian amphibians.

Below we suggest priority areas for conservation together with the justification for each:

1 - The Rio Juruá basin - an area of high amphibian diversity, and which is representative of the western extremity of the Brazilian Amazon; a region with no established conservation areas able to ensure conservation of the local fauna.

2 - The region between the Juruá and the Purus rivers - an area of high amphibian diversity, and which is representative of the western extremity of the Brazilian Amazon; a region with no established conservation areas able to ensure conservation of the local fauna; moderate similarity between the fauna of the Juruá and Purus regions, facilitating conservation of species of both regions.

3 - The region between the Purus and the Madeira rivers - an area where inventories along the rivers indicate high amphibian diversity; important for ensuring representation of amphibians of central Amazonia; a region with no established conservation areas able to ensure conservation of the local fauna; moderate to high similarity between the fauna of the Purus and the Madeira regions, facilitating conservation of species of both regions.

4 - The Amazon portion of the Rio Madeira basin - an area of high amphibian diversity and important for ensuring representation of the fauna of central Amazonia, since only 40% of its fauna is similar to that of the Manaus region; a region with no established conservation areas able to ensure conservation of the local fauna.

5 - The northern portion of the area between the Tapajós and Xingu rivers - an area whose fauna is still unknown, which is at risk of high anthropogenic impacts due to its easy accessibility and to the rapid advance of the line of deforestation. This area is able to act as a corridor between two conservation areas established to the northwest (Amazonia National Park) and to the southeast (Tapirapé Biological Reserve and Igarapé Gelado Environmental Protection Area) in the State of Pará.

6 - The border area of the states of Pará and Mato Grosso - an area whose fauna is still unknown, which is at risk of high anthropogenic impacts due to its easy accessibility and to the rapid advance of the line of deforestation. This area is able to act as a corridor between two conservation areas established to the northwest (Amazonia National Park) and southeast (Tapirapé Biological Reserve and Igarapé Gelado Environmental Protection Area) in the State of Pará. An area influenced by the savannah of central Brazil, possibly with a fauna shared among forest environments and open areas.

7 - The Alter do Chão region in the State of Pará - an enclave area of Amazonian savannah with characteristic fauna and low similarity to neighboring forest areas; a potential area of tourist development threatened by real estate speculation and accidental fires caused by ranching and agriculture.

8 - The region of the Tapajós National Forest - an area representative of regional forest fauna with low similarity to other areas of the central Amazon and neighboring areas.

9 - The border region of Suriname and French Guiana - fauna on the Brazil side is still unknown, but there are high levels of endemism in the neighboring countries; a region with no established conservation areas able to ensure conservation of the local fauna.

10 - The region of the Serra do Navio, State of Amapá - fauna characteristic of the region; ensures inclusion of high altitude habitats.

11 - Northeastern Pará - although the region does not have as rich an anurofauna as areas of western Amazon, it reveals around 50% similarity with neighboring inventoried regions. Since

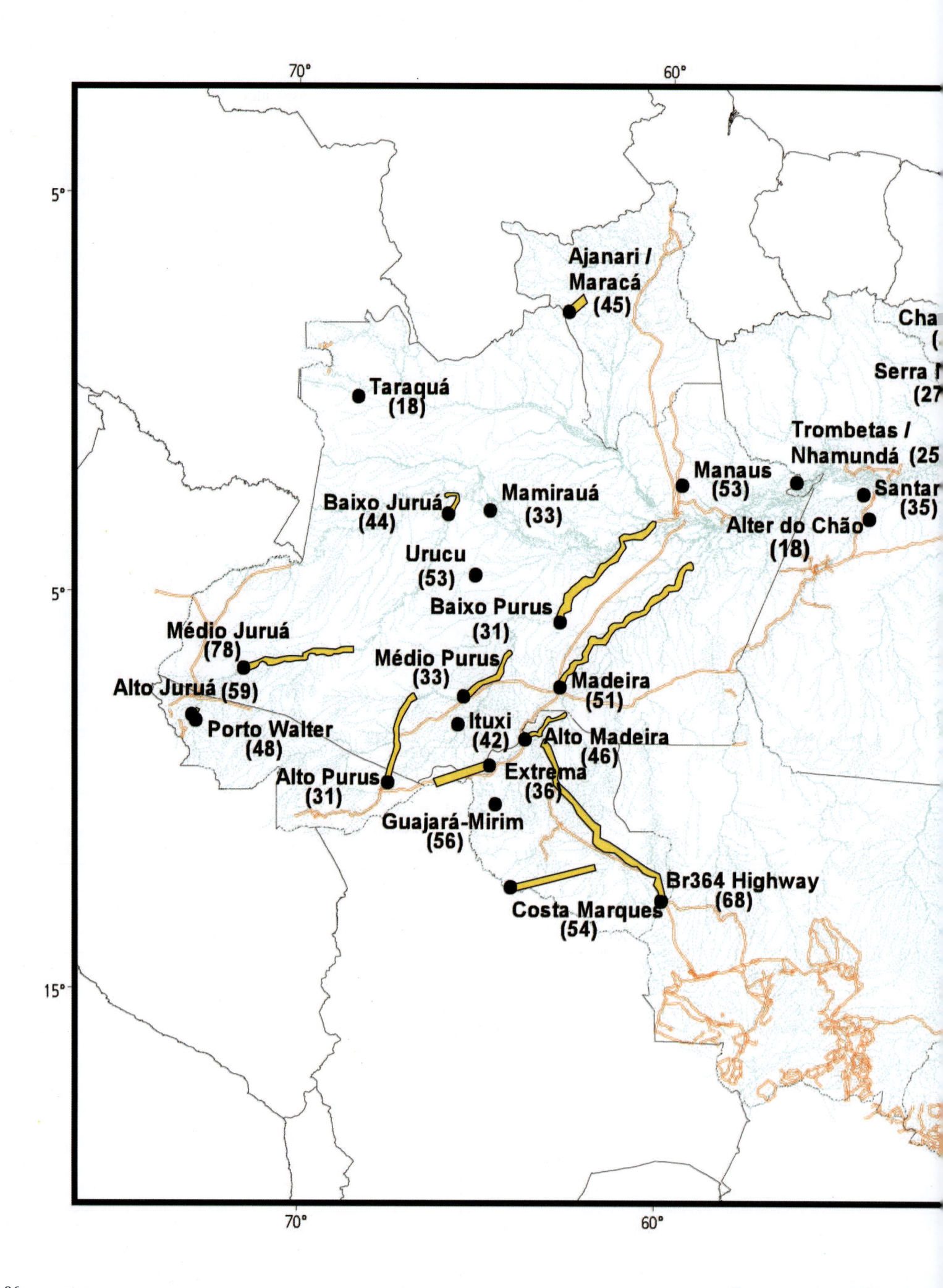

- Ajanari / Maracá (45)
- Taraquá (18)
- Cha...
- Serra... (27)
- Trombetas / Nhamundá (25)
- Manaus (53)
- Santar... (35)
- Baixo Juruá (44)
- Mamirauá (33)
- Alter do Chão (18)
- Urucu (53)
- Baixo Purus (31)
- Médio Juruá (78)
- Médio Purus (33)
- Alto Juruá (59)
- Madeira (51)
- Porto Walter (48)
- Ituxi (42)
- Alto Madeira (46)
- Alto Purus (31)
- Extrema (36)
- Guajará-Mirim (56)
- Br364 Highway (68)
- Costa Marques (54)

Figure 3. Location of inventoried areas for amphibians in the Brazilian Amazon in relation to the river and highway networks of the region. The numbers show the total of species found in each location.

the Caixuanã National Reserve provides protection for regional species between the Xingu and the Tocantins rivers and the area around Belém has already been significantly degraded, a conservation area in northeastern Pará could ensure the maintenance of fauna in an area undergoing extreme anthropogenic impact as a result of its easy accessibility by road, high lumber exploitation and intense conversion from forest to agricultural ecosystems.

12 - Ilha de Marajó - an area whose fauna is still unknown; a conservation area on this island would enable the maintenance of an island community representative of both open and seasonally flooded areas.

Discussion

The amount of data on the distribution of amphibian species in the Amazon region has considerably increased since the last workshop on the assessment of priority areas for conservation in Amazonia, which took place in 1990.

However, this knowledge is still very fragmented and not widely available through the specialist literature. The majority of inventories were carried out either along the margins of the main Amazon tributaries or in regions well served by the road network. Many areas still lack any type of information, for example the regions between the main Amazon tributaries.

The richness of the amphibian species as shown in this paper represents the minimum number known and is biased towards anurous species (toads and frogs). Information on *Gymnophiona* (Caecilians) is rare and, although only one species of salamander has been described for the Brazilian Amazon (*Bolitoglossa altamazonica*), little is known about its geographic distribution.

Apparently, endemism is not a useful variable for guiding the selection of conservation areas for Amazonian amphibians since the number of endemic species found was very low. Nor are there references to species regarded as endangered.

The average similarity of fauna between localities was 0.40, which indicates the specificity of the fauna of each region of Amazonia. The effect of this for conservation policies is that conservation of any particular locality would ensure preservation of less than half the amphibian diversity of Amazonia. Furthermore, the farther apart the areas are from each other, the less similar their fauna are. This strongly suggests that conservation areas should be established and maintained on both the north-south and the east-west axes. General concepts of species diversity have also been noted in this study of amphibians. Areas with higher rainfall tend to display a higher degree of diversity. In general, regions of western Amazonia display a higher degree of diversity than the eastern region.

New areas for inventories and for conservation have been proposed in this paper. However, as large areas of the Amazon remain unknown, we suggest that studies in the areas surrounding the arc of deforestation be given priority in light of the rapid conversion of forests into other ecosystems and, as a consequence, the higher risk of loss of information on the local fauna and flora.

Bibliography

(Dates of unpublished data refer to year of collection)

AZEVEDO-RAMOS, C. *A exploração madeireira manejada e tradicional:* impacto sobre a diversidade animal e programa de educação ambiental na Amazônia Oriental. Technical report. Belém/PA: Fundo Estadual de Ciência e Tecnologia do Pará, 1999.

AZEVEDO-RAMOS, C.; MAGNUSSON, W. E.; BAYLISS, P. Predation as the Key Factor Structuring Tadpole Assemblages in a Savannah Area in Central Amazonia, *Copeia*, n. 1, p. 22-33, 1999.

BERNARDI, J. A. R.; ESTUPIÑÁN, R. A.; GALATTI, U. New Records of Anuran Amphibians in the Floresta Nacional de Caxiuanã, Eastern Amazon, Brazil. Submitted to *Herp. Review*, unpublished.

CALDWELL, J. P. C. NSF Project DEB-9200779. Laurie J. Vitt and Janalee P. Caldwell, Oklahoma Museum of Natural History, University of Oklahoma. Inventory and ecologia of the herpetofauna of Amazonia. Rio Ajarani, BR-210, Roraima, Brasil. <http://www.omnh.ou.edu/personnel/herpetology/NSF/DEB_9200779/RR93AmphList.html>, unpublished, 1993.

_____. NSF Project DEB-9200779. Laurie J. Vitt and Janalee P. Caldwell, Oklahoma Museum of Natural History, University of Oklahoma/Museu Paraense Emílio Goeldi. Inventory and ecologia of the herpetofauna of Amazonia. Alter do Chão/CEMEX, Santarém/PA, Brasil. <http://www.omnh.ou.edu/personnel/herpetology/NSF/DEB_9200779/ParaAmphList.html>, unpublished, 1995.

_____. NSF Project DEB-9505518. Laurie J. Vitt and Janalee P. Caldwell, Oklahoma Museum of Natural History, University of Oklahoma/Museu Paraense Emílio Goeldi. Inventory and ecologia of the herpetofauna of Amazonia. Rio Juruá, Porto Walter/AC, Brasil. <http://www.omnh.ou.edu/personnel/herpetology/NSF/DEB_9505518/AcreAmphList.html>, unpublished, 1996.

_____. NSF Project DEB-9505518. Laurie J. Vitt and Janalee P. Caldwell, Oklahoma Museum of Natural History, University of Oklahoma/Museu Paraense Emílio Goeldi. Inventory and ecologia of the herpetofauna of Amazonia. Rio Ituxi, Amazonas, Brasil. <http://www.omnh.ou.edu/personnel/herpetology/NSF/DEB_9505518/ItuxiAmphList.html>, unpublished, 1997.

_____. NSF Project DEB-9505518 (Laurie J. Vitt and Janalee P. Caldwell, Oklahoma Museum of Natural History, University of Oklahoma/Museu Paraense Emílio Goeldi. Inventory and ecologia of the herpetofauna of Amazonia. Rio Formoso, Guajará Mirim, Rondônia, Brasil. http://www.omnh.ou.edu/personnel/herpetology/NSF/DEB_9505518/RondAmphHabData.html, unpublished, 1998.

COLLI, G. Avaliação ecológica rápida na área da Chamflora. In: *Herpetofauna*. Amapá: Champion Papel e Celulose, unpublished.

CRUMP, M. L. Quantitative Analysis of the Ecological Distribution of a Tropical Herpetofauna. In: *Occas.* Pap. Mus. Nat. Hist. Univ. Kansas 3, 1971. p. 1-62.

DE QUADRO, M. F. L. ET AL. Centro de Previsão de Tempo e Estudos Climáticos/Instituto Nacional de Pesquisas Espaciais - CPTEC/INPE. *Boletim de Monitoramento e Análise Climática. Climatologia de precipitação e Temperatura*. <http://www1.cptec.inpe.br/products/climanalise>.

ESTUPIÑÁN, R. A.; GALATTI, U. La fauna anura en areas con diferentes grados de intervención antropica de la Amazonia oriental brasileña, *Revista de Instituto de Ciencias Naturales de la Universidad Nacional de Colombia José Jerônimo Triana*, no prelo.

ESTUPIÑÁN, R. A.; BERNARDIM, J. A. R.; GALATTI, U. La fauna anura en la floresta Nacional de Caxiuanã. In: LISBOA, P. (Ed.). *Caxiuanã*, vol. 2. Belém: Museu Paraense Emílio Goeldi, forthcoming.

DUELLMAN, W. E. Herpetofaunas in Neotropical Rainforests: Comparative Composition, History, and Resources Use. In: GENTRY, A. H. (Ed.). *Four Neotropical Rainforests*. New Haven: Yale Univ. Press, 1990, p. 455-505.

DUELLMAN, W. E. Amphibian Species of the World: Additions and Corrections, *Univ. Kansas Mus. Nat. Hist. Spec. Publ.*, n. 21, p. 1-372, 1993.

FROST, D. R. (Ed.). *Amphibian Species of the World*. Lawrence, Kansas: Allen Press, 1985.

GALATTI, U. *Inventário da herpetofauna da área sob influência do Projeto Salobo, Floresta Nacional Tapirapé-Aquiri, Parauapebas, Pará*. Final report. Belo Horizonte: Brandt Meio Ambiente, 1998.

_____. Avaliação ecológica rápida da Reserva Biológica Estadual Rio Ouro Preto, Guajará-Mirim, Rondônia. In: *Inventário da herpetofauna da Res. Biol. rio Ouro Preto*. Relatório final. United Nations Development Programme/Plano Agropecuário e Florestal de Rondôdia (UNDP/PLANAFLORO), 1999.

GASCON, C. *Inventário da herpetofauna ao longo do rio Juruá, 1991/1992*, unpublished.

_____. Amphibian Litter Fauna as River Barrier in Flooded and Non-Flooded Amazonian Rainforest, *Biotropica*, v. 28, n. 1, p. 136-140, 1996.

GASCON, C.; PEREIRA, O. S. Preliminary Checklist of the Herpetofauna of the Upper Rio Urucu, Amazonas, Brazil, *Rev. Brasil. Zool.*, v. 10, n. 1, p. 179-183, 1993.

HENZL, M.; GALATTI, U. *Formas de vida e biologia de anuros da Amazônia*. Vienna/Belém: University of Vienna/Museu Paraense Emílio Goeldi, Missão Taraquá, Amazonas & Floresta Nacional de Caxiuanã/PA. 1996, unpublished.

HERO, J.-M. An Illustrated Key to Tadpoles Occurring in the Central Amazon Rainforest, Manaus, Amazonas, Brasil, *Amazoniana*, v. 11, n. 2, p. 201-262, 1990.

HEYER, W. R. Taxonomic Notes on Frogs from the Madeira and Purus Rivers, Brazil, *Papéis Avulsos de Zoologia*, v. 31, n. 8, p. 141-162, 1977.

HOOGMOED, M. S.; ÁVILA-PIRES, T. C. S. The Herpetofauna. In: LISBOA, P. (Ed.). *Caxiuanã*. Belém: Museu Paraense Emílio Goeldi, 1997, p. 389-401.

_____. *Inventário preliminar da herpetofauna na região do rio Urucu, Amazonas*. 1989, unpublished.

_____. *Inventário preliminar da herpetofauna na região do interflúvio rio Nhamundá/rio Trombetas, Pará*. 1988, unpublished.

_____. *Inventário preliminar da herpetofauna na região da serra do Navio, Amapá*. 1988, unpublished.

_____. *Inventário preliminar da herpetofauna na Reserva Biológica de Mamirauá, Amazonas*. 1994, unpublished.

_____. *Inventário preliminar da herpetofauna na região de São Félix do Xingú, Pará*. 1999, unpublished.

KREBS, C. J. *Ecological Methods*. New York: Harper & Row, Publishers, 1989.

MARTINS, M. The Frogs of the Ilha de Maracá. In: MILLIKEN, W.; RATTER, J. A. (Ed.). *Maracá:* Biodiversity and Environment of an Amazonian Rainforest. John Wiley and Sons Ltd., 1998, p. 285-306.

MOREIRA, G. R. et al. Relatório final da área temática herpetofauna. In: *Macrozoneamento socio-econômico-ecológico do Estado de Rondônia*. Porto Velho: Planafloro, 1997.

OLIVEIRA, S. N. et al. *Diversity and Distruibution of Frogs along the Banks of the Tapajós River at the Edge of an Area of Amazonian Savannah in Brazil*, unpublished.

VANZOLINI, P. E. Levantamento herpetológico da área do estado de Rondônia sob influência da rodovia BR 364. In: *Programa Polonoroeste, Subprograma Ecologia Animal, Relatório de Pesquisa*, n. 1. MCT/ CNPq, 1986.

ZIMMERMAN, B. L.; RODRIGUES, M. T. Frogs, Snakes, and Lizards of INPA-WWF Reserves near Manaus, Brasil. In: GENTRY, A. H. (Ed.). *Four Neotropical Rainforests*. New Haven/London: Yale University Press, 1990, p. 426-454.

ZIMMERMAN, B. L.; SIMBERLOFF, D. An Historical Interpretation of Habitat Use by Frogs in Central Amazonian Forest, *Journal of Biogeography*, v. 23, n. 1, p. 27-46, 1996.

Reptile biodiversity of the Amazon Forest biome and priority action for its conservation

Richard C. Vogt *Universidad Autónoma del México*
Gláucia Maciel Moreira *Instituto Nacional de Pesquisas da Amazônia*
Ana Cristina de Oliveira Cordeiro Duarte *Instituto Nacional de Pesquisas da Amazônia*
Collaborators: T. C. S. Ávila-Pires, Márcio Martins, Laurie Vitt e P. E. Vanzolini

Introduction

The Brazilian Amazon is the world's largest tropical forest. Its vegetation is not homogenous, consisting of terra firme forest, floodplains, savanna, grassland, and open rocky areas. This combination of high vegetation diversity, high forest structure diversity, and non-forest areas is responsible for the great diversity of land reptiles found in the region (Vitt 1996).

In addition to the large number of bodies of water associated with the forest itself, there are many rivers (varying in size and nutrient quality), igapós (seasonally flooded forests), igarapés (streams and channels), lakes, and pools that offer immense habitat diversity and favor population isolation and the formation of new species.

The fact that the Amazon basin is bounded to the west by the Andes, to the south by savanna, and to the north by several mountain ranges also contributes to its high levels of biodiversity.

State of knowledge of reptiles

Faunistic studies of the Amazon region are extremely incomplete, especially in relation to certain reptile groups. The most complete data available are on the distribution, taxonomy, status, and ecology of caiman and turtle species. This may be due to the smaller number of species of these groups (compared to snakes, for example), and to their greater economic importance. As a result of historically greater commercial interest in turtle and caiman species, there is greater knowledge of their distribution and an increasing interest in the conservation of their populations.

Dixon's maps (1979) on the distribution of snakes and lizards in South American tropical rain forests do not reveal the presence of these reptiles in the central Amazon basin in Brazil. Twenty six years later, Ávila-Pires' maps (1995) of the distribution of lizards in Amazonia continued to show many central areas of the basin with no record of these species. The present type of publication is important for confirming the need to carry out collecting in areas for which inventories are lacking and to assess the importance of these areas for biodiversity conservation. A number of inventories (Ávila Pires 1995; Ávila-Pires & Hoogmoed 1997; Vitt 1996; Vitt unpublished 1993, 1995, 1996, 1997, 1998) have recently been published on lizard distribution and ecology in the Brazilian Amazon basin. Such lists are important sources of data on species distribution in general and on population status in different locations. The problem, however, is that such lists are usually compiled over a very short time frame, and do not constitute reliable samples of herpetofauna communities as a whole. Whilst they may be a useful contribution to the documentation on species records, they do not help to determine the distribution range of these species.

In general, distribution records for snake species are also extremely inadequate. It is not possible to draw up reliable recommendations for conservation areas on basis of the existing research on these reptiles in Amazonia.

Reptile diversity

According to Dixon (1979), there are 550 reptile species recorded for the Amazon basin, 62% of which are endemic. Muller (1973) found four endemic centers for birds: Guyana, Madeira, Napo, and Pará. Some amphibian species seem to follow this pattern, such as the *Hyla rostrata* (Duellman 1972) and *Dendrobates* (Silverstone 1975) groups. Is this a true arc of species distribution in the Amazon (Linche 1979), or does it just reflect the lack of collection efforts?

The orders and suborders of reptile groups are internally extremely diversified, and their study must therefore be approached in different ways. Turtles and caimans are closely linked to the ecology of the watercourse, unlike most lizard, snake, and amphisbaenian species. A further factor is that the turtle and crocodile groups have a considerably smaller number of species than snakes and lizards. Bearing in mind that, as a result of their economic importance, the distribution areas and population status of turtles and caimans are better known, it is advisable to establish separate conservation priorities for each reptile group.

Chelonia

Most Amazonian turtle species are better protected than turtles in other parts of the world. Three marine turtle species nest on islands and beaches along the coast of Amazonia, but these are not considered to be part of the Amazonian fauna.

The two land turtle species, *Geochelone denticulata* and *Geochelone carbonaria* are widely found in Amazonia. *G. denticulata* is more plentiful in forest environments, whereas *G. carbonaria* is more common outside Amazonia, although its presence has been recorded in the region (Vanzolini 1994). Both species are found within conservation areas, but there are no conservation programs to ensure maintenance of population levels.

There are 14 fresh-water turtle species in Amazonia. More data are available on the distribution areas of those species with greater economic value, which are more frequently found in local markets. There is less information on those species of lower commercial value. For a long time many of these were considered to be rare or even extinct. However, with systematic collection being undertaken in their habitats, many species are being located throughout the region and the blank areas in Iverson's maps (1996) are being filled in. Collecting mainly took off after a workshop in 1990, following which the fieldwork of Vogt and other researchers resulted in a substantial volume of data from various parts of Amazonia (Table 1); hence the changes in the picture since then.

Other than a new species, *Trachemys adiutrix*, endemic to the state of Maranhão, no other turtle species found in the Amazon is endemic to Brazil. However, the distribution of some species in Brazil is confined to this region.

Table 1 - Sites surveyed specifically for turtles

River	Type of water	no. of species	Source	Study time
Trombetas	clear	12	Vogt & Zwink	5 years
Tapajós	clear	5	Vogt	2 months
Guaporé	clear-black	8	Vogt	3 years
Rio Negro (Barcelos)	black	8	Vogt	2 years
Rio Solimões (Mamirauá Res.)	white	10	Vogt & Fachin	3 years
Purus	white	6	Vogt & Pezutti	1 year
Ducke Reserve	black	3	Vogt	10 years
Jaú	black	11	Rebelo & Vogt	3 years

Pelomedusidae

All the five species of this family in Brazil are threatened by human activity, through consumption of their eggs and the meat of adult animals.

Podocnemis expansa

This species is threatened everywhere it occurs outside Brazil. Conservation of the populations to be found in the Brazilian Amazon is due to the protection programs for beaches and hatching sites established by the National Amazonia Chelonia Center (*Centro Nacional de Quelônios da Amazônia* or *Cenaqua*) in all the Amazonian states. In Amapá, the program operates on the islands at the mouth of the Amazon river; in Amazonas, on the Rio Purus (the large populations of the Rio Juruá still lack protection); in Pará, the program covers beaches of the Trombetas, Tapajós, and Xingu rivers; in Roraima, it is being carried out on the Rio Branco; in Acre, on the Rio Purus; in Rondônia, on the Rio Guaporé; in Mato Grosso, on the Rio das Mortes; and in Goiás, on the Araguaia river. The program has managed to reduce the commercial exploitation of this species. Despite its lack of funds for inspection and control, the absence of the program itself would have resulted in the extinction of the species. For instance, in August 1999 a boat was seized on the Rio Purus with a cargo of 38,000 'bichos de casca' ('shelled creatures') – the regional name for turtles.

In the past, the population density of this species was high throughout the whole of Amazonia. Its numbers started declining in the 19th century and have reached alarmingly low levels today, mainly to hunting and to the taking of eggs by humans.

The protection of this species needs to be rapidly extended to all the river beaches in the region (especially those of the Juruá river, in the state of Amazonas). It is particularly important to incorporate both banks of the river into the protected area. No aquatic species can be protected if only one side of the river is part of the reserve. The size of the reserves must also be increased to cover feeding habitats and migration routes.

This may well be the most difficult species to protect. However, as the reptile of greatest economic value in the whole of the Amazon region, it serves as a 'flagship' species for the protection of other species that are less valuable economically, but of equal ecological importance. *P. expansa* is found throughout the whole of the Amazon region, in Brazil and outside. Its populations are protected in 28 national parks or biological reserves, in white and black water rivers. This species needs wide rivers with available hatching sites.

Podocnemis unifilis

This species occurs in all types of rivers and is widely found throughout Amazonia. Populations suffer less from hunting than *P. expansa* and, as both species use the same hatching sites, the species benefits from the same Cenaqua protection program. There are *P. unifilis* populations in 26 protected areas.

Podocnemis sextuberculata

The ecology of this species is more distinct; it only lives in clear water rivers, and is more plentiful in white waters. Some of its hatching sites are protected by the Cenaqua project, such those on the Purus, Trombetas, Tapajós, and Branco rivers. The Mamirauá Project also protects this turtle in some beaches of the Rio Solimões basin. There are fairly large populations of this species in at least 11 protected areas.

Podocnemis erythrocephala

This is the smallest of the Amazonian turtles and its distribution range is the most restricted, mainly because it is found in black water rivers. It is particularly abundant in the Rio Negro, in the state of Amazonas, where there are populations in five protected areas. However, there are also large populations in an unprotected section of the same river, in the municipality of Barcelos, and a legally protected reserve should be created in this area. The Cenaqua protection program does not include any hatching sites of this species. There are some populations on tributaries of the Rio Tapajós, but the numbers are very small.

Peltocephalus dumerilianus

This turtles inhabits mainly black waters and is abundant in 14 protected areas. As its hatching grounds are dispersed, the species has a greater chance of survival.

Chelidae

As species of this family are not normally captured for food or sale, their population numbers tend to be higher. However, little is actually known about these populations and their distribution in Amazonia.

Chelus fimbriatus

This species inhabits both white and black waters. It is most frequently recorded near the coast, although it seems that its distribution covers the whole of the Amazon basin. It can be found in approximately 30 protected areas and does not require any special protection program, since its meat is not sought for human consumption. Nevertheless, there is a lack of inventory studies of this species throughout Amazonia.

Phrynops geoffroanus

Inhabiting exclusively the upper areas of the Amazon basin, this species is common in the Guaporé river, where it is not eaten by humans. Research on the headwaters of other rivers is needed to increase the sample size of this species.

Phrynops gibbus

This small species inhabits forest pools in the Amazon basin. Its occurrence seems to be more common in lowlands. Present in at least eight reserves, it also lacks inventory programs throughout the region.

Phrynops raniceps

This species is found throughout the greater part of the Brazilian Amazon. Although it is found in clear and white waters, it seems to be more common in black water rivers. It is found in 16 protected areas in Amazonia, but does not require any extra protection, since its meat is not eaten.

Phrynops rufipes

A supposedly rare species in the Amazon, with records for only three areas in Brazil. In the last 10 years, five new sites for this species have been found in forest streams. Not taken for human consumption, it is very secretive species, although it has no special habitat. It may well be the most abundant turtle in the Amazon, yet its presence is poorly documented due to the lack of samples. Populations are known to exist in four protected areas, but the species probably also occurs in other areas still unknown.

Phrynops vanderhaegei

This small species inhabits pools in the middle of open areas on the edge of the Amazon basin. Surveys are necessary to determine its distribution.

Platemys platycephala

Another small species, which inhabits pools in the heart of the forest. Inventories for this species are lacking throughout Amazonia. It is however found in at least 31 protected areas.

Kinosternidae

Kinosternon scorpioides

A small species inhabiting swamps and pools in the middle of open areas of the Amazon basin. Widely distributed from Mexico to Bolivia, it is abundant in Brazilian coastal swamps and widely captured in Belém and in the state of Maranhão. New recordings of this species have recently been made in the state of Roraima, in the Rio Solimões valley, and in the Mamirauá reserve. There are at least eight conservation areas among the distribution sites of this turtle. Inventories for the species are needed throughout Amazonia.

Emydidae

Rhinoclemmys punctularia

This species inhabits streams and small tributaries in the lower reaches of the Amazon basin. It is apparently more abundant along the coast, extending inland as far as the border between the states of Pará and Amazonas. No priority protection program is needed for this species, as it is not taken for its meat; it does, however, need an inventory to determine its abundance and distribution.

Trachemys adiutrix

A recently described species (Vanzolini 1995), endemic to the state of Maranhão, where it inhabits coastal lakes and swamps. It is essencial that studies are carried out to better understand its distribution and abundance. Given both that it is hunted for its meat, and that it is an endemic species of restricted distribution, a special management plan for this turtle is needed.

CAIMANS

There are four caiman species found throughout the whole of the Amazon basin: *Caiman crocodilus*, *Melanosuchus niger*, *Paleosuchus trigonatus*, and *Paelosuchus palpebrosus*. Caimans suffer from two problems: 1) uncontrolled hunting for its meat (domestic market) and skin (overseas markets) and 2) environmental change.

The species most affected by commercial hunting are *C. crocodilus* and *M. niger*. Two thirds of all caiman skins on the world market are *C. crocodilus*, and Brazil is the largest producer of illegally exported skins (Rebelo et al. 1990). *M. Niger* was the most sought-after species when hunting was legal (prior to 1967), and since 1990 it seems that populations have not recovered (Rebelo et al. 1990). More recently, however, the *Melanosuchus* populations of the Mamirauá Reserve and of the Anavilhanas have recovered and are at levels high enough to allow commercialization (Ronis de Silveira pers. com.). From 1987 to 1989, Rebelo et al. (1990) studied the distribution of all Amazonian species, sampling 71 sites in 12 states and territories. Some locations, however, still have to be sampled: the Juruá, Purus, Japurá, Tapajós, and Trombetas rivers.

Critical areas

There are two special situations to do with caimans in the Guaporé-Madeira basin: 1) *C. c. crocodilus* and *C. c. yacare* populations are hybridizing along 800 km of the Rio Madeira; 2) there are *M. niger* populations on the upper Rio Guaporé, in the state of Mato Grosso, and on the lower Rio Madeira, separated by more than 1,500 km. The area in between is where hunting is most intensive (the Guaporé valley between Costa Marques and Abunã), and where prospecting is taking place (between Guajará-Mirim and Porto Velho). *M. Niger* populations were last recorded in these areas 20 years ago, and by 1989 the species appeared to have become totally extinct here. These fragmented *M. niger* populations need to be protected through the creation of conservation areas in those stretches where the species still occurs.

Since 1989, *M. niger* also seems to have disappeared almost entirely from the Araguaia-Tocantins system, with the possible exception of the northern part of the Ilha do Bananal, inside the National Park. Even *C. crocodilus* populations were found to be low in this river system. Rebelo et al. discovered one of the largest populations of this species in the state of Amapá, in the Piratuba Lake Biological Reserve, as well as in the Maracá Islands Ecological Station in the state of Roraima. Outside these protected areas, hunting is widespread. Another problem at places where these reptiles occur is habitat destruction caused by extensive buffalo raising.

There are no historical records for *M. niger* in the far eastern part of the Amazon, only for *C. crocodilus*. In the Mearim-Pindaré valley, in the Maranhão lowlands, and in the Tocantins valley, Rebelo et al. (1990) found low *M. niger* population densities in the areas of high human population densities. *M. niger* has practically disappeared from the lower Rio Negro when compared to other Amazonian areas. Even the *C. crocodilus* populations of this region, 70 km from Manaus, in the Ariau valley, mainly comprise young individuals. The Anavilhanas Ecological Station is located in this area, but it is an open reserve with intense river traffic.

Five *M. niger* populations have recently been located, three of which, in the upper Guaporé valley (Mato Grosso), Borba (Amazonas), and Pracuuba (Amapá), are large (Rebelo et al. 1990). Nine populations have been found at sites where the occurrence of this species had not previously been recorded. There are *M. Niger* populations in the Trombetas Reserve, in Itaituba, in the Mamirauá Reserve, and in the Anavilhanas. The populations in Anavilhanas are in a better condition now than in 1990 (Ronis de Silveira pers. com.).

Paleosuchus trigonatus

This caiman of forest streams shares its habitat with *Phrynops rufipes*. Like *P. rufipes*, it has no commercial value, and its occurrence in the region is still not well known. Rebelo et al. (1990) found it in the Abuna, Mamoré, and Madeira rivers.

Paleosuchus palpebrosus

This species is abundant in the Mamoré and Pacaás rivers. In Rondônia, Rebelo et al. (1990) recorded three *Paleosuchus* for each *C. c. yacare*; the normal ratio is 1:20. Research on the distribution and current population density of this species is also lacking.

Lizards

There are three distribution patterns for lizards in Amazonia:

Diffuse distribution

Twenty species are included here, eight (*) of which are also found outside the Amazon: Gekkonidae: *Coleodactylus amazonicus,* *Gonatodes humeralis, Thecodactylus rapicauda;* Iguanidae: *Anolis chrysolepis,* *Anolis ortonii,* *Anolis punctatus,* *Iguana iguana, Plica plica, Plica umbra,* *Polychrus marmoratus, Uranoscodon superciliosum;* Scincidae: *Mabuya bistriata;* Teiidae: *Ameiva ameiva Arthrosaura reticulata,* *Cercosaura ocellata, Cnemidophorus lemniscatus, Iphisa elegans,* *Kentropyx calcarata, Leposoma percaninatu,* and *Neusticurus bicarinatus;*

Restricted distribution

Gekkonidae: *Coleodactylus septentrionalis* (N, NE), *Gonatodes annularis* (NE), *Gonatodes concinnatus* (W), *Gonatodes hasemani* (S, SW), *Hemidactylus palaichtus* (N, NE), *Lepidoblepharis festae* (NW), *Lepidoblepharis heyerorum* (SW); Iguanidae: *Anolis bombiceps* (W), *Enyalioides cofanorum* (NW), *Enyalioides laticeps* (W), *Enyalioides palpebralis* (W), *Enyalioides praestabilis* (W), *Polychrus liogaster* (W); Teiidae: *Alopoglossus atriventris* (W), *Alopoglossus buckleyi* (W), *Alopoglossus copii* (W), *Gymnophthalmus underwoodi* (NE), *Kentropyx borckiana* (NE), *Kentropyx pelviceps* (W), *Leposoma guianense* (NE), *Leposoma parietale* (NW), *Neusticurus cochranae* (W), *Neusticurus strangulatus* (W), *Prionodactylus eigenmanni* (SW), *Prionodactylus manicatus* (W), *Tretioscincus agilis* (NE); Anguidae: *Diploglossus fasciatus* (SW) (Vanzolini 1988); and

Endemic distribution

Neusticurus cochranae, Neusticurus strangulatus, Tropidurus insularis, which are endemic to the region of the Serra do Cachimbo.

There are at least 89 lizard species in the Brazilian Amazon, belonging to nine families (Ávila-Pires 1995). Of these, 26 to 29% also occur outside this region. Some are restricted to the open areas of the Amazon, and others to open grasslands of the rest of Brazil. Other species have distribution areas that extend as far as the southern edge of Amazonia, along the gallery forests. Some species have disjointed distribution patterns, in southwestern Amazonia and in western Brazil (Ávila-Pires 1995). Whether these distribution patterns reflect reality or merely illustrate the specimen data available in museums is not yet clear. Data on the largest number of Amazonian lizards, held by the University of São Paulo Zoological Museum, have not been included in this analysis. Of the 89 species listed for the Amazon, 10 are widely distributed in the region; nine occur practically throughout the region, with the exception of a few western areas (possibly due to insufficient collecting); three taxa are distributed throughout the whole of eastern Amazonia, as far as Negro and Madeira rivers; four other species do not occur in southern Amazonia, some are restricted to the north and the Guianas; other taxa typical of open vegetation in the Guianas occur in open areas along the banks of Amazonian rivers; some lizards are only found in the north, 13 species are restricted to western Amazonia, many are present on both banks of the Amazon river, five are only known to the south of Amazonia; 13 taxa are confined to the southwest of Amazonia; in southeastern Amazonia, nine are associated with the open vegetation of the forest fringes. Species confined to open areas in southern Amazonia are *Stenocercus dumerlilii, Gonatodes eladioi, G. tapojonicus,* and *Anolis phyllorhinus.*

Snakes

Compared to other Amazonian reptile groups, very little is known about the distribution, abundance, and state of snake populations (Table 2). Dixon (1979) listed 63 genera and 284 species of tropical forest snake in South America at altitudes below 1,000 meters, including Amazonian areas outside Brazil and the Atlantic Forest. With the description of many new species in the last twenty years, we should not be surprised if the number of Amazonian species exceeds 300. Dixon and Soini (1975) found 166 snake species in one region alone (Iquitos, Peru).

During twenty years of collecting, Cunha and Nascimento (1993) recorded 86 species in an area of approximately 50,000 square kilometers in eastern Pará. Vanzolini (1986) collected 57 snake species in six months in the state of Rondônia. The results of Márcio Martins' research on snake fauna in the Ducke Reserve are comparable to those obtained by Cunha and Nascimento in Pará.

Cunha and Nascimento recorded 86 species in eight families:
Typhlopidae, *Typhlops* (2 species)
Anomalepididae, *Liotyphlops* (1 species) and *Typhlophis* (1)
Leptotyphopidae, *Leptotyphlops* (2)
Anilidae, *Anilius* (1)
Boidae *Boa* (1), *Corallus* (2), *Epicrates* (1), and *Eunectes* (1)
Colubridae (35 genera) *Apostolepis* (1 species), *Atractus* (4), *Chironius* (5), *Cleia* (1), *Dendrophidion* (1), *Dipsas* (4), *Drepanoides* (1), *Drymarchon* (1), *Drymoluber* (1), *Erythrolamprus* (1), *Helicops* (4), *Hydrodynastes* (1), *Hydrops* (2), *Imantodes* (2), *Leptodeira* (1), *Leptophis* (1), *Liophis* (7), *Mastigodryas* (2), *Oxybelis* (3), *Oxyrhopus* (3), *Philodryas* (1), *Pseudoboa* (1), *Pseudoeryx* (1), *Pseustes* (2), *Rhadinaea* (2), *Rhinobothryum* (1), *Sibon* (1), *Sipholophis* (1), *Spilotes* (1), *Tantilla* (1), *Thamnodynastes* (1), *Tripanurgos* (1), *Uromacerina* (1), *Xenodon* (2) and *Xenopholis* (1).

Many of these genera (28) have only one species; nine of them have two.

Endemic and threatened herpetofauna species

Turtles

Threatened: *Podocnemis expansa*, *Podocnemis erythrocephala*, *Podocnemis sextuberculata*, *Podocnemis unifilis* and *Peltocephalus dumerilianus*
Endemic: *Trachemys adiutrix*

Caimans

Threatened: *Caiman crocodilus* and *Melanosuchus niger*
Endemic: *Neusticurus cochranae*, *Neusticurus strangulatus*, *Tropidurus insularis*, endemic to the region of the Serra do Cachimbo.

Snakes

Threatened: *Boa constrictor*

TABLE 2 - LIZARD AND SNAKE SAMPLING AREAS

Area Inventoried	Number of species (lizards/snakes)	Number of individuals (lizards/snakes)	Study time	Author
Rio Xingu	25/(?)			Vitt 1991c
East of the Rio Tapajós	22/(?)			Vitt unpublished
Balbina	19/(?)			Martins 1991
WWF-INPA	23/62	(?)/126	35 days/20 months	Zimmerman & Rodriguez 1990
Carajás	25/(?)			Cunha et al. 1990
Rio Jammari	17/(?)			Vitt unpublished
Rondônia	41/57	1.492/141	6 months	Vanzolini 1986
Belém	21/(?)			Crump 1971
Lavrado area	8/(?)			Vitt & Carvalho 1995
Alter do Chão	10/(?)		20 years	Vitt & Magnusson unpublished
Tapajós	24/(?)		35 days	M. Rodriguez unpublished
Trombetas	17/(?)		15 days	M. Rodriguez unpublished
Rio Urucuí	12/10		9 days	Gascon & Pereira 1993
Rio Ituxi	27/32	313/90	2 months	Vitt unpublished
Ilha de Marajó	25/38		Museum – 94 years	Nascimento et al. 1991
Eastern Pará	(?)/87		20 years	Cunha & Nascimento 1993
Amazonas	89/(?)		Museum – 200 years	Ávila-Pires 1995
Anavilhanas	16/22		2 months	Moreira et al. 1997
Pres. Figueiredo	23/51		Museum – 20 years	Duarte 1998
Mamirauá	16/14		Museum – 10 years	Eem
Caxiuanã	28/43	502/48	?	Bernardi et al.

* In the second column, the number before the slash represents lizard species; the number after the slash refers to snakes.
** A very specific variation between time and surveyed area can be observed.

Priority areas in Amazonia for new reptile fauna inventories

Re-examining the lizard distribution maps of Ávila-Pires (1995) and Dixon (1979), we can see that there are no collection data for the central Amazon region. General studies such as these are helpful for identifying areas in need of survey. The samplings carried out by Vanzolini (1986) and Cunha and Nascimento (1995) in Rondônia are good examples of time and effort employed in reptile biodiversity studies over extensive areas. There are practically no samplings such as these for snakes and lizards in the rest of Amazonia. A large number of Amazonian specimens can be found in the museum of the University of São Paulo. These data are now being mapped and it will thus become possible to identify the locations lacking information on lizards and snakes. The Goeldi Museum also has a large number of Amazonian specimens; however, as these data have not yet been digitized, it has not been possible to include them in this report. The collection of the National Institute for Amazonian Research has not been digitized either, but the collection sites have already been mapped. When all this information is put together into a single document, more precise recommendations will be possible. Pending this, we can do no more than suggest areas for which there appear to be no studies.

Sites lacking amphibian studies also lack research on lizards and snakes; sampling of these fauna can therefore be done simultaneously. It is important to sample all Amazonian habitats in different geographical regions. Turtle and caiman collection sites, however, are very different and need a different approach.

We can identify several river basins for which general reptile studies are lacking:

1. Upper and middle Rio Negro
2. Rio Branco as far as the Rio Jari
3. Rio Tapajós
4. Rio Xingu
5. Rio Tocantins
6. Rio Araguaia
7. Amanã Reserve
8. Rio Japurá
9. Rio Purus
10. Rio Juruá
11. Rio Madeira

Priority areas for reptile conservation in the Amazon

Areas of intense human activity and complete degradation of natural habitats, such as the states of Rondônia, Acre, some regions of Pará, and the north of Mato Grosso should be urgently selected for sampling. Their reptile communities and diversity should be surveyed as soon as possible, before the populations totally disappear.

Places where the pressure of economic interests is intense are not suitable for the creation of conservation areas. It would be better to concentrate efforts on establishing reserves in areas that are not subject to human pressure. Even 'paper parks' in untouched areas have a better chance of serving their purpose.

It is urgent and essential that stretches of all the major Amazonian rivers be designated as conservation areas and a system for identifying these should be put in place. Not having such a system can lead to the complete loss of the diversity of Amazonian aquatic fauna.

Contrary to current practice, reserves created in aquatic ecosystems need to have both riverbanks protected. This is essential for the conservation of aquatic animals. In the Rio Trombetas reserve, for instance, only one side of the river is within the protected area. On the opposite bank, the river's resources are exploited without restriction. Management and control are impossible under such conditions.

It is essential that reserves for the protection of turtles and caimans be created in the following river basins: 1) Guaporé river; 2) upper and middle Rio Negro; 3) Rio Branco; 4) Rio Trombetas, through expanding the existing reserve to cover both riverbanks; 5) Rio Purus, through expanding the existing reserve to cover both riverbanks; 6) Rio Juruá; 7) areas in the Amanã Reserve for the preservation of turtles and caimans, by giving priority to the protection of the animal populations over the economic activities of the human populations; 8) Rio Tapajós; 9) Rio Xingu; 10) Rio Araguaia; 11) Rio das Mortes; 12) Rio Japurá.

There are already conservation areas in some of the locations mentioned above, but many of them are inadequate. It is impossible to protect turtles without controlling a stretch of at least 100 km on both sides of the river. Notwithstanding the importance of hatching beaches for the preservation of turtles, these are only part of the species' habitat. The populations are still at risk unless their feeding habitats and migration routes are also protected. The preservation of river corridors protects not only turtles, but many forest animals with no economic value. The use of commercially valuable species as 'flagship' species can help to attract public attention to the need to protect certain areas. Otherwise how can we convince people of the importance of conserving 100,000 hectares of forest to protect an endemic poisonous snake or a small lizard? Ideally, what should be considered are large reserves and whole hydrographic basins in different geographical regions throughout Amazonia. In this way there can be a real chance of protecting a high percentage of the biodiversity without wasting time trying to conserve everything in small areas.

It is true that levels of knowledge of Amazonian species have increased significantly since the 1990 workshop. However, even with the added data and records of species for the region, little is really known about the distribution of its reptiles. The creation of a database of all the specimens in museums worldwide, and a great sampling effort in sites with no recorded species of this fauna might mean that we would learn a little more about these groups. This would possibly take 20 to 30 years. Therefore, until hard data on the Amazonian herpetofauna are available, conservations areas of a substantial size should be created in all basins listed above in order to preserve the different types of habitats in all the different geographical zones of the region.

Bibliography

ÁVILA-PIRES, T. C. S. Lizards of Brazilian Amazonia (Reptilaia: *Squamata*), *Zool. Verh.*, p. 3-706, 1995.

ÁVILA-PIRES, T. C. S.; HOOGMOED M. S. The Herpetofauna. In: LISBOA, P. (Org.). *Caxiuanã*. Belém: Museu Paraense Emílio Goeldi, 1997. p. 389-401.

BRAZAITIS, P.; YAMASHITA, C.; REBELO, G. Report of the CITES Central South America Caiman Study: Phase I: Brasil. November 1988.

CAMPBELL, K. E. Jr. The Geological Basis of Biogeographic Patterns in Amazonia. In: PETERS, G.; HUTTERER. R. (Eds.). *Vertebrates in the Tropics*. Bonn: Mus. Alexander Koenig, 1990, p. 33-43.

COLLI, G. *Avaliação ecológica rápida na área de Chamflora*. Amapá: Champion Papel e Celulose, Herpetofauna, unpublished.

CORDEIRO DUARTE, A. C. Fauna. In: *Diagnóstico ambiental: levantamento do meio físico/biótico do município de Presidente Figueiredo*, 4.2. 1998, p. 153-179.

CUNHA, O. R. da; NASCIMENTO F. P. do. Ofídios da Amazônia: as cobras da região do Pará. *Bol. Mus. Paraense Emílio Goeldi, Zool.* 9, p. 1-191, 1993.

CUNHA, O. R. da; NASCIMENTO, F. P. do; ÁVILA-PIRES, T. C. S. de. Os répteis da área de Carajás, Pará, Brasil (Testudeines e Squamata). Contribuições do Museu Paraense Emilio Goeldi ao *Projeto Carajás*, n. 40, p. 1-92, 1985.

DIXON, J. R. Origin and Distribution of Reptiles in Lowland Tropical Rainforests of South America. In: DUELMANN, W. E. (Org.). *The South American Herpetofauna: its Origin, Evolution and Dispersal*. Monogr. Mus. Nat. Hist. Univ. Kansas, 7. 1979, p. 271-240.

DUELLMAN, W. E. Herpetofaunas in Neotropical Rainforests: Comparative Composition, History, and Resource Use. In: GENTRY, A. H. (Org.). *Four Neotropical Rainforests*. New Haven: Yale Univ. Press, 1990, p. 455-505.

GALATTI, U. Inventário da herpetofauna da área sob influência do Projeto Salobo Floresta Naional Tapirapé-Aquiri, Parauapebas, Pará. *Relatório final Brandt meio ambiente*. Belo Horizonte, 1988.

_____. Avaliação ecológica rápida da reserva biológica estadual rio Ouro Preto, Guajará-Mirim, Rondônia. In: *Inventário de herpetofauna da Res. Biol. Rio Ouro Preto*. Final report. United Nations Development Program: Plano Agropecuário e Florestal de Rondônia (UNDP/Planafloro), 1989.

GASCON, C. *Inventário da herpetofauna ao longo do rio Juruá*. 1991/1992, inédito.

GASCON, C.; PEREIRA, O. S. Preliminary Checklist of the Herpetofauna of the Upper Rio Urucu, Amazonas, Brazil, *Brasil. Zool.*, v. 10, n. 10, p. 179-183, 1993.

HOOGMOED, M. S.; ÁVILA-PIRES, T. C. S. *Inventário preliminar da herpetofauna na região do Rio Urucu, Amazonas*. 1989, unpublished.

_____. *Inventário preliminar da herpetofauna na região do interflúvio rio Nhamundá/rio Trombetas, Pará*. 1988, unpublished.

_____. *Inventário preliminar da herpetofauna na região da Serra do Navio, Amapá*. 1988, unpublished.

_____. *Inventário preliminar da herpetofauna na Reserva Biológica Sustentável de Mamirauá, Amazonas*. 1994, unpublished.

_____. *Inventário preliminar da herpetofauna na região de São Félix do Xingu, Pará*. 1999, unpublished.

IVERSON, J. B. A. *Revised Checklist with Distribution Maps of the Turtles of the World*. Richmond, Indiana: Privately Printed, 1992.

LAURENT, R. B. A. Parallel Survey of Equatorial Amphibians and Reptiles in Africa and South America. In: MEGGERS, B. J.; AYENSU, E. S.; DUCKWORTH, W. D. (Eds.). *Tropical Forest Ecosystems in Africa and South America, a Comparative Review*. Washington D.C.: Smithsonian Institution Press, 1973, p. 259-266.

MAGNUSSON, W. E. The Correlates of Foraging Mode in a Community of Brazilian Lizards, *Herpetologica*, n. 41, p. 324-332, 1985.

MARTINS, M. The Lizards of Balbina, Central Amazonia, Brazil: A Qualitative Analysis of Resource Utilization, *Studies of Neotropical Fauna and Environment*, n. 26, p. 179-190, 1991.

MOREIRA, G. R. et al. *Relatório final da área temática herpetofauna. Macrozoneamento sócio-economico-ecológico do Estado do Rondônia*. Porto Velho: Planafloro, 1997.

MOREIRA, G. R. et al. *Levantamento da herpetofauna na estação ecológica de Anavilhanas:* final report. 1997, unpublished.

NASCIMENTO, F. P.; ÁVILA-PIRES, T. C. S.; CUNHA, O. R. Os répteis da área de Carajás, Pará, Brasil (*Squamata*), *Bol. Mus. Paraense Emílio Goeldi, Nova Série Zoológica*, n. 3, p. 33-65, 1987.

_____. Répteis *squamata* de Rondônia e Mato Grosso coletados através do programa Polonoroeste, *Bol. Mus. Paraense Emílio Goeldi, Nova Série Zoológica*, n. 4, p. 21-66, 1988.

PRITCHARD, P. C. H.; TREBBAU, P. The Turtles of Venezuela, *Soc. Stud. Amphib. Rept. Contrib. Herpetol.*, n. 2, p. 1-403, 1984.

REBELO, G. H.; YAMACHITA, C.; BRAZAITIS, P. Conservação de jacarés na Amazônia. *Workshop 90 Ms*. 1990, unpublished.

RODRIGUES, M. T. Sistemática, ecologia e zoogeografia dos *Tropidurus* do grupo *torquatus* ao sul do rio Amazonas (*Sauria, Iguanidae*), *Arq. Zool. S. Paulo*, n. 31, p. 105-230, 1987.

_____. A New Species of Micrablepharus Squamata: Gymnophthalmidae, from Brazil, *Herpetologica*, n. 52, p. 535-541, 1996.

SILVA, N. J. Jr.; SITES, J. W. Jr. Patterns of Diversity of Neotropical Squamate Reptile Species with Emphasis on the Brazilian Amazon and the Conservation Potential of Indigenous Reserves, *Cons. Biol.*, v. 9, p. 873-901, 1995.

VANZOLINI, P. E. *Levantamento herpetológico da área do estado de Rondônia sob a influência da Rodovia BR-364*. Brasília: Conselho Nacional do Desenvolvimento Científico e Tecnológico, Assessoria Editorial, 1986.

_____. Distribution Patterns of South American Lizards. In: HEYER, W. R.; VANZOLINI, P. E. (Orgs.) *Proceedings of a Workshop on Neotropical Distribution Patterns*. Rio de Janeiro: Academia Brasileira de Ciências, 1988, p. 317-343.

_____. On the Distribution of Certain South American Turtles (*Testudines: testudinidae & Chelidae*), *Smithsonian Herpetological Information Service*, n. 97, p. 1-10, 1994.

VANZOLINI, P. E.; CARVALHO, C. M. Two Sibling and Sympatric Species of Gymnophthalmus in Roraima, Brasil (*Sauria, Teiidae*), *Pap. Av. Zool. S. Paulo*, n. 37, p. 173-226, 1991.

VITT, L. J. Ecology and Life History of the Scansorial Arboreal Lizard *Plica plica* (*Iguanidae*) in Amazonian Brazil, *Canadian J. Zool.*, n. 69, p. 504-511, 1991.

_____. Ecology and Life History of the Wide-Foraging Lizard *Kentropyx calcarata* (*Teiidae*) in Amazonian Brazil, *Canadian J. Zool.*, n. 69, p. 2791-2799, 1991.

_____. Ecology of Isolated Open-Formation *Tropidurus* (*Reptilia: Tropiduridae*) in Amazonian Lowland Rain Forest, *Canadian J. Zool.*, n. 71, p. 2370-2390, 1993.

_____. Biodiversity of Amazonian Lizards. In: GIBSON, A. C. (Ed.). *Neotropical Biodiversity and Conservation*. Los Angeles: Mildred E. Mathias Botanical Garden, UCLA, 1996. p. 89-108.

_____. NSF Project DEB-9200779. Rio Ajarnai, BR-210, Roraima, Brasil. In: *Inventário e ecologia da herpetofauna da Amazônia*. 1993, unpublished.

_____. NSF Project DEB-9200779. Alter do Chão/CEMEX, Santarém, Pará, Brasil. In: *Inventário e ecologia da herpetofauna da Amazônia*. 1995, unpublished.

_____. NSF Project DEB-9505518. Rio Juruá, Porto Walter, Acre, Brasil. In: *Inventário e ecologia da herpetofauna da Amazônia*. 1996, unpublished.

_____. NSF Project DEB-9505518. Rio Ituxi, Amazonas, Brasil. In: *Inventário e ecologia da herpetofauna da Amazônia*. 1997, unpublished.

_____. NSF Project DEB-9200779. Rio Formoso, Guajará Mirim, Rondônia, Brasil. In: *Inventário e ecologia da herpetofauna da Amazônia*. 1998, unpublished.

VITT, J. L.; BLACKBURN, D. G. *Ecology and Life History of the Viviparous Lizard* Mabuya bistriata *(Scincidae) in the Brazilian, Amazon*. Copeia, 1991, p. 916-927.

VITT, L. J.; COLLI, G. R. Geographical Ecology of a Neotropical Lizard: *Ameiva ameiva* (*Teiidae*) in Brazil, *Canadian J. Zool.*, n. 72, p. 1986-2008, 1994.

ZIMMERMAN, B. L.; RODRIGUES M. T. Frogs, Snakes and Lizards of the INPA-WWF Reserves near Manaus, Brazil. In: GENTRY, A. H. (Ed.). *Four Neotropical Rainforests*. New Haven: Yale Univ. Press, 1990, p. 426-454.

The biogeography and conservation of birds in the Amazon region

David C. Oren *Museu Paraense Emílio Goeldi*

The Amazon region: geographical context

Of the different concepts that can be used to define Amazonia, this study will use that of the political boundaries of the 'Legal Amazon', which comprises the total area of the states of Acre, Amapá, Amazonas, Mato Grosso, Pará, Rondônia, Roraima, and Tocantins, as well as the westernmost two thirds of the state of Maranhão. Besides tropical forest vegetation, the Legal Amazon contains important enclaves of open vegetation, such as cerrados (woody grasslands), white sand campinas (treeless grasslands), várzea (floodplain) and high grasslands, and babassu palm groves. Although it uses the concept of the Legal Amazon, this study will concentrate on the Amazon Forest biome, as bird conservation priorities in cerrado areas have already been addressed in a special workshop (Silva 1998c). The total area included in this study covers over 5,200,000 square kilometers, between 44° W and 74° W, and 3° N and 18° S.

The geology of the Legal Amazon comprises five main formations: the Precambrian Guiana shields (north) and Brazil shields (south); Paleozoic marine deposits on, respectively, the southern and northern sides of the shields; Tertiary sediments occupying most of the upper Amazonas/Solimões and its tributaries, as well as the banks of the Amazon river valley (the 'Barreiras' or 'Alter do Chão' formation); Cretaceous sediments (in southeastern Amazonas, southeastern Rondônia, and northwestern Mato Grosso); and Quaternary sediments (located in the present day floodplains as well as most of the area of the river mouth) (Bigarella and Ferreira 1985).

Ornithological inventory

There is a tendency in the ornithological literature to confuse the sites indicated in the basic reference book *Ornithological Gazetteer of Brazil* (Paynter and Traylor 1991) with collection efforts. Simply mapping the sites in the book exaggerates the supposed inventory work, as the sole criterion for the inclusion of a geographical location in the book was its having been mentioned in the ornithological literature, regardless of whether it was an inventory site or not. Therefore, in addition to sites where scientific collection had been undertaken, the book also included references to transit and overnight sites, to transportation changeover points, and other temporary locations. In an analysis of the inventory of the avifauna of the cerrado, Silva (1995) concluded that only 80 of the more than 500 sites for the cerrado included in the *Gazetteer* could be considered to represent minimum inventories. It is therefore necessary to be cautious and to establish criteria for any mapping of ornithological inventory efforts on the basis of Paynter & Traylor's book. It is especially important to base mapped sites on the specialized literature. A list of the most significant avifauna research conducted in the Brazilian Amazon region would include: Beebe (1916), Borges (1994), Camargo (1957), Cohn-Haft et al. (1997), Dégallier et al. (1992), Friedmann (1948), Fry (1970), Goeldi & Hagmann (1902), Graves & Zusi (1990), Griscom & Greenway (1941), Gyldenstolpe (1945, 1951), Hagmann (1907), Hellmayr (1905, 1906, 1907a, 1907b, 1907c, 1910, 1912), Henriques & Oren (1997), Lovejoy (1974), Morrison et al. (1986), Moskovitz et al. (1985), Naumberg (1930), Novaes (1957, 1958, 1960, 1969, 1970, 1973, 1974, 1976, 1978, 1980), Novaes & Lima (1991, forthcoming), Novaes & Pimentel (1973), Oren (1991), Oren & Parker (1997), Pacheco (1995), Parker et al. (1997), Pelzeln (1868-1870), Peres & Whittaker (1991), Pinto (1938a, 1938b, 1944, 1947, 1953, 1966), Pinto & Camargo (1948, 1952, 1954, 1961), Ridgely & Tudor (1989, 1994), Riker (1890-1891), Schubart et al. (1965), Sclater & Salvin (1967), Sick (1997), Silva (1998a, 1998b), Silva et al. (1997), Snethlage (1908a, 1908b, 1909, 1912, 1913, 1914), Stone (1928), Stotz & Bierregaard (1989), Slotz et al. (1992, 1997), Staufer & Bierregaard (1995), Whittaker & Oren (forthcoming), Willis (1997), and Zimmer et al. (1997). In the case of unpublished research, the ideal would be to have access to the collectors' field notes in order to map inventory sites with the utmost precision.

Haffer (1974) published an excellent gazetteer of ornithological collection sites based on the scientific collections containing neotropical material he reviewed for his revision of toucans and jacamars. Oren & Albuquerque (1991) updated this to establish priority areas for new avian inventories in the Brazilian Amazon. The authors established the criterion that a site could only be mapped if its collection represented at least 100 specimens. Oren & Albuquerque's work has been updated for the present study (Table 5) using the same criterion and arrives at a total of 247 avian inventory sites. The priority areas for new inventories are the same as those indicated in Oren & Albuquerque's work, with a few remarkable exceptions resulting from recent fieldwork efforts. These include the regions of the upper and middle Juruá, now partially inventoried thanks to a great number of expeditions sponsored by the Wildlife Conservation Society, the MacArthur Foundation, and The Nature Conservancy, the latter carried out as part of the development of the management plan of the Serra do Divisor National Park. The Emílio Goeldi Museum of Pará (MPEG), sponsored by the MacArthur Foundation, conducted avian inventories in the lower Juruá (three sites), in Caitau-Uará on the middle Solimões, in the far southeast of Pará (the municipality of Santana do Araguaia), and in the west of the Ilha de Marajó. With funding from the Department of Science, Technology, and the Environment of the State of Pará (Sectam), the MPEG also conducted important research in the Serra das Andorinhas State Park, in the municipality of São Geraldo do Araguaia (Pará). The Smithsonian Institute (Washington DC, USA) collected birds on the right bank of the Xingu. Recently, the Planaforo project in Rondônia has sponsored ornithological collections in the Rio Ouro Preto extractive reserve, with funding from the United Nations. Ornithological research for the Jaú National Park management plan has revealed exciting new finds, such as the rediscovery of *Nonnula amaurochephala* (Whittaker et. al 1995), but unfortunately hardly any collecting has been done.

The state of Tocantins, where only three sites have so far been inventoried, is one of the most important priority areas for new inventories. Southern Maranhão is also poorly covered for ornithological data collection. Other regions totally unknown in terms of avian inventories include the upper and middle stretches of rivers draining the Guiana shield, northwestern Roraima, the upper Japurá, the upper Javari, the Tarauacá and the upper Purus in Acre, the right bank tributaries of the Madeira, the Juruena, the upper reaches of the Teles Pires, the upper Iriri, and the middle Xingu above Cachoeira Grande. It is important to bear in mind that the state of Tocantins and the upper courses of the Purus, Madeira, Juruena, Teles Pires, and Xingu are located within the Brazilian Amazon's 'Arc of Deforestation' and, in addition to lacking basic data on their fauna and flora, these areas are undergoing high rates of environmental change, making biological inventory efforts an urgent priority.

Species richness

Assessing species richness by comparing lists of sites in the Brazilian Amazon, or even the neotropical region as a whole (Remsen 1994), poses serious problems. Research efforts, methods, and experience vary from site to site; there is no standard size for research areas; resident and migrant species are not differentiated, and so on. In an attempt to compare the composition of neotropical mammalian fauna, Voss & Emmons (1996) found only ten sites from Mexico to southern Brazil with sufficiently complete data to allow useful comparisons, only two of which are in the Brazilian Amazon. Any attempt to compare species richness in Amazonian bird communities would lead to similar frustration. This, however, has not inhibited attempts. Haffer (1990) compared 15 sites for richness of neotropical bird communities, four of which are in the Brazilian Amazon: north of Manaus, Cachoeira Nazaré, the lower Xingu, and the Amazonia National Park (Tapajós). An example of the inherent problems is the number of *Dendrocolaptidae* (woodcreepers) Haffer recorded for the Tapajós National Park: 14. Later cross-referenced research on the same area identified 19 species of woodcreepers for the park (Oren and Parker 1997), exceeding the site 'richest' in representatives of this family, Cachoeira Nazaré (18). For this and other reasons, establishing conservation priorities on the basis of assessments of species richness in Amazonian avian communities is either unfeasible or must recognize that serious inaccuracies will occurr.

Endangered species, endemic species, and species of limited distribution

Endangered species (Tables 1 and 2) have been identified on the basis of Bernardes et al. (1990), who use the official IBAMA list plus two other species (*Synallaxis kollari* and *Formicarius rufifrons*) listed in the World Conservation Union's Red Book as 'vulnerable' (Collar et al. 1992). Five other species are mentioned in this work (*Crax globulosa*, *Synallaxis cherriei*, *Clytoctantes atrogularis*, *Pipra vilasboasi*, and *Todirostrum senex*); however, they are all listed as 'insufficiently known' or of 'undetermined' status. As this does not justify their classification as truly endangered species, they are not included in the present list. Nevertheless, they do appear in other lists below, either as endemic species, or species of limited distribution. Tables 1 and 2 list 15 endangered species and 11 potentially endangered species.

A list of all Amazonian endemic species would add up to hundreds of species. However, as the Amazon territory includes Brazil and seven neighboring countries, only 32 species out of the 1,000 found in the Brazilian Amazon are endemic to Brazil (Table 3). In order to allow a more consistent and complete analysis, Table 4 lists Brazilian Amazon bird species of limited

TABLE 1 - Endangered bird species	
Species	Distribution
Eudocimus ruber	Coast of Amapá, Pará and Maranhão
Phoenicopterus ruber	Coast of Amapá and Marajó
Falco deiroleucus	Widespread distribution
Harpia harpyja	Widespread distribution
Morphnus guianensis	Widespread distribution
Spizastur melanoleucus	Widespread distribution
Crax fasciolata pinima	Rio Tocantins to Maranhão
Anodorhynchus hyacinthinus	Rio Tapajós to Maranhão, estuary islands and Amapá
Guaruba guarouba	Rondônia to Maranhão
Nyctibius leucopterus	North of Manaus, Jaú National Park, Serra do Divisor National Park
Synallaxis kollari	Roraima (seasonal flooded forests)
Cercomacra carbonaria	Roraima (gallery forests)
Formicarius rufifrons	Upper Juruá
Hemitriccus minimus	Lower Tapajós, Jaú National Park, Alta Floresta (Mato Grosso)
Oryzoborus maximiliani	Widespread distribution

TABLE 2 - POTENTIALLY ENDANGERED BIRD SPECIES	
Species	Distribution
Leucopternis kuhli	South of the Solimões/Amazonas from the western borders to Maranhão
Spizaetus ornatus	Widespread distribution
Crax globulosa	Western Amazonia to the Negro and Madeira
Penelope pileata	Rio Madeira to Maranhão
Neomorphus squamiger	Rio Tapajós (both banks) to the Xingu
Nyctibius aethereus longicaudatus	Probably widespread distribution
Nyctibius bracteatus	North of Manaus
Avocettula recurvirostris	Widespread distribution
Myrmotherula klagesi	Islands and floodplains of the middle Amazonas
Pipra vilasboasi	Upper Tapajós (Rio Cururu)
Oryzoborus crassirostris	Rio Negro to Amapá

TABLE 3 - ENDEMIC SPECIES (32)	
Species	Distribution
Ortalis ruficeps	Rio Tapajós to the Araguaia
Ortalis superciliaris	Rio Tocantins to Maranhão
Penelope pileata	Rio Madeira to Maranhão
Aramides mangle	Belém to Maranhão (and as far as Rio de Janeiro)
Psophia viridis	Rio Madeira to Maranhão
Guaruba guarouba	Rondônia to Maranhão
Pionopsitta vulturina	Rio Madeira to Maranhão
Amazona kawalli	South of the Amazonas/Solimões, from the Juruá to the east of the Tapajós
Neomorphus squamiger	Rio Tapajós (both banks) to the Xingu
Nonnula amaurocephala	Northern bank of the lower Solimões and the Jaú National Park
Capito brunneipectus	West bank of the Tapajós
Selenidera gouldii	Lower Madeira to Maranhão
Picumnus varzeae	Islands and banks of the middle Amazonas
Xiphorhynchus necopinus	Floodplains of the Solimões/Amazonas basin
Furnarius figulus	Lower Amazonas (and widespread distribution beyond Amazonia)
Synallaxis simoni	Rio Araguaia basin
Sakesphorus luctuosus	Riverside forests of the Amazonas (both banks) to the Araguaia
Myrmotherula klagesi	Island and forest floodplains of the middle Amazonas
Myrmotherula iheringi	South bank of the Solimões to the Tapajós
Cercomacra ferdinandi	Middle and lower Araguaia
Rhegmatorhina gymnops	Tapajós-Xingu interfluve
Rhegmatorhina hoffmannsi	Madeira east bank drainage
Rhegmatorhina berlepschi	Madeira west bank drainage
Skutchia borbae	Madeira-Tapajós interfluve
Conopophaga roberti	Rio Tocantins to Maranhão
Xipholena lamellipennis	West bank of the Tapajós to Maranhão
Pipra iris	Tapajós to Maranhão
Pipra vilasboasi	Upper Tapajós (Rio Cururu)
Hemitriccus minima	Lower Tapajós, Jaú National Park, Alta Floresta (Mato Grosso)
Hemitriccus inornatus	Rio Içana and north of Manaus
Todirostrum senex	Borba
Paroaria baeri	Rio Araguaia basin, upper Xingu

distribution, defined here as those occurring in only one of the larger divisions of the region. The basin has been divided into three sub-basins: Rio Negro to the Atlantic Ocean; Rio Madeira or Rio Tapajós to the state of Maranhão; and the remaining western area (Rio Negro and Rio Madeira or Rio Tapajós to the country's western borders). Also included in Table 4 are a few species (such as *Neochen jubata*) that are widely distributed but of rare and localized occurrence. In all, there are 283 species which are rare or of limited distribution.

It should be emphasized that the present lists are based on the current taxonomy. There is a worldwide tendency towards accepting a phylogenetic rather than a biological concept of species. In practical terms, this implies raising many taxa currently considered as subspecies to the level of species (Zink and McKitrick 1995). It is not possible in the present study to draw up a list of all 'subspecies' with limited distribution, as this would require taxonomic revision of all Amazonian bird species. What matters here is to point out that an analysis of conservation priorities based on birds requires the use of lists containing many distinct 'subspecies', as these represent the true avian biodiversity units of the basin.

Priority conservation areas

In its well-known analysis of global conservation priorities, BirdLife International (Bibby et al. 1992) uses bird distribution to delimit the most important areas worldwide. In relation to the Brazilian Amazon, only northern Roraima is considered important in global terms. It is essential to understand the reason for this. The methodology used by the authors consisted of mapping birds with a geographical distribution of up to 50,000 square kilometers (the so-called hotspots analysis). In the Brazilian Amazon, only a few species occupying the table-top mountains (tepuis) of Roraima have such a limited distribution. The basic biodiversity subregions in the Amazon are the interfluves, and many endemic species are restricted to only one or two interfluves (between the Madeira and Tapajós rivers, for example). The total area of the smallest Amazonian interfluve (between the Xingu and Tocantins rivers) is 250,000 square kilometers or five times the maximum area allowed for in the BirdLife analysis.

Therefore, as a result of the methodology adopted, which only considers species with geographical range of less than 50,000 square kilometers, the greater part of the region is not considered to be of importance. The Amazon has so much biodiversity distributed over such immense areas that the region does not appear in the analysis. This does not mean that it is not a priority region for biodiversity conservation. On the contrary, based on the number of bird species in the region, it is estimated that 11% of all species in the world are located in the Brazilian Amazon.

Based on the presence of bird species in the Red Book, Wege & Long (1995) proposed 15 priority sites for the establishment of conservation areas in the Brazilian Amazon, as follows: 1) Conceição do Maú (Roraima; 3°38' N, 59°53' W), 2) Rio Surumu (Roraima; 3°22' N, 60°19' W), 3) Boa Vista (Roraima; 2°55' N,

60°36' W), 4) Rio Mucajaí (Roraima; 2°32' N, 61°02' W), 5) Amapá savannas (Amapá; 0°02' S, 51°03' W [sic]), 6) Mamirauá (Amazonas; 2°13' S, 65°49' W), 7) Ilhas Codajás (Amazonas; 3°50' S, 62°05' W), 8) Borba (Amazonas; 4°24' S, 59°35' W), 9) Rio Tapajós (Pará/Amazonas; 4°16' S, 56°52' W), 10) Serra dos Carajás (Pará; 5°00' S, 51°00' W), 11) Kayapó (Pará; 7°30' S, 52°00' W), 12) Serra do Cachimbo (Pará; 9°00' S, 55°15' W), 13) Jamari (Rondônia; 9°07' S, 62°54' W), 14) Cachoeira Nazaré (Rondônia; 9°44' S, 61°53' W), and 15) Alta Floresta (Mato Grosso; 10°00' S, 55°30' W). There are at most two species from the Red Book in each area. No doubt they are important locations, but many others were omitted, as the preparation of the list was limited by the methodology and its dependence upon the findings of only a few of the researchers working in the area.

The results of the 'Workshop 90' represent the best attempt so far to identify priority sites for bird conservation (Sanaiotti et al. ms.). The bird thematic group recommended 69 different areas for the Amazon region as a whole, 45 of them in the Brazilian Amazon. This group constitutes the best qualified group ever assembled for this type of analysis in the Amazon region (its membership can be found in Sanaiotti et al.). Although some other groups were unable to support their recommendations with lists of species and other data, in the case of the bird thematic group all the proposed areas are accompanied by precise information, albeit not always detailed. It is recommended that the manuscript resulting from this effort be published, or at least made available on the Internet, so that all those interested can have access to the material. It is an essential starting point for any new effort to determine bird conservation priorities in the Brazilian Amazon (and, by extension, biodiversity conservation priorities as a whole).

TABLE 4 - RARE SPECIES OR SPECIES OF LIMITED DISTRIBUTION

Family	Species	Distribution
Tinamidae	Tinamus tao	Madeira to Maranhão
	Crypturellus erythropus	Negro to Amapá
	Crypturellus atrocapillus	Upper Juruá
	Crypturellus duidae	Rio Uaupés
	Crypturellus casiquiare	Upper Rio Negro
Threskiornithidae	Eudocimus ruber	Coasts of Amapá, Pará and Maranhão
	Cercibis oxycerca	Rio Negro, Roraima, Rio Guaporé
	Platalea ajaja	Rare, local
Phoenicopteridae	Phoenicopterus ruber	Coasts of Amapá and Marajó
Anatidae	Neochen jubata	Rare, local
Accipitridae	Leucopternis melanops	North of the Amazonas
Cracidae	Ortalis guttata	Western Amazonia to the Negro and the Tapajós
	Ortalis motmot	Negro to Amapá
	Penelope marail	Rio Branco to Amapá
	Crax globulosa	Western Amazonia to the Negro and the Madeira

continues

Family	Species	Distribution
Cracidae	Crax alector	Negro to Amapá
	Mitu tomentosa	Upper Rio Negro to the east of Rio Branco
	Nothocrax urumutum	Western Amazonia to the Negro and the Tapajós
Odontophoridae	Colinus cristatus	Roraima, plains to the north of the Amazonas, Amapá
	Odontophorus stellatus	Western Amazonia
Psophiidae	Psophia leucoptera	South of the Solimões to the Madeira
Rallidae	Aramides calopterus	Rare, Upper Juruá and north of Manaus
	Anurolimnas castaneiceps	Rio Abunã
	Laterallus fasciatus	Western Amazon (Solimões and Purus)
Burhinidae	Burhinus bistriatus	Amapá and Roraima plains
Columbidae	Uropelia campestris	Isolated populations in Marajó and Amapá
Psittacidae	Ara couloni	Upper Purus and Juruá (Acre)
	Ara auricollis	Ilha do Bananal and vicinity (scattered populations)
	Aratinga s. solstitialis	Roraima to Amapá, Santarém
	Aratinga weddellii	Left bank of the Solimões to the Madeira
	Aratinga pertinax	Isolated populations in Roraima, upper Rio Negro, upper Cururu
	Pyrrhura perlata	Rio Madeira to Maranhão (3 taxons)
	Pyrrhura rupicola	Acre
	Brotogeris cyanopterus	Western Amazonia to the Negro and the Purus
	Brotogeris sanctithomae	Amazonas/Solimões valley to its mouth
	Nannopsittaca dachilleae	Serra do Divisor National Park
	Touit huetii	Rare, local
	Pionopsitta barrabandi	Western Amazonia to the Negro and the Madeira
	Pionopsitta caica	Rio Negro to Amapá
	Amazona dufresniana	Rio Oiapoque
	Amazona festiva	Amazonas/Solimões valley to its mouth
	Graydidascalus brachyurus	Amazonas/Solimões valley to its mouth
Cuculidae	Neomorphus pucheranii	Western Amazonia, from the Solimões to the Purus
	Neomorphus rufipennis	Upper Rio Negro
Steatornithidae	Steatornis caripensis	Roraima-Venezuela border

continues

Family	Species	Distribution
Nyctibiidae	*Nyctibius leucopterus*	North of Manaus, Jaú National Park, Serra do Divisor National Park
	Nyctibius bracteatus	North of Manaus
Caprimulgidae	*Caprimulgus cayennensis*	Rio Negro to Amapá
Apodidae	*Cypseloides phelpsi*	Cerro Urutani (Roraima)
	Aeronautes montivagus	Cerro Urutani (Roraima)
Trochilidae	*Phaethornis malaris*	Rio Negro to Amapá
	Phaethornis philippii	South of the Solimões and east of the Madeira
	Phaethornis rupurumii	Roraima, plains north of the Amazonas, and lower Tapajós and Xingu
	Phaethornis griseogularis	Neblina National Park
	Phaethornis longuemareus	Lower Tapajós and the Anavilhanas
Trochilidae	*Colibri delphinae*	Roraima
	Campylopterus hyperythrus	Cerro Uei-Tepuí (Roraima)
	Lophornis ornata	Rio Negro to Amapá
	Lophornis gouldii	Maranhão, Serra do Cachimbo, Upper Xingu (Tocantins)
	Lophornis pavonina	Cerro Urutani (Roraima)
	Chrysuronia oenone	Upper Solimões
	Leucippus chlorocercus	Rio Solimões valley to Manaus
	Amazilia chionopectus	Rio Mucajaí (Roraima)
	Amazilia leucogaster	Mangrove swamps from Amapá to Maranhão
	Amazilia lactea	Amazonas
	Amazilia viridigaster	Roraima table-tops
	Polyplancta aurescens	Solimões valley, Marajó, Serra do Cachimbo
	Heliodoxa schreibersii	Upper Rio Negro, Benjamin Constant
	Heliodoxa xanthogonys	Roraima table-tops
	Topaza pyra	Western Amazonia from the Negro and the Purus westwards
Trogonidae	*Pharomachrus pavoninus*	Western Amazonia from the Negro and right bank of the Tapajós westwards
	Trogon personatus	Roraima table-tops and Amazonas
Momotidae	*Electron platyrhynchum*	South of the Amazonas from the Juruá to the Tocantins
Galbulidae	*Galbalcyrhynchus leucotis*	Rio Solimões valley
	Galbacyrhynchus purusianus	Upper Purus and Juruá
	Galbula tombacea	Rio Solimões valley to the mouth of the Madeira
	Galbula cyanescens	Western Amazonia from the south of the Solimões to the Madeira
	Galbula albogularis	Upper Purus and Juruá

Family	Species	Distribution
Galbulidae	*Trogon personatus*	Roraima and Amazonas table-tops
Momotidae	*Electron platyrhynchum*	South of the Amazonas from the Juruá to the Tocantins
Galbulidae	*Galbalcyrhynchus leucotis*	Rio Solimões valley
	Galbacyrhynchus purusianus	Upper Purus and Juruá
	Galbula tombacea	Solimões valley to the mouth of the Madeira
	Galbula cyanescens	Western Amazonia from the south of the Solimões to the Madeira
	Galbula albogularis	Upper Purus and Juruá
Bucconidae	*Notharchus ordii*	Upper Rio Negro, middle Solimões, middle Amazonas
	Bucco macrodactylus	Western Amazonia to the Negro and the Tapajós
	Nystalus striolatus	Rio Madeira to Maranhão
	Malacoptila fusca	Rio Negro to Amapá
	Malacoptila semicincta	Upper Juruá
	Micromonacha lanceolata	South of the Solimões to the Purus
	Nonnula sclateri	South of the Solimões to the Madeira
	Monasa atra	Rio Negro to Amapá
	Monasa flavirostris	Western Amazonia to the Negro and the Purus
Capitonidae	*Capito aurovirens*	Western Amazonia to the Negro and the Purus
	Eubucco richardsonii	South of the Solimões to the Madeira
	Eubucco tucinkae	Upper Juruá, Serra do Divisor National Park
Ramphastidae	*Aulacorhynchus derbianus*	Roraima table-tops
	Aulacorhynchus prasinus	Upper Juruá
	Pteroglossus pluricinctus	North bank of the Solimões to the Rio Negro and the Rio Branco
	Pteroglossus bitorquatus	Rio Madeira to Maranhão
	Pteroglossus azara	North bank of the upper Solimões to the Rio Negro
	Pteroglossus mariae	South bank of the upper Solimões to the Madeira
	Pteroglossus beauharnaesii	South bank of the Solimões to the Xingu
	Selenidera nattereri	Middle Solimões to the Rio Branco
	Selenidera culik	Lower Rio Negro and Rio Branco to Amapá
	Selenidera reinwardtii	Upper Solimões to the Madeira
Picidae	*Celeus spectabilis*	Upper Juruá
	Celeus torquatus	Rio Madeira to Maranhão
	Veniliornis cassini	Rio Negro to Amapá

continues

Family	Species	Distribution
Picidae	Veniliornis kirkii	Roraima table-tops
	Picumnus rufiventris	Western Amazonia to the Purus
	Picumnus castelnau	Upper Solimões to the Japurá
	Picumnus s. spilogaster	Roraima
	Picumnus spilogaster pallidus	Rio Tocantins to Maranhão
	Picumnus lafresnayi	North bank of the Solimões to the upper Rio Negro
Dendrocolaptidae	Dendrocincla unicoloroptera	Xingu-Tocantins interfluve
	Dendrexetastes paraensis	The Tocantins to Maranhão
	Hylexetastes perrotii	Rio Negro to Amapá
	Hylexetastes uniformis	The Madeira to the Xingu
	Hylexetastes brigidai	Xingu-Tocantins interfluve
	Hylexetastes stresemanni	Western Amazonia to the Negro and the Purus
	Dendrocolaptes hoffmannsi	Rio Madeira to the Xingu
	Xiphorhynchus spixii	The Tapajós to Maranhão
	Xiphorhynchus juruanus	Rio Juruá to the Madeira
	Xiphorhynchus pardalotus	Rio Negro to Amapá
	Lepidocolaptes souleyetii	Roraima
Furnariidae	Synallaxis macconnelli	Western Amapá
	Synallaxis albigularis	Grassy islands of the Solimões
	Synallaxis propinqua	Widespread throughout fluvial islands
	Synallaxis cherriei	Rondônia, Mato Grosso and southern Pará
	Poecilurus kollari	Roraima (seasonal flooded forest)
	Certhiaxis mustelina	Islands and floodplains of the Solimões
	Cranioleuca muelleri	Floodplains of the lower Amazonas
	Cranioleuca demissa	Roraima and Amazonas table-tops
	Thripophaga fusciceps	Floodplains of the lower Amazonas (both banks), from the Madeira to the Tapajós
	Metopothrix aurantiacus	The Purus and the Solimões
	Roraimia adusta	Cerro Uei-Tepui (Roraima)
	Ancistrops strigilatus	Acre to the Tapajós
	Simoxenops ucayalae	Acre to the southern Pará
	Automolus rubiginosus	Rio Negro to Amapá

Family	Species	Distribution
Funariidae	Automolus melanopezus	Upper Juruá, upper Purus, Cachoeira Nazaré
	Automolus roraimae	Roraima and Amazonas table-tops
	Sclerurus albigularis	Rondônia
Thamnophilidae	Cymbilaimus sanctaemariae	Bamboo groves from the upper Solimões to Rondônia
	Frederickena viridis	Rio Negro to Amapá
	Frederickena unduligera	Western Amazonia to the Negro and the Madeira
	Percnostola lophotes	Upper Juruá
	Thamnophilus nigrocinereus	Rio Negro and Amazonas floodplains to the mouth
	Thamnophilus cryptoleucus	Islands and floodplains of the Solimões and tributaries
	Thamnophilus insignis	Roraima and Amazonas table-tops
	Neoctantes niger	Western Amazonia to the Tapajós
	Clytoctantes atrogularis	Cachoeira Nazaré, Rondônia
	Thamnomanes ardesiacus	North bank of the Solimões/Amazonas to Amapá
	Thamnomanes saturninus	South bank of the Solimões/Amazonas to the Tapajós
	Thamnomanes schistogynus	South bank of the Solimões, from the Javari to the Purus
	Myrmotherula gutturalis	North bank of the lower Amazonas and Amapá
	Myrmotherula obscura	Upper Solimões to Tefé
	Myrmotherula sclateri	South bank of the Solimões to the Tapajós
	Myrmotherula ambigua	Upper Rio Negro and western Roraima
	Myrmotherula cherriei	Rio Negro and tributaries
	Myrmotherula guttata	Rio Negro to Amapá
	Myrmotherula ornata	Rio Madeira to the Tocantins
	Myrmotherula sunensis	Upper Juruá
	Myrmotherula erythrura	Western Amazonia to the upper Rio Negro and Tefé
	Myrmotherula behni	Roraima and Amazonas table-tops
	Herpsilochmus sticturus	Óbidos
	Herpsilochmus dorsimaculatus	Rio Negro basin to Faro
	Herpsilochmus roraimae	Roraima table-tops
	Drymophila devillei	Rondônia to the Curuá (Pará)
	Terenura spodioptila	Rio Negro to Amapá
	Terenura humeralis	South bank of the Solimões to Rondônia
	Cercomacra laeta	Tocantins to Maranhão and north of Manaus

continues

Family	Species	Distribution
Thamnophilidae	Cercomacra serva	Upper Juruá
	Cercomacra carbonaria	Roraima
	Cercomacra manu	Alta Floresta (Mato Grosso)
	Pyriglena leuconota	Rio Guaporé to Maranhão
	Myrmoborus lugubris	Floodplains and islands of the Solimões/Amazonas to the Tocantins
	Hypocnemis hypoxantha	Solimões-Negro and Tapajós-Xingu interfluves
	Myrmochanes hemileucus	Floodplains and islands of the Solimões to Manaus
	Percnostola rufifrons	Rio Negro to Amapá
	Percnostola schistacea	Upper Solimões (both banks) to Tefé
	Percnostola lophotes	Upper Juruá
	Percnostola caurensis	Roraima
	Myrmeciza longipes	Roraima to Amapá
	Myrmeciza ferruginea	Rio Negro to Amapá, Madeira-Tapajós interfluve
	Myrmeciza pelzelni	Upper Rio Negro
	Myrmeciza hemimelaena	South of the Solimões to the Xingu
	Myrmeciza hyperythra	Floodplains of the Solimões, Purus and Juruá
	Myrmeciza melanoceps	Upper Solimões and Juruá
	Myrmeciza goeldii	Upper Purus
	Myrmeciza fortis	Solimões (both banks) to the Purus
	Pithys albifrons	Rio Negro to Amapá
	Gymnopithys rufigula	Rio Negro to Amapá
	Gymnopithys leucaspis	Solimões-Negro interfluve
	Gymnopithys salvini	South bank of the Solimões to the Madeira
	Rhegmatorhina cristata	Japurá-Negro interfluve
	Rhegmatorhina melanosticta	Upper Solimões to the Madeira
	Phlegopsis erythroptera	Western Amazonia to the Negro and the Madeira
Formicariidae	Chamaeza nobilis	South of the Solimões/Amazonas to the east bank of the Tapajós (Santarém)
	Formicarius rufifrons	Upper Juruá
	Grallaria guatimalensis	Serra da Curupira, Roraima
	Grallaria eludens	Benjamin Constant and upper Juruá
	Hylopezus berlepschi	Both banks of the Madeira to the Tocantins
	Myrmothera simplex	Roraima and Amazonas table-tops
Conopophagidae	Conopophaga melanogaster	Rio Madeira to the Tocantins

Family	Species	Distribution
Conopophagidae	Conopophaga peruviana	Upper Juruá and Purus
Tyrannidae	Elaenia pelzelni	Amazonas/Solimões islands
	Mecocerculus leucophrys	Roraima and Amazonas table-tops
	Phylloscartes chapmani	Roraima and Amazonas table-tops
	Lophotriccus eulophotes	Upper Purus and Juruá
	Atalotriccus pilaris	Northeastern Roraima
	Hemitriccus josephinae	Rio Negro to Amapá
	Hemitriccus iohannis	Solimões, Juruá, Japurá and Purus
	Hemitriccus flammulatus	Rio Mequenes (Rondônia)
	Poecilotriccus capitalis	Rondônia, Alta Floresta (Mato Grosso) and Carajás
	Todirostrum pictum	Rio Negro to Amapá
	Todirostrum russatum	Roraima table-tops
	Todirostrum latirostre	Islands and floodplains of the Solimões/Amazonas and southern tributaries to the Tapajós
	Cnipodectes subbrunneus	Western Amazonia to the Negro and the Madeira
	Ramphotrigon fuscicauda	Bamboo groves in Acre, southern Pará and Mato Grosso
	Myiophobus roraimae	Roraima and Amazonas table-tops
	Contopus albogularis	Mountain ranges of Amapá
	Contopus fumigatus	Roraima table-tops
	Knipolegus orenocensis	Solimões/Amazonas floodplains to the Xingu
	Attila bolivianus	Solimões/Amazonas floodplains to its mouth
	Attila citriniventris	Upper Rio Negro and Tefé
	Rhytipterna immunda	Rare; white sand grasslands
	Myiozetetes granadensis	Western Amazonia to the Madeira and the Japurá
Pipridae	Pipra chloromeros	Upper Juruá
	Pipra serena	Rio Negro to Amapá
	Pipra iris	Lower Tapajós to Maranhão
	Pipra nattereri	Rio Madeira to the upper Xingu
	Pipra filicauda	Western Amazonia to the Negro and the Purus
	Corapipo gutturalis	Serra do Navio
	Chloropipo uniformis	Cerro Uei/Tepui (Roraima)
	Heterocercus flavivertex	Rio Negro basin to the Rio Trombetas
	Neopelma chrysocephalum	Rio Negro basin
	Tyranneutes virescens	Rio Negro to Amapá

continues

Family	Species	Distribution
Pipridae	*Schiffornis major*	Western Amazon floodplains to the Tapajós
Cotingidae	*Porphyrolaema porphyrolaema*	Western Amazon to the Negro and the Purus
	Conioptilon mcilhennyi	Upper Juruá
	Iodopleura fusca	Rio Negro to Amapá
	Lipaugus streptophorus	Cerro Uei-Tepui (Roraima)
	Procnias alba	Locally to the east of the Rio Negro and in the Serra dos Carajás
	Rupicola rupicola	Mountain ranges from the Rio Negro to Amapá
Corvidae	*Cyanocorax violaceus*	Western Amazonia to the Rio Purus and Roraima
	Cyanocorax heilprini	Upper Rio Negro
Troglodytidae	*Campylorhynchus griseus*	Roraima
	Odontorchilus cinereus	Rio Madeira to the Xingu
	Thryothorus griseus	Rio Javari to the Purus
	Troglodytes rufulus	Roraima and Amazonas table-tops
	Henicorhina leucosticta	Roraima to Amapá
	Microcerculus ustulatus	Roraima and Amazonas table-tops
Turdidae	*Cichlopsis leucogenys*	Roraima table-tops
	Platycichla leucops	Roraima and Amazonas table-tops
	Turdus olivater	Roraima (Maracá) and Pico da Neblina
Vireonidae	*Hylophilus sclateri*	Roraima and Amazonas table-tops
	Hylophilus muscicapinus	Rio Negro to Amapá, Madeiras-Tapajós interfluve
Vireonidae	*Hylophilus burnneiceps*	Upper Rio Negro to western Roraima
Parulidae	*Myioborus miniatus*	Roraima and Amazonas table-tops
	Myioborus castaneocapillus	Roraima and Amazonas table-tops
	Basileuterus bivittatus	Roraima and Amazonas table-tops
Thraupidae	*Conothraupis speculigera*	Upper Juruá
	Mitrospingus oleagineus	Cerro Uei-Tepui (Roraima)
	Tachyphonus rufiventer	The Javari and the Juruá
	Piranga leucoptera	Roraima
	Euphonia plumbea	Rio Negro to Amapá
	Euphonia finschi	Gallery forests in Roraima
	Tangara schrankii	Western Amazonia to the Purus
	Tangara guttata	Cerro Uei-Tepui and Serra Parima
Thraupidae	*Tangara xanthogastra*	Solimões and the slopes of the table-tops
	Tangara cyanoptera	Roraima table-tops
	Tangara callophrys	The Javari to the Purus
	Dacnis albiventris	The Cururu
	Diglossa major	Roraima table-tops
	Diglossa duidae	Pico da Neblina
	Conirostrum margaritae	Solimões/Amazonas valley to the Nhamundá
Emberizidae	*Sporophila intermedia*	Roraima
	Oryzoborus crassirostris	Rio Negro to Amapá
	Dolospingus fringilloides	Rio Negro basin
	Catamenia homochroa	Roraima (slopes of the table-tops)
	Arremonops conirostris	Roraima
	Atlapetes personatus	Roraima
	Caryothraustes humeralis	Right bank of the Solimões to the Tapajós and Carajás
Icteridae	*Ocyalus latirostris*	Upper Juruá
	Psarocolius oseryi	Upper Juruá
	Icterus nigrogularis	Roraima
	Lampropsar tanagrinus	Western Amazonia to the Negro and the Madeira
	Macroagelaius imthurni	Roraima
	Quiscalus lugubris	Eastern Amapá

continues

Table 5 - Main ornithological collection sites in the Brazilian Amazonia
(negative latitude = west; negative longitude = south)

Location	Latitude	Longitude
Açailândia	-47.50689	-4.94588
Acajutuba	-60.27021	-3.11631
Aiapuá (lake)	-62.12627	-4.45820
Aldeia Zé Gurupi	-45.76802	-2.98392
Alenquer	-54.73696	-1.93806
Alta Floresta, rio Teles	-55.93333	-9.70000
Altamira	-52.20503	-3.19972
Alvorada do Oeste, line 64	-62.41666	-11.41666
Amapá	-50.73661	2.09606
Anibá / Rio Anebá	-58.26117	-2.78024
Araguatins	-48.12661	-5.65152
Arimã	-63.62652	-5.76998
Aripuanã	-59.42630	-10.50236
Arumanduba	-52.45364	-1.45803
Arumatéua	-49.70437	-3.60228
Aveiro	-55.33153	-3.60470
Baião / Ilha Pirunum	-49.67234	-2.78650
Balbina	-59.82838	-1.57517
Barcelos	-62.92401	-0.97382
Barra do Corda	-45.24550	-5.50478
Barro Vermelho	-68.76667	-6.46667
Base Camp./Serra do Roncador	-51.22449	-11.87905
Belém et al.	-48.48333	-1.45000
Belém-Brasilía highway, km 86-92	-47.55000	-2.50000
Benevides	-48.24539	-1.35636
Benjamin Constant	-70.03431	-4.37737
Boa Vista	-60.67161	2.82525
Boca do Tejo	-72.80637	-8.94303
Boim	-55.24514	-3.11970
Bom Jesus da Mata	-45.91571	-2.37787
Bom Lugar	-45.03894	-4.21894
Borba	-59.59375	-4.38694
BR-230 highway, km 25, Tapacurazinho	-55.90000	-4.30000
Bragança	-46.76177	-1.05114
Breves-Anajás highway, km 18	-50.41667	-1.58333
Breves-Castanhal-R.Caruac	-50.35000	-1.50000
Buriticupu-CVRD reserve	-46.05199	-4.08113
Cachoeira	-65.95767	-7.68999
Cachoeira Arari, povoado Pedras	-48.75000	-1.15000
Cachoeira Nazaré, Jipara river	-61.88333	-9.73333
Cachoeira de Pederneira	-65.32507	-9.51261
Cachoeira Grande	-52.62789	-3.93015
Cachoeira Muíra	-54.38486	-1.72731
Cachoeira Porteira	-57.04381	-1.05129
Caitau-uará, Solimões river	-65.61253	-2.63883
Calama	-62.87570	-8.02697
Camanaós	-66.29133	-0.34786
Cametá / Ilha Taiuna	-49.49299	-2.23942
Canoal	-49.66666	-4.16666
Capanema	-47.18006	-1.19079
Carajás, Manganês	-50.40000	-6.16666
Carajás, Pojuca	-50.50000	-5.91666
Carauari	-66.89283	-4.86969
Caviana Faz. São Luiz	-49.97803	0.00433
Caxiricatuba	-55.03771	-2.83326
Caxiuanã	-51.47000	-1.75000
Certeza	-46.76470	-9.41454
Codajás	-62.05679	-3.83578
Colônia do Apiaú	-61.30000	2.56667
Conceição do Araguaia	-49.26451	-8.25819
Cruzeiro do Sul	-72.66907	-7.62892
Cruzeiro do Sul, Juruá river	-72.76667	-8.80000
Cruzeiro do Sul Sobral	-72.83333	-8.38333
Cuçari	-53.34760	-1.90543
Cunani	-51.12250	2.86370
Curuá-una, Santarém	-54.08333	-2.40000
Diauarum	-53.23249	-11.13969
Estirão do Equador	-71.60433	-4.54472
Faro	-56.74709	-2.16772
Fazenda Canto da Onça / Graj	-46.12694	-6.22917
Fazenda Casemiro	-50.75000	1.38333
Fazenda Itapoã	-50.93333	2.06667
Fazenda São Bento	-50.78333	1.33333
Fazenda Sta. Bárbara	-46.63499	-3.06605
Fazenda Vitória/Paragominas	-47.26876	-2.75515
Flexal	-57.06312	-5.52716
Fordlândia	-55.29816	-3.55830
Garapu	-52.49214	-13.79712
Genipauba-Jacundá	-49.50000	-4.50000
Gorotire	-51.13429	-7.75806
Guajará-Mirim (Rondônia)	-65.34051	-10.78199
Huitanaã	-65.75822	-7.66882
Humaitá	-63.02188	-7.50530
Iauaretê	-69.19514	0.59674
Igarapé Açu	-47.62082	-1.12570
Igarapé Anil, upper Moa	-73.65378	-7.32636
Igarapé do Gordão/Grande (Amazonas)	-69.81634	-6.50370
Igarapé Preto, tributary Juruá-Mirim	-73.25000	-8.28333
Igarapé Ramon	-73.76349	-7.44170
Igarapé do Castanha	-61.34527	-3.85747
Ilha Caviana	-50.26361	0.05202
Ilha de Maracá (Roraima)	-61.88750	3.31626
Ilha de Maracá	-50.48813	2.07618
Ilha Mexiana	-49.75282	-0.10534
Imperatriz	-47.50824	-5.46217
Itaboca	-62.66907	-4.87284
Itacoatiara	-58.43924	-3.13183
Itaituba	-55.98347	-4.27526
Jaburu	-64.04673	-5.58837
Jacaré (Mato Grosso)	-52.84440	-12.96530
Jacareacanga	-57.65822	-6.22260
Ji-paraná	-61.94692	-10.84811
João Pessoa / Eirunepé	-69.87411	-6.66063
Lábrea	-64.79793	-7.25783
Lago do Baptista	-58.24370	-3.30474
Lago Grande	-69.55388	-6.61176
Lago Paricá	-65.70994	-1.84613
Lago Verde	-44.93971	-4.04808
Limoal	-55.19187	-2.83115
Locality facing Maguari	-65.40293	-1.90918
Macapá	-51.06502	0.04255
Macapá EMBRAPA research station	-50.94493	0.45840
Maguari	-65.39734	-1.84675
Maloca do Manoelzinho	-54.85668	-7.34153
Maloquinha	-55.79118	-5.52019
Maloquinha	-56.04758	-4.29896
Manacapuru	-60.61274	-3.28444
Manaquiri	-60.32723	-3.32455
Manaus, km 38	-59.80000	-2.63333
Manaus	-60.02088	-3.09258
Manicoré	-61.29411	-5.84584

continues

Location	Latitude	Longitude
Manuas, agricultural district	-59.76667	-2.00694
Marabá	-49.11876	-5.36782
Marabitanas	-66.87259	0.91017
Marapanim	-47.70019	-0.71778
Marmellos	-61.84840	-6.12019
Maruins / Milho	-61.92601	-9.00849
Mazagão	-51.28994	-0.11527
Mexiana Fazenda Santana	-49.72547	-0.11873
Miritiba / Humberto Campos	-43.46326	-2.59754
Missión Padauiri	-64.08266	1.12985
Mocajuba	-49.50712	-2.58222
Monte Alegre	-54.06798	-2.00406
Monte Cristo	-61.92222	-10.15268
Monte Verde	-67.43877	-8.74317
Mosqueiro	-48.40000	-1.11666
Mouth of the Gurupi	-46.13367	-1.25883
Nova Olinda do Norte	-59.09403	-3.88722
Nova Olinda	-64.27990	-5.62612
Óbidos	-55.51965	-1.91411
Oriximiná	-55.86474	-1.76196
Ourém	-47.10000	-1.55000
Ouro Preto do Oeste	-62.25000	-11.08333
Outeiro	-48.45000	-1.25000
PA-263 highway, km 18	-49.39078	-3.78389
Palhão in Santarém (Pará)	-54.63772	-2.53667
Parabrilho	-50.90000	0.80000
Paragominas	-47.35494	-2.99503
Parintins	-56.73674	-2.62839
Paru do Leste Aldeia Apal	-54.34264	0.92554
Paru do Leste Igarapé Castanho	-54.35148	0.79967
Patauá	-54.96769	-1.75542
Pedra Chata	-46.28080	-2.17312
Pedra Gavião	-61.70959	-1.39254
Pedral / Bacaba	-47.06183	-1.84774
Peixe	-48.54169	-12.06586
Peixe-Boi	-47.31117	-1.19226
Pimenta Bueno	-61.19448	-11.67208
Pimentel, Tapajós river	-56.20000	-4.56666
Plácido de Castro	-67.17475	-10.28143
Ponta de Pedras	-48.87157	-1.39064
Porangaba	-72.81667	-8.75000
Portel	-50.81976	-1.93191
Porto Alegre	-67.83836	-8.95417
Porto de Móz	-52.23697	-1.74470
Porto Franco	-47.34880	-6.33277
Porto Velho	-63.90489	-8.76235
Príncipe da Beira (Rondônia)	-64.41681	-12.41898
Redenção	-50.03119	-8.02785
Ouro Preto Biological Reserve	-64.75000	-10.83333
Samuel Ecological Reserve	-63.41667	-8.78333
Restauração	-72.26667	-9.03333
Ribeirão	-65.26232	-10.25517
Rio Acará	-48.22969	-1.99167
Rio Amajaú	-61.94111	-1.29460
Rio Branco	-67.80989	-9.97395
Rio Capim	-47.79823	-1.69820
Rio Curuá	-54.41551	-5.38206
Rio Cururu	-57.79247	-7.48586
Rio Iriri, upper reaches	-54.50221	-4.61208
Rio Itinga	-47.46666	-4.50000
Rio Juruá/N. S. Aparecida	-72.78333	-8.88333
Rio Moju	-48.75647	-1.87534
Rio Mucajaí	-60.89789	2.43517
Rio Peixoto de Azevedo	-54.72989	-10.32622
Rio Sororó, CVRD reserve	-49.21573	-5.58653

Location	Latitude	Longitude
Rio Tejo, 5 km upstream, left bank	-72.70000	-9.00000
Rio Teles Pires, right bank	-55.90000	-9.68333
Rio Uasseipeiú	-52.95021	2.14837
Rio Urubu	-58.54945	-2.91303
Rio Xié / Marcelino	-67.17367	0.92287
Rosarinho (Sampaio Lake)	-59.13330	-3.69676
Rosário	-44.23715	-2.93365
Salinópolis	-47.35462	-0.61380
Salobo, serra dos Carajás	-50.51667	-5.80000
Salto do Huá	-65.41456	0.83281
Salto Grande	-55.65196	-6.31590
Santa Helena, Maranhão	-45.30009	-2.23086
Santa Isabel /Tapurucuará	-65.01607	-0.41357
Santa Rosa	-48.08849	-0.88156
Santana do Araguaia	-50.19595	-9.67119
Santarém	-54.69821	-2.44207
Santarém-Cuiabá highway km 84	-55.00000	-3.11666
Santarém Novo	-47.40000	-0.90000
São Gabriel /Uaupés	-67.08447	-0.12009
São Paulo de Olivença	-68.87186	-3.37733
Ser. Conceição Amarante	-46.75241	-5.56707
Seringal Oriente	-72.75781	-8.79852
Serra Carauman (Gr. Serra)	-60.65002	2.57803
Serra das Andorinhas	-48.57724	-6.33241
Serra do Cachimbo	-56.28272	-8.93094
Serra do Navio	-52.00085	0.89922
Serra Norte	-50.52377	-5.98933
Silves	-58.19763	-2.81275
Smithsonian camp	-52.34191	-3.67394
Sta. Isabel do Rio Negro	-65.02602	-0.38557
Sto. Antônio da Cachoeira	-52.49879	-0.66761
Sumaúma	-60.20790	-7.88250
Sumaúma (Pará)	-55.36855	-3.57223
Tapajós National Forest	-55.14363	-3.35970
Tapajós National Park	-56.61634	-4.62365
Tapirapoã	-57.69262	-15.16174
Taraquá	-68.41599	0.05686
Tatu / Umarituba	-67.24904	0.02981
Tefé	-64.70854	-3.34779
Tocantins / 12 km S Jacundá	-49.45000	-4.61666
Tocantins / 20 km S Jacundá	-49.58333	-4.66666
Tomar	-63.85316	-0.38635
Tomé-Açu	-48.15270	-2.41918
Tonantins	-67.77296	-2.76796
Toototobi	-63.42128	1.86863
Tucuruí, Chiquerão	-49.53333	-4.33333
Tucuruí / Sítio Calandrini	-49.58333	-4.36666
Tucuruí + Vale do Caraipé	-49.73595	-3.83561
Turiaçu	-45.37032	-1.65965
Upper Moa, left bank	-73.66667	-7.45000
Utiariti	-58.27481	-13.02658
Valparaíso	-72.90000	-8.33333
Vila Braga	-56.28333	-4.41666
Villarinho do Monte	-51.28333	-1.60297
Vista Alegre	-60.57681	-7.67789
Vitória do Jari	-52.41041	-0.91383
Vitória do Mearim	-44.87299	-3.45900
Vitória do Xingu	-52.00864	-2.87638
Vl. Bella / S. Fco. Xavier	-59.95431	-14.84900
Yucabí / Iucaí	-67.10330	-0.16469

continues

BIBLIOGRAPHY

BEEBE, C. W. Notes on the birds of Pará, Brazil. *Zoologica*, n. 2, p. 55-106, 1916.

BERNARDES, A. T.; MACHADO, A. B. M.; RYLANDS, A. B. *Fauna brasileira ameaçada de extinção*. Belo Horizonte: Fundação Biodiversitas, 1990.

BIBBY, C. J. et al. *Putting Biodiversity on the Map: Priority Areas for Global Conservation*. Cambridge: International Council for Bird Preservation, 1992.

BIGARELLA, J. J.; FERREIRA, A. M. M. Amazonian Geology and the Pleistocene and Cenozoic Environments and Paleoclimates. In: PRANCE, G. T.; LOVEJOY, T. E. (Eds.). *Key Environments: Amazonia*. Oxford: Pergamon Press., 1985, p. 49-71.

BORGES, S. H. Listagem e novos registros de aves para a região de Boa Vista, Roraima, Brasil. *Bol. Mus. Paraense Emílio Goeldi*, n. 10, p. 191-202, 1994.

CAMARGO, E. A. Resultados ornitológicos de uma excursão ao estado do Maranhão. *Papéis Avulsos Departamento de Zoologia*, n. 13, p. 75-84, 1957.

COHN-HAFT, M.; WHITTAKER, A.; STOUFFER, P. A New Look at the 'Species-Poor' Central Amazon: Updates and Corrections to the Avifauna North of Manaus, Brazil. *Ornithol. Monogr.*, n. 48, p. 205-235, 1987.

COLLAR, N. J. et al. *Threatened birds of the Americas*. Washington D. C.: Smithsonian Institution Press, 1992.

DÉGALLIER, N. et al. As aves como hospedeiras de arbovírus na Amazônia brasileira, *Bol. Mus. Paraense Emílio Goeldi, série Zoologia*, n. 8, p. 69-111, 1992.

FRIEDMANN, H. Birds Collected by the National Geographic Society's Expeditions to Northern Brazil and Southern Venezuela, *Proc. U. S. Nat. Mus.*, n. 97, p. 373-570, 1948.

FRY, C. H. Ecological Distribution of Birds in Northeastern Mato Grosso State, Brazil, *Anais Acad. Brasil. Cien.*, n. 42, p. 275-318, 1940.

GOELDI, E. A.; HAGMANN, G. Lista das aves amazônicas, *Bol. Mus. Paraense Emílio Goeldi*, n. 3, p. 276-327, 1902.

GRAVES, G. R.; ZUSI, R. L. Avian Body Weights from the Lower Rio Xingu, *Bull. Brit. Ornith. Club*, n. 110, p. 20-25, 1990.

GRISCOM, L.; GREENWAY Jr., J. C., Birds of Lower Amazonia, *Bull. Mus. Comp. Zool.*, n. 81, p. 83-344, 1941.

GYLDENSTOLPE, N. The Bird Fauna of the Rio Juruá in Western Brazil. Kungl. Svenska Vent.-akad, *Handl* 30 Ser. Band 22, n. 3, p. 1-338. 1945.

_____. The Ornithology of the Rio Purus Region in Western Brazil, *Ark. Zool*, v. 2, n. 2, p. 1-320, 1951.

HAFFER, J. Avian Speciation in Tropical South America, with a Systematic Survey of the Toucas (*Ramphastidae*) and Jacamars (Galbulidae), *Publ. Nuttall Ornith. Club*, n. 14, p. 1-390, 1974.

HAGMANN, G. Die Vögelwelt der Insel Mexiana, Amazonenström, *Zoolog. Jahrb. Abt. Syst.*, n. 26, p. 11-62, 1907.

HELLMAYR, C. E. Notes on a Collection of Birds, Made by Mons. A. Robert in the District of Pará, *Novit. Zool.*, n. 12, p. 269-305, 1905.

_____. Notes on a Second Colleciton of Birds from the District of Pará, Brazil, *Novit. Zool.*, n. 13, p. 305-352, 1906.

_____. Another Contribution to the Ornithology of the Lower Amazons, *Novit. Zool.*, n. 14, p. 1-39, 1907.

_____. On a Collection of Birds from Teffé, Rio Solimões, Brazil, *Novit. Zool.*, n. 14, p. 40-91, 1907.

_____. On a Collection of Birds Made by Mr. Hoffmanns on the Rio Madeira, Brazil, *Novit. Zool.*, n. 14, p. 343-412, 1907.

_____. The Birds of the Rio Madeira, *Novit. Zool.*, n. 17, p. 257-428, 1910.

_____. Zoologische Ergebnisse einer Reise in das Mündungsgebiet des Amazonas (org. L. Müller) – II. Vögel, *Abh. Bayern Akad.* Wiss. Math.-phys. Kl., v. 26, n. 2, p. 1-142, 1912.

HENRIQUES, L. M. P.; OREN, D. C. The Avifauna of Marajó, Caviana and Mexiana Islands, Amazon River estuary, Brazil, *Rev. Brasil. Biol.*, n. 57, p. 357-382, 1997.

LOVEJOY, T. E. Bird Diversity and Abundance in Amazon Forest Communities, *Living Bird*, n. 13, p. 127-191, 1974.

MORRISON, R. I. G.; ROSS, R. K.; ANTAS, P. T. Z. Distribuição de maçaricos, batuíras e outras aves costeiras na região do salgado paraense e reeentrâncias maranhenses, *Espaço, Ambiente e Planejamento*, n. 4, p.1-135, 1986.

MOSKOVITZ, D.; FITZPATRICK, J. W.; WILLARD. Lista preliminar das aves da estação ecológica de Maracá, território de Roraima, Brasil e áreas adjacentes, *Papéis Avulsos Depto. Zool.*, n. 36, p. 51-68, 1985.

NAUMBURG, E. M. B. The Birds of Mato Grosso, Brazil, *Bull. Amer. Mus. Nat. Hist.*, n. 60, p. 1-432, 1930.

NOVAES, F. C. Contribuições à ornitologia do noroeste do Acre, *Bol. Mus. Paraense Emílio Goeldi, nova série Zool.*, n. 9, p. 1-30, 1931.

_____. As aves e as comunidades bióticas no alto rio Juruá, território do Acre, *Bol. Mus. Paraense Emílio Goeldi, nova série Zool.*, n. 14, p. 1-13, 1958.

_____. Sobre uma coleção de aves do sudeste do Estado do Pará, *Arq. Zool.*, n. 11, p. 133-146, 1960.

_____. Análise ecológica de uma avifauna da região do rio Acará, Estado do Pará, *Bol. Mus. Paraense Emílio Goeldi, Zool.*, n. 69, p. 1-52, 1969.

_____. Distribuição ecológica e abundância das aves em um trecho de mata do baixo rio Guamá (Estado do Pará), *Bol. Mus. Paraense Emílio Goeldi, Zool.*, n. 71, p. 1-54, 1970.

_____. Aves de uma vegetação secundária na foz do Amazonas, *Publ. Avul. Mus. Par. Emílio Goeldi*, n. 21, p. 1-88, 1973.

_____. Ornitologia do território do Amapá, I, *Publ. Avul. Mus. Par. Emílio Goeldi*, n. 25, p. 1-121, 1974.

_____. As aves do rio Aripuanã, estados de Mato Grosso e Amazonas, *Acta Amazonica*, v. 6, n. 4, p. 61-85, 1976.

_____. Ornitologia do território do Amapá, II, *Publ. Avul. Mus. Par. Emílio Goeldi*, n. 29, p. 1-75. 1978.

_____. Observações sobre a avifauna do alto curso do rio Paru do leste, estado do Pará, *Bol. Mus. Paraense Emílio Goeldi, Zool.*, n.100, p. 1-58, 1980.

NOVAES, F. C.; LIMA, M. F. C. As aves do rio Peixoto de Azevedo, Mato Grosso, Brasil, *Rev. Bras. Zool.*, n. 7, p. 351-381, 1991.

_____. *As aves de grande Belém*. Belém: Secretaria de Ciência, Tecnologia e Meio Ambiente do Estado do Pará, forthcoming.

NOVAES, F. C.; PIMENTEL, T. Observações sobre a avifauna dos campos de Bragança, Estado do Pará, *Publ. Avul. Mus. Para Emílio Goeldi*, n. 20, p. 229-246, 1973.

OREN, D. C. Aves do Estado do Maranhão, Brasil, *Goeldiana Zool.*, n. 9, p. 1-57, 1991.

_____. Conservação da natureza na Amazônia brasileira: uma orientação sobre prioridades baseada em aves, *Bol. Mus. Paraense Emílio Goeldi, sér. Zool.*, n. 8, p. 259-268, 1992.

OREN, D. C.; ALBUQUERQUE, H. G. Priority Areas for New Avian Collections in Brazilian Amazonia, *Goeldiana Zool.*, n. 6, p. 1-11, 1990.

OREN, D. C.; PARKER III, T. A. Avifauna of the Tapajós National Park and Vicinity, Amazonian Brazil, in *Ornithol. Monogr.*, n. 48, p. 493-525, 1997.

PACHECO, J. F. New Distributional Records for Some Birds from Várzea Forest at Mamirauá, Western Brazilian Amazon, *Ararajuba*, n. 3, p. 83-87, 1995.

PARKER III, T. A.; STOTZ, D. F.; FITZPATRICK, J. W. Notes on Avian Bamboo Specialists in Southwestern Amazonian Brazil, *Ornithol. Monogr.*, n. 48, p. 543-547, 1997.

PAYNTER Jr., R. A.; TRAYLOR Jr., M. A., *Ornithological Gazetteer of Brazil*. Cambridge (Mass.): Museum of Comparative Zoology, 1991.

PELZELN, A. *Zur Ornithologie Brasiliens. Resultate von Johann Natterers Reisen in den Jahren 1817 bis 1835*. Viena: Druck und Verlag von A. Pichler's Witwe & Sohn, p. 1868-1870.

PERES, C. A.; WHITTAKER, A. Annotated Checklist of the Bird Species of the Upper Rio Urucu, Amazonas, Brazil, *Bull. Brit. Ornithol. Club*, n. 111, p. 156-171, 1991.

PINTO, O. M. de O. Catálogo das aves do Brasil, primeira parte, *Rev. Mus. Paulista*, n. 22, p. 1-566, 1938.

_____. Nova contribuição à ornitologia amazônica. Estudo crítico de uma coleção de aves do baixo Solimões e do alto rio Negro, *Rev. Mus. Paulista*, n. 23, p. 493-604, 1938.

_____. *Catálogo das aves do Brasil, segunda parte*. São Paulo: Publ. Depto. Zool., Sec. Agric., Ind. e Comércio, 1944.

_____. Contribuição à ornitologia do baixo Amazonas: estudo crítico de uma coleção de aves do Estado do Pará, *Arq. Zool*, n. 5, p. 311-482, 1947.

_____. Sobre a coleção Carlos Estêvão de peles, ninhos e ovos das aves de Belém (Pará), *Papéis Avulsos Depto. Zool.*, n. 11, p. 111-224, 1953.

_____. Estudo crítico e catálogo remissivo das aves do território federal de Roraima, *Cadernos da Amazônia*, n. 8, p. 1-176, 1966.

PINTO, O. M. de O.; CAMARGO, E. A. de. Sobre uma coleção de aves do rio das Mortes (Estado de Mato Grosso), *Papéis Avulsos, Depto. Zool.*, n. 8, p. 287-336, 1948.

_____. Nova contribuição à ornitologia do rio das Mortes, *Papéis Avulsos, Depto. Zool.*, n.10, p. 213-234, 1952.

_____. Resultados ornitológicos de uma expedição ao território do Acre pelo Departamento de Zoologia, *Papéis Avulsos, Depto. Zool.*, n. 12, p. 371-418, 1954.

_____. Sobre uma coleção de aves da região de Cachimbo (sul do Estado do Pará), *Arq. Zool.*, n. 11, p. 193-284, 1961.

REMSEN Jr., J. V. Use and Misuse of Bird Lists in Community Ecology and Conservation, *Auk*, n. 111, p. 225-227, 1994.

RIDGELY, R. S.; TUDOR, G. *The Birds of South America, vol. 1. The Oscine Passerines*. Austin: Univ. Texas Press, 1989.

_____. *The Birds of South America, vol. 2. The Subocine Passerines*. Austin: Univ. Texas Press, 1994.

RIKER, C. B. A List of Birds Observed at Santarém, Brazil, with Annotations by F. M. Chapman, *Auk*, n. 7, p. 131-137, 265-271; n. 8, p. 24-31, 158-164, 1890-1891.

SANAIOTTI, T. et al. Priority Sites for Bird Conservation in the Amazon. In: *Workshop 90*, Manaus, AM, Brasil, janeiro de 1990, patrocínio Ibama, Conservation International, INPA.

SCHUBART, O.; AGUIRRE, A. C.; SICK, H. Contribuição para o conhecimento da alimentação das aves brasileiras, *Arq. Zool.*, n. 12, p. 95-249, 1965.

SCLATER, P. L.; SALVIN, O. List of Birds Collected by Mr. Wallace on the Lower Amazon and Rio Negro, *Proc. Zool. Soc. London*, p. 566-596, 1867.

SILVA, J. M. C. Avian Inventory of the Cerrado Region, South America: Implications for Biological Conservation, *Bird Conserv. Intern.*, n. 5, p. 291-304, 1995.

_____. Birds of the Ilha de Maracá. In: MILLIKEN, W.; RATTER, J. (Orgs.). *Maracá: the Biodiversity and Environment of an Amazonian Rainforest*. London: John Wiley & Sons, 1998. p. 211-229.

_____. As aves. In: LISBOA, P. L. B. (Org.). *Caxiuanã*: ambiente físico e diversidade biológica. Belém: Museu Paraense Emílio Goeldi, 1998, p. 403-415.

_____. Biogeografia e conservação de aves na região do cerrado e pantanal. <http://www.bdt.org/workshop/cerrado/br/aves>, 1998.

SILVA, J. M. C. da; LIMA, M. F. C.; MARCELIANO, M. L. V. Pesos de aves de duas localidades na Amazônia oriental, *Ararajuba*, n. 1. p. 99-104, 1990.

SILVA, J. M. C. da et al. Composition and Distribution Patterns of the Avifauna of an Amazonian Upland Savanna, Amapá, Brazil, *Ornith. Monogr.*, n. 48, p. 743-762, 1997.

SNETHLAGE, E. Eine Vogelsammlung vom Rio Purus, Brasilien, *Journ. für Ornith.*, 56, 1908, p. 7-24, 1908.

_____. Ornithologisches von Tapajoz und Tocantins, *Journ. für Ornith.*, n. 56, p. 493-539, 1908.

_____. Sobre uma coleção de aves do rio Purús, *Bol. Mus. Paraense Emílio Goeldi*, n. 5, p. 43-76, 1909.

_____. A travessia entre o Xingu e o Tapajos, *Bol. Mus. Paraense Emílio Goeldi*, n. 7, p. 49-539, 1912.

_____. Über die Verbreitung der Vogelarten in Unteramazonien, *Journ. für Ornith.*, n. 61, p. 469-539, 1913.

_____. Catálogo das aves amazônicas, *Bol. Mus. Paraense Emílio Goeldi*, n. 8, p. 1-530, 1914.

STONE, W. On a Collection of Birds from the Pará Region, Eastern Brazil, *Proc. Acad. Nat. Sci.*, n. 80, p. 149-176, 1928.

STOTZ, D. F.; BIERREGAARD Jr., R. O. The Birds of the Fazendas Porto Alegre, Esteio and Dimona North of Manaus, Amazonas, Brazil, *Rev. Brasil. Biol.*, n. 49, p. 861-872, 1989.

STOTZ, D. F et al. The Status of North American Migrants in Central Amazonian Brazil, *Condor*, n. 94, p. 608-621.

STOTZ, D. F. et al. An Avifaunal Survey of Two Tropical Forest Localities on the Middle Rio Jiparaná, Rondônia, Brazil, *Ornithol. Monogr.*, n. 48, p. 763-781, 1997.

STOUFER, P. C.; BIERREGAARD, R. O. Use of Amazonian Forest Fragments by Understory Insectivorous Birds: Effects of Fragment Size Surrounding Secondary Vegetation, and Time Since Isolation, *Ecology*, n. 76, p. 2429-2445, 1995.

VOSS, R. S.; EMMONS, L. H. Mammalian Diversity in Neotropical Lowland Rainforests: a Preliminary Assessment, *Bulletin of the American Museum of Natural History*, n. 230, p. 1-115, 1996.

WEGE, D. C.; LONG, A. J. *Key Areas for Threatened Birds in the Neotropics*. Cambridge: BirdLife International, 1995.

WHITTAKER, A.; CARVALHÃES, A. M. P.; PACHECO, J. F. Rediscovery of the Chestnut-headed Nunlet *Nonnula amaurocephala* in Amazonian Brazil, *Cotinga*, n. 3, p. 48-50, 1995.

WHITTAKER, A.; OREN D. C. Important Ornithological Records from the Rio Juruá, Western Amazonia, Including Twelve Additions to the Brazilian Avifauna, *Bull. Brit. Orn. Club*, forthcoming.

WILLIS, E. O. Lista preliminar das aves da parte noroeste e áreas vizinhas da Reserva Ducke, Amazonas, Brasil, *Rev. Bras. Biol.*, n. 37, p. 585-601, 1977.

ZIMMER, K. J. et al. Survey of a Southern Amazonian Avifauna: the Alta Floresta Region, Mato Grosso, Brazil, *Ornithol. Monogr.*, n. 48, p. 887-918, 1997.

ZINK, R. M.; MCKITRICK, M. C. The Debate Over the Species Concept and its Implications for Ornithology, *Auk*, n.112, p. 701-719, 1995.

Biogeography and Conservation of Mammals in the Brazilian Amazon Forest

Maria Nazareth F. da Silva *Instituto Nacional de Pesquisas da Amazônia*
Anthony B. Rylands *Universidade Federal de Minas Gerais e Fundação Biodiversitas*
James L. Patton *Museum of Vertebrate Zoology, University of California*
Collaborators: Carlos A. Peres, Leonora Pires Costa, Marc van Roosmalen, Pedro M. R. S. Santos, Suely Aparecida Marques-Aguiar, Robert Voss and Yuri Leite

Introduction

The Amazon extends from the Atlantic Ocean to the eastern foothills of the Andes, up to an altitude of approximately 600 meters (Ab'Saber 1977), and forms parts of nine South American countries. In Brazil, the Amazon comprises the states of Acre, Amapá, Amazonas, Pará, Rondônia and Roraima and parts of the states of Mato Grosso, Maranhão and Tocantins, corresponding to an area of approximately five million square kilometers (INPE 1999).

Given its great size, species richness and habitat diversity, the gaps in our knowledge of Amazonian mammals are still enormous. For this reason, museum collections, especially those from the interfluve areas, are also incomplete (Figure 1). In general, for most of the locations inventoried only a few groups of mammals were addressed and sampling was insufficient to plot cumulative species-area curves. Preparing relatively complete inventories is a task that requires not only spending long periods of time in the field (five months or longer), but also use of multiple sampling methods (Voss and Emmons 1996; Simmons and Voss 1998) In the five million square kilometers of the Brazilian Amazon, Voss and Emmons (1996) found only two sites for which relatively complete inventories of mammalian species had been made. Comprehensive inventories have therefore yet to be drawn up for practically the entire region.

Considering the size of Amazonia and the threats to which it is exposed, the small number of areas which have been studied is worrying, to say the least. In view of this, even drawing up a list of the mammalian species found in the Brazilian Amazon becomes a difficult task, for such a list would be unlikely to accurately reflect the species diversity in the region, especially

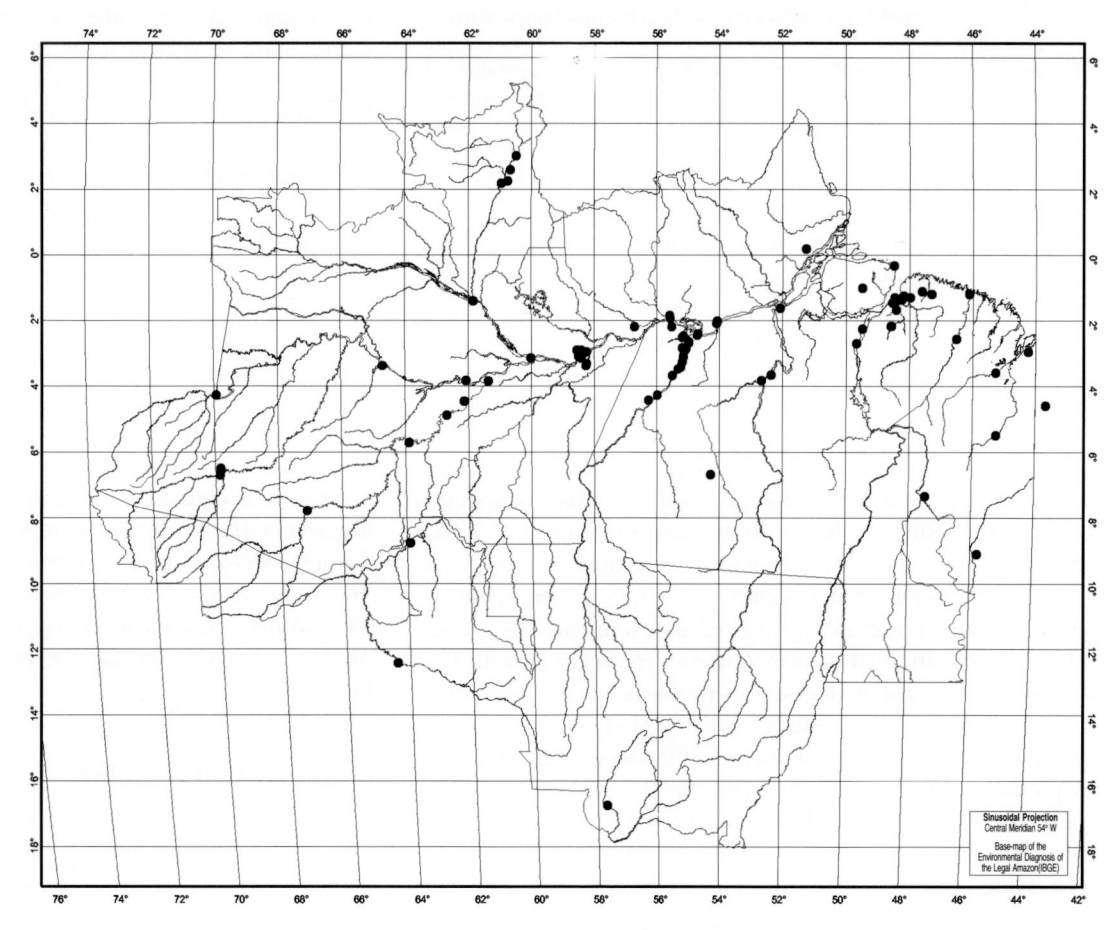

Figure 1.
Locations of collecting sites of mammals deposited in the Field Museum of Natural History.

of rodents, marsupials and bats, which account for two thirds of total mammalian diversity.

This paper presents a list of species from the forested areas of the Brazilian Amazon only. It is based on various sources, but mostly on documented records of witness-species held in museum collections. Data records for these species from specialized literature, especially from older publications, have proved unreliable due to uncertainty regarding the taxonomic methods employed. Added to this is the problem that imprecise information can be harmful when conservation decisions are involved. The authors have therefore sought to draw upon records from the main museums in both Brazil and the United States that hold material collected in the Brazilian Amazon. In some cases, the authors examined specimens, whilst in others, studies were based on computerized information held in data bases. The margin of error of these has not been estimated, for example as regards the identification of species and localities, and this may also jeopardize the final result. The authors have mainly used recent general reviews, such as those by Musser et al. (1998) and Simmons and Voss (1998), especially the study by Voss and Emmons on mammalian diversity in the forests of neotropical lowlands. This study provides an excellent summary of the current state of knowledge, as well as of the problems and needs in respect of describing the diversity of mammals in neotropical forests.

In view of the limitations discussed above, the information presented here should be regarded with the necessary caution. This paper represents an attempt to summarize the knowledge of mammalian zoology currently available.

The state of knowledge on mammalian fauna

> '[...] we simply do not know enough about the distribution of mammals in this region (southwestern Amazonia) to be able to identify areas of endemism or those of crucial importance for conservation [...] with the possible exception of primates, nothing is known about the extent of species distribution that would help in planning conservation strategies.'
>
> Robert S. Voss

Statements such as this are frequent and often shared by large numbers of mammal zoologists. Unbelievable as it may seem, such statements depict the current situation of the mammalian zoology of Amazonia, particularly of Brazilian Amazonia, where our knowledge of the diversity and the endemism of the majority of mammals is still quite precarious.

A simple glance at Figure 1, which plots the collecting sites for mammals from the Brazilian Amazon held by the Chicago Field Museum of Natural History, or even the tables of species sorted by collecting site from various other museums (Tables 2, 3 and 4), will demonstrate this dramatic situation. In 1996, Voss and Emmons listed ten neotropical forest sites where mammalian inventories could be considered as exemplary. Of these, only two were in the Brazilian Amazon. However as with the other sites, these also reveal serious problems such as very variable sampling, non-asymptotic cumulative species curves, omission of essential sampling methods in the inventories, and data on predatory hunting collected prior to the studies. Voss and Emmons (1996) have found that useful comparisons of diversity are impossible to make without greater investment in field work, even in localities already inventoried. To the above list, one can add other areas (albeit so few in number as to be able to be counted on the fingers of one hand) where relatively complete inventories either have been or are being conducted.

With the possible sole exception of the primates and larger mammals such as ungulates and carnivores, knowledge of the species richness of mammalian communities inhabiting neotropical forests is limited. New taxa are constantly being discovered when large-scale inventories, combined with modern analytical techniques and methods, are carried out in areas insufficiently sampled. Proof of this is the recent discovery of at least four new taxa of primates in the mid-eastern Amazon (Mittermeier et al. 1992; Ferrari and Lopes 1992; Queiroz 1992; Roosmalen et al. 1998).

As for small mammals, the situation is even more striking. As a result of an annual inventory along the Juruá, nine species were described, representing 20% of the total number of species of rodents and marsupials recorded for this region (Patton and Silva 1995; Silva 1998; Patton et al. forthcoming). It is important to emphasize that some of these taxa were found in areas which had not even been identified as priority areas on the 'Workshop 90' map. It is equally important to note that knowledge of both ecological and geographical distribution, population demography and of basic parameters of natural history (in other words, virtually all aspects of natural history) is practically nonexistent for the majority of species living in neotropical forests.

Mammalian diversity

In recent years, a large number of mammalian species has been described for the Brazilian Amazon (Mittermeier et al. 1992; Ferrari and Lopes 1992; Queiroz 1992; Patton and Silva 1995; Roosmalen et al. 1998; Silva 1998; Patton et al. forthcoming) and it is certain that many other species have yet to be described. It is important to note that, as far as many of these species are concerned, we are dealing not with taxonomic reclassification but rather with the results of fieldwork in poorly studied areas, which have revealed new taxa to science.

Therefore, on the basis of the list of species shown in Table 1, there are currently 311 species of mammals recorded for the Brazilian Amazon: 22 species of marsupials, 11 edentates, 124 bats, 57 primates, 16 carnivores, 2 cetaceans, 5 ungulates, 1 sirenian, 72 rodents and 1 lagomorph. These numbers must be viewed as estimates only, for they will certainly change as new taxonomic reviews are performed and new areas are sampled. This lack of taxonomic knowledge is critical, especially when it comes to marsupials, rodents and bats, which represent about 70.1% of the taxa, but for which the total number of species is not yet well defined. The most noteworthy examples include the genera *Marmosa*, *Marmosops*, *Micoureus*, *Monodelphis*, *Philander*, *Micronycteris*, *Choeroniscus*, *Platyrrhinus*, *Molossus*, *Microsciurus*, *Sciurus*, *Neacomys*, *Nectomys*, *Oecomys*, *Oryzomys*, *Rhipidomys*, *Coendou*, *Dasyprocta*, *Myoprocta*, *Echimys*, *Mesomys*, *Proechimys* and the primate genus *Aotus* (Voss and Emmons 1996).

Mammal communities

The environmental and biogeographical factors that determine the differences in the structure of communities and in the mammalian diversity in Amazonia are not yet well understood.

Emmons (1984) concluded that soil fertility and the density of the undergrowth are the ecological factors that account for local species richness, and that the amount of rainfall or rainfall patterns are relatively less important. Emmons also found a decrease in the number of species going from western to eastern Amazonia. Peres (1997) links species richness among primate communities to the type of forest, with terra firme forests richer, but displaying a lower density and biomass than floodplain forests. He suggests that primate species richness is related to habitat diversity, just as biomass and density are influenced by soil fertility. For the rodents and marsupials of the Juruá, Patton et al. (forthcoming) found a pattern of richness and density similar to that of primates. However, the number of arboreal species was equivalent in both types of forest and the largest difference occurred among terrestrial species, whose numbers, on average, are twice those of the terra firme. The researchers also found that, along the Juruá, the change in species composition is greater on terra firme than on the floodplains and drew attention to the contrasting bio-geographic patterns of the two types of forest. The authors conclude that patterns of regional diversity (gamma diversity) vary according to the type and stratum of the forest.

When Patton et al. (forthcoming) examined the relationship between the composition of non-flying mammal communities on the Juruá and at fourteen other sites in Amazonia, they found two clearly defined geographic groups. The two groups represented two distinct areas, one in eastern Amazonia and one in western Amazonia, bounded by the Rio Negro to the north of the Solimões-Amazon axis and by a region not yet well defined, between the Madeira and the Xingu, to the south. Although a significant variation in the composition of species is found within each of these areas, the differences between them are remarkable and are, in general, consistent with the subdivision proposed for mammals by Voss and Emmons (1996) and with the patterns found for reptiles in the Amazon region (Silva and Sites 1995). This north-south axis was identified over a century ago by A. R. Wallace (1852) as the dividing line for primate communities. From a conservationist viewpoint, acknowledging the existence of this division is extremely important, for these areas constitute independent evolutionary units in Amazonia and should therefore be considered as distinct and complementary areas when defining conservation areas.

Biogeographic patterns

Based on species distribution maps, Voss and Emmons (1996) established a number of biogeographical patterns for Amazonian mammals. Generally speaking, mammalian diversity is probably greater in western Amazonia (west of the Negro and the Madeira), where as many as 200 species may be sympatric in some localities, smaller in the region of the Guianas (east of the Negro and north of the Amazon), and intermediate in southwestern Amazon (east of the Madeira and south of the Amazon). These authors affirm that the mammalian fauna of the western Amazon is the most diverse of the Americas and possibly in the world. However, Roosmalen (personal comment) argues that in central Amazonia, taking a radius of 10 kilometers around the city of Novo Aripuanã at the confluence of the Madeira and the Aripuanã, a primate diversity of more than 21 species (or 23+ taxa) is found, which would certainly be the highest in the world. It is interesting to note that a comparison of the avifauna of the Manaus region with that of the Manu National Park and of the Tambopata reserve, both in Peru, reveals a similar species richness in the terra firme forest areas of the three localities, something also reported by Cohn-Haft et al. (1997).

These authors also affirm that habitat heterogeneity is a determining factor for patterns of species richness of birds in Amazonia, echoing the conclusions of Peres (1997) for primates. However, Voss and Emmons (1996) argue that the crucial factor for levels of mammalian diversity in southwestern Amazonia is possibly not habitat diversity alone, but the continuity over time of primary production in habitats with asynchronous and irregular fructification peaks. In central Amazonia, in areas of high habitat heterogeneity on the middle and lower courses of white water rivers, Roosmalen (personal comment) has found very high primate diversity and noted signs that in these areas frugivorous fauna perform lateral migrations between the various habitats, supporting the suggestion of Voss and Emmons (1996).

These authors also argue that geographic variations in mammalian diversity in Amazonia mainly involves marsupials, bats, primates and rodents, rather than edentates, carnivores, and ungulates, whose faunas are exceptionally uniform throughout the region. In relation to other biomes, the authors conclude that mammalian diversity, which is measured by the richness of sympatric species, is higher in tropical forest lowlands and decreases along gradients of increasing latitude, elevation, and aridity. The conclusions of Mares (1992) that the 'arid areas' in South American contain a higher number of species than the Amazon forest, and that the latter has a smaller number of endemic species, were strongly rejected by Voss and Emmons (1996, note 26). These authors argue that the 'arid areas' referred to by Mares (1992) bring together ecosystems as diverse as the llanos, caatinga, savanna (cerrado), chaco, pampas, paramo, puna and coastal deserts into a single unit, and it is therefore not surprising that they should present a greater number of species than the Amazon forest.

Silva and Patton (1998) examined, on the basis of sequences of mitochondrial genes of Amazonian rodents and marsupials, the relationships between different areas of the region and came up with a general summary of those geographical areas with marked molecular differences. The regions with more marked phylogeographical divisions (i.e. with higher levels of divergence between clades) are the lower Rio Negro region northwest of Manaus, followed by the middle Juruá and the upper Solimões regions. However, levels of divergence between localities on opposite margins of the Amazonas downstream from Manaus are lower. This pattern is similar to that found by Ayres and Clutton-Brock (1992), according to which primate community structures on this stretch of the Amazonas are more similar than those upstream from Manaus. Patton et al (forthcoming) have also shown that the relationships between geographical areas in Amazonia present a relatively uniform pattern. In the same way as the composition of mammal communities, the phylogeographical patterns of the majority of the taxa of Amazonian rodents and marsupials examined also divide into two groups, one in the east and the other in the west, separated by the north-south axis formed by the Negro and Madeira rivers. There are a few exceptions to this pattern, but since the geographic samplings and the number of taxa studied are still relatively limited, we cannot say that these variations will continue to hold. It can therefore be inferred that different areas of Amazonia reveal high differentiation and comprise diverse groups of taxa.

The studies of Patton and Silva (Patton et al. 1996; Silva 1995; Silva and Patton 1998, forthcoming) show, perhaps for the first time, a high degree of coincidence between the areas of phylogeographical transition and the presence of geological structures, such as the Iquitos arc and the Acre and Amazonas paleobasins. This suggests a relationship between the evolution of landscapes in western Amazonia and the phylogeographical patterns observed. Overlapping patterns in the diversification of taxa suggest an important vicarious role for the paleobasins of the upper Amazon. If, through collecting and further research, these patterns could be confirmed for other areas, the paleobasins, as geologically defined, could become important targets for the identification of conservation areas.

Inventoried areas

Materials held by the Field Museum of Natural History in Chicago clearly illustrate that most collecting in Amazonia has been performed in a relatively few localities along the main rivers of the region, probably because of an easier access to these areas (Figure 1). The present paper has also sought to determine the localities for which there are witness-species deposited in museums. To do this, the authors consulted data collections of the American Museum of Natural History (AMNH, Table 2); the Field Museum of Natural History (FMNH, Table 3); the National Museum of Natural History and the National Amazon Research Institute (Instituto Nacional de Pesquisas Amazônicas, Table 4). Information was also requested from the National Museum in Rio de Janeiro (MNRJ), the Zoological Museum of the University of São Paulo (MZ-USP) and the Emílio Goeldi Museum of Pará (MPEG). Once again, the likely existence of errors in these data collections regarding identification of species and localities needs to be stressed, despite continual efforts at taxonomic verification and updating. However, even allowing for a certain degree of inaccuracy, it is possible to build up an approximate picture of the representativity of the mammal species and the areas of Amazonia held in museums.

The collections of the Goeldi Museum (MPEG) feature materials mainly from disturbed areas such as the Carajás region, Tucuruí, and the Ilha de Marajó in Pará; Balbina in Amazonas; and the Polonoroeste project area comprising Rondônia and Mato Grosso. The museum also features materials from inventories carried out in parks, reserves, and biological stations (for example, the Trombetas and Caxiuanã biological reserves). The collections also contain samples of materials used in research on tropical pathogenic agents by the World Health Organization, consisting mainly of bats and rodents (for example, from Acre, Amapá, and along the Transamazônica highway in the states of Pará and Amazonas). The museum collection currently contains over 26,000 samples from a wide range of localities, the great majority in Amazonia. Chiroptera is the order with the largest number of samples in the collection, about 12,000 recorded species and 5,000 still to be recorded. Rodentia is second with approximately 5,000 specimens, then come Primates (3,500 specimens), Marsupialia (2,500 specimens) plus other orders, totaling some 3,000 species. The collection includes old samples of species threatened with extinction such as the jaguar (*Panthera onca*) and the manatee (*Trichechus inunguis*). The collection shows an average growth rate of 2,000 samples.

Looking at the collections of the American Museum of Natural History, the Field Museum of Natural History and the National Amazon Research Institute, we can see that they contain materials from only ten or fewer localities per catchment area or state in the case of more than 85% of the records (Tables 2, 3, and 5 respectively). The number of species by catchment area is also extremely low, varying from 1 to 110 species. However, fewer than 50 species have been recorded for the great majority of the locations and the highest numbers related to collections of bats. A similar pattern has also been observed in the collections of the Smithsonian National Museum of Natural History (Table 4). Bearing in mind the estimates given by Voss and Emmons (1996, Table 11), of approximately 150 to 215 sympatric species in different areas of Amazonia, we may conclude that very little of the mammalian fauna of Amazonia is represented in museums either in Brazil or abroad.

In view of this, it is little wonder that Voss and Emmons (1996) consider that relatively complete surveys were performed at only two sites in the Brazilian Amazon. These are the reserves of the 'Biological Dynamics of Forest Fragments' project located approximately 60-90 kilometers north of Manaus (2°30'S, 60°W), and on the lower Xingu about 54 km south-southwest from Altamira, Pará (3°39'S, 52°22'W). Considering mammalian fauna as a whole, even these inventories are incomplete and methodologically geared to only a few groups.

The other areas known to us where inventories of mammalian fauna have been or are being carried out are: the Belém region (Pine 1973); the Urucu river (Peres 1997, 1999); the Juruá river (Peres 1993, 1997, 1999; Patton and Silva 1995; Patton et al. 1994, 1996, forthcoming; Silva 1998); the Jaú National Park in the state of Amazonas (Patton et al., forthcoming); and the Tapajós river (Ferrari et al., work in progress). The other localities where communities of primates have been studied are referred to Voss and Emmons (1996, Appendix 12) and Peres and Janson (forthcoming).

Priority areas for inventories

These are:

1. Interfluves in almost the entire Amazon basin;

2. Transition areas of vegetation, such as the transition forest between Amazonia and the non-Amazonian region to the south, dry forests (the transitional band between the Araguaia and the Amazon forest), and semi-deciduous forests;

3. Bamboo forests (*Guadua spp*), campinarama, savanna enclaves on the edges of the closed canopy forests of the pre-Amazon, and the buriti palm (*Mauritia flexuosa*) forests of the western Amazon;

4. Western Brazilian Amazonia to the south of the Solimões, especially along the Madeira and the Purus: areas of high forest biomass, subject to logging and the focus of development programs;

5. Western Brazilian Amazonia to the north of the Solimões and west of the Rio Negro. This is a region apparently still extensively forested, but poorly sampled for mammals;

6. The states of Amazonas, Pará and Amapá, to the north of the Amazon and to the east of the Rio Negro;

7. Southeastern Amazonia, a region extremely degraded in many areas and where sampling of mammals has been confined to a few localities on the Xingu and around Belém, where intact mammalian fauna can no longer be found.

8. Areas along the Solimões-Amazonas axis and on the lower and middle reaches of regional rivers, including the Branco where there is high habitat heterogeneity in close contact, including floodplains, terra firme, lakes and igapós.

Priority areas for conservation

Areas of high diversity and areas of endemism

Voss and Emmons (1996) convincingly advance some of the reasons why identification of areas of high diversity and of endemism in Amazonia is still not feasible in respect of mammalian fauna as a whole. Some of these difficulties have been discussed in this paper. In the light of these, one way to proceed from now on might be to use our accumulated knowledge of primates as an indicator of areas of high mammalian diversity and endemism. However, it should be pointed out that, in such cases, the indication would be biased and could give the impression that other areas of equal or greater species richness were not important in this respect, when in reality they simply had not been properly studied.

Although high diversity and endemism are standard criteria, in recent years there has been a growing tendency among conservationists to be concerned not only with ecological diversity, but also with evolutionary diversity, which encompasses both genetic diversity and the phylogenetic relationships between taxa (Costa 1998).

Descriptions of biodiversity based solely on the distribution of vegetation types or of endemic species may not properly represent the evolutionary diversity of a certain biota (Fjeldsa 1994, *apud* Costa 1998). Historical processes are relevant for current efforts towards species conservation and for efficient management of natural resources because many such processes reflect natural properties intrinsic to specific areas and which may influence the generation and maintenance of biological diversity (Fjeldsa and Rahbek 1997).

Better appreciation of the geographical patterns of vicariance, and specifically those temporal and spatial processes which have led to the current distribution of diversity, will improve our ability to plan conservation strategies that take into account both evolutionary and species diversity. Such planning will require not only detailed knowledge of current patterns, but also an assessment of the interaction between these patterns and those that applied in the past. As Moritz et al. (1997) stress, any methodologies used in planning reserves which ignore these historical and contemporary processes are clearly inadequate for ensuring the long term feasibility of the systems which they intend to conserve (Costa 1998).

Areas suffering high anthropogenic pressure

These are:
1. Areas under the influence of the Transamazonica highway: areas where farming, ranching and human settlements (e.g. Apuí) are expanding;
2. Areas along the Amazon deforestation belt in the Amazon (INPE 1999): critical areas are southeastern Acre; Porto Velho; Humaitá; southern Pará, especially the Marabá region; and regions of contact between different types of forest;
3. Areas susceptible to forest fires in their undergrowth, such as the lower Tapajós valley, and the southern Amazonia arc;
4. Settlements along the BR-369 (Manaus-Porto Velho) highway;
5. The remaining forests in Rondônia;
6. The remaining forests in eastern Amazonia, especially southern Pará;
7. Northern Mato Grosso (Alta Floresta, Serra do Roncador, etc.);
8. Further north, the colonization front on the upper Jatapu.

Summary of the main biogeographical and ecological patterns

From a conservation viewpoint, some of the biogeographical and ecological patterns related to Amazonian mammal fauna which have to be considered are:

1. The available data suggest a decrease in species richness from west to east across Amazonia. However, knowledge of community structures is still relatively deficient and few areas have been properly sampled;

2. The acknowledgment of an east-west divide in Amazonia, separating at least two independent evolutionary spaces with large numbers of organisms;

3. The congruent patterns in taxa diversification suggest an important vicariate role for the paleobasins of the upper Amazon. If these patterns are confirmed in other areas, the paleobasins, as geologically defined, could constitute important targets for the identification of conservation areas;

4. Studies suggest that local primate species richness, and possibly of other groups of mammals, is related to local habitat diversity;

5. Species richness among communities of primates, rodents and marsupials is greater in terra firme than in floodplain areas, although densities and biomass are smaller. However, floodplain communities represent a unique complement and an increase in the beta diversity of species which live along the rivers of Amazonia.

6. Both floodplain and terra firme forests show distinct biogeographical patterns, probably as a result of the action of different forces and evolutionary processes, and therefore both deserve conservation efforts;

7. Preliminary studies of rodents and marsupials suggest a richness of similar species in both white and black water systems in Amazonia, and the relative abundance of much smaller species in black water basins (Silva and Patton, unpublished data), suggesting that black water systems may be much more sensitive to human activity in these forests.

Conclusion

There is an enormous need to support studies aimed at gaining greater knowledge of Amazonia mammal fauna, for which basic information on a wide range of aspects of its natural history, population demography, limits of ecological and geographic distribution, amongst others, is still lacking.

Amazonia has not yet been properly inventoried. Considerable sampling efforts are needed to identify the patterns and the processes which define the ecological structure of sympatric communities, the geographical distribution of species, and the biogeographical gradients, among other things. These efforts need to be followed by taxonomic reviews of the most problematic groups, using modern analytical methods and approaches. Even in the case of the larger mammal fauna widely distributed throughout the Amazon basin, there is still no understanding of the degree of genetic or geographical structuring of these species. Conservation agencies can make a significant contribution by adopting policies for supporting faunistic inventory projects.

TABLE 1 - LIST OF SPECIES OF MAMMALS IN THE BRAZILIAN AMAZON BASED ON EMMONS & FEER (1997), EXCEPT WHERE OTHERWISE INDICATED; GEOGRAPHYC DISTRIBUTION IN SOUTH AMERICA FROM EMMONS & FEER (1997), WILSON & REEDER (1993) AND KOOPMAN (1982)

Order	Sub-order	Taxon	Distribution	Source
Didelphimorphia	Didelphidae	*Caluromys lanatus*	Colombia, Guyana, Ecuador, Peru, Paraguay, Argentina, Brazil	
		Caluromys philander	Venezuela, Guianas, Brazil, Bolivia	
		Caluromysiops irrupta *	Peru, Brazil	
		Chironectes minimus	Venezuela, Colombia, Ecuador, Peru, Bolivia, Brazil, Guianas, Paraguay, Argentina	
		Didelphis marsupialis	Colombia, Venezuela, Guianas, Bolivia, Paraguay, Argentina, Brazil	
		Glironia venusta *	Ecuador, Brazil, Peru, Bolivia	
		Gracilinanus emiliae *	Colombia, Suriname, French Guyana, Brazil	
		Marmosa murina *	Venezuela, Guianas, Colombia, Ecuador, Peru, Bolivia, Brazil	
		Marmosa lepida *	Colombia, Ecuador, Peru, Bolivia, Brazil	
		Marmosops impavidus	Colombia, Peru, Bolivia, Brazil	
		Marmosops neblina	Venezuela, Ecuador, Brazil	
		Marmosops noctivagus *	Ecuador, Peru, Brazil, Bolivia	
		Marmosops parvidens * a	Venezuela, Colombia, Guianas, Brazil, Peru	
		Metachirus nudicaudatus	Colombia, Venezuela, Guianas, Bolivia, Paraguay, Argentina, Brazil	
		Micoureus demerarae b	Colombia, Argentina, Paraguay, Brazil, Peru, Bolivia, Venezuela, Guianas	
		Micoureus regina *	Ecuador, Colombia, Peru, Brazil, Bolivia (?)	
		Monodelphis brevicaudata	Colombia, Venezuela, Guianas, Peru, Bolivia, Brazil, Argentina	
		Monodelphis domestica	Bolivia, Paraguay, Brazil	
		Monodelphis emiliae *	Brazil, Peru, Bolivia	
		Philander andersoni *	Venezuela, Colombia (?), Ecuador, Brazil	Patton et al. forthcoming
		Philander mcilhennyi *	Peru, Brazil	Patton et al. forthcoming
		Philander opossum	Peru, Paraguay, Argentina, Guianas, Bolivia, Brazil	Patton et al. forthcoming
Xenarthra	Bradypodidae	*Bradypus tridactylus* *	Venezuela, Guianas, Brazil	
		Bradypus variegatus	Ecuador, Venezuela, Colombia, Bolivia, Brazil, Argentina	
	Megalonychidae	*Choloepus didactylus* *	Venezuela, Guianas, Ecuador, Peru, Brazil	
		Choloepus hoffmanni	Ecuador, Venezuela, Peru, Brazil, Bolivia	
	Dasypodidae	*Cabassous unicinctus*	Colombia, Venezuela, Guianas, Suriname, Ecuador, Peru, Bolivia, Brazil	
		Dasypus novemcinctus	Ecuador, Colombia, Venezuela, Guianas, Brazil, Peru, Bolivia, Paraguay, Argentina, Uruguay	
		Dasypus kappleri *	Colombia, Venezuela, Guianas, Ecuador, Peru, Bolivia, Brazil	
		Priodontes maximus	Colombia, Venezuela, Guianas, Ecuador, Peru, Bolivia, Paraguay, Argentina, Brazil	

continues

Order	Sub-order	Taxon	Distribution	Source
Xenarthra	Myrmechophagidae	*Cyclopes didactylus*	Ecuador, Colombia, Venezuela, Guianas, Brazil, Peru, Bolivia	
		Myrmecophaga tridactyla	Ecuador, Colombia, Venezuela, Guianas, Brazil, Peru, Bolivia, Paraguay, Argentina, Uruguay	
		Tamandua tetradactyla	Ecuador, Colombia, Venezuela, Guianas, Brazil, Peru, Bolivia, Paraguay, Argentina, Uruguay	
Chiroptera	Emballonuridae	*Centronycteris maximiliani*	Venezuela, Guianas, Brazil	Simmons & Voss 1998
		Cormura brevirostris	Peru, Brazil, Colombia, Venezuela, Guianas	Marinho-Filho & Sazima 1998
		Cyttarops alecto	Guyana, Brazil	Marinho-Filho & Sazima 1998
		Diclidurus albus	Colombia, Venezuela, Guianas, Ecuador, Peru, Bolivia, Brazil	Marinho-Filho & Sazima 1998
		Diclidurus ingens	Colombia, Venezuela, Guyana, Brazil	Marinho-Filho & Sazima 1998
		Diclidurus isabellus *	Venezuela, Brazil	Marinho-Filho & Sazima 1998
		Diclidurus scutatus *	Brazil, Venezuela, Peru, Guyana, Suriname	Marinho-Filho & Sazima 1998
		Peropteryx kappleri	Colombia, Venezuela, Guianas, Suriname, Ecuador, Peru, Bolivia, Brazil	Marinho-Filho & Sazima 1998
		Peropteryx leucoptera	Peru, Colombia, Brazil, Venezuela, Guianas, Suriname	Voss & Emmons 1996, Marinho-Filho & Sazima 1998
		Peropteryx macrotis [c]	Peru, Colombia, Brazil, Venezuela, Guianas, Suriname, Paraguay	Voss & Emmons 1996, Marinho-Filho & Sazima 1998
		Rhynchonycteris naso	Ecuador, Colombia, Venezuela, Guianas, Brazil, Peru, Bolivia	Marinho-Filho & Sazima 1998
		Saccopteryx bilineata	Ecuador, Colombia, Venezuela, Guianas, Suriname, Brazil, Peru, Bolivia	Voss & Emmons 1996, Marinho-Filho & Sazima 1998
		Saccopteryx canescens	Ecuador, Colombia, Venezuela, Guianas, Suriname, Brazil, Peru	Voss & Emmons 1996, Marinho-Filho & Sazima 1998
		Saccopteryx gymnura *	Brazil, French Guiana	Marinho-Filho & Sazima 1998
		Saccopteryx leptura	Ecuador, Colombia, Venezuela, Guianas, Suriname, Brazil, Peru, Bolivia	Voss & Emmons 1996
	Noctilionidae	*Noctilio albiventris*	Ecuador, Colombia, Venezuela, Guianas, Suriname, Brazil, Peru, Bolivia, Paraguay, Argentina	Simmons & Voss 1998, Marinho-Filho & Sazima 1998
		Noctilio leporinus	Ecuador, Colombia, Venezuela, Guianas, Suriname, Brazil, Peru, Bolivia, Paraguay, Argentina	Simmons & Voss 1998, Marinho-Filho & Sazima 1998
	Mormoopidae	*Pteronotus gymnonotus*	Colombia, Venezuela, Brazil, Guyana, Peru, Bolivia	Marinho-Filho & Sazima 1998
		Pteronotus parnellii	Colombia, Venezuela, Guianas, Suriname, Brazil, Peru, Bolivia	Simmons & Voss 1998, Marinho-Filho & Sazima 1998
		Pteronotus personatus	Colombia, Venezuela, Guyana, Suriname, Brazil, Peru, Bolivia	Marinho-Filho & Sazima 1998
	Phyllostominae	*Chrotopterus auritus*	Colombia, Venezuela, Guianas, Suriname, Brazil, Ecuador, Peru, Bolivia, Paraguay, Argentina	Simmons & Voss 1998, Marinho-Filho & Sazima 1998
		Glyphonycteris daviesi	Colombia, Venezuela, Guianas, Suriname, Brazil, Peru, Bolivia	Simmons & Voss 1998
		Glyphonycteris sylvestris	Colombia, Venezuela, Guianas, Suriname, Brazil, Peru	Simmons & Voss 1998
		Lonchorhina aurita	Colombia, Venezuela, Guianas, Suriname, Brazil, Peru, Bolivia	Marinho-Filho & Sazima 1998
		Macrophyllum macrophyllum	Colombia, Venezuela, Guianas, Suriname, Brazil, Ecuador, Peru, Bolivia, Paraguay, Argentina	Simmons & Voss 1998, Marinho-Filho & Sazima 1998
		Micronycteris behnii	Brasil, Peru, Bolivia	Marinho-Filho & Sazima 1998

continues

Order	Sub-order	Taxon	Distribution	Source
Chiroptera	Phyllostominae	*Micronycteris brachyotis*	Colombia, Venezuela, Guianas, Suriname, Brazil	Marinho-Filho & Sazima 1998
		Micronycteris hirsuta	Colombia, Venezuela, Guyana, Peru, Brazil	Marinho-Filho & Sazima 1998
		Micronycteris homezi	Colombia, Venezuela, French Guiana, Brazil	Bernard (personal com.)
		Micronycteris megalotis [d]	Colombia, Venezuela, Guianas, Suriname, Brazil, Ecuador, Peru, Bolivia	Koopman 1993
		Micronycteris minuta	Colombia, Venezuela, Guianas, Suriname, Brazil, Ecuador, Peru, Bolivia	Marinho-Filho & Sazima 1998
		Micronycteris pusilla *	Colombia, Brazil	Marinho-Filho & Sazima 1998
		Micronycteris schmidtorum	Venezuela, Brazil, Peru	Marinho-Filho & Sazima 1998
		Micronycteris sylvestris	Colombia, Venezuela, Guianas, Suriname, Brazil, Peru	Marinho-Filho & Sazima 1998
		Mimon. bennettii	Colombia, Venezuela, Guianas, Suriname, Brazil	Marinho-Filho & Sazima 1998
		Mimon crenulatum	Colombia, Venezuela, Guianas, Suriname, Brazil, Ecuador, Peru, Bolivia	Simmons & Voss 1998
		Phylloderma stenops	Colombia, Venezuela, Guianas, Brazil, Peru, Bolivia	Marinho-Filho & Sazima 1998
		Phyllostomus discolor	Colombia, Venezuela, Guianas, Suriname, Brazil, Ecuador, Peru, Bolivia	Simmons & Voss 1998, Marinho-Filho & Sazima 1998
		Phyllostomus elongatus	Colombia, Venezuela, Guianas, Suriname, Brazil, Ecuador, Peru, Bolivia	Simmons &Voss 1998, Marinho-Filho & Sazima 1998
		Phyllostomus hastatus	Colombia, Venezuela, Guianas, Suriname, Brazil, Ecuador, Peru, Bolivia	Simmons & Voss 1998, Marinho-Filho & Sazima 1998
		Tonatia brasiliense	Colombia, Venezuela, Guianas, Suriname, Brazil, Ecuador, Peru, Bolivia	Simmons & Voss 1998, Marinho-Filho & Sazima 1998
		Tonatia carrikeri	Suriname, Venezuela, Guianas, Brazil, Bolivia	Marinho-Filho & Sazima 1998, Gribel & Taddei 1989
		Tonatia saurophila [e]	Ecuador, Colombia, Venezuela, Guianas, Suriname, Brazil, Peru, Bolivia	Williams et al. 1995
		Tonatia schulzi	Suriname, Brazil	Marinho-Filho & Sazima 1998, Marques & Oren 1987, Gribel & Taddei 1989
		Tonatia silvicola	Colombia, Venezuela, Guianas, Suriname, Brazil, Ecuador, Peru, Bolivia, Paraguay, Argentina	Voss & Emmons 1996, Marinho-Filho & Sazima 1998
		Trachops cirrhosus	Ecuador, Colombia, Venezuela, Guianas, Brazil, Peru, Bolivia	Simmons & Voss 1998, Marinho-Filho & Sazima 1998
		Trinycteris nicefori	Colombia, Venezuela, Guianas, Suriname, Brazil, Peru, Bolivia	Simmons & Voss 1998
		Vampyrumspectrum	Colombia, Venezuela, Guianas, Suriname, Brazil, Peru, Bolivia	Simmons & Voss 1998, Marinho-Filho & Sazima 1998
	Glossophaginae	*Anoura geoffroyi*	Colombia, Venezuela, Guianas, Suriname, Brazil, Peru, Bolivia Ecuador	Marinho-Filho & Sazima 1998
		Anoura caudifera	Colombia, Venezuela, Guianas, Suriname, Brazil, Ecuador, Peru, Bolivia, Argentina	Voss &Emmons 1996, Marinho-Filho & Sazima 1998
		Choeroniscus intermedius	Peru, Guianas, Suriname, Brazil	Marinho-Filho & Sazima 1998
		Choeroniscus minor	Colombia, Venezuela, Guianas, Suriname, Brazil, Ecuador, Peru, Bolivia	Voss & Emmons 1996, Marinho-Filho & Sazima 1998
		Glossophaga commissarisi	Ecuador, Colombia, Brazil, Peru	Marinho-Filho & Sazima 1998

continues

Order	Sub-order	Taxon	Distribution	Source
Chiroptera	Glossophaginae	*Glossophaga longirostris*	Ecuador, Colombia, Venezuela, Guyana	Marinho-Filho & Sazima 1998
		Glossophaga soricina	Colombia, Venezuela, Guianas, Suriname, Brazil, Ecuador, Peru, Bolivia, Paraguay, Argentina	Voss & Emmons 1996, Marinho-Filho & Sazima 1998
		Lichonycteris obscura f	Colombia, Venezuela, Guianas, Suriname	Koopman 1993
		Lionycteris spurrelli	Colombia, Brazil, Peru, Bolivia	Marinho-Filho & Sazima 1998
		Lonchophylla thomasi	Colombia, Venezuela, Guianas, Suriname, Brazil, Ecuador, Peru, Bolivia	Simmons & Voss 1998, Marinho-Filho & Sazima 1998
		Scleronycteris ega *	Brazil, Venezuela	Marinho-Filho & Sazima 1998
	Carollinae	*Carollia brevicauda*	Colombia, Venezuela, Guianas, Suriname, Brazil, Ecuador, Peru, Bolivia	Simmons & Voss 1998, Marinho-Filho & Sazima 1998
		Carollia castanea	Peru, Bolivia, Venezuela, Brazil	Koopman 1993, Marinho-Filho & Sazima 1998
		Carollia perspicillata	Colombia, Venezuela, Guianas, Suriname, Brazil, Ecuador, Peru, Bolivia, Paraguay	Simmons & Voss 1998
		Rhinophylla fischerae *	Colombia, Ecuador, Peru, Brazil	Simmons & Voss 1998, Marinho-Filho & Sazima 1998
		Rhinophylla pumilio	Colombia, Venezuela, Guianas, Suriname, Brazil, Ecuador, Peru, Bolivia	Simmons & Voss 1998, Marinho-Filho & Sazima 1998
	Stenodermatinae	*Ametrida centurio*	Venezuela, Guianas, Brazil	Simmons & Voss 1998, Marinho-Filho & Sazima 1998
		Artibeus (Artibeus) jamaicensis	Colombia, Venezuela, Guianas, Suriname, Brazil, Ecuador, Peru, Bolivia, Paraguay	Simmons & Voss 1998, Marinho-Filho & Sazima 1998
		Artibeus (Artibeus) lituratus	Colombia, Venezuela, Guianas, Suriname, Brazil, Ecuador, Peru, Bolivia, Paraguay, Argentina	Simmons & Voss 1998, Marinho-Filho & Sazima 1998
		Artibeus (Artibeus) obscurus	Colombia, Venezuela, Guianas, Suriname, Brazil, Ecuador, Peru, Bolivia	Simmons & Voss 1998, Marinho-Filho & Sazima 1998
		Artibeus (Artibeus) planirostris	Colombia, Venezuela, Guianas, Suriname, Brazil, Ecuador, Peru, Bolivia, Paraguay, Argentina	Marinho-Filho & Sazima 1998
		Artibeus (Dermanura) anderseni	Brazil, Ecuador, Peru, Bolivia	Marinho-Filho & Sazima 1998
		Artibeus (Dermanura) cinereus	Colombia, Venezuela, Guianas, Suriname, Brazil, Ecuador, Peru, Bolivia	Simmons & Voss 1998, Marinho-Filho & Sazima 1998
		Artibeus (Dermanura) gnomus g*	Brasil, Ecuador, Peru, Venezuela, French Guiana	Handley 1987
		Artibeus (Koopmania) concolor	Colombia, Venezuela, Guianas, Suriname, Brazil, Peru	Simmons & Voss 1998, Marinho-Filho & Sazima 1998
		Chiroderma trinitatum	Colombia, Venezuela, Guianas, Suriname, Brazil, Ecuador, Peru, Bolivia	Simmons & Voss 1998, Marinho-Filho & Sazima 1998
		Chiroderma villosum	Colombia, Venezuela, Guianas, Suriname, Brazil, Ecuador, Peru, Bolivia	Simmons & Voss 1998, Marinho-Filho & Sazima 1998
		Mesophylla macconnelli	Ecuador, Colombia, Venezuela, Guianas, Brazil, Peru, Bolivia	Simmons & Voss 1998, Marinho-Filho & Sazima 1998
		Platyrrhinus brachycephalus	Colombia, Venezuela, Guianas, Suriname, Brazil, Ecuador, Peru, Bolivia	Marinho-Filho & Sazima, 1998
		Platyrrhinus helleri	Colombia, Venezuela, Guianas, Suriname, Brazil, Ecuador, Peru, Bolivia	Simmons & Voss 1998, Marinho-Filho & Sazima 1998
		Platyrrhinus infuscus	Colombia, Brazil, Ecuador, Peru, Bolivia	Marinho-Filho & Sazima 1998

continues

Order	Sub-order	Taxon	Distribution	Source
Chiroptera	Stenodermatinae	*Platyrrhinus lineatus*	Colombia, Brazil, Ecuador, Peru, Bolivia	Marinho-Filho & Sazima 1998
		Sphaeronycteris toxophyllum	Venezuela, Colombia, Peru, Brazil, Bolivia	Marinho-Filho & Sazima 1998
		Sturnira bidens *	Peru, Ecuador, Colombia, Venezuela, Brazil	Marinho-Filho & Sazima 1998, Marques & Oren 1987
		Sturnira lilium	Colombia, Venezuela, Guianas, Suriname, Brazil, Ecuador, Peru, Bolivia, Paraguay, Argentina, Uruguay	Simmons & Voss 1998, Marinho-Filho & Sazima 1998
		Sturnira tildae	Brazil, Guianas, Venezuela, Colombia, Ecuador, Peru, Bolivia	Simmons & Voss 1998, Marinho-Filho & Sazima 1998
		Uroderma bilobatum	Colombia, Venezuela, Guianas, Suriname, Brazil, Ecuador, Peru, Bolivia	Simmons & Voss 1998, Marinho-Filho & Sazima 1998
		Uroderma magnirostrum	Colombia, Venezuela, Brazil, Peru, Bolivia	Simmons & Voss 1998, Marinho-Filho & Sazima 1998
		Vampyressa bidens	Colombia, Venezuela, Guianas, Suriname, Brazil, Ecuador, Peru, Bolivia	Marinho-Filho & Sazima 1998
		Vampyressa brocki *	Colombia, Guyana, Suriname, Brazil	Simmons & Voss 1998, Marinho-Filho & Sazima 1998
		Vampyrodes caraccioli	Colombia, Venezuela, Guianas, Suriname, Brazil, Peru, Bolivia	Marinho-Filho & Sazima 1998
	Desmodontinae	*Desmodus. rotundus*	Ecuador, Colombia, Venezuela, Guianas, Brazil, Peru, Bolivia, Paraguay, Argentina, Uruguay	Marinho-Filho & Sazima 1998
		Diaemus youngi	Ecuador, Colombia, Venezuela, Guianas, Brazil, Peru, Bolivia, Paraguay, Argentina	Marinho-Filho & Sazima 1998
		Diphylla ecaudata	Colombia, Ecuador, Peru, Bolivia, Brazil	Marinho-Filho & Sazima 1998
	Natalidae	*Natalus stramineus*	Colombia, Venezuela, Guianas, Suriname, Brazil	Marinho-Filho & Sazima 1998
	Furipteridae	*Furipterus horrens*	Colombia, Venezuela, Guianas, Peru, Brazil	Simmons & Voss 1998, Marinho-Filho & Sazima 1998
	Thyropteridae	*Thyroptera discifera*	Colombia, Venezuela, Guianas, Suriname, Brazil, Peru, Bolivia	Marinho-Filho & Sazima 1998
		Thyroptera tricolor	Colombia, Venezuela, Guianas, Suriname, Brazil, Peru, Bolivia	Simmons & Voss 1998, Marinho-Filho & Sazima 1998
	Vespertilionidae	*Eptesicus brasiliensis*	Ecuador, Colombia, Venezuela, Guianas, Suriname, Brazil, Peru, Bolivia, Paraguay, Argentina, Uruguay	Simmons & Voss 1998, Marinho-Filho & Sazima 1998
		Eptesicus furinalis	Ecuador, Colombia, Venezuela, Guianas, Suriname, Brazil, Peru, Bolivia, Paraguay, Argentina	Marinho-Filho & Sazima 1998
		Eptesicus melanopterus	Brazil	Simmons & Voss 1998
		Lasiurus blossevillii [h]	Ecuador, Colombia, Venezuela, Guianas, Suriname, Brazil, Peru, Bolivia	Simmons & Voss 1998
		Lasiurus ega	Ecuador, Colombia, Venezuela, Guianas, Suriname, Brazil, Peru, Bolivia, Paraguay, Argentina, Uruguay	Marinho-Filho & Sazima 1998
		Myotis albescens	Ecuador, Colombia, Venezuela, Guianas, Suriname, Brazil, Peru, Bolivia, Paraguay, Argentina, Uruguay	Simmons & Voss 1998, Marinho-Filho & Sazima 1998
		Myotis nigricans	Ecuador, Colombia, Venezuela, Guianas, Suriname, Brazil, Peru, Bolivia, Paraguay, Argentina	Simmons & Voss 1998, Marinho-Filho & Sazima 1998

continues

Order	Suborder	Taxon	Distribution	Source
Chiroptera	Vespertilionidae	*Myotis riparius*	Ecuador, Colombia, Venezuela, Guianas, Suriname, Brazil, Peru, Bolivia, Paraguay, Argentina, Uruguay	Simmons & Voss 1998, Marinho-Filho & Sazima 1998
		Myotis simus	Ecuador, Colombia, Brazil, Peru, Bolivia, Paraguay	Marinho-Filho & Sazima 1998
		Rhogeessa tumida	Colombia, Ecuador, Venezuela, Guianas, Bolivia, Brazil	Marinho-Filho & Sazima 1998
	Molossidae	*Eumops auripendulus*	Ecuador, Colombia, Venezuela, Guianas, Suriname, Brazil, Peru, Bolivia, Paraguay	Marinho-Filho & Sazima 1998
		Eumops bonariensis	Ecuador, Colombia, Venezuela, Guianas, Suriname, Brazil, Peru, Bolivia, Paraguay, Argentina, Uruguay	Marinho-Filho & Sazima 1998
		Eumops glaucinus	Ecuador, Colombia, Venezuela, Guianas, Suriname, Brazil, Peru, Bolivia, Paraguay, Argentina	Marinho-Filho & Sazima 1998
		Eumops hansae	Venezuela, Guianas, Brazil, Peru, Bolivia	Marinho-Filho & Sazima 1998
		Eumops trumbulli [i]		Simmons & Voss 1998
		Molossops abrasus	Colombia, Venezuela, Guianas, Suriname, Brazil, Peru, Bolivia, Paraguay	Simmons & Voss 1998, Marinho-Filho & Sazima 1998
		Molossops greenhalli	Ecuador, Colombia, Venezuela, Guianas, Suriname, Brazil	Marinho-Filho & Sazima 1998
		Molossops matogrossensis	Venezuela, Guyana, Brazil	Marinho-Filho & Sazima 1998
		Molossops neglectus *	Suriname, Brazil, Peru	Marinho-Filho & Sazima 1998
		Molossops planirostris	Colombia, Venezuela, Guianas, Suriname, Brazil, Peru, Bolivia, Paraguay	Marinho-Filho & Sazima 1998
		Molossus molossus [j]	Ecuador, Colombia, Venezuela, Guianas, Suriname, Brazil, Peru, Bolivia, Paraguay, Argentina, Uruguay	Koopman 1993
		Molossus rufus [l]	Ecuador, Colombia, Venezuela, Guianas, Suriname, Brazil, Peru, Bolivia, Paraguay	Simmons & Voss 1998
		Neoplatymops mattogrossensis	Venezuela, Guyana, Brazil	Simmons & Voss 1998
		Nyctinomops aurispinosus	Ecuador, Colombia, Venezuela, Guianas, Suriname, Brazil, Peru, Bolivia	Marinho-Filho & Sazima 1998
		Nyctinomops laticaudatus	Ecuador, Colombia, Venezuela, Guianas, Suriname, Brazil, Peru, Bolivia, Paraguay, Argentina	Marinho-Filho & Sazima 1998
		Nyctinomops macrotis	Ecuador, Colombia, Venezuela, Guianas, Suriname, Brazil, Peru, Bolivia, Paraguay, Argentina, Uruguay	Marinho-Filho & Sazima 1998
		Promops nasutus	Ecuador, Venezuela, Suriname, Brazil, Peru, Bolivia, Paraguay, Argentina	Marinho-Filho & Sazima 1998
Primates	Callimiconidae	*Callimico goeldii* *	Brazil, Bolivia, Peru, Colombia	
	Callitrichidae	*Callithrix argentata* *	Brazil	Rylands et al. 1993, Rylands et al. 1998
		Callithrix chrysoleuca *	Brazil	Rylands et al. 1998
		Callithrix emiliae *	Brazil	Rylands et al. 1993, Rylands et al. 1998
		Callithrix humilis *	Brazil	Roosmalen et al. 1998, Rylands et al. 1998
		Callithrix humeralifer *	Brazil	Rylands et al. 1993, Rylands et al. 1998

continues

Order	Suborder	Taxon	Distribution	Source
Primates	Callitrichidae	Callithrix intermedia *	Brazil	Rylands et al. 1998
		Callithrix leucippe *	Brazil	Rylands et al. 1998
		Callithrix marcai *	Brazil	Alperin 1993, Rylands et al. 1998
		Callithrix mauesi *	Brazil	Mittermeier et al. 1992, Rylands et al. 1998
		Callithrix melanura	Brazil, Bolivia, Paraguay	Rylands et al. 1998
		Callithrix nigriceps *	Brazil	Ferrari & Lopes 1992 Rylands et al. 1998
		Callithrix saterei *	Brazil	Silva & Noronha, forthcoming Rylands et al. 1998
		Cebuella pygmaea		
		Cebuella pygmaea pygmaea	Brazil, Colombia, Ecuador, Peru	
		Cebuella pygmaea niveiventris	Bolivia, Brazil, Peru	
		Saguinus bicolor *	Brazil	Rylands et al. 1993, Rylands et al. 1998
		Saguinus bicolor bicolor		
		Saguinus bicolor martinsi		
		Saguinus bicolorochraceus		
		Saguinus fuscicollis		Roosmalen et al. 1998, Rylands et al. 1998
		Saguinus fuscicollis avilapiresi *	Brazil	
		Saguinus fuscicollis cruzlimai	Brazil (?)	
		Saguinus fuscicollis fuscicollis	Brazil, Peru	
		Saguinus fuscicollis fuscus	Brazil, Colômbia	
		Saguinus fuscicollis melanoleucus *	Brazil	
		Saguinus fuscicollis primitivus *	Brazil	
		Saguinus fuscicollis weddelli	Brazil, Bolivia, Peru, Colombia	
		Saguinus imperator		Rylands et al. 1998
		S. imperator imperator	Brazil, Peru	
		S. imperator subgrisescens	Brazil, Bolivia, Peru	
		Saguinus inustus	Brazil, Colombia	Rylands et al. 1998
		Saguinus labiatus		Rylands et al. 1998
		Saguinus labiatus labiatus	Brazil, Bolivia, Peru	
		Saguinus labiatus thomasi *		
		Saguinus midas		Rylands et al. 1998
		Saguinus midas midas	Brazil, French Guiana, Guyana, Suriname	
		Saguinus midas niger *	Brazil	
		Saguinus mystax		Rylands et al. 1998
		Saguinus mystax mystax mystax	Brazil, Peru	
		Saguinus mystax mystax pileatus *	Brazil	
		Saguinus mystax mystax pluto *	Brazil	
	Cebidae	Aotus infulatus *	Brazil	Rylands et al. 1998
		Aotus nancymaae	Brazil, Colombia, Peru	Rylands et al. 1998
		Aotus nigriceps	Brasil, Colombia, Peru	Rylands et al. 1998
		Aotus trivirgatus	Brazil, Colombia, Venezuela	Rylands et al. 1998
		Aotus vociferans	Colombia, Brazil, Ecuador, Peru	Rylands et al. 1998
		Alouatta seniculus		Rylands et al. 1998
		Alouatta seniculus amazonica *	Brazil	
		Alouatta seniculus juara	Brazil, Peru	
		Alouatta seniculus macconnelli	Brazil, French Guiana, Guyana, Suriname, Venezuela	
		Alouatta seniculus puruensis	Bolivia, Brazil	
		Alouatta seniculus seniculus	Colombia, Bolivia, Brazil, Ecuador, Peru, Venezuela	
		Alouatta belzebul *		Rylands et al. 1998
		Alouatta belzebul belzebul	Brazil	

continues

Order	Suborder	Taxon	Distribution	Source
Primates	Cebidae	*Alouatta belzebul discolor*	Brazil	
		Alouatta belzebul nigerrima	Brazil	
		Alouatta belzebul ululata	Brazil	
		Ateles belzebuth belzebuth	Colombia, Brazil, Ecuador, Peru, Venezuela	Rylands et al. 1998
		Ateles chamek	Bolivia, Brazil, Peru	Rylands et al. 1998
		Ateles marginatus *	Brazil	Rylands et al. 1998
		Ateles paniscus	Brazil, French Guiana, Guyana, Suriname	Rylands et al. 1998
		Cacajao calvus		Rylands et al. 1998
		Cacajao calvus calvus *	Brazil	
		Cacajao calvus novaesi *	Brazil	
		Cacajao calvus rubicundus	Brazil, Colombia	
		Cacajao melanocephalus		Rylands et al. 1998
		Cacajao melanocephalus melanocephalus	Brazil, Venezuela	
		Cacajao melanocephalus ouakary	Brazil, Colômbia	
		Callicebus brunneus	Brazil, Peru	Rylands et al. 1998
		Callicebus caligatus	Brazil, Peru	Rylands et al. 1998
		Callicebus cinerascens *	Brazil	Rylands et al. 1998
		Callicebus cupreus cupreus	Brazil, Peru	Rylands et al. 1998
		Callicebus dubius *	Brazil	Rylands et al. 1998
		Callicebus hoffmannsi		Rylands et al. 1998
		Callicebus hoffmannsi hoffmannsi *	Brazil	
		Callicebus hoffmannsi baptista *	Brazil	
		Callicebus moloch *	Brazil	
		Callicebus torquatus		
		Callicebus torquatus lucifer	Brazil, Colombia, Peru	Rylands et al. 1998
		Callicebus torquatus lugens	Brazil, Colombia, Venezuela	Rylands et al. 1998
		Callicebus torquatus purinus *	Brazil	Rylands et al. 1998
		Callicebus torquatus regulus *	Brazil	Rylands et al. 1998
		Callicebus torquatus torquatus *	Brazil	Rylands et al. 1998
		Cebus apella		Rylands et al. 1998
		Cebus apella apella	Brazil, Colombia, French Guiana, Guyana, Suriname, Venezuela	
		Cebus apella macrocephalus	Brazil, Peru	
		Cebus apella maranonis	Brazil, Colombia, Ecuador, Peru	
		Cebus apella peruanus	Brazil, Peru	
		Cebus albifrons		Rylands et al. 1998
		C. a. unicolor	Colombia, Bolivia, Brazil, Peru, Venezuela	
		C. a. cuscinus	Bolivia, Brazil, Peru	
		Cebus olivaceus olivaceus		Rylands et al. 1998
		Cebus kaapori	Brazil	Rylands et al. 1998
		Chiropotes albinasus *	Brazil	Rylands et al. 1998
		Chiropotes satanas		Rylands et al. 1998
		Chiropotes satanas chiropotes	Brazil, French Guiana, Guyana, Suriname, Venezuela	
		Chiropotes satanas satanas *	Brazil	
		Chiropotes satanas utahicki *	Brazil	
		Lagothrix lagotricha		Rylands et al. 1998
		Lagothrix lagotricha cana	Brazil, Peru	
		Lagothrix lagotricha lagotricha	Brazil, Colombia, Ecuador, Peru	
		Lagothrix lagotricha poeppigii	Brazil, Ecuador, Peru	
		Pithecia albicans *	Brazil	Rylands et al. 1998

continues

Order	Suborder	Taxon	Distribution	Source
Primates	Cebidae	*Pithecia irrorata*		Rylands et al. 1998
		Pithecia irrorata irrorata	Bolivia, Brasil, Peru	
		Pithecia irrorata vanzolinii *	Brazil	
		Pithecia monachus monachus	Brazil, Colombia, Ecuador, Peru	Rylands et al. 1998
		Pithecia pithecia		Rylands et al. 1998
		Pithecia pithecia chrysocephala *	Brazil	
		Pithecia pithecia pithecia	Brazil, French Guiana, Guyana Suriname, Venezuela	
		Saimiri boliviensis		
		Saimiri boliviensis boliviensis	Bolivia, Brazil, Peru	Rylands et al. 1998
		Saimiri boliviensis pluvialis *	Brazil	Rylands et al. 1998
		Saimiri boliviensis jaburuensis *	Brazil	Rylands et al. 1998
		Saimiri sciureus		
		Saimiri sciureus sciureus	Brazil, French Guiana, Guyana, Suriname	Rylands et al. 1998
		Saimiri sciureus macrodon	Brazil, Colombia, Ecuador, Peru	Rylands et al. 1998
		Saimiri sciureus cassiquiarensis	Brazil, Colombia, Venezuela	Rylands et al. 1998
		Saimiri ustus *	Brazil	Rylands et al. 1998
		Saimiri vanzolinii	Brazil	Rylands et al. 1998
Carnivora	Canidae	*Atelocynus microtis*	Brazil, Peru, Ecuador, Colombia, Bolivia, Paraguay, Argentina	
		Speothos venaticus	Bolivia, Paraguay, Brazil, Peru, Ecuador, Colombia, Venezuela, Guyana, French Guiana, Suriname	
	Felidae	*Herpailurus yaguarondi*	Argentina, Bolivia, Brazil, Colombia, Guianas, Paraguay, Peru, Suriname, Venezuela	
		Leopardus pardalis	Argentina, Bolivia, Brazil, Colombia, Ecuador, Guianas, Paraguay, Peru, Suriname, Venezuela, Uruguay	
		Leopardus wiedii	Argentina, Bolivia, Brazil, Colombia, Ecuador, Guianas, Paraguay, Peru, Suriname, Venezuela, Uruguay	
		Panthera onca	Argentina, Bolivia, Brazil, Colombia, Guianas, Paraguay, Peru, Suriname, Venezuela	
		Puma concolor	Argentina, Bolivia, Brazil, Colombia, Chile, Ecuador, Guyana, Paraguay, Peru, Suriname, Venezuela	
	Mustelidae	*Eira barbara*	Colombia, Venezuela, Guianas, Suriname, Brazil, Ecuador, Peru, Bolivia, Argentina	
		Galictis vittata	Colombia, Venezuela, Guianas, Suriname, Brazil, Ecuador, Bolivia, Peru	
		Lontra longicaudis	Colombia, Venezuela, Guianas, Suriname, Brazil, Ecuador, Bolivia, Peru, Paraguay, Argentina, Uruguay	
		Mustela africana	Peru, Ecuador, Brazil	
		Pteronura brasiliensis	Argentina, Bolivia, Brazil, Colombia, Ecuador, Venezuela, Guyana, Suriname	
	Procyonidae	*Bassaricyon alleni*	Ecuador, Peru, Bolivia, Brazil	Patton et al. forthcoming

continues

Order	Suborder	Taxon	Distribution	Source
Carnivora	Procyonidae	*Nasua nasua*	Colombia, Venezuela, Guianas, Suriname, Brazil, Ecuador, Bolivia, Peru, Paraguay, Argentina, Uruguay	
		Potos flavus	Colombia, Venezuela, Guianas, Suriname, Brazil, Ecuador, Bolivia, Peru	
		Procyon cancrivorus	Colombia, Venezuela, Guianas, Suriname, Brazil, Ecuador, Bolivia, Peru, Paraguay, Argentina, Uruguay	
Cetacea	Platanistidae	*Inia geoffrensis*	Colombia, Venezuela, Brazil, Ecuador, Bolivia, Peru	
	Delphinidae	*Sotalia fluviatilis*	Colombia, Brazil, Ecuador, Peru	
Perissodactyla	Tapiridae	*Tapirus terrestris*	Colombia, Venezuela, Guianas, Suriname, Brazil, Ecuador, Bolivia, Peru, Paraguay, Argentina	
Artiodactyla	Tayassuidae	*Tayassu pecari*	Colombia, Venezuela, Guianas, Suriname, Brazil, Ecuador, Bolivia, Peru, Paraguay, Argentina	
		Pecari tajacu	Colombia, Venezuela, Guianas, Suriname, Brazil, Ecuador, Bolivia, Peru, Paraguay, Argentina	Voss & Emmons 1996
	Cervidae	*Mazama americana*	Colombia, Venezuela, Guianas, Suriname, Brazil, Ecuador, Bolivia, Peru, Paraguay, Argentina	
		Mazama gouazoupira	Colombia, Venezuela, Guianas, Suriname, Brazil, Ecuador, Bolivia, Peru, Paraguay, Argentina, Uruguay	Voss & Emmons 1996
Sirenia	Trichechidae	*Trichechus inunguis*	Ecuador, Peru, Brazil, Guianas	
Rodentia	Sciuridae [o]	*Microsciurus flaviventer*	Peru, Colombia, Ecuador, Brazil	
		Sciurillus pusillus	Peru, Colombia, Suriname, French Guyana, Brazil	
		Sciurus aestuans	Venezuela, Guianas, Suriname, Brazil	
		Sciurus gilvigularis [m]	Venezuela, Guyana, Brazil	Voss & Emmons 1996
		Sciurus ignitus	Argentina, Bolivia, Brazil, Peru	
		Sciurus igniventris	Brazil, Colombia, Ecuador, Peru, Venezuela	
		Sciurus pusillus	Peru, Colombia, Suriname, French Guyana, Brazil	
		Sciurus spadiceus	Ecuador, Peru, Bolivia, Brazil	
	Muridae [o]	*Holochilus sciureus*	Venezuela, Guianas, Brazil, Colombia, Ecuador, Peru, Bolivia	Patton et al. forthcoming
		Neacomys guianae	Guianas, Suriname, Brazil	Patton et al. forthcoming, Voss & Emmons 1996
		Neacomys musseri	Peru, Brazil	Patton et al. forthcoming
		Neacomys minutus	Brazil	Patton et al. forthcoming
		Neacomys spinosus	Colombia, Bolivia, Brazil	Patton et al. forthcoming
		Nectomys apicalis	Ecuador, Brazil, Peru, (?)	Patton et al. forthcoming
		Nectomys mattensis	Venezuela, Brazil, Peru	Patton et al. forthcoming
		Oecomys bicolor	Colombia, Ecuador, Venezuela, Guianas, Brazil, Peru, Bolivia	Patton et al. forthcoming, Musser & Carleton 1993
		Oecomys concolor	Colombia, Venezuela, Brazil, Bolivia	Voss & Emmons 1996; Musser & Carleton 1993
		Oecomys paricola	Venezuela, Guianas, Brazil	Voss & Emmons 1996; Musser & Carleton 1993

continues

Order	Suborder	Taxon	Distribution	Source
Rodentia	Muridae [o]	Oecomys rex	Venezuela, Guianas, Brazil	Voss & Emmons 1996; Musser & Carleton 1993
		Oecomys roberti	Venezuela, Guianas, Brazil, Peru, Bolivia	Patton et al. forthcoming; Musser & Carleton 1993
		Oecomys sp	Brazil	Patton et al. forthcoming; Musser & Carleton 1993
		Oecomys superans	Colombia, Ecuador, Peru, Brazil	Patton et al. forthcoming; Musser & Carleton 1993
		Oecomys trinitatis	Guianas, Colombia, Brazil, Peru	Patton et al. forthcoming; Musser & Carleton 1993
		Oligoryzomys fulvescens	Ecuador, Guianas, Brazil	Voss & Emmons 1996
		Oligoryzomys microtis	Brazil, Bolivia, Peru, Paraguay, Argentina	Patton et al. forthcoming; Musser & Carleton 1993
		Oryzomys emmonsae *	Brazil	Musser et al. 1998
		Oryzomys macconnelli *	Brazil, Colombia, Ecuador, Guianas, Venezuela, Peru	Musser et al. 1998; Patton et al. forthcoming
		Oryzomys megacephalus	Brazil, Venezuela, Guianas, Suriname, Paraguay	Musser et al. 1998; Patton et al. forthcoming
		Oryzomys nitidus	Brazil, Ecuador, Bolivia, Peru	Musser et al. 1998; Patton et al. forthcoming
		Oryzomys perenensis	Brazil, Peru, Bolivia	Patton et al. forthcoming
		Oryzomys yunganus *	Colombia, Ecuador, Peru, Bolivia, Brazil	Musser et al. 1998; Patton et al. forthcoming
		Oxymycterus amazonicus	Brazil	Voss & Emmons 1996
		Oxymycterus inca	Peru, Bolivia, Brazil	
		Rhipidomys gardneri	Peru, Brazil	Patton et al. forthcoming
		Rhipidomys leucodactylus	Brazil, Venezuela, Guianas, Ecuador, Peru	Patton et al. forthcoming; Musser & Carleton 1993
		Rhipidomys mastacalis	Brazil, Venezuela, Colombia, Ecuador, Peru	Voss & Emmons 1996; Musser & Carleton 1993
		Rhipidomys nitela	Brazil, Venezuela, Guianas	Voss & Emmons 1996; Musser & Carleton 1993
		Scolomys juruaense	Brazil	
	Erethizontidae [o]	Coendou bicolor	Bolivia, Peru, Ecuador, Colombia, Brazil	Patton et al. forthcoming
		Coendou prehensilis	Colombia, Venezuela, Guianas, Suriname, Brazil, Ecuador, Bolivia, Peru, Paraguay, Argentina	
		Coendou melanurus	Colombia, Venezuela (?), Guianas, Suriname, Brazil	
		Coendou nycthemera	Brazil	Voss & Angermann 1997
	Dinomyidae [o]	Dinomys branickii	Brazil, Colombia, Ecuador, Bolivia, Venezuela, Peru	
	Hydrochaeridae	Hydrochaeris hydrochaeris	Colombia, Venezuela, Guianas, Suriname, Brazil, Ecuador, Bolivia, Peru, Paraguay, Argentina	
	Dasyproctidae [o]	Dasyprocta fuliginosa	Brazil, Colombia, Ecuador, Bolivia, Venezuela, Peru	
		Dasyprocta leporina [n]	Venezuela, Guianas, Suriname, Brazil	Voss & Emmons 1996
		Dasyprocta prymnolopha	Brazil	
		Myoprocta acouchy	Guianas, Suriname, Brazil	
		Myoprocta pratti	Venezuela, Brazil, Colombia, Ecuador, Peru	
	Agoutidae	Agouti paca	Colombia, Venezuela, Guianas, Suriname, Brazil, Ecuador, Bolivia, Peru, Paraguay	
	Echimyidae [o]	Dactylomys boliviensis	Ecuador, Bolivia, Peru, Brazil	Patton et al. forthcoming
		Dactylomys dactylinus	Brazil, Venezuela, Bolivia	

continues

Order	Suborder	Taxon	Distribution	Source
Rodentia	Echimyidae [o]	*Echimys chrysurus*	Guianas, Suriname, Brazil	
		Isothrix bistriata	Venezuela, Colombia, Ecuador, Peru, Bolivia, Brazil	
		Isothrix pagurus	Brazil	
		Lonchothrix emiliae	Brazil	Patton et al. forthcoming
		Makalata grandis	Brazil	
		Makalata didelphoides	Brazil, Bolivia, Guianas	
		Makalata macrura	Colombia, Venezuela, Peru, Bolivia, Brazil	Patton et al. forthcoming
		Mesomys hispidus	Colombia, Ecuador, Venezuela, Guyana, Bolivia, Peru	
		Mesomys occultus	Brazil	Patton et al. forthcoming
		Mesomys stimulax	Brazil	Patton et al. forthcoming
		Proechimys brevicauda	Bolívia, Ecuador, Peru, Brazil	Patton et al. forthcoming
		Proechimys cayennensis	Venezuela, Guianas, Brazil	Voss & Emmons 1996
		Proechimys cuvieri	Peru, Brazil, Venezuela, Guianas, Suriname	Patton et al. forthcoming
		Proechimys echinothrix	Brazil, Colombia (?), Peru (?)	Patton et al. forthcoming
		Proechimys gardneri	Bolivia, Brazil	Patton et al. forthcoming
		Proechimys goeldii	Brazil	Voss & Emmons 1996
		Proechimys kulinae	Peru, Brazil	Patton et al. forthcoming
		Proechimys oris	Brazil	Voss & Emmons 1996
		Proechimys pattoni	Peru, Brazil	Patton et al. forthcoming
		Proechimys quadruplicatus	Ecuador, Peru, Colombia, Venezuela, Brazil	Patton et al. forthcoming
		Proechimys simonsi	Colombia, Peru, Bolivia, Brazil	Patton et al. forthcoming
		Proechimys steerei	Peru, Brazil, Bolivia	Patton et al. forthcoming
Lagomorpha	Leporidae	*Sylvilagus brasiliensis*	Colombia, Venezuela, Peru, Bolivia, Brazil, Argentina	

a: *Marmosops parvidens* (polytypical, probably a complex of three or four distinct species); b: *Micoureus demerarae* (includes *M. constantinae*); c: *Peropteryx macrotis* (probably a complex of more than one species); d: *Micronycteris megalotis* (includes *M. microtis*); e: *Tonatia saurophila* (formerly known as *T. bidens*); f: *Lichonycteris obscura* (includes *L. degener*); g: *Artibeus gnomus* (cf. Koopman 1993, included in *A. glaucus*); h: *Lasiurus blossevillii* (includes *L. borealis*, cf. Koopman 1993); i: *Eumops trumbulli* (cf. Koopman 1993, included in *E. perotis*); j: *Molossus molossus* (includes *M. coibensis*); l: *Molossus rufus* (called *M. ater* by Koopman 1993 and others); m: *Sciurus gilvigularis* (included in *S. aestuans* by some authors); n: *Dasyprocta leporina* (includes *D. aguti*); o: the majority of genera of the order Rodentia need revising; the majority of the species here probably represent a complex of species; *: geographic distribution restricted to Amazonia.

TABLE 2 - NUMBER OF MAMMALIAN SPECIES AND INVIDIVUALS, BY LOCATION OF COLLECTION IN THE BRAZILIAN AMAZON, HELD BY THE AMERICAN MUSEUM OF NATURAL HISTORY (AMNH), NEW YORK, USA

River or State	Locality	no. of species	no. of individuals
Acre (AC)	Rio Branco	1	1
	Total	1	1
Rio Amazonas	Parintins	64	603
	Sto. Antônio do Amatary	11	14
	Marajó	8	39
	Rio Andira	4	4
	Tamoury	3	13
	Serra De Espelli	2	5
	Rio Paratuca	1	11
	Cussary	1	1
	(indication lacking)	2	14
	Total	75	704
Rio Branco	Frechal	4	6
	Isla do Cantanlial	1	1
	(indication lacking)	4	5
	Total	7	12
Rio Cotinga	Limão	8	78
	Total	8	78
Rio Madeira	Rosarinho	52	543
	Avara Igarapé	42	341
	Borba	36	121
	Sto. Antônio Uayara	19	56
	Total	80	1061
Rio Majary	Recreio	27	95
	Total	27	95
Rio Negro	Manaus	24	145
	Tatu	23	208
	Cacao Pereira	21	211
	Tabacal	11	22
	Miripinima	8	91
	Javanari	8	22
	Serra De Cucuhy	7	134
	São Gabriel	7	27
	Yucali	6	10
	Monte Curycuryari	4	8
	Santa Isabel	2	9
	Santa Maria	2	2
	Prigueza	1	1
	Tinahy	1	1
	Taurarate	1	2
	Vacara	1	1
	Camanaos	1	1

continues

River or State	Locality	no. of species	no. of individuals
Rio Negro	Pira-pucu	1	1
	(indication lacking)	3	18
	Total	74	914
Rio Nhamundá	Faro	43	356
	(indication lacking)	1	6
	Total	44	362
Pará (PA)	Curralinho	18	235
	Capim	11	65
	Belém	9	23
	Patagônia	8	36
	Otinga	3	8
	Vorsladt	1	2
	Rio Piratucu	1	2
	Total	39	371
Rondônia (RO)	Piedras Negras	7	144
	Costa Marques	5	6
	Rio Itenez	2	2
	8 Km. N. Santa Cruz	1	1
	Príncipe da Beira	1	1
	Baures	1	1
	Total	16	155
Roraima (RR)	Mte. Roraima	8	15
	(indication lacking)	6	16
	Total	14	31
Rio Solimões	Lago Tefé	20	70
	Tefé	5	9
	(indication lacking)	6	21
	Total	28	100
Rio Tapajós	Igarapé Brabo	47	270
	Igarapé Amorin	47	264
	Tauary	40	233
	Caxiricatuba	32	144
	Aramanay	28	129
	Piquiatuba	27	58
Rio Tapajós	Limoal	27	75
	Limontuba	21	51
	Inajatuba	19	97
	Fordlândia	18	
	Santarém	7	29
	Aquiatuba	6	12
	Pimental	1	1
	Boim	1	2
	Burburé	1	1
	(indication lacking)	2	1
	Total	110	1432
Rio Tocantins	Ilha do Taiuna	49	662
	Baiao	44	244
	Mocajuba	19	68
	Cometa	18	129
	Arumathina	3	10
	Marapiri Island	2	2
	(indication lacking)	2	2
	Total	72	1117
Rio Uraricoera	Uaica	13	47
	Total	13	47
Rio Vaupés	Tahuapunta	26	93
	Iauraté	5	18
	Bella Vista	2	36
	Apuri	1	1
	(indication lacking)	4	15
	Total	32	163
Rio Xingu	Villarinho do Monte	29	98
	Tapará	20	93
	Porto do Moz	17	34
	Total	42	229
Undetermined		8	14
Total Brazilian Amazon		223	6886

continues

TABLE 3 - NUMBER OF MAMMALIAN SPECIES AND INDIVIDUALS, BY COLLECTION SITE IN THE BRAZILIAN AMAZON, HELD BY THE FIELD MUSEUM OF NATURAL HISTORY (FMNH), CHICAGO, USA

River or State	Locality	no. of species	no. of individuals
Rio Amazonas	Ilha de Urucurituba	19	76
	Itacoatiara	13	60
	Lago do Baptista	9	49
	Jacuara	5	19
	Igarapé Aneba	4	4
	Urumanduba	3	16
	Lago do Serpa	2	2
	Baixo rio Urubu	1	1
	Igarapé Piaba	1	2
	Lago Canacari	1	1
	Lago Tapaiuna	1	1
Rio Amazonas	Tamucury	1	1
	(indication lacking)	1	1
	Total	61	233
Rio Branco	Boa Vista	7	7
	Conceição	4	8
	Serra Grande	2	2
	Total	13	17
Rio Guaporé	Príncipe da Beira	1	5
	Total	1	5
Rio Juruá	Eirunepe/João Pessoa	9	15
	Igarapé Grande	4	5
	Santo Antônio	3	8
	Rio Juruá	2	2
	Igarapé do Gordão	1	2

continues

River or State	Locality	no. of species	no. of individuals
Rio Juruá	Lago Grande	1	1
	Santa Cruz	1	1
	Total	21	34
Rio Madeira	Porto Velho	12	17
	Total	12	17
Rio Maruanum	Bem Querer	1	1
	Macapá	1	1
	Total	2	2
Rio Negro	Manaus	11	17
	Total	11	17
Rio Nhamundá	Faro	5	7
	Fazenda Paraíso	1	1
	Total	6	8
Pará (PA)	Belém	34	389
	Ilha de Marajó	10	18
	Murutucun	5	5
	Estrada de Ferro de Bragança	4	7
	BR-010, km 87-94	3	43
	Icoraci	2	46
	Iltingo	2	2
	Igarapé Amorcu	1	2
	Ilha das Onças	1	2
	Lago Jauari	1	2
	(others)	7	8
	Total	60	524
Rio Purus	Lago Mapixi	5	11
	Lago Aiapua	3	3
	Igarapé do Castanha	1	1
	Itaboca	1	1
	Pauini	1	1
	Total	10	17
Roraima (RR)	Serra da Lua	18	48
	Mt. Roraima	1	2

River or State	Locality	no. of species	no. of individuals
Roraima (RR)	Rio Takutu	1	1
	Total	20	51
Rio Solimões	Codajas	8	8
	Tefé	2	2
	Tabatinga	1	1
	Total	11	11
Rio Tapajós	Fordlândia	31	97
	Tapaiuna	13	29
	Santarém	12	13
	Caxiricatuba	7	9
	Tavio	7	15
	Arara	6	12
	Irocanga	4	4
	Tauari	4	4
	Belterra	3	4
	Aveiros	2	3
	Boim	2	3
	Marai	2	3
	Piquiatuba	2	2
	Patinga	1	1
	São Raimundo	1	1
	Vila Braga	1	1
	Total	63	200
Rio Tocantins	Cameta	10	17
	Baião	2	2
	Indet.	2	2
	Ilha da Tainna	1	2
	Ilha de Manapiri	1	1
	Total	13	24
Rio Xingu	Cachoeira do Espelho	3	11
	Tapara	1	1
	Total	4	12
Total Brazilian Amazon		164	1172

continues

TABLE 4 - NUMBER OF MAMMALIAN SPECIES AND INDIVIDUALS, BY COLLECTION SITE IN THE BRAZILIAN AMAZON, HELD BY THE INSTITUTO NACIONAL DE PESQUISA NA AMAZÔNIA (INPA), MANAUS, BRASIL

River or State	Locality	no. of species	no. of individuals
Rio Amazonas	Itacoatiara	6	17
	Lago dos Reis	3	3
	Belém	1	1
	Lago do Puraquequara	1	3
	(indication lacking)	2	3
	Total	12	27
Amazonas (AM)	PDBFF Reserves	79	595
	BR-319	15	60
	Rio Riozinho – Petrobrás	13	36

River or State	Locality	no. of species	no. of individuals
Amazonas (AM)	1501 WWF Reserve	11	12
	Cabo Frio Reserve	8	8
	AM 010	7	12
	Pico da Neblina	6	20
	BR-174	6	7
	Caverna Maroaga	5	69
	BR-364	4	4
	Rio Araca	3	8
	Rio Demeni	3	3
	Bolixu, rio Quiuine	2	4
	Manaus	2	2
	Reserva Biológica da Campina	2	3
	AM 240	1	1
	BR-310	1	1

continues

River or State	Location	no. species	no. individuals
Amazonas (AM)	Ilha do Curari	1	1
	Piraua Sucam	1	3
	Reserva Ducke	1	2
	Rio Cuiuini	1	1
	Santo Antônio	1	1
	Rio Jauari	1	1
	Rio Nhamundá	1	1
	Rio Preto da Eva	1	1
	(non indicated)	3	3
	Total	107	860
Rio Japurá	Lago Amanã	15	48
	Lago Urini	2	3
	Total	14	51
Rio Juruá	Barro Vermelho	3	7
	Altamira	2	6
	Vira-Volta	2	2
	Igarapé Porongaba	1	6
	Penedo	1	2
	Seringal Condor	1	5
	Sobral	1	2
	Total	7	30
Rio Madeira	Lago Mamori	2	3
	Comunidade Santa Cruz	1	1
	Lago Matupiri	1	2
	Seringal São Luiz	1	1
	Total	4	7
Rio Negro	Manaus	37	105
	Parque Nacional do Jaú	21	33
	Comunidade Colina, rio Tiquié	3	9
	Tarumã	2	2
	Fazenda P. Alegre	1	2
	Rio Cuivini	1	1
	(non indicated)	1	1
	Total	55	153
Pará (PA)	Floresta Nacional Tapirapé-Aquiri	20	95
	Rio Mapuera	10	19
	Rio Curuá-Una	4	11
	Total	31	125
Rio Pitinga	Igarape Água-branca	22	66
	UHE rio Pitinga	12	57
	Total	30	123
Rio Purus	Lago Mapixi	9	19
	Tapauá	6	24
	Beruri	4	8
	Total	14	51
Rondônia (RO)	BR-364	12	60
	Jaciparana	5	5
	Rio Pacas Novas	1	1
	Porto Velho	1	1
	(non indicated)	1	2
	Total	15	69

River or State	Location	no. species	no. individuals
Roraima (RR)	BR-401	5	28
	UHE Samuel, rio Jamari	3	8
	Rio Jamari	2	15
	BR-174	1	1
	RR 205	1	1
	(non indicated)	3	3
	Total	15	56
Rio Solimões	Jandira	3	4
	Tefé	3	3
	Ilha do Curari	1	4
	Tabatinga	1	1
	Rio Sanabani	1	3
	(non indicated)	1	1
	Total	7	14
Rio Tapajós	Alter do Chão	21	41
	Total	20	4
Rio Tocantins	Tucuruí	5	7
	Jacundazinho	1	1
	Total	4	8
Rio Trombetas	Cachoeira Porteira	35	183
	Igarapé Tramalhetinho	23	43
	Rio Mapuera	21	41
	Igarapé Ricardão	13	19
	Igarapé Cutravá	3	3
	Cachoeira Porteira	2	3
	Igarapé Caxipacore	2	2
	BR-163 km67	1	1
	Igarapé da Avicunha	1	1
	Jandira	1	1
	Total	63	297
Rio Uatumã	Balbina	48	201
	Igarapé Caititu	44	227
	Rio Pitinga	14	23
	Igarapé Caititu	10	22
	Igarapé Mão Branca	10	17
	Rio Pitinga	5	6
	Cachoeira Porteira	3	3
	(right bank)	3	4
	Cachoeira Morena	1	1
	Igarapé Tucumai	1	1
	(non indicated)	3	3
	Total	79	508
Rio Uraricoera	Ilha de Maracá	64	243
	Igarapé Trairão	3	5
	Fazenda Aprazível	1	3
	Total	61	251
Rio Urucu	Alto rio Urucu	17	28
	Total	17	28
Total Brazilian Amazon		199	2701

continues

Acknowledgments

The preparation of this paper could not have been undertaken without access to the data collection of several museums. We would like to thank the following curators and their respective institutions for having made this information available to us: Michael D. Carleton, National Museum of Natural History, Smithsonian Institute, Washington DC, USA; Bruce D. Patterson, Field Museum of Natural History, Chicago, USA; Robert S. Voss, American Museum of Natural History, New York, USA; Suely Aparecida Marques-Aguiar, Museu Paraense Emílio Goeldi, Brazil; and the Instituto Nacional de Pesquisas da Amazônia, Manaus, Brazil. We also gratefully acknowledge the great help given by Glenn H. Shepard Jr. in the preparation of Tables 2-5.

Bibliography

AB'SABER, A. N. Os domínios morfoclimáticos na América do Sul: primeira aproximação. *Geomorfologia*, n. 52, p. 1-23, 1977.

ALPERIN, R. *Callithrix argentata* (Linneus, 1771): considerações taxonômicas e descrição de subespécie nova. *Bol. Mus. Paraense Emílio Goeldi*, sér. Zool., v. 9, n. 2, p. 317-28, 1993.

AYRES, J. M.; CLUTTON-BROCK, T. H. River Boundaries and Species Range Size in Amazonian Primates. *Amer. Nat.*, n. 140, p. 531-7, 1992.

BERNARD, E. (ms. in prep.); (espécime INPA 2605, identificação confirmada por Dr. C. Handley).

COHN-HAFT, M.; WHITTAKER, A.; STOUFFER, P. C. A New Look at the 'Species-Poor' Central Amazon: the Avifauna North of Manaus, Brazil. *Ornithological Monographs*, n. 48, p. 205-35, 1997.

COSTA, L. P. *A importância das florestas do Brasil central na história evolutiva dos pequenos mamíferos da Amazônia e da Mata Atlântica*. Proposal approved by World Wildlife Fund (WWF-Brazil), in the context of the 'Natureza e Sociedade' program, 1998.

EMMONS, L. H. Geographic Variation in Densities and Diversities of Non-Flying Mammals in Amazonia. *Biotropica*, n. 16, p. 210-22, 1984.

EMMONS, L. H.; FEER F. *Neotropical Rainforest Mammals*: A Field Guide, 2nd ed. Chicago: Univ. of Chicago Press, 1997.

FERRARI, S. F.; LOPES, M. A. A New Species of Marmoset, Genus *Callithrix* Erxleben, 1777 (Callitrichidae, Primates), from Western Brazilian Amazonia, *Goeldiana Zoologia*, n. 12, p. 1-13, 1992.

FJELDSA, J. Geographical Patterns for Relict and Young Species of Birds in Africa and South America and Implications for Conservation Priorities, *Biodiversity and Conservation*, n. 3, p. 207-26, 1994.

FJELDSA, J.; RAHBEK, C. Species Richness and Endemism in South American Birds: Implications for the Design of Networks of Natural Reserves. In: LAURANCE, W. F.; BIRREGAARD Jr., R. O. (Eds.). *Tropical Forest Remnants: Ecology, Management, and Conservation of Fragmented Communities*. Chicago: Univ. of Chicago Press, 1997. p. 466-82.

FONSECA, G. A. B. da et al. (Orgs.). *Livro vermelho dos mamíferos brasileiros ameaçados de extinção*. Belo Horizonte: Fundação Biodiversitas, 1994.

GRIBEL, R. & TADDEI, V. A. Notes on the Distribution of *Tonatia schulzi* and *Tonatia carrikeri* in the Brazilian Amazon, *J. Mamm.*, v. 70, n. 4, p. 871-3, 1989.

HANDLEY Jr., C. O. New Species of Mammals from Northern South America: Fruit-Eating Bats, Genus *Artibeus* Leach, *Fieldiana Zool.*, n. 39, p. 163-72, 1987.

INPE. *Relatório Projeto PRODES*, <http://www.inpe.br/Informaçoes_Eventos/amz/amz.html>. 1999.

KOOPMAN, K. F. Biogeography of Bats of South America. In: MARES, M. A.; GENOWATS, H. H. (Eds.). *Mammalian Biology in South America*. Linesville/Pa: Pymatuning Laboratory of Ecology, Univ. of Pittsburg, 1982. p. 273-302.

_____. Order Chiroptera. In: WILSON, D. E.; REEDER, D. M. (Orgs.). *Mammal Species of the World*, 2nd ed. Cambridge/MA: Mus. Comp. Zool., 1993. p. 137-241.

MARES, M. A. Neotropical Mammals and the Myth of Amazonian Biodiversity, *Science*, n. 255, p. 976-9, 1992.

MARINHO-FILHO, J.; SAZIMA, I. Brazilian Bats and Conservation Biology a First Survey. In: KUNZ, T. H.; RACEY, P. A. (Eds.). *Bat Biology and Conservation*. Washington/London: Smithsonian Institute Press, 1998. p. 282-94.

MARQUES, S. A.; OREN, D. C. First Brazilian Record for *Tonatia schulzi* and *Sturnira bidens* (Chiroptera: Phyllostomidae), *Bol. Mus. Paraense Emílio Goeldi*, sér. Zool., n. 3, p. 159-60, 1987.

MITTERMEIER, R. A.; SCHWARZ, M.; AYRES, J. M. A New Species of Marmoset, Genus *Callithrix* Erxleben 1777 (Callitrichidae, Primates) from the Rio Maués Region, State of Amazonas, Central Brazilian Amazonia, *Goeldiana Zoologia*, n. 14, p. 1-17, 1992.

MORITZ, C. et al. Molecular Perspectives on Historical Fragmentation of Australian Tropical and Subtropical Rainforests: Implications for Conservation. In: LAURANCE, W. F.; BIRREGAARD Jr., R. O. (Eds.). *Tropical Forest Remnants: Ecology, Management, and Conservation of Fragmented Communities*. Chicago: Univ. of Chicago Press, 1997. p. 442-54.

MUSSER, G. G.; CARLETON, M. D. Family Muridae. In: WILSON, D. E.; REEDERS, D. M. (Eds.). *Mammal Species of the World*, 2nd ed. Cambridge/MA: Mus. Comp. Zool., 1993. p. 501-755.

MUSSER, G. G. et al. Systematic Studies of Oryzomyine Rodents (*Muridae, Sigmodontinae*): Diagnoses and Distributions of Species Formely Assigned to *Oryzomys 'capito'*, *Bul. Am. Mus. Nat. Hist.*, n. 236, 1998.

PATTON, J. L.; SILVA, M. N. F. da. A New Species of Spiny Mouse (*Scolomys*, Sigmodontinae, Muridae) from the Western Amazon of Brazil. In: *Proceedings of the Biological Society of Washington*, v. 108, n. 2, p. 319-37, 1995.

_____. Rivers, Refuges, and Ridges: the Geography of Speciation of Amazonian Mammals. In: HOWARD, D.; BERLOCHER, S. (Eds.). *Endless Forms: Modes and Mechanisms of Speciation*. Oxford, England: Oxford Univ. Press, 1998. p. 202-13.

PATTON, J. L.; SILVA, M. N. F.; MALCOLM, J. R. Gene Genealogy and Differentiation among Arboreal Spiny Rats (Rodentia: Echimyidae) of the Amazon Basin: A Test of the Riverine Barrier Hypothesis, *Evolution*, v. 48, n. 4, p. 1314-23, 1994.

_____. Hierarchical Genetic Structure and Gene Flow in Three Sympatric Species of Amazonian Rodents. *Journal of Molecular Ecology*, n. 5, p. 229-38, 1996

_____. Mammals of the Rio Juruá: Evolutionary and Ecological Diversification in the Western Amazon. *Bulletin of the American Museum of Natural History*, no prelo.

PATTON, J. L. et al. Diversity, Differentiation, and the Historical Biogeography of Non-Volant Small Mammals of the Neotropical Forests. In: LAURENCE, W. F.; BIERREGAARD Jr, R. O; MORITZ, C. (Eds.). *Tropical Forest Remnants: Ecology, Management and Conservation of Fragmented Communities*. Chicago: Univ. of Chicago Press, 1997. p. 455-65.

PERES, C. A. Notes on the Primates of the Juruá River, Western Brazilian Amazonia, *Folia Primat*, n. 61, p. 97-103, 1993.

_____. Primate Community Structure at Twenty Western Amazonian Flooded and Unflooded Forests. *J. Trop. Ecol.*, n. 13, p. 381-405, 1997.

_____. The Structure of Non-Volant Mammal Communities in Different Amazonian Forest Types. In: EISENBERG, J. F.; REDFORD, K. H. (Eds.). *Mammals of the Neotropics: the Central Neotropics*. Chicago: Univ. of Chicago Press, 1999. p. 564-81.

PERES, C. A.; JANSON, C. H. Species Coexistence, Distribution, and Environmental Determinants of Neotropical Primate Richness: A Community-Level Zoogeographical Analysis. In: FLEAGLE; REED; JANSON (Eds.). *Primate Communities*. Cambridge: Cambridge Univ. Press, 1999.

PINE, R. H. Mammals (Exclusive of Bats) of Belém, Pará, Brazil, *Acta Amazonica*, n. 3, p. 47-79, 1973.

QUEIROZ, H. L. A New Species of Capuchin Monkey, Genus Cebus Erxleben, 1777 (Cebidae: Primates) from Eastern Brazilian Amazonia, *Goeldiana Zoologia*, n. 15, p. 1-13, 1992.

ROOSMALEN, M. G. M. et al. A New and Distinctive Species of Marmoset (Callitrichidae, Primates, from the lower Rio Aripuanã, State of Amazonas, Central Brazilian Amazonia), *Goeldiana Zoologia*, n. 22, p. 1-27, 1998.

RYLANDS, A. B.; COIMBRA-FILHO, A. F.; MITTERMEIER, R. A. Systematics, Geographic Distribution, and Some Notes on the Conservation Status of the Callitrichidae. In: RYLANDS, A. B. (Ed.). *Marmosets and Tamarins: Systematics, Behaviour, and Ecology*. Oxford: Oxford Univ. Press, 1993. p. 11-77.

RYLANDS, A. B; MITTERMEIER, R. A.; KONSTANT, W. R. Apendices. In: ROOSMALEN, M. G. M. et al (Eds.). A New and distinctive Species of Marmoset (Callitrichidae, Primates, from the lower Rio Aripuanã, State of Amazonas, Central Brazilian Amazonia), *Goeldiana Zoologia*, n. 22, p. 1-27, 1998.

SILVA, M. N. F. da. *Systematics and Phylogeography of Amazonian Spiny Rats of the Genus Proechimys (Rodentia: Echimyidae)*, 1995. Thesis (PhD in Zoology) – Zoology Department, University of California, Berkeley, Berkeley, USA.

_____. Four New Species of Spiny Rats of the Genus *Proechimys* (Rodentia: Echimyidae) from the Western Amazon of Brazil, *Proceedings of the Biological Society of Washington*, v. 111, n. 2, p. 436-71, 1998.

SILVA, M. N. F. da; PATTON, J. L. Molecular Phylogeography and the Evolution and Conservation of Amazonian Mammals, *Mol. Ecol.*, n. 7, p. 475-86, 1998.

SILVA Jr., N. J. da; SITES Jr., J. W. Patterns of Diversity of Neotropical Squamate Reptile Species with Emphasis on the Brazilian Amazon and the Conservation Potential of Indigenous Reserves, *Conserv. Biol.*, n. 9, p. 873-901, 1995.

SILVA Jr., J. S.; NORONHA M. de A. On a New Species of Bare-Eared Marmoset, Genus Callithrix Erxleben, 1777, from Central Amazonia, Brazil (Primates: Callitrichidae), *Goeldiana Zoologia*, n. 18, forthcoming.

SIMMONS, N. B. A New Species of *Micronycteris* (Chiroptera: Phyllostomidae) from Northeastern Brazil, with Comments on Phylogenetic Relationships, *Bul. Am. Mus. Nat. Hist.*, n. 3158, 1996.

SIMMONS, N. B.; VOSS, R. S. The Mammals of Paracou, French Guiana: A Neotropical Lowland Rainforest Fauna Part I. Bats, *Bul. Am. Mus. Nat. Hist.*, n. 237, 1998.

VOSS, R. S.; EMMONS, L. H. Mammalian Diversity in Neotropical Lowland Rainforests: A Preliminary Assessment, *Bul. Am. Mus. Nat. Hist.*, n. 230, 1996.

VOSS, R. S.; ANGERMANN, R. Revisionary Notes on Neotropical Porcupines (Rodentia: Erethizontidae). 1. Type Material Described by Olfers (1818) and Kuhl (1820) in the Berlin Zoological Museum, *Bul. Am. Mus. Nat. Hist.*, n. 3214, 1997.

WALLACE, A. R. On the Monkeys of the Amazon. *Proc. Zool. Soc. London*, n. 20, p. 107-110, 1852.

WILLIAMS, S. L.; WILLIG, M. R.; REID, F. A. Review of the *Tonatia bidens* Complex (Mammalia: Chiroptera), with Descriptions of Two New Subspecies, *J. Mamm.*, v. 76, n. 2, p. 612-26, 1995

Quantitative floristic inventory and conservation status of vegetation types in the Brazilian Amazon

Bruce W. Nelson *Instituto Nacional de Pesquisas da Amazônia*
Alexandre A. de Oliveira *Universidade Paulista*

Abstract

This chapter deals with the selection of priority conservation areas in the Brazilian Amazon. It is divided into two parts, based on current knowledge of the flora: the first part considers the 'Current State of Knowledge of Amazonian Flora' and the second the 'Geographical Occurrence, Characteristics, and Conservation Status of Amazonian Vegetation Types'.

The first part describes the major studies providing quantitative inventories of Amazonian vegetation; this is followed by an overview of current knowledge on the distribution of plant species; and the section concludes with a synthesis of these studies and considerations on investments in future research to support demands for conservation planning solutions. A prior quantitative study, analyzing the distribution patterns of 729 species, demonstrated the relative homogeneity of the Amazon forest, as compared to other neotropical forests, with respect to geographic variation in diversity and concentrations of local endemism. Two other studies, using ordination of quantitative inventories, suggest that the composition of Amazonian forest plots varies as a function of physiognomy and distance between sites.

The second part analyzes the status of and priorities for conservation of different Amazonian vegetation types. The selection of the 21 vegetation types defined in this study was made on the basis of maximizing the floristic differences between types, so as to deal with distinct groups of species. Based on the premise that conservation of plant diversity will be more effective when protected areas are evenly distributed across the whole area of occurrence of each vegetation type, priority areas are identified for each physiognomic group. The identification of priority areas for conservation is also based on distance from existing conservation areas and on the threat of anthropogenic degradation. These criteria are analyzed using conservation area maps (at two levels of protection) and a map showing areas of anthropogenic impacts up to 1991. This leads to suggestions, which should be treated as approximate and flexible, for new conservation areas, with three levels of priority for each vegetation type. Finally there are suggestions on how to improve the process of selection of priority areas to include: 1) incorporation of new criteria; 2) use of an algorithm to indicate the level of conservation of the flora at a given point within the map of a single vegetation type, based on the size of surrounding conservation areas and of surrounding anthropogenic areas, both weighted by distance to the point in question; and 3) overlay of the resultant 21 maps in order to detect high priority areas in proximity to each other.

Current state of knowledge of Amazonian flora

Quantitative inventories of trees

Terra firme

Terra firme forests are treated here as dense non-alluvial rain forests, following the classification system of Veloso et al. (1991). For practical reasons, open rain forests dominated by bamboos, vines, or palms are included as well (after Veloso et al. 1991).

The oldest quantitative tree inventory for a neotropical forest was conducted by Davis and Richards (1934) in Moraballi Creek in British Guiana, now Guyana. In each of the five primary forest types they identified, the authors inventoried all trees with a diameter at breast height (DBH) of more than 10 cm in 1.5 hectare (122 x 122 m) plots, which resulted in 59 to 94 species, and 460 to 919 trees for each plot. They found that each forest type was more or less limited to a specific type of soil and has its own community structure characteristics, though a great number of species were found in more than one type of forest. The method of species identification was based on the common name given by local field assistants, which were based primarily on the characteristics of the trunk and the cut wood.

Bastos (1948), concerned with assessing timber potential for charcoal production, published the first quantitative study of an Amazonian forest in Brazil. For this he used a sample area of one hectare divided into discontinuous plots of 20 x 50 m, totaling 891 trees with a DBH of more than 15 cm. He identified 46 species of trees with a DBH ≥ 30 cm, out of 124 individuals.

In the 1950s, researchers at the Northern Institute of Agronomy (Instituto Agronômico do Norte – IAN), stimulated by the research of Davis and Richards (1933-1934) and influenced by a visit to Brazil by Theodosius Dobzhansky, conducted forest inventory studies in the Amazon, the most important of which were those by Black, Dobzhansky and Pavan (1950) and Pires, Dobzhansky and Black (1953).

Black et al. (1950) sampled two plots in terra firme forest and one in igapó (seasonally flooded forest), all of one hectare (100 x 100 m). They studied the Rio Guamá igapó and the Mocambo terra firme forest close to Belém and found, respectively, 60 species among 564 trees and 97 species among 423 trees with a DBH of 10 cm or more. In a terra firme forest in Tefé, in western Amazonia, they found 79 species among 230 trees with a DBH of more than 20 cm. Observing the low similarity among the plots and the high percentage of rare species, the authors concluded, based on Preston's (1948) octave scale, that little more than half the species of one association are found in one hectare, and suggested that it is not possible to reach generalized conclusions about composition and structure based on sampling of small plots.

With the aim of estimating the number of tree species in the terra firme community of the state of Pará, Pires et al. (1953) inventoried individuals with a DBH of ≥ 10 cm in 3.5 hectares in the locality of Castanhal, totaling 1,482 trees sampled and 179 species (108 species for the first hectare). Using statistical analyses of the expected random distribution of species, according to the Poisson distribution, and of what was found in the plots, they concluded that the distribution of the more common species was uniform. Applying Preston's (1948) octave method, they inferred that approximately 70 species occurring in the association were not sampled in the survey. Comparisons with the plot close to Belém, studied by Black et al. (1950), revealed great differences in composition and diversity between relatively close terra firme areas (Pires et al. 1953).

The study conducted by Cain et al. (1956) was the first in the Amazon to use phyto-sociological parameters – such as density, frequency, and importance value (Curtis and Macintosh 1951) – and the vegetation characterization methodology based on life forms and leaf size developed by Raunkier (1934). In an area close to that studied by Black et al. (1950), in a two-hectare plot (200 x 100 m) Cain et al. (1956) found 897 trees and 153 species with a DBH of ≥ 10 cm, 144 species of which were present in the first hectare sampled. The authors observed that: 1) there is no dominance of a single species or of a few species in this type of forest, as there is in temperate forests; 2) there is some dominance only at the family level; 3) most species show low frequency; and 4) the specific similarity is very low compared to other terra firme forests.

The first tree inventory in the mid Amazon River region was conducted by Robert Lechthaler in one hectare of terra firme forest in the Ducke Forest Reserve, in the municipality of Manaus. With the aim of surveying the region's timber potential, all trees with a DBH of more than 8 cm were inventoried and classified according to wood color. The trees were identified by their common name, and the methodology used for this identification was not described. Among the 735 sampled individuals, at least 76 common names were listed (Lechthaler 1956).

The FAO mission to the Amazon, together with the Agency for the Amazon Economic Growth Plan (Superintendência do Plano de Valorização Econômica da Amazônia – SPVEA), produced various forest surveys which were submitted as reports to the Brazilian government (Glerum 1960, 1962a, 1962b; Glerum and Smith 1960, 1962; Heinsdijk 1957, 1958a, 1958b, 1958c, 1960, 1964, 1965, 1966; Heinsdijk and Bastos 1965; Bastos 1960). Most did not circulate widely, but were later published together in a single volume by the Amazon Development Agency (Superintendência do Desenvolvimento da Amazônia – SUDAM, the successor to the SPVEA). The mission analyzed at least 1,362 hectares, where trees with a DBH of ≥ 25 cm or in some cases of more than 45 cm were measured and identified by specialized field technicians. Four hundred species from 47 families were inventoried, the most representative of which were Leguminosae, Lecythidaceae, Sapotaceae, Burseraceae, Lauraceae, and Chrysobalanaceae. Amazonian terra firme forests were divided into two types: *Pouteria* association and *Eschweilera-Pouteria* association, both divided into 24 facies or variations according to their composition. For the first and only time, floristic similarities were highlighted by comparing one hectare on the Madeira River, with 111 individuals and 60 species, with one hectare close to Belém, with 133 individuals and 42 species. These inventories, of plots approximately 1,200 km apart, revealed 22 shared species, with more than half the individuals in either of the plots belonging to species present in both. Qualitatively, the similarity between these two plots is small, 27.5% according to the Jaccard index. In other words, they are less similar than was argued by the authors (SUDAM 1974).

In the 1960s, Takeuchi studied various types of Amazon forests using vegetation profiles to analyze physiognomy. For terra firme forest, the most important were the studies of the region close to Manaus (Takeuchi 1960, 1961[1]) and of the upper Rio Negro (Takeuchi 1962). The size of his profiles varied greatly and diversity data were not presented, as the sampled areas, 500 m^2 on average, were too small for species density analysis.

Rodrigues (1963), using a minimum DBH of 15 cm, found 461 trees and 96 species in 1.5 hectares (100 x 150 m) at Serra do Navio, in the state of Amapá. In another plot of 1.1 hectare (100 x 110 m) he calculated 347 trees and 84 species. He found 78 and 80 species, respectively, for the first hectare sampled in each plot. The author presented data on wood volume, frequency and density, as well as 100 x 5 m profile diagrams for trees over 3 m high for each of the sample areas.

Grubb et al. (1963) studied the physiognomy and structure of small plots (465 m^2) of lowland (terra firme) and montane forest in Ecuador, and found between 27 and 42 species, and 42 and 101 trees over 6 m high per plot. The results obtained contradicted the supposed stratification of tropical rain forests and revealed a family composition similar to the Amazonian Hileia. In conclusion, the authors proposed a slightly different nomenclature to that used by Richards (1952) for tropical formations, introducing the term Tropical Lowland Rain Forest.

In his study along the recently opened Manaus-Itacoatiara highway, Rodrigues (1967) sampled trees with a DBH of ≥ 25 cm in 27 hectares, and trees with a DBH of ≥ 45 cm in another 27.5 hectares. He found the families Leguminosae, Chrysobalanaceae, Lauraceae, Sapotaceae, and Lecythidaceae to be the most representative in terms of numbers of species and individuals.

In the 1970s, the RadamBrasil Project conducted the biggest inventory in the Brazilian Amazon in an area of approximately two thousand hectares, including in the sampling all trees with a circumference at breast height (CBH) equal to or greater than 100 cm (DBH ≥ 32 cm). These data, however, were presented in separate reports (RadamBrasil 1968-1978), and a partial synthesis of the results was only presented in the 1990s (Rollet 1993). This compilation analyzed data collected in the regions of Boa Vista, Manaus, and the Purus (volumes 8, 17 and 18 of the RadamBrasil reports), which cover an area of approximately 840,000 km^2, of which around 74% was forest. The 612 hectares investigated revealed 558 species, of which the most abundant were: *Eschweilera odora*[2] (Poepp.) Miers (Lecythidaceae), *Goupia glabra* Aubl. (Celastraceae), *Cariniana micrantha* Ducke (Lecythidaceae), *Licania membranacea* Sagot ex Lanes. (Chrysobalanaceae), and *Pouteria guianensis* Eyma (Sapotaceae) (Rollet 1993).

---

1. This publication is the English version of the previous one.
2. Synonymous with *E. coriacea* (DC.) Mori, in Mori and Prance (1990).

Ramos et al. (1972) surveyed the timber potential of the agribusiness district of the Manaus Free Trade Zone using methods to obtain the volume of wood per hectare. However, the authors do not make it clear what the minimum diameter for inclusion was, nor provide any reference to the species sampled. This inventory, therefore, contributes very little to any discussion of the composition, structure, and diversity of Amazon forests.

Researchers from the National Institute for Amazon Research (INPA) and the Federal University of Rio Grande do Sul (UFRGS) published two important studies on the phyto-sociology of different types of habitats in terra firme forest close to Manaus (Prance et al. 1976, Porto et al. 1976). Prance et al. (1976) produced the first, and for a long time the only, quantitative study of terra firme forest in the region by collecting specimens from all trees for identification at species level. They found 179 species and 350 trees with a DBH of ≥ 15 cm in a one hectare plot (125 x 80 m), and 56 other different species, with a DBH of 5 to 15 cm, sampled in a subplot of 200 m^2, totaling 235 species. Prance (1990) republished the data of this inventory showing *Eschweilera odora* (Poepp.) Miers and *Scleronema micranthum* (Ducke) Ducke (Bombacaceae) to be the species with the highest Species Importance Value (SIV, after Curtis and Macintosh 1951). Using the Family Importance Value (FIV) described by Mori et al. (1983)[3], they determined the main families in the area to be Lecythidaceae, Moraceae, Sapotaceae, Burseraceae, Caesalpiniaceae and Chrysobalanaceae.

Porto et al. (1976) published the first phyto-sociological study of 'mata-de-baixio', a floodplain vegetation of igarapés (small streams) associated with terra firme forest. Different inclusion criteria (DBH of 5, 10, and 30 cm) were used in different sampling areas, totaling one hectare divided into 10 discontinuous plots of 10 x 100 m. The authors draw attention to the internal similarity of flora in this formation and its floristic differentiation in relation to the adjacent terra firme forest. Following the classification of Mueller-Dombois and Ellenberg (1974), they named this community *Vitex-Micrandra*. The species of greatest density and frequency were *Vitex sprucei* Briq. (Verbenaceae) and *Carapa guianensis* Aubl. (Meliaceae), and the most representative families were Leguminosae, Myristicaceae, Sapotaceae, Meliaceae, Palmae, Euphorbiaceae, Annonaceae, and Bombacaceae.

Pires and Prance (1977) presented data on the vertical, horizontal and diameter size distribution of trees in terra firme, igapó (tidally and seasonally flooded by clear water) and várzea (seasonally flooded by muddy water) forests. All trees with a CBH ≥ 30 cm (DBH ≥ 9.55 cm) in an area of 15.5 hectares were sampled, totaling 8,996 individuals, 342 species, and an average of 580 trees per hectare. Of this total, 5.7 hectares and 224 species were recorded in the terra firme forest of the Mucambo Reserve, close to Belém; 4.7 hectares and 180 species in the igapó forest of the Catú Reserve, on the edge of the Mucambo area; and 5 hectares and 196 species in the várzea forest of Aurá. They found that 43% of the species were common to both terra firme and igapó forests, 38% to terra firme and várzea; 40% to várzea and igapó, and 83 species (24%) occurred in all three types of forest. The authors did not detect in the areas studied any evidence of the stratification suggested by Richards (1952) and predicted that, despite the absence of dominant species, in any study of Amazonian trees with a CBH greater than 30 cm, 5 to 15 species will make up approximately 50% of the total number of individuals. According to the authors, these species should be considered as characteristic of the area and, on this basis, they consider the implications for conservation in Amazonia.

In Altamira, Pará, in a total area of 1.5 hectares of fertile *terra roxa* soil on terra firme, and with an inclusion CBH of at least 30 cm, 101 species (577 individuals) were found in the one-hectare plot (100 x 100 m), and 89 species (300 individuals) in the half-hectare plot. Subplots were also used for sampling trees with a CBH of 15 to 30 cm and for individuals with a CBH of less than 15 cm and over 2 m high (Dantas and Müller 1979).

Dantas et al. (1980) described the phyto-sociology of forest on yellow lateritic soils in Capitão Poço, Pará, comprising 121 species and 503 trees with a CBH ≥ 30 cm in a one hectare plot. The most diversified families were Leguminosae, Sapotaceae and Moraceae; the most numerous were Lecythidaceae and Burseraceae. The species with the greatest number of individuals was *Eschweilera odora* (Poepp.) Miers.

Uhl and Murphy (1981) investigated the composition, structure, and regeneration of a terra firme forest in southeastern Venezuela. They found, in mature forests, 83 species and 744 trees in a one hectare plot; and in two 0.5-hectare plots they recorded, respectively, 79 and 63 species among 387 and 335 trees. The diversity found in sampling a half-hectare plot of secondary forest was very similar, with 68 species among 259 trees. The floristic composition of the area was not fully investigated, nevertheless some aspects relating to the community's Species Importance Value (SIV) were analyzed. For the one-hectare plot, 18 species made up 79.3% of the total importance value, and the most important of these was *Licania sp*, with 19.1% of the total SIV. The SIV of this species varied significantly between primary forest sites, and the authors concluded that a species may be common in one sample and rare or absent in another nearby site.

In his study on the behavior and ecology of the primates *Chiropotes albinasus* and *Chiropotes satanas*, Ayres (1981) presented data from a survey of eight hectares of terra firme forest for the purpose of analyzing the environment and obtaining information about the species used by these monkeys. In seven one-hectare plots in Aripuanã, Mato Grosso, he found an average of 272.4 individuals per hectare, and between 28 and 33 families for trees with a DBH of ≥ 15 cm. The dominant[4] families were Leguminosae, Moraceae, and Myristicaceae, with variations in the ranking of these three families for the different plots. Using the Bray and Curtis (1957) family similarity index, he found similarity values of 55% to 80% between four one-hectare plots at varying distances, on the basis of which he suggested that 'within small areas of Amazonian terra firme, the forest is homogeneously heterogeneous.' In a one-hectare plot in Aripuanã, plants with a DBH of over 15 cm were identified at species level. Among 266 trees he found 123 species, with *Tetragastris altissima* (*Aubl.*) Swart showing the highest density. Using the Shannon index with log base 2 gave a diversity level of 6.18.

Campbell et al. (1986) investigated three hectares (3000 x 10 m) of terra firme forest and 0.5 hectare (500 x 10 m) of várzea on the Xingu using transect sampling and an inclusion criterion of DBH ≥ 10 cm. The reason for using this methodology was that

---

3. The FIVs of the survey by Prance et al. (1976) were calculated here, therefore this is the first publication of this type of phytosociological data for an Amazonian forest.

4. Dominance is employed by the author meaning higher density or higher number of individuals.

the authors wanted to 'sample the highest possible number of species per unit of area.' In the terra firme forest, 1,420 individuals, 39 families and 265 species were found, with *Cenostigma macrophyllum* Tul. (Leguminosae) and *Orbignya sp* (Arecaceae) the most important (SIV) species, and Leguminosae, Palmae, Lecythidaceae, Moraceae and Bombacaceae the best represented families. In each hectare 393, 460 and 567 trees, and 133, 118 and 162 species were found, respectively. Although the two species above were shown to be the most representative for any of the terra firme plots, composition varied significantly between the plots. Only 40 species (15%) were recorded in all three hectares, and the similarity ranged from 26% to 33% (Jaccard index)[5] for all two hectare pairings. The authors concluded that the forest's high diversity was due to the large number of rare species, each contributing very little to the community's total SIV, and that the Amazon is a mosaic of different types of forests. Thus, conclusions about larger areas cannot be reached by extrapolation from data on species analysis and richness in small sample areas.

Using a rectangular one-hectare (10 x 1000 m) plot of terra firme forest in Bolivia, Boom (1986) described the composition of the forest's dominant stratum (DBH ≥ 10 cm). The data were later used for a quantitative ethnobotanical study in a community of Chácobo indians (Boom 1987). The survey found 649 individuals belonging to 94 species, with *Iryanthera juruensis* Warb. (Myristicaceae), *Pseudolmedia laevis* (R.&P.) Macbr. (Moraceae), *Euterpe precatoria* Mart. (Arecaceae), *Pseudolmedia macrophylla* Tréc. (Moraceae), *Socratea exorrhiza* (Mart.) H. Wendl (Arecaceae), and *Vochysia vismiifolia* Spruce x Warming (Vochysiaceae) as the species with the highest SIV; and Moraceae, Myristicaceae, Palmae, Leguminosae, Melastomataceae, and Cecropiaceae as the families with the highest FIV. The difference in family importance ranking compared to other Amazonian studies, the high importance of Melastomataceae in the sample, and the community's low basal area all suggested to the author that this forest was undergoing a secondary regeneration phase following previous disturbance.

Mori and Boom (1987) and Mori et al. (1989) used the point-centered quarter method (Cottam and Curtis 1956) and an inclusion DBH of 10 cm to describe the vegetation of, respectively, La Fumée mountain at Saül in French Guiana and Camaipi in Amapá.

In the Saül reserve in French Guiana they found 295 species among 800 trees sampled, with Burseraceae, Sapotaceae, Lecythidaceae, Mimosaceae, and Caesalpiniaceae as the families with the highest FIV, and *Tetragastris altissima* (Aubl.) Swart (Burseraceae), *Quararibea turbinata* Poir. (Bombacaceae), *Virola michelii* Heckel (Myristicaceae), *Protium apiculatum* Swart (Burseraceae), *Couratari stellata* A. C. Smith and *Eschweilera coriacea* (DC.) Mori (Lecythidaceae) as the species with the highest SIV. Taking the known total number of Lecythidaceae species in the region and the total number of species in the sample, they predicted the reserve's expected richness. Based on the quantity of species of this one family collected throughout the whole reserve, they estimated the number of expected tree species with a DBH ≥ 10 cm to be 513, and concluded that the 800 sampled trees included only 53% of the arboreal species (Mori and Boom 1987).

In the Camaipi forest, in Amapá, 205 species were found among 1,000 trees, with *Geissospermum argenteum* Woods. (Apocynaceae) as the species with the highest SIV, followed by *Tachigalia myrmecophila* Ducke (Leguminosae), *Tetragastris panamensis* (Engl.) O. Kuntze (Burseraceae), *Lecythis persistens* Sagot. (Lecythidaceae), and *Protium tenuifolium* (Engl.) Engl. (Burseraceae). The most important families were Apocynaceae, Sapotaceae, Mimosaceae, Burseraceae, and Lecythidaceae (Mori et al. 1989).

Absy et al. (1986-1987) inventoried six one-hectare (10 x 1000 m) plots, in adjoining pairs, in a terra firme forest close to the Cuiabá-Porto Velho (BR-364) highway. They found 103 to 136 species with a DBH of ≥ 10 cm per hectare, out of a total of 278 species and 2,235 individuals. Despite the proximity between the hectare plots, the most important species in each varied significantly: of the ten most important species in all the plots, only two were common to all six: *Tetragastris altissima* (Aubl.) Swart and *Pseudolmedia laevis* (R.&P.) Macbr. The families with the highest FIV, for any single plot, were Leguminosae, Moraceae, Sapotaceae, Lecythidaceae, and Burseraceae.

Using the point-centered quarter method and an inclusion DBH of at least 10 cm in a survey in the Ecuadorian Amazon, Balslev et al. (1987) compared a terra firme area with an adjacent várzea (floodplain) forest in the Yasuni National Park. Of a total of 804 trees in the terra firme forest, they found 244 species, an estimate of 728 trees and 228 species[6] per hectare. The species with the highest SIV were *Iriartea deltoidea* R.&P. (Arecaceae), *Rinorea cf. apiculata* Hekking (Violaceae), *Pseudolmedia laevis* (R.&P.) Macbr. (Moraceae), *Cedrelinga catenaeformis* Ducke (Leguminosae), and *Cecropia sciadophylla* Mart. (Cecropiaceae). The families with the highest FIV were Arecaceae, Meliaceae, Mimosaceae, and Caesalpiniaceae.

In the late 1980s, researchers at the Emílio Goeldi Museum (MPEG) conducted various studies on the arboreal component of terra firme forests in the Serra dos Carajás, Pará (Silva et al. 1986, 1987; Salomão et al. 1988; Silva and Rosa 1989) and Rondônia (Maciel and Lisboa 1989; Lisboa 1989; Salomão and Lisboa 1989).

Silva et al. (1986) recorded 516 trees and 125 species with a CBH ≥ 30 cm for one transect (20 x 500 m) and, considering also the shrub and herbaceous strata, noted that Leguminosae, Moraceae, Rubiaceae, Bignoniaceae, and Sapindaceae were the most diversified families.

Silva et al (1987) analyzed a one-hectare transect (1000 x 10 m) and recorded 103 species with a CBH = 30 cm. The species with the highest density was *Theobroma speciosa* Willd. (Sterculiaceae), and *Bertholletia excelsa* H. & B. (Lecythidaceae) was the species with the greatest basal area. The families with the greatest number of species were Mimosaceae (13), Burseraceae (8), Moraceae (8), Caesalpiniaceae (8), and Papilionaceae (7).

Using two 500 x 10 m transects, Salomão et al. (1988) also studied the terra firme forest of the Serra dos Carajás region, sampling 484 individuals and 122 tree species with a DBH ≥ 10 cm, with Leguminosae, Sapotaceae, Vochysiaceae, Lauraceae, and Melastomataceae as the families with the highest FIV, and *Erisma uncinatum* Warm. (Vochysiaceae) as the species with the highest SIV.

---

5. The similarities presented in the paper are incompatible with the data. For some reason the species common to the three hectares were excluded from the calculation; the data here presented were recalculated to take these species into account.

6. According to Mori (1987) and Mori et al. (1989), the point-centered quarter method, which is based on the sampling of individuals, and has area as an indirectly related measure, should not be used to estimate species richness per area.

Silva and Rosa (1989) surveyed two terra firme areas over copper deposits in Carajás using 10 x 1000 m transects and CBH ≥ 30 cm inclusion. They found 552 individuals and 119 species, and 470 individuals and 121 species respectively in the transects. Sapotaceae, Mimosaceae, Papilionaceae, Euphorbiaceae, and Caesalpiniaceae were the families with the highest FIV in the first plot, and Burseraceae, Mimosaceae, Moraceae, Lecythidaceae, and Lauraceae were the most important in the second.

In Rondônia, Salomão and Lisboa (1988) and Maciel and Lisboa (1989) studied the arboreal vegetation, with a CBH ≥ 30 cm, in a sampling area of 500 x 20 m, and at least ten subplots of 5 x 1 m for shrub-herbaceous vegetation. For the arboreal stratum, Salomão and Lisboa found 171 species among 573 individuals, with Moraceae, Leguminosae, Burseraceae, Palmae, and Sapotaceae as the most important families, and *Tetragastris altissima* (Aubl.) Swart (Burseraceae) as the species with the highest SIV, followed by *Bertholletia excelsa* H. & B. (Lecythidaceae) (Salomão and Lisboa 1988). Maciel and Lisboa (1989) recorded 603 individuals belonging to 90 species and 33 families in the arboreal stratum, with *Theobroma cacao* L. (Sterculiaceae) and *Guarea kunthiana* Adr. Juss. (Meliaceae) as the species with the highest SIV, and Sterculiaceae, Meliaceae, Moraceae, Leguminosae, and Palmae as the families with the highest FIV.

Also in Rondônia, Lisboa (1989) studied secondary forest and recorded data on all 760 individuals with a CBH ≥ 15 cm in a half-hectare (500 x 10 m) plot. The families with the highest FIV were Leguminosae, Euphorbiaceae, Cochlospermaceae, Moraceae, and Titliacea; of the 113 species found, the most important were *Cochlospermum orinocense* (Kunth) Steud. (Cochlospermaceae), *Sapium marmieri* Huber (Euphorbiaceae), and *Inga edulis* Mart. (Leguminosae).

In order to identify the different vegetation types of the Serra dos Carajás, Morellato and Rosa (1991) established plots along the transects. For the mature terra firme arboreal stratum (DBH ≥ 5 cm), 100 species were found among 437 individuals, with *Erisma uncinatum* Warm. (Vochysiaceae), *Aparisthium cordatum* (Juss.) Baill, and *Neea sp* as the species with the highest SIV. The authors also presented composition and structure data for the other vegetation types identified.

Balée (1986-1987) conducted two inventories in terra firme forest with the objective of studying the ethnobotany of two indigenous communities, the Ka'apor indians in Maranhão, and the Tembé in Pará, and found that they used 100% of the species sampled in the surveys. In a 20 x 500 m transect in the pre-Amazon forest of Maranhão, he found 519 individuals, 117 tree species and six vine species with a DBH ≥ 10 cm (Baleé 1986). In the Gurupi river basin, in Pará, he sampled a one-hectare plot (10 x 1000 m) with 456 trees and 138 species, of which *Eschweilera sp* (Lecythidaceae) and *Sagotia racemosa* Baill. (Euphorbiaceae) were the species with the greatest density (Balée 1987).

Beginning in the 1980s, Alwyn H. Gentry published a series of studies on patterns of diversity of neotropical plants (Gentry 1982, 1986, 1988b, 1992; Gentry and Emmons 1987). In 1986 he presented data on the diversity of two 0.1-hectare plots in Colombia, with an impressive average of 262 species with a DBH ≥ 2.5 cm. In his inventory conducted in seven one-hectare plots close to Iquitos, in Peru, he found between 283[7] and 275 tree species with a DBH ≥ 10 cm (Gentry 1988a). The data were compared to other inventories and the author concluded that the western Amazon contained the highest tree alpha-diversity in the world, due to its relatively fertile soils and heavy rainfall without marked seasonality (Gentry 1998a). In the same year, Gentry published a report compiling and comparing forest composition and diversity data from 67 studies by various authors from 25 different countries (Gentry 1988b).

Faber-Langendoen and Gentry (1991) described the composition of a forest in the Colombian Chocó, sampling trees with a DBH ≥ 10 cm in plots of one hectare (100 x 100 m) and 0.5 hectare (50 x 100 m), and individuals with a DBH ≥ 2.5 cm in subplots of 0.1 hectare in each of the larger plots. For trees with a DBH ≥ 10 cm, 252 species were found in the one-hectare plots, and 154 species in the 0.5-hectare plots. The families with the highest FIV were Arecaceae, Sapotaceae, Myristicaceae, Clusiaceae, and Fabaceae, and the most important species[8] were *Jessenia bataua* (Mart.) Burret, *Socratea exorrhiza* Mart., and *Wettinia quinaria* (Cook & Doyle) Burret (Arecaceae) for the one-hectare samples, and *Jessenia bataua* (Mart.) Burret, *Otoba lehmannii* (A. C. Sm.) A. H Gentry (Myristicaceae), and *Eschweilera panamensis* Pittier (Lecythidaceae) for the 0.5-hectare plots.

Salomão (1991) studied terra firme forest vegetation in the municipality of Marabá, Pará, sampling all individuals with a DBH ≥ 10 cm in six transects (1000 x 10 m), in adjoining pairs. Between 104 and 109 species were found per hectare, out of a total of 237. The most important families for the total sample were Euphorbiaceae, Burseraceae, Mimosaceae, Moraceae, and Lecythidaceae. *Sagotia brachysepala* (Muell.Arg.) R. Secco (Euphorbiaceae) was the most important species in four hectares, and *Tetragastris altissima* (Aubl.) Swart (Burseraceae) was the species with the highest SIV in the other two.

With the aim of comparing different sampling methodologies in quantitative forest inventories, Korning et al. (1991) established a one hectare (100 x 100 m) plot in an area adjacent to that studied by Balslev et al. (1987) in Ecuador. They found a density of 734 individuals belonging to 153 species, with *Quararibea ochrocalyx* (Schum.) Vischer (Bombacaceae), *Jessenia bataua* (Mart.) Burret (Arecaceae) and *Virola elongata* (Benth.) Warb. (Myristicaceae) as the species with the highest SIV, and Bombacaceae, Arecaceae and Moraceae as the families with the highest FIV. The authors observed that the square plot revealed less richness, while the point-centered transect included a greater variety of habitats and, consequently, greater species richness. They concluded that both methods showed the same dominance patterns, but that comparisons of community structure and diversity are only possible when based on the same sampling method.

Surveying four transects (10 x 1000 m) of forest in the Juruá basin, Silva et al. (1992) recorded 556 species (213 to 270 species per hectare) and 3,158 individuals with a DBH ≥ 10 cm, one of the highest tree alpha-diversity levels found in the Brazilian Amazon to this day, and one of the highest in the world with this diameter inclusion criterion. The families presenting the highest FIV among the four hectares were Chrysobalanaceae, Lecythidaceae, Leguminosae, and Sapotaceae, although not necessarily in this order. *Eschweilera odora* (Poepp.) Miers

---

7. This was for a long time the quantitative inventory with highest number of sampled species per hectare, adding up to 300, considering also woody lianas.
8. The names of the authors of the species mentioned in the paper were not given.

(Lecythidaceae) and *Ragala sanguinolenta* Pierre (Sapotaceae) showed the highest SIV in transects 1 and 2 respectively, and *Eschweilera alba* Kunth. (Lecythidaceae) was the most important in the other two. They were followed in importance by *Pourouma ovata* Tréc. (Cecropiaceae) in transect 1, *Jessenia bataua* (Mart.) Burret in transects 2 and 3, and *Eschweilera odora* (Poepp.) Miers in transect 4.

Rankin-de-Merona et al. (1992) published preliminary data on a 70-hectare terra firme forest survey conducted close to Manaus, in the Biological Dynamics of Forest Fragments Project (PDBFF) reserve. They found 698 morphospecies, and the most abundant families in individuals and species richness were Lecythidaceae, Leguminosae, Sapotaceae, and Burseraceae.

Thompson et al. (1992) studied physical factors, forest structure, and leaf chemistry in six plots of 0.25 hectare each in a late secondary terra firme forest on Maracá Island, Roraima. They found 630 trees and 84 species with a DBH ≥ 10 cm, with Moraceae and Sapotaceae as the families with the greatest basal area.

Milliken et al (1992) presented the preliminary data of a one-hectare (500 x 20 m) forest tree survey conducted during their ethnobotanical study of the Waimiri-Atroari indians in the state of Amazonas, subsequently published in its final version (Milliken 1998). This study found 200 tree and 14 liana species, 81% of which were in some way useful to the indians. The families with the greatest number of individuals were Leguminosae, Lecythidaceae, Burseraceae, Sapotaceae, and Chrysobalanaceae, and the most numerous species were *Clathrotopis macrocarpa* Ducke (Leguminosae), *Eschweilera coriacea* (A. DC.) Mori (Lecythidaceae), *Protium hebetatum* Daly, *P. apiculatum* Swart. (Burseraceae), and *Oenocarpus bacaba* Mart (Arecaceae).

In a survey carried out at the Ferreira Pena Scientific Station in Caxiuanã, Pará, 2,441 individuals of 338 species were sampled in four hectares of terra firme forest. The number of species per hectare varied between 147 and 196, and the number of individuals ranged between 527 and 727. The most abundant species were *Laetia procera* Eichl. (Flacourtiaceae), *Astrocaryum aculeatum* G.F.W. Mey (Arecaceae), *Goupia glabra* Aubl. (Celastraceae), and *Eschweilera coriacea* (A.DC.) Mori (Lecythidaceae). The hypothesis of an increasing diversity gradient running from east to west in the eastern Amazon was not borne out by the comparison of data from this survey to that of other studies conducted in the region (Almeida et al. 1993).

Muniz et al. (1994a, 1994b) studied the structure and composition of a pre-Amazonian terra firme forest in the region of São Luís, Maranhão. They found 419 individuals and 46 arboreal species with a CBH ≥ 15 cm (DBH ≥ 4.77) in 50 plots of 10 x 10 m. *Licania cf. incana* Aubl., *Guarea guidonia* (L.) Sleumer and *Copaifera langsdorffii* Desf. were the species with the highest SIV within the community (Muniz et al. 1994b).

Two hectares were sampled in the northwest of Guyana where, respectively, 59 and 85 species, and 493 and 504 individuals with a DBH ≥ 10 cm were found. The most important species in both hectares was *Eschweilera pedicellata* (Rich.) Mori (Lecythidaceae), followed by *Aspidosperma excelsum* Benth. ex Ducke (Apocynaceae) in the first plot and *Mora gonggrijpii* (Kleinh.) Sandw. (Caesalpiniaceae) in the second. Despite being second in importance in one plot, *Mora gonggrijpii* was completely absent from the other. (Comiskey et al. 1994).

In Ecuador, Valencia et al. (1994) sampled the hectare (100 x 100 m) with the highest tree alpha-diversity in the world to date, where 473 species with a DBH ≥ 5 cm, and 307 species with a DBH of at least 10 cm were found. In the latter category, *Jessenia bataua* (Mart.) Burret (Arecaceae) and *Eschweilera aff. coriacea* (Lecythidaceae) were the species with the highest density, and Leguminosae, Lauraceae, Sapotaceae, Moraceae, and Burseraceae were the most numerous families.

In one hectare of terra firme forest in the municipality of Jenaro Herrera, Peru, 504 trees and 227 species with a DBH ≥ 10 cm were sampled. *Jessenia bataua* (Mart.) Burret (Arecaceae), *Eschweilera coriacea* (A.DC.) Mori, and *Osteophloeum platyspermum* (A.DC.) Warb (Myristicaceae) were the species showing the highest SIV, and Leguminosae, Sapotaceae, and Moraceae were the families with the highest FIV (Spichiger et al. 1996).

In the Colombian Amazon, Duivenvoorden (1995, 1996) used 95 sampling units of 0.1 hectare each, in discontinuous areas, to study different types of forest. The plots were established along a section of the Caquetá river, with a minimum distance of 250 m between each. A total of 1,077 morphospecies was found, 525 of which were identified at the species level. In the 40 terra firme plots, he found an average of 38 ± 1.4 morphospecies per plot, 252 ± 21 species per hectare, and a total of 668 morphospecies. The study demonstrated a positive correlation between species density and canopy height, and showed that density of taxa in different forest formations is related to soil quality and environmental adversity (Duivendoorden 1996).

Studying the forests of the Urucu region, in the state of Amazonas, Amaral (1996) found the highest beta-diversity ever registered in Brazil. In one-hectare plots (100 x 100 m), covering the transition between upland, hillside, and lowland forest, he found 253, 269, and 322 tree species with a DBH of over 10 cm for each plot. This study demonstrates that, in addition to the high point diversity recorded in other research, there is also high replacement of species across environmental gradients. It is interesting to observe that this high beta-diversity is also related to a difference in forest structure: the most diverse hectare contained 769 individuals, a very high tree per hectare density.

In the Brazilian Amazon, close to Manaus, three one-hectare plots were established in terra firme forest with similar edaphic conditions and no more than 400 m apart. The authors found between 280 and 285 species per hectare and a total of 513 tree species with a DBH ≥ 10 cm, one of the highest species densities ever recorded for tropical rain forests (Oliveira and Mori 1999, Oliveira 1997). The alpha-diversity was attributed to the confluence of phyto-geographical regions, probably due to recent vicarious events (Oliveira and Daly 1999, Oliveira 1997). The plots showed low levels of similarity, sharing less than 36% of the species between any two plots. *Eschweilera coriacea* (A.DC.) Mori (Lecythidaceae), *Pouteria anomala* (Pires) T. D. Penn. (Sapotaceae), and *Scleronema micranthum* (Ducke) Ducke (Bombacaceae) were, respectively, the species with the highest SIV in each plot. Only *S. micranthum* (Ducke), *Protium hebetatum* Daly (Burseraceae), and *Minquartia guianensis* Aubl. (Olacaceae) appeared among the ten highest SIV species in the three plots, which indicates the inconsistencies in community identification that occur when using this index for samples of one hectare size in terra firme forests (Oliveira 1997).

In the Jaú National Park, Ferreira and Prance (1998) analyzed four discontinuous hectares of terra firme forest, counting all individuals with a DBH ≥ 10 cm. Sample similarity was very low: only 40 (13%) of the 315 species sampled were common to all four plots, and only 24% to 44% were common to any two. The number of species varied between 137 and 168, and the number of individuals between 639 and 713 per hectare. The families Burseraceae, Leguminosae, and Myristicaceae presented the highest tree density in three plots, not necessarily in this order; and Arecaceae, Chrysobalanaceae, and Leguminosae were the highest density families in the other. The most abundant species in number of individuals were *Alexa grandiflora* Ducke (Leguminosae) and *Iryanthera laevis* Markgr. (Myristicaceae) in hectares 1 and 3; *Scleronema micranthum* (Ducke) Ducke (Bombacaceae) and *Protium grandifolium* Engl. (Burseraceae) in hectare 2; and *Oenocarpus bacaba* Mart. (Arecaceae) and *Couepia obovata* Ducke (Chrysobalanaceae) in hectare 4.

Using data from large-scale inventories on the Guiana shield, Steege (1998) identified five forest regions, included two further regions on the basis of additional information, and by means of analysis established a strategy for identifying areas for nature protection. He analyzed 1,029 plots, totaling 212 hectares and 15,397 trees with a DBH greater than 30.5 cm. Caesalpiniaceae, Lecythidaceae, Fabaceae, Chrysobalanaceae, Sapotaceae, Mimosaceae and Lauraceae were the families with the highest density of individuals in each region.

In the Bolivian Amazon, close to the Andes, Dewalt et al. (1999) established two one-hectare plots in the province of Iturralde to study the quantitative ethnobotany of the Tacana community, one in seasonally flooded forest and the other in terra firme. They found 618 and 566 individuals with a DBH ≥ 10 cm belonging to 117 and 122 species, respectively. The most representative families in both plots were Arecaceae, Moraceae, Fabaceae, Annonaceae, and Meliaceae by FIV (after Mori et al. 1983). Palms comprised 30% of the individuals found on the floodplain as against 16% in terra firme, and constituted the family with highest tree density in both samples. *Iriatea deltoide* Ruíz; Pavon, *Euterpe precatoria* Mart., and *Jessenia bataua* (Mart.) Burret. were the species with highest SIV (after Curtis and Macintosh 1951) in the floodplain, and *Dipteryx odorata* (Aubl.) Willd., *Trichilia pleena* (Juss.) C.DC., and *Astrocaryum gratum* Kahn & Millán showed the highest SIV in terra firme. Of the 185 species found, 115 were used by the Tacana, 40 (22%) of which for medicinal purposes. According to the data, only 29% of the species were common to both plots (Dewalt et al. 1999).

Seasonally flooded forests

This section analyzes the forests occurring on the lowland terraces of the Quaternary floodplains along large rivers. In the Amazon region, these areas are popularly known as 'várzea' or 'igapó', according to the level of flooding. In the scientific literature, these denominations are adapted to mean forests inundated by muddy water (várzea) or by black/transparent water (igapó) (Pires 1974, Prance 1979). In the system used by Veloso et al. (1991), várzeas and igapós are brought together under the category Alluvial Dense Rain Forest.

Studies describing the flora and composition of seasonally flooded forests in Amazonia are very scarce, despite the efforts of pioneering Amazon researchers who sought to better understand these environments (Huber 1906, Ducke and Black 1950). There are only a few known igapó forest inventories in Brazil, most of them concentrating on the region near Manaus (Rodrigues 1961, Keel and Prance 1979, Revilla 1981, Piedade 1985, Worbes 1986 apud Ferreira 1997, Ferreira 1991). Others were carried out near Amanã lake (Ayres 1993), the Xingu River (Campbell et al. 1986), the Jaú National Park (Ferreira 1997), and the outskirts of Belém, where Pires and Prance (1977) studied and compared igapó, várzea, and terra firme forests. In addition to this last study, only six other quantitative inventories of seasonally flooded várzea forests have so far been carried out in Brazil (Black et. al 1950, Pires and Koury 1959, Rankin-de-Merona 1988, Campbell et al. 1992, Worbes et. al. 1992, Ayres 1993), adding up to a total of only 15 inventories in seasonally flooded forests. The most relevant data from these studies have been selected and are presented in this section.

In 1961, Rodrigues studied the floristic composition of an island in the Anavilhanas archipelago north of Manaus, on the lower Rio Negro. He found the most representative families to be Leguminosae, Annonaceae, and Rubiaceae. Among the 51 species recorded, *Unonopsis guatterioides*, *Swartzia laevicarpa*, and *Eschweilera sp.* stand out as emergent species, and *Heisteria sp.*, *Pseudoxandra polypheba*, and *Psychotria lupulina* were the most important in the intermediate stratum.

In 1962[9], Takeuchi described the environments of seasonally flooded forests close to Manaus. The species he records as characteristic of the Rio Negro igapó are *Eugenia inundata* D.C. associated with *Symmeria paniculata* Benth., *Eschweilera sp.* (probably *E. tenuifolia*, very common in the region), and *Simaba guinensis* Engl. In addition, he describes the species *Licania heteromorpha* Benth., *Campsiandra laurifolia* Benth., *Copaifera guianensis* Desf., *Pithecolobium cauliflorum* Mart., and *Ouratea aquatica* Engl. as occurring frequently at lower levels on the white-sand beaches. Amongst other observations, the author mentions the floristic similarities between igapós on river margins, on islands, and on lakes, where muddy waters become black following decantation.

Keel and Prance (1979) also studied the floristic composition, community structure and diversity of an igapó forest on the lower Rio Negro, recording all individuals over 1 m high in twelve 10 x 15 m plots. They found 51 species and 1,028 individuals, with Myristicaceae, Leguminosae, Apocynaceae, and Euphorbiaceae as the families most numerous in species and individuals. The authors noted distinct zoning within the igapó, with the most abundant species changing in accordance with the duration of the flooding to which they were subjected. In the lower areas of the igapó they found *Myrciaria dubia*, *Remijia tenuifolia*, *Tococa subciliata*, and *Turnera acuta*; the middle part was dominated by *Eugenia cachoeirensis*, *E. chrysobalanoides*, and *Schistostemon macrophyllum*; while the higher area, which has a shorter flooding season, was dominated by *Eugenia patrisii*, *Pera distichophylla*, and *Pithecellobium adiantifolium*. As the occurrence of *Eugenia inundata* is here recorded only in the permanently flooded areas of the igapó, it can be concluded that the difference in composition between this site and that studied by Takeuchi (1962) is due to the different flooding characteristics in both areas.

In his description of seasonal igapó forests and their arthropod fauna, Adis (1984) compiles data from botanical surveys and divides the igapó into three habitats each with a distinct composition: low igapó, high igapó, and island igapó. The data were taken from previous studies, especially those of Keel and Prance (1979), Revilla (1981), Adis (1981), Adis et al. (1979), Takeuchi (1962), and Rodrigues (1961).

Campbell et al. (1986) compared terra firme forest with the vegetation of a seasonally flooded forest adjacent to the Xingu River, and their main conclusions are summarized in the previous

---

9. Republished in Portuguese in 1967.

section on terra firme. In this section we shall simply attempt to summarize the floristic characteristics of seasonally flooded forest. In a half-hectare plot, 220 trees and 40 species with a DBH ≥ 10 cm were found and the most abundant families were Violaceae, Leguminosae, and Tiliaceae. The most abundant species were *Mollia lepidota* with 22% of the individuals, *Leonia glicocarpa* with 21%, and *Etaballia guianensis* with approximately 5% of the individuals in the sample.

At the Mamirauá Ecological Station on the middle Solimões, Ayres studied vegetation composition and structure in order to describe the habitat of the White Uakari (*Cacajao calvus calvus*). In this study he sampled sixteen 25 x 25 m plots totaling one hectare randomly distributed on both banks of the Taboca river, a black-water tributary on the right bank of Lake Amanã. For trees with a DBH ≥ 10 cm, the most numerous families were Leguminosae, Sapotaceae, Chrysobalanaceae, Euphorbiaceae, Clusiaceae, Annonaceae, and Lecythidaceae. Five species contributed more than 25% of the total number of trees sampled: *Pouteria elegans*, *Caraipa densifolia*, *Erisma calcaratum*, and *Eschweilera cf. rodriguesiana*. In the Lake Teiú várzea forest, also in the Mamirauá Ecological Station, the author studied transects adding up to 10 x 100 m, and 16 discontinuous 25 x 25 m plots, a total sampling area of two hectares. The study recorded all individuals with a DBH ≥ 10 cm, adding up to 996 trees and 174 species. Two communities were identified through analysis of their main components: high levees, where the water level never exceeded 2.6 m, and low levees, where the high water level rose was deeper than 2.6 m. The dominant families by numbers of individuals in the high levee were Annonaceae (16.4%), Euphorbiaceae (10.5%), Leguminosae (7.8%), Apocynaceae (7.4%), Lecythidaceae (6%), and Lauraceae (5.2%). Of the 137 species found, the most common were *Malouetia cf. tamaquirensis* (4.6%), *Guatteriopsis kuhlmanii* (4%), *Tapura amazonica* (3.3%), and *Pseudoxandra polyphleba* (2.8%). Some of the tallest Amazonian trees were also found in this environment: *Ceiba pentandra*, *Hura crepitans*, and *Parinari excelsa*. On the low levee, the most abundant families were Euphorbiaceae (18.8%), Leguminosae (16%), Lecythidaceae (7%), Annonaceae (5.5%), and Myrtaceae; the most common species were *Pterocarpus amazonicus*, *Eschweilera albiflora*, *Piranhea trifoliolata*, and *Pouteria elegans*. Of the 174 species found in both hectares, 41 and 67 occurred exclusively in the low and high levees respectively. This means that only 37.9% of the species were common to both environments, which indicates high community differentiation associated with flooding levels (Ayres 1993).

Ferreira (1991) studied the composition, regeneration, and phenology of igapó species on the Tarumã-Mirim river, north of Manaus. He found 165 species undergoing clear substitution along the forest flooding gradient, with some species restricted to certain zones, and others distributed throughout the whole gradient. He also noticed that the number of species increases as the duration of flooding decreases, and that there is intraspecific variation in the reproductive phenophase relating to the individual's position on the flooding gradient.

At the Jaú National Park, Ferreira (1997) studied three different environments in igapó forests: lake, riverbank, and igarapé (small stream). In each of these environments, he recorded all individuals with a DBH ≥ 10 cm in a one-hectare area and found, respectively, 44, 103, and 137 species among 777, 941, and 1,111 individuals in the lake, riverbank, and igarapé plots. The families with the greatest number of individuals were Euphorbiaceae, Leguminosae, and Malpighiaceae in the lake; Leguminosae, Sapotaceae, and Euphorbiaceae in the riverbank; and Leguminosae, Sapotaceae, and Chrysobalanaceae in the igarapé. The most abundant species also varied among the three environments: *Amanoa oblongifolia* and *Macrolobium acaciaefolium* were predominant in the lake, *Pouteria elegans* and *Amanoa oblongifolia* in the riverbank, and *Sclerolobium sp* and *Aldina latifolia* in the igarapé.

The várzea forests close to Manaus present floristic and structural differences related to their successional stage (Worbes et al. 1992). The várzea forest vegetation of this region was sampled under different conditions of anthropogenic disturbance, and correlations were found between average tree age, wood density, time elapsed since disturbance, and floristic composition. Mature or climax forests tend to possess bigger trees, denser wood, lower dominance, and higher diversity. The most characteristic species of this phase are *Piranhea trifoliata*, *Eschweilera sp*, *Manilkara sp*, a non-determined species, and *Vatairea gianensis*. The authors of this work list 75 common species in Amazon forest surveys and argue that, although there are species widely distributed throughout northern South America, few of the species shared among the várzeas of Manaus occur beyond the central Amazon. They also observe that more than half the listed trees are not restricted to flooded forest environments and can occur in terra firme forests. Other species common to várzeas may also appear as typical of igapó environments: *Alchornea castaneaefolia*, *Tabebuia barbata*, *Piranhea trifoliolata*, *Triplaris surinamensis*, and *Macrolobium acaciaefolium* (Worbes et al. 1992).

If we take a one-hectare plot to be the average survey size, we have survey sizes of around ten hectares to describe 15,000 km² of igapó, and of less than ten hectares to describe the estimated 50,000 km² of várzea in Brazil. This amounts to less than one hectare sampled for each 325,000 hectares of seasonally flooded forest and reflects a state near total lack of knowledge of the flora and community structure for this type of environment.

Synthesis of quantitative tree inventories

Inventories carried out in Amazonia have shown that strict terra firme forests, that is to say forests on clay plateaus or slopes, show high diversity, a high percentage of low-density species, and low floristic similarity between neighboring plots. These patterns were established early in the history of quantitative forest inventories (Davis and Richard 1934; Black et al. 1950; Pires et al. 1953; Cain et al. 1956) and very little has been added since then with respect to typical community structural and floristic patterns of these forests at the species level.

Comparisons between different studies have been hampered by the great variety of research methodologies employed, especially regarding shape and size of sample areas, and of diameter inclusion criteria (Table 1). Moreover, the great efforts needed to obtain good collections of botanical material and the complexity of identifying specimens have made floristic and structural comparisons at the species level even more difficult.

It is hard to single out any species that are of uniformly great importance in the structure of terra firme forests. The matamatá, (*Eschweilera coriacea* (A.DC.) Mori (Lecythidaceae), synonymous with *E. odora* Miers according to Mori and Prance (1990)), is one of the few high density species to occur in different regions of Amazonia (Oliveira 1997, Valencia et al. 1994, Rollet 1993,

Silva et al. 1992, Prance et al. 1976, Sudam 1974, Cain et al. 1956, Pires et al. 1953). The patauá palm, (*Oenocarpus bataua* Mart., synonymous with *Jessenia bataua* (Mart.) Burret according to Henderson et al. (1995)), shows high density levels in the terra firme forests of western Amazonia (Faber-Langendoen and Gentry 1991, Korning et al. 1991, Silva et al. 1992, Valencia et al. 1994, Spichiger et al. 1996), occurs exclusively in low periodically flooded forests in central Amazonia close to small streams (Porto et al. 1976; personal observation) and is not found at all in eastern Amazonia (Henderson et al. 1995). The low density of most species hinders floristic comparisons between plots; nevertheless, some attempts have been made to extract family and genus patterns from the existing data.

Floristic composition

The present study shows that, with rare exceptions, the families with the highest density and diversity in the primary forest canopy are Leguminosae (broadly defined), Arecaceae, Lecythidaceae, Sapotaceae, Burseraceae, Chrysobalanaceae, Moraceae, and Lauraceae. Palms are particularly predominant in transition forests between the Amazon and other biomes, in disturbed environments – close to indigenous or traditional communities – and in seasonally waterlogged streamside forests, while Leguminosae are among the most abundant families in any region.

Terborgh and Andresen (1998), analyzing data on the sixteen most representative families in 39 inventories of terra firme and seasonally flooded Amazonian forests, report that Leguminosae and Arecaceae are among the best represented families. According to the authors, Chrysobalanaceae and Lecythidaceae are important families on the Guiana plateau, but are less important in the Amazonian tree community. Using multivariate analysis at the family level, they demonstrate that there is greater distinction between more distant plots than among those with different edaphic conditions in the same region (terra firme versus seasonally flooded forest).

More recently, Steege et al. (2000a, 2000b) used the same methodology adopted by Terborgh and Andresen (1998) in a group of 268 terra firme and várzea plots, distributed mainly in Amazonia and the Guiana plateau. In this analysis, Leguminosae were found to be the most abundant family, accounting for an average of 16% of the individuals in the plots. The authors also demonstrated that Leguminosae are particularly abundant in eastern Amazonia and the Guiana plateau, especially in seasonally flooded forests or on sandy soil. Lecythidaceae and Chrysobalanaceae are abundant on the Guiana plateau and in central Amazonia, with Lecythidaceae also having an important presence in the forests further east. Burseraceae are common in eastern and central Amazonia, and Sapotaceae are among the most predominant families along the middle Amazon. In the forests of western Amazonia, the most representative families, in addition to Leguminosae, are Arecaceae and Moraceae. The differences observed in relation to the study conducted by Terborgh and Andresen (1998) are mainly due to the latter lacking information on the middle Amazon and Guiana regions (Steege et al. 2000a, 2000b).

Using the data available in the literature and unpublished data from other plots, Oliveira and Nelson (2000) compared the plot composition and community structure of 32 terra firme inventories in 16 different regions, all at the genus level. Classification and ordination analyses showed that changes in composition of terra firme plots are associated with forest type (physiognomy) and geographic distance, with a clear differentiation between mature forests, forests with a history of disturbance, and the more open forests in transitional areas of the Brazilian Amazon. Oliveira-Filho and Ratter (1995) also mention the transitional character of open forests in Amazonia, demonstrating their closer floristic and structural affinity to the forests of central Brazil than to other Amazonian forests.

Patterns of tree diversity

Using currently available inventory data, Gentry (1988a) described an east-west tree diversity gradient in which the plots closest to the Andes show greater richness (Gentry 1988a, 1988b). He related this phenomenon to climatic and edaphic factors, and showed that climates with more rain and less seasonality, and soils that are relatively richer in nutrients, support greater tree diversity (Gentry 1988a). Other authors relate diversity in tropical forest plots to the natural dynamics of tree mortality – forests with higher mortality and recruitment rates will be richer in species (Phillips et al. 1994). Climatic seasonality seems to be an important factor in explaining the differences in tree diversity in the Amazon. Different studies (Gentry 1992; Phillips et al. 1994; Clinebell II et al. 1995) suggest that forests in less seasonal climates, without distinct dry seasons, show higher tree diversity.

Steege et al. (2000a, 2000b), using more than 250 inventoried plots in Amazonia and the Guiana highlands, show that forest type and plot location are closely correlated to species richness, while the relationship between rainfall and richness, although significant, is less pronounced.

The present study suggests that western Amazonian inventories show higher tree diversity than those carried out in the far east of Amazonia (Table 1). However, species density for trees (DBH ≥ 10 cm) in middle Amazonian inventories are very close to those found in western Amazonian inventories (Gentry 1988a, Valencia et al. 1994, Oliveira 1997; Oliveira and Mori 1999, Steege et al. 2000a, 2000b), which is not fully consistent with the idea of a longitudinal east-west gradient pattern. This high species density in central Amazonian plots further contradicts the posited relationships between tree diversity, seasonality, rainfall, and dynamics. Research on the geographical distribution of arboreal species in central Amazonia suggests that high diversity here could be related to the overlap of distinct phyto-geographical regions, bringing together species from different regions (Oliveira and Daly 1999).

We can therefore see that, at the present time and despite all the efforts to understand the structure and composition of Amazonian forests, little is known about community structural patterns and regional floristic differences. Moreover, the structure and composition data obtained in one-hectare sampling plots cannot be extrapolated to the surrounding forest, even in areas that are close to each other and show similar topographic and soil conditions (Oliveira 1997).

Geographical distribution of species

This section analyzes the geographical distribution of Amazonian plant species, focusing on issues relevant to conservation, such as restricted geographical distribution (local endemism) and sites of high diversity. The data are drawn from three main studies: Lleras et al. (1992), Williams et al. (1996), and Oliveira and Daly (1999).

Table 1 - Principal studies on the tree component of Amazonia and related species richness

Author	Locality	Plot size (m)	DBH (cm)	no. of individuals	no. of species	sp/ha
Oliveira 1997	Brazil, Manaus	3 (100 x 100)	10	1916	513	280-285
Duivenvoorden 1996	Colombia, Caquetá	40 (20 x 50)	10	2874	668	252 ± 21
Valencia et al. 1994	Ecuador	100 x 100	10	693	307	307
Almeida et al. 1993	Brazil, Caxiuanã	4 (25 x 400)	10	2441	338	147-196
Milliken et al. 1992	Brazil, Maré	20 x 500	10	643	201	201
Silva et al. 1992	Brazil, Juruá	4 (10 x 1000)	10	3158	556	213-271
Faber-Langendoen & Gentry 1991	Colombia, Chocó	100 x 100	10	675	258	258
Salomão 1991	Brazil, Marabá	3 (20 x 1000)	10	3147	237	101-109
Maciel & Lisboa 1989	Brazil, Rondônia	1 ha	9.55	602	90	90
Mori et al. 1989	Brazil, Amapá	CQ	10	1000	205	-
Silva & Rosa 1989	Brazil, Carajás	2 (10 x 1000)	9.55	1022	>121	118-121
Salomão & Lisboa 1988	Brazil, Ji-Paraná	500 x 20	9.55	564	164	164
Salomão & Lisboa 1988	Brazil, Carajás	2* 500 x 10	10	484	122	122
Gentry 1988a	Peru, Yanamono	1 ha	10	508	283	283
Gentry 1988a	Peru, Mishana	1 ha	10	842	275	275
Gentry 1988a	Peru, Cocha Cashu	1 ha	10	650	189	189
Gentry 1988a	Peru, Cabeza de Mono	1 ha	10	520	169	169
Gentry 1988a	Peru, Tambopata	1 ha	10	585	168	168
Gentry 1988a	Brazil / Venezuela	1 ha	10	493	89	89
Balée 1987	Brazil, També	1 ha	10	456	138	138
Balslev et al. 1987	Ecuador, Yasuní	CQ	10	804	244	228
Mori & Boom 1987	French Guiana	CQ	10	800	295	-
Silva et al. 1987	Brazil, Carajás	10 x 1000	9.55	456	210	210
Absy et al. 1986-1987	Brazil, Jaru	6 (10 x 1000)	10	2235	278	103-136
Balée 1986	Brazil, Maranhão	20 x 500	10	498	117	117
Boom 1986	Bolivia, Allto Ivon	10 x 1000	10	649	94	94
Campbell et al. 1986	Brazil, Xingu	10 x 3000	10	1420	265	118-133
Silva et al. 1986	Brazil, Carajás	20 x 500	9.55	516	125	125
Uhl & Murphy 1981	Venezuela, San Carlos	1 ha	10	744	83	83
Dantas et al. 1980	Brazil, Capitão Poço	40* (10 x 25)	9.55	504	120	120
Dantas & Müller 1979	Brazil, Transamazônica	40* (10 x 25)	9.55	578	101	101
Prance et al. 1976	Brazil, Manaus	125 x 80	15	350	179	179
Rodrigues 1963	Brazil, Amapá	11* (10 x 100)	15	347		
Rodrigues 1963	Brazil, Amapá	15* (10 x 100)	15	307	96	96
Cain et al. 1956	Brazil, Belém	20* (10 x 100)	10	1188	173	144
Pires et al. 1953	Brazil, Belém	3,5 ha	10	1482	179	108
Black et al. 1950	Brazil, Belém	100 x 100	10	423	87	87

CQ: point-centered quarter; –: data not available; *: number of plots.

Lleras et al. (1992) studied the geographical occurrence of approximately three thousand species, using data from the Flora Neotropica monographs (New York Botanical Garden Press) and herbarium collections (see Figure 32). The authors stress the difficulties interpreting results due to the lack of botanical collections, which leads to a false increase in the number of local endemisms and of species diversity for those regions where highest collecting effort has occurred. Despite this problem, they highlight Manaus and the upper Rio Negro as regions of high diversity and, therefore, priority conservation areas.

Williams et al. (1996) interpret the distribution of 729 species from five botanical families common in Amazonia and the Andes. Species occurrence data are interpolated to draw a map indicating the probable occurrence of each species, thus reducing the effect of differential collecting efforts. The Neotropical region was divided into 1,751 blocks of one degree latitude by one degree longitude, in each of which species diversity and rarity level are analyzed. For any given block, the rarity level increases when more species with registered ranges are found in the block. The results suggest high species diversity throughout the Amazon region for this group of families (see Figure 6a). It can also be seen that the high diversity in the Manaus region is not repeated in Belém, which would be expected if these results derived solely as a result of collecting effort, since collecting activities in Belém have been greater than in Manaus (Nelson et al. 1990). The axis of high diversity along the Solimões, Amazonas, and Negro valleys, as well as in the Guianas, seen in Figure 6a, may result in part from collecting activities. The degree of rarity map developed by Williams et al. (1996), in which sites with a greater incidence of small scale endemism have higher scores (Figure 6b), reveals that Amazonian species show a wider geographical distribution than those of other biomes, suggesting that a uniform pattern of conservation areas would be an adequate strategy for conserving the floristic diversity of Amazonia. The hot spots of small scale endemism occur mainly on Caribbean islands and in mountain regions outside Amazonia: the Andes, the Guiana Shield, the upper Orinoco and upper Rio Negro, and the Atlantic Forest. In Amazonia, the areas with apparent low levels of endemism correspond to the regions with the lowest levels of collecting, clearly an artifact. There are also five centers of local endemism, albeit of modest levels and small size as follows: 2°-3° S, 59°-61° W (Manaus, Amazonas); 5°-6° S, 45°-46° W (Barra do Corda, Maranhão); 10°-11° S, 63°-64° W (Ariquemes, Rondônia); 12°-13° S, 59°-60° W (Nambiquara Indigenous Area, Mato Grosso); and 15°-16° S, 49°-50° W (Goianésia, Goiás). It is interesting to note that three of these areas – Barra do Corda, the Nambiquara Indigenous Area and Goianésia – do not appear as sites of high collecting activity on the map developed by Nelson et al. (1990).

An analysis of the distribution of 354 species occurring in the terra firme (strict sense) forests of Manaus (Table 2), based on data from the Flora Neotropica monographs (New York Botanical Garden Press) and herbarium records, demonstrates that 82.7% of these species occur exclusively in Amazonia and the Guianas, but that only 19.1% are restricted to the middle Amazon region (Oliveira and Daly 1999; Oliveira 1997).

In the same studies (Oliveira and Daly 1999; Oliveira 1997), Manaus appears as the farthest point of geographical distribution of a great number of species occurring in different areas of Amazonia (Figure 7 c-f). This shows that, although these species are, in general, widely distributed throughout Amazonia, there is a difference between the floras of the large forest blocks delimited by the Amazonas-Solimões and the Negro-Madeira. This difference is difficult to detect because of the effects of the varied levels of collecting.

Differences in botanical collecting efforts hamper phyto-geographical analysis and impede studies of species distribution. In the case of angiosperms, the majority of the centers of non-edaphic endemism found are the result of the lack of occurrence data for those regions poorly studied. As a result of five years of intensive collecting, the Flora of the Ducke Reserve project (INPA/DFID) was able to double the number of species recorded in the reserve, which is on the urban limits of Manaus (Hopkins, personal communication). This region was considered by Nelson et al. (1990) to be, in floristic terms, one of the best-known in Amazonia prior to the project. Facts such as these serve as a warning against basing decisions on conservation priorities on analyses of the distribution of plant species. There is an urgent need to improve existing species distribution databases (Lleras et al. 1992; Williams et al. 1996) by incorporating species information held in important Amazonian collections (in Manaus, Belém, São Paulo and New York) and information on species occurrence in those regions where little collecting has taken place, as indicated by Nelson et al. (1990).

Geographical occurrence, characteristics and conservation status of Amazonian vegetation types

Background

In this section we will use, with some modification and updating, the methodology developed by Fearnside and Ferraz (1995) to define priority conservation areas. These authors employed a map of vegetation types in Brazil available at the time (IBGE/IBDF 1988) to define the vegetation formations needing protection in each state in the Amazon. At a scale of 1:5,000,000, this map showed 28 different vegetation types for the region. Fearnside and Ferraz (1995) digitized vegetation type polygons and overlaid these on the boundaries of conservation units and of Brazilian Amazon states. They excluded semi-protected areas from the analysis: national forests, areas of managed forest, extractive reserves, and indigenous areas. They were thus able to define how many protected and unprotected vegetation types there were in each state. The number of vegetation types varied from 4 (in Acre) to 18 (in Roraima). The two states with the lowest proportion of protected vegetation types were Maranhão (with only 1 out of 10 types) and Pará (2 out of 16). The states with the best situation were Amapá (5 out of 8) and Amazonas (10 out of 17). The authors recommended that each state establish strict conservation areas to include examples of every vegetation type present in the state. This would require the conservation of parts of 111 separate types of polygons, using the state by vegetation type combinations. Of these 111 classes, 74 lay outside strict conservation areas at the time of the analysis. Fearnside and Ferraz proposed 44 new conservation areas as a means of ensuring the partial conservation of all vegetation types in each state.

According to Fearnside and Ferraz (1995), strict conservation areas represented 2.6% of the Brazilian Legal Amazon and semi-protected conservation areas added up to 823,000 km^2, or 16.4%. With the creation of new reserves reported by IBGE as of

TABLE 2 - NUMBER OF SPECIES IN EACH DISTRIBUTION PATTERN; PERCENTAGE OF TOTAL NUMBER OF SPECIES FOUND; AND THE NUMBER AND THE PERCENTAGE OF SPECIES FOR WHICH MANAUS IS THE LIMIT OF OCCURRENCE.

Distribution pattern	no. of species	Limit at Manaus
Wide distribution		
Neotropical	11 (3.0%)	-
Amazon-Central America	11 (3.0%)	-
Tropical South America	13 (3.6%)	1 (7.6%)
Disjoined distribution		
Amazon-Atlantic Forest	20 (5.5%)	1 (5.0%)
Restricted distribution		
Extra-Amazonian		
Amazon-Central Brazil	8 (2.2%)	-
Amazonian		
Whole of Amazonia	112 (30.8%)	13 (11.6%)
Southern Amazonia	5 (1.4%)	5 (100%)
Northern Amazonia	13 (3.6%)	11 (84.6%)
East-central Amazonia	34 (9.3%)	30 (88.2%)
West-central Amazonia	51 (14.0%)	38 (74.5%)
Central Amazonia-Guianas	16 (4.4%)	12 (75%)
Middle Amazonas		
Whole of Middle Amazonas	11 (3.0%)	7 (63.6%)
Mid-south Amazonas	14 (3.8%)	14 (100%)
Mid-north Amazonas	19 (5.2%)	18 (94.7%)
Endemic		
Manaus	26 (7.1%)	-

Source: Oliveira 1997.

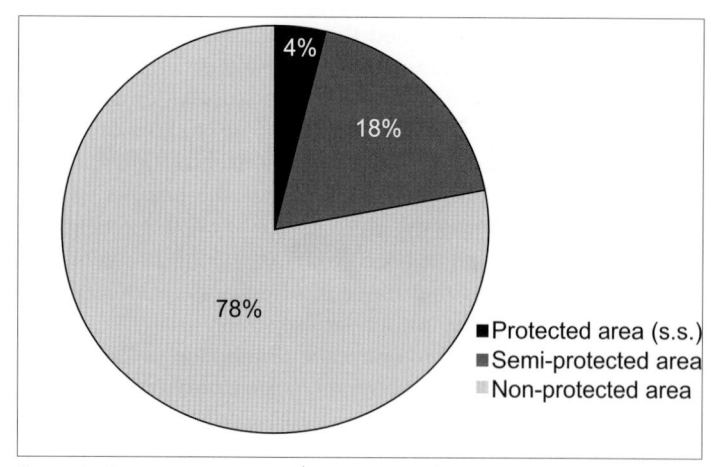

Figure 1. Conservation areas as a percentage of the area of the Legal Amazon based on IBGE (1997).

1997, strict conservation areas later added up to 185,000 km²; and semi-protected areas to 894,000 km², or 3.7% and 17.8% of the Legal Amazon[10], respectively (Table 3). The total of strict and semi-protected conservation areas, leaving out overlaps, was 1,078,000 km² or 21.5% of the Legal Amazon (IBGE 1997; Figures 1-3).

The summary that follows modifies the methodology used by Fearnside and Ferraz in five ways:

Inclusion of semi-protected conservation areas

Semi-protected conservation areas were not considered when Fearnside and Ferraz (1995) made their recommendations for new conservation areas. The new analysis of overlays of vegetation types and conservation areas will be made for both levels of protection. Indigenous areas, although not officially designated as conservation areas, will be included in the semi-protected conservation area category in this study. Areas occupied by traditional and indigenous populations are very extensive and may enjoy better chances of protection than those conservation areas which do not allow presence of human populations and where levels of inspection are very deficient. Near the city of Marabá, in a region renowned for its frequent disputes over ownership of rural land, the Mãe Maria Indigenous Area of the Gavião indians appears in a Landsat image (Figure 8) as an intact forest island with straight borders and no apparent invasions. Similar situations can be observed in indigenous areas in Maranhão and Mato Grosso. These are, therefore, important de facto conservation areas, and in 1997 added up to 69.4% of the total extent of all conservation areas, in the broad sense, in the Legal Amazon.

Geographic stratification of plant physiognomies

Fearnside and Ferraz (1995) geographically subdivided each vegetation type using state boundaries. A state-level approach has its advantages when presenting conservation priorities to decision-makers; however, using such boundaries makes no biological sense. The Amazonian states vary in size: Amazonas is ten times larger than Rondônia. Such an approach therefore does not favor conservation in states with extensive territories. A more rational subdivision would be one based either on a simple latitudinal and longitudinal grid or on floristic criteria.

Prance (1977, 1987) subdivided the Amazon into different floristic or 'phytochorial' regions (Figure 9) based on several plant families. These units are not evident in more recent studies on centers of endemism (Williams et al. 1996; see Figures 6a and 6b) that are based on the geographical distribution of species of the same plant families. Even though they employed interpolated species distribution maps, the regional variations in endemism in Amazonia detected by Williams et al. (1996) are very subtle. A comparison between the endemism map and the collecting density map (Nelson et al. 1991; see Figure 10) indicates that the low levels of endemism in some areas are related to low levels of collecting intensity and not to real phyto-geographical patterns. Although it contains great diversity, the Amazon region is internally homogeneous as to the distribution of plant species, at least when compared to other neotropical forests (Williams et al. 1996; see Figure 6a and 6b). This conclusion is reinforced by analysis of the distribution of 364 species found in Manaus (Oliveira 1997; Oliveira and Daly 1999), where only 19.1% of these species are restricted to central Amazonia (Table 2).

Using the abundance of the main families in 28 quantitative inventories in the Amazon and other places outside the region, a DCA ordination carried out by Terborgh and Andresen (1998) demonstrated the effect of geographical distance on grouping tendencies in Amazonia (see Figure 5). Another ordination of quantitative inventories relating to genus, including 15 Amazonian sites (Oliveira and Nelson 2000),

---

10. Areas overlapping *stricto sensu* UCs were excluded from the total area calculation of semi-protected UCs.

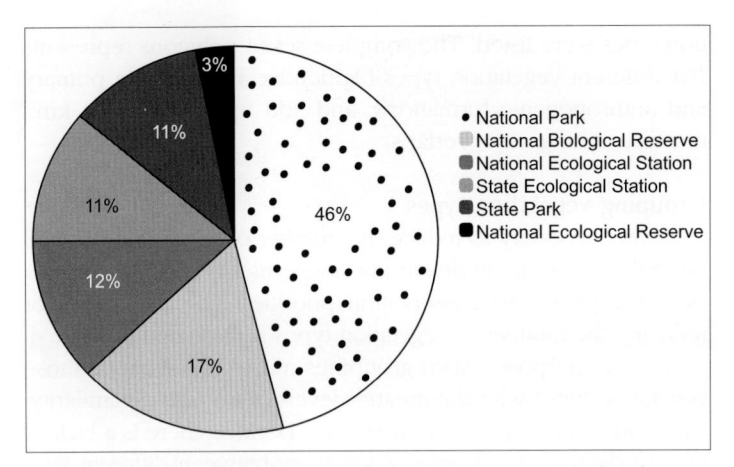

Figure 2. Breakdown of strictly protected conservation areas in the Legal Amazon (total = 184,000 km²).

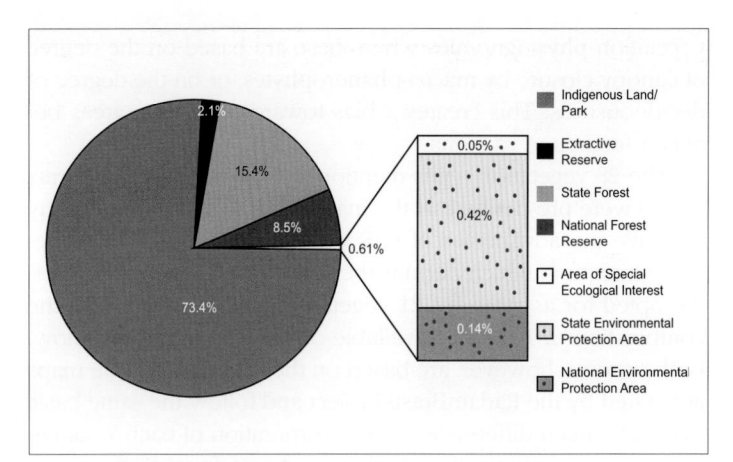

Figure 3. Semi-protected conservation areas in the Legal Amazon.

TABLE 3 - STRICTLY PROTECTED AREAS AND SEMI-PROTECTED AREAS[1] IN THE LEGAL AMAZON (LA)					
Strictly protected areas	km²	% of LA	Semi-protected areas	km²	% of LA
State Ecological Station	19,852	0.40	Indigenous Park / Land	748,634	14.95
National Ecological Station	22,350	0.45	Extractive Reserve	21,680	0.43
National Ecological Reserve	6,035	0.12	State Forest	156,479	3.12
National Biological Reserve	31,197	0.62	National Forest Reserve	86,397	1.72
State Biological Reserve	1,892	0.04	Area of Special Ecological Importance	496	0.01
State Park	9,493	0.39	State Environmental Protection Area	4,318	0.09
National Park	84,137	1.68	National Environmental Protection Area	1,470	0.03
Total	184,276	3.68	Total[2]	893,630	17.84

1. Estimated by polygon raster scanning of 1280 x 1024 screen capture.
2. The total excludes overlaps with strict protected areas.
Source: IBGE 1997.

does not reveal a strong influence of geographical distance on plots of dense and mature terra firme forest, but infers strong differences among forests with distinct physiognomies (see Figures 4a and 4b).

The data from Oliveira and Nelson (2000) demonstrate the value of using vegetation types as indicators of geographical variation in the composition of Amazonian flora, while the analysis of Terborgh and Andresen (1998) indicates the importance of stratifying some vegetation types by distance. We suggest, therefore, that the planning of conservation areas in Amazonia should follow a two-stage stratification process: first, guaranteeing the presence of reserves in each physiognomic unit; and second, locating reserves in a regular geographical pattern throughout the area of occurrence of each vegetation type, paying special attention to outliers or disjunctures of the plant formation.

Fragmented reserves

The 44 reserves recommended by Fearnside and Ferraz (1995) are small and constitute a fragmented group. Current conservation strategies aim at creating corridors to minimize the effects of fragmented forests (Brazil/MMA 1998). Is it interesting to observe that the automated logical procedures of geographic information systems (GIS) can lead to diametrically opposite results. An algorithm optimized for filling occurrence gaps would suggest new reserves as far away as possible from existing reserves; whereas an algorithm for creating corridors would locate the new reserves adjacent to existing reserves. In order to supply decision-makers with a wider range of options, we do not suggest specific reserves. Instead, we show the whole coverage of each vegetation type, indicating where it is protected and the unprotected gaps.

Classification of 'zones of ecological tension'

The five examples of contact between formations found in the IBGE/IBDF (1988) map are considered ecotones by Fearnside and Ferraz (1995) and are given the same consideration as other plant formations. But these contact zones are more a consequence of mapping scale than real ecotones. When two formations are extensively mixed, it becomes impossible to show the boundaries between them on a small-scale map. If these were true ecotones, the ecological tension polygons would be consistently present in all climatic transects, which is not the case. True Amazonian ecotones are found in well defined sequences of plant formations in the vegetation type system used here, such as the sequence: dense rain forest – open rain forest – forested seasonal savanna – woodland seasonal savanna – open seasonal savanna; or the sequence – dense rain forest – campinarana (white-sand) rain forest – moist campinarana woodland – moist open campinarana. In our analysis we give less importance to a 'zone of tension' between two vegetation types, usually incorporating it into the plant formation of lower canopy height or lower canopy closure (Table 4).

Choice of vegetation types

The choice of the vegetation type classification system is a difficult and basic step towards a good conservation strategy. Small areas of climatic transition tend to have a large number of vegetation physiognomies when these are based on the degree of canopy closure by macro-phanerophytes, or on the degree of deciduousness. This creates a bias towards transition areas between forest and savanna.

The 28 vegetation types mentioned by Fearnside and Ferraz (1995) were pre-defined by the map available at the time. Today we have the advantages of GIS with its capacity for more detailed mapping, which permits the selection of vegetation types. We opted for a system of 21 vegetation types derived from the combination of 161 types available on GIS, as described below. Both systems, however, are based on the 1:1,000,000 scale maps generated by the RadamBrasil Project and follow the same basic logic. The main difference is the incorporation of each 'ecological tension zone' into the smaller vegetation formation.

The vegetation classification system adopted

The system used is that proposed by Veloso et al. (1975) to develop 'phyto-ecological' maps for the RadamBrasil Project. The classification was later adapted to a universal system (Veloso et al. 1991) which uses physiognomy (life forms, size of woody elements, deciduousness, canopy uniformity), abiotic environmental factors (substratum, rainfall pattern, altitude) and succession stage (pioneer, climax) as a means of classifying natural vegetation types. Veloso's system was adopted for three main reasons:

1. Other classification systems (Pires and Prance 1985; Prance 1987) are based on this one;

2. It is the only system transformed into the detailed vegetation maps required for the assessment that needs to be undertaken of the conservation status of each vegetation type and for making recommendations on the location of new conservation areas;

3. The phyto-ecological RadamBrasil maps were recently incorporated into a user-friendly geographic information system (GIS) (IBGE 1997).

Vegetation types of Veloso et al. (1991) and IBGE (1997)

Appendix 2 provides a synthesis of the system of Veloso et al. (1991) adapted by IBGE (1997). At the first hierarchical level, there are 14 'formation classes' based on the dominant life forms. At the second level are five 'formation subclasses', based on water deficit or flood regime criteria. The IBGE system ignores the category 'formation groups' used by Veloso et al. (1991) and proceeds to 'formation subgroups' as the third level, where the categories describe mainly the size and spacing of woody elements. At the fourth hierarchical level are the 'formations' and at the fifth level, the 'sub-formations'.

A vegetation type is defined by the choice of one of the 14 options at the first level, to which are added as modifiers the adjectives given at the other four hierarchical levels (we have excluded the sixth level).

A specific adjective at the lower levels matches only one or a few choices at the upper levels. This logical structure is not found in the IBGE (1997) documentation and does not strictly follow the system of Veloso et al. (1991). All real combinations are presented in Appendix 3, based on a GIS report for all 5,929 vegetation polygons. The report was generated by requesting all 14 vegetation groups at the first hierarchical level, leaving all the other levels blank. This way, the GIS was prompted to list all vegetation polygons, each with its vegetation type defined down to the sixth level. The report was then sorted into alphabetical and hierarchical order to determine how many distinct vegetation types were listed. The complete set of polygons represents 161 different vegetation types (Appendix 3), including primary and anthropogenic formations, and add up to 4,970,514 km^2, not discounting any overlaps.

Grouping vegetation types

It was necessary to reduce the number of vegetation types to be analyzed, grouping similar physiognomies in order to permit a clearer approach to conservation priorities. The procedure for reducing the number of vegetation types is illustrated in Table 4.

For our purposes, such groupings must keep separate those vegetation types with the greatest levels of floristic dissimilarity. Decisions on grouping are subjective, because there is a lack of precise data on the degree of similarity between different vegetation types. A simplification of the hierarchical tree, successively eliminating levels five, four, three and so on, so as to reach a system with few classes, does not lead to satisfactory results. This procedure leads to the mixture of categories with notoriously distinct flora, such as open forests with bamboo and open forests with palms.

Maps of vegetation types and conservation areas

The geographical coverage of the IBGE (1997) geographic information system is the Brazilian Legal Amazon, and our approach will thus be limited to Brazil. The same GIS includes other databases with their respective polygons that are useful for cross-referring to the vegetation type polygons, as follows:

- The conservation areas recommended by the *Workshop-90* (with no differentiation of levels of importance or criteria);
- All state and federal conservation areas;
- All indigenous areas;
- Anthropogenic impacts to 1991;
- 18 categories of land use for agriculture and ranching;
- Roads; and
- Soil types.

In order to consider the conservation status of each vegetation type, it is necessary to query these different geospatial databases to create new maps that will help answer the following questions:

- What is the total area of each vegetation type and what percentage of each type is protected or semi protected?
- Considering that floristic composition can change across a very extensive vegetation type, how are the conservation areas to be distributed throughout each type?
- Knowing that the process of degradation of natural forests increases with proximity to the front lines of deforestation and other anthropogenic impacts (Nepstad et al. 1999), what is the degree of threat to each vegetation type arising from deforestation, from fires in the understory, or from mechanized logging operations?

In the IBGE (1997) GIS, the vegetation type polygons and their characteristics are stored in a separate database, and this spreadsheet cannot be cross-queried against those containing information on levels of threats or on conservation areas. This restriction could be overcome by exporting the IBGE (1997) database to another GIS with interactive spreadsheets, but such a reorganization of data would take a long time.

Another, quicker, solution was adopted: exporting a digital map of each vegetation type to image processing software that identifies the areas of intersection of the polygons derived from different raster layers. The details of this process are described in Appendix 1.

TABLE 4 - TWENTY-ONE VEGETATION TYPES ADOPTED AND HOW THEY ARE DERIVED FROM THE IBGE HIERARCHICAL SYSTEM (1997)

	Level 1	Level 2	Level 3	Level 4	Level 5
Vegetation type 1a: evergreen montane forest	forest	wet/moist	dense	montane	
	forest	wet/moist	open	montane	
Vegetation type 1b: seasonally deciduous montane forest	forest	seasonal	deciduous	montane	
	forest	seasonal	semi-deciduous	montane	
Vegetation type 2a: rocky shrubland on isolated mountain tops (600 to 2000 m altitude)	refugium		shrub	montane	
	refugium		herbaceous	montane	
	refugium			montane	
Vegetation type 2b: rocky shrubland on isolated mountain tops (> 2000 m altitude)	refugium		herbaceous	high-montane	
Vegetation type 3a: dense forest on terra firme submontane lowlands (5 to 100 m altitude)	forest	wet/moist	dense	lowland	
Vegetation type 3b: dense forest on terra firme submontane highlands (100 to 600 m altitude)	forest	wet/moist	dense	sub-montane	
Vegetation type 4a: várzea and igapó (periodically flooded riparian and lacustrine forests of all water types)	forest	wet/moist	dense	alluvial	
	forest	seasonal	deciduous	alluvial	
	forest	seasonal	semi-deciduous	alluvial	
Vegetation type 4b: herbaceous and other primary sucession in várzea and igapó (recent fluvial and lacustrine deposits)	pioneer	fluvial influence	herbaceous	alluvial	
	pioneer	fluvial influence	shrub	alluvial	
	pioneer	fluvial influence	buriti palm grove	alluvial	
Vegetation type 5a: woody primary succession in coastal environments: mangroves and dunes	pioneer	fluvial/tidal influence	tree-covered		
	pioneer	marine influence	shrub		
Vegetation type 5b: herbaceous primary sucession in coastal environments: periodically flooded savannas	pioneer	tidal influence	herbaceous		
	pioneer	marine influence	herbaceous		
Vegetation type 6a: 'open' terra firme forest (5 to 600 m altitude) dominated by large palms	forest	wet/moist	open	lowland	with palms
	forest	wet/moist	open	sub-montane	with palms
Vegetation type 6b: 'open' terra firme forest (5 to 600 m altitude) dominated by lianas or Phenakospermum	forest	wet/moist	open	lowland	with vines/lianas
	forest	wet/moist	open	sub-montane	with vines/lianas
	forest	wet/moist	open	sub-montane	with *Phenakospermum*
Vegetation type 7: 'open' terra firme forest (100 to 600 m altitude) dominated by arborescent bamboos of the genus Guadua	forest	wet/moist	open	sub-montane	with bamboos
	forest	wet/moist	open	sub-montane	with bamboos
Vegetation type 8a: seasonally semi-deciduous terra firme 'transition' forests (5 to 600 m altitude)	tropical moist and seasonal forest				
	forest	seasonal	semi-deciduous	lowland	
	forest	seasonal	semi-deciduous	sub-montane	
Vegetation type 8b: seasonally deciduous terra firme 'transition' forests (5 to 600 m altitude)	forest	seasonal	deciduous	lowland	
	forest	seasonal	deciduous	sub-montane	
Vegetation type 9a: mixed contact zone: savanna and closed-canopy forest	tropical moist forest/savanna				
	seasonal forest / savanna				
Vegetation type 9b: savanna woodland, broken tree and shrub canopy with grassy understory; cerradão	savanna	seasonal	forested		
	steppe savanna	seasonal	forested		
Vegetation type 10a: seasonally dry savanna parkland, scattered low trees and shrubs; cerrado	savanna	seasonal	tree-covered		
	steppe savanna	seasonal	tree-covered		

continues

	Level 1	Level 2	Level 3	Level 4	Level 5
Vegetation type 10b: seasonally dry open savanna, trees and shrubs absent or sparse	savanna	seasonal	park		
	steppe savanna	seasonal	park		
	savanna	seasonal	grassy-woody		
	steppe savanna	seasonal	grassy-woody		
	savanna steppe savanna				
Vegetation type 11a: closed-canopy forest on white sand (podzol): campinarana	campinarana	wet/moist	forested		
	campinarana/ tropical moist forest				
Vegetation type 11b: grass or shrub savanna on white sand (podzol), no prolonged dry season.	campinarana	wet/moist	tree-covered		
	campinarana	wet/moist	grassy-woody		

The IBGE (1997) GIS only allows the export of vector maps through screen capture. This mode of polygon to raster conversion leads to an overestimation of the polygon area, and the error is greater in the case of small polygons or polygons with irregular borders. In order to estimate the error and obtain a correction factor, all the 134 demarcated indigenous areas polygons found in the database were rasterized by screen capture. The true area of each polygon is known from the database. All areas included in this report are based on a 1,280 x 1,024 pixel screen capture and corrected by the factor 0.894 (Table 5). It is important to stress that the real correction factor for a given polygon varies according to its size and the shape of its perimeter. The areas given in this study for groups of polygons are therefore estimates.

In this study we will evaluate, in visual rather than quantitative terms, the following: 1) the level of threat a specific vegetation type is exposed to – indicated by the distance from anthropogenic impacts – and 2) the spatial distribution of conservation areas within each vegetation type, using the latitude/longitude grid as the reference.

Level of threat map

The IBGE (1997) GIS includes indicators of anthropogenic threats in four different databases. Four maps were produced with the following criteria:
- Vegetation: the sum of the following polygons defined at level 1: farming and ranching + reforestation + secondary vegetation.
- Land use: the sum of ten agriculture categories and eight ranching categories.
- Roads: the sum of paved and unpaved roads.
- Anthropogenic impacts: the union of five temporal sets of altered vegetation cover (mainly deforestation) between 1971 and 1991.

The first map seems to be wrong as it does not match the anthropogenic impacts map, even in areas of original forest cover. The second map includes both severe human impacts and those less severe, such as the use of natural grasslands for pasture, low-intensity plant extractive activities, shifting agriculture of indigenous populations, and traditional fishing. Some of these activities, such as the crab fishery in mangrove forests or the collection of non-timber forest products, constitute activities that

TABLE 5 - CORRECTION FACTORS IN THE RASTER CAPTURE PROCESS OF THE IBGE MAPS (1997)		
Screen resolution	800 x 600	1280 x 1024
Pixel size	35.86 km^2	10.27 km^2
Estimated area	406,253 km^2	371,106 km^2
Real area	331,853 km^2	331,853 km^2
Overestimate (%)	22.4%	11.83%
Correction factor	0.817	0.894

favor, rather than threaten, conservation of the natural vegetation. With the exception of some long-abandoned roads, the road map coincides with the anthropogenic impact map. For these reasons the distance to anthropogenic landscapes between 1971 and 1991 has been adopted as the sole indicator of degree of threat.

Conservation status indicators and suggestions for new conservation areas

In an attempt to ensure more balanced levels of conservation for all vegetation types, a two-step procedure was developed: 1) assessment of the conservation status of the vegetation type and 2) suggestions for new priority areas for its conservation.

In the first step, three assessment criteria were employed: (i) the percentage of the area of the vegetation type in conservation areas broadly defined (direct use conservation areas + strict conservation areas + indigenous areas), (ii) the percentage in strict conservation areas, and (iii) the geographical distribution of both these general types of conservation areas. Assessment categories were established for the analysis of the protection percentages and of the geographic distribution of conservation areas within each vegetation type, as shown in Table 6. The final assessment rating – good, fair or poor – refers to the general status of the vegetation type as a whole.

The second step – the choice of priority conservation areas for each vegetation type – identified those regions which lacked conservation areas and/or were under threat, by superimposing four layers: 1) the occurrence of the vegetation type, 2) the areas of the vegetation type under strict protection, 3) semi-protected areas within the vegetation type and 4) the extent of anthropogenic impacts up to 1991. Three levels of conservation priority were proposed: 1) maximum priority, 2) medium priority and 3) low priority. Maximum priority was always given to sites distant from existing protected areas – with additional weight given to sites close to areas of human impact – in an attempt to distribute protected areas evenly within the vegetation type. Regions considered to be of medium priority were those areas within each vegetation type with greater proximity to protected or semi-protected areas, or with only semi-protected areas nearby, with the aim of achieving an even distribution of these two types of conservation categories. Regions considered to be of low conservation priority were those near protected areas; however, these were small in relation to the total area of the vegetation type. In the case of those vegetation types that were rated 'Good' in each of the three assessment categories, new conservation areas were not suggested.

TABLE 6 - CRITERIA USED ASSESSING PROTECION LEVELS FOR AMAZONIAN VEGETATION TYPES

Assessment	Criteria		
	% in conservation areas broadly defined	% in strict conservation areas	Geographical distribution
Good	> 20%	> 10%	Throughout the area
Fair	10% a 20%	5% a 10%	Uneven
Poor	< 10%	< 5%	Concentrated

Results

The 21 maps that show the conservation status of the vegetation types according to the three categories assessment, the extent of anthropogenic areas and the suggested new conservation areas can be found in Figures 11-31. Table 7 provides, for each vegetation type, the dimensions of the areas under the two general levels of protection, as obtained from these maps.

More than 10% of the areas of all 21 vegetation types analyzed here is protected by conservation areas, in the broad sense, with an average of 31% ± 23%. The conservation picture for Amazonia changes when we consider only conservation areas under strict use regimes. This category amounts to only 3.7% of the Legal Amazon area (Figure 1). The 21 vegetation types show an average of 12% ± 22% of their area in this conservation category. The large standard deviation is due to the great variation in the degree of protection among the different vegetation types. There are some extreme cases, such as that of 'rocky shrubland on isolated mountain tops (over 2000 m altitude)' (type 2B), whose distribution is restricted to the Pico da Neblina National Park and is therefore 100% within a strict protection conservation area and, at the opposite extreme, 'seasonally deciduous montane forest' (type 1B), which is not represented in any strict protection conservation area.

Discussion

Conservation status of the vegetation types of the Legal Amazon

The total area of conservation units in the broad sense, those that involve some sort of use restriction, amounted to 21.5% of the Legal Amazon when the IBGE (1997) data was digitized (Figure 1), which is an encouraging state of affairs. Indigenous areas[11] make up 69.4% of this total. Bearing in mind the difficulties of supervising areas that do not contain indigenous and traditional populations, and recalling the example of indigenous areas where the physiognomy of the natural landscape has been maintained, with well-defined forest limits surrounded by totally altered adjacent areas, it is reasonable to infer that this category must be included in an analysis of future conservation action. At the same time, we should not forget that the maintenance of the vegetation

---
11. Indigenous Park and Land *sensu* IBGE (1997).

type does not guarantee the preservation of all the groups of organisms present in semi-protected areas, and that the pressures of hunting and of other extractive and supposedly sustainable activities can render these resources scarce and at risk of exhaustion, especially when demand increases. For the maintenance of biological diversity we therefore feel that it is important to take these two conservation categories into account, with a view to a more equitable division between protected and semi-protected conservation areas, provided there is effective control over human activities, in accordance with applicable legislation.

Our suggestions for priority conservation areas consider biodiversity at its principal levels. By prioritizing areas throughout all environments across the whole extent of each vegetation type, these recommendations should protect the *genetic variability* of plant *populations*. They include the species present in the different *environments* of each *vegetation type*, thus maximizing complementarity (beta-diversity) that these different *landscape units* (environments and vegetation types) represent. However, many important issues are not considered here because of the restrictions imposed by the methodology. In some cases very distinct environments, which should properly be analyzed separately, are included in a single vegetation type, such as the plateau, slope and stream floodplain forests of terra firme, all included in the 'dense forest on terra firme lowlands' vegetation type. A further consideration relates to the quality of some soil types and to other environmental variables important in the distribution of species and communities, but which are ignored in the vegetation classification, such as the distinction between várzea and igapó forests. In some cases, the distribution of vegetation types mapped by RadamBrasil/IBGE is deficient, with isolated areas missing, as is the case for the open white sand vegetation in the Tucuruí region and in the Trombetas basin. We have also noted that the areas of occurrence of some vegetation types are underestimated, as in the case of the bamboo forests of Acre. The classification of areas of anthropogenic impacts according to level of threat to the remaining original vegetation would also be useful, as would the ability to distinguish areas of anthropogenic impacts within certain vegetation types (for example, pastures in areas of natural grasslands). Such methodological restrictions are inherent in an analysis like this, ambitious in its scope and complexity, and do not detract from the great practical utility of the suggestions put forward in this study.

Limitations of the methodology

Suggestions for new conservation areas

It is important to note that the suggestions for new conservation areas are not rigid and other areas could also meet the criteria used here. A more detailed approach would be to award a degree of priority to each pixel within a raster image of a vegetation type, on the basis of an algorithm that takes into

Table 7 - Conservation status of the twenty-one vegetation types in the Legal Amazon (code follows Table 4)

Code	Area in km²			Percentage by vegetation type		
	Strict protection	Semi-protected	No protection	Strict protection	Semi-protected	Total protected
1A	3,398	20,691	6,961	10.9	66.6	77.6
1B	0	992	2,939	0.0	25.2	25.2
2A	707	1,286	928	24.2	44.0	68.2
2B	37	0	0	100.0	0.0	100.0
3A	47,812	106,947	760,595	5.2	11.7	16.9
3B	46,673	252,815	664,200	4.8	26.2	31.1
4A	40,088	83,344	474,965	6.7	13.9	20.6
4B	9,000	19,516	87,651	7.7	16.8	24.5
5A	2,507	83	16,412	13.2	0.4	13.6
5B	569	0	928	38.0	0.0	38.0
6A	28,029	203,507	480,622	3.9	28.6	32.5
6B	3,086	93,685	262,183	0.9	26.1	27.0
7	2,278	11,370	53,460	3.4	16.9	20.3
8A	3,683	52,302	227,036	1.3	18.5	19.8
8B	266	8,706	52,615	0.4	14.1	14.6
9A	129	3,453	16,935	0.6	16.8	17.5
9B	3,848	32,759	162,326	1.9	16.5	18.4
10A	5,529	50,236	437,412	1.1	10.2	11.3
10B	8,844	50,098	246,276	2.9	16.4	19.3
11A	8,385	44,606	69,991	6.8	36.3	43.1
11B	6,741	1,212	64,839	9.3	1.7	10.9
Averages				11.6	19.4	31.0
Standard deviation				22.2	15.8	23.4

account (1) coverage coefficient of the surrounding conservation areas within different radii of distance from the pixel and (2) a similar metric for coverage and distance from anthropogenic impacts. The result would be an image with differently shaded pixels, corresponding to a linear scale of conservation priority. Subsequently the 21 images would be overlaid in order to search for high priority cases, adjacent to each other. In the present study, priority conservation areas are proposed for each vegetation type, with the proviso that the identification of future conservation areas can be flexible. The next step would be a more quantitative (non-binary) definition of conservation priority, which would also be more accurate with respect to the size, quantity and location of the new areas. This subsequent approach should based on a more detailed assessment of factors such as threat, conservation status, viable populations of rare species, difficulty of access, and potential for effective control of these new reserves, preferably based on complementary *in loco* environmental diagnosis.

An attempt was made to define priority in quantitative terms, using an algorithm that takes into account the distance between each pixel and the factors considered. This experimental software, called Lacuna, transforms each pixel of a given vegetation type into an index based on a 50 pixel radius. The index represents the average distance of this pixel from conservation areas containing the vegetation type in question, semi-protected conservation areas containing the vegetation type, and the distance to areas of anthropogenic impacts. The first two factors were computed in direct proportion to priority, with the second divided by half, while the third was computed in inverse proportion to conservation priority. For the purposes of illustration, we have reproduced the occurrence map of vegetation type 3a (dense lowland terra firme forest), where the different green shades represent the levels of priority (Figure 33). This is still a preliminary analysis and needs some adjustments with respect to the index and the area to be considered in the calculation of each pixel, and is included here only as an illustration.

Definition of the vegetation types

The system adopted, based exclusively on vegetation types, presents a few problems:

1. There is no distinction between environments seasonally flooded by black or muddy waters (igapós and várzeas);
2. Dense terra firme rain forest, responsible for a large part of the floristic diversity of Amazonia, is divided into only two categories, based on a small difference of altitude; and
3. Two important abiotic factors are not directly considered: soil and rainfall

Rainfall

There is evidence that the species richness of one-hectare plots of dense terra firme forest increases with rainfall, with ichness saturating at about 2,500 mm/year (revision by Oliveira 1997; Amaral 1996). Below 2,000 mm/year the vegetation type itself can be used as a rainfall indicator. Although Nepstad et al. (1994) found evidence that dense forest is sustained by deep water, these forests become partially deciduous and susceptible to fire after only two years of extreme drought, clearly a common occurrence in places with low annual rainfall averages.

Ancient disturbances by ground fires of anthropogenic (indigenous) origin may have been the mechanism for transforming extensive dense forest areas into open forests, and their subsequent maintenance (Sombroek 1992, Nelson and Irmão 1998, cf. Balée 1989). Three open forest formations were mapped by RadamBrasil and are analyzed in this report.

Soil

It would be interesting in the future to develop criteria for a pedological subdivision of both dense and open forests using soil data available in the IBGE (1997) GIS. In the present study only the criterion of altitude subdivides the dense terra firme forests, although this also tends to distinguish, albeit imperfectly, between two distinct classes of soil: (a) fertile soils, formed *in situ* by igneous rock of the shield, and (b) ancient continental deposits doubly impoverished, first by the process of river transportation from the shield, and then by millions of years of leaching.

However, the lower lands also include extensive paleo-floodplains uplifted by land movements and/or sea level changes.

These paleo-floodplains will show differing levels of fertility depending on their age. Data from Peru (Ruokolainen et al. 1995, 1997) suggest that soil fertility is responsible for floristic changes in dense terra firme forests, even when the obvious effects of podzols are excluded. In the state of Acre, extensive areas of terra firme have soils and tree communities similar to those of várzeas, although they no longer show the geomorphologic features that indicate fluvial deposition. They are fluvial or tidal deposits of the Miocene (Rasanen et al. 1995) preserved by their depth from weathering, but now put within reach of forest roots through high rates of mechanical surface removal, a phenomenon peculiar to this region. In this case, the distribution of bamboo-dominated canopies can serve as an indicator, which is why bamboo forests are classified as a distinct vegetation type in this study.

Bibliography

ABSY, M. L.; PRANCE, G. T.; BARBOSA, E. M. Inventário florístico de floresta natural na área da estrada Cuiabá-Porto Velho (BR-364). *Acta Amazon*, no. 16/17 (supplement), p. 85-121, 1986-1987.

ADIS, J. Comparative Ecological studies of the terrestrial arthropod fauna in Central Amazonian inundation forests. *Amazoniana*, no. 7, p. 87-173, 1981.

_____. Seasonal *igapó*-forests of Central Amazonian black water rivers and their terrestrial arthropod fauna. In: SIOLI, H. (Ed.). *The Amazon liminology and landscape ecology of a mighty tropical river and its basis*. Dordrecht: Dr. Junk Publisher, 1984.

ADIS, J.; FURCH, K.; IRMLER, U. Litter production of a Central Amazonian black water inundation forest. *Trop. Ecol.*, no. 20, p. 235-45, 1979.

ALMEIDA, S. S.; LISBOA, P. L. B.; SILVA, A. S. Diversidade florística de uma comunidade arbórea na estação científica 'Ferreira Pena', em Caxiuanã (Pará). *Bol. Mus. Paraense Emílio Goeldi, Bot.*, v. 9, no. 1, p. 93-128, 1993.

AMARAL, I. L. *Diversidade florística em floresta de terra firme, na região de Urucu, AM*. 1996. Master's dissertation – Instituto Nacional de Pesquisas da Amazônia (INPA)/Fundação Universidade do Amazonas (FUA), Manaus, Amazonas.

AYRES, J. M. *Observações sobre a ecologia e o comportamento dos Cuxiús (Chiropotes albinasus e C. satanus)*, 1981. Master's dissertation. INPA, Manaus.

_____. *As matas de várzea do Mamirauá*. Brasília: MCT/CNPq, 1993.

BALÉE, W. The culture of Amazonian forests. In: POSEY, D. A.; BALÉE, W. (Orgs.). *Resource management in Amazonia:* Indigenous and Folk Strategies (Advances in Economic Botany, v. 7). New York: The New York Botanical Garden, 1989. p. 1-22.

_____. Análise preliminar de inventário florestal e a etnobotânica Ka'apor (Maranhão). *Bol. Mus. Paraense Emílio Goeldi*, v. 2, no. 2, p. 141-67, 1986.

_____. Etnobotânica quantitativa dos índios Tembé (Rio Gurupi, Pará). *Bol. Mus. Paraense Emílio Goeldi*, v. 3, no. 1, p. 29-50, 1987.

_____. Biodiversidade e os índios amazônicos. In: CASTRO, E. V.; CUNHA, M. C. (Eds.). *Amazônia:* etologia e história indígena. São Paulo: NHI/USP/Fapesp, 1993. p. 385-93.

BALSLEV, H. et al. Composition and structure of adjacent unflooded and floodplain forest in Amazonian Ecuador. *Opera Botanica*, no. 92, p. 37-57, 1987.

BASTOS, A. M. As matas de Santa Maria do Vila Nova. *Anuário Brasileiro de Economia Florestal*, Ministério da Agricultura, Serviço Florestal, Setor de Inventários Florestais, no. 1, p. 281-8, 1948.

_____. A floresta do Amapari-Matapi-Cupixi (inventário florestal). *Serviço Florestal, Boletim 2*, p. 54, 1960.

BLACK, G. A.; DOBZHANSKY, T. H.; PAVAN, C. Some attempts to estimate species diversity and population density of trees in Amazonian forests. *Bot. Gaz.*, v. 111, no. 4, p. 413-25, 1950.

BOOM, B. M. A Forest inventory in Amazonian Bolivia. *Biotropica*, v. 18, no. 4, p. 413-25, 1986.

_____. Ethnobotany of the Chácobo indians, Beni, Bolivia. *Advances Econ. Bot.*, no. 4, p. 1-68, 1987.

BRASIL/MMA. *Primeiro relatório nacional para a convenção sobre diversidade biológica*. Brasília: Ministério do Meio Ambiente, dos Recursos Hídricos e da Amazônia Legal, 1998.

BRAY, J. R.; CURTIS, C. T. An Ordination of upland forest communities of Southern Wisconsin. *Ecol. Monogr.*, no. 27, p. 325-49, 1957.

CAIN, S. A. et al. Application of some phytosociological techniques to Brazilian rain forest. *Amer. J. Bot.*, no. 43, p. 911-41, 1956.

CAMPBELL, D. C.; STONE, J. L.; ROSAS, A. A comparison of the phytosociology and dynamics of three floodplain (várzea) forests of known ages, Rio Juruá, Western Brazilian Amazon. *Bot. J. Linnean Soc.*, no. 108, p. 213-37, 1992.

CAMPBELL, D. C. et al. Quantitative ecological inventory of terra firme and várzea tropical forest on the Rio Xingú, Brazilian Amazonia. *Brittonia*, v. 38, no. 4, p. 369-93, 1986.

CLINEBELL II, R. R. et al. Prediction of Neotropical tree and Liana species richness from soil and climatic data. *Biodiversity and conservation*, no. 4, p. 56-90, 1995.

COMISKEY, J. A.; AYMARD, G.; DALLMEIER, F. Structure and composition of lowland mixed forest in the Kwani region of Guyana. *Bollania*, no. 10, p. 13-28, 1994.

CONDIT, R. Research in large, long-term tropical forest plots. *Trends ecol. and evol.*, no. 10, p. 18-22, 1995.

CONDIT, R. et al. Species-area and species-individual relationships for tropical trees: a comparison of three 50-ha plots. *J. Ecol.*, no. 84, p. 549-62, 1996.

COTTAM, G.; CURTIS, J. T. The use of distance measures in phytosociological sampling. *Ecology*, v. 37, no. 3, p. 451-60, 1956.

CURTIS, J. T.; MACINTOSH. An upland forest continum in the prairie-forest border region of Wisconsin. *Ecology*, no. 32, p. 476-96, 1951.

DANTAS, M.; MULLER, N. A. M. Estudos fito-ecológicos do trópico úmido brasileiro II. Aspectos fitossociológicos de mata sobre latossolo amarelo em Capitão Poço, Pará. *Boletim de Pesquisa*, Cpatu/Embrapa, Belém, no. 9, 1979.

DANTAS, M.; MULLER, N. A. M.; RODRIGUES, I. A. Estudos fito-ecológicos do trópico úmido brasileiro I. Aspectos fitossociológicos de mata sobre terra roxa na região de Altamira, Pará. In: *Congresso Nacional de Botânica*, 30, 1980, Anais da Sociedade Botânica do Brasil.

DAVIS, T. A. W.; RICHARDS, P. W. The vegetation of Moraballi Creek, British Guiana: an ecological study of a limited area of tropical rain forest I. *J. Ecol.*, v. 21, no. 2, p. 350-84, 1933.

_____. The vegetation of Moraballi Creek, British Guiana: an ecological study of a limited area of tropical rain forest II. *J. Ecol.*, no. 22, p. 106-55, 1934.

DEWALT, S. J. et al. Ethnobotany of the Tacana: qualitative inventories of two permanent plots of Northwestern Bolivia. *Economic Botany*, v. 53, no. 3, p. 237-60, 1999.

DUIVENVOORDEN, J. F. Tree species composition and rain forest-environment relationships in the Middle Caquetá area, Colombia, NW Amazonia. *Vegetatio*, no. 120, p. 91-113, 1995.

_____. Patterns of tree species richness in rain forests of the Middle Caquetá Area, Colombia, NW Amazonia. *Biotropica*, v. 28, no. 2, p. 142-58, 1996.

FABER-LANGENDOEN, D.; GENTRY, A. H. The structure and diversity of rain forests at Bajo Calima, Chocó region, Western Colombia. *Biotropica*, v. 23, no. 1, p. 2-11, 1991.

FEARNSIDE, P. M.; FERRAZ, J. A Conservation gap analysis of Brazil's Amazonian vegetation. *Conservation Biology*, v. 9, no. 5, p. 1134-47, 1995.

FELFILI, J. M. Diversity, structure and dynamics of a gallery forest in Central Brazil. *Vegetatio*, no. 117, p. 1-15, 1995.

FERREIRA, L. V.; PRANCE, G. T. Species richness and floristic composition in four hectares in the Jaú National Park in upland forests in Central Amazonian. *Biodiversity and conservation*, v. 7, no. 10, p. 1349-64, 1998.

FERREIRA, L. V. Effects of the duration of flooding on species richness and floristic composition in three hectares in the Jaú National Park in floodplain forests in Central Amazonia. *Biodiversity and conservation*, no. 6, p. 1353-63, 1997.

_____. O efeito do período de inundação na zonação de comunidades, fenologia e regeneração em floresta de igapó na Amazônia Central. 1991. Master's dissertation, INPA/FUA, Manaus.

GENTRY, A. H. Patterns of Neotropical plant species diversity. *Evol. biol.*, no. 15, p. 1-84, 1982.

_____. An overview of Neotropical phytogeographic patterns with an emphasis on Amazonia. In: *Anais do 1º Simpósio do Trópico Úmido*, 1986, Brasília.

_____. Tree species richness of upper Amazonian Forests. *Procl. Natl. Acad. Sci. USA*, no. 85, p. 156-9, 1988a.

_____. Changes in plant community diversity and floristic composition on environmental and geographical gradients. *Ann. Missouri. Bot. Gard.*, v. 75, no. 1, p. 1-34, 1988b.

_____. Tropical forest diversity: distributional patterns and their conservational significance. *Oikos*, v. 63, no. 1, p. 19-28, 1992.

GENTRY, A. H.; EMMONS, L. H. Geographical variation in fertility, phenology, and composition of the understory of Neotropical forests. *Biotropica*, v. 19, no. 3, p. 216-27, 1987.

GLERUM, B. B. Levantamento florestal na região entre o rio Caeté e o rio Maracassumé. *Relatório FAO*, no. 1250, 1960.

_____. Levantamento florestal na região de Ucuúba no rio Tocantins. *Relatório FAO*, no. 1492, 1962a.

_____. Levantamento florestal piloto na região de Mogno nos Estados de Goiás e Pará. *FAO Report*, no. 1562, 1962b.

GLERUM, B. B.; SMITH, G. Inventário florestal total na região do rio Curuá-Una (Santarém). *FAO Report*, no. 1271, 1960.

_____. Levantamento combinado floresta-solo ao longo da rodovia BR-14 entre São Miguel e Imperatriz. *FAO Report*, no. 1483, 1962.

GRUBB, P. J. et al. A Comparison of montane and lowland rain forest in Ecuador I. The forest structure, physiognomy, and floristics. *J. ecol.*, v. 51, no. 3, p. 567-601, 1963.

HEINSDIJK, D. Levantamento florestal na região entre o rio Tapajós e o rio Xingu. *FAO Report*, no. 601, 1957.

_____. Levantamento florestal na região entre o rio Xingu e o rio Tocantins. *FAO Report*, no. 949, 1958a.

_____. Levantamento florestal na região entre o rio Madeira e o rio Tapajós. *FAO Report*, no. 969, 1958b.

_____. Levantamento florestal na região entre o rio Tocantins e os rios Guamá e Capim. *FAO Report*, no. 992, 1958c.

_____. As florestas de terra firme nos solos Terciário e Quaternário ao sul do rio Amazonas. *FAO Report*, no. 1284, 1960.

_____. Amostragem 'zero' nos levantamentos florestais. *Boletim do Ministério da Agricultura*, no. 8, 1964.

_____. A distribuição dos diâmetros nas florestas brasileiras. *Boletim do Ministério da Agricultura*, no. 11, 1965.

_____. Inventário florestal. *FAO Report*, no. 2159, 1966.

HEINSDIJK, D.; BASTOS, A. M. Inventários florestais na Amazônia. *FAO Report*, no. 2159, 1965.

HUBBELL, S. P.; FOSTER, R. B. Commonness and rarity in a Neotropical forest: implications for tropical tree conservation. In: SOULÉ, M (Ed.). *Conservation biology: the science of scarcity and diversity*. Massachusetts: Sunderland, 1986.

HUBBELL, S. P. Tree Dispersion, abundance and diversity in a tropical dry forest. *Science*, no. 203, p. 1299-309, 1979.

HUBER, J. La vegetation de la vallé du rio Purus (Amazonas). *Bull. De L'Herbier Boissier*, no. 4, p. 249-76, 1906.

IBGE. *Diagnóstico ambiental da Amazônia Legal*. Rio de Janeiro, 1997. 1 CD-ROM.

IBGE/IBDF. *Mapa da Vegetação do Brasil*. Brasília, 1988. Scale 1:5.000.000.

KELL, S. H. K.; PRANCE, G. T. Studies of the vegetation of white-sand blackwater igapó (rio Negro, Brasil). *Acta Amaz.*, v. 9, no. 4, p. 645-55, 1979.

KORNING, J.; THOMSEN, K.; ÖLLGAARD, B. Composition and structure of a species rich Amazonian rain forest obtained by two different sampling methods. *Nordic J. Bot.*, no. 11, p. 103-11, 1991.

LECHTHALER, R. Inventário de árvores de um hectare de terra firme. *Botânica*, no. 3, INPA, 1956.

LISBOA, P. L. B. Estudo florístico da vegetação arbórea de uma floresta secundária, em Rondônia. *Bol. Mus. Paraense Emílio Goeldi Bot.*, v. 5, no. 2, p. 145-62, 1989.

LLERAS, E. et al. *Definição de áreas de alta diversidade e endemismo na Amazônia brasileira*. In: PROJETO BRA/89/006 (Selected Baseline Data for Compilation and Processing, and Training for Systematic Agroecologic-Economic Zoning for Susteainable Development of the Amazon Region). Report to United Nations (UNDEP and FAO), 1992, 63 p.

MACIEL, U. N.; LISBOA, P. L. B. Estudo florístico de 1 hectare de mata de terra firme no km 15 da rodovia Presidente Médici-Costa Marques (RO-429), Rondônia. *Bol. Mus. Paraense Emílio Goeldi Bot.*, v. 5, no. 1, p. 25-37, 1989.

MILLIKEN, W. Structure and Composition of one hectare of Central Amazonian terra firme forest. *Biotropica*, v. 30, no. 4, 1998.

MILLIKEN, W. et al. *Ethnobotany of the Waimiri Atroari indians of Brazil*. Kew: Royal Botanic Gardens, 1992.

MORELLATO, P. L. C.; ROSA, N. A. Caracterização de alguns tipos de vegetação na região amazônica, Serra dos Carajás, Pará, Brasil. *Rev. Brasil. Bot.*, no. 14, p. 1-14, 1991.

MORI, S. A.; BOOM, B. The forest. In: MORI, S. A. (Ed.). The Lecythidaceae of a lowland Neotropical forest: la fumée mountain, French Guyana. *Mem. New York Bot. Gard*, no. 44, p. 9-29, 1987.

MORI, S. A. et al. Ecological importance of Myrtaceae in an eastern Brazilian moist forest. *Biotropica*, no. 15, p. 68-9, 1983.

_____. Composition and structure of an eastern Amazonian forest at Camapai, Amapá, Brasil. *Bol. Mus. Paraense Emílio Goeldi*, v. 5, no. 1, p. 3-18, 1989.

MUELLER-DOMBOIS, D.; ELLENBERG, H. *Aims and methods of vegetation ecology*. New York: John Wiley, 1974.

MUNIZ, F. H.; CESAR, O.; MONTEIRO, R. Aspectos florísticos quantitativos e comparativos da vegetação arbórea da Reserva Florestal do Sacavém, São Luís, Maranhão (Brasil). *Acta Amazonica*, v. 24, no. 3/4, p. 189-218, 1994a.

_____. Fitossociologia da vegetação arbórea da Reserva Florestal do Sacavém, São Luís, Maranhão (Brasil). *Acta Amazonica*, v. 24, no. 3/4, p. 219-36, 1994b.

NELSON, B. W. Inventário florístico na Amazônia e a escolha racional de áreas prioritárias para conservação. In: VAL, A. L.; FIGLIOULO, R.; FELDBERG, E. (Eds.). *Bases científicas para estratégias de preservação e desenvolvimento na Amazônia: fatos e perspectivas* (v. 1). Manaus: INPA, 1991. p. 173-83.

NELSON, B.; IRMÃO, M. N. Fire penetration in standing Amazon forest. In: *IX Simpósio Brasileiro de Sensoriamento Remoto*, 1998, São José dos Campos, INPE. 1 CD-ROM, p. 1-12.

NELSON, B. et al. Endemism centers, refugia and botanical collection density in the Brazilian Amazon. *Nature*, no. 345, p. 714-6, 1990.

NEPSTAD, D. C. et al. The role of deep roots in the hydrological and carbon cycles of Amazonian forests and pastures. *Nature*, no. 372, p. 666-9, 1994.

_____. Large-scale impoverishment of Amazonian forests by logging and fire. *Nature*, no. 398, v. 6727, p. 505-8, 1999.

OGUTU, Z. A. Multivariate analysis of plant communities in Narok District, Kenya: the influence of environmental factors and human disturbance. *Vegetatio*, no. 126, p. 181-9, 1996.

OLIVEIRA, A. A. de. *Diversidade, estrutura e dinâmica do componente arbóreo de uma floresta de terra firme de Manaus, AM*. 1997. Doctorate Thesis – Instituto de Biociências, Universidade de São Paulo, São Paulo, 187 p.

OLIVEIRA, A. A. de.; DALY, D. Geographic distribution of tree species in the region of Manaus, Brazil: implications for regional diversity and conservation. *Biodiversity and Conservation*, no. 8, v. 9, p. 1245-59, 1999.

OLIVEIRA, A. A. de.; MORI, S. A. A Central Amazonian terra firme forest I. High tree species richness on poor soils. *Biodiversity and Conservation*, v. 8, no. 9, p. 1219-44, 1999.

OLIVEIRA, A. A. de.; NELSON, B. Floristic relationship of terra firme forests in the Brazilian Amazon. *Forest ecology and management*, 146 (1-3), p. 169-79, 2001.

OLIVEIRA-FILHO, A. T.; RATTER, J. A. A Study of the origin of Central Brazilian forests by the analysis of plant species distribution patterns. *Edinburgh. J. Bot*, v. 52, no. 2, p. 141-94, 1995.

PHILLIPS, O. L. et al. Dynamics and species richness of tropical rain forests. *Proc. Natl. Acad. Sci. USA.*, 1994.

PIEDADE, M. T. F. *Ecologia e biologia reprodutiva de Astrocaryum jauari Mart. (Palmae) como exemplo de população adaptada às áreas inundáveis do rio Negro (igapós)*. INPA, 1985.

PIRES, J. M. Tipos de vegetação da Amazônia. *Brasil Floresta*, v. 5, no. 17, p. 48-58, 1974.

PIRES, J. M.; KOURY, H. M. Estudo de um trecho de mata de várzea próximo a Belém. *Bol. Téc. Inst. Agron. Norte*, no. 36, p. 3-44, 1959.

PIRES, J. M.; PRANCE, G. T. The Amazon Forest: a natural heritage to be preserved. In: PRANCE, G. T.; ELIAS, T. S. (Eds.). *Extinction is forever*. New York: New York Botanical Garden, 1977.

_____. The vegetation types of the Brazilian Amazon. In: PRANCE, G. T.; LOVEJOY, T. E. (Eds.). *Key environments, Amazonia*. New York: Pergamon Press, 1985. p. 109-145..

PIRES, J. M.; DOBZHANSKY, T. H.; BLACK, G. A. An estimate of the number of trees in an Amazonian forest community. *Bot. Gaz.*, v. 114, no. 4, p. 467-77, 1953.

PORTO, M. L. et al. Levantamento fitossociológico em área de 'mata-de-baixio' na estação experimental de silvicultura tropical – INPA – Manaus - Amazonas. *Acta Amazon*, v. 6, no. 3, p. 301-18, 1976.

PRANCE, G. T. The Phytogeographic subdivisions of Amazonia and their influence on the selection of biological reserves. In: PRANCE, G. T.; ELIAS, T. S. (Eds.). *Extinction is Forever*. New York: The New York Botanical Garden, 1977.

_____. Notes on the vegetation of Amazonia III. The terminology of Amazonian forest types subject to innundation. *Brittonia*, no. 31, p. 26-38, 1979.

_____. Vegetation. In: WHITMORE, T. C.; PRANCE, G. T. (Eds.). *Biogeography and quaternary history in tropical America*: Oxford Monographs on Biogeography no 3. Oxford: Clarendon Press, 1987. p. 28-45.

_____. The floristic composition of the forests of Central Amazonian Brazil. In: GENTRY, A. H. (Ed.). *Four Neotropical Rainforests*. New Haven: Yale Univ. Press, 1990.

PRANCE, G. T.; RODRIGUES, W. A.; SILVA, M. F. Inventário florístico de um hectare de mata de terra firme km 30 da Estrada Manaus-Itacoatiara. *Acta Amazonica*, v. 6, no. 1, p. 9-35, 1976.

PRESTON, F. W. The commonness and rarity of species. *Ecology*, v. 29, no. 3, p. 254-83, 1948.

RADAMBRASIL. *Levantamento de recursos naturais*. v. 1-18. Rio de Janeiro: Ministério de Minas e Energia, Departamento Nacional de Produção Mineral, 1968-1978.

RAMOS, A. A. et al. Levantamento florestal do distrito agropecuário da Zona Franca de Manaus. *Rev. Floresta*, v. 4, no. 1, p. 40-53, 1972.

RANKIN-DE-MERONA, J. M. *Conditions écologiques et economiques de la production d'une ile de várzea: L'ile du Careiro, Part 4: les relations poisson-forêt*. Paris/Manaus: Final Report/ORSTOM/INPA, 1988, p. 202-228.

RANKIN-DE-MERONA, J. M. et al. Preliminary results of a large-scale tree inventory of upland rain forest in the Central Amazon. *Acta Amazon*, v. 22, no. 4, p. 493-534, 1992.

RASANEN, M. E. et al. Late miocene tidal deposits in the Amazonian foreland basin. *Science*, no. 269, p. 386-90, 1995.

RAUNKIAER, C. *The Life forms of plants and statistical geography*. Oxford: Clarendon Press, 1934.

REVILLA, J. D. *Aspectos florísticos e fitossociológicos de floresta inundável (igapó) Praia Grande, rio Negro, Amazonas, Brasil*. 1981. Master's Thesis, INPA/FUA, Manaus.

RICHARDS, P. W. *The Tropical Rainforest: an Ecological Study*. London, 1952, 450 p.

RODRIGUES, W. A. Estudo preliminar de mata de várzea alta de uma ilha do baixo rio Negro de solo argiloso e úmido. *Publicação do INPA (botânica)*, no. 10, p. 1-50, 1961.

_____. Estudo de 2,6 hectares de mata de terra firme da serra do Navio, território do Amapá. *Bol. Mus. Paraense Emílio Goeldi*, no. 19, p. 1-42, 1963.

_____. Inventário florestal piloto ao longo da estrada Manaus-Itacoatiara, estado do Amazonas: dados preliminares. In: *Simpósio Biota Amazônica*, 1967, *Atas...*, v. 2, p. 257-67.

ROLLET, B. Tree populations in natural tropical rain forest. *Bois et Forêsts des tropiques*, v. 236, no. 2, p. 43-55, 1993.

RUOKOLAINEN, K.; LINNA, A.; TUOMISTO, H. Use of Melastomataceae and Pteridophytes for revealing phytogeographical patterns in Amazonian rain forests. *Journal of tropical ecology*, no. 13, p. 243-56, 1997.

RUOKOLAINEN, K. et al. Tree species distribution in Peruvian rain forests: correlation with satellite image patterns and edaphic factors. In: RUOKOLAINEN, K. (Ed.). *Floristic and environmental variation in the rain forests of Peruvian Amazonia*: Reports from the Department of Biology. Turku: Univ. of Turku, 1995.

SALOMÃO, R. P. Uso de parcela permanente para estudo da vegetação da floresta tropical úmida. I. Município de Marabá, Pará. *Bol. Mus. Paraense Emílio Goeldi*, v. 7, no. 2, p. 543-604, 1991.

SALOMÃO, R. P.; LISBOA, P. L. B. Análise ecológica da vegetação de uma floresta pluvial tropical de terra firme, Rondônia. *Bol. Mus. Paraense Emílio Goeldi*, v. 4, no. 2, p. 195-233, 1988.

SALOMÃO, R. P.; SILVA, M. F. F.; ROSA, N. A. Inventário ecológico em floresta pluvial tropical de terra firme, serra Norte, Carajás, Pará. *Bol. Mus. Paraense Emílio Goeldi*, v. 4, no. 1, p. 1-46, 1988.

SILVA, A. S. L; LISBOA, P. L. B.; MACIEL, U. N. Diversidade florística e estrutura em floresta densa da bacia do rio Juruá. *Bol. Mus. Paraense Emílio Goeldi*, v. 8, no. 2, p. 203-58, 1992.

SILVA, M. F.; ROSA, N. A. Análise do estrato arbóreo da vegetação sobre jazidas de cobre na serra dos Carajás-PA. *Bol. Mus. Paraense Emílio Goeldi*, v. 5, no. 2, p. 175-205, 1989.

SILVA, M. F.; ROSA, N. A.; OLIVEIRA, J. Estudo botânico na área do projeto ferro Carajás. 3. Aspectos florísticos da mata do aeroporto da serra Norte-PA. *Bol. Mus. Paraense Emílio Goeldi*, v. 2, no. 2, p. 169-87, 1986.

_____. Estudo botânico na área do projeto ferro Carajás. 5. Aspectos florísticos da mata do rio gelado, Pará. *Bol. Mus. Paraense Emílio Goeldi*, v. 3, no. 1, p. 1-20, 1987.

SOMBROEK, W. Biomass and carbon storage in Amazonian ecosystems. *Interciência*, no. 17, v. 5, 1992.

SPICHIGER, R. et al. Tree species richness of a South-Western Amazonian forest (Jenaro Herrera, Peru, 73°40'W/ 4°54'S). *Candollea*, no. 51, p. 559-77, 1996.

STEEGE, H. T. The use of forest inventory data for a national protected area strategy in Guyana. *Biod. Conserv.*, v. 7, no. 11, p. 1457-83, 2000b.

STEEGE, H. T. et al. A regional perspective: analysis of Amazonian floristic composition and diversity that includes the Guiana Shield. In: STEEGE, H. T. (Ed.). *Plant diversity in Guyana: with recommendations for a protected areas strategy*: Tropenbos series 18. The Wageningen: Tropenbos Foundation, 2000a. p. 19-34.

_____. An analysis of the floristic composition and diversity of Amazonian forests that includes the Guiana Shield. *Journal of Tropical Ecology*, no. 16, p. 829-39. 2000b.

SUDAM. *Levantamentos florestais realizados pela missão FAO na Amazônia*, v. 2. Belém: 1974.

TAKEUCHI, M. A estrutura da vegetação na Amazônia I – A mata plúvia-tropical. *Bol. Mus. Paraense Emílio Goeldi*, no. 6, p. 1-29, 1960.

_____. The structure of the Amazonian vegetation II. Tropical rain forest. *J. Fac. Sci. Univ. Tokyo III*, v. 8, no. 1, p. 1-26, 1961.

_____. The structure of the Amazonian vegetation V. Tropical rain forest near Uaupés. *J. Fac. Sci. Univ. Tokyo III*, v. 8, no. 4-7, p. 289-96, 1962a.

_____. The structure of the Amazonian vegetation VI. Igapó. *J. Fac. Sci. Tokyo*, Sect. Bot., no. 8, p. 297-304, 1962b.

TERBORGH, J.; ANDRESEN, E. The Composition of Amazonian forests: patterns at local and regional scales. *J. Trop. Ecol.*, no. 14, p. 645-64, 1998.

THOMPSON, J. et al. Ecological studies on a lowland evergreen rain forest on Maracá island, Roraima, Brazil, I. Physical environment, forest structure and leaf chemistry. *J. Ecol.*, no. 80, p. 689-703, 1992.

UHL, C.; MURPHY, P. G. Composition, structure and regeneration of terra firme in the Amazon basin of Venezuela. *Tropic. Ecol.*, v. 22, no. 2, p. 219-37, 1981.

VALENCIA, R.; BALSLEV, H.; PAZ Y MINO, G. C. High tree alpha-diversity in Amazonian Ecuador. *Biodiv. Conserv.*, no. 3, p. 21-8, 1994.

VELOSO, H. P. et al. IV-Vegetação. *Brasil-Departamento Nacional de Produção Mineral. Projeto RADAMBRASIL (v. 8) Folha NA 20 Boa Vista e Parte das Folhas NA 21 Tumucumaque, NB 20 Roraima e NB 21*. Rio de Janeiro, p. 307-404, 1975.

VELOSO, H. P., RANGEL-FILHO, A. L. R.; LIMA, J. C. A. *Classificação da vegetação brasileira, adaptada a um sistema universal*. Rio de Janeiro: IBGE, 1991.

WILLIAMS, P.H.; PRANCE, G. T.; HUMPHRIES, C. J.; EDWARDS, K. S. Promise and problems in applying quantitative complementary areas for representing the diversity of some Neotropical plants (families Dichapetalaceae, Lecythidaceae, Caryocaraceae, Chrysobalanaceae and Proteaceae). *Biological Journal of the Linnean Society*, no. 58, p. 125-57, 1996.

WORBES, M.; HANS, K.; REVILLA, J. D.; MARTIUS, C. On the dynamics, floristic subdivision and geographical distribution at várzea forests in Central Amazonia. *J. Veget. Science*, no. 3, p. 553-64, 1992.

APPENDICES

Appendix 1 – Procedures for preparing the conservation status maps for each vegetation type

In order to determine the level of conservation of a given vegetation type, the spatial database of the IBGE (1997) GIS was queried twice, resulting in two maps: (1) the map showing the polygons of the vegetation type under review; and (2) the map of conservation areas in two colors, one for the polygons of conservation areas under strict protection and the other for the polygons of semi-protected conservation areas. The GIS used by the IBGE does not permit the display of intersecting polygons and only allows the export of the maps by means of screen capture. Thus the two maps were produced in separate frames in the GIS, each with a white background, and the polygons of the attribute in question (conservation unit or vegetation type) were filled in with different solid colors. Subtractive primary colors were used: yellow for the vegetation type, cyan for strict conservation areas and magenta for semi-protected conservation units. In the GIS the two maps were displayed separately, using the same scale and exactly the same position on the screen (display option Fit Features). The presence of the latitude-longitude grid and border is essential for fixing the scale. The screens were captured at a resolution of 1,280 x 1,024 pixels (key printscreen). The maps were displayed in digital raster image processing software, where they were superimposed in a perfect fit. The two maps (conservation areas and vegetation types) were merged through the 'multiply colors' option. The intersecting pixels thus take on one of two additive primary colors, green or red.

The result is a map with polygons in five colors, three of which interest us:
- green = the portion of the vegetation type under strict protection regimes;
- red = the portion of the vegetation type that is semi-protected; and
- yellow = the portion of the vegetation type with no use restrictions.

Finally all three classes are measured by counting pixels.

Appendix 2 - Synthesis of the classification of Amazonian vegetation types proposed by Veloso et al. (1991) and adapted by IBGE (1997)

	Formation classes	Formation subclasses	Formation groups	Formation subgroups	Formations	Sub-formations
Terminology used by Veloso et al. (1991)	Structure / Life Forms	Climate / water deficit	Physiology/ transpiration and fertility	Physiognomies [growth habits]	Environment / relief	Specific physiognomies
Criteria adopted by Veloso et al. (1991)						
Hierarchical level in IBGE's GIS (1997)	1	2	--	3	4	5
Options available in IBGE's GIS (1997)	- Pioneer - Savanna - Steppe-savanna - Campinarana - Forest - 'Refuge' [isolated mountain tops] - Savanna / Seasonal forest contact - Savanna / Rain forest contact zone - Savanna / Steppe-savannah contact - Campinarana/ Rain forest contact - Rain Forest / Seasonal Forest contact - Secondary vegetation - Reforestation - Farming and ranching	- Wet/moist - Seasonal - Fluvial influence - Tidal influence [within river] - Marine influence	--	- Grassy-woody - Herbaceous - Shrubby - Wooded - Forested - Park - Arboreal - Open - Dense - Semi-deciduous - Deciduous - Buriti palm grove	- Alluvial [várzea and igapó] - Lowland [terra firme < 100 m] - Sub-montane [terra firme 100 to 600 m] - Montane [600 to 2000 m] - High-montane [> 2000 m]	- With gallery forest - Without gallery forest - With palms - Without palms - With bamboos - Bamboo grove - With vines - With sororocas - With emergents in canopy - With uniform canopy - Cyclical crop - Eucalyptus - Fruit trees - Pines - Ranching

Appendix 3 - Table of the 161 distinct vegetation types available in IBGE's (1997) GIS obtained from the report of all 5,929 polygons in the database. The grouping system adopted for the 21 maps is shown in Table 4.

no. polygons	Area (km²)	Symbol	Primary or secondary	Hierarchical levels					
				1	2	3	4	5	6
35	12,031	Acc	S	farming and ranching				cyclical crop	
353	40,879	Ap	S	farming and ranching				ranching	
43	15,983	Lap3	P	campinarana	wet/moist	wooded		with palm trees	3
57	14,267	Lap	P	campinarana	wet/moist	wooded		with palm trees	

continues

no. polygons	Area (km²)	Symbol	Primary or secondary	Hierarchical levels					
				1	2	3	4	5	6
2	593	Las	P	campinarana	wet/moist	wooded		with palm trees	
12	3,338	La3	P	campinarana	wet/moist	wooded			3
21	16,275	La	P	campinarana	wet/moist	wooded			
8	6,143	Ldp	P	campinarana	wet/moist	forested		with palm trees	
38	32,359	Ld3	P	campinarana	wet/moist	forested			3
102	58,181	Ld	P	campinarana	wet/moist	forested			
1	1,381	Lg3	P	campinarana	wet/moist	grassy-woody			3
16	3,872	Lg	P	campinarana	wet/moist	grassy-woody			
19	24,352	LO	P	campinarana	wet/moist				
1	935	Cau	P	forest	seasonal	deciduous	alluvial	with uniform canopy	
1	98	Ca4	P	forest	seasonal	deciduous	alluvial		4
2	1,201	Cbe4	P	forest	seasonal	deciduous	lowland	with emergents in canopy	4
7	5,214	Cb	P	forest	seasonal	deciduous	lowland		
2	280	Cme2	P	forest	seasonal	deciduous	montane	with emergents in canopy	2
1	253	Cme4	P	forest	seasonal	deciduous	montane	with emergents in canopy	4
1	156	Cm2	P	forest	seasonal	deciduous	montane		2
5	2,455	Cse2	P	forest	seasonal	deciduous	sub-montane	with emergents in canopy	2
17	8,688	Cse4	P	forest	seasonal	deciduous	sub-montane	with emergents in canopy	4
2	232	Cse7	P	forest	seasonal	deciduous	sub-montane	with emergents in canopy	7
4	5,232	Cse	P	forest	seasonal	deciduous	sub-montane	with emergents in canopy	
9	9,001	Cs4	P	forest	seasonal	deciduous	sub-montane		4
25	20,705	Cs	P	forest	seasonal	deciduous	sub-montane		
7	5,533	Fae4	P	forest	seasonal	semi-deciduous	alluvial	with emergents in canopy	4
39	20,145	Fae	P	forest	seasonal	semi-deciduous	alluvial	with emergents in canopy	
29	5,526	Fa4	P	forest	seasonal	semi-deciduous	alluvial		4
2	67	Fa	P	forest	seasonal	semi-deciduous	alluvial		
4	991	Fbu2	P	forest	seasonal	semi-deciduous	lowland	with uniform canopy	2
3	1,105	Fbu4	P	forest	seasonal	semi-deciduous	lowland	with uniform canopy	4
1	97	Fme2	P	forest	seasonal	semi-deciduous	montane	with emergents in canopy	2
3	728	Fme4	P	forest	seasonal	semi-deciduous	montane	with emergents in canopy	4
1	118	Fme	P	forest	seasonal	semi-deciduous	montane	with emergents in canopy	
2	278	Fm4	P	forest	seasonal	semi-deciduous	montane		4
4	580	Fm	P	forest	seasonal	semi-deciduous	montane		
32	156,294	Fse2	P	forest	seasonal	semi-deciduous	sub-montane	with emergents in canopy	2
71	41,377	Fse4	P	forest	seasonal	semi-deciduous	sub-montane	with emergents in canopy	4
37	36,652	Fse	P	forest	seasonal	semi-deciduous	sub-montane	with emergents in canopy	
6	2,910	Fsu2	P	forest	seasonal	semi-deciduous	sub-montane	with uniform canopy	2
7	2,214	Fsu	P	forest	seasonal	semi-deciduous	sub-montane	with uniform canopy	

continues

no. polygons	Area (km²)	Symbol	Primary or secondary	Hierarchical levels					
				1	2	3	4	5	6
14	7,076	Fs4	P	forest	seasonal	semi-deciduous	sub-montane		4
10	2,282	Fs	P	forest	seasonal	semi-deciduous	sub-montane		
6	905	Abc1	P	forest	wet/moist	open	lowland	with vines	1
42	21,092	Abc	P	forest	wet/moist	open	lowland	with vines	
23	7,075	Abp1	P	forest	wet/moist	open	lowland	with palms	1
3	839	Abp2	P	forest	wet/moist	open	lowland	with palms	2
27	12,043	Abp3	P	forest	wet/moist	open	lowland	with palms	3
223	158,459	Abp	P	forest	wet/moist	open	lowland	with palms	
3	367	Ab	P	forest	wet/moist	open	lowland		
2	326	Amc2	P	forest	wet/moist	open	montane	with vines	2
2	364	Amc	P	forest	wet/moist	open	montane	with vines	
3	463	Amp	P	forest	wet/moist	open	montane	with palms	
2	182	Am	P	forest	wet/moist	open	montane		
1	948	Asb1	P	forest	wet/moist	open	sub-montane	with bamboos	1
36	24,884	Asb	P	forest	wet/moist	open	sub-montane	with bamboos	
36	22,709	Asc1	P	forest	wet/moist	open	sub-montane	with vines	1
24	12,610	Asc2	P	forest	wet/moist	open	sub-montane	with vines	2
171	252,807	Asc	P	forest	wet/moist	open	sub-montane	with vines	
57	28,363	Asp1	P	forest	wet/moist	open	sub-montane	with palms	1
5	1,335	Asp2	P	forest	wet/moist	open	sub-montane	with palms	2
9	11,075	Asp3	P	forest	wet/moist	open	sub-montane	with palms	3
1	227	Asp6	P	forest	wet/moist	open	sub-montane	with palms	6
249	444,831	Asp	P	forest	wet/moist	open	sub-montane	with palms	
6	6,974	Ass	P	forest	wet/moist	open	sub-montane	with Phenakospermum	
49	32,052	Asb*	P	forest	wet/moist	open	sub-montane	bamnoo grove	
1	156	As1	P	forest	wet/moist	open	sub-montane		1
1	142	As	P	forest	wet/moist	open	sub-montane		
3	1,767	Dae1	P	forest	wet/moist	dense	alluvial	with emergents in canopy	1
7	5,221	Dae3	P	forest	wet/moist	dense	alluvial	with emergents in canopy	3
216	192,054	Dae	P	forest	wet/moist	dense	alluvial	with emergents in canopy	
8	3,308	Dau3	P	forest	wet/moist	dense	alluvial	with uniform canopy	3
23	7,437	Dau6	P	forest	wet/moist	dense	alluvial	with uniform canopy	6
136	121,831	Dau	P	forest	wet/moist	dense	alluvial	with uniform canopy	
4	835	Da1	P	forest	wet/moist	dense	alluvial		1
22	1,341	Da3	P	forest	wet/moist	dense	alluvial		3
352	90,110	Da	P	forest	wet/moist	dense	alluvial		
18	5,768	Dbe1	P	forest	wet/moist	dense	lowland	with emergents in canopy	1
5	2,289	Dbe2	P	forest	wet/moist	dense	lowland	with emergents in canopy	2
52	61,791	Dbe3	P	forest	wet/moist	dense	lowland	with emergents in canopy	3
1	1,384	Dbe6	P	forest	wet/moist	dense	lowland	with emergents in canopy	6
302	804,632	Dbe	P	forest	wet/moist	dense	lowland	with emergents in canopy	
4	2,088	Dbu1	P	forest	wet/moist	dense	lowland	with uniform canopy	1
3	358	Dbu2	P	forest	wet/moist	dense	lowland	with uniform canopy	2
4	1,667	Dbu3	P	forest	wet/moist	dense	lowland	with uniform canopy	3

continues

no. polygons	Area (km²)	Symbol	Primary or secondary	Hierarchical levels					
				1	2	3	4	5	6
1	116	Dbu6	P	forest	wet/moist	dense	lowland	with uniform canopy	6
70	54,451	Dbu	P	forest	wet/moist	dense	lowland	with uniform canopy	
2	721	Db1	P	forest	wet/moist	dense	lowland		1
4	917	Db3	P	forest	wet/moist	dense	lowland		3
17	5,083	Db	P	forest	wet/moist	dense	lowland		
14	13,043	Dme	P	forest	wet/moist	dense	montane	with emergents in canopy	
28	10,829	Dmu	P	forest	wet/moist	dense	montane	with uniform canopy	
3	132	Dm	P	forest	wet/moist	dense	montane		
42	18,417	Dse1	P	forest	wet/moist	dense	sub-montane	with emergents in canopy	1
1	3,834	Dse2	P	forest	wet/moist	dense	sub-montane	with emergents in canopy	2
36	11,912	Dse3	P	forest	wet/moist	dense	sub-montane	with emergents in canopy	3
1	246	Dse6	P	forest	wet/moist	dense	sub-montane	with emergents in canopy	6
701	638,234	Dse	P	forest	wet/moist	dense	sub-montane	with emergents in canopy	
6	7,328	Dsu1	P	forest	wet/moist	dense	sub-montane	with uniform canopy	1
2	1,375	Dsu2	P	forest	wet/moist	dense	sub-montane	with uniform canopy	2
4	1,252	Dsu3	P	forest	wet/moist	dense	sub-montane	with uniform canopy	3
212	169,622	Dsu	P	forest	wet/moist	dense	sub-montane	with uniform canopy	
10	1,489	Ds	P	forest	wet/moist	dense	sub-montane		
2	1,086	ON	P	wet or moist / seasonal forest					
13	1,543	Pap	P	pioneer	fluvial influence	shrub	alluvial	with palms	
8	13,450	Pas	P	pioneer	fluvial influence	shrub	alluvial	without palms	
69	9,189	Paa	P	pioneer	fluvial influence	shrub	alluvial		
12	2,786	Pab	P	pioneer	fluvial influence	buriti palm grove	alluvial		
3	360	Phs6	P	pioneer	fluvial influence	herbaceous	alluvial	without palms	6
38	5,256	Phs	P	pioneer	fluvial influence	herbaceous	aluvial	without palms	
75	50,831	Pah	P	pioneer	fluvial influence	herbaceous	alluvial		
93	10,955	Pfm	P	pioneer	fluvial/tidal influence	arboreal			
7	869	Pfh	P	pioneer	fluvial/tidal influence	herbaceous			
1	137	Pmb	P	pioneer	marine influence	shrub			
1	52	Pmh	P	pioneer	marine influence	herbaceous			
1	44	Re	S	reforestation				eucalyptus	
1	22	Rf	S	reforestation				fruit trees	
2	227	Rp	S	reforestation				pines	
5	363	rmb	P	refugium		shrub	montane		
1	17	rlh	P	refugium		herbaceous	high-montane		

continues

no. polygons	Area (km²)	Symbol	Primary or secondary	Hierarchical levels					
				1	2	3	4	5	6
2	39	rmh	P	refugium		herbaceous	montane		
16	1,221	rm	P	refugium			montane		
1	1,983	Saf1	P	savanna	seasonal	wooded		with gallery forest	1
49	31,021	Saf4	P	savanna	seasonal	wooded		with gallery forest	4
99	300,963	Saf	P	savanna	seasonal	wooded		with gallery forest	
5	1,089	Sas1	P	savanna	seasonal	wooded		without gallery forest	1
35	34,204	Sas4	P	savanna	seasonal	wooded		without gallery forest	4
1	123	Sas5	P	savanna	seasonal	wooded		without gallery forest	5
205	110,359	Sas	P	savanna	seasonal	wooded			
29	11,920	Sa1	P	savanna	seasonal	wooded			1
44	7,724	Sa	P	savanna	seasonal	wooded			
42	31,649	Sd1	P	savanna	seasonal	forested			1
71	59,466	Sd4	P	savanna	seasonal	forested			4
212	55,971	Sd	P	savanna	seasonal	forested			
22	13,044	Sgf	P	savanna	seasonal	grassy-woody		with gallery forest	
2	1,061	Sgs4	P	savanna	seasonal	grassy-woody		without gallery forest	4
5	1,459	Sgs5	P	savanna	seasonal	grassy-woody		without gallery forest	5
26	10,958	Sgs	P	savanna	seasonal	grassy-woody		without gallery forest	
3	715	Sg1	P	savanna	seasonal	grassy-woody			1
9	14,476	Sg	P	savanna	seasonal	grassy-woody			
2	811	Spf1	P	savanna	seasonal	park		with gallery forest	1
131	146,388	Spf	P	savanna	seasonal	park		with gallery forest	
3	805	Sps1	P	savanna	seasonal	park		without gallery forest	1
5	4,304	Sps4	P	savanna	seasonal	park		without gallery forest	4
1	1,747	Sps5	P	savanna	seasonal	park		without gallery forest	5
83	26,485	Sps	P	savanna	seasonal	park		without gallery forest	
13	6,631	Sp1	P	savanna	seasonal	park			1
3	1,182	Sp4	P	savanna	seasonal	park			4
33	9,975	Sp	P	savanna	seasonal	park			
19	10,651	SN	P	savanna/ seasonal forest					
8	6,329	SO	P	savanna/ tropical moist forest					
1	4,089	ST	P	savanna / steppe-savanna					
2	123	Ta	P	steppe-savanna	seasonal	wooded			
11	2,751	Td	P	steppe-savanna	seasonal	forested			

continues

no. polygons	Area (km²)	Symbol	Primary or secondary	Hierarchical levels					
				1	2	3	4	5	6
1	835	Tgs5	P	steppe-savanna	seasonal	grassy-woody		without gallery forest	5
1	127	Tgs	P	steppe-savanna	seasonal	grassy-woody		without gallery forest	
3	8,701	Tp	P	steppe-savanna	seasonal	park			
13	45,028	Vsp	S	secondary vegetation				with palms	
34	51,467	Vss	S	secondary vegetation				without palms	
21	3,267	Vs	S	secondary vegetation					
Total:	4,970,514								

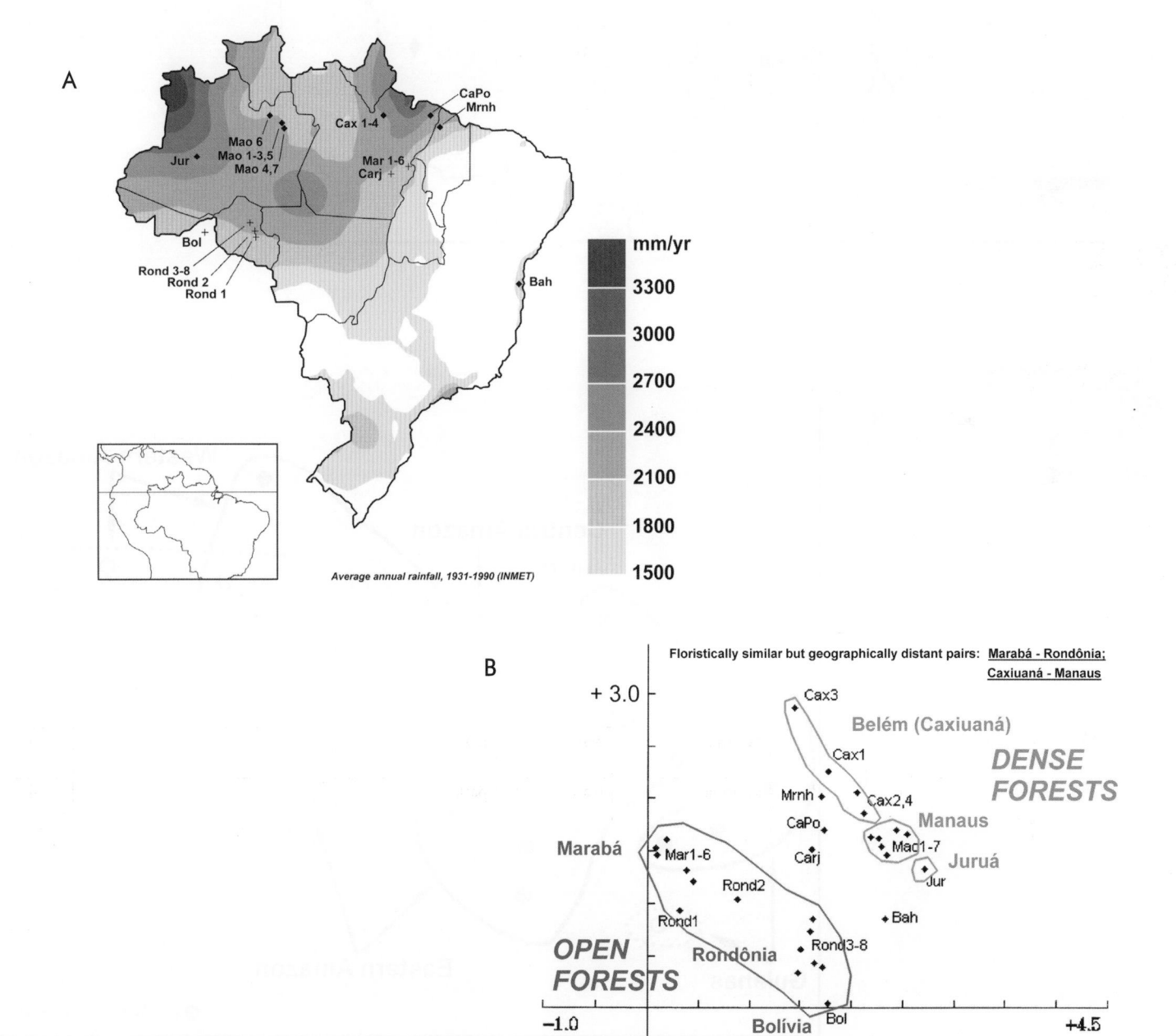

Figure 4. Location (A) and ordination (B) by Detrended Correspondence Analysis (DCA) of different inventories of terra firme, at genus level, using tree abundance to indicate importance. (Source: Oliveira and Nelson 2000).

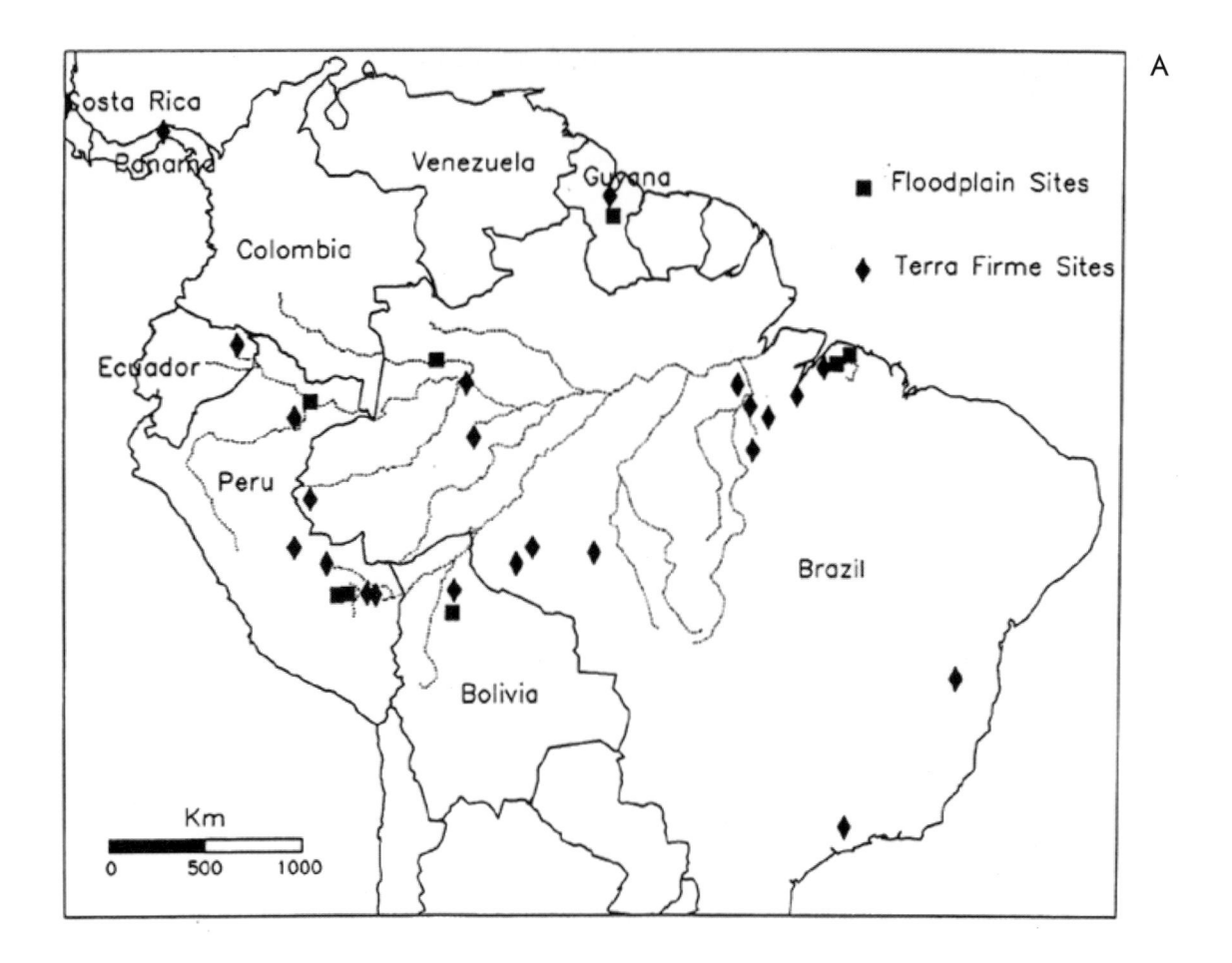

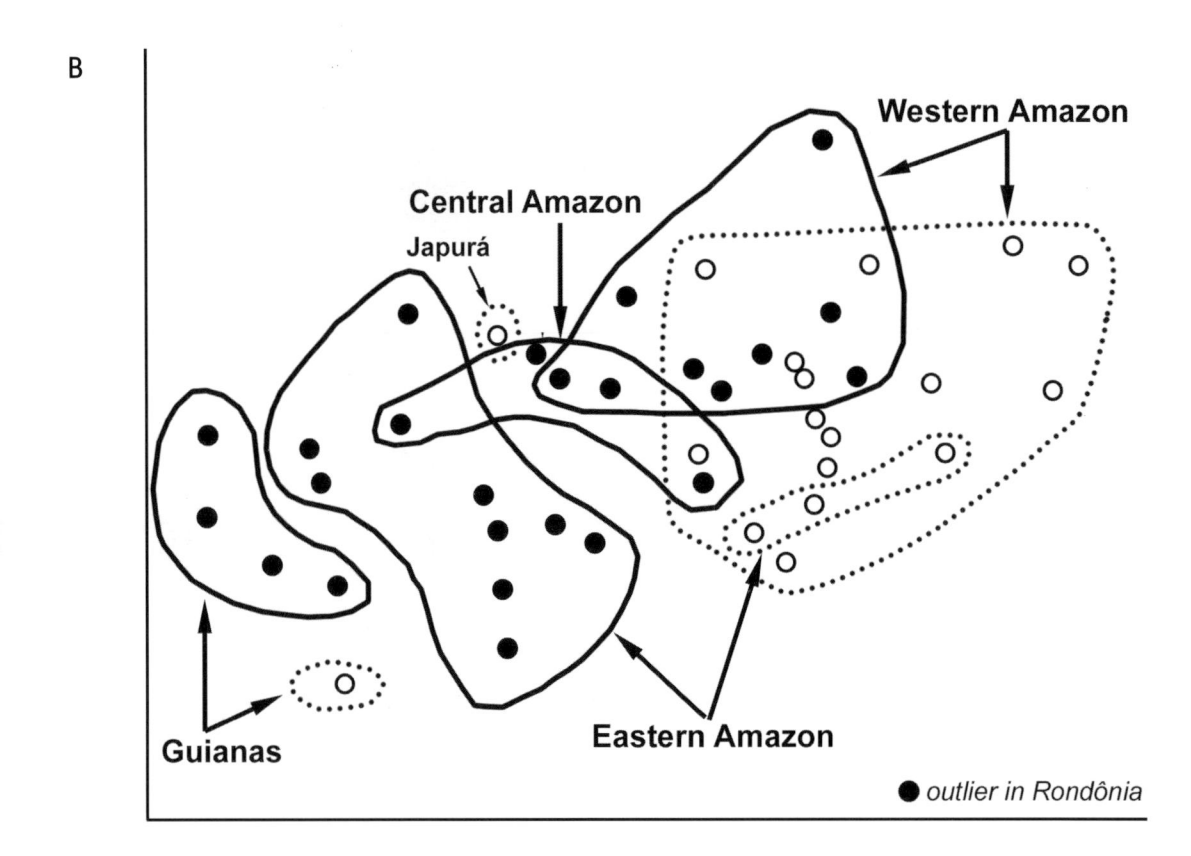

Figure 5. (A) Location of 29 inventory sites and (B) Decorrelated Correspondence Analysis at family level for 44 forests plots in Amazonia and the Guianas (four extra-Amazonian sites not shown), based on abundance of trees in 92 families. Solid outlines and solid dots indicate terra firme plots; dashed outlines and open dots indicate seasonally inundated riparian forests. Modified from Terborgh and Andresen 1998.

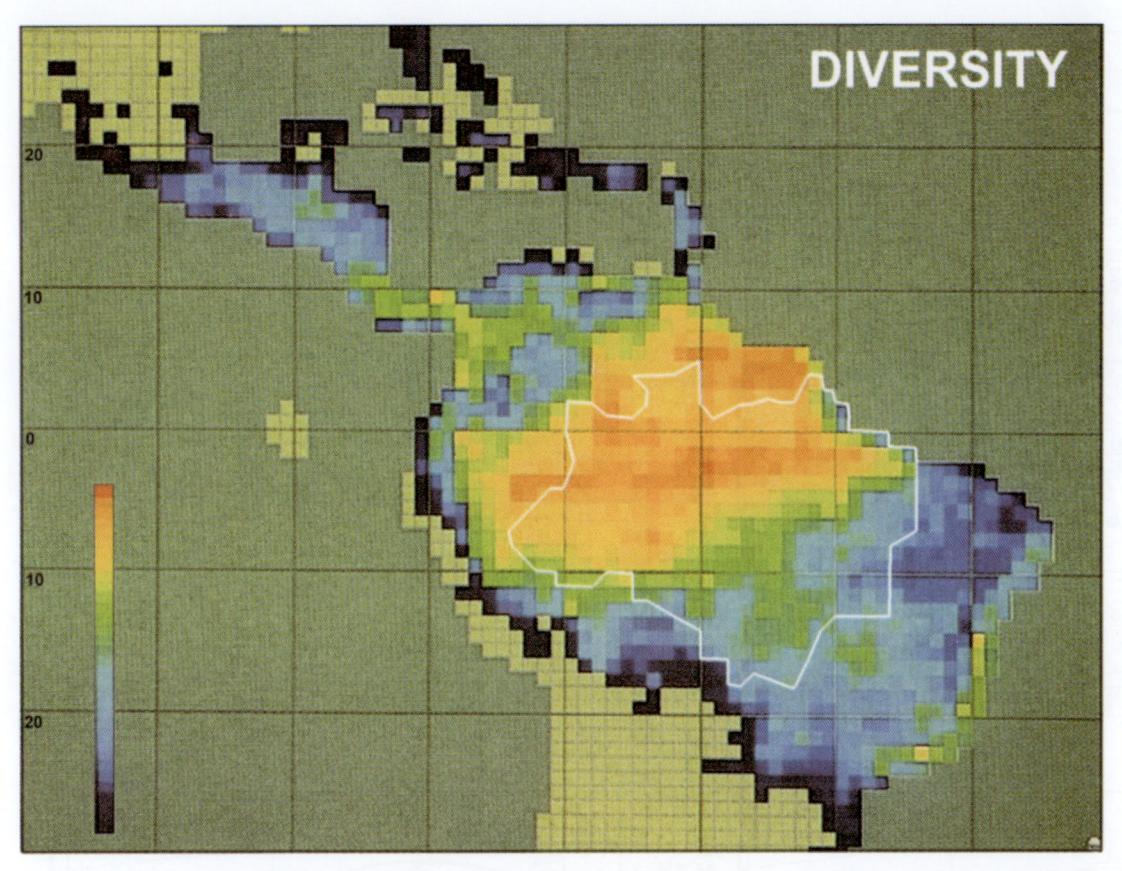

Figure 6a. Spatial analysis of Neotropical diversity on the basis of 729 species of five woody angiosperm families: Lecythidaceae, Chrysobalanaceae, Dichapetalaceae, Caryocaraceae, and Proteaceae. Presence counts were summed for each of 1,751 1° x 1° blocks based on 729 distribution maps, and the total distribution area for each species was interpolated between the collection sites to reduce the effect of variable collecting effort. (Source: Williams et al. 1996.)

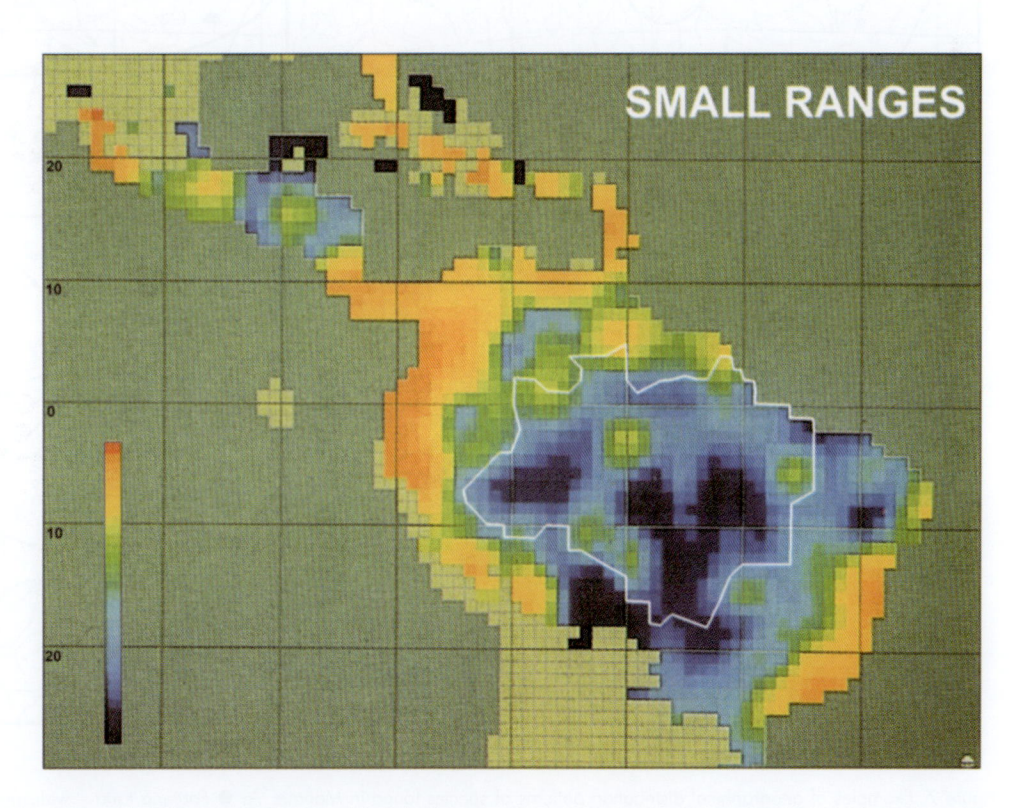

Figure 6b. Local endemism (or rarity) map in 1° x 1° blocks based on the same 729 interpolated distribution maps from Figure 6a. For a given 1° x 1° block, the rarity index is the sum of rarity scores for all species in the block, and each species' rarity score is inversely proportional to its geographic range size. Areas of sparse collecting will have an artificially low rarity index. (Source: Williams et. al 1996).

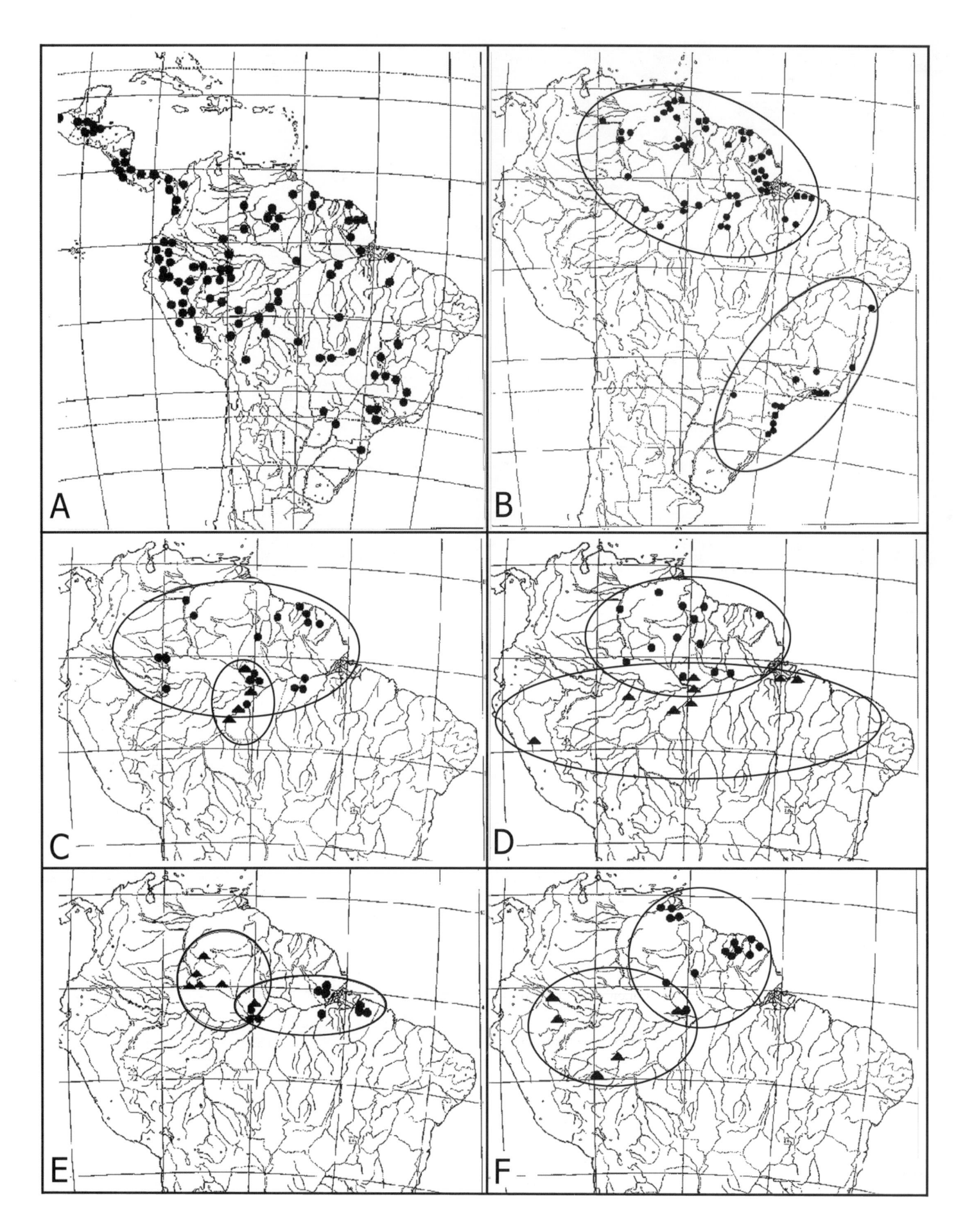

Figure 7. Examples of geographical distribution patterns of species found in Manaus. A: ● *Pouteria torta* – widespread; B: ● *Pouteria venosa* – disjunct distribution between Amazonia and Atlantic Forest; C: ● *Couratari stellata* – widespread in Amazonia; ▲ *Couepia magnoliifolia*, mid-south Amazon; D: ● *Licania coriacea* – middle Amazon/Guianas; ▲ *Pouteria opposita* – southern Amazonia; E: ● *Couepia robusta* – mid to east Amazon; ▲ *Micropholis splendens* – mid Amazon and north; F: ● *Eschweleira collina* – middle Amazon/Guianas; ▲ *Couepia macrophylla* – mid Amazon and west. (Source: Oliveira and Daly 2000).

Figure 8. Mãe Maria Indigenous Area of the Gavião indians near Marabá, showing the coincidence between the reserve boundaries and the limits of deforestation. (Landsat Thematic Mapper Image. Source: National Space Research Institute (Instituto Nacional de Pesquisas Espaciais – INPE)).

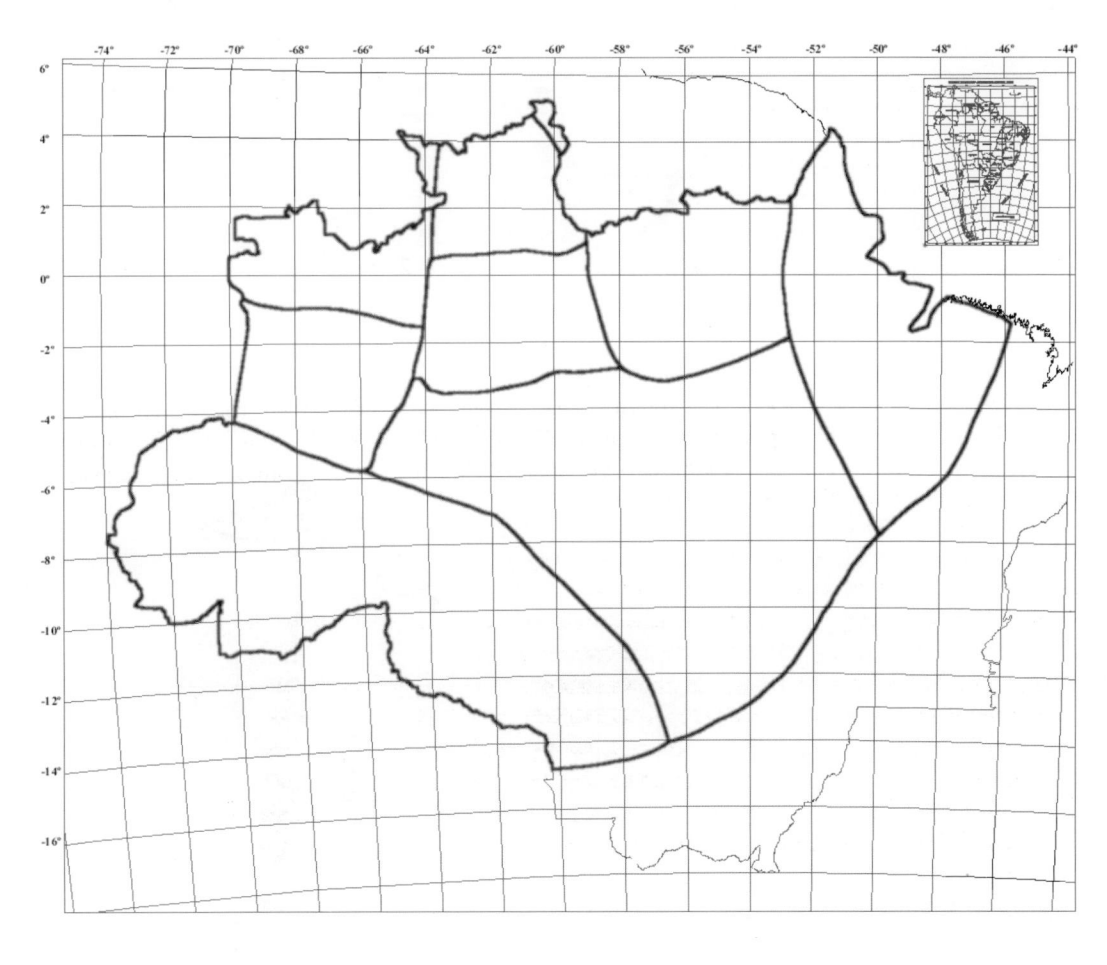

Figure 9. Phyto-geographical regions of Amazonia according to Prance (1977, 1987; map reproduced in Daly and Prance 1989), geometrically corrected and superimposed on the IBGE base map.

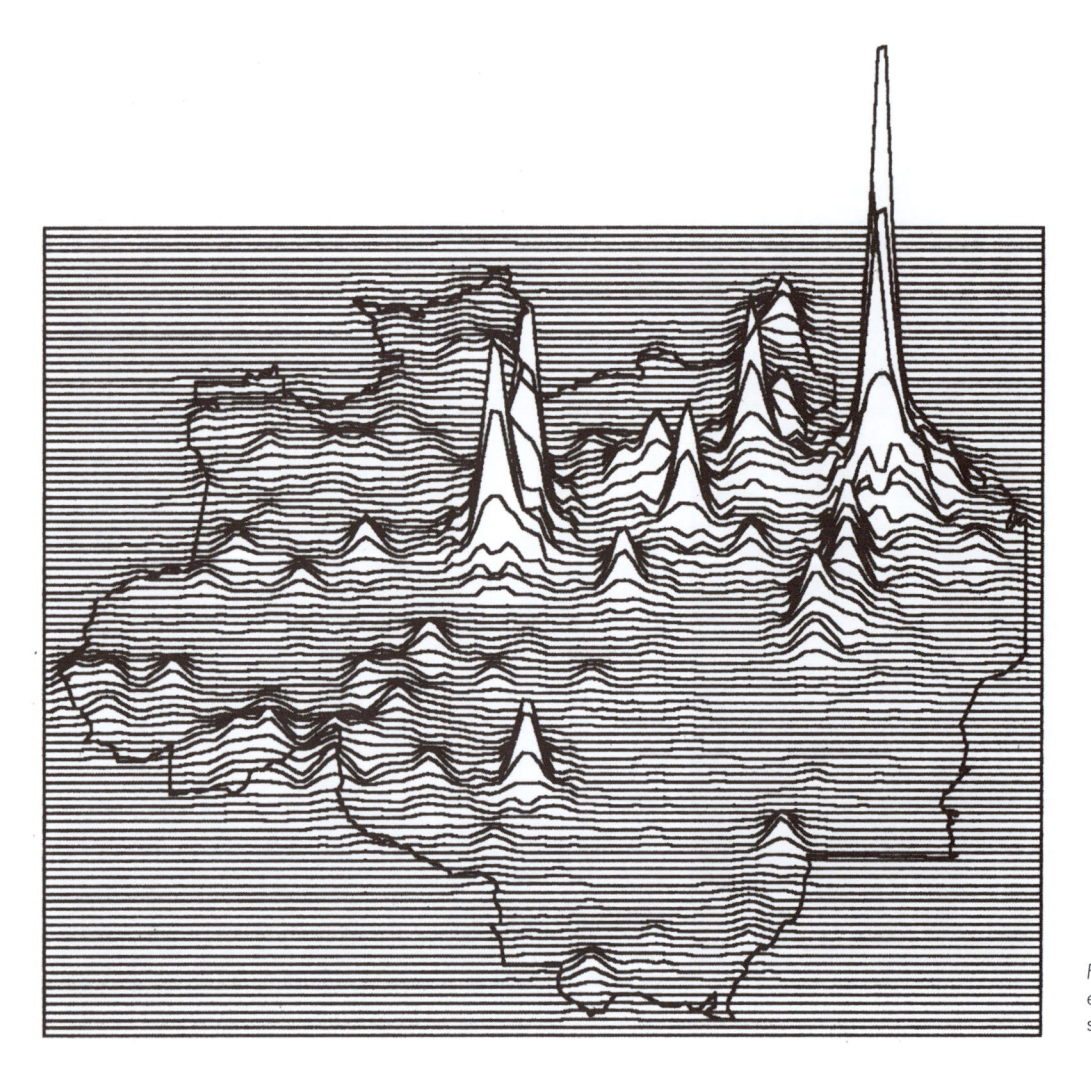

Figure 10. Map of angiosperm collection efforts in the Brazilian Amazonia, on the basis of the genus *Inga* (Nelson 1991).

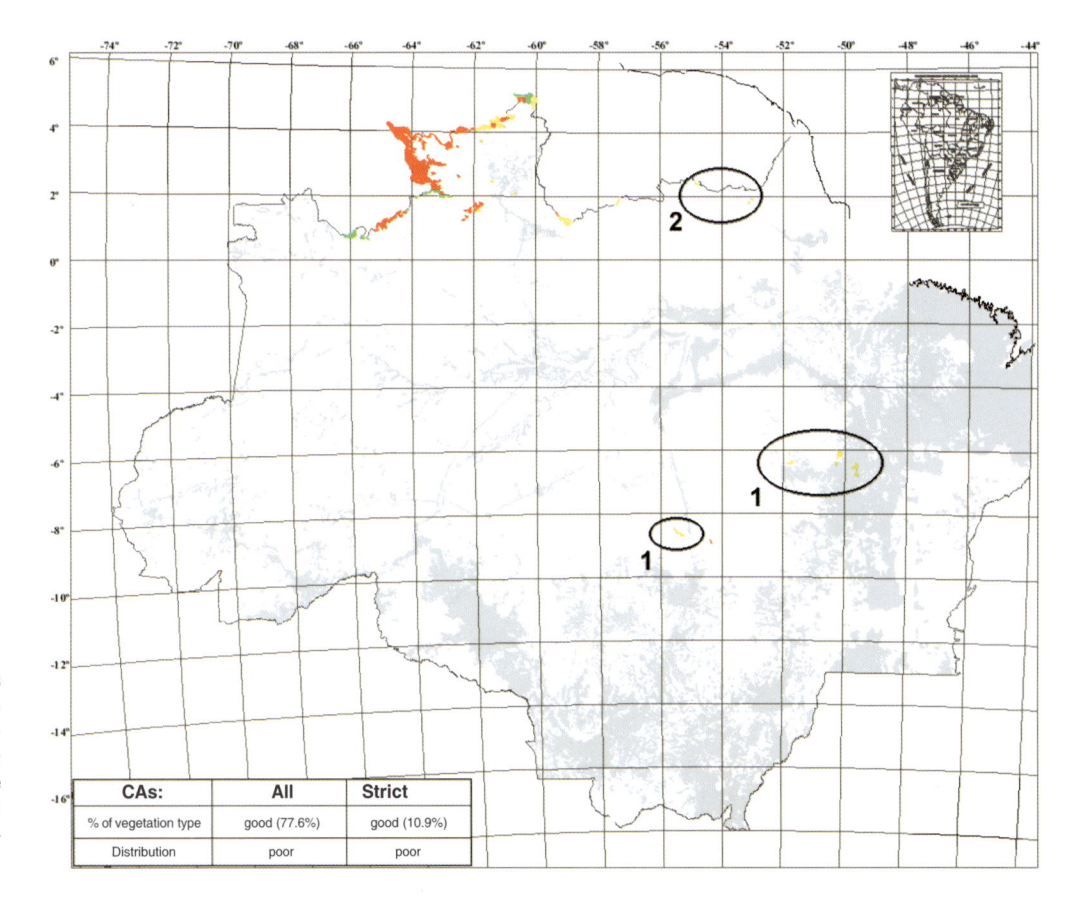

Figure 11. Distribution, conservation status and suggestions for new conservation areas for vegetation type 1a: evergreen montane forest (green = strict conservation area; red = semi-protected area; yellow = no use restrictions). Proposed conservation areas: 1 = maximum priority, 2 = medium priority, 3 = low priority.

CAs:	All	Strict
% of vegetation type	good (77.6%)	good (10.9%)
Distribution	poor	poor

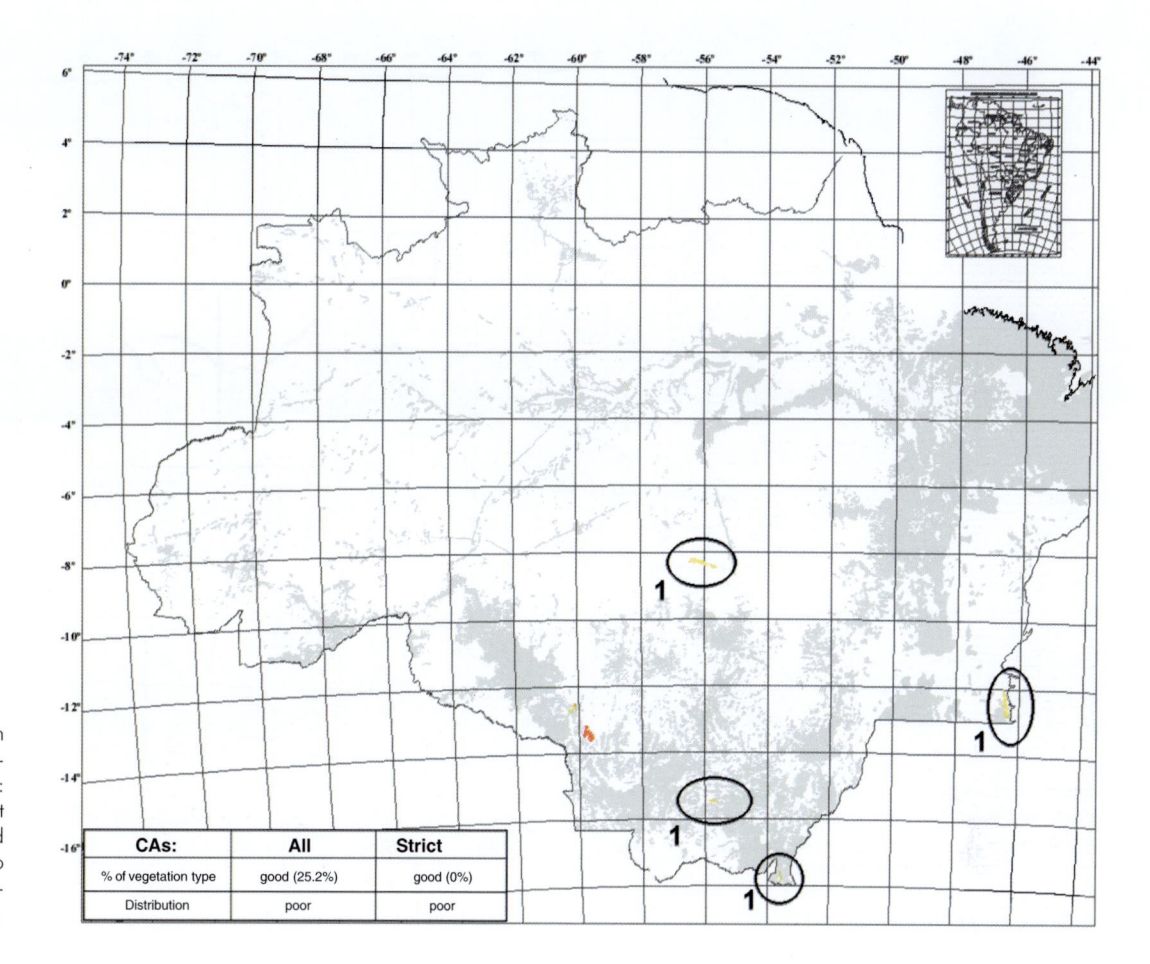

Figure 12. Distribution, conservation status and suggestions for new conservation areas for vegetation type 1b: seasonally deciduous montane forest (green = strict conservation area; red = semi-protected area; yellow = no use restrictions). Proposed conservation areas: 1 = maximum priority.

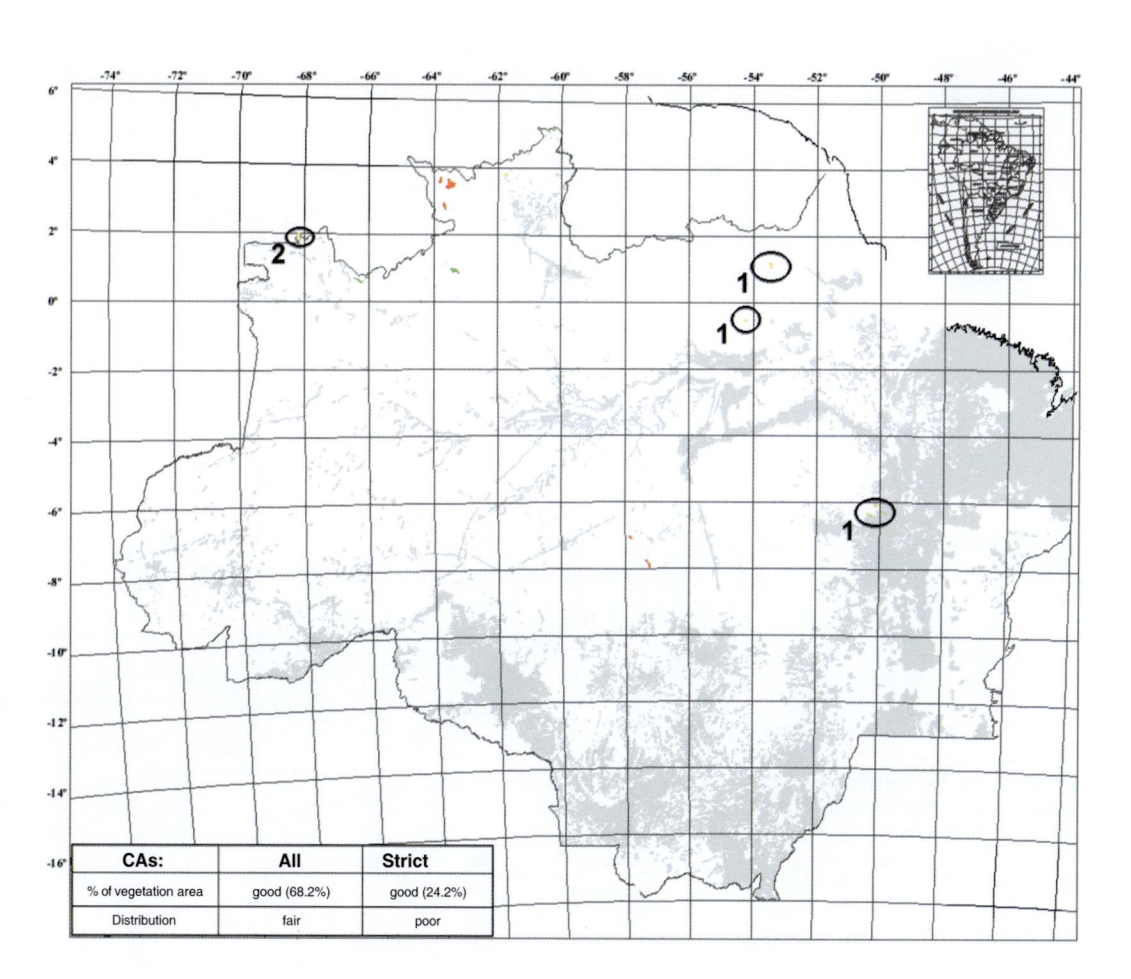

CAs:	All	Strict
% of vegetation type	good (25.2%)	good (0%)
Distribution	poor	poor

Figure 13. Distribution, conservation status and suggestions for new conservation areas for vegetation type 2a: rocky shrubland on isolated mountain tops, 600 to 2000 m altitude (green = strict conservation area; red = semi-protected area; yellow = no use restrictions). Proposed conservation areas: 1 = maximum priority, 2 = medium priority, 3 = low priority.

CAs:	All	Strict
% of vegetation area	good (68.2%)	good (24.2%)
Distribution	fair	poor

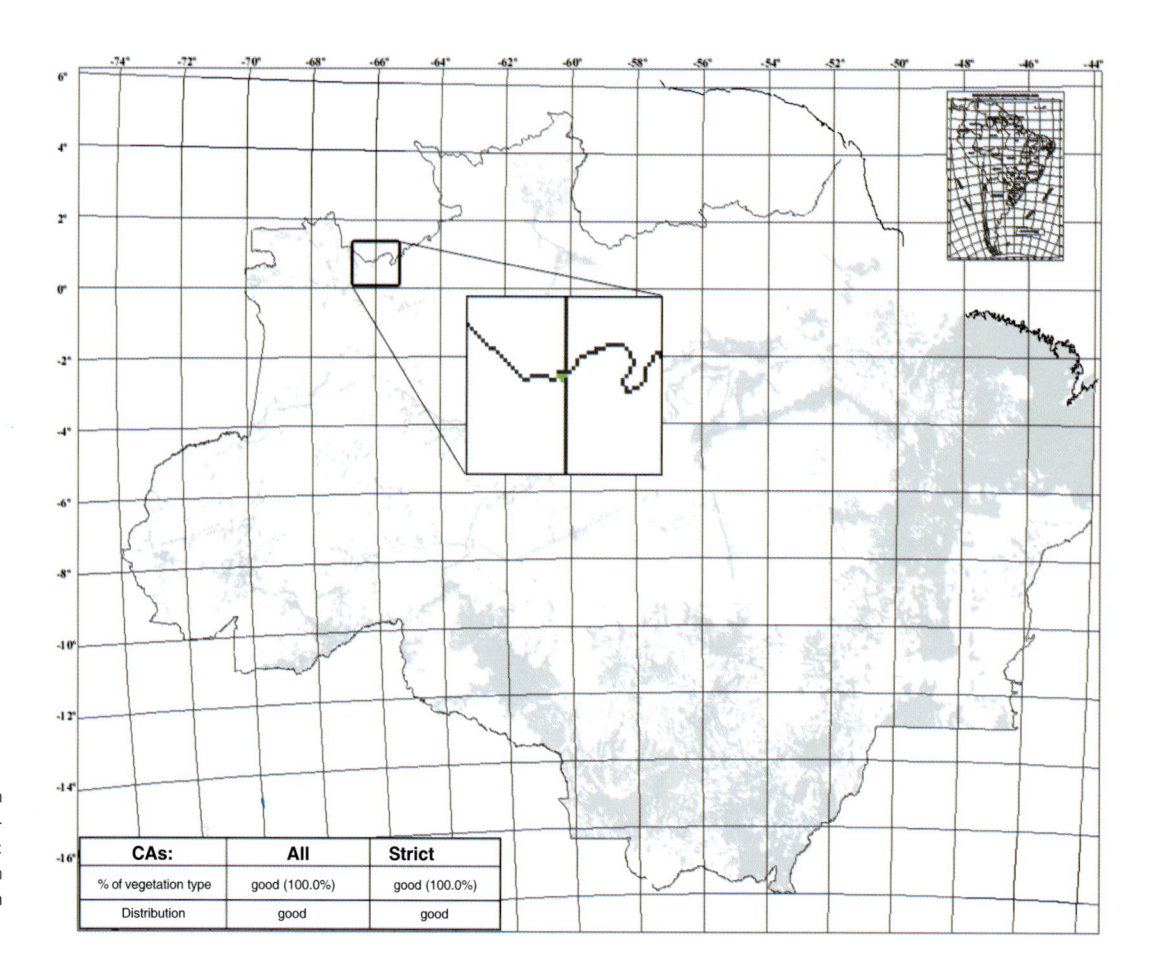

Figure 14. Distribution, conservation status and suggestions for new conservation ares for vegetation type 2b: rocky shrubland on isolated mountain tops, > 2000 m alt. Entire vegetation is already strictly protected (green).

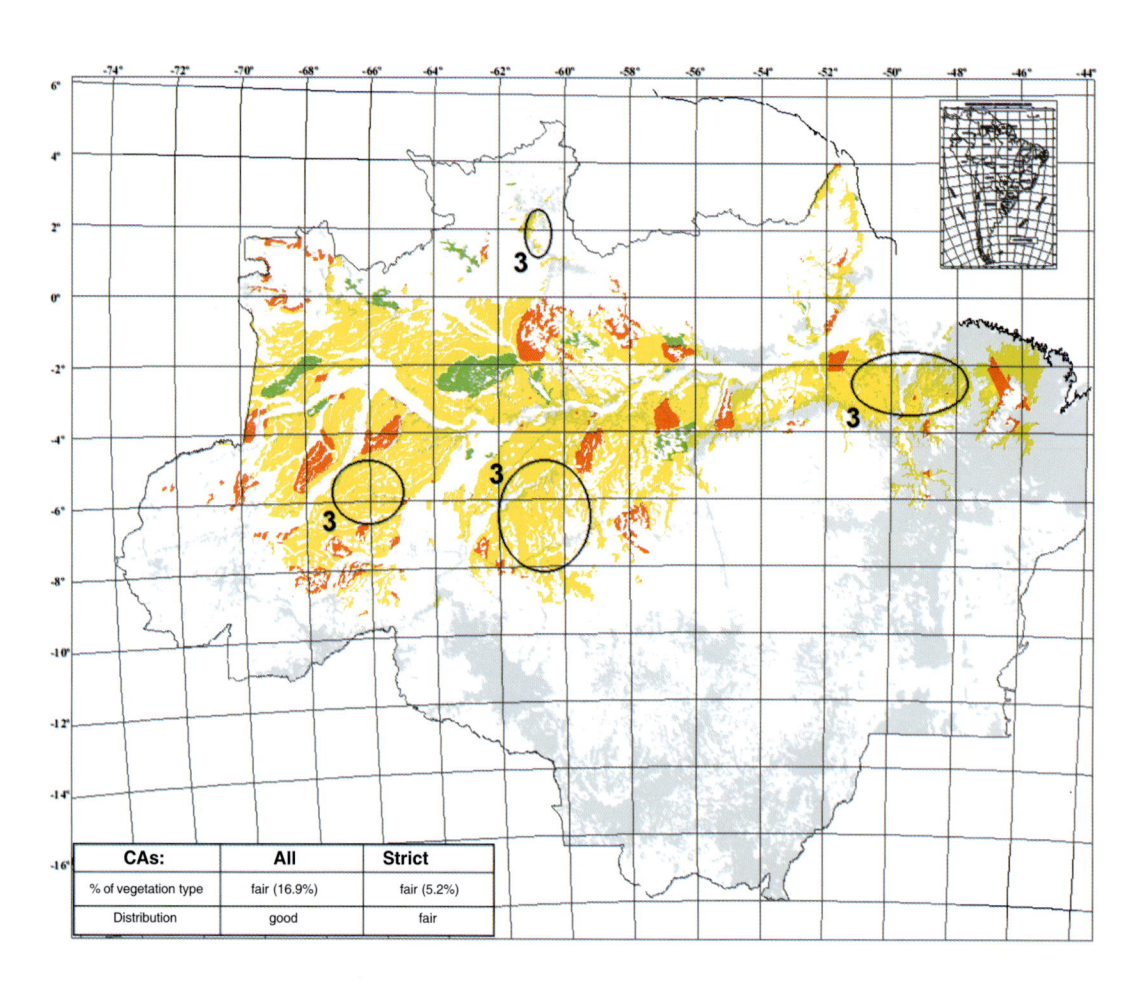

CAs:	All	Strict
% of vegetation type	good (100.0%)	good (100.0%)
Distribution	good	good

Figure 15. Distribution, conservation status and suggestions for new conservation areas for vegetation type 3a: dense forest on terra firme lowlands, 5 to 100 m altitude (green = strict conservation area; red = semi-protected area; yellow = no use restrictions). Proposed conservation areas are all scored 3 = low priority.

CAs:	All	Strict
% of vegetation type	fair (16.9%)	fair (5.2%)
Distribution	good	fair

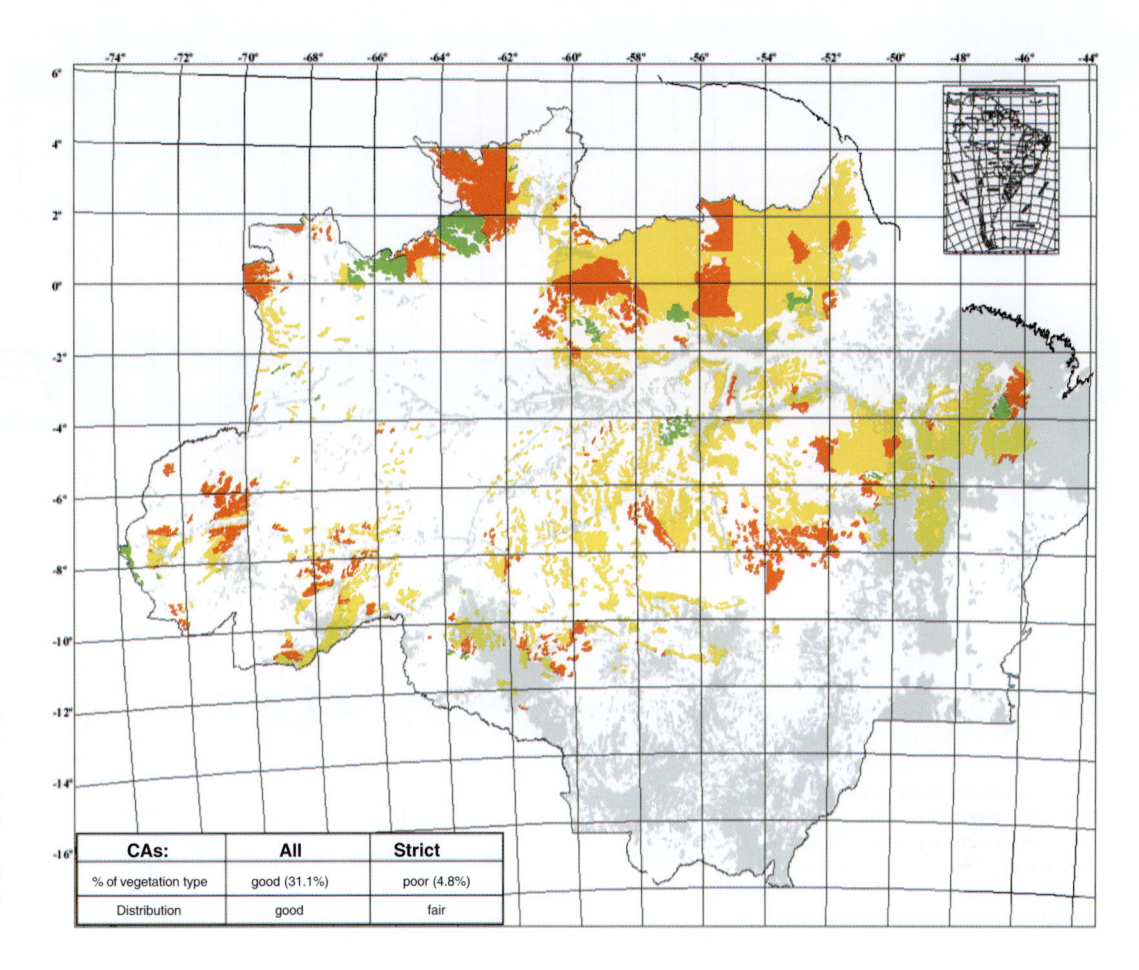

Figure 16. Distribution, conservation status and suggestions for new conservation areas for vegetation type 3b: dense forest on terra firme sub-montane, 100 to 600 m altitude (green = strict conservation area; red = semi-protected area; yellow = no use restrictions). No conservation areas are proposed.

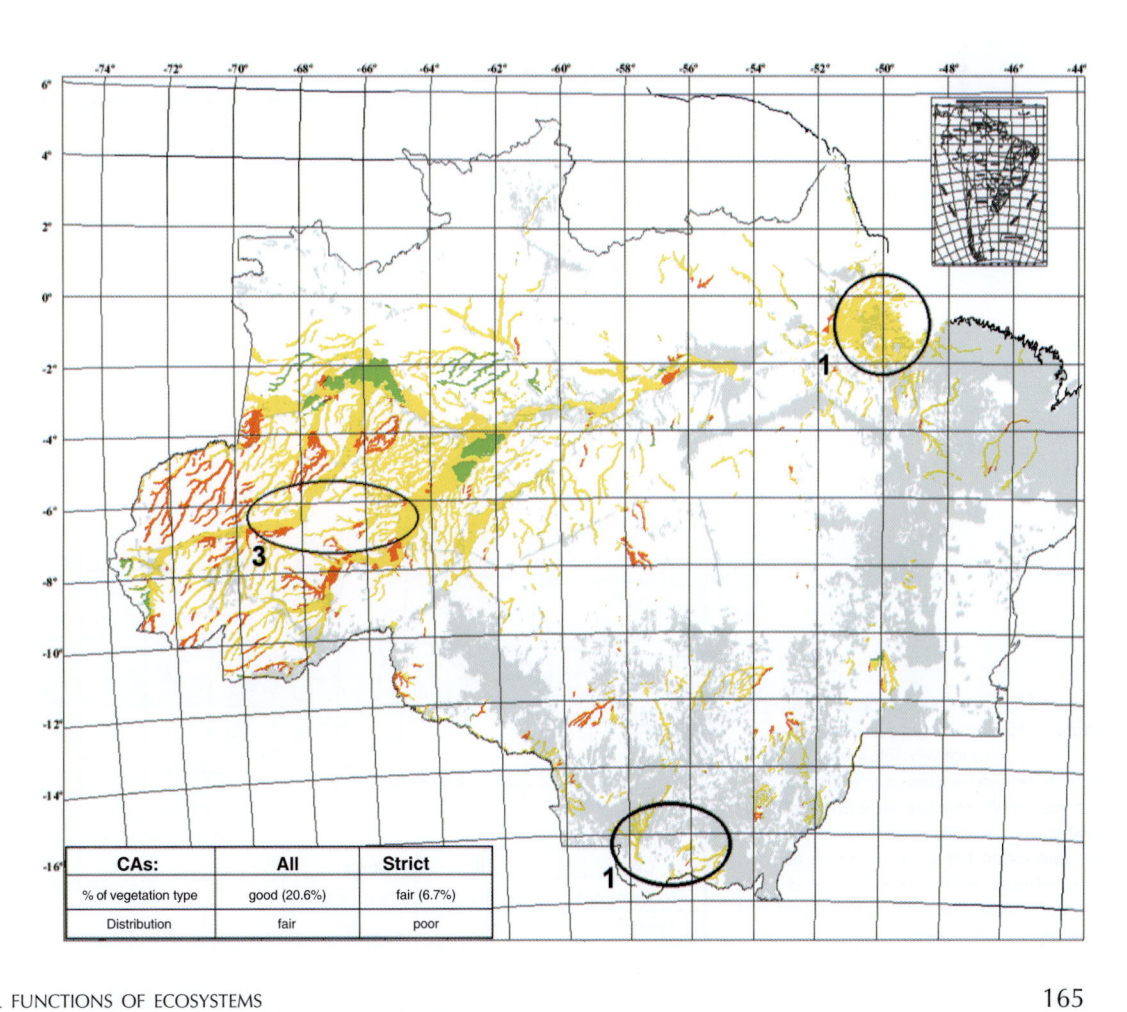

CAs:	All	Strict
% of vegetation type	good (31.1%)	poor (4.8%)
Distribution	good	fair

Figure 17. Distribution, conservation status and suggestions for new conservation areas for vegetation type 4a: várzea and igapó forests (periodically flooded riparian and lacustrine forests of all water types) (green = strict conservation area; red = semi-protected area; yellow = no use restrictions). Proposed conservation area: 1 = maximum priority, 3 = low priority.

CAs:	All	Strict
% of vegetation type	good (20.6%)	fair (6.7%)
Distribution	fair	poor

BIODIVERSITY AND THE ECOLOGICAL FUNCTIONS OF ECOSYSTEMS

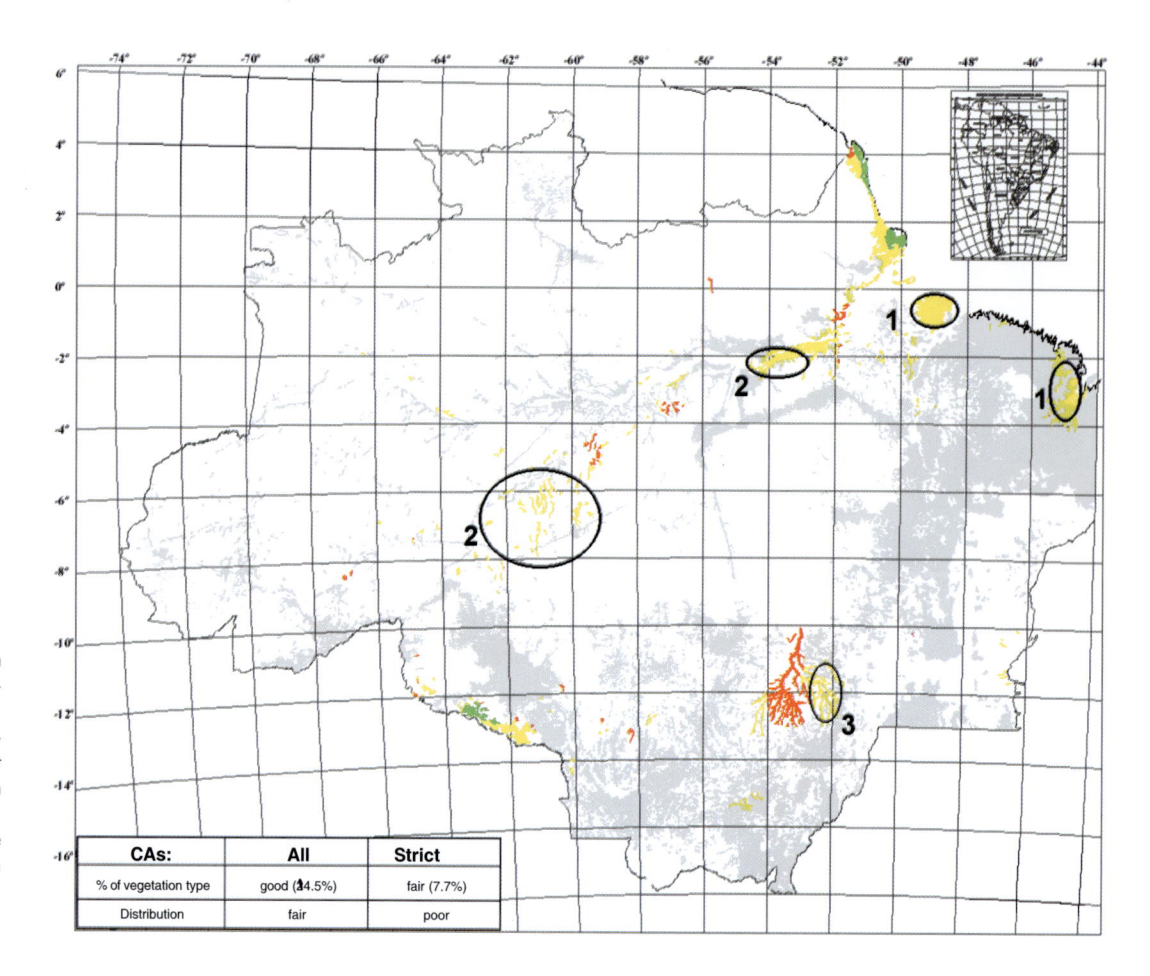

Figure 18. Distribution, conservation status and suggestions for new conservation areas for vegetation type 4b: herbaceous and other primary succession in várzea and igapó (on recent fluvial and lacustrine deposits) (green = strict conservation area; red = semi-protected area; yellow = no use restrictions). Proposed conservation areas: 1 = maximum priority, 2 = medium priority, 3 = low priority.

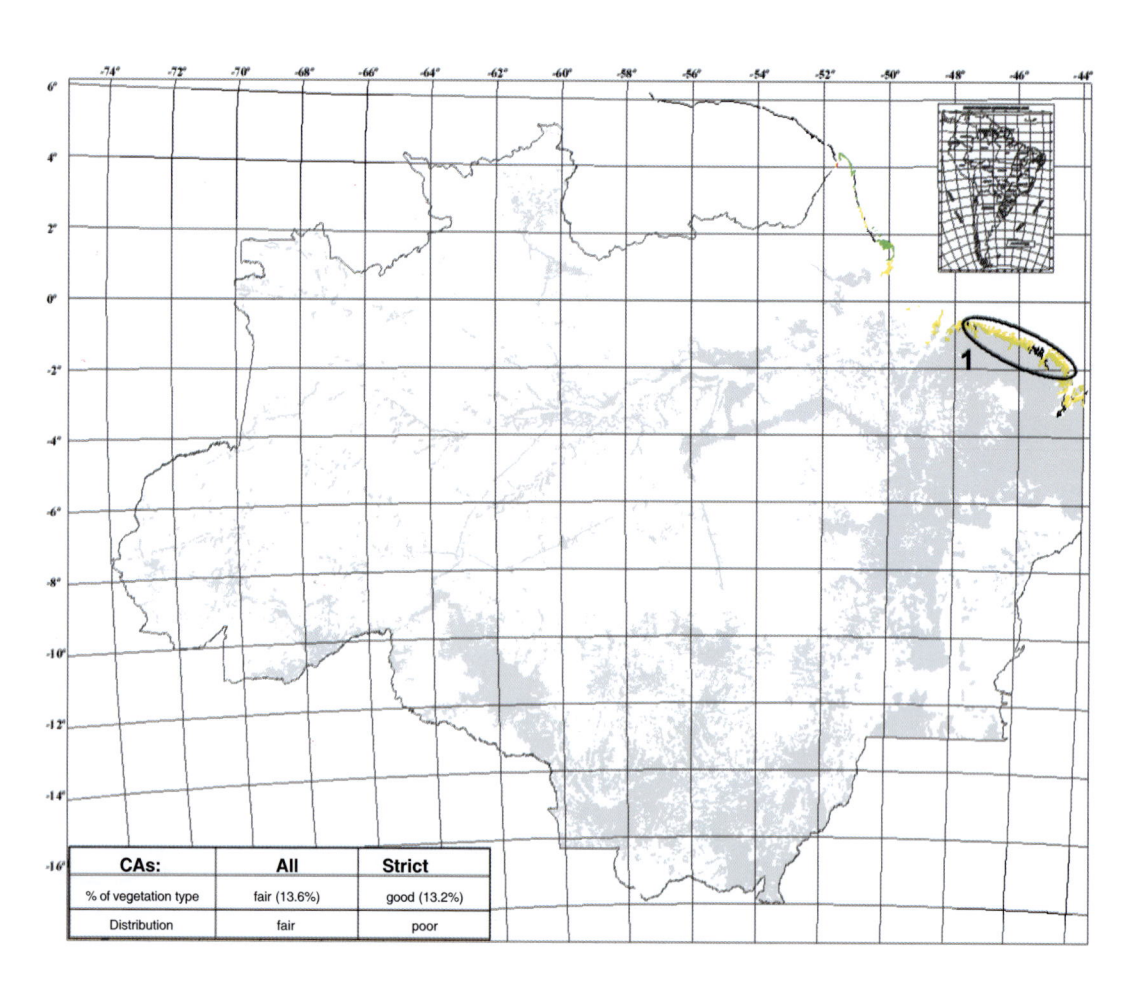

CAs:	All	Strict
% of vegetation type	good (14.5%)	fair (7.7%)
Distribution	fair	poor

Figure 19. Distribution, conservation status and suggestions for new conservation areas for vegetation type 5a: woody primary succession in coastal environments: mangroves and dunes (green = strict conservation area; red = semi-protected area; yellow = no use restrictions). Proposed conservation area is scored as 1 = maximum priority.

CAs:	All	Strict
% of vegetation type	fair (13.6%)	good (13.2%)
Distribution	fair	poor

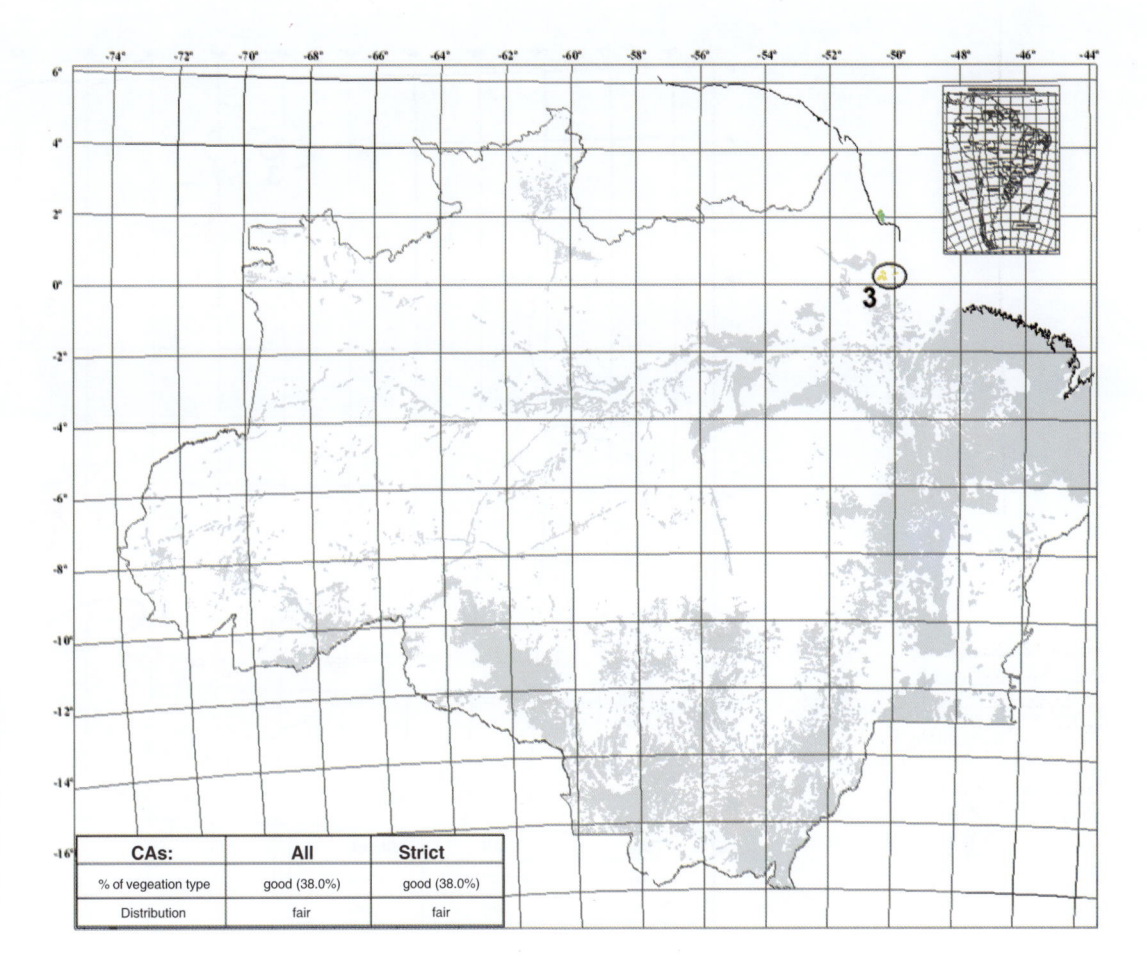

Figure 20. Distribution, conservation status and suggestions for new conservation areas for vegetation type 5b: herbaceous primary succession in coastal environments: periodically flooded savannas (green = strict conservation area; red = semi-protected area; yellow = no use restrictions). Proposed conservation area is scored as 3 = low priority.

CAs:	All	Strict
% of vegetation type	good (38.0%)	good (38.0%)
Distribution	fair	fair

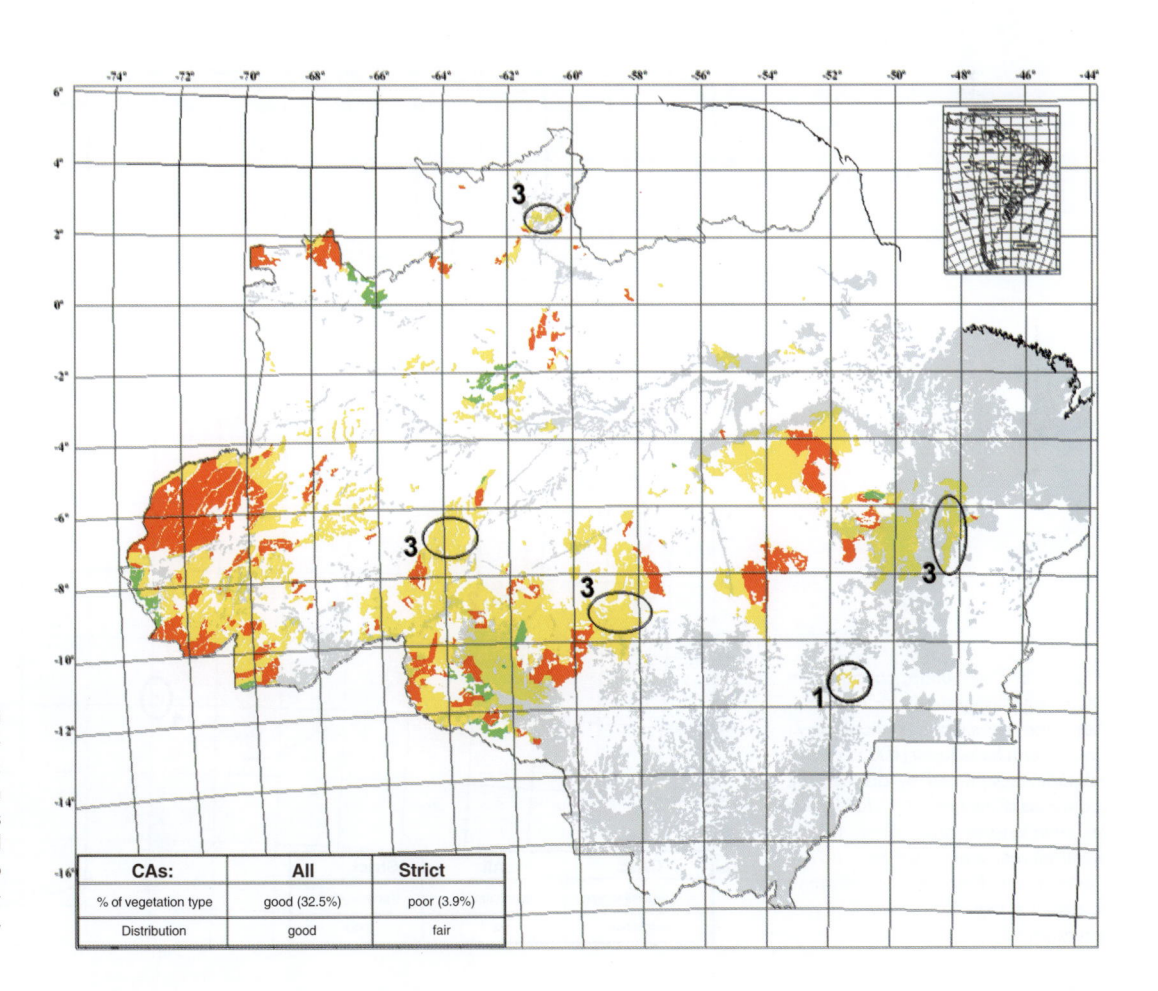

Figure 21. Distribution, conservation status and suggestions for new conservation areas for vegeation type 6a: 'open' terra firme forest (5 to 600 m altitude) dominated by large palms (green = strict conservation area; red = semi-protected area; yellow = no use restrictions). Proposed conservation areas: 1 = maximum priority, 3 = low priority.

CAs:	All	Strict
% of vegetation type	good (32.5%)	poor (3.9%)
Distribution	good	fair

BIODIVERSITY AND THE ECOLOGICAL FUNCTIONS OF ECOSYSTEMS

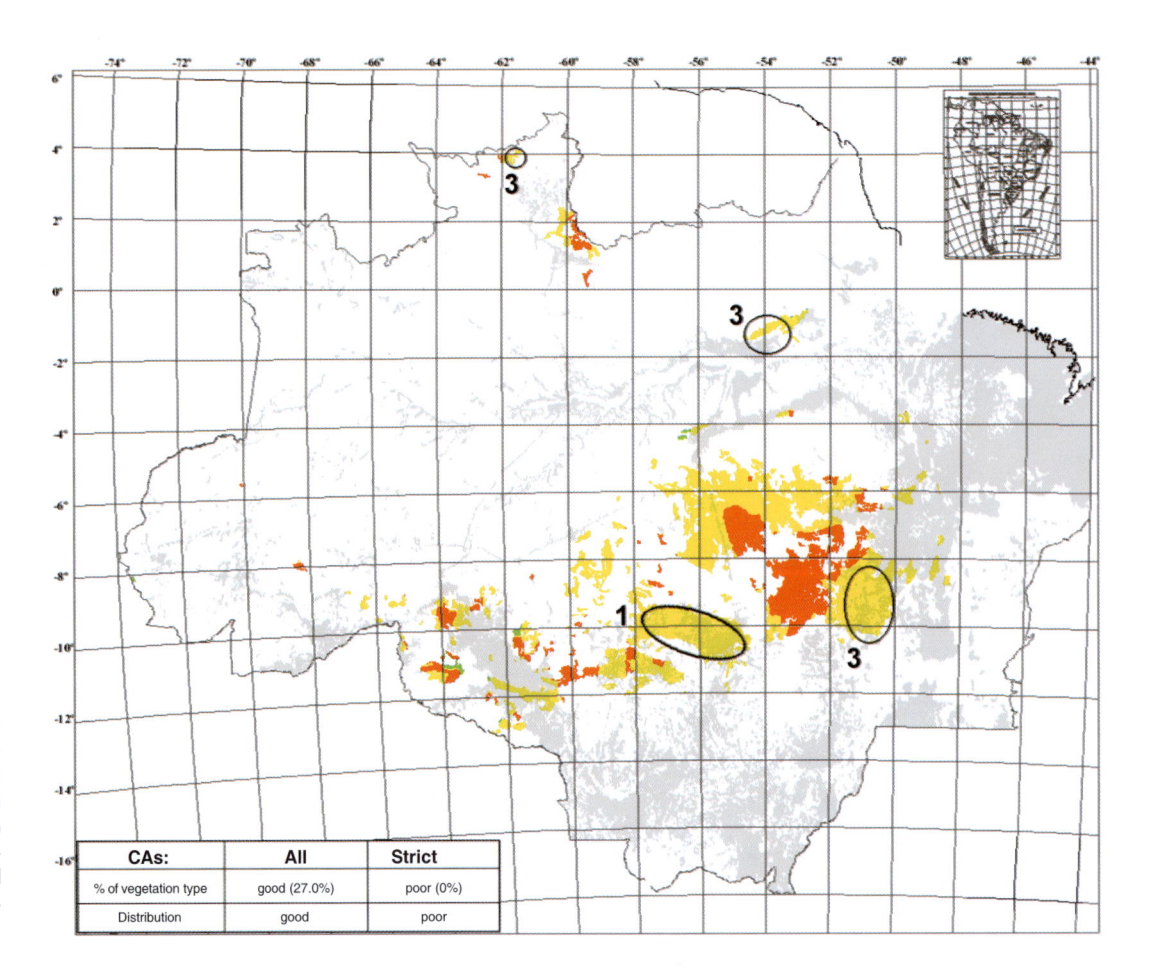

Figure 22. Distribution, conservation status and suggestions for new conservation areas for vegetation type 6b: 'open' terra firme forest (5 to 600 m altitude) (green = strict conservation area; red = semi-protected area; yellow = no use restrictions). Proposed conservation areas: 1 = maximum priority, 3 = low priority.

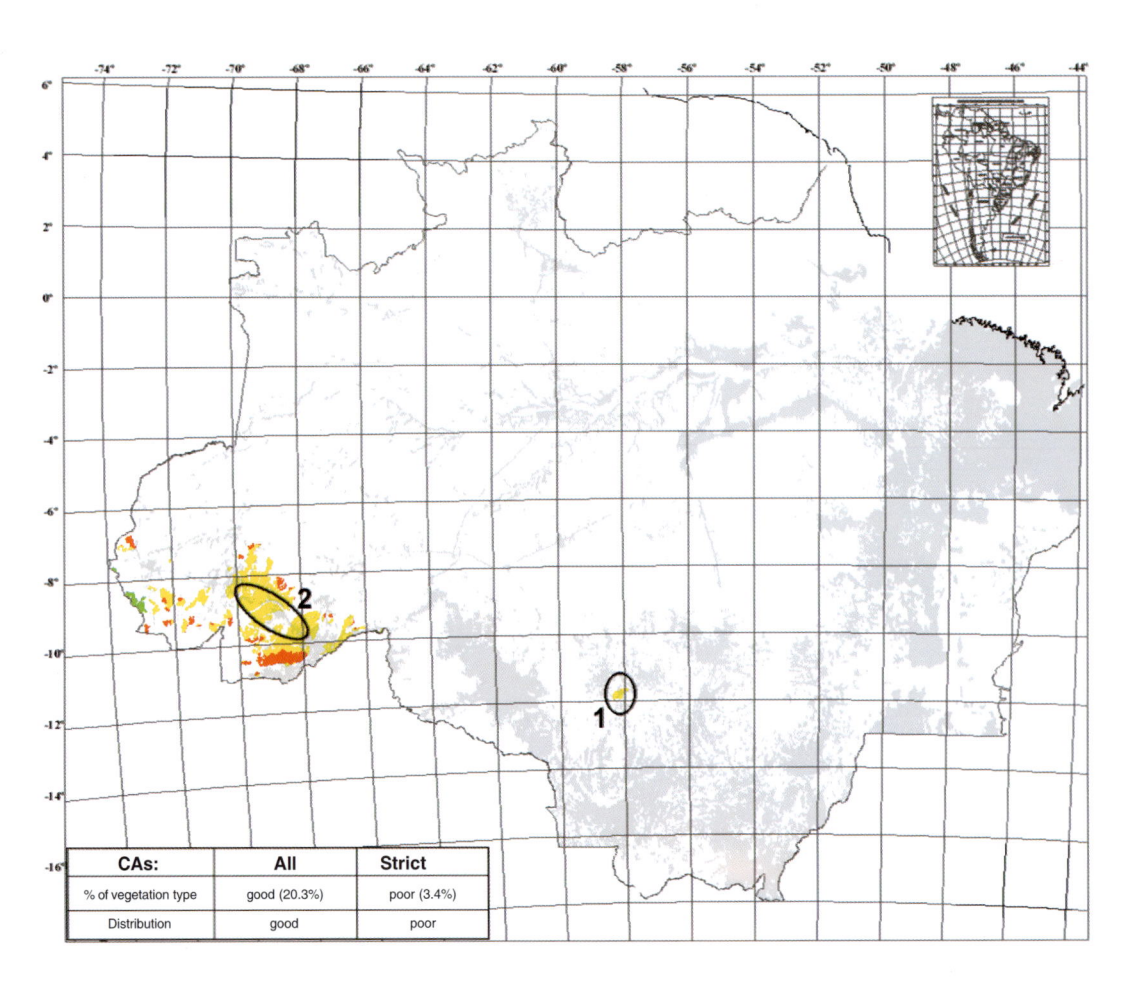

CAs:	All	Strict
% of vegetation type	good (27.0%)	poor (0%)
Distribution	good	poor

Figure 23. Distribution, conservation status and suggestions for new conservation areas for vegetation type 7: 'open' terra firme forest (100 to 600 m altitude) dominated by arborescent bamboos of the genus *Gradua* (green = strict conservation area; red = semi-protected area; yellow = no use restrictions). Proposed conservation areas: 1 = maximum priority, 2 = medium priority.

CAs:	All	Strict
% of vegetation type	good (20.3%)	poor (3.4%)
Distribution	good	poor

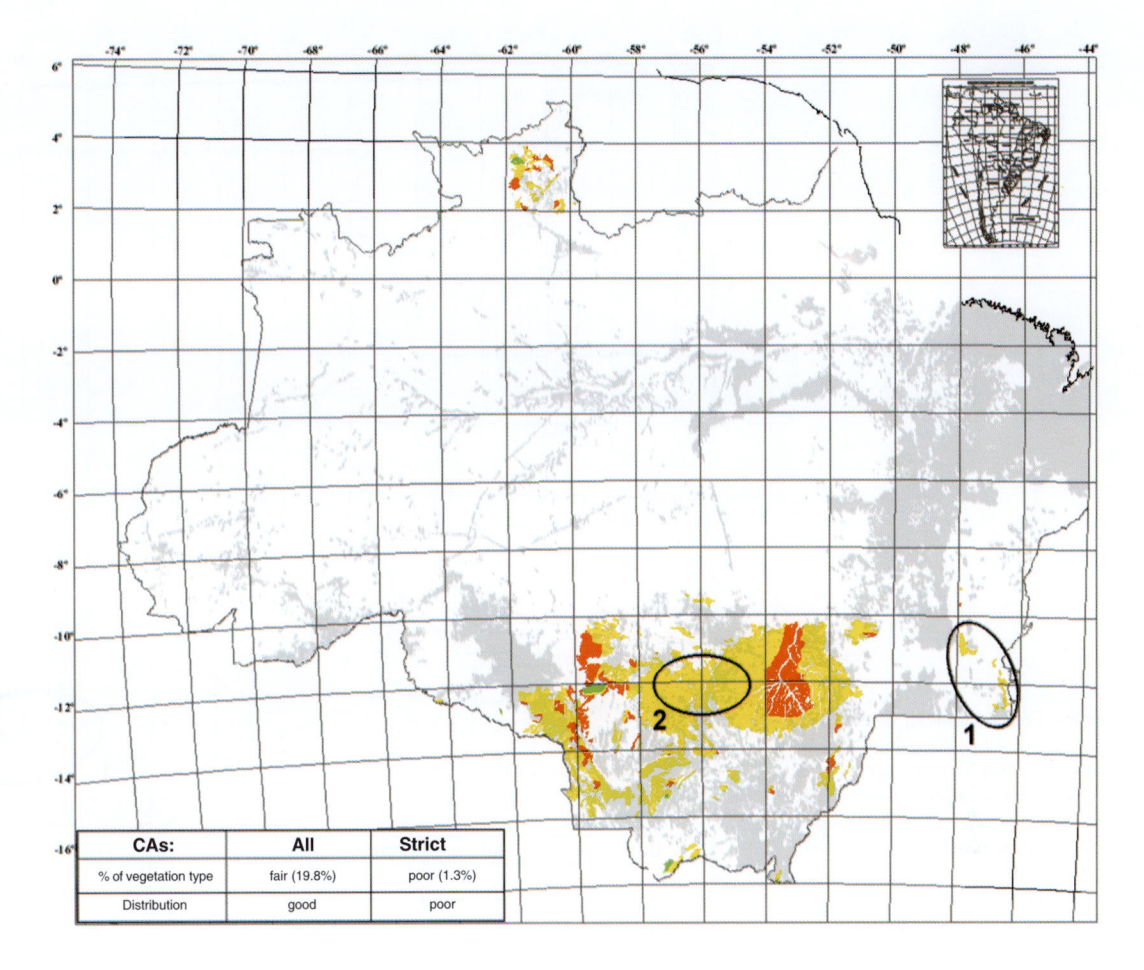

Figure 24. Distribution, conservation status and suggestions for new conservation areas for vegetation type 8a: seasonally semi-deciduous terra firme 'transition' forests, 5 to 600 m altitude (green = strict conservation area; red = semi-protected area; yellow = no use restrictions). Proposed conservation areas: 1 = maximum priority, 2 = medium priority.

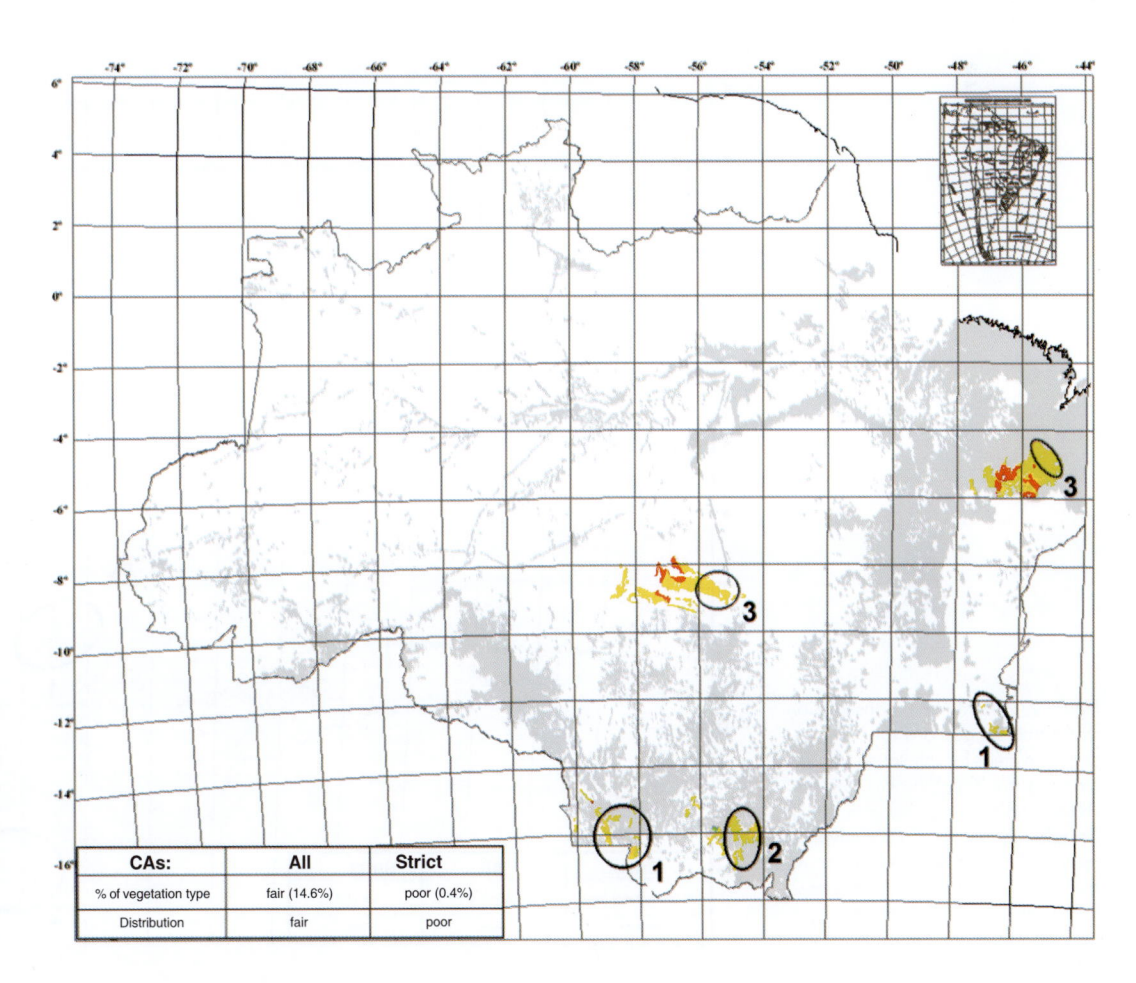

CAs:	All	Strict
% of vegetation type	fair (19.8%)	poor (1.3%)
Distribution	good	poor

Figure 25. Distribution, conservation status and suggestions for new conservation areas for vegetation type 8b: seasonally deciduous terra firme 'transitional' forest, 5 to 600 m altitude (green = strict conservation area; red = semi-protected area; yellow = no use restrictions). Proposed conservation areas: 1 = maximum priority, 2 = medium priority, 3 = low priority.

CAs:	All	Strict
% of vegetation type	fair (14.6%)	poor (0.4%)
Distribution	fair	poor

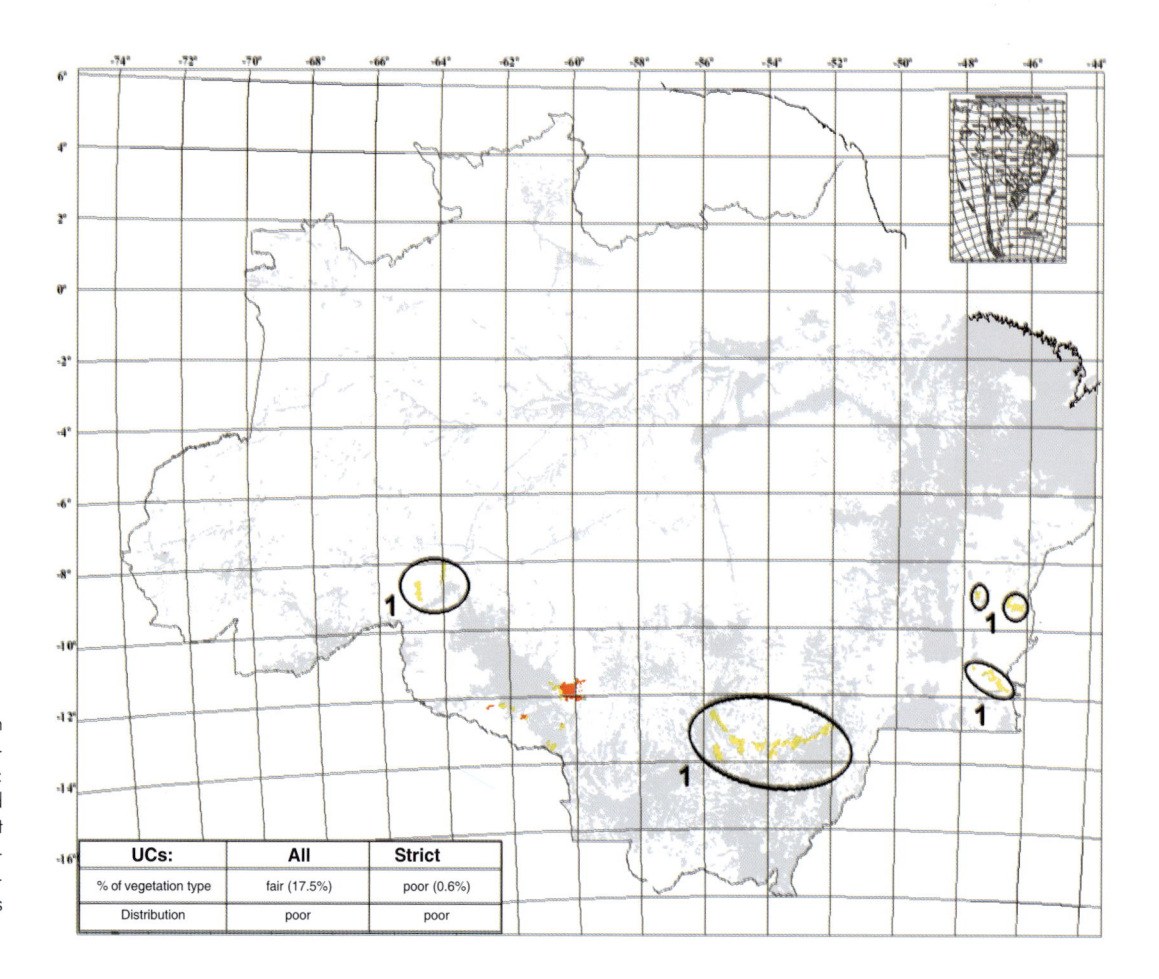

Figure 26. Distribution, conservation status and suggestions for new conservation areas for vegetation type 9a: mixed contact zone: savanna and closed-canopy forest (green = strict conservation area; red = semi-protected area; yellow = no use restrictions). Proposed conservation areas are all: 1 = maximum priority.

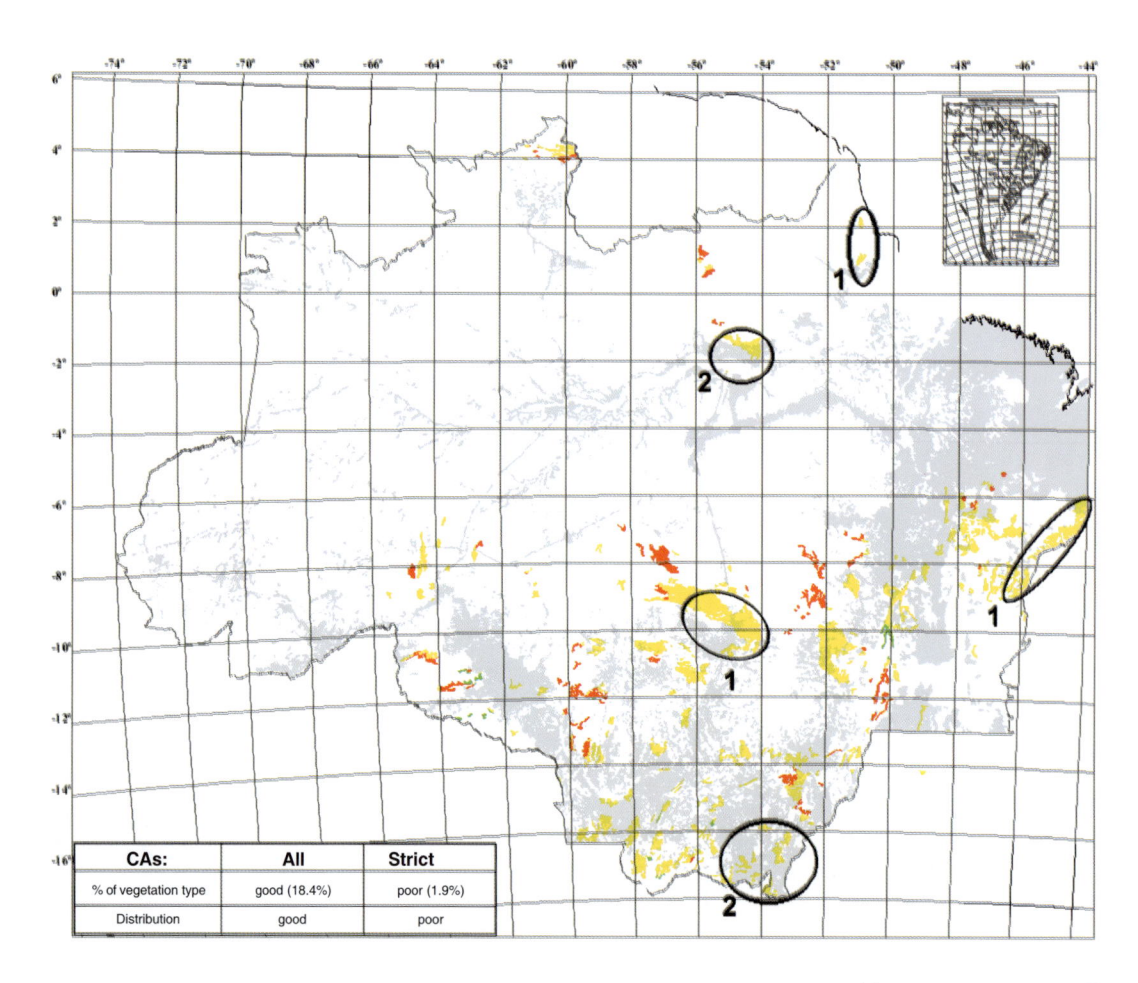

UCs:	All	Strict
% of vegetation type	fair (17.5%)	poor (0.6%)
Distribution	poor	poor

Figure 27. Distribution, conservation status and suggestions for new conservation areas for vegetation type 9b: savanna woodland, broken tree and shrub canopy with grassy under story, cerradão (green = strict conservation area; red = semi-protected area; yellow = no use restrictions). Proposed conservation areas: 1 = maximum priority, 2 = medium priority.

CAs:	All	Strict
% of vegetation type	good (18.4%)	poor (1.9%)
Distribution	good	poor

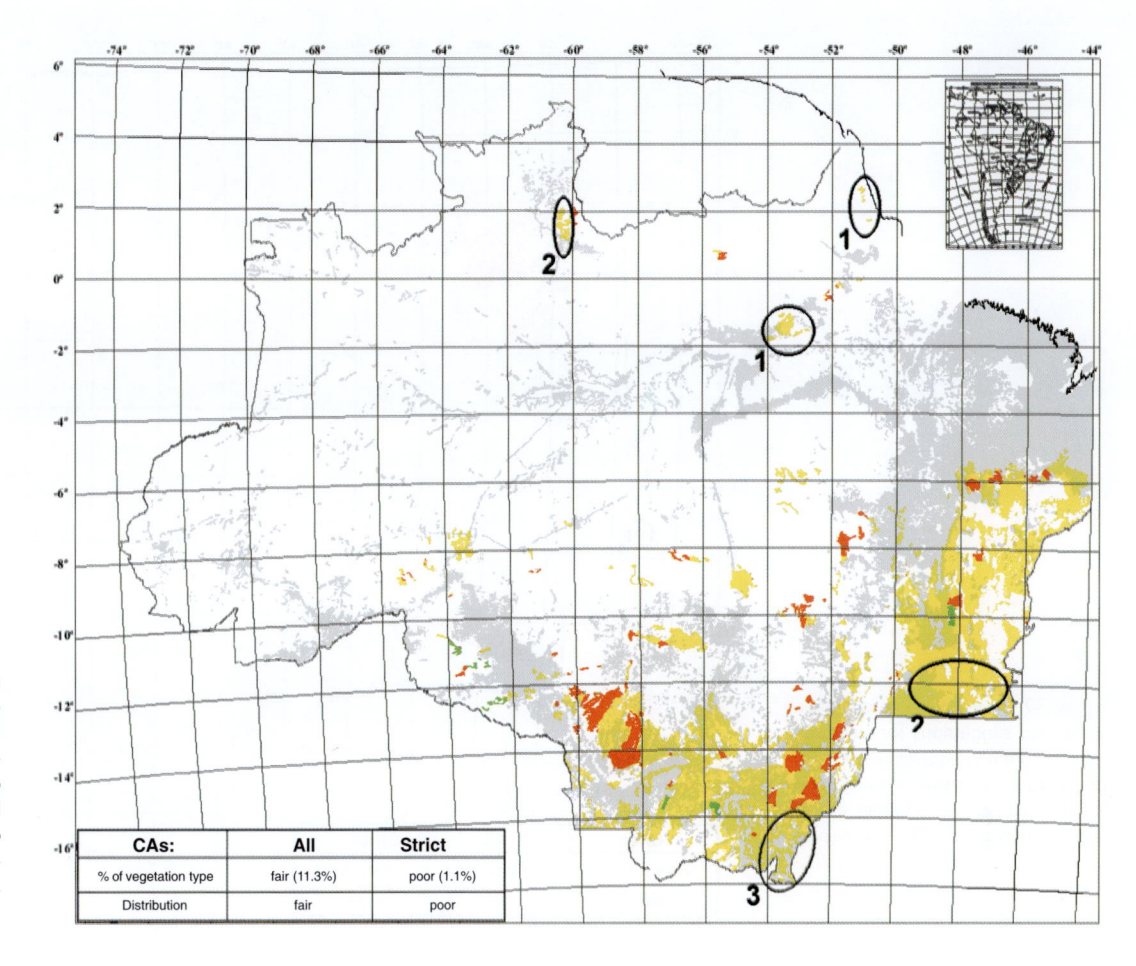

Figure 28. Distribution, conservation status and suggestions for new conservation areas for vegetation type 10a: seasonally dry savanna parkland, scattered low trees and shrubs; cerrado (green = strict conservation area; red = semi-protected area; yellow = no use restrictions). Proposed conservation areas: 1 = maximum priority, 2 = medium priority, 3 = low priority.

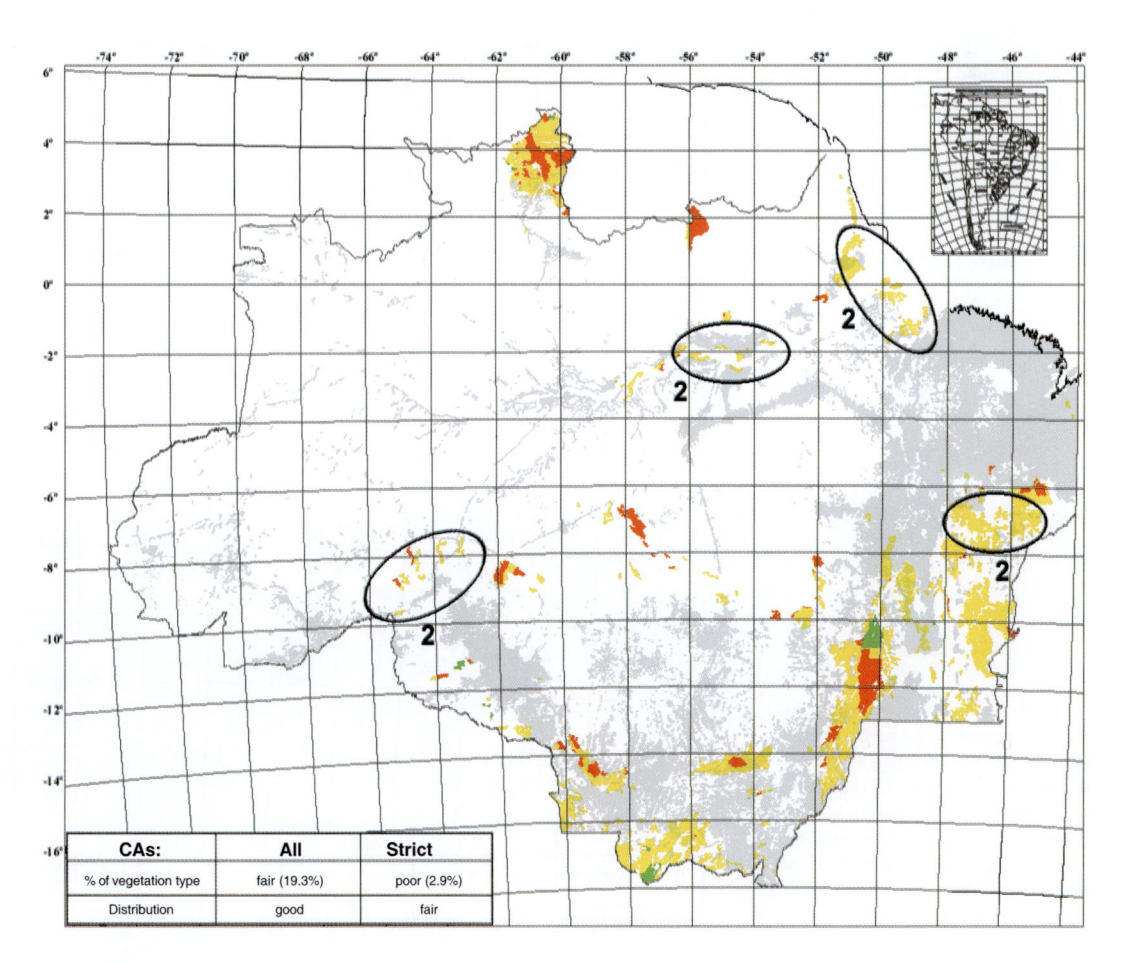

CAs:	All	Strict
% of vegetation type	fair (11.3%)	poor (1.1%)
Distribution	fair	poor

Figure 29. Distribution, conservation status and suggestions for new conservation areas for vegetation type 10b: seasonally dry open savanna, trees and shrubs absent or sparse (green = strict conservation area; red = semi-protected area; yellow = no use restrictions). Proposed conservation areas are all: 2 = medium priority.

CAs:	All	Strict
% of vegetation type	fair (19.3%)	poor (2.9%)
Distribution	good	fair

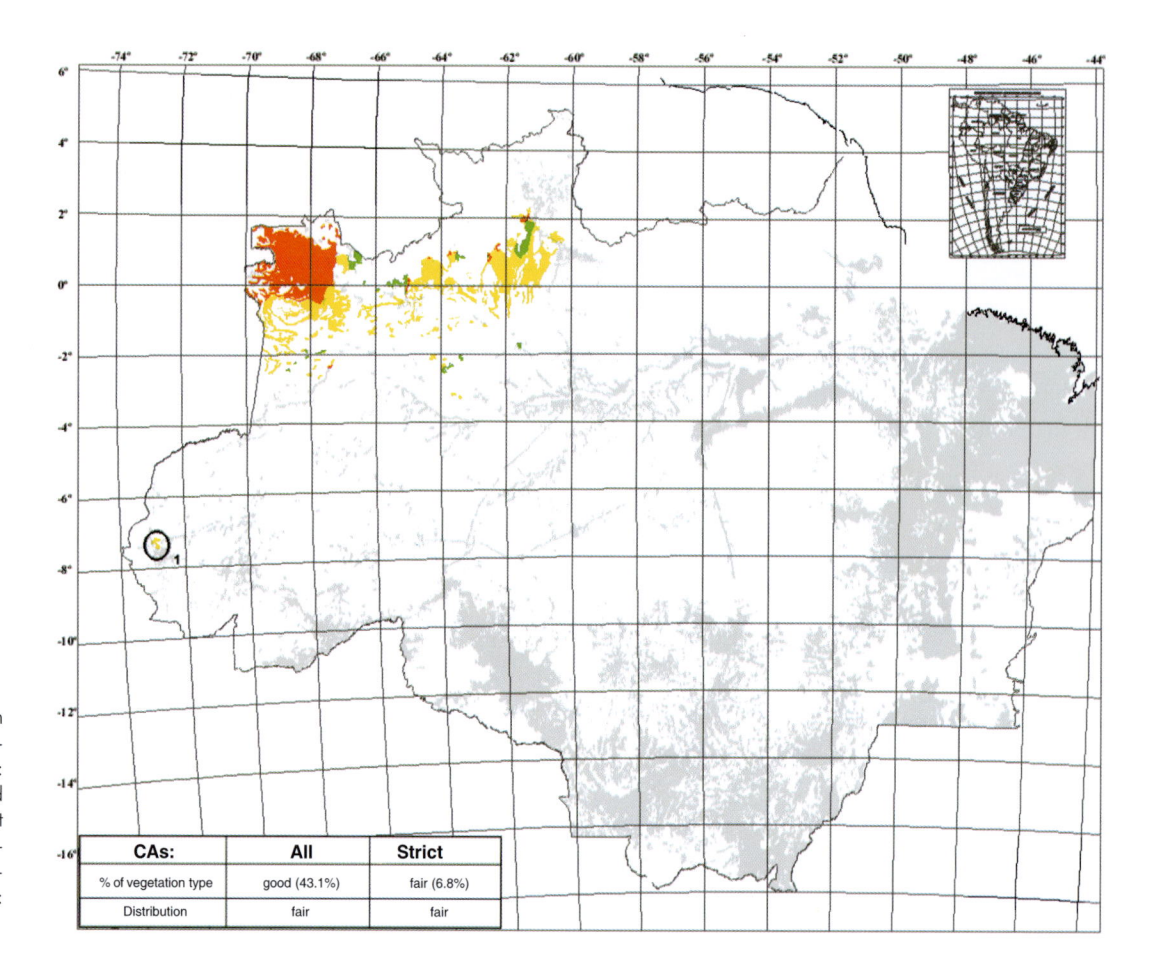

Figure 30. Distribution, conservation status and suggestions for new conservation areas for vegetation type 11a: closed-canopy forest on white sand (podzol): campinarana (green = strict conservation area; red = semi-protected area; yellow = no use restrictions). Proposed conservation area: 1 = maximum priority.

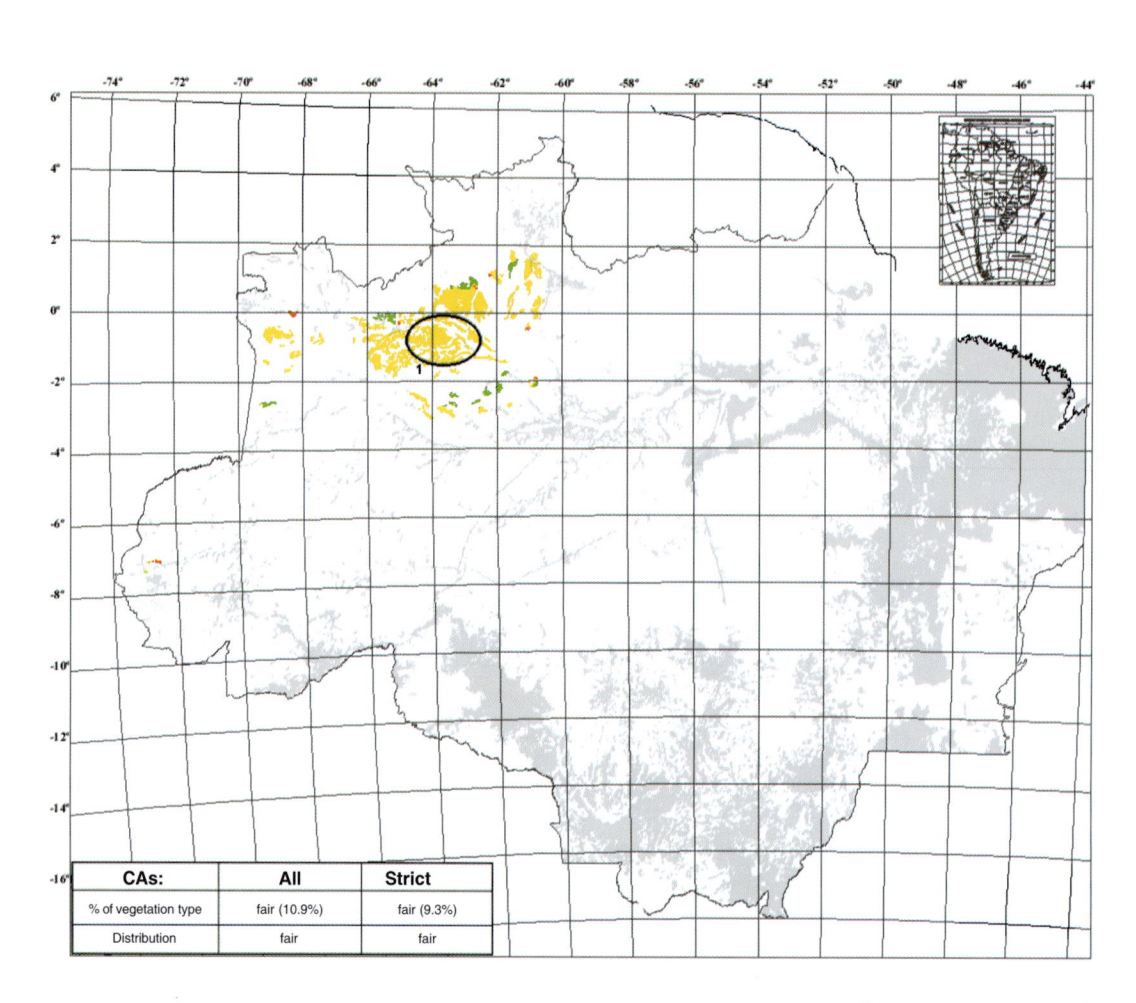

CAs:	All	Strict
% of vegetation type	good (43.1%)	fair (6.8%)
Distribution	fair	fair

Figure 31. Distribution, conservation status and suggestions for new conservation areas for vegetation type 11b: grass, sedge or shrub on white sand (podzol), no prolonged dry season: campina (green = strict conservation area; red = semi-protected area; yellow = no use restrictions). Proposed conservation area: 1 = maximum priority.

CAs:	All	Strict
% of vegetation type	fair (10.9%)	fair (9.3%)
Distribution	fair	fair

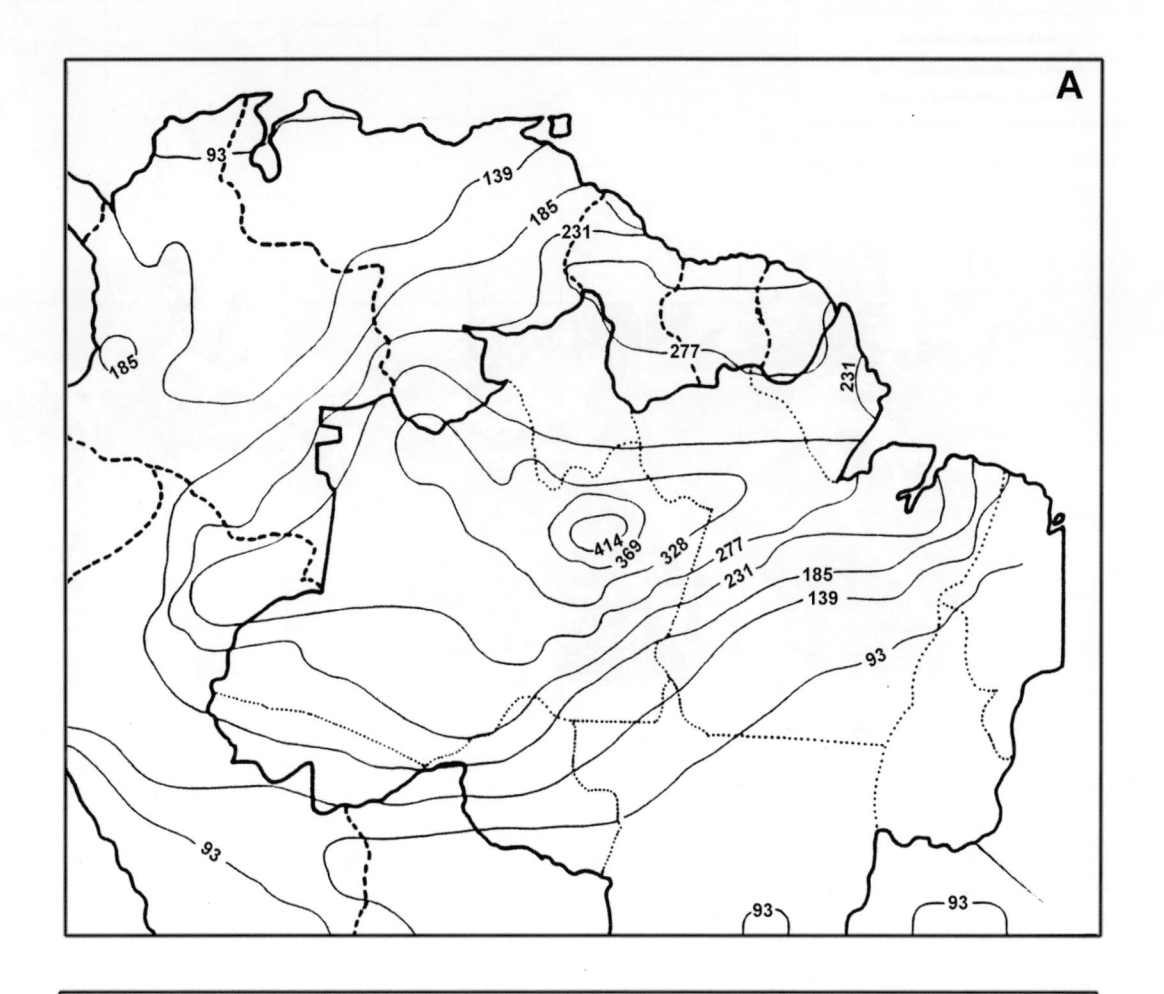

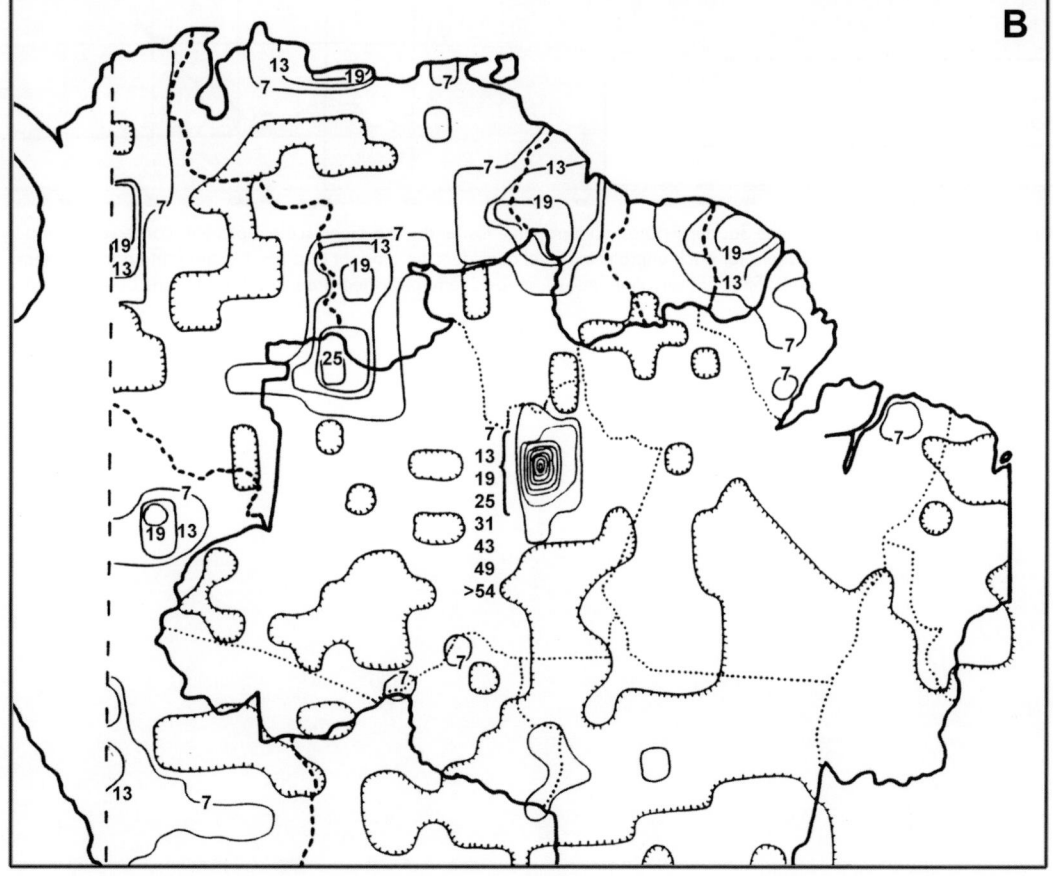

Figure 32. Diversity (A) and local endemism (B) of over three thousand plant species (modified from Lleras et al. 1992).

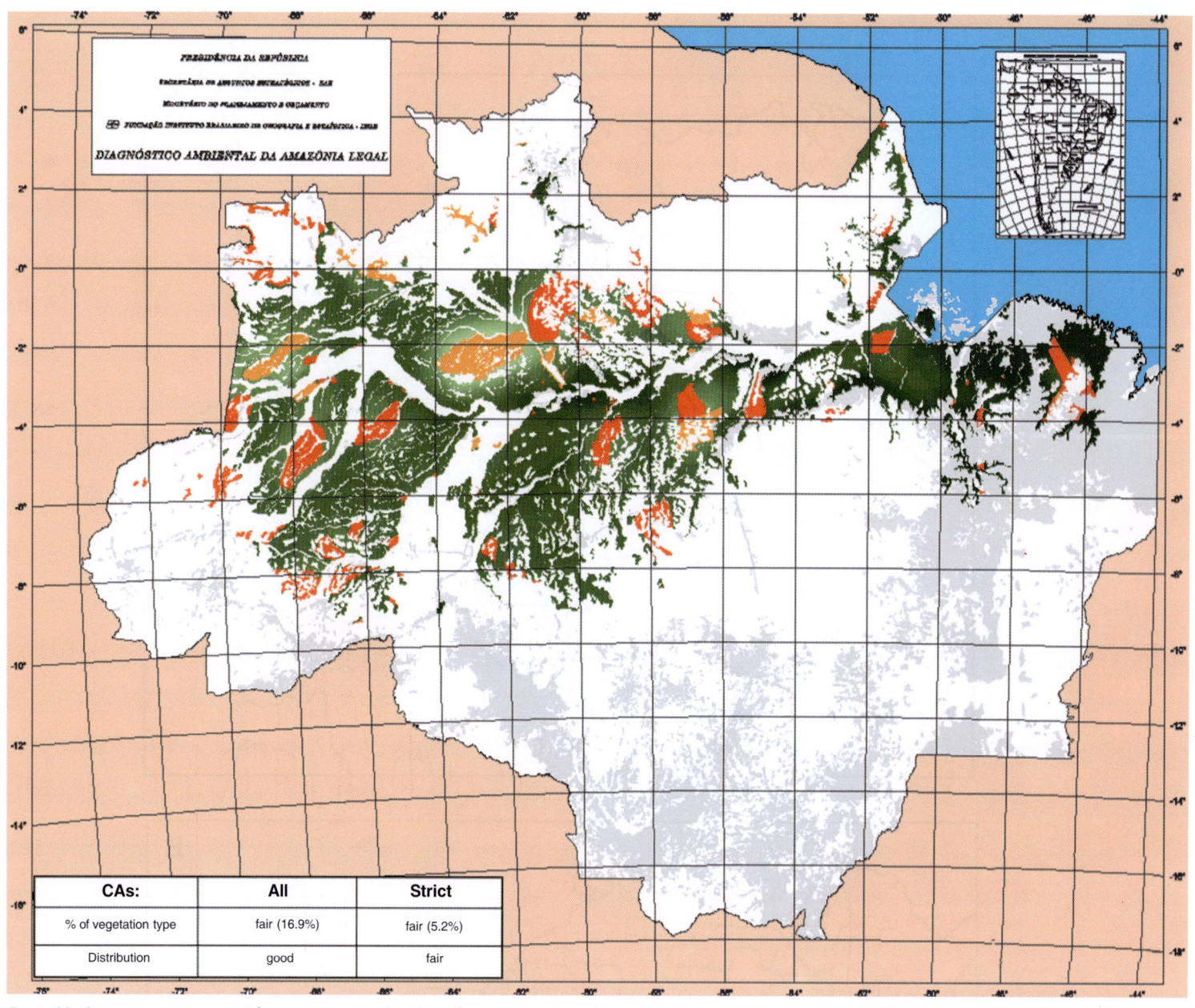

CAs:	All	Strict
% of vegetation type	fair (16.9%)	fair (5.2%)
Distribution	good	fair

Figure 33. Quantitative priority map for vegetation type 3a: dense forest on terra firme lowlands. The green scale represents conservation priority levels for this vegetation type, with darker tones signifying higher priority. Priority score for each unprotected pixel considers the amount of protected area and anthropogenic area within successively larger rings around the pixel, out to a distance of 50 pixels. Strict conservation areas (orange), semi-protected areas (red), and areas of anthropogenic impacts (grey).

The ecological functions of forest ecosystems: implications for the conservation and use of Amazonian biodiversity

Paulo Moutinho *Instituto de Pesquisa Ambiental da Amazônia*
Daniel Nepstad *Instituto de Pesquisa Ambiental da Amazônia*

Introduction

What is the value of one cubic meter of water released from the Amazon forest through evaporation, which then returns as rain and maintains the region's humid climate? What is the value of the nutrients accumulated in the trunks and barks of centuries-old trees? What damage would the fires in Amazonia cause if they did not die out at the edges of the forests? What is the value of one kilogram of carbon not released into the atmosphere because it remains stored in the forest? All these questions are related to the value of what we can call the 'ecological services' supplied by the forests of Amazonia, and whose importance becomes clear when we imagine a 'deforested Amazonia' scenario. If the majority of the vast extent of existing forest was removed, not only would an enormous number of species disappear, but the planet's atmosphere would end up containing much more CO_2 (a gas that contributes to the greenhouse effect and to global warming), the region's rainfall would be reduced by 20 to 30%, and the temperature would be higher. In addition, there would be greater surface runoff during heavy rains, which would carry nutrients from the highlands into the rivers and igarapés, and cause floods. A drier and hotter climate would facilitate the occurrence of fires, resulting in the burning of large areas including, without doubt, those forests protected in parks and conservation areas.

This paper, one of the thematic documents arising out of the *Seminar on Amazonian Biodiversity*, briefly analyzes some functional aspects of Amazonian forests that are considered especially important for the conservation and sustainable use of the region's biodiversity. Its intention is to provide background information to assist the discussions during the seminar within the different thematic groups. Given the diversity of professional expertise taking part, it was decided to provide a general overview of the issues. More detailed information can be found in the authors referred to in the text.

The specific objective is to make clear the importance of the 'ecological services' of Amazonian forests to (1) the carbon cycle and global warming, (2) the maintenance of the regional climate, and (3) as a barrier to the spreading of large-scale fires. The main argument that will be made is that action for the conservation and sustainable use of the biodiversity of Amazonia must first focus on the conservation of these forest services. It must also start from the premise that Amazonia in the future will probably be drier, and the intensity of droughts in the region will be closely related to the area of forest remaining, especially in the eastern region. In this context, the forests that are threatened by human activity (eastern and southern Amazonia) are precisely those that play the most important role in the maintenance of the regional climate and in inhibiting accidental fires.

The Amazon and global warming

The planet's temperature is increasing at a rate of 0.2 degrees Celsius per decade. According to over a thousand scientists, responsible for the highly respected report of the Intergovernmental Panel on Climate Change (IPCC 1996), this increase is probably a result of the emission into the atmosphere of gases that retain heat, especially carbon dioxide (CO_2) and methane (CH_4). Some geological evidence supports this conclusion. For example, the planet's temperature in the last 160,000 years was highest when the concentration of CO_2 was also high (Figure 1). However, the concentration of this gas in the atmosphere has undergone an increase greater than would be expected within a geological time scale (Figure 2). The present concentration is 37% higher than before the Industrial Revolution, and a warming of more than 0.7 degrees C has been recorded over the last 100 years.

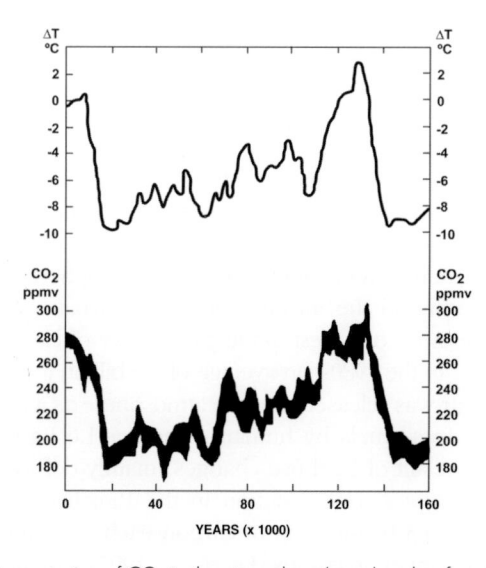

Figure 1. Concentration of CO_2 in the atmosphere (ppmv) and surface temperature changes over the last 160,000 years. The results were obtained from the analysis of glacial ice from Vostok in Antarctica. Temperatures were estimated on the basis of deuterium concentration measurements (source: Barnola et al. 1987).

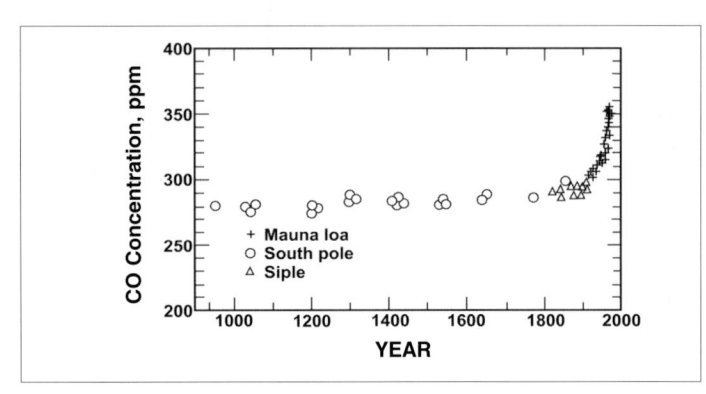

Figure 2. Concentration of atmospheric CO_2 during the last thousand years calculated through analysis of air (Mauna Loa, Hawaii) and Antarctic ice (South Pole and Siple stations). Source: Houghton 1995.

Computer models indicate that, if the concentration of greenhouse gases doubles, the earth could experience a warming of 1.5 to 4.5 degrees C. It may not sound much, but in relative terms it is a very significant increase. (The temperature during the last ice age was only 5 degrees C lower than now.) With a 7 degrees C increase, the sea level would rise by two meters and flood many coastal cities, causing great ecological impacts on species and ecosystems.

But how does the Amazon forest affect the composition of the global atmosphere? Photosynthesis by forest vegetation absorbs a vast quantity of carbon from the atmosphere each year (approximately 12 tons per year per hectare x 500 million hectares = 6 billion tons – 10% of the planet's terrestrial photosynthesis). This absorption is offset, however, by the release of carbon through decomposition of organic matter. Thus, the main effect of the Amazon forest is to function as a giant stable carbon storehouse. A typical forest of the region will contain an average of 460 tons of biomass per hectare, corresponding to 230 tons of carbon per hectare (Fearnside 1997). However, when this forest is logged and burnt, this carbon is released into the atmosphere in the form of CO_2, and the ecological service of storing carbon is disturbed.

Until recently, the scientific community thought that there was an equilibrium, whereby the carbon absorbed by the Amazon forest through photosynthesis and that released by the decomposition of organic matter were equal. Recent studies, however, demonstrate that the primary forest absorbs more carbon than it releases (Philips et al. 1998; Grace et al. 1996; Maine et al. 1997). In other words, the forest is growing. These studies suggest that forests take up approximately 0.4 tons of carbon per hectare per year, increasing the importance of the Amazon forest in the chemical composition of the planet's atmosphere. Thus, deforestation not only increases the emission of carbon, but also eliminates the forest's function of removing it from the atmosphere.

Considering all the information above, what is the importance of the Amazon forest in the global flow of carbon into the atmosphere? In the 1980s, an average of 5.5 billion tons of carbon (Pg C) a year was released into the atmosphere as a result of the burning of fossil fuels by humans. Another 1.6 Pg C were released as a result of land use changes (mainly deforestation) in the humid tropics. Deforestation in the Brazilian Amazon releases about 0.3 billion tons of carbon each year, representing 5% of total human emissions (Fearnside 1997) and also reduces the quantity of carbon removed from the atmosphere by the forest. The 30 million hectares of deforested land that are not covered by secondary forests, for example, can mean 12 million tons of carbon (0.4 t/ha/year x 30 million hectares) that are not removed annually from the atmosphere.

The calculation of carbon emissions caused by deforestation is based on estimates of the area deforested each year (INPE 1998) multiplied by estimates of the biomass contained in the felled forests (Fearnside 1997). These figures, however, still underestimate Amazonian carbon emissions because they do not consider the contribution of logging activities and fires, which together affect each year an area of forest equal to that affected by deforestation (Nepstad et al. 1999a). When the carbon released by logging and forest fires is added to that released by deforestation, emissions in the Brazilian Amazon can reach 10% of the global emissions from human activities in years of severe drought, when many fires occur (Nepstad et al. 1999a).

Although efforts to reduce the emission of CO_2 into the atmosphere must necessarily include the reduction and more efficient use of fossil fuel, the conservation of forests (primary or otherwise) in the Amazon is very important for the maintenance of the great quantity of carbon stored in the vegetation, an amount almost equivalent to that released into the atmosphere by human activities over a ten-year period. The conservation of carbon in the forest must be made possible, therefore, through (1) preserving large areas of intact forest, (2) switching from rural production systems requiring deforestation to systems that depend on forests, (3) expanding or restorating forest areas on abandoned land, and (4) reforestation.

The Amazon forest: a drier future?

Three basic mechanisms link deforestation to climatic and hydrological changes in the Amazon. Deforestation (1) reduces the evapotranspiration that supplies water vapor to the atmosphere (which cools the air and facilitates rainfall), (2) increases air and soil temperatures, (3) alters the drainage and runoff of surface water (usually causing floods by increasing the volume of water in the rivers), and finally, (4) the vegetation that replaces the forest has less rooting capacity and, as a result, evapotranspiration is reduced.

Every year, the Amazon forest releases around 7 trillion[1] tons of water into the atmosphere via evapotranspiration. This process is very important for the climate of the Amazon, as it supplies the necessary water vapor for the formation of cumulus clouds, which are responsible for most of the rainfall. Furthermore, the conversion of water into vapor cools the air, making the forests act as giant air conditioners. Various experiments using climatic models have shown that the deforestation of Amazonia could lead to a reduction of 20 to 30% in the amount of rainfall, and to an increase in air temperature (Lean and Warrilow 1989, Shukla et al. 1990, Nobre et al. 1991, Henderson-Sellers et al. 1993). Under a drier climate, even intact forests conserved in parks and reserves would be threatened with disappearance, or at least would undergo drastic alterations in their structure and species diversity, as well as becoming vulnerable to fire. Therefore, strategies for the conservation of the biological wealth of Amazonia should take into consideration the fact that the region's future will probably be drier, and the intensity of the dry seasons will depend closely on the area of the remaining standing forest.

---

1. (500,000,000 ha of forest x (365 x 4 mm of water/day) x 10 tons/mm – which evaporates from leaves per day).

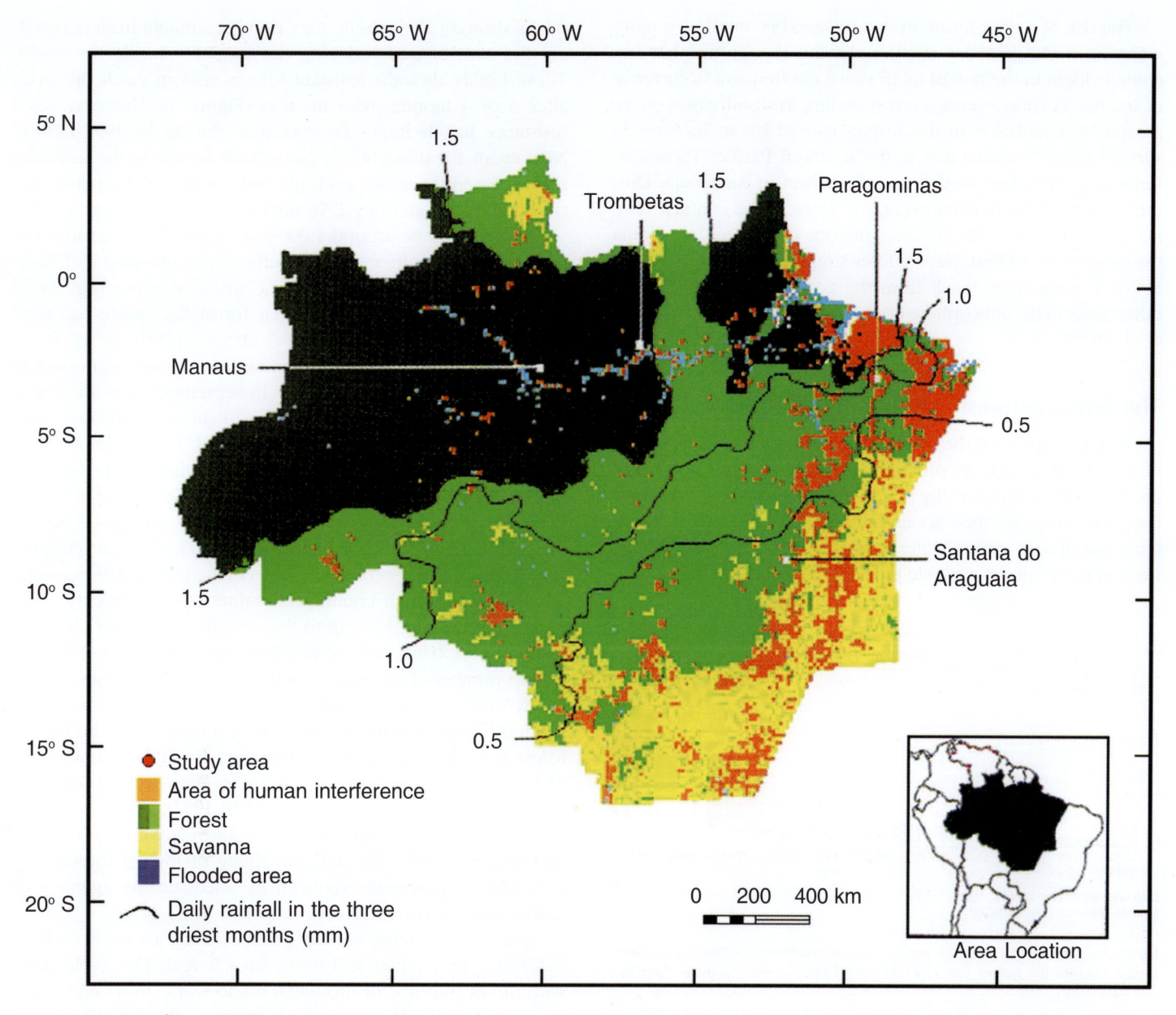

Figure 3. Amazonian forest areas that use deep ground water supplies to stay evergreen (light green), even during the typical dry season in the eastern region. The lines delimit daily rainfall during the dry season. Source: Nepstad et al. 1994.

In the same way that the Amazon forests found along the Atlantic coast are fed with rain originated in water vapor from the ocean, the forests in the interior of the region depend on rain formed by the water vapor produced by forests hundreds of kilometers to the east (Victoria et al. 1991). In the interior of Amazonia, half the rainfall is produced by the forest itself. Paradoxically, a large part of the water vapor released by the Amazon forest into the atmosphere comes from regions that experience seasonal droughts. The forests of southern and eastern Amazonia suffer three to five months of severe drought starting in April or June, during which the quantity of rainfall is smaller in terms of water quantity than that which the forest releases into the atmosphere by evapotranspiration. This is possible because these forests have a root system that is capable of drawing water from deep below ground (> 10 m) during the annual droughts (Nepstad et al. 1994, Figure 3). If the forests of this region were replaced by pastures, the volume of water vapor released into the atmosphere would be severely reduced, since evaporation from pastures is 15% lower than that from forests (Jipp et al. 1998). Thus, given seasonal droughts, these forests

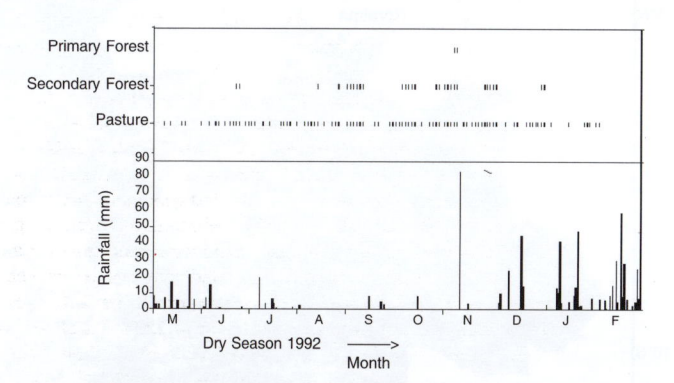

Figure 4. Forest and pasture inflammability in eastern Amazonia, Paragominas, Pará. The small bars in the upper part indicate inflammable state. Inflammability was estimated based on data related to rainfall and drying rates of combustible material reported by Uhl and Kauffman (1990). The figure records daily rainfall. Source: Nepstad et al. 1995.

that cover one third of the area of Amazonia must be given priority in conservation plans because of their role in maintaining the regional climate, and because they are currently under severe risk of deforestation.

The risk of a drier future in the Amazon becomes even more worrying if we consider another climatic change that has become evident in the last 10 to 15 years: the frequent occurrence of intense El Niño events, corresponding to disturbances in atmospheric circulation in the tropics caused by an increase in surface water temperatures in the southern Pacific. These disturbances mean less rainfall and more heat in Amazonia. During the 1997-1998 El Niño event, the worst of the century, rainfall levels fell by 70% in some regions of eastern Amazonia (Nepstad et al. 1999b). New studies suggest that the increase of El Niño events may result from the accumulation of CO_2 and other gases in the atmosphere (Trenbarth et al. 1997; Timmerman et al. 1999).

The Amazon forest: a future in flames?

Besides supplying the atmosphere with enormous quantities of water vapor, forests provide another ecological service of great importance, especially in regions where seasonal droughts are more frequent: they act as fire-breaks. Thanks to root systems that absorb groundwater from depths of up to 10 meters, trees in these forests are able to retain their foliage during periods of drought. As a result, they prevent sunlight from penetrating the canopy and reducing the humidity inside the forest. These highly drought resistant forests seldom catch fire even after 3 or 4 months with no rain (Figure 4). However, such resistance has its limit. For example, during the 1997-1998 El Niño event, the drought was particularly severe. In the Santarém region, for instance, the accumulated rainfall for the period between July 1997 and July 1998 did not reach 600 mm, whereas it would normally be around 1,800 mm (Figure 5). The forest did not receive water in a quantity sufficient to maintain its foliage and humidity. The same thing occurred in other regions of Amazonia. As a result, substantial forest fires were recorded during this period. In May 1998, about 14,000 km² of forest caught fire in the state of Roraima (an area almost equivalent to the total area anually deforested). In September 1998 an area of Amazonia larger than the state of São Paulo (270,000 km²) was at high risk of catching fire (Nepstad et al. 1999a, Figure 6). In the same year the area of standing forest that caught fire may have reached 30,000 km² (Nepstad et al. 1999a), representing twice the average area deforested annually. Alongside severe drought, logging, which affects 10 to 15,000 km² a year (Nepstad et al. 1999a), also contributes to fires in the region. For example, when a tree of high commercial value is felled, twenty other trees are damaged, leading to the opening of various clearings in the forest (Uhl and Vieira 1989; Veríssimo et al. 1992). A greater number of clearings in turn increases the forest's vulnerability to fires during the dry season, as this allows sunlight to reach the interior of the forest, making it drier. Once the logged forest is burnt, usually by a spreading fire a few centimeters high, substantial tree mortality, of up to 40%, occurs (Cochrane and Schulze 1999; Holdsworth and Uhl 1997). If the fire strikes the same area again, more than 70% of the trees will die (Cochrane and Schulze 1999). The inflammability of logged forests can, however, be potentially reduced by adequate management of timber extraction (Holdsworth and Uhl 1997).

In a drier Amazon, the danger of creating a vicious cycle of deforestation, logging and forest fires is real. This cycle starts with the occurrence of droughts, made worse by El Niño, and logging, which increase the forest's vulnerability to fires. Once burnt, the forest becomes even more vulnerable to future fires, causing a reduction in evapotranspiration, which in turn provokes a reduction in rainfall; and the cycle repeats itself (Cochrane et al. 1999; Nepstad et al. 1999b; Figure 7).

All the evidence suggests that the forests of the region are losing their capacity to act as fire-breakers, one of their most important ecological services, increasing the likelihood of the occurrence of mega-fires. Under a drier climate, therefore, the greatest threat to the biodiversity of Amazonia in the near future is fire. This threat will be greatest in eastern Amazonia, where the forests experience seasonal droughts, and where the frontier of human occupation is to be found, which itself advances through deforestation by the use of fire. The conservation of eastern Amazonia represents a guarantee not only for the climate and for biodiversity, but also for the economic activities and the quality of life of local populations.

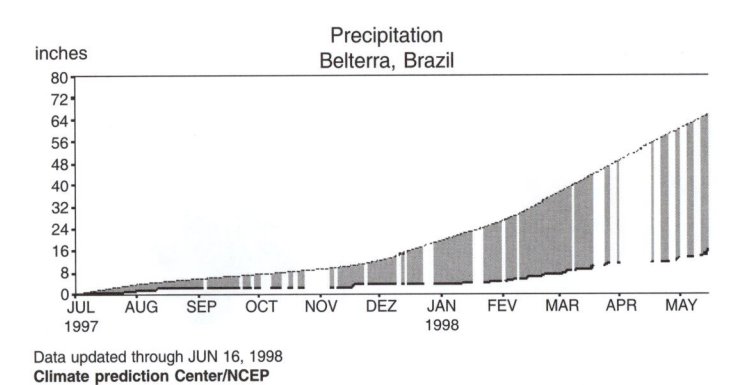

Figure 5. Accumulated observed precipitation (lower line) and monthly averages (upper line) for the period July 1997 to June 1998. Source: Climate Prediction Center (NCEP).

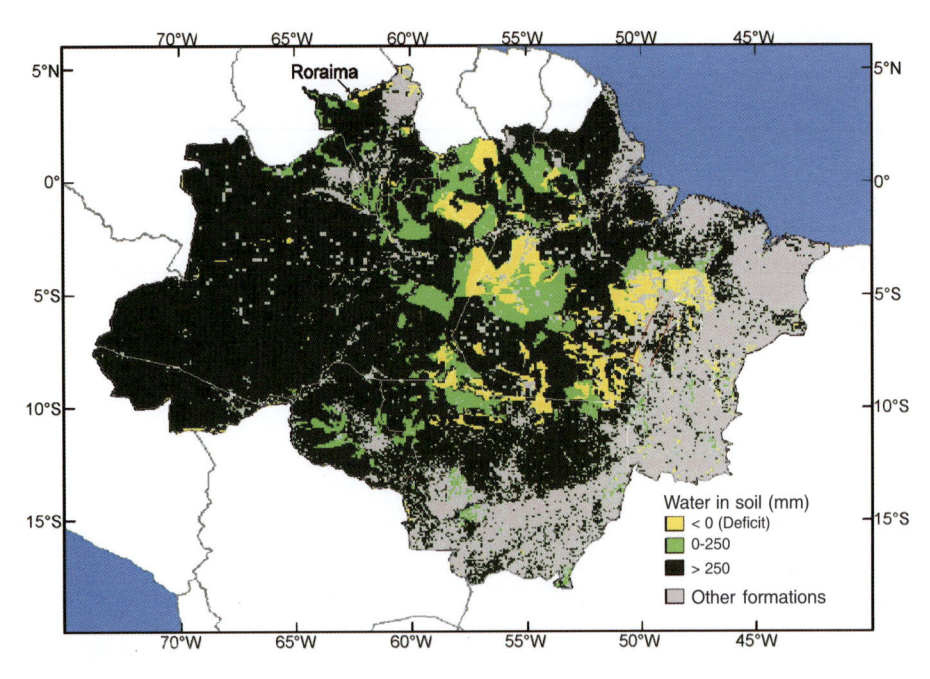

Figure 6. Fire risk areas in the Amazon determined by the quantity of groundwater (up to 5 m deep) available for plants at the end of the 1998 dry season (September 30). The forests where water was exhausted (0 mm, yellow) were considered highly inflammable. Source: Nepstad et al. 1999.

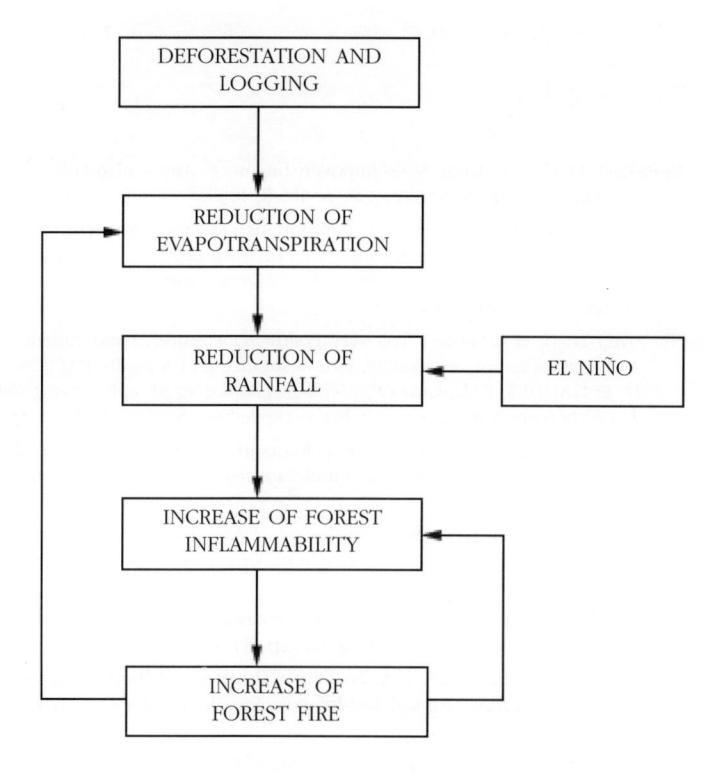

Figure 7. Inflammability of primary forest caused by deforestation and logging. Logging and deforestation reduce evapotranspiration, which in turn causes a reduction in rainfall, increasing the forest's inflammability and vulnerability to fire. Once the forest is burnt, evapotranspiration is even further reduced, and the forest becomes more inflammable and susceptible to future fires. The El Niño phenomenon further intensifies this cycle. Source: Nepstad et al. 1995.

The value of the ecological services of the forest and conservation strategies

What is the value of the ecological services provided by the forests of Amazonia? The answers to such questions have been sought by many researchers, and have provided support for an approach to defining actions and priorities for the conservation and sustainable use of biodiversity that is different from an approach based on species diversity or endemism. For example, Constanza et al. (1997) calculated that the economic value of the planet's ecosystem services is around US$ 33 trillion (1.8 times global GDP). Of this, the most valuable service is nutrient recycling, which corresponds to US$ 17 trillion, more than half the total. In comparison, genetic resources are valued at US$ 78 billion (0.2% of the total). Around 38% of the total value of services is supplied by terrestrial ecosystems. Forests provide services worth US$ 4.7 trillion, such as nutrient recycling, raw materials, climate regulation and erosion control. The genetic resources of forests, however, do not add up to more than 2% of the total (US$ 80 billion).

Although such estimates are often debatable and difficult to determine, actions for biodiversity conservation and use that start from this perspective can open up new horizons. For example, the main objective of actions and strategies for the conservation and sustainable use of biodiversity could be to ensure the functioning of the biogeochemical cycles that maintain the biosphere or ecosystem (Lovelock 1998, McGrath 1997). Another issue arises from this objective: maintenance of ecosystem functioning does not necessarily mean keeping it free from human interference. In extractive reserves, for example, despite the impact on fauna and flora caused by the extractive activities (Nepstad et al. 1992), the forest is still able to maintain many of its original ecological functions (such as evapotranspiration and resistance of fire). From this point of view, the conservation value of inhabited forests becomes as important as that of intact forests. This is an approach to conservation that is different from the traditional approach which advocates biodiversity conservation (taken to mean conservation of species diversity) through the establishment of parks and reserves that are free of human presence (Terborgh 1999, Redford and Mansour). In this view, the issue of the preservation of tropical forests involves a choice between 'conserving (preservation of forests in good condition and uninhabited) *versus* destroying nature (i.e. the inevitable outcome of human presence in the forest)' (Schwartzman et al., submitted). For Amazonia, however, it's more of a choice between maintaining forested areas, in most cases inhabited (less than 5% of the area of Amazonian forests is conserved as parks or uninhabited reserves), versus maintaining and expanding areas of pasture for cattle. More than five million peasants and 60% of the country's indigenous population (living on 372 reserves occupying around 900,000 km^2) live off or in the region's forests. To consider them as enemies of nature is to lose a great opportunity for conserving the ecological services of the forests where they live. This opportunity arises from the recognition that forests under human occupation can have a high value in terms of the conservation of their ecological functions and even of species conservation. Exploiting this potential on a large scale needs to take place through strong local organizations, guarantees of land ownership, provision of basic government services, and the application and development of means and strategies to add value to and market non-timber forest products.

The strategy of conserving the biodiversity of Amazonia through maintaining the ecological services of the ecosystem values not only the conservation of inhabited forests, but also of secondary forests. Depending on the region, the value of secondary forests in Amazonia, typically growing on abandoned pastures, can be very high. For example, a secondary forest in eastern Amazonia less than 20 years old can release into the atmosphere practically the same quantity of water as a primary forest (Jipp et al. 1998), or even restore the nutrient cycle (Nepstad et al. forthcoming). Furthermore, these forests can harbor a significant number of native animal and plant species (Gascon and Moutinho 1998; Nepstad et al. 1996). Areas with growing secondary forests, therefore, should be considered important for conservation strategies, especially in areas where the original vegetation cover is now absent (for example, the Bragantina region in northern Pará).

Preservation the ecological services of the Amazon forest must be a priority for regional strategies for the conservation and use of biodiversity. These strategies should consider ecosystems and/or landscapes, and not only species, as the objects of conservation. In this way, those basic functions that keep the biosphere active are conserved and, as a result, so are existing species (known and unknown).

Acknowledgments

We are very grateful to Claudia Azevedo-Ramos and Cristina M. Oliveira for comments on the text, and to Karen Schwalbe for help with the figures and references. The U.S. Agency for International Development (USAID) provided financial support to the authors.

Bibliography

BARNOLA J. M. et. al. *Nature*, n. 324, p. 408-14, 1987.

COCHRANE, M. A.; SCHULZE, M. D. Fire as a Recurrent Event in Tropical Forests of the Eastern Amazon: Effects on Forest Structure, Biomass, and Species Composition, *Biotropica*, v. 31, n. 1, p. 2-16, 1999.

COCHRANE, M. A. et al. Positive Feedbacks in the Fire Dynamic of Closed Canopy Tropical Forests, *Science*, n. 284, p. 1832-5, 1999.

FEARNSIDE, P. M. Greenhouse Gases from Deforestation in Brazilian Amazonia: Net Committed Emissions, *Climatic Change*, n. 35, p. 321-360, 1997.

FRANKLYN, J. F. Preserving Biodiveristy: Species, Ecosystems, or Landscapes?, *Ecological Applications*, n. 3, p. 202-5, 1993.

GRACE, J. et al. The Use of Eddy Covariance to Infer the Net Carbon Dioxide Uptake of Brazilian Rain Forest, *Global Change Biology*, n. 2, p. 209-217, 1996.

GASCON, C.; MOUTINHO, P. *Floresta Amazônica: dinâmica, regeneração e manejo*. Manaus: Editora do INPA, 1998.

HENDERSON-SELLERS, A. et al. Tropical Deforestation: Modelling Local to Regional-Scale Climate Change, *Journal Geophysics Research*, n. 98, p. 7289-7315, 1993.

HOUGHTON, R. A. Terrestrial Carbon Storage: Global Lessons for Amazonian Research, *Ciência & Cultura*, n. 49, p. 58-72, 1997.

_____. Carbon Cycle, *Encyclopedia of Energy Technology and the Environment*, n. 4, p. 491-504, 1995.

HOLDSWORTH, A. R.; UHL, C. Fire in Amazonian Selectively Loggeg Rain Forest and the Potential for Fire Reduction, *Ecological Application*, n. 7, p. 713-25, 1997.

INPE. *Monitoring of the Brazilian Amazonian Forest by Satellite 1997-1998*. São José dos Campos, February 1999.

JIPP, P.; NEPSTAD, D.; CASSLE, K. Deep Soil Moisture Storage and Transpiration in Forests and Pastures of Seasonally-Dry Amazonia, *Climatic Change*, v. 39, n. 2-3, p. 395-412, 1998.

LEAN, J.; WARRILOW, D. A. Simulation of the Regional Climatic Impact of Amazon Deforestation, *Nature*, n. 342, p. 411-413, 1989.

LOVELOCK, J. *The Ages of Gaia*. New York: Bantam Books, 1988.

MACGRATH, D. Biosfera ou biodiversidade: uma avaliação crítica do paradigma da biodiversidade. In: XIMENES, T. (Ed.). *Perspectivas do desenvolvimento sustentável: uma contribuição para a Amazônia 21*. Belém: Editora da UFPA, 1997.

NEPSTAD, D. C.; MOREIRA, A.; ALENCAR, A. *Flames in the Rainforest:* Origins, Impacts and Alternatives to Amazonian Fire. Brasília, Brasil: World Bank, Pilot Program for the Conservation of the Brazilian Rainforest, 1996.

NEPSTAD, D. C.; MOUTINHO, P.; MARKEWITZ, D. The Recovery of Biomass, Nutrient Stocks, and Deep Soil Function in Secondary Forests. In: McCLAIN, R.; VITORIA, R.; RICHEY, J. (Eds.). *Biogeochemistry of the Amazon*. Oxford: Oxford University Press, forthcoming.

NEPSTAD, D. C. et al. Large-Scale Impoverishment of Amazonian Forests by Logging and Fire, *Nature*, n. 398, p. 505-8, 1999.

NEPSTAD, D. C. et al. The Ecological Importance of Forest Remnants in an Eastern Amazonian Frontier Landscape. In: SCHELHAS, J.; GREENBERG, R. (Eds.). *Forest Patches in Tropical Forest Landscapes*. Washington D.C.: Island Press, 1996. p. 133-150.

NEPSTAD D. C. et al. Forest Recovery Following Pasture Abandonment in Amazonia: Canopy Seasonality, Fire Resistance and Ants. In: RAPPORT, D. J.; GAUDET, C. L.; CALOW, P. (Eds.). *Evaluating and Monitoring the Health of Large-Scale Ecosystems*. Berlin/Heidelberg: Springer-Verlag, 1995.

NEPSTAD, D. C. et al. The Role of Deep Roots in the Hydrological and Carbon Cycles of Amazonian Forests and Pastures, *Nature*, n. 372, p. 666-9, 1994.

NEPSTAD, D. C. et al. Biotic Impoverishment of Amazonian Forests by Rubber Tappers, Loggers and Cattle Ranchers, *Advances in Economic Botany*, n. 9, p. 1-14, 1992.

NOBRE, C. A.; SELLERS, P. J.; SHUKLA, J. Amazonian Deforestation and Regional Climate Change, *J. Climate*, n. 4, p. 957-988, 1991.

REDFORD, K. H.; MANSOUR, J. A. Traditional Peoples and Biodiversity Conservation in Large Tropical Landscapes. In: *The Nature Conservancy*. Arlington, VA: 1996

SALATI, E.; VOSE, P. B.; LOVEJOY, T. E. Amazon Rainfall, Potential Effects of Deforestation, and Plans for Future Research. In: PRANCE, G. T. (Ed.). *Tropical rainforest and the World Atmosphere*. Boulder, Colorado: Westview Press, 1996.

SCHWARTZMAN, S.; MOREIRA, A.; NEPSTAD, D. Requiem for Nature or Conservation Caprice?, *Conservation Biology*, submitted.

SHUKLA, J.; NOBRE, C. A.; SELLERS, P. Amazon Deforestation and Climate Change, *Science*, n. 247, p. 1322-1325, 1990.

TERBORGH, J. *Requiem for Nature*. Island Press: 1999.

TRENBERTH, K. E.; HOAR, T. J. El Niño and Climate Change, *Geophysical Research Letters*, v. 24, n. 23, p. 3057-3060.

TIMMERMANN, A. et al. Increased El Niño Frequency in a Climate Model Forced by Future Greenhouse Warming, *Nature*, n. 398, p. 694-697, 1999.

UHL, C.; VIEIRA, I. C. G. Ecological Impacts of Selective Logging in the Brazilian Amazon: A Case Study from the Paragominas Region of the State of Pará, *Biotropica*, n. 21, p. 98-106, 1989.

VERÍSSIMO, A. et al. Logging Impacts and Prospects for Sustainable Forest Amangement in an Old Amazonian Frontier: the Case of Paragominas, *Forest Ecology and Management*, n. 55, p. 169-199, 1992.

VICTORIA, R. L. et al. Mechanisms of Water Recycling in the Amazon Basin: Isotopic Insights, *Ambio*, n. 20, p. 384-387, 1991.

Thematic documents 2

Sociodiversity and traditional knowledge

Traditional populations and environmental conservation

Manuela Carneiro da Cunha *University of Chicago*
Mauro W. B. Almeida *Universidade Estadual de Campinas*

In a surprising change of ideological direction, the traditional populations of Amazonia, who until recently were considered to be a hindrance to 'development', or at best to be candidates for this development, have been promoted to the frontline of modernity. The reason for this change is essentially due to the association between these populations and their traditional knowledge and environmental conservation. At the same time, indigenous communities, previously despised or harassed by neighbors on the frontier, have suddenly been transformed into models for the other dispossessed peoples of Amazonia.

The present summary has been written in large measure in response to two common misunderstandings. The first of these consists in questioning the basis of the commitment of traditional populations to conservation: Could it be that this commitment is a fraud? Or, putting the question more mildly, might not this be a case of the western world projecting its ecological concerns onto an arbitrarily created 'good ecological savage'? The second misunderstanding, linked to the first, claims that non-governmental organizations and 'foreign' ideologies are responsible for the new link between biodiversity conservation and traditional populations. In Brazil, this misunderstanding has led to a strange convergence of interests between the military and the left. In order to refute these conceptions we will devote some time to clarifying the historical context in which this process has occurred and the respective roles of different actors in the making of this linkage. Finally, we will discuss the significance that this linkage has taken on locally, its importance for Brazil and the international community, and some of the necessary pre-conditions for its success.

Who are the traditional populations?

The use of the term 'traditional populations' is deliberately broad. However, this breadth should not be confused with conceptual confusion.

Defining traditional populations on the basis of adherence to tradition would run counter to current anthropological understanding. Defining them as population groups with low environmental impacts, in order to be able to them describe them as ecologically sustainable, would be mere tautology. If we describe them as populations beyond the reach of markets, it would be difficult to find any nowadays. In academic and legal textbooks, categories are generally described by means of the properties or characteristics of those elements by which they are constituted. But social categories can also be described 'by extension' – that is, by simple enumeration of the elements that make them up. For the time being, we feel it would be better to define 'traditional populations' 'by extension', in other words by listing current 'members' or candidates for 'membership'. This approach matches the emphasis we will give to the creation and appropriation of categories and, more importantly, also points to the formation of subjects by means of new practices.

This is nothing new here. Terms such as 'indian', 'indigenous', 'tribal', 'native', 'aborigine', and 'negro' are all metropolitan creations, fruits of the colonial encounter. And although they are generic and artificial at the moment of their creation, such terms have been inhabited over time by flesh and blood people. This is what happens, although not necessarily, when the terms gain administrative or legal status. We cannot help noticing the fact that peoples who have started out being forced to inhabit these categories have frequently been able to take possession of them, transforming terms laden with prejudice into campaign banners. In this case, deportation to a foreign conceptual territory has led to the occupation and defense of that territory. It is from this moment on that the category, initially defined 'by extension', starts being redefined on the basis of its properties.

At the moment the term 'traditional populations' is still in its early phase of life. It is a thinly populated category, but it already numbers a few members and has candidates at the door. To begin with, it has administrative existence: the *Centro Nacional de Populações Tradicionais* (CNPT – National Center for Traditional Populations), a unit within Ibama. At first, the category consisted of rubber tappers and brazil-nut gatherers from the Amazon region. It then expanded to include other groups, ranging from cockle collectors in Santa Catarina to babassu nut gatherers in southern Maranhão and 'quilombolas'[1] in Tocantins. What all these groups have in common is the fact that they have, at least to some extent, a history of low environmental impact, and that they currently have an interest in maintaining or recovering control over the territory they exploit. And, above all, they are willing to negotiate: in exchange for control over their territory, they commit themselves to supplying environmental services[2].

---

1. 'Quilombolas' are members of a 'quilombo', a community originating from a settlement of fugitive slaves established prior to the abolition of slavery in 1888 (cf. 'Maroons' in the West Indies and Guianas). (Editor's note)
2. Although traditional populations have followed the example of the indigenous populations, as we will try to show, the category 'traditional populations' does not include indigenous populations. There exists a fundamental legal distinction: indigenous territorial rights are not defined in terms of conservation, even when we see that indigenous lands act as 'islands' of environmental conservation in a context of accelerating devastation. In order to highlight the specific nature of the Brazilian legislation that distinguishes indigenous from 'traditional' populations, we will not include the former in this category and, when necessary, will use the expression 'indigenous and traditional populations'.

How (little) people make history

During the last twenty years, indigenous peoples in Amazonia region have made considerable progress. In the 1970s, the governing class had no compunctions about referring to them as 'obstacles to progress'. Right-wing politicians and the military were suspicious, believing that the only explanation for international concern over indigenous peoples was an envious desire to access the resources of Amazonia. At the time it was a cliché to lament the 'end of the indian'. Some attributed this 'end of the indian' to the inexorable march of development, whereas left-wing intellectuals put it down to the equally inexorable march of history. The quick marches of these battalions did not allow for survivors. The noise concealed more pressing causes of suffering, although less impressive and inexorable than the armies of history: corruption on multiple levels, cooptation by logging and mining interests, eviction of peasants who found themselves driven to invade indigenous lands, and above all government policies providing infrastructure projects and tax breaks for agribusiness. Correspondingly, what would alter the course of events would be the political mobilization of a wide range of Brazilian and international actors, and not a history without agents.

By the end of the 1970s, indian issues had become important national concerns[3]. In the 1934 Constitution and in all subsequent Brazilian Constitutions (those of 1937, 1946, 1967 and 1969), indigenous lands and their resources were reserved for the collective and exclusive use of defined ethnic groups. The ownership of the land belongs to the federal government and indigenous lands can neither be sold nor alienated. In compensation, the 1916 Civil Code assigns indigenous peoples to the category of the 'relative capable', a category designed to cover all citizens over 16 but under 21. It was a last minute fix, given that the Civil Code did not address indigenous issues. 'Persons of relative capacity', deemed to be easily taken advantage of, enjoy special protection in matters of commerce. Although the concept of guardianship over indigenous populations appears, to say the least, paternalistic and anachronistic, in practice it has provided them with effective legal protection. Any business undertaken to the detriment of indians and without legal assistance can by law be challenged and annulled. Additionally, since Brazilian law does not provide for cases of collective legal title to land, the legal status of tutelage becomes increasingly understood as the basis for the anomalous status of indigenous land rights. This however is an error, since it is their prior occupation (in other words, history) which provides the basis for indigenous rights to land.

In 1978, a government minister proposed legislation for the emancipation of so-called 'acculturated indians'. The proposal provided for them to receive individual title to property, which could be placed on the market. In other words, indigenous lands could be sold. The effects of such a measure are easy to imagine, given past precedents in Brazilian history: the laws of 1850 and 1854, for instance, resulted in a thirty-year sell-off of titles to indigenous lands (Cunha 1993).

In 1978, the military dictatorship also clamped down all political demonstrations. To the surprise of many people, repressed dissatisfaction found its channel of expression through indigenous issues. The ban on political demonstrations may have been the reason why the so-called emancipation project – an issue somewhat distant from the concerns of the majority of urban Brazilians – managed to channel such widespread protests. The emancipation project was eventually dropped, although periodically brought back to life under different disguises. However, the campaign against the emancipation of indigenous lands marked the beginning of a decade of intense mobilization around indigenous causes. The first nation-wide indigenous organization was founded[4], as well as a significant number of 'pro-indian committees' comprising volunteers, anthropologists and lawyers. CIMI (*Conselho Indigenista Missionário* – the Indian Missionary Council), a member of the influential CNBB (*Conferência Nacional de Bispos do Brasil* – National Conference of Bishops of Brazil), was strengthened through the inclusion of activist lawyers. The *Associação Brasileira de Antropologia* (ABA – Brazilian Anthropological Association), which at the time had approximately 600 members, was also actively involved in the issue of indigenous rights. The main institutions which supported this type of work were ICCO, the Dutch interchurch organization for development cooperation, the Ford Foundation, through its office in Rio de Janeiro and, to a lesser degree, some German NGOs and Oxfam UK. Legal actions were started (the majority were successful), as well as campaigns for the demarcation and protection of indigenous lands.

Despite the differing results of such campaigns, they had important consequences. In the first place, they helped to identify the main threats facing indigenous populations. In addition, they gave rise to coalitions based on the mutual trust that resulted from shared research, goals and campaigns. We will refer to just two examples.

The first was the alliance between anthropologists and the *Ministério Público Federal* (the federal prosecution service), arising from the government's need to defend itself against the (generally fraudulent) compensation claims brought by supposed owners of indigenous lands. After losing several lawsuits, and dissatisfied with the advice received from Funai (*Fundação Nacional do Índio* – the federal indian affairs agency), the Prosecutor General's office[5] asked the Brazilian Anthropological Association to help with its investigation. The positive outcome

---

3. The only comparable national mobilization around the issue of indigenous lands had occurred in the first decade of the twentieth century and resulted in the creation of the SPI (Serviço de Proteção aos Índios). Examples form the colonial era are less clear although one could, anachronistically, include the Jesuit campaigns of the eighteenth century against indigenous slavery among the large scale movements. The creation of the Xingu national park in 1961, although it had wide support in the cities, was an isolated event to the point of often being considered to be no more than an attempt to project a picture-postcard image of Brazil. The massacres, evictions, and other forms of violence were not normally considered to be national concerns, but instead regrettable instances of localized violence. The structural conditions leading to such forms of violence went unperceived.

4. The *União das Nações Indígenas* (UNI - Union of Indigenous Nations) would play an important role in the 1980s, despite its urban roots (or possibly precisely because of them). This organization would give way at the end of the 1980s and during the 1990s to ethnically or regionally-based indigenous organizations.

5. As part of its mandate, the *Ministério Público Federal* acts as the public defender of the national heritage; the environment; and collective rights and interests, especially those of indigenous communities, the family, children and the aged. The *Procuradoria-Geral da República* (Prosecutor-General's office) can institute civil investigations and public civil action to protect constitutional rights; the national heritage; the environment; properties and rights of artistic esthetic, historic or landscape value; inalienable individual and collective rights related to indigenous communities, the family, children, adolescents, the aged, ethnic minorities and consumers. (Editor's note)

cemented a lasting relationship of mutual trust, which would bear fruit in the drafting of the Constitution of 1988.

The other example is the support of CONAGE (*Coordenação Nacional de Geólogos* – the National Association of Geologists) concerning the prohibition of mineral prospecting in indigenous lands, with the aim of protecting Brazil's mineral reserves in the face of a powerful lobby of national and multinational mining companies. This support was built around a collaborative project developed by CEDI (*Centro Ecumênico de Documentação e Informação* – the Ecumenical Documentation and Information Center) to map the overlap of indigenous lands and areas for which prospecting permits had been sought. The RadamBrasil Project, a radar-based survey of Amazonia carried out in the 1970s, had raised expectations of mineral wealth and caused a rush for prospecting and mining concessions. Since in law the ownership of land does not include ownership of the subsoil, which is federal property, a fierce battle was fought to decide whether or not research and mining could be carried out in the subsoil of indigenous lands.

In 1987, when the Constituent Assembly began to consider the new federal constitution, an effective coalition of indigenous leaders, anthropologists, lawyers and geologists was established. There was a clear understanding of the indian rights that needed to be secured under the new constitution, and almost complete unanimity as to the program for the Constituent Assembly, with the partial exception of CIMI.

It will come as no surprise that the most controversial issues concerned approval for the construction of hydroelectric plants and access to indians lands by non-indians and mining companies for the purpose of prospection. Private companies were extremely interested in mining issues. During the discussions of the draft text of the constitution, under which any type of access to the subsoil of indian land was prohibited, an enormous press campaign against indian rights was organized. On the eve of the submission of a revised text, leading newspapers in five state capitals gave front page coverage for a week to an alleged international conspiracy to keep tin prices high. The fictious argument was that cassiterite mining on indian lands was being blocked in order to prevent Amazonian tin from reaching the market and causing prices to drop. Another battery of accusations was directed towards CIMI, who persisted in using the term 'nations' in relation to indigenous societies – an archaic term, as a matter of fact, commonly found in historical documents prior to the late 19th century, when it was replaced by the word 'tribe'. The use of the term 'nations', the press insinuated, could imply a claim for autonomy. A petition containing the signatures of members of the Austrian public in support of indian rights was held to be proof of the foreign conspiracy that was hiding behind the banner of indian rights. These and other similarly creative accusations, together with the publication of forged documents, kept the heat up until the new constitutional draft was released. It was no surprise to find that in this version indian rights had been drastically mutilated. To have clawed back the majority of these rights in the final text of the Constitution was a political achievement that was made possible thanks to the massive presence of indians, above all of the Kayapó, in Brasília, the negotiating skills of the late senator Severo Gomes, and the effectiveness of a large number of NGOs.

In the end indigenous rights gained their own chapter in the Constitution of 1988. The definition of indigenous land in its article 231 explicitly included not only inhabited spaces and areas of cultivation, but also the territory required for the 'preservation of the environmental resources necessary for the well-being of the indigenous populations, as well as the land necessary for their physical and cultural reproduction, in conformity with their habits, customs and traditions'.

The rights to indigenous land were declared to be 'originário', a legal term implying over-riding precedence, and which limits the role of the state to recognizing such rights, but not to granting them. This formulation has the virtue of linking territorial rights to their historical roots (and not to cultural status or a situation of tutelage). The legal personality of indigenous groups and associations was recognized and, in particular, their ability to start legal proceedings in their own name, independently of the opinion of the legal guardian, with the Prosecutor General's office having responsibility for assisting them before a court of law. All these procedures constitute basic instruments for guaranteeing their rights (Cunha 1989).

Throughout this process the success of indigenous claims to land gained visibility, and had the unexpected and paradoxical result that other dispossessed sectors of society, such as 'quilombolas' and, as we will see, 'seringueiros' (rubber-tappers) began to copy them.

SERINGUEIROS AND ENVIRONMENTALISTS

In 1975 the government of the state of Acre published newspaper advertisements inviting anyone interested to 'plant in Acre and export to the Pacific'. The economic decline of the old 'seringais' (rubber estates) based on a system of debt bondage had opened up opportunities for buying up low-priced land. The fact that these lands did not have legal titles meant that the first task of the buyers was to expel the seringueiros, who could claim squatters rights. As a reaction to the invasion of ranchers and speculators, who saw in the cheap lands of Acre a new frontier for making easy money, from 1977 onward a network of rural workers' unions, with the support of the Catholic church, organized the seringueiros' resistance to eviction. This fight against the clearing of the forests took the form of 'empates' (obstructions)[6] originally under the leadership of Wilson Pinheiro, the president of the rural workers' union (*Sindicato dos Trabalhadores Rurais* – STR) of Brasiléia. This grassroots leader was assassinated in the early 1980s, but Chico Mendes, a union leader from the neighboring municipality of Xapuri, continued and extended the use of empates. At that time the activities of the unions were supported by the Catholic church (through its Rio Purus diocese, but not by the Rio Juruá diocese) and by new organizations supporting the struggles of indians and seringueiros.

At the national meeting of CONTAG[7] in 1984, a number of Amazonian unions proposed a land reform solution for seringueiros which provided for a minimum land module of 600 hectares, something which shocked many of their colleagues who could not understand why a single family would need so much forest. And from 1985 onwards, Chico Mendes audaciously

---

6. Seringueiros and their families would occupy en masse areas about to be cleared, preventing the laborers hired by the rancher from clearing the forest. The term comes from the verb 'empatar' - to block, delay, or obstruct. (Editor's note)
7. Confederação Nacional dos Trabalhadores na Agricultura – National Confederation of Agricultural Workers.

began to bring the empates movement out of the defensive posture into which it had been put. One such action consisted in appealing to the residents of the cities to participate in the empates: this is why in 1986 the young teacher and union leader Marina Silva, two agronomists, one anthropologist and a photographer took part in an empate alongside a hundred seringueiros, with the difference that the movement was now clearly aimed at the country as a whole, just like the civil disobedience movements organized by Gandhi in India and Martin Luther King in the USA. The 1986 empate, under the emerging leadership of Marina Silva and the command of Chico Mendes, ended with the occupation of the offices of IBDF, the federal forestry agency[8], and press attention on irregularities in the granting of forest clearance permits.

Another of Chico Mendes' actions consisted of proposing to Mary Allegretti[9] the organization of a high-impact public act in support of the seringueiros' cause. In response, Mary organized an astonishing meeting in Brasília, with the support of government and non-governmental bodies, at which 120 union leaders representing seringueiros from all over Amazonia met face-to-face with government officials responsible for rubber policy, with members of congress and ministers, with intellectuals and experts. By the end of the meeting they had created an equally strange and unplanned body: the *Conselho Nacional dos Seringueiros* (National Rubber-Tappers Council), whose name reflected that of the *Conselho Nacional da Borracha* (National Rubber Council), on which they had no representatives. Another equally significant outcome was the development of a statement of principles, which included in its section on land the demand for the creation of 'reservas extrativistas' (extractive reserves) for seringueiros, without division into individual plots and with modules of at least 300 hectares.

Although seringueiros had been fighting for years for a land reform that would permit the continuation of their extractive activities, this was the first time that the word 'reserve' had been used, deliberately establishing a direct association with the language of protection of indigenous lands. In the following years, the seringueiros realized that the connection between their actions to prevent deforestation and the program of conserving forests in the form of extractive reserves had the potential to attract powerful allies.

Seringueiros, who a few years previously had constituted a category believed to be destined for rapid disappearance, had by the end of the 1980s taken on a leadership role in terms of environmental mobilization. At the end of 1988 an alliance for the defense of the forests and its inhabitants emerged in Acre under the name of the Alliance of Forest Peoples, made up of seringueiros and indigenous groups in the form of the two national organizations recently created: the *Conselho Nacional dos Seringueiros* and the *União das Nações Indígenas*. The meeting at Altamira (February 1989), organized by the Kayapó against the Xingu dam project, had an explicit environmental connotation. By the end of the 1980s, the environmental connection had become explicit. In contrast to the Yellowstone model, which sought to create an 'untouched' North American environment with no human population, it was argued that local communities, who had protected the environment on which their way of life was based, should be the partners and not the victims of environmental conservation.

On the contrary, in order to protect the environment, local communities should take on responsibility for the management and control of the natural resources in the environment in which they lived. The new factor was the active role attributed to local communities. At the beginning of 1992 the explicit link between indigenous populations and conservation gained international prominence with the creation of the International Alliance of Tribal and Indigenous Populations of Tropical Forests, of which one of the founder organizations was COICA (*Confederação das Organizações Indígenas da Bacia Amazônica* – Confederation of Indigenous Organizations of the Amazon Basin). The Convention on Biological Diversity and Agenda 21, approved in 1992, explicitly recognized the important role played by indigenous and local communities. In 1996, Colombia put into practice on a large scale the idea of making indigenous populations officially responsible for large areas of tropical forest. In Brazil, as we will see below, the same idea was applied six years earlier than in Colombia, on a smaller yet no less important scale, in the form of extractive reserves. The first protagonists of this experiment were the seringueiros, rather than indigenous groups.

INDIAN LANDS AND CONSERVATION AREAS

It is calculated that the indigenous population of Brazil amounts to approximately 310,000 individuals, of whom 280,000 live on indian lands. Although this population is relatively small, its social diversity is extremely rich. There are 206 indigenous societies, 160 of them in the Amazon region, and approximately 195 different languages. It is estimated that there are 50 isolated indigenous groups, with no regular contact with the outside world.

With the exception of the brief and violent rubber boom, which lasted from 1870 to 1910, the major part of Amazonia, away from the main channel of the Amazon river, remained a relative stranger to the process of human occupation. As a consequence, the majority of the surviving indigenous groups and the major part of the lands they succeeded in preserving are found within Amazonia, where almost 99% of the total area of indigenous lands in Brazil is concentrated.

Although dispersed, the extent of indigenous lands as a whole is impressive. Indians have a constitutional right to almost 12% of the Brazilian territory, made up of 574 different areas and encompassing 20% of Brazilian Amazonia. Conservation areas where human presence is permitted, direct use conservation areas, cover another 8.4% of the Amazon region.

In the 1980s, the extent of the indian lands in Brazil seemed an exaggeration: 'too much land for too few Indians'. This focus has changed. The cover story of *Veja* magazine of June 20th, 1999, told of the 3,600 indians of the Xingu who 'preserved an ecological paradise' of the size of Belgium. The point was that a small number of Indians could take good care of a vast territory. The idea that the people who are most qualified to care for the conservation of an area are those who live off it in a sustainable way is also the premise for the creation of extractive reserves.

It is clear that not all conservation areas can be administrated by their pre-existing inhabitants. But it is also clear that serious and viable environmental policy in Brazil must include

---

8. Instituto Brasileiro de Desenvolvimento Florestal - Brazilian Institute for Forestry Development (merged with other federal agencies in 1989 to form IBAMA).
9. Anthropologist, subsequently Secretary for Amazon Coordination, Ministry of the Environment from 1999 to 2003. (Editor's note)

local populations. Not least, to evict people from conservation areas without offering them alternative means of subsistence is a course leading towards certain disaster.

Are traditional populations really conservationists?

The enemies of the participation of traditional populations in conservation argue (1) that not all traditional societies are conservationists and (2) that even those who are today may change for the worse when they gain access to the market.

For a long time there existed among anthropologists, conservationists, government leaders and the populations themselves an idealization of the relationship between traditional populations and the environment. A set of ideas, presenting indigenous groups as conservationists by nature, led to what has been called 'the myth of the good ecological savage' (Redford and Stearman 1991, 1993). It is obvious that natural conservationists do not exist. Nevertheless, even after translating 'natural' into 'cultural', the question remains: can traditional populations be described as 'cultural conservationists'?

Environmentalism can describe a set of practices and can refer to an ideology. There are, however, three different situations, which tend to be confused when using a single term to all three.

First, there can be ideology without effective practice – take the case of verbal support for conservation. Next, there are those cases where both sustainable practices and cosmology are present. Many indigenous societies of Amazonia subscribe to a kind of Lavoisierian ideology according to which nothing is lost and everything is recycled, including life and souls. Such societies believe in the limited exploitation of natural resources, where human beings are the stewards of the equilibrium of the universe, which includes both the natural and the supernatural. Values, food and hunting taboos, and institutional or supernatural sanctions provide them with the instruments for acting in accordance with this ideology. Such societies can easily be put into the category of cultural conservationists. The example of the Yagua in Peru immediately comes to mind (Chaumeil 1983).

Finally, there can be cultural practices without ideology (Gonzales 1992). In this case, we can think of populations who, despite not having an explicit conservation ideology, follow cultural rules regarding to the use of natural resources that, when population density and the territory in which they are applied are taken into account, are sustainable. It is worth nothing that, to preserve resources, a society does not need to avoid predatory practices completely, just to keep them within limits. If a society agrees to the killing of a group of monkeys, including females and offspring, and if this massacre, offensive as it may be to some, does not alter population levels, then the society is not infringing the practice of conservation. What one can ask is whether the habits in question are compatible with sustainable use, and not whether they are morally wrong. We may object to sport hunting in our own society; but the fact is that North American associations, who have their origin in hunting organizations, such as the National Wildlife Federation, were and are important for environmental conservation. In the same way, indigenous groups have been able to conserve and manage the environments in which they live, with creativity and competence.[10] However, this does not necessarily flow from a cosmology of the equilibrium of nature and may result rather from considerations linked to the desire to maintain resource stocks.

In fact, indigenous groups and even some newcomer groups, such as seringueiros, have protected and perhaps even enriched the biodiversity of neotropical forests. Amazonian forests are dominated by species that control access to sunlight. Human groups, by cutting small clearings in the forest, create opportunities for oppressed species to have a window of access to sunlight – when, for instance, a large tree comes down (Balée 1994: 119-23).

The second argument suggests that, although traditional societies may in the past have exploited the environment in a sustainable way, the frontier populations with whom they interact will influence them to adopt short-sighted resource use strategies. In the absence of adequate institutions and with little information about alternatives, anomie can lead to the moral dissolution of social groups as younger members with an entrepreneurial spirit come into greater conflict with older customs and values of reciprocity.

According to this line of argument, although 'traditional culture' has ensured conservation in the past, needs arising from the linking to market economies will inevitably lead to cultural change and to the overexploitation of natural resources. It is true that change is certain, but it is not necessarily true that overexploitation is. What the state of equilibrium prior to contact also implies is that, under certain structural conditions, traditional populations can play an important role in conservation.

What this scenario fails to recognize is that the situation has changed, and with it the validity of old paradigms. Traditional populations are no longer outside the central economy, nor are they simply on the periphery of the global system. Traditional populations and their organizations no longer deal only with farmers, loggers and prospectors, but have become partners of institutions at the centre, such as the United Nations, the World Bank and powerful first world NGOs.

Neither is the market in which traditional populations operate today the same as before. Until recently, in order to earn money, indigenous societies had to supply first-generation goods: raw materials such as rubber, Brazil-nuts, minerals and timber. They by-passed the second generation of goods with industrial added value, and scarcely touched the third generation goods and services. They have begun participating in the information economy, fourth generation goods, by means of value added to indigenous and local knowledge (Cunningham 1991; Nijar 1996; Brush 1996; Cunha et al. 1998 and 1999). They have also entered the emerging market of 'existence values', such as biodiversity and natural landscapes. For example, in 1994 purchasers could buy a certificate for a square meter of Central American forest, despite knowing that they would never see their square meter.

---

10. Balée provides a detailed review of the evidence that Amazonian societies have enriched natural resources, whether they be rivers, soils, animals or botanical diversity (see Balée 1989, Balée and Gely 1989, Anderson 1991, Kaplan and Kopischke 1992).

How does conservation acquire local meaning?

A case study

One difficulty about involving local communities in conservation projects is that, generally speaking, these projects are usually started by someone in a position of power and only afterwards do local groups become 'involved'. But even in cases in which the origin of the conservation project lies in the initiative of a local group, there remains the difficulty of aligning action plans at different levels, seeking external resources, and acquiring the necessary technical capacity.

We will now briefly describe the process of combining conservation and land reform, which resulted in the invention of extractive reserves. In doing this, we will go into seemingly minute detail, in order to show the role played by local initiatives, by universities, and by governmental and non-governmental organizations, Brazilian and foreign.

On January 23, 1990, by decree 98,863, the Upper Juruá extractive reserve was established. It was the first conservation area of its kind, a territory of half a million hectares about to pass from the control of private owners to the legal status of federal land, destined for the exclusive use of its inhabitants, through concession contracts, and whose management would by law be undertaken by means of agreements between the government and representative local associations.

This achievement was the result of the joint efforts of organizations and individuals at different levels, including local union activists, the leadership of the *Conselho Nacional dos Seringueiros* (whose head offices were in the capital of Acre), researchers and advisers, the *Banco Nacional de Desenvolvimento Econômico e Social* (BNDES – the Brazilian national development bank), the Prosecutor General's office and a number of Brazilian and foreign NGOs. It was also the result of unexpected events and serendipitous connections, an effect of the 'unequal and combined development', which placed one of the most remote and isolated regions of the country, where the struggle of the seringueiros was not against the farmers, but against trading-post bosses, at the frontline of the environmental debate (Almeida 1996c).

Over the previous period the idea of the extractive reserve had been successfully disseminated in Brazil and abroad, associated to notions of sustainable development programs based on local communities (Allegretti 1990, Schwartzman 1989). When in 1985 the word 'reserve' was spoken in public, read out by Chico Mendes as part of the final declaration of the national meeting of seringueiros held in Brasília, it did not yet have a precise meaning. What it was meant to suggest, according to the delegation from Rondônia that introduced it into the text, was that the lands of seringueiros should enjoy the same protection as indian reserves.

The term only acquired a more specific meaning in December 1986 in the interior of the municipality of Brasiléia, Acre, in the middle of a clutch of surviving Brazil nut trees in an otherwise devastated landscape. At this meeting, which included members of the *Conselho Nacional de Seringueiros* and a small group of advisers, one of the topics was the basis for extractive reserves under agrarian law. The draft in the document at Brasiléia stated only that the land could not be 'divided into lots', and that the traditional settlement system should be maintained. An anthropologist with experience in Funai explained the legal situation of indigenous lands and the other land law alternatives. The preference of the socialist seringueiro leaders was for the indian lands system, since this was the only one which completely prevented any possibility of re-privatization of the forest through land sale. Thus, after a closed door discussion, with no input from the advisory group, the Council voted for the 'federal property' solution and for the 'exclusive (collective) use of the land' by seringueiros.

Another important topic of this Brasiléia meeting was the economic question. Up to that point, all the seringueiro union leaders, including Chico Mendes, were convinced that the production of Amazonian rubber was of fundamental importance to the national economy. This belief was apparently reinforced by the importance of extractive activities for the economy of the state of Acre. A presentation by one of the advisers summarized some basic facts. The Amazon region supplied only a small part of the rubber used by Brazilian industry, and only as a result of government prices support, since it was cheaper for companies to import rubber than to buy it internally. Even if the entire workforce of all traditional rubber estates were to receive government subsidy, total production in the Amazon region would probably not exceed the 40,000 tons reached at the peak of the rubber boom in 1911, an amount well below the needs of Brazilian industry and an almost insignificant amount in global terms. Moreover, at the time in 1986, the price support mechanisms and the subsidies granted to rubber estate owners began to be withdrawn. One of the leaders present at the meeting, the same person who had defended the case for collective ownership of the reserves and who had previously enquired what 'ecology' was, broke the silence by saying that if people did not want rubber, at least there were those who wanted ecology. And this seringueiros knew how to deliver.

In 1987, the link between the land reform of the seringueiros and the environmental question was strengthened by means of an alliance between seringueiros and environmentalists (Mendes 1989; Hecht and Cockburn 1989; Shoumatoff 1991). But by now extractive reserves were part of a land reform rather than an environmental program, and the first legal steps were directed towards Incra (*Instituto Nacional de Colonização e Reforma Agrária* – the federal National Institute for Colonization and Agrarian Reform) and not Ibama. In fact, prior to 1988, only a small number of people, such as Mary Allegretti, conceived of the possibility of establishing extractive reserves as conservation areas. For the seringueiros, the real issues continued to be land reform and labor unions.

In October 1989, the PT (*Partido dos Trabalhadores* – the Workers' Party) lost the presidential elections in the second round, with the victory of Collor over Lula. Given the right-wing support base of the newly elected president, hopes for land reform at the federal level evaporated. In fact, such hopes had been seriously undermined by the defeat of the land reform program of the left in 1985. However there was a possibility: if extractive reserves were established as conservation areas, the necessary procedures for expropriation would avoid the difficulties of going through Incra. Thus, soon after the October elections, the *Conselho Nacional dos Seringueiros*, using the specific case of the Upper Juruá extractive reserve – half a million hectares that did not figure in Incra's plans – agreed to look for a solution in the context of Ibama. After the Juruá extractive reserve was established by decree on January 23, 1990, representing a victory of the seringueiros of that remote region over the bosses led by

Orleir Cameli[11], three other projects along the same lines were prepared and quickly submitted. These three projects – one in Acre (the Chico Mendes extractive reserve), one in Rondônia and one in Amapá – were approved in the evening of the last day of office of the government of President Sarney, on March 15, 1990, following intense scrutiny by the military.

The conservation alliance was thus a strategy, and categorizing extraction reserves as conservation areas was a tactical choice. However, to say that the conservation alliance was a strategy does not mean that it was false, either in substance or as a project. As to the project, this is still being adapted at the local level. As to the substance, seringueiros really were protecting biodiversity. As previously explained, in the Upper Juruá rubber had been exploited for more than 120 years, and the area was proven to be a biodiversity hot spot, with 616 species of birds, 102 species of amphibians and 1,536 species of butterfly, including 477 Nymphalidae (Brown Jr. and Freitas, forthcoming).

It is true that, like M. Jourdain who had been speaking prose without knowing it, seringueiros may not have been aware they were conserving biodiversity. They thought they were producing rubber and not biodiversity. Rubber is tangible and production is individual. Despite price variation, its value was relatively stable in terms of the purchasing power of the national currency. At a time when inflation affected the whole country and when salaries at the end of the month were worth less than half what they were at the beginning, seringueiros managed to measure the value of their work in rubber, both when bartering amongst themselves and for external purchases. If someone wanted to hire the services of a seringueiro as a day laborer, the daily wages were equivalent to the value of ten kilos of rubber. Compared to the rest of the country, this was a good rate. It does not mean that every seringueiro produced ten kilos of rubber a day. The average seringueiro exploited two estradas (circuits) of rubber trees and each tree was tapped twice a week for, at most, eight months of the year. With two estradas the seringueiro would work four days a week, and for the remainder of the time would hunt during the winter and fish during the dry season. Moreover, ten kilos of rubber did not represent the productivity of the entire region, but rather a benchmark for the most productive areas. However, as a daily wage these ten kilos represented dignity and independence: what seringueiros could earn in a day if they wanted to. In its monetary aspect, this is what economists call the opportunity cost of work labor. (The rare entrepreneurs who tried to establish rubber plantations in the Upper Juruá soon found out that one of the main problems was finding labor). A seringueiro household depends simultaneously on rubber extraction (to obtain cash), swidden crops (to obtain manioc flour, the basis of the diet), some poultry and livestock (as a safeguard for the future), and hunting and fishing. Seasonal collecting of palm tree fruits and other medicinal and food items, as well as material for building, is important. Even when they are not making rubber, seringueiros are far from being unemployed.

It is well-known that rubber plantations do not do well in Amazonia mainly because of leaf disease – at least when planted at the same density as Asian plantations. The rubber tree remains healthy when it is dispersed throughout the forest. An estrada consists of about 120 trees of the genus *Hevea*. A seringueiro household manages on average two, and sometimes three, estradas and, in the case of two, the total area will cover at least 300 hectares or 3 km². This is the minimum area, but if we consider the whole forest, including those tracts not transected by estradas, but inhabited by game, households in the Upper Juruá extractive reserve cover on average 500 hectares or 5 km² each. The natural low density of rubber trees in the forest thus explains the low population density within the seringais (rubber estates) of about 1.2 people per square kilometer (i.e. a six-person household occupying 5 km²). This density is compatible with the conservation of the forest. In this whole area the extent of deforestation by seringueiros for small garden clearings, even including the pastures of small farms along the banks of Juruá), barely reaches 1%.

As one would expect, local adaptation of the conservation project varied in accordance with local situations and plans. While in eastern Acre, land purchasers from the state of São Paulo ('paulistas') felled the forest and confronted the seringueiros, in the western part of the state the old system of seringais lasted into the 1980s. Some companies from São Paulo had bought land, not for immediate use but as a speculative investment, anticipating the future paving of BR-364 highway. In the meantime, they leased the forest to local landowners such as Orleir Cameli, who, in turn, subleased it to others. At the mouth of each important river there would be a store advancing supplies on credit, where the seringueiro was taken on as the 'titleholder' of a pair of estradas, on condition of paying 33 kilos of rubber a year for each. Thus, the head of the household was on one hand the lessee of the estradas from the local boss, and on the other, the creditor of that same boss for the goods supplied.

What mattered to the rubber bosses was to maintain the monopoly over the rubber trade. They sought to control the movement of rubber in order to stop indebted seringueiros (the large majority) selling rubber to river traders and peddlers, something that nevertheless always occurred to a certain extent. This forbidden commerce would result in the eviction of the seringueiros by the boss, with police from the city called in for this purpose.

Thus, the seringueiros of the Juruá, in contrast to those of eastern Acre, were considered cativos (captive or in thrall). The seringueiros of the Acre valley in the east of the state, abandoned by the old bosses who had sold their title to newly arriving ranchers, were libertos (free), who could sell rubber to whoever they wanted. In practice, it was impossible to control people scattered throughout a wide area of forest. During the 1980s, the most economically successful of the Juruá rubber bosses were those who offered an abundant of goods in their stores, a result of easy subsidized loans from the Banco do Brasil. The worth of a boss was measured by the size of his debts, as was the worth of a seringueiro.

The legal basis of the property ownership of the large landowners of Acre, who also controlled trade, was very weak. In the 1980s if a landowner held any type of legal title at all, this would typically cover only a small fraction of the land in question, perhaps 10% at most. The payment of 33 kilos of rubber for each estrada, rather than for the land itself, was a pre-capitalist form of rent. Being fixed and payable in kind, it depended neither on the actual or potential production of the estradas, nor on current prices. Rather, it represented the recognition on the part of the seringueiro that the boss was the 'dono das estradas' (the 'owner' of the rubber trees) and thus legitimized the dubious status of the ownership which the bosses enjoyed: as *de facto*, but not *de jure*,

---
11. Subsequently state governor, 1995-1998. (Editor's note)

owners. The battle of the seringueiros of the Upper Juruá was not directed against the large landholders, but against a humiliating situation of servitude. The basic objectives of the first union meetings were to refuse to pay rent and to protest against the violence used to prohibit free trade. The first skirmishes in this fight, long before the extractive reserve project, were related to exemption from rent payments (in the case of those seringueiros who had opened their estradas), and subsequently to the fight against all payment of rent (Almeida 1993).

The rebellion against lease payments and against the violence of the monopoly exploded in 1988, following a meeting of 700 seringueiros in the small town of Cruzeiro do Sul, the main town of western Acre. In this same year, the meetings took place at which the proposal for extractive reserves had begun to be discussed. At the beginning of 1989, following the assassination of Chico Mendes at the end of 1988, an association of seringueiros was founded in the Tejo valley to administer a cooperative revolving loan fund established by the BNDES. Together with the refusal to pay rent, this represented a direct challenge to the monopoly of the landowners. After successfully overcoming requests for injunctions filed by the UDR[12], violent conflicts, imprisonment and threats, by May 1989 a procession of 'cooperative' boats triumphantly entered the Rio Tejo in what would later become the extractive reserve, loaded with merchandise, a glorious symbolic cargo representing the end of an era.[13] This first attempt to create a cooperative trading system ran down the capital after two or three years. One of the reasons for this was that almost nobody had any management experience, particularly in a situation of extremely high inflation. Another problem was that many seringueiros did not pay their off their debts, influenced by landowners spreading rumors that 'it's government money, you don't need to pay it back'.

The main importance of the initiative was that, after the first year of activities of the association, on January 23rd, 1990 the Upper Juruá extractive reserve was created under the jurisdiction of Ibama. This was a solution to the agrarian and social problems (including evidence of debt bondage in a rubber estate leased by Orleir Cameli), but was also a solution to the conservation problem, supported by the opinions of experts and reports by biologists.

In contrast to the conflicts surrounding the felling of forests in Xapuri, the movements in the Juruá was not openly ecological, except for the fact that the union leaders foresaw the imminent start of mahogany logging as practiced by Orleir Cameli, and criticized negligence in relation to the unkeep of estradas. However following the creation of the reserve, and alongside the cooperative activities, there began a phase of setting up new institutions around the *Associação dos Seringueiros e Agricultores*, (Association of Rubber-Tappers and Farmers), starting with the *Plano de Utilização* (management plan) developed and approved at an assembly in late 1991. Health programs were launched, as well as a project that involved research, advice and staff training, sponsored by bodies ranging from the McArthur Foundation to Fapesp[14] and the CNPT – Ibama[15], and involving a number of Brazilian universities, with the objective of showing that under appropriate conditions it was possible for local populations to manage a conservation area. Such conditions include well-defined legal rights, adequate quality of life, democratic institutions at the local event, and access to technological and scientific resources. The project supported the association in many activities, from developing cadastral records, maps and projects to mediating contacts with national and international organizations. In a subsequent phase, Ibama itself channeled resources from European countries to the area, as one of the conservation 'pilot experiments' of the PPG-7.[16]

The impacts of these policies on all aspects of life in the upper Juruá were marked, but it is no surprise that such impacts were very different from those that had been expected. One example is that the population of the Juruá developed its own version of environmental conservation. While younger people tended to enter the political arena by means of the association and then local politics, the more mature and respected men constituted a cadre of 'community inspectors', whose activities were modeled on those of the old 'mateiros' (backwoodsmen) of the rubber estates. These were specialized workers who supervised the state of the estradas and who could impose sanctions on seringueiros who put the life of trees at risk by careless tapping. The new 'community inspectors', in contrast to the old mateiros, did not have the authority to impose punishment and, after much complaining, Ibama gave them the status of 'fiscais colaboradores' (collaborative inspectors) with a limited authority to serve violation notices.

With or without formal authority, the community inspectors carried out their duties with great zeal. The main violations related to hunting. All forms of hunting activity were prohibited by the Forest Code and the punishments were draconian; but locally this severe legislation was interpreted basically as a policy of social equity. Therefore, as part of the *Plano de Utilização* approved by the assembly after much debate, the seringueiros not only prohibited commercial hunting (there was a small local market for game in the village of Thaumaturgo, soon afterwards designated the municipal seat), but also 'hunting with dogs'. There are two types of dogs in the area: 'country dogs' and expensive 'paulista dogs'. Nobody knows for sure whether these mongrel dogs really came from São Paulo, or whether the name comes from their impressive predatory skills, but at any rate 'paulistas' are dogs which follow big game with great persistence and without being distracted once they have located it, whereas the small 'country dogs' go after any kind of animal whose trail they come across. The problem with 'paulista dogs', according to the population of Juruá, is that they frighten the game ('when they don't kill the game, they scare it off') and make the hunting of larger animals (deer, wild pigs) almost impossible for those who do not have them. There was thus a local conflict around equal access to game and the seringueiros decided to go for the lowest common denominator: nobody could have dogs. This ban became the main plank of local conservation. Not having dogs, initially 'paulista dogs' and later any kind of dogs, became the public sign of having adhered to the reserve project, maybe even to a greater extent than buying from the cooperative and not from the bosses, who continued to act as traveling merchants.

---

12. *União Democrática Ruralista*, a national organization of landowners and agribusiness interests.
13. A reference to the literature on Melanesian cargo cults.
14. *Fundação de Amparo à Pesquisa do Estado de São Paulo* (the State of São Paulo Research Foundation).
15. *Centro Nacional de Populações Tradicionais* (National Center for Traditional Populations).
16. The Pilot Program to Conserve the Brazilian Rain Forests, first proposed at the 1990 G-7 summit and operational since 1995. (Editor's note)

There is an important distinction linked to the very notion of producing and maintaining biodiversity. As mentioned above, what the seringueiros thought they were producing was first of all their sustenance and, to this end, rubber destined for the market. There were general rules relating to everything found in the forest: moderation and the sharing of food with groups of neighbors and relatives, magical precautions and pacts of different kinds struck with 'mothers' and protectors of what we can call 'realms', such as the mother-of-the-rubber-tree, the mother-of-hunting and so forth. Agriculture, in contrast, does not have a 'mother'. Here, the entire process is thought to be controlled by people. This is why there is a radical difference between what is exploited in nature and what is controlled by men and women, a sharp division between the domesticated and the wild. This can be seen, for instance, in the fact that no category exists corresponding to what we call 'plants'. The word 'plant' exists, obviously, but refers only to what we would call cultivated plants (a meaning which, by the way, will be obvious to those who know that 'plant' comes from 'to plant'). Since wild species are not planted, how can they be called 'plants'? Clearly the forest also contains trees, reeds, vines, shrubs, and so on.

Another clue in the same direction is the distinction between 'brabo' and 'manso'. In regional usage, 'brabo' can be roughly translated as 'savage, wild, uncivilized or uncouth', as opposed to 'manso' (tame, domesticated). In more general terms, it can refer to the contrast between creatures that flee from humans and those that are not afraid of them. In the more restricted sense of not domesticated or untamed, the word 'brabo' is applied to newcomers, those who are inexperienced in working and surviving in the forest. During the Second World War, the soldados da borracha[17] were called 'brabos' or 'selvagens' (savages), which is somewhat surprising. They were left in the forest with food and instructions, sometimes under the guidance of more experienced seringueiros, in order to become 'amansados' (tamed).

The contrast between wild and tamed is wide and extreme. 'With everything in this world, there is the wild and there is the tame: there is the tapir and there is the cow, there is the deer and there is the kid goat, there is the coati and the rat, the tinamou and the chicken. Even people have their tame and their wild, which are the indians' (Sr. Lico, community inspector).

Producing biodiversity, producing nature, these are oxymorons, contradictions in (local) terms. But this is exactly what the resources of the G-7 are funding. How can this be translated into political terms? A direct economic response would be to pay the seringueiros directly for what the world market is currently really interested in, which is biodiversity. But this runs counter to the local perception. Biodiversity is a by-product of a way of life, the equivalent of what economists call positive externality. Externalities are products that result from an activity of the producer and which are freely 'consumed' by others, such as the smoke of a factory inhaled by its neighbors (negative externality) or the security on the street resulting from a well-protected house (positive externality). The market ignores externalities. But biodiversity and environmental services (and disservices) have begun to be taken into account, and their benefits have begun to be treated as something to be paid for. This, by the way, is a consequence of an enhanced notion of what the system is as a whole. If environmental services were paid for directly at the reserve, this would invert foreground and background: what was a by-product, an unplanned consequence of a way of life, would become the product itself.

In contrast, Ibama and other agencies have concentrated their efforts on developing so-called sustainable forest products and hope that these will make the reserves economically viable, without including ecological services on the balance sheet. The problem might be resolved by means of a careful combination of good quality forest products, for instance, a source of cash income for the families, and a fund that would remunerate overall biological diversity by providing collective benefits relating to the well-being of the population, as well as resources to finance local collective organizations and sustainable projects. It should be remembered that so far, on the basis of the notion that forest peoples are essentially conservationists, nobody has provided permanent funding to cover the costs of local forest governance, despite the very high travel costs for all the leaders who live on the upper rivers.

This is now starting to happen. Conservation was initially a political weapon in a battle for freedom and land rights. Today, the resources for conservation are being used to obtain outboard motors, boats, schools, and health facilities. Conservation is in the process of becoming a part of local projects and its importance is growing.

Revisiting traditional populations

We began with a definition 'by extension' and argued that an analytical definition would emerge in its own time. From what we have seen we can already take some steps in this direction and argue that traditional populations are groups that have gained or are fighting to gain (by practical and symbolical means) a public identity which includes some but not necessarily all of the following characteristics: the use of low impact environmental techniques, equitable forms of social organization, the presence of institutions with the necessary legitimacy to have their rules obeyed, local leadership, and, finally, cultural features that are selectively reaffirmed and re-worked.

Therefore, although it would be tautological to say that 'traditional populations' have a low destructive impact on the environment, it is not tautological to say that a specific group such as the cockle collectors of Santa Catarina are, or have become, a 'traditional population', since we are dealing with a process of self-constitution. Internally, this self-constitution process requires the establishment of conservation rules, as well as leaders and legitimate institutions. Externally, there is a need for alliances with organizations outside and inside government.

It should now be clear that the category of 'traditional populations' is one filled by political actors who are willing to give it substance, who are willing to strike a bargain: to agree to a set of practices in exchange for some sort of benefit, above all land rights. From this perspective, even those societies who are culturally conservationist are, nevertheless and in a certain sense, neo-traditional or neo-conservationist.

---

17. Men recruited, mainly in north-eastern Brazil, to work as seringueiros in the western Amazon region as part of the agreement between Brazil and the USA to re-vitalize the Amazon rubber industry to supply the Allies following Japanese occupation of Malaya (Editor's note).

Bibliography

ALLEGRETTI, M. H. Extractive Reserves: An Alternative for Reconciling Development and Environmental Conservation in Amazonia. In: ANDERSON, A. (Ed.). *Alternatives for Deforestation: Steps Toward Sustainable Use of the Amazon Rain Forest*. New York: Columbia Univ. Press, 1990. p. 252-64.

ALMEIDA, M. W. B. As colocações como forma social, sistema tecnológico e unidade de recursos naturais. *Terra Indígena*, n. 54, p. 29-39, 1990.

_____. *Rubber Tappers of the Upper Juruá River, Acre: The Making of a Forest Peasantry*, 1993. Doctoral Thesis, University of Cambridge, Cambridge.

_____. The Management of Conservation Areas by Traditional Populations: the Case of the Upper Juruá Extractive Reserve. In: REDFORD, K. H.; MANSOUR, J. A. (Eds.). *Traditional Peoples and Biodiversity Conservation in Large Tropical Landscapes*. Arlington: America Verde Publications and The Nature Conservancy, 1996a. p. 137-58.

_____. Le Droit Foncier et les reserves d'extraction en Amazonie. In: SACHS, I. (Ed.). *Cahiers du Brésil contemporain*. Paris: Maison des Sciences de l'Homme, 1996b.

_____. *The Struggles of Rubber Tappers*. Massachusetts, 1996c.

ANDERSON, A. B. Forest Management Strategies by Rural Inhabitants in the Amazon Estuary. In: GOMEZ-POMPA, A.; WHITMORE, T. C.; HADLEY, M. (Eds.). *Rain forest regeneration and management*. UNESCO, 1991. p. 351-60.

BALÉE, W. *Footprints of the Forest Ka'apor Ethnobotany: the Historical Ecology of Plant Utilization by an Amazonian People*. New York: Columbia Univ. Press, 1994.

_____. The Culture of Amazonian Forests. *Advances in Economic Botany*, n. 7, p. 1-21, 1989.

BALÉE, W.; GELY, A. Managed Forests Succession in Amazonia: the Ka'apor Case. *Advances in Economic Botany*, n. 7, p. 129-58, 1989.

BROWN Jr., K.; FREITAS, A. V. Diversidade biológica no Alto Juruá: avaliação, causas e manutenção. In: CUNHA, M. C. da; ALMEIDA, M. (Eds.). *Enciclopédia da Floresta: o alto Juruá*. São Paulo: Companhia das Letras, 2001.

BRUSH, S. Indigenous Knowledge of Biological Resources and Intellectual Property Rights: the Role of Anthropology. *American Anthropologist*, v. 95, n. 3, p. 653-86, 1996.

CUNHA, M. C. da. L'État brésilien, les indiens, la nouvelle constitution. In: CUNHA, M. C.; ALMEIDA, M. (Eds.). *L'État et les autochtones en Amérique latine et au Canada*. Symposiums du Congrès annuel. Association Canadienne des études latino-américaines et Caraibeennes, 1989, p. 133-45. Université de Laval (republished in *Ethnies*, n. 11-12, p.12-15, 1990).

_____. *Legislação indigenista no século XIX*. São Paulo: Edusp/Comissão Pró-Índio, 1993.

_____. Populações tradicionais e a convenção da diversidade biológica. *Revista do Instituto de Estudos Avançados*, 1999. (Also published as: Populations traditionnelles et Convention sur la Diversite Biologique: l'exemple du Bresil. *Journal d'Agriculture Traditionnelle et de Botanique Appliquee*, 1999.)

CHASE-SMITH, R. Biodiversity won't Feed our Children. Biodiveristy Conservation and Economic Development in Indigenous Amazonia. In: SEMINAR TRADITIONAL PEOPLES AND BIODIVERISTY: CONSERVATION IN LARGE TROPICAL LANDSCAPES. The Nature Conservancy, Panama, 14-17 November 1994, Mss., paper presented, 24 p.

CHAUMEIL, J.-P. *Voir, Savoir, Pouvoir. Le chamanisme chez les Yagua du Nord-Est Peruvien*. Paris: Editions de l'Ecole des Hautes Etudes en Sciences Sociales, 1983, 352 p.

CUNHA, M. C. da et al. Exploitable Knowledge Belongs to the Creators of it: a Debate. *Social Anthropology*, v. 6, n. 1, p. 109-26, 1998.

CUNNINGHAM, A. B. Indigenous Knowledge and Biodiversity: Global Commons or Regional Heritage?. *Cultural Survival Quarterly*, Summer, p. 1-4, 1991.

DAVIS, S. H. *Victims of the Miracle: Development and the Indians of Brazil*. Cambridge/New York: Cambridge Univ. Press, 1977.

GONZALES, N. We are not Conservationists. *Cultural Survival Quarterly*, Fall, p. 43-5, 1992, Interview conducted by Celina Chelala.

HECHT, S.; COCKBURN A. *The Fate of the Forest: Developers, Destroyers and Defenders of the Amazon*. London: Verso, 1989.

KAPLAN, H.; KOPISCHKE, K. Resource Use, Traditional Technology and Change Among Native Peoples of Lowland South America. In: REDFORD, K; PADOCH, C. (Eds.). *Conservation of Neotropical Forests: Working from Traditional Resource Use*. New York: Columbia Univ. Press, 1992, p. 83-107.

MENDES, C. *Fight for the Forest: Chico Mendes in his own words*. London: Latin American Bureau, 1989.

MENDES Jr., J. *Os indígenas brasileiros, seus direitos individuais e politicos*. São Paulo: Comissão Pró-Indio, 1980 [1912] (Facsimile edition).

NIJAR, G. S. *In Defense of Local Community Knowledge and Biodiversity*. Third World Network Paper, 1996, 62 p.

REDFORD, K.; STEARMAN A. M. The Ecologically Noble Savage. *Cultural Survival Quarterly*, v. 15, n. 1, p. 46-8, 1991.

_____. Forest Dwelling Native Amazonians and the Conservation of Biodiversity: Interests in Common or in Collision?. *Conservation Biology*, v. 7, n. 2, p. 248-55, 1993.

SALICK, J. Amuesha Forest Use and Management: an Integration of Indigenous Use and Natural Forest Management. In: REDFORD, K.; PADOCH, C. (Eds.). *Conservation of Neotropical Forests: Working from Traditional Resource Use*. New York: Columbia Univ. Press, 1992, p. 305-32.

SCHWARTZMAN, S. Extractive Reserves: The Rubber Tappers' Strategy for Sustainable Use of the Amazon Rainforest. In: BROWDER, J. (Ed.). *Fragile Lands of Latin America: Strategies for Sustainable Development*. Westview Press, 1989, p. 151-63.

SHOUMATOFF, A. *Murder in the Forest: the Chico Mendes Story*. London: Fourth Estate, 1991.

SPONSEL, L. The Environmental History of Amazonia: Natural and Human Disturbances, and the Ecological Transition. In: STEEN, H. K.; TUCKER, R. P. (Eds.). *Changing Tropical Forests*. Durham: Forest History Society, 1992, p. 233-25.

Contemporary native sociodiversity in Brazil and biodiversity in the Amazon

Beto Ricardo *Instituto Socioambiental*

Brazil, which turned 500 in 2000, is neither familiar with nor aware of the immense contemporary sociodiversity of its indigenous peoples. We do not even known for certain how many peoples or native languages exist. The, as yet partial, (ac)knowledge(ment) of this diversity does not extend beyond restricted specialist academic circles.

Today for example, a student or a teacher wanting to know more about contemporary Brazilian 'indians' would encounter many difficulties. Firstly, there are few channels or spaces on the national cultural and political scene for direct indigenous expression. Usually living in 'places of difficult access', with basically oral traditions of communication, usually monolingual, and with poor knowledge of Portuguese, the different ethnic groups need to overcome a series of barriers in order to be able to express themselves freely to the non-Indian world. Their points of view are generally removed from the context in which they live, mediated by frequently unreliable interpreters and, finally, recorded as fragments and in Portuguese. For example, there are very few written records in Brazil of what might be called oral art. There is no publication that covers even a selection of the genres currently practiced, and indigenous museums, published literature or videos directed by indians are very rare[1].

Secondly, little is known about 'the indians'. Suffice it to say, for instance, that a mere half of the 210 ethnic groups mentioned in this book (out of more than a thousand estimated to have existed in this part of the world before the arrival of the Europeans[2]), and of the 170 or so native languages existing today in Brazil, have been the subject of basic ethnological and linguistic research[3], and the result has been a specialized bibliography (books and articles) that remains unpublished or only accessible in a foreign language[4].

The general public interested in knowing more about indians is faced with a cultural black hole and must be content with watered-down textbook bibliographies, often prejudiced or ill-informed[5]. For example, of the encyclopedias on the market, only one[6], of the sort sold on newsstands and aimed at elementary school students, contains entries about contemporary ethnic groups in Brazil, but even so only in the form of short four line texts. There are a handful of publications which constitute

---

1. There are some exceptions, for example: the Magüta Museum of the Ticuna, which has been functioning since 1992 in Benjamin Constant (Amazonas) or the Cultural Center of Foirn (*Federação das Organizações Indígenas do Rio Negro* – Federation of the Indigenous Organizations of Rio Negro) in São Gabriel da Cachoeira (Amazonas), inaugurated in April 1995. The books *Antes o mundo não existia: a mitologia heróica dos índios Desâna* ['Previously the world did not exist: the heroic mythology of the Desâna indians'] by Umúsin Panlõn and Tolamãn Kenhíri (Portuguese version, São Paulo: Livraria Cultura, 1980; re-published by Foirn/Unirt in 1995 in a revised and extended version as the first in the series 'Indigenous Narrators from Rio Negro') and *Torü Duü'ügü, nosso povo* ['Torü Duü'ügü, our people'] (oral narratives of two Ticuna, bilingual edition, Rio de Janeiro: Museu Nacional/SEC/MEC/SEPS/FNDE, 1985) are unique works of their genre. There are a few literary compositions by indigenous authors, in native languages, written especially for textbooks used in unofficial educational programs. Collections of myths are more frequent, but this is only one of the genres. In any case, the most complete compilations have been published abroad. There are published recordings of indigenous music, almost always fragments and also mainly published abroad. In Brazil there are a small number of exceptions, of which the most important are, in chronological order: *A arte vocal dos Suyá* ['The vocal art of the Suyá'] (Tacape, Série Etnomusicologia, São João Del Rei, 1982); *Paiter Marewá* (Memória Discos e Edições, São Paulo, 1984); *Kaapor, cantos de pássaros não morrem* ['Kaapor, birdsongs never end'] (Unicamp/MinC/Seac, 1988); *Bororo vive* ['The Bororo live'] (Museu Rondon/UFMT, Cuiabá, 1989) and the CD *Etenhiritipá, cantos da tradição Xavante* ['Etenhiritipá, songs of the Xavante tradition'] (Associação Xavante de Pimentel Barbosa e Núcleo de Cultura Indígena/SP, 1994). With respect to video, the 1980s saw some indigenous video makers appearing on the scene, among them Siã Kaxinauá from Acre, one of the few whose films have been shown in festivals in Brazil and abroad. Another highlight is the *Projeto Vídeo nas Aldeias* ['Video in the Villages project'] by the *Centro de Trabalho Indigenista* (São Paulo). Coordinated by the video maker Vincent Carelli, the project encourages cultural exchange between different indigenous peoples through the use of video, by training and assisting indigenous video makers, such as Raimundo Xontapi Gavião Parkatejê (Pará) and Kasiripinã Waiãpi (Amapá), and also by producing its own videos, the special feature of which is direct recording in native language with subtitling into Portuguese and other languages.
2. See the article *Línguas Indígenas: 500 anos de descobertas e perdas* ['Indigenous Languages: 500 years of discoveries and losses'] by Aryon Dall'Ignia Rodrigues, published in *Ciência hoje*, the scientific magazine of the SBPC [*Sociedade Brasileira pelo Progresso da Ciência* - Brazilian Society for the Advancement of Science], v. 16, n. 95, p. 20-6, Nov. 1993.
3. 'Of the 170 indigenous languages in Brazil, approximately 80 have received some kind of description, typically relating to segmental phonology or grammatical details. Less than 10% of the languages have been fully described to a good scientific standard' (cf. Moore, D. and Storto, L. *Lingüística indígena no Brasil*, Belém: MPEG, mimeogr., 1993, p.3).
4. There is no up to date assessment of the status of ethnological or linguistic research on indians in Brazil. The most recent bibliographical surveys are: A. Seeger & E. Viveiros de Castro *Pontos de vista sobre os índios brasileiros: um ensaio bibliográfico* ['Points of view about Brazilian indians: a bibliographical essay'], (Boletim informativo e bibliográfico de ciências sociais, Iuperj, no 2, 1977); Aryon Dall'Ignia Rodrigues *The Present State of the Study of the Indigenous Languages of Brazil* (1985); and the article by Moore & Storto, referred to above, to be published in the magazine *América indígena* (Mexico). It is worth mentioning a series of reference works, highly regarded by specialists in this subject, entitled *Bibliografia crítica da etnologia brasileira* [Critical Bibliography of Brazilian Ethnology] (v. I, São Paulo, 1954, and v. II, Hannover, 1968, both by Herbert Baldus, and v. III, Berlin, 1984, by Thekla Hartmann).
5. See *A questão indígena na sala de aula* ['The indigenous question in the classroom'], resources for primary and secondary school teachers, organized by Aracy Lopes da Silva (São Paulo: Brasiliense, 1987, 253 p.), which contains a critical analysis in the first part and practical guidance in the second.
6. The *Larousse Enciclopédia, Brasil A/Z*, São Paulo: Universo, 1988.

exceptions to this state of affairs[7], and the Instituto Socioambiental is currently producing an encyclopedia, *Povos Indígenas no Brasil* (Indigenous Peoples in Brazil), whose entries are gradually being made available on the Internet.

WE DON'T EVEN KNOW THEIR NAMES

The indigenous peoples who lived in what would eventually be called Brazil had unwritten languages, and still today the majority does not read or write. They were – and continue to be – 'baptized' in a written form by 'whites', even before anybody was capable of understanding their languages. Since many native population groups do not express themselves in Portuguese and have not been studied by anthropologists or linguists, and many others still live 'in isolation' and are unknown, the field is open for all kinds of semantic and orthographic mistakes, over and above changes arising out of corrections and additions based on new information.

There are considerable variations in the way names of indigenous peoples are written in Brazil. To give one example, one of the indigenous societies currently inhabiting areas in the state of Acre has its name written in at least four different ways: 'caxinuá', 'cashinaua', 'kaxinawá' and 'kaxináua'.

What we can call the 'convention on official indian names', as used by Funai, follows no rules, using terms originating from its fieldworkers and mixed with others borrowed from anthropologists. Different sets co-exist and there are constant changes. Various peoples are known by names that first appeared in the anthropological literature. The main reason for anthropologists choosing to spell a name in a given way has to do with the choice of the alphabet in which the words of the language of that people are to be written. As these languages have sounds that cannot be represented directly by the letters of the Brazilian alphabet, anthropologists are forced to resort to other letters and combinations of letters. Certain letters of our alphabet have a different sound to their counterparts in other languages. The *c* placed before the *e*, for instance, sounds like an *s* (se), and when placed before the *a* (ca), like a *k*. In other languages the *c* in this position has the sound of a *ts*. *Q* and *c* are complicated letters and for this reason anthropologists avoid using these consonants in the spelling of names of peoples. They try to use letters whose sound corresponds to the International Phonetic Alphabet used by linguists worldwide.

In addition to the reasons that lead anthropologists to use forms of spelling that are pronounced in broadly the same way in all languages (forms therefore that are unlikely to correspond to those of Brazilian Portuguese), we also need to consider the fact that some of these peoples do not live exclusively in Brazil (see in Table 1, in the 'Name' column, those marked by an asterisk). In such cases the national borders that history ended up imposing to delimit nation states in South America were superimposed on indigenous societies in such a way as to make some of them live under the political and administrative jurisdiction of two, three, or even four, different countries.

There is a 'Convention for the spelling of tribal names', approved by the Brazilian Anthropological Association (ABA) on November 14th, 1953. Some aspects of this convention are still respected by anthropologists, but many have never been. The most notable aspects are the use of an initial capital letter for tribal names, even when the name is used in the adjectival form, and the non-use of the plural form. The first provision stems from the direct influence of the rules of English grammar, according to which proper nouns are written with an initial capital (e.g. the Brazilians). The reason for not using the plural form lies in the fact that, in most cases, given that the names are words that already exist in indigenous languages, the addition of an 's' constitutes hybridization. In addition, there are the dangers that the words are already in the plural form or that the plural form is unknown in the language in question.

We may ask why we should be bound by a rule of English grammar, and this clearly has to do with the fact that the greater part of the anthropological literature of the world has been written in English. It is true that, when the name of an indigenous group appears in the adjectival form, it can be written with an initial lower-case ('the araweté language', for example). In the case of proper nouns however it is better to retain the upper-case form. Whilst it is true that these societies do not have corresponding countries (unlike the French of France, for example), it is appropriate since these proper names signify the collective unity of a society or people, and not just the sum of a set of individuals.

The style guides of newspapers have imposed rules of 'Portuguese-ness' on the spelling of the names of indigenous peoples, forbidding the use of the letters 'w', 'y' and 'k'(!), and certain combinations of letters that do not exist in Portuguese, such as 'sh'.[8] These rules are not consistent, for example always writing proper names in lower case or inflecting number but not gender. Thus if *krahô* has to be written *craô*, then *Kubitscheck* should be written *Cubicheque*, and *Geisel*, *Gáisel*.[9] Why then does the same editorial manual which recommends the spellings ianomâmi and the ianomâmis veto the gender inflection when the word is

---

7. A general classic, still available, is *Índios do Brasil* ['Indians of Brazil'], by the anthropologist Julio Cesar Melatti (7th ed., São Paulo/Brasilia: Hucitec/Editora da UnB, 1993, 220 p.). For the past, see Curt Nimuendajú's impressive *Mapa etno-histórico* ['Ethno-historical map'], (Rio de Janeiro: IBGE, 1981, 97 p. + map), the compilation *História dos índios do Brasil* ['History of the indians of Brazil'], organized by Manuela Carneiro da Cunha (São Paulo: Companhia das Letras/SMCSP, 1992, 611 p.), and another classic, *Os índios e a civilização* ['Indians and civilization'] by Darcy Ribeiro (Petrópolis: Vozes, 1982, 509 p.), which specifically deals with relations between indians and non-indians in Brazil in the first half of the twentieth century. For a deeper dive into the universe of a specific indigenous population, see *Araweté, o povo do Ipixuna* ['Aaweté, the people of Ipixuna'] by Eduardo Viveiros de Castro (São Paulo: CEDI, 1992, 192 p.), a version for the general public of a full length academic monograph, as well as the video documentary *Araweté* by Murilo Santos (CEDI, VHS, 1992, 28'). For a wide-ranging contemporary survey of the various regional situations facing indigenous peoples and their relations with the national and international scene, see *Aconteceu - especial: povos indígenas no Brasil* (a series published since 1980 by CEDI, São Paulo), especially the volume covering the period from 1987 to 1990 (592 p., with photos, maps, figures, news and analytical articles), and the volumes published by the Instituto Socioambiental covering the periods from 1991 to 1995 and 1996 to 2000. See also *A temática indígena na escola: Novos subsídios para professores de 1º e 2º graus* ['The indigenous issue in school: new resources for primary and secondary teachers'], by Aracy Lopes da Silva and Luís Donisete B. Grupione (eds.), Brasilia: MEC/MARI/Unesco, 1995, 575 p. Literature for children also includes some good books, such as those by Ciça Fittipaldi and Rubens Matuck.
8. The *Manual de redação e estilo* [Editorial and Style Manual] of *O Estado de São Paulo* states that 'the names of indigenous tribes will have singular and plural forms, and will be adapted to the Portuguese language and written in lower-case', and 'as adjectives, they will only have the plural form, but not the feminine form' (São Paulo, 1990, entry 'índio', p. 185). The *Novo manual de redação* [New Editorial Manual] of the *Folha de São Paulo* (entry 'indígena/índio', p. 81), only rules that the names of indigenous tribes must be inflected, and through the examples it offers, agrees with the previous rules.
9. *Krahô* is an indigenous group, Kubitschek and Geisel were presidents of Brazil (1956 to 1961 and 1974 to 1979, respectively). (Editor's note)

used as an adjective ('as mulheres ianomâmis' – the ianomâmi women), leading to a halfway Portuguese-ness?

There are various aspects of this semantic confusion, that is to say on the significance of the names of ethnic groups, that need to be considered. Members of nation states, like us, think that each society should have its own name. This is as false a premise as supposing that each society should have a chief. A large number of the names used, today as in the past, to identify indigenous peoples in Brazil are not self-denominations. Many were given by other groups, often enemies and, for this reason, are charged with pejorative connotations. This is the case, for example, with the well-known *Kayapó*, a generic designation given to them by the Tupi-speaking groups with whom they warred until recently, and which means 'similar to monkeys'. Other names were given by sertanistas (indian agency fieldworkers) belonging to the old SPI (*Serviço de Proteção aos Índios*) or to Funai (*Fundação Nacional do Índio*), often straight after the first contacts made by the so-called 'expedições de atração'.[10]

In such cases, where there is no knowledge of the language, mistakes are inevitable and certain peoples end up being known by names that are given to them for totally random reasons. One such case is that of the Araweté, a Tupi-speaking group living in the middle Xingu region in the state of Pará, who were given this name for the first time by a Funai sertanista, who considered he could understand their language, immediately following the 'first contact' in the mid-1970s. Thus the name, coined for the first time by a federal employee in an administrative report, ended up as the official public identity of this people, and was later incorporated into the name of an area of land officially granted to them in 1992 as the Araweté Indigenous Area of the Igarapé Ipixuna. But an anthropologist who studied the Araweté a few years later and who learned their language found that the members of this people did not originally use a noun to denominate themselves, but rather, when referring to the group to which they belonged, used only the word *bïdé*, a pronoun that means 'we, the humans'.[11]

At these moments of first contact and of tenuous communication with 'unknown tribes', some came to be called by the name of individual members or of sub-groups. There are also cases of names imposed in Portuguese, such as the *Beiço de Pau* ('wooden lip' used to refer to the *Tapayúna* in Mato Grosso) or the *Cinta-Larga* ('wide belt') of Rondônia, so called by Funai sertanistas because they wore wide belts made of bark when they were contacted at the end of the 1960s.

'Attracting and pacifying' indians, the mantra of the indian policy of the Brazilian State, and arbitrarily imposing names and leaders, is historically linked to colonial practices of social control: spatial concentration of the population (with the consequent spread of diseases and post-contact depopulation); feeble and paternalistic systems of social assistance; territorial confinement; and exploitation of available natural resources. All of this took place in the name of the 'integration of indians into national society'. To the contrary, recognizing and respecting their specific identities, learning their languages, and understanding their traditional forms of social organization, of occupation of the land and of their use of natural resources is linked to diplomatic gestures of cultural exchange and respect for special collective rights.[12]

Despite all these reservations, it has been possible to prepare a list containing the basic information available about existing indigenous groups in Brazil. The list is contained in Table 1 on the following pages. The spelling of the names in the first column follows the practice used by CEDI's *Programa Povos Indígenas no Brasil*.[13] The column 'other names or spellings' contains only those variations currently in use, which does not by any means exhaust the possibilities. This list reflects current practices among people (anthropologists, linguists, missionaries, indigenistas, etc.) and institutions working with Indians, members of the program's network of collaborators. It has makes no claim, therefore, to any normative value. The third column shows the Brazilian states where the ethnic groups are located and, where appropriate, the neighboring countries.

This list, clearly incomplete, is above all subject to constant revision in the light of new and better information, and of the fact that Brazil is a country in formation in which ethnic groups considered extinct emerge and reconstruct their identities[14], and others, still 'isolated', will appear on the scene in the future.[15] Consequently, the trend in the near future will be one of growth both in the number of population groups and of the overall population. However, the population of some individual groups may decline (as is currently the case with the Yanomani, for instance), and the spectrum of sociodiversity may suffer irreparable losses as a result of the historically non-viable status of some contemporary native micro-societies.

THE TOTAL POPULATION, GROWING

As far as demography is concerned, once again what we know about the present situation of indians in Brazil is very little. The demographic data shown in the table are somewhat heterogeneous as regards their origin, date and methods of collection. Pulling them together involved assembling a jigsaw puzzle, finding scattered information, much of which is the result of estimates and not of direct counting. Even when the figures are the result of direct counting, census takers will rarely have mastered

---

10. Official SPI or Funai expeditions to contact 'uncontacted' indigenous groups. (Editor's note).
11. See E. Viveiros de Castro, *Araweté, o povo do Ipixuna*. São Paulo: CEDI, 1992
12. Regarding the special collective rights of indians, see Social Order chapter VIII in the Federal Constitution of Brazil (1988) and the draft *Estatuto das sociedades indígenas* [Statute of indigenous societies] being considered by the National Congress.
13. CEDI (*Centro Ecumênico de Documentação e Informação* - Ecumenical Documentation and Information Center) was a private non-profit organization, based in São Paulo, which in the 1970s began collecting, organizing, editing and publishing information and analysis on the current situation of indians in Brazil. After the winding-up of CEDI in 1995, the *Programa Povos Indígenas no Brasil* [Indigenous Peoples in Brazil Program] became part of the Instituto Socioambiental, a new NGO also based in São Paulo and with offices in Brasília and São Gabriel da Cachoeira (Amazonas).
14. On the question of the emergence of native identity see, for example, the *Atlas das Terras Indígenas do Nordeste* [Atlas of Indigenous Lands in the Northeast], Rio de Janeiro: PETI/Museu Nacional, December 1993.
15. Today there are indications of the existence of 54 indigenous groups with no regular or known contact with the national society, all of them in the Amazon region. These indications derive from references in technical reports by staff of Funai, by missionaries or by NGO fieldworkers, from remarks made by other Indians and/or local populations, or as a result of direct observation of indian settlements and clearings sighted from the air. Funai acknowledges only 12. In the publication *Terras indígenas no Brasil* (CEDI/PETI, 1990), the 54 indications are listed, with their approximate location: 31 are located in indigenous lands that have already been demarcated or are to some extent officially recognized by the federal government.

TABLE 1 - LIST OF INDIGENOUS PEOPLE IN PRESENT-DAY BRAZIL
(SOURCE: DATA COLLECTION OF THE INDIGENOUS PEOPLES IN BRAZIL PROGRAM OF ISA, AUG/2003)

	Name	Other names or spelling	Language group / Language	State (Brazil) / neighboring countries	Population** (census /estimate)	Year
1	Aikanã	Aikaná, Massaká, Tubarão, Cassupá, Corumbiara	Aikanã	Rondônia	264	1995
2	Ajuru		Tupari	Rondônia	77	2001
3	Akunsu	Akunt'su	?	Rondônia	7	1998
4	Amanayé	Amanaié	Tupi-Guarani	Pará	192	2001
5	Amondawa		Tupi-Guarani	Rondônia	83	2003
6	Anambé		Tupi-Guarani	Pará	132	2000
7	Aparai	Apalai	Karíb	Pará	415	1998
8	Apiaká	Apiacá	Tupi-Guarani	Mato Grosso	192	2001
9	Apinayé	Apinajé, Apinaié	Jê	Tocantins	990	1999
10	Apolima Arara		Portuguese	Acre	?	2002
11	Apurinã		Aruák	Amazonas	2,779	1999
12	Aranã		Portuguese	Minas Gerais	?	2000
13	Arapaso	Arapaço	Tukano	Amazonas	328	2001
14	Arara	Ukarãgmã, Ukarammã	Karíb	Pará	195	1998
15	Arara	Shawanauá	Pano	Acre	200	1999
16	Arara do Aripuanã	Arara do Beiradão	?	Mato Grosso	150	1994
17	Araweté	Arauetê	Tupi-Guarani	Pará	278	2000
18	Arikapu	Aricapu	Jaboti	Rondônia	19	2001
19	Aruá		Mondé	Rondônia	58	2001
20	Ashaninka*	Kampa	Aruák	Acre	813	1999
				Peru	(55,000)	1993
21	Asurini do Tocantins	Akuáwa	Tupi-Guarani	Pará	303	2002
22	Asurini do Xingu	Awaeté	Tupi-Guarani	Pará	106	2001
23	Atikum	Aticum	Portuguese	Pernambuco	2,743	1999
24	Avá-Canoeiro		Tupi-Guarani	Tocantins/Goiás	16	2000
25	Aweti	Aueti	Aweti	Mato Grosso	138	2002
26	Bakairi	Kurâ, Bacairi	Karíb	Mato Grosso	950	1999
27	Banawa Yafi	Banawa	Arawá	Amazonas	215	1999
28	Baniwa*	Baniua, Baniva, Walimanai, Wakuenai	Aruák	Amazonas	5,141	2002
				Colombia	6,790	2000
				Venezuela	3,236	2000
29	Bará	Waípinõmakã	Tukano	Amazonas	39	2001
				Colombia	296	1988
30	Barasana*	Hanera	Tukano	Amazonas	61	2001
				Colombia	939	1988
31	Baré		Nheengatu	Amazonas	2,790	1998
				Venezuela	(1,210)	1992
32	Bororo	Boe	Bororo	Mato Grosso	1,024	1997
33	Chamacoco*		Samuko	Mato Grosso do Sul	40	1994
				Paraguay	(908)	1992
34	Chiquitano	Chiquito	Chiquito	Mato Grosso	2,000	2000
				Bolivia	(40,000)	2000
35	Cinta Larga	Matétamãe	Mondé	Mato Grosso / Rondônia	1,032	2001
36	Deni		Arawá	Amazonas	672	2000
37	Desana*	Desano, Dessano, Wira, Umukomasã	Tukano	Amazonas	1,531	2001
				Colombia	(2,036)	1998
38	Enawenê-Nawê	Salumã	Aruák	Mato Grosso	320	2000
39	Ewarhuyana			Pará	12	2001
40	Fulni-ô		Yatê	Pernambuco	2,930	1999
41	Galibi*	Galibi do Oiapoque	Karíb and creoulo language, patois	Amapá	28	1993
				French Guyana	(2,000)	1992
42	Galibi Marworno	Galibi do Uaçá, Aruã, Uaçauara, Mum Uaçá	Kheoul (creoulo language, patois)	Amapá	1,764	2000
43	Gavião	Digüt	Mondé	Rondônia	436	2000
44	Gavião	Parkatejê, Gavião do Mãe Maria	Timbira Oriental	Pará	338	1998
45	Gavião	Pukobiê, Pykopjê, Gavião do MA	Jê	Maranhão	250	1998
46	Guajá	Awá, Avá	Tupi-Guarani	Maranhão	280	1998

continues

	Name	Other names or spelling	Language group / Language	State (Brazil) / neighboring countries	Population** (census /estimate)	Year
47	Guajajara	Tenethehara	Tupi-Guarani	Maranhão	13,100	2000
48	Guarani *		Tupi-Guarani	Mato Grosso do Sul / São Paulo / Rio de Janeiro /Paraná / Espírito Santo / Santa Catarina / Rio Grande do Sul	35.000	1998
	Kaiowá	Pãi Tavyterã	Tupi-Guarani	Mato Grosso do Sul, Paraguay	(25,000) Paraguay	1995
	Ñandeva	Avakatueté, Chiripá	Tupi-Guarani	Mato Grosso do Sul / São Paulo / Paraná / Paraguay		
	M'bya		Tupi-Guarani	São Paulo / Rio de Janeiro / Espírito Santo / Paraná / Santa Catarina / Rio Grande do Sul/ Argentina/Paraguay	In Brazil, 2.640	1997
49	Guató		Guató	Mato Grosso do Sul	372	1999
50	Hyskariana	Hiskariana		Pará / Roraima	?	?
51	Ikpeng	Txikão	Karíb	Mato Grosso	319	2002
52	Ingarikó*	Ingaricó	Karíb	Roraima	675	1997
		Akawaio, Kapon		Guyana	(4,000)	1990
				Venezuela	(728)	1992
53	Iranxe	Irantxe	Iranxe	Mato Grosso	326	2000
54	Jabuti	Jeoromitxi	Jaboti	Rondônia	123	2001
55	Jamamadi	Yamamadi, Jeoromitxi, Kapaná, Kapinamari, Kanamanti	Arawá	Amazonas	800	2000
56	Jarawara	Jarauara	Arawá	Amazonas	160	2000
57	Javaé	Karajá (biggest unit in which it is included), Itya Mahãdu	Karajá	Tocantins	919	2000
58	Jiahui	Djahui, Diarroi, Kagwahiva	Tupi-Guarani	Amazonas	50	2000
59	Jiripancó	Jeripancó	Portuguese	Alagoas	1,500	1999
60	Juma	Yuma	Tupi-Guarani	Amazonas	7	2000
61	Kaapor	Urubu-Kaapor, Ka'apor, Kaaporté	Tupi-Guarani	Maranhão	800	1998
62	Kadiweu	Caduveo, Cadiuéu, Ejiwaijigi	Guaikuru	Mato Grosso do Sul	1,592	1998
63	Kaiabi	Caiabi, Kayabi	Tupi-Guarani	Mato Grosso / Pará	1,000	1999
64	Kaimbé	Caimbé	Portuguese	Bahia	1,270	2001
65	Kaingang	Caingangue	Jê	São Paulo / Paraná / Santa Catarina / Rio Grande do Sul	25,000	2000
66	Kaixana	Caixana	Portuguese	Amazonas	224	1997
67	Kalabaça			Ceará	?	
68	Kalankó			Alagoas	230	1999
69	Kalapalo	Calapalo	Karíb	Mato Grosso	417	2002
70	Kamaiurá	Camaiurá	Tupi-Guarani	Mato Grosso	355	2002
71	Kamba	Camba	?	Mato Grosso do Sul	?	
72	Kambeba	Cambeba, Omágua	Tupi-Guarani	Amazonas	156	2000
73	Kambiwá	Cambiuá	Portuguese	Pernambuco	1,578	1999
74	Kanamari	Tüküná, Canamari	Katukina	Amazonas	1,327	1999
75	Kanela Apaniekra	Canela, Timbira	Jê	Maranhão	458	2000
76	Kanela Rankokamekra	Canela, Timbira	Jê	Maranhão	1,337	2001
77	Kanindé		Portuguese	Ceará	?	
78	Kanoê	Canoê, Kapinaxã	Kanoê	Rondônia	95	2002
79	Kantaruré	Cantaruré	Portuguese	Bahia	353	2003
80	Kapinawá	Capinauá	Portuguese	Pernambuco	422	1999
81	Karajá	Carajá, Iny	Karajá	Mato Grosso / Tocantins / Pará	2,500	1999
82	Karapanã*	Carapanã, Muteamasa, Ukopinõpõna	Tukano	Amazonas	42	2001
				Colombia	(412)	1988
83	Karapotó	Carapotó	Portuguese	Alagoas	796	1999
84	Karipuna	Caripuna	Tupi-Guarani	Rondônia	21	2001

continues

	Name	Other names or spelling	Language group / Language	State (Brazil) / neighboring countries	Population** (census /estimate)	Year
85	Karipuna do Amapá	Caripuna	French Creoulo	Amapá	1,708	2000
86	Kariri	Cariri	Portuguese	Ceará	?	
87	Kariri-Xocó	Cariri-Chocó	Portuguese	Alagoas	1,500	1999
88	Karitiana	Caritiana	Arikem	Rondônia	206	2001
89	Karo	Arara	Ramarama	Rondônia	184	2000
90	Karuazu		Portuguese	Alagoas	?	
91	Katukina	Tüküná	Katukina	Amazonas	289	2000
92	Katukina		Pano	Acre / Amazonas	318	1998
93	Katxuyana		Karíb	Pará	69	1998
94	Kaxarari	Caxarari	Pano	Amazonas / Rondônia	269	2001
95	Kaxinawá*	Huni-Kuin, Cashinauá, Caxinauá	Pano	Acre	3,964	1999
				Peru	1,400	2000
96	Kaxixó		Portuguese	Minas Gerais	?	
97	Kayapó (subgroups Gorotire, A'ukre, Kikretum, Mekrãnoti, Kuben-Kran-Ken, Kokraimoro, Metuktire, Xikrin and Kararaô)	Mebengokre (self-denominated), Caiapó	Jê	Mato Grosso / Pará	7,096	2003
98	Kiriri		Portuguese	Bahia	1,401	2003
99	Kocama*	Cocama	Tupi-Guarani	Amazonas	622	1989
				Peru	(10,705)	1993
				Colombia	(236)	1988
100	Korubo		Pano	Amazonas	250	2000
101	Krahô	Craô, Kraô, Timbira, Mehim	Timbira Oriental	Tocantins	1,900	1999
102	Krenak	Borun, Crenaque	Krenak	Minas Gerais	150	1997
103	Krikati	Krinkati, Timbira	Jê	Maranhão	620	2000
104	Kubeo*	Cubeo, Cobewa, Kubéwa, Pamíwa	Tukano	Amazonas	287	2001
				Colombia	(4,238)	1988
105	Kuikuro	Kuikuru	Karíb	Mato Grosso	415	2002
106	Kujubim	Kuyubi	Txapakura	Rondônia	27	2001
107	Kulina Madihá*	Culina, Madija, Madiha	Arawá	Acre / Amazonas	2,318	1999
				Peru	(300)	1993
108	Kulina Pano	Culina	Pano	Amazonas	20	1996
109	Kuripako*	Curipaco, Coripaco	Aruák	Amazonas	1,115	2002
				Colombia	?	
110	Kuruaia	Curuaia	Munduruku	Pará	115	2002
111	Kwazá	Coaiá, Koaiá	Isolated language	Rondônia	25	1998
112	Machineri	Manchineri, Yine	Aruák	Acre	459	1999
113	Macurap	Makurap	Tuparí	Rondônia	267	2001
114	Maku* (subgroups Yuhupde, Hupdá, Nadöb, Dow, Cacua and Nucak)	Macu	Maku	Amazonas	2.548	1998
				Colombia	678	1995
115	Makuna*	Macuna, Yebamasã	Tukano	Amazonas	168	2001
				Colombia	528	1988
116	Makuxi*	Macuxi, Macushi, Pemon	Karíb	Roraima	16,500	2000
				Guyana	7,500	1990
117	Manoki	Myky, Menki	Iranxe	Mato Grosso	78	2000
118	Marubo		Pano	Amazonas	1,043	2000
119	Matipu		Karíb	Mato Grosso	119	2002
120	Matis		Pano	Amazonas	239	2000
121	Matsé*	Mayoruna	Pano	Amazonas	829	2000
				Peru	(1,000)	1988
122	Maxakali	Maxacali, Monacó bm, Kumanuxú, Tikmuún	Maxakali	Minas Gerais	802	1997
123	Mehinako	Meinaku, Meinacu	Aruak	Mato Grosso	199	2002
124	Miranha	Mirãnha, Miraña	Bora	Amazonas	613	1999
				Colombia	(445)	1988
125	Mirity-Tapuya	Miriti-Tapuia, Buia-Tapuya	Tukano	Amazonas	95	1998
126	Munduruku	Mundurucu	Munduruku	Pará	7,500	1997
127	Mura		Mura	Amazonas	5,540	2000
128	Nahukuá	Nafuquá	Karib	Mato Grosso	105	2002

continues

	Name	Other names or spelling	Language group / Language	State (Brazil) / neighboring countries	Population** (census /estimate)	Year
129	Nambikwara	Anunsu, Nhambiquara	Nambikwara	Mato Grosso / Rondônia	1,145	2001
	Nambikwara do Campo	Halotesu, Kithaulu, Wakalitesu, Sawentesu				
	Nambikwara do Norte	Negarotê, Mamaindê, Latundê, Sabanê, Manduka, Tawandê				
	Nambikwara do Sul	Hahaintesu, Alantesu, Waikisu, Alaketesu, Wasusu, Sararé				
130	Naruvoto		Karib	Mato Grosso	78	2003
131	Náua		Portuguese	Acre	458	2001
132	Nukini	Nuquini	Pano	Acre	458	2001
133	Ofaié	Ofayé-Xavante	Ofaié	Mato Grosso do Sul	56	1999
134	Oro Win		Txapakura	Rondônia	50	2000
135	Paiaku	Jenipapo-Kanindé	Portuguese	Ceará	220	1999
136	Pakaa Nova	Wari (self-denomination), Pacaás Novos	Txapakura	Rondônia	1,930	1998
137	Palikur*	Aukwayene, Aukuyene Paliku'ene	Aruák	Amapá	918	2000
				French Guyana	(470)	1980
138	Panará	Krenhakarore, Krenakore, Krenakarore, Índios gigantes, Kreen-Akarore	Jê	Mato Grosso / Pará	202	2000
139	Pankararé	Pancararé	Portuguese	Bahia	1,500	2001
140	Pankararu	Pancararu	Portuguese	Pernambuco	4,146	1999
141	Pankaru	Pancaru	Portuguese	Bahia	84	1999
142	Parakanã	Paracanã, Apiterewa	Tupi-Guarani	Pará	746	1999
143	Pareci	Paresi, Haliti	Aruák	Mato Grosso	1,293	1999
144	Parintintin		Tupi-Guarani	Amazonas	156	2000
145	Patamona*	Kapon	Karíb	Roraima	50	1991
				Guyana	(5,500)	1990
146	Pataxó		Portuguese	Bahia	2,790	2001
147	Pataxó Hã-Hã-Hãe		Portuguese	Bahia	1,865	2001
148	Paumari	Palmari	Arawá	Amazonas	870	2000
149	Pipipã		Portuguese	Pernambuco	?	
150	Pirahã	Mura Pirahã	Mura	Amazonas	360	2000
151	Piratuapuia*	Piratapuia, Piratapuyo, Pira-Tapuia, Waíkana	Tukano	Amazonas	1,004	2001
				Colombia	(400)	1988
152	Pitaguari		Portuguese	Ceará	871	1999
153	Potiguara		Portuguese	Pernambuco	7,575	1999
154	Poyanawa	Poianáua	Pano	Acre	403	1999
155	Rikbaktsa	Canoeiros, Erigpaktsa	Rikbaktsa	Mato Grosso	909	2001
156	Sakurabiat	Mekens, Sakirabiap, Sakirabiar	Tupari	Rondônia	89	2001
157	Sateré-Mawé	Sataré-Maué	Mawé	Amazonas / Pará	7,134	2000
158	Shanenawa	Katukina	Pano	Acre	178	1998
159	Siriano*	Siria-Masã	Tukano	Amazonas	17	2001
				Colombia	665	1988
160	Suruí	Aikewara	Tupi-Guarani	Pará	185	1997
161	Suruí	Paíter	Mondé	Rondônia	765	2000
162	Suyá	Suiá	Jê	Mato Grosso	334	2002
163	Tabajara		Portuguese	Ceará	?	
164	Tapayuna	Beiço-de-Pau	Jê	Mato Grosso	58	1995
165	Tapeba	Tapebano, Perna-de-pau	Portuguese	Ceará	2,491	1999
166	Tapirapé	Tapi'irape	Tupi-Guarani	Mato Grosso	438	2000
167	Tapuio	Tapuia-Xavante, Tapuio	Portuguese	Goiás	235	1998
168	Tariana*	Tariano, Taliaseri	Aruák	Amazonas	1,914	2001
				Colombia	(205)	1988
169	Taurepang *	Taulipang	Karíb	Roraima	532	1998
		Pemon, Arekuna		Venezuela	20,607	1992
170	Tembé	Timbé, Tenetehara	Tupi-Guarani	Pará / Maranhão	820	1999
171	Tenharim	Kagwahiva	Tagwahiva, of the Tupi-Guarani family	Amazonas	585	2000
172	Terena		Aruák	Mato Grosso do Sul	15,795	1999

continues

	Name	Other names or spelling	Language group / Language	State (Brazil) / neighboring countries	Population** (census /estimate)	Year
173	Ticuna*	Tikuna, Tukuna, Magüta	Ticuna	Amazonas	32,613	1998
				Peru	(4,200)	1988
				Colombia	(4,535)	1988
174	Tingui Botó		Portuguese	Alagoas	350	2002
175	Tiriyó* (subgroups: Tsikuyana and Kah'yana)	Trio, Tarona, Yawi, Pianokoto	Karíb	Pará	735	1998
				Suriname	(376)	1974
176	Torá		Txapakura	Amazonas	51	1999
177	Tremembé		Portuguese	Ceará	1,511	1999
178	Truká		Portuguese	Pernambuco	1,333	1999
179	Trumai		Trumai	Mato Grosso	92	1999
180	Tsohom Djapá	Tsunhum-Djapá, Tyonhwak Dyapa, Tucano	Katukina	Amazonas	100	1985
181	Tukano*	Tucano, Ye'pâ-masa, Dasea	Tukano	Amazonas	4,604	2001
				Colombia	6,330	1988
182	Tumbalalá		Portuguese	Bahia	900	2001
183	Tupari		Tuparí	Rondônia	338	2001
184	Tupinambá		Portuguese	Bahia	?	
185	Tupiniquim		Portuguese	Espírito Santo	1,386	1997
186	Turiwara		Tupi-Guarani	Pará	60	1998
187	Tuxá		Portuguese	Bahia / Pernambuco	1,630	1999
188	Tuyuka*	Tuiuca, Dokapuara, Utapinõmakãphõnã	Tukano	Amazonas	593	2001
				Colombia	570	1988
189	Umutina	Omotina, Barbados	Bororo	Mato Grosso	124	1999
190	Uru-Eu-Wau-Wau	Urueu-Uau-Uau, Urupain	Tupi-Guarani	Rondônia	87	2003
191	Wai Wai (subgroups: Karafawyana, Xereu, Katuena and Mawayana)	Waiwai	Karíb	Roraima / Amazonas / Pará	2,020	2000
				Guyana	130	2000
192	Waiãpi*	Wayampi, Oyampi, Wayãpy, Wayãpi	Tupi-Guarani	Amapá	525	1999
				French Guyana	412	1992
193	Waimiri-Atroari	Kinã, Kinja	Karíb	Roraima / Amazonas	931	2001
194	Wanana*	Uanano, Wanano	Tukano	Amazonas	447	2001
				Colombia	1,113	1998
195	Wapixana*	Uapixana, Vapidiana, Wapisiana, Wapishana	Aruák	Roraima	6,500	2000
				Guyana	(4,000)	1990
196	Warekena*	Uarequena, Werekena	Aruák	Amazonas	491	1998
				Venezuela	(409)	1992
197	Wassu		Portuguese	Alagoas	1,447	1999
198	Wauja	Uaurá, Waurá	Waurá, of the Aruák family	Mato Grosso	321	2002
199	Wayana*	Waiana, Uaiana	Karíb	Pará	415	1999
				Suriname	(400)	1999
				French Guyana	(800)	1999
200	Witoto*	Uitoto, Huitoto	Witoto	Amazonas	?	
				Colombia	(5,939)	1988
				Peru	(2,775)	1988
201	Xakriabá	Xacriabá	Jê	Minas Gerais	6,000	2000
202	Xambioá	Karajá do Norte, Ixybiowa, Iraru mahãdu	Karajá	Tocantins	185	1999
203	Xavante	A'uwe (self-denomination) Akwe, Awen	Jê	Mato Grosso	9,602	2000
204	Xerente	Akwen (self-denomination), Akwe, Awen	Jê	Tocantins	1,814	2000
205	Xetá	Hetá	Tupi-Guarani	Paraná	8	1998
206	Xikrin	Put Karot	Kayapó, of the family Jê	Pará	1,052	2000
207	Xipaya	Shipaya	Juruna	Pará	595	2003
208	Xokleng	Shokleng, Laklanô	Jê	Santa Catarina	757	1998
209	Xokó	Xocó, Chocó	Portuguese	Sergipe	250	1987
210	Xukuru	Xucuru	Portuguese	Pernambuco	6,363	1999
211	Xukuru Kariri	Xucuru-Kariri	Portuguese	Alagoas	1,820	1996
212	Yaminawá	Jaminawá, Iaminawa, Xixinawá, Yawanawá, Bashonawá, Marinawá	Pano	Acre	618	1999
				Peru	324	1993
				Bolivia	630	1993

continues

	Name	Other names or spelling	Language group / Language	State (Brazil) / neighboring countries	Population** (census /estimate)	Year
213	Yanomami* (subgroups: Yanomam, Sanumá and Ninam)	Ianomâmi, Ianoama, Xirianá	Yanomami	Roraima / Amazonas	11,700	2000
				Venezuela	(15,193)	1992
214	Yawalapiti	Iaualapiti	Aruák	Mato Grosso	208	1999
215	Yawanawá	Iauanauá	Pano	Acre	450	1999
216	Yekuana*	Maiongong, Ye'kuana, Yekwana	Karíb	Roraima	426	2000
				Venezuela	(3,632)	1992
217	Yudjá	Juruna, Yuruna	Juruna	Pará / Mato Grosso	278	2001
218	Zo'é	Poturu	Tupi-Guarani	Pará	152	1998
219	Zoró	Pageyn	Mondé	Mato Grosso	414	2001
220	Zuruahã	Sorowaha, Suruwaha	Arawá	Amazonas	143	1995

(*) Peoples present in more than one country.
(**) Numbers in brackets refer to the indigenous population in other countries and are not included in the overall calculation of the indigenous population of Brazil. The Tupi-Guarani, Awetí, Munduruku, Mawé, Tupari, Arikem, Mondé, Ramarama and Juruna linguistic families are part of the Tupi language group. The Jê, Maxakali, Krenak, Yatê, Karajá, Ofaié, Guató, Rikbaktsa and Bororo linguistic families are part of the Macro-Jê language group.

Peoples speaking Portuguese are those who have suffered linguistic loss and/or represent cases of emerging identities. Numbers in this list are approximate as a result of problems with the census data, especially in the cases of ethnic groups occupying more than one indian land, where censuses were carried out at different times and by different bodies.

the language or understood the social organization and the spatial and seasonal dynamics of the indigenous societies. They therefore produce, to a greater or lesser degree, inconsistent information and wrong totals. Even so, the data as a whole represent the best and most up to date set of information available.[16] Data on indigenous peoples from the 1991 national census are published, without further explanations, as estimates and linked to indian lands, which does not always allow the figures to be linked to particular ethnic groups.[17] For this reason the census figures have not been taken into account in this table.

Some reservations still need to be made about the population data that appear in the table:

1) there is no information on those parts of the population of some ethnic groups who live away from their lands, for instance in urban areas such as Manaus (Amazonas), Boa Vista (Roraima), in a number of towns in Mato Grosso do Sul (where the Terena live), or the Kamba in Corumbá (Mato Grosso), or even the Pankararu who live in a shanty town in the city of São Paulo;

2) for some of the groups listed there are no population data, or the totals are underestimates, because they share, totally or partially, the same indigenous area with other groups and the census data available does not distinguish between these groups. This is the case with the Issé, Witoto, Miranha, Kaixana and Kambeba of the Méria, Miratu and Barreira da Missão indigenous areas; the Ajuru, Arikapu, Aruá, Kanoe, Jaboti, Makurap, Mequem and Columbiara of the Guaporé and Rio Branco indigenous areas; and the the Xereu, Katuena, Mawayana, Kaxuyana, Hyxkaryana, Karafawyana of the Nhamundá indigenous area;

3) there is also no information available on those cases of 'emerging' groups, such as the Kantaruré, Kariri and Pitaguari, all in the northeast, and the Kaxixó in Minas Gerais;

4) the figure does not contain the so-called 'isolated' population groups, for which, obviously, there is no population data;.

5) in the calculations, information on indigenous populations residing beyond the boundaries of Brazil was not included, although this data does appear in brackets in the table. This has the effect of distorting the classification of demographic patterns in the cases, for example, of the Kampa (99% in Peru), the Guarani (70% or more in Paraguay, Bolivia and Argentina), the Yanomami (50% in Venezuela), the Wapixana and the Makuxi (45% and 30%, respectively, in Guyana).

The data calculated from the table, with the reservations noted, allow us to say that the total indigenous population in Brazil today is approximately 300,000; this is 0.2% of the national population. The major part of indigenous population groups in Brazil, from a demographic standpoint, is formed by micro-societies. Of the 210 indigenous population groups which appear in the table, 63 have a population of less than 200 individuals. There are 46 groups with a population of between 201 and 500 individuals, and 34 of between 501 and 1,000. In other words, about 68% of all indigenous groups in Brazil have a population of less than a thousand individuals. There are 40 population groups in the range of 1,000 to 5,000, eight (the Sateré-Mawé, Potiguara, Xavante, Yanomami, Munduruku, Kayapó, Xakriabá and Wapixana) of between 5,000 and 10,000, three (the Guajajara, Terena and Makuxi) with more than 10,000 but less than 20,000, two others with rather more than 20,000 (the Kaingang and Ticuna) and only (the Guarani) with around 30,000 (in Brazil).

On the basis of the monitoring carried out by the *Programa Povos Indígenas* no Brasil/CEDI (now part of the Instituto Socioambiental) during the last 20 years, with the support of an extensive network of collaborators and the periodic publication of tables such as this, it is possible to confirm that the total indigenous population in Brazil is gradually increasing for the first time since 1500.

---

16. Once again, this is the result of the systematic collection of information carried out by Fany P. Ricardo, of the *Programa Povos Indígenas no Brasil*/CEDI, from field reports, academic monographs, Brazilian and foreign publications, and firsthand contact with members of the program's network of collaborators. Given the nature of the present publication, the extensive list of sources of the population data is omitted.
17. I am referring to the data published in chapter 14 (*Áreas Especiais*) of the *Anuário Estatístico do Brasil*, 1992, section I, IBGE (*Instituto Brasileiro de Geografia e Estatística*), p. 176-8.

Rights and lands

The Federal Constitution, which entered into force in October 1988, contains a chapter and other provisions addressing the special rights of indigenous peoples. These constitute the expression of the struggle of the indians, and of the organizations that had assisted them over the previous decade, to establish a positive – and highly symbolic – correlation between the rights of indigenous peoples and the process of re-democratization of the country.

In this period, confounding the pessimistic and catastrophic predictions of the early 1970s, the conviction grew that, far from disappearing and being relegated to the status of a transitional social category on the Brazilian historical landscape, to whom legislators should concede only temporary rights, indians were here to stay and should be treated accordingly.

In context of this new paradigm of the so-called 'indigenous question', the 1988 Constitution breaks with the tradition of assimilation and recognizes indians' rights to the lands they traditionally occupy, and the legitimacy of their taking legal action to defend and secure these rights.

Indigenous rights to land, for instance, have been safeguarded in law since the colonial legislation of the early seventeenth century. During the Republican period, the 1934 Constitution already formally guaranteed indians' inalienable rights of title to their lands. But it is the 1988 Constitution that, for the first time, devotes a special chapter to (collective) indigenous rights, enshrining and expanding the principle by which indians are the first and natural owners of the lands that they traditionally occupy, defined as 'those they have permanently inhabited, those used for productive activities, those essential to their welfare and necessary for their cultural and physical reproduction, in accordance with their uses, customs and traditions' (Article 231).

Such lands are inalienable federal property. Indians are granted original and imprescriptable rights to them, that is to say rights of permanent possession and exclusive usufruct of the riches of the soil, rivers and lakes to be found on them.

Although the rights of indians to a particular area of land is independent of any formal recognition, the same Constitution of 1988 requires the State to formally enact this recognition by means of what is commonly known as demarcation. Article 67 of the Transitory Provisions of the Constitution provides for the completion of such demarcations by October 5th, 1993. This did not happen. This official procedure for recognizing indigenous lands has however a merely declaratory function. It does not in itself constitute the indigenous right, but does have the political value of clearly and publicly defining the real extent of the indigenous title.

With the entry into force of the *Estatuto do Índio* (the Statute of the Indian (Law 6.001 of 1973)), this formal recognition of indigenous territorial rights became subject to administrative procedures, which can be changed by Executive decree.

What is currently called demarcation of indigenous lands is nothing more than the set of administrative procedures by which the federal government acknowledges the incidence of the elements described in paragraph 1 of Article 231 of the Constitution, referred to above.

In accordance with presidential Decree no. 22 (February 4th, 1991), which establishes the official demarcation procedures presently in force, demarcation of a given indian land will pass through the following stages: (1) it is initially *identificada* (identified) by a technical working group of Funai, whose report, once approved, is published in the *Diário Oficial da União* and the file is transferred to the Ministry of Justice; (2) approval by the Minister of Justice results in the issue of an order for the area's *delimitação* (delimitation), which is also published in the *Diário Oficial da União* and which contains the geographical

Table 2 - Legal status of indian lands in Brazil (Source: ISA, 25/08/1999)				
Stages	Number	%	Size (hectares)	%
Awaiting identification (2 with access restricted)	65	11.44	2,697,000	2.58
Being identified (4 with access restricted)	79	13.91	3,757,863	3.58
With use restrictions	8	1.41	696,270	0.66
Forwarded to Ministry of Justice	1	0.18	4,900	-
Approved/Funai subject to appeal	24	4.23	4,216,770	4.03
Delimited (undergoing demarcation)	50	8.80	17,697,725	16.90
Ratified	64	11.27	17,188,593	16.41
Reserved without registration	15	2.65	74,966	0.06
Registered CRI and/or SPU	262	46.13	58,384,427	55.77
Total	568	100.00	104,718,514	100.00

Table 3 - Legal status of indian lands in Brazilian Amazonia (Source: ISA, 25/08/1999)				
Stages	Number	%	Size (hectares)	%
Awaiting identification (2 with access restricted)	36	9.75	2,697,000	2.61
Being identified (4 with access restricted)	51	13.83	3,742,918	3.62
With use restriction	6	1.63	694,050	0.67
Approved/Funai subject to appeal	20	5.42	4,205,554	4.06
Delimited	32	8.67	17,566,059	16.98
Ratified	41	11.11	17,107,779	16.53
Reserved without registration	2	0.54	58	
Registered CRI and/or SPU	181	49.05	57,457,728	55.53
Total	369	100.00	103,471,146	100.00

coordinates of the area, thus making its *demarcação física* (physical demarcation) technically possible, provided resources are available; (3) once the demarcation is concluded, the area is ready to be *homologada* (ratified) by presidential decree and, finally, *registrada* (registered) with the *Serviço de Patrimônio da União* (the office of federal assets) and in the land registry (or registries) of the corresponding judicial district(s).

Tables 2 and 3 give the situation in respect of official recognition of indigenous lands in Brazil as of August 25th, 1999.

Even when demarcated, a large proportion of these lands are invaded (by loggers, prospectors, squatters and homesteaders) or claimed in the name of public interests (infrastructure services, for example) and private interests (such as applications by mining companies). In April 1998, 7,203 mining titles and applications in 126 indigenous lands were registered with the *Departamento Nacional de Produção Mineral* (National Department of Mineral Production).[18]

Even the Xingu Indigenous Park, the country's showcase indigenous area, where no doubts exist about the legitimacy of the indians' rights or the extent and physical boundaries of the area, presents a worrying picture for the future. Although the environment inside the park is fully conserved, the health of the park is threatened by the predatory model of natural resource use by large farming, ranching and lumber companies in the surrounding areas. This is a particular problem because the sources of all the rivers which form the Xingu remained outside the Park's boundaries when it was created at the beginning of the 1960s. There are already indigenous communities living in the park who need to travel beyond its borders to obtain clean drinking water.[19]

THE FUTURE

If it is true that the possibility of the physical disappearance of indians in Brazil no longer exists and that therefore we are not, as was previously feared, dealing with a 'lost cause', it is also true that the future of the Indians will depend first of all, though not entirely, on themselves. As a general rule, demographically weakened and subject to increasing pressure from the economic frontier expanding onto their lands and natural resources, indians frequently find themselves in the middle of the interplay of extremely unfavorable regional power dynamics which possible support networks (the media, support from Brazilian and foreign NGOs, legal action, community projects) will not be able to overcome in the long term.

At the moment, 40% of the country's indigenous population lives in the most populated regions of northeastern, eastern and southern Brazil, confined within 1.2% of the total of indian lands. On the other hand, 60% of the present indigenous population, living in the mid-western and northern regions (Amazonia and the cerrado), is formally entitled to 98.8% of the total indian land. History teaches us that at each stage of the advance of the expanding frontiers of national society, under specific political conditions, the State revises its calculations with respect to indian lands, imposing a pattern of increasing confinement on lands ever more reduced in size.

Will it be possible for today's indians to retain future control over their extensive and unbroken lands in the mid-western and northern regions? Or, in other words, will the Amazonia of tomorrow be the Mato Grosso do Sul of today?

Although they are not 'ecologists by nature', indians deserve historic credit for having managed their natural resources gently, causing little environmental disturbance prior to the arrival of the European conquistadors. Faced with the real, constant and usually unpunished, albeit illegal, pressures of the predatory forms of natural resource use prevailing in Amazonia today, it is also true that some indigenous populations have actively bought into such models, in the form of junior partners. This was recently and notoriously the case with the involvement of the Kayapó in Pará in the illegal extraction of gold and mahogany on their lands. On the other side of the coin are the emerging links between the resources found on indigenous lands and so-called green capitalism.

Either way, amongst the various alternatives on the table, bringing together indigenous projects and non-indigenous strategies for the sustainable use of natural resources, whether public or private, would in theory increase indians' chances of favorably reconciling in the future their possession of extensive lands with their low demography, and would contribute enormously to the conservation and sustainable use of biodiversity, particularly in Amazonia.

In the same way, it is absolutely necessary to have a clear State compensation policy which would give practical effect to constitutional rights and would strategically value native sociodiversity and its connection to biodiversity.

---

18. See 'Interesses Minerários' ['Mineral Interests'] in *Terras Indígenas na Amazônia Legal Brasileira* [Indigenous Lands in the Brazilian Legal Amazon] (ISA, 1999).
19. See the cartographic studies prepared by the Instituto Socioambiental in partnership with the indigenous communities of the Parque do Xingu between 1994 and 1995.

Traditional populations and biodiversity in Amazonia: a GIS-based bibliographical survey

Antonio Carlos Diegues *Núcleo de Apoio à Pesquisa sobre Populações Humanas e Áreas Úmidas Brasileiras*

Geraldo Andrello *Instituto Socioambiental*

Márcia Nunes *Instituto Socioambiental e Núcleo de Apoio à Pesquisa sobre Populações Humanas e Áreas Úmidas Brasileiras*

Introduction

This text provides some details of a bibliographic survey carried out by Nupaub-USP[1] of studies on the traditional knowledge of communities in the Amazon region. In addition to the bibliography below, which provides references to studies carried out in the Amazon region, a map showing their spatial distribution has also been prepared to assist the workshop on *Assessment and Identification of Priority Actions for the Conservation, Sustainable Use and Benefit Sharing of the Biodiversity of the Brazilian Amazon*. It should be noted that the survey *Biodiversity and Traditional Communities in Brazil in the context of the Convention on Biological Diversity* (1999) was also conducted by Nupaub under the auspices of Probio.[2]

We wish to emphasize that, although not fully comprehensive, this survey is the first systematic inventory of research on this topic. The mapping of these data is equally important, since it allows us to see which areas have been covered by research and, importantly, where there are significant gaps. Mapping thus serves as a tool both for evaluating the current situation and as a basis for decisions on future research to cover the large number of still unknown areas in Amazonia.

The project *Biodiversity and traditional communities in Brazil in the context of the Convention on the Biological Diversity* (1999)

The project *Biodiversity and Traditional Communities in Brazil* (1999) was conducted by Nupaub at the request of the Biodiversity Department of the Ministry of the Environment, and its objective was to compile an inventory of studies on traditional knowledge related to the natural world and biodiversity. Three thousand publications (theses, books, articles, reports), located in various databases and research institutions in different regions of Brazil were reviewed by means of keywords. Of these studies, 923 relevant to the topic were selected and analyzed on the basis of eleven variables, including types of traditional population (indigenous or non-indigenous), ecosystems, subjects and topics, traditional knowledge, traditional management system, etc.)

Of these studies, selected for their relevance, 55.6% referred to traditional non-indigenous peoples (caiçaras, jangadeiros, ribeirinhos, caboclos[3], etc.), and 44.4% to indigenous peoples. Since this is a new topic, above all in the area of human sciences, more than 85% of the studies are from the 1980s onwards. The publications which give most details on the types and areas of knowledge (botany, zoology, ichthyology, etc.) are those with an ethno-scientific focus – a new field for anthropologists, botanists, ichthyologists, and biologists and which basically came into being after the 1970s. This field of knowledge grew significantly during the 1990s, when more than 48% of the studies selected were carried out.

The Amazon region

The majority of the studies (471), representing 51% of the total, are concentrated on the Amazon region. This is followed by those focused on the coastal region (18.9%), the cerrado (savannas) (17.4%), and the caatinga (semi-arid region) (5.4%). The remainder is shared among the Pantanal, the middle-northern region, pine forests, seasonal forests, and the extreme south.

Of the studies carried out in the Amazon region relating to *indigenous populations*, the following topics are prominent: the botany of cultivated species (especially in shifting agriculture), the botany of collected species (extractive activities), pharmacology, traditional technology, ichthyology, and zoology. A significant part of these studies provide information on the traditional knowledge of the peoples studied, in particular those of the Kaiapó (51 of the 55 titles included in the Nupaub database), Yanomami (15 of 18 titles in the database), and Urubu-Kaapor (12 of 13 titles in the database). Many studies also describe forms of natural resources management. In the case of

---

1. *Núcleo de Apoio à Pesquisa sobre Populações Humanas e Áreas Úmidas Brasileiras* - USP (Support Unit for Research on Human Populations and Wetlands in Brazil, University of São Paulo).
2. *Projeto de Conservação e Utilização da Diversidade Biológica Brasileira* (Conservation and Sustainable Use of Brazilian Biological Diversity Project).
3. Caiçaras = traditional coastal communities of Rio de Janeiro, São Paulo and Paraná states; jangadeiros = raft fishing communities of northeastern Brazil; ribeirinhos = traditional riparian communities, especially in Amazonia; caboclos = rural communities of mixed European and indigenous descent. (Editor's note)

studies on the Kaiapó and Tukano, for example, more than 65% provide information about management techniques.

Of the studies on non-indigenous peoples, we find a large number devoted to the botany of collected species (extractive activities), especially among ribeirinhos, followed by technology, the botany of cultivated species, ichthyology, and pharmacology. In the studies carried out among the praieiros (seashore communities) of the coast of Pará, the most recurring theme is technology (principally that related to fishing), followed by ichthyology and the botany of collected species. In the studies on quilombolas [4], the main issue is the botany of collected species, followed by the botany of cultivated species and pharmacology. In the studies on babaçueiros [5], it is the botany of collected species, followed by traditional technology and the botany of cultivated species. The theme of traditional knowledge occurs in 9 of the 18 studies on quilombolas, in 12 of the 29 on praieiros, in 54 of the 168 on ribeirinhos, and in 2 of the 7 on babaçueiros. As for descriptions of natural resource management systems, the numbers are as follows: there is information in 52 of the 168 studies on ribeirinhos; in 4 of the 18 on quilombolas; in 4 of the 29 on praieiros, and in 1 of the 7 on babaçueiros.

To sum up, the studies reviewed show that, over the course of generations, the traditional peoples of Amazonia have built up a considerable body of knowledge and practices concerning the natural world and biodiversity, and that this is fundamental to their survival in the forest and on the riverbanks and lakeshores.

Preparation of the map

Of the total number of studies identified by Nupaub for Amazonia (471)[6], 302 were plotted on the map (see pages 380-381): 140 refer to indigenous peoples and 162 to non-indigenous traditional peoples (Amazonian ribeirinhos, quilombolas, praieiros, babaçueiros, etc.). It is important to emphasize that this map shows only those studies on non-indigenous peoples of high and medium relevance, and those on indigenous peoples of high relevance.[7] In other words, there are various other studies that are not included in this first attempt to map scientific output about the biodiversity knowledge of traditional peoples. Any analysis made will have to take these limitations into account.

The georeferencing of the bibliographical survey was carried out using the base map "*Carta do Brasil ao Milionésimo*"; scale 1:3,500,000; sinusoidal projection, covering the area of the Legal Amazon as defined by IBGE.[8]

The number of studies associated with each location is represented by five color classes (1; 2-3; 4-9; 10-19; 11-29). These locations are represented by two spatial categories:

- Dots: represent the exact location of the research sites by means of geographic coordinates or direct citation of the municipalities or smaller administrative units; they are represented on the map by squares.
- Polygons:
    a) plotted on the map in accordance with the description or delimitation given in the studies.
    b) conservation areas and indian lands are represented in their overall extents, as there were no exact descriptions of the locations of the research areas.

Extracting information from the map

The map reveals the high concentration of research on non-indigenous peoples carried out in the Tocantins estuary region, the Marajó bay area and the adjacent coastal zone. This concentration is due to the presence of important research institutions based in Belém – the *Universidade Federal do Pará* (UFPA, Federal University of Pará), the *Museu Paraense Emílio Goeldi* (MPEG, the Emílio Goeldi Museum of Pará), and the *Núcleo de Alto Estudos da Amazônia* (NAEA, Institute of Advanced Studies of Amazonia) – which maintain a tradition of many decades of research on local populations. The same situation occurs, to a smaller degree, in the area surrounding Manaus, as a result of the research undertaken by the *Instituto Nacional de Pesquisas da Amazônia* (INPA, National Amazon Research Institute), which is located there.

On the other hand, there are enormous gaps throughout practically the entire Amazon region. However, over the last few years we can see the emergence of studies of populations living inside conservation areas (such as the Alto Juruá extractive reserve (ref. 1028), the Chico Mendes extractive reserve (ref. 1037), the Mamirauá sustainable development reserve (refs. 817 and 904), the Tapajós national forest (refs. 176, 190, 647, and 824), the Jaú national park (refs. 1, 297, 298, 299, 237, and 1029), the Rio Trombetas biological reserve (ref. 19), the Maraca-Jipioca biological station (ref. 82), the Marajó Archipelago environmental protection area (refs. 103, 144, 251, 252, and 335), the right bank of the Rio Negro (refs. 181 and 315), the Reetrâncias Maranheses (refs. 697, 95, and 48), and the Baixada Maranhense (refs. 620 and 995). In other words, research has been carried out in at least 10 of the 154 conservation areas currently existing in the Amazon region (both federal and state conservation areas, fully protected or sustainable use). The recent nature of these studies demonstrates the emergence of resident populations in conservation areas as a topic for research. As far as indigenous peoples are concerned, we have found studies in 50 of the 369 indian lands (TI) in the Amazon region. If we had

---

4. Quilombolas = members of communities of descendents of escaped slaves (quilombos). (Editor's note)
5. Babaçueiros = collectors of the nuts of the babaçu palm (*Orbignya martiana* and *O. oleifera*). (Editor's note)
6. The studies were classified according to their relevance (high/medium/low) in terms of the level of detail they provide about communities' traditional knowledge and management of biodiversity. Of the 471 studies, 264 deal with indigenous peoples and 207 with non-indigenous peoples.
7. This decision was taken because of the limited time available for the preparation of the map.
8. The first step was to locate the studies on the base map and identify them by means of codes (cod_pub) related to each publication, in accordance with the nomenclature of the textual database created by Nupaub as a complement to the bibliographical survey. Three distinct situations occurred with regard to the bibliographical survey: areas with an occurrence of one study; areas with the occurrence of more than one study (e.g. Belém – 6 studies; codes: 9, 700, 701, 716, 808, 1021); studies in more than one area (e.g. Prance, Ghillean T. - "An ethnobotanical comparison of four tribes of Amazonian Indians". In: Acta Amazônica, 2(2), s/d: 7-27; this research was carried out in four different areas, all of them georeferenced using the same code: 837).

also included those studies considered to be of medium and low relevance, we would certainly have arrived at a much higher number. To sum up, the need for new research is clear, in the case both of conservation areas with resident populations and of the large number of indian areas that have not yet been studied.

Among other things, new research studies will assist in the search for compatibility between the establishment of conservation areas and indian lands in places of significant biodiversity and the presence of human populations. In both cases, the objective will be to understand the specific forms by which so-called traditional peoples in Amazonia will be able to make a positive contribution to and to participate in the conservation and sustainable use of biodiversity.

Preliminary Conclusions

a) Various studies analyzed during the course of the survey carried out by Nupaub (Balé 1993; Balick and Cox 1996; Anderson, May and Balick 1991; Descola 1997) suggest that species, ecosystem, and genetic diversity is not just a natural phenomenon, but is also a cultural phenomenon, in other words it is also the result of human action. According to these studies, human populations not only co-exist with the forest and know its inhabitants, but they also manage it, that is to say they manipulate its organic and non-organic components. Consequently, as Ribeiro (1990) emphasizes, the management of natural species by Amazonian peoples results in the increase of plant communities and their integration with animal species and with humans.

b) Thus, what natural scientists (botanists, biologists, ichthyologists) call biodiversity, translated into long lists of plant and animal species and viewed out of its cultural context, is different from the concept of biodiversity that is, to a large extent, materially and symbolically constructed and adopted by traditional peoples.

c) The selection of priority areas for biodiversity conservation in Amazonia should not start from the premise that human activities in this biome always pose a threat to biodiversity. While this may be true in the case of some categories of human populations and their technologies, it is not the case for many traditional populations.

d) The selection of such areas should constitute a true interdisciplinary exercise that includes both natural and social scientists, and the effective participation of traditional populations.

e) In those cases where the location of significant biodiversity coincides with the existence of traditional populations, the creation of such conservation areas should be made compatible with the presence of these human groups and their contribution to biodiversity.

Bibliography

BALÉE, W. *Footprints of the Forest: Kaápor Etnobotany, the Historical Ecology of Plant Utilization by Amazonian People*. New York: Columbia University Press, 1993.

BALICK, M.; COX, P. *Plants, People and Culture: the science of ethnobotany*. New York: Scientific American Library, 1996.

DESCOLA, P. Ecologia e cosmology. In: CASTRO, E.; PINTON, F. (Eds.). *Faces do trópico unido: conceitos e questões sobre desenvolvimento e meio ambiente*. Belém: CEJUP, 1997.

RIBEIRO, B. *Amazônia urgente: cinco séculos de história e ecologia*. Belo Horizonte: Itatiaia, 1990.

Research on the Biodiversity Knowledge of Traditional Peoples
(refer to map on p. 380-381)

001 PUBLICATION: Durigam, C. C. *Biologia extrativismo do Cipó-Titica (Heteropsis spp. - Araceae): Estudo para a avaliação dos impactos da coleta sobre a vegetação de terra firme no Parque Nacional do Jaú UA*. Manaus: INPA, 1998. p. 50.
TRADITIONAL KNOWLEDGE: No • ENVIRONMENTAL MANAGEMENT: Yes • Non-indigenous • RELEVANCE: High • SUBJECTS: Botany of cultivated species/Botany of collected species/Pharmacology/Medicine/Technology/Material culture • LOCATION: Jaú National Park • POPULATION: Other/Ribeirinhos/Caboclos/Seringueiros/Castanheiros.

004 PUBLICATION: Fearnside, P. M. Agroforestry in Brazil's Amazonian Development Policy: the Role and Limits of a Potential Use for Degraded Lands. In: Clüsener-Godt, M.; Sachs, I. *Brazilian Perspectives on Sustainable Developmente of the Amazon Region*, v. 15. Unesco Paris and The Parthenon Publishing Group, 1995. p. 125-148.
TRADITIONAL KNOWLEDGE: No • ENVIRONMENTAL MANAGEMENT: Yes • Non-indigenous • RELEVANCE: Fair • SUBJECTS: Botany of cultivated species/Botany of collected species • LOCATION: Amazon Region • POPULATION: Ribeirinhos/Caboclos/Seringueiros/Castanheiros

006 PUBLICATION: Ferreira, M. R. C. *Les plantes Medicinales a Manaus: utilisation et commercialisation*. L'Universite Pierre et Marie Curie, Laboratoire de Botanique Tropicale/Etudes Superieures Universitaires de Biologie Vegetale Tropicale, 1992. p. 81.
TRADITIONAL KNOWLEDGE: Yes • ENVIRONMENTAL MANAGEMENT: No • Non-indigenous • RELEVANCE: High • SUBJECTS: Botany of cultivated species/Botany of collected species/Pharmacology/Medicine/Technology/Material culture • LOCATION: Manaus, Amazonas • POPULATION: Ribeirinhos/Caboclos/Seringueiros/Castanheiros.

009 PUBLICATION: Figueiredo, N. Questões metodológicas na pesquisa do uso recente das plantas medicinais de folk em Belém, Estado do Pará, Brasil. *Cadernos Antropologia*, 1. Centro de Filosofia e Ciências Humanas, UFPA.
TRADITIONAL KNOWLEDGE: Yes • ENVIRONMENTAL MANAGEMENT: No • Non-indigenous • RELEVANCE: Fair • SUBJECTS: Botany of cultivated species/Botany of collected species • LOCATION: Belém • POPULATION: Ribeirinhos/Caboclos/Seringueiros/Castanheiros.

010 PUBLICATION: Fleming-Moran, M. The Folk View of Natural Causation and Disease in Brazil and Its Relation to Traditional Curing Pratices. *Bol. Mus. Paraense Emílio Goeldi*, Antropologia, v. 8, n. 1, CNPq/INPA, 1992, p. 65-156.
TRADITIONAL KNOWLEDGE: Yes • ENVIRONMENTAL MANAGEMENT: No • Non-indigenous • RELEVANCE: High • SUBJECTS: Pharmacology/Medicine • LOCATION: Agrovila Vila Roxa – Transamazonica Highway, Iriru watershed between Altamira and Brasil Novo • POPULATION: Ribeirinhos/Caboclos/Seringueiros/Castanheiros.

012 PUBLICATION: Fonseca, V. S. da. Situación de los estudios de etnobotánica y botánica económica en ecosistemas costeros de Brasil: nota preliminar. *Usos y Manejo de Recursos Vegetales, Memorias del Segundo Simposio Ecuatoriano de Etnobotánica y Botánica Económica*. Rios. Montserrat y Pedersen, Henrikb. Quito, Ecuador, Abya-Yala, 1997, p. 57-81.
> TRADITIONAL KNOWLEDGE: Yes • ENVIRONMENTAL MANAGEMENT: No • Nonindigenous • RELEVANCE: Fair • SUBJECTS: Botany of cultivated species/Botany of collected species • LOCATION: State of Pará. • POPULATION: Caiçaras/Ribeirinhos/Caboclos/Seringueiros/Castanheiros.

014 PUBLICATION: Forsberg, M. C. S. Manejo agrícola dos caboclos do Rio Xingu: um ponto de partida para a sustentação de populações em áreas degradadas na Amazônia brasileira. In: MANEJO E REABILITAÇÃO DE ÁREAS DEGRADADAS E FLORESTAS SECUNDÁRIAS NA AMAZÔNIA. *Anais...*, Santarém, Pará, Porto Rico, Brazil/Porto Rico, MAB, UNESCO, 1993. p. 93-97.
> TRADITIONAL KNOWLEDGE: Yes • ENVIRONMENTAL MANAGEMENT: Yes • Nonindigenous • RELEVANCE: High • SUBJECTS: Botany of cultivated species/Pedology • LOCATION: Arroz Cru Settlement, city of José Porfírio (3°16' S - 52° W) • POPULATION: Ribeirinhos/Caboclos/Seringueiros/Castanheiros.

019 PUBLICATION: Acevedo, R.; Castro, E. *Negros do Trombetas guardiães de matas e rios*. Belém: UFPA/NAEA, 1993, p. 261.
> TRADITIONAL KNOWLEDGE: Yes • ENVIRONMENTAL MANAGEMENT: Yes • Nonindigenous • RELEVANCE: High • SUBJECTS: Botany of cultivated species/Botany of collected species/Pharmacology/Medicine/Icthyology/Fishing techniques/Technology/Material culture • LOCATION: Upper Rio Trombetas, Erepecuru, Curimã (along these rivers, below the falls) • POPULATION: Quilombolas.

030 PUBLICATION: Amorozo, M. C. de M. Algumas notas adicionais sobre o emprego de plantas e outros produtos com fins terapêuticos pela população cabocla do Município de Barcarena, PA, Brasil. *Bol. Mus. Paraense Emílio Goeldi, Botânica*, v. 9, n. 2, MCT/CNPq, 1993, p. 249-266.
> TRADITIONAL KNOWLEDGE: Yes • ENVIRONMENTAL MANAGEMENT: No • Nonindigenous • RELEVANCE: High • SUBJECTS: Botany of cultivated species/Botany of collected species/Pharmacology/Medicine • LOCATION: Barcarena (Pará), Vila Itupanema and Vila Nova do Piry • POPULATION: Ribeirinhos/Caboclos/Seringueiros/Castanheiros.

031 PUBLICATION: Amorozo, M. C. de M.; Gély, A. Uso de plantas medicinais por caboclos do Baixo Amazonas. Barcarena, PA, Brasil. *Bol. Mus. Paraense Emílio Goeldi, Botânica*, v. 4, n. 1, MCT/CNPq, 1988, p. 47-131.
> TRADITIONAL KNOWLEDGE: Yes • ENVIRONMENTAL MANAGEMENT: Yes • Nonindigenous • RELEVANCE: High • SUBJECTS: Pharmacology/Medicine • LOCATION: Barcarena (Pará), Vila Itupanema and Vila Nova do Piry • POPULATION: Ribeirinhos/Caboclos/Seringueiros/Castanheiros.

032 PUBLICATION: Anderson, A. B. W. Extraction and Forest Management by Rural Inhabitants in the Amazon Estuary. *Alternatives to Deforestation: Steps Toward Sustainable Use of the Amazon Rain Forest*. New York: Columbia University Press, 1990, p. 65-85.
> TRADITIONAL KNOWLEDGE: No • ENVIRONMENTAL MANAGEMENT: Yes • Nonindigenous • RELEVANCE: High • SUBJECTS: Botany of cultivated species/Botany of collected species • LOCATION: Ilha das Onças • POPULATION: Ribeirinhos/Caboclos/Seringueiros/Castanheiros.

033 PUBLICATION: Anderson, A. B. W. Forest Management Patterns in the Flood Plain of the Amazon Estuary. Submitted to Conservation Biology, 25.
> TRADITIONAL KNOWLEDGE: Yes • ENVIRONMENTAL MANAGEMENT: Yes • Nonindigenous • RELEVANCE: High • SUBJECTS: Botany of cultivated species/Botany of collected species/Technology/Material culture • LOCATION: Sacará island (Boca do Tocantins), Ilha das Onças, Jubinha island (Tocantins river) • POPULATION: Ribeirinhos/Caboclos/Seringueiros/Castanheiros.

034 PUBLICATION: Anderson, A. B. W. et al. Um sistema agroflorestal na várzea do estuário amazônico (Ilha das Onças, Barcarena, Pará.). *Acta Amazônica*, supl. v.15, n. 1-2, 1985, p. 195-224.
> TRADITIONAL KNOWLEDGE: No • ENVIRONMENTAL MANAGEMENT: Yes • Nonindigenous • RELEVANCE: High • SUBJECTS: Botany of cultivated species/Botany of collected species/Technology/Material culture • LOCATION: Ilha das Onças • POPULATION: Ribeirinhos/Caboclos/Seringueiros/Castanheiros.

035 PUBLICATION: Anderson, A. B. W. Use and Management of Native Forests Dominated by Açaí Palm (*Euterpe oleracea* Mart.) in the Amazon Estuary. In: Ballick, M. J. *Economic Botany*, ed. 6, NYBG, 1988, p. 144-154.
> TRADITIONAL KNOWLEDGE: No • ENVIRONMENTAL MANAGEMENT: Yes • Nonindigenous • RELEVANCE: High • SUBJECTS: Botany of cultivated species/Botany of collected species/Technology/Material culture • LOCATION: Ilha das Onças • POPULATION: Ribeirinhos/Caboclos/Seringueiros/Castanheiros.

036 PUBLICATION: Anderson, A. B. W. Management of Native Palm Forest: A Comparison of Case Studies in Indonesia and Brazil. In: Gholz, H. L. (Ed.). *Agroforestry: Realities, Possibilities and Potencial*. Dordrecht, Netherlands, Martinus Nijhoff Publishers, 1987, p. 13.
> TRADITIONAL KNOWLEDGE: No • ENVIRONMENTAL MANAGEMENT: No • Nonindigenous • RELEVANCE: High • SUBJECTS: Botany of collected species • LOCATION: General Amazon • POPULATION: Babaçueiros.

037 PUBLICATION: Anderson, A. B. W.; Ioris, E. M. The Logic of Extraction: Resources Management and Income Generation by Extractive Producers in the Amazon Estuary. In: *Populações humanas rios e mares da Amazônia/ IV Encontro de Ciências Sociais e o Mar no Brasil*. São Paulo, Brazil, PPCAUB/USP/Museu Paraense Emílio Goeldi/UFPA, 1992, p. 238-265.
> TRADITIONAL KNOWLEDGE: Yes • ENVIRONMENTAL MANAGEMENT: Yes • Nonindigenous • RELEVANCE: High • SUBJECTS: Botany of collected species/Technology/Material culture • LOCATION: Combu island (Guamá river, near Belém) • POPULATION: Ribeirinhos/Caboclos/Seringueiros/Castanheiros.

038 PUBLICATION: Anderson, A. B. W.; Ioris, E. M. Valuing the Rain Forest: Economic Strategies by Small-Scale Forest Extractivists in the Amazon Estuary. *Human Ecology*, v. 20, n. 3, Plenum Publishing Corporation, 1992, p. 337-369.
> TRADITIONAL KNOWLEDGE: No • ENVIRONMENTAL MANAGEMENT: Yes • Nonindigenous • RELEVANCE: High • SUBJECTS: Botany of cultivated species/Botany of collected species/Technology/Material culture • LOCATION: Combu island (Guamá river, near Belém) • POPULATION: Ribeirinhos/Caboclos/Seringueiros/Castanheiros.

041 PUBLICATION: Anderson, A. B. W.; May, P. H. A palmeira de muitas vidas. *Ciência Hoje*, v. 4 n. 20, SBPC, 1985, p. 59-64.
> TRADITIONAL KNOWLEDGE: No • ENVIRONMENTAL MANAGEMENT: No • Nonindigenous • RELEVANCE: High • SUBJECTS: Botany of collected species • LOCATION: State of Maranhão • POPULATION: Babaçueiros.

048 PUBLICATION: Araújo, M. *Breve memória das comunidades de Alcântara*. São Luís, Brazil, Sioge, 1990, p. 250.
> TRADITIONAL KNOWLEDGE: No • ENVIRONMENTAL MANAGEMENT: No • Nonindigenous • RELEVANCE: High • SUBJECTS: Botany of cultivated species/Botany of collected species/Pharmacology/Medicine/Icthyology/Fishing techniques • LOCATION: Alcântara, Maranhão • POPULATION: Praieiros/Sitiantes.

055 PUBLICATION: Barthem, R.; Goulding, M. *Os bagres balizadores: ecologia, migração e conservação de peixes amazônicos*. Tefé: Sociedade Civil Mamirauá Brasília, MCT/CNPq/IPAAM, 1997, p.129.
> TRADITIONAL KNOWLEDGE: Yes • ENVIRONMENTAL MANAGEMENT: No • Nonindigenous • RELEVANCE: Fair • SUBJECTS: Icthyology/Fishing techniques techniques/Technology/Material culture • LOCATION: Amazon Region • POPULATION: Ribeirinhos/Caboclos/Seringueiros/Castanheiros.

057 PUBLICATION: Bastos, M. de N. do C. A importância das formações vegetais da restinga e do manguezal para as comunidades pesqueiras, *Bol. Mus. Paraense Emílio Goeldi*, v. 11, n. 1, MCT/CNPq, 1995, p. 41-56.
> TRADITIONAL KNOWLEDGE: Yes • ENVIRONMENTAL MANAGEMENT: No • Nonindigenous • RELEVANCE: Fair • SUBJECTS: Botany of collected species/Pharmacology/Medicine • LOCATION: Marapanim, Pará • POPULATION: Praieiros.

058 PUBLICATION: Begossi, A.; Braga, F. M. de S. Food Taboos and Folk Medicine Among Fishermen From the Tocantins River (Brazil), *Amazoniana*, v. XII, n. 1, Kiel, 1992, p.101-118.
> TRADITIONAL KNOWLEDGE: Yes • ENVIRONMENTAL MANAGEMENT: No • Non-

indigenous • RELEVANCE: High • SUBJECTS: Icthyology/Fishing techniques techniques • LOCATION: Imperatriz, Porto Franco, Tocantinópolis, Estreitos (cities on the Tocantins river) • POPULATION: Ribeirinhos/Caboclos/Seringueiros/Castanheiros.

062 PUBLICATION: Begossi, A.; Garavello, J. C. Notes on the ethnoicthyology of fishermen from the Tocantins river (Brazil), *Acta Amazonica*, v. 20, unique, 1990, p. 341-351.

TRADITIONAL KNOWLEDGE: Yes • ENVIRONMENTAL MANAGEMENT: No • Non-indigenous • RELEVANCE: High • SUBJECTS: Icthyology/Fishing techniques • LOCATION: Middle Tocantins, between the cities of Imperatriz and Estreito • POPULATION: Ribeirinhos/Caboclos/Seringueiros/Castanheiros.

073 PUBLICATION: Benatti, J. H. P. *Agro Ecológica*: um estudo das concepções jurídicas sobre os apossamentos de camponeses agroextrativistas na Amazônia. Belém: Ipam, 1996, p. 96.

TRADITIONAL KNOWLEDGE: No • ENVIRONMENTAL MANAGEMENT: Yes • Non-indigenous • RELEVANCE: Fair • SUBJECTS: Botany of cultivated species/Botany of collected species • LOCATION: Amazon Region • POPULATION: Quilombolas/Ribeirinhos/Caboclos/Seringueiros/Castanheiros.

077 PUBLICATION: Brabo, M. J. C. *Os roceiros de Muaná*. Belém: Publicações Avulsas, n. 32. CNPq/Mus. Par. Emílio Goeldi, 1979, p. 78.

TRADITIONAL KNOWLEDGE: Yes • ENVIRONMENTAL MANAGEMENT: No • Non-indigenous • RELEVANCE: Fair • SUBJECTS: Botany of cultivated species/Botany of collected species/Technology/Material culture • LOCATION: Muaná (Ilha de Marajó), Pará • POPULATION: Ribeirinhos/Caboclos/Seringueiros/Castanheiros.

078 PUBLICATION: Brabo, M. J. C. Palmiteiros de Muaná: estudo sobre o processo de produção no beneficiamento do açaizeiro, *Bol. Mus. Paraense Emílio Goeldi, Antropologia*, n. 73, MCT/CNPq, 1979, p. 129.

TRADITIONAL KNOWLEDGE: No • ENVIRONMENTAL MANAGEMENT: No • Non-indigenous • RELEVANCE: Fair • SUBJECTS: Botany of collected species/Technology/Material culture • LOCATION: Muaná (Ilha de Marajó), Pará • POPULATION: Ribeirinhos/Caboclos/Seringueiros/Castanheiros.

082 PUBLICATION: Bruck, E. C. *Estudos Iniciais de Implantação da estação Ecológica de Maracá - Jipioca - AP*. FBCN, no date, p. 91.

TRADITIONAL KNOWLEDGE: No • ENVIRONMENTAL MANAGEMENT: No • Non-indigenous • RELEVANCE: Fair • SUBJECTS: Icthyology/Fishing techniques/Zoology • LOCATION: Maracá-Jipioca Ecological Station • POPULATION: Praieiros.

084 PUBLICATION: Câmara, E. P. L.; McGrath, D. G. A viabilidade da reserva de lago como unidade de manejo sustentável dos recursos da várzea amazônica. *Bol. Mus. Paraense Emílio Goeldi, Antropologia*, v. 11, n. 1, MCT/CNPq, 1995, p. 87-132.

TRADITIONAL KNOWLEDGE: No • ENVIRONMENTAL MANAGEMENT: Yes • Non-indigenous • RELEVANCE: High • SUBJECTS: Icthyology/Fishing techniques/Technology/Material culture • LOCATION: Ituqui island (Santarém, Pará) • POPULATION: Ribeirinhos/Caboclos/Seringueiros/Castanheiros.

085 PUBLICATION: Camargo, M. T. L. de A. *Plantas medicinais e de rituais afro-brasileiros*, v. I. São Paulo: ALMED, 1988, p. 97.

TRADITIONAL KNOWLEDGE: Yes • ENVIRONMENTAL MANAGEMENT: No • Non-indigenous • RELEVANCE: Fair • SUBJECTS: Botany of cultivated species/Botany of collected species/Pharmacology/Medicine/Cosmology • LOCATION: Amazon region • POPULATION: Quilombolas.

095 PUBLICATION: Carvalho, J.

TRADITIONAL KNOWLEDGE: No • ENVIRONMENTAL MANAGEMENT: No • Non-indigenous • RELEVANCE: Fair • SUBJECTS: Botany of cultivated species/Botany of collected species/Technology/Material culture • LOCATION: Turiaçu, Maranhão • POPULATION: Ribeirinhos/Caboclos/Seringueiros/Castanheiros.

099 PUBLICATION: Castro, C. F. de A. *Biodiversidade e quintais*. Eng. Florestal, UFMG.

TRADITIONAL KNOWLEDGE: Yes • ENVIRONMENTAL MANAGEMENT: No • Non-indigenous • RELEVANCE: Fair • SUBJECTS: Botany of cultivated species/Botany of collected species/Technology/Material culture • LOCATION: Amazon region • POPULATION: Caiçaras/Ribeirinhos/Caboclos/Seringueiros/Castanheiros.

100 PUBLICATION: Diegues, A. C. S. Sustainable Development and Peoples Participation in Wetland Ecosystem Conservation in Brazil: Two Comparative Studies. In: Ghai, D.; Vivian, J, M. *Grassroots Environmental Action:* Peoples Participation in Sustainable Development. Canada, Routledge, 1992, p. 141-158.

TRADITIONAL KNOWLEDGE: No • ENVIRONMENTAL MANAGEMENT: No • Non-indigenous • RELEVANCE: Fair • SUBJECTS: Pharmacology/Medicine/Icthyology/Fishing techniques/Technology/Material culture • LOCATION: Vale do Rio Guaporé, Rondônia • POPULATION: Ribeirinhos (non-Amazonian)/Ribeirinhos/Caboclos/Seringueiros/Castanheiros.

103 PUBLICATION: Castro, F. de et al. Estratégias de obtenção de recursos na região do Lago Arari. In: POPULAÇÕES HUMANAS RIOS E MARES DA AMAZÔNIA - IV ENCONTRO DE CIÊNCIAS SOCIAIS E O MAR NO BRASIL. São Paulo: PPCAUB/UFPA, 1992, p. 142-156.

TRADITIONAL KNOWLEDGE: No • ENVIRONMENTAL MANAGEMENT: No • Non-indigenous • RELEVANCE: High • SUBJECTS: Icthyology/Fishing techniques/Zoology • LOCATION: Arari Lake (Ilha de Marajó, Pará) • POPULATION: Ribeirinhos/Caboclos/Seringueiros/Castanheiros.

131 PUBLICATION: Diegues, A. C. S. Repensando e recriando as formas de apropriação comum dos espaços e recursos naturais. In: Vieira, P. F.; Guerra, M. (Eds.). *Biodiov. Biotec. & Ecodesenvolv. – O Sol é nosso: perspectivas de ecodesenvolvimento para o Brasil*. Florianópolis: Universidade Federal de Santa Catarina, 1994, p. 69-86.

TRADITIONAL KNOWLEDGE: Yes • ENVIRONMENTAL MANAGEMENT: Yes • Non-indigenous • RELEVANCE: Fair • SUBJECTS: Botany of collected species/Technology/Material culture • LOCATION: Amazon Region • POPULATION: Caiçaras/Ribeirinhos/Caboclos/Seringueiros/Castanheiros.

140 PUBLICATION: Furtado, L. G. *Curralistas e rendeiros de Marudá pescadores do litoral do Pará. Ministério da Ciência e Technology*. Belém: Museu Paraense Emílio Goeldi/MCT/CNPq, 1987, p. 366.

TRADITIONAL KNOWLEDGE: No • ENVIRONMENTAL MANAGEMENT: Yes • Non-indigenous • RELEVANCE: High • SUBJECTS: Botany of cultivated species/Botany of collected species/Pharmacology/Medicine/Icthyology/Fishing techniques/Technology/Material culture • LOCATION: Marudá island, Marapanim (Pará) • POPULATION: Praieiros.

141 PUBLICATION: Furtado, L. G. Sem barco, como pescar? Notas de viagens pelas águas costeiras e ribeirinhas do Pará. In: Ximenes (Ed.). *Embarcações, homens e rios na Amazônia*. Belém: Editora Universitária UFPA, 1992, p. 31-51.

TRADITIONAL KNOWLEDGE: Yes • ENVIRONMENTAL MANAGEMENT: No • Non-indigenous • RELEVANCE: Fair • SUBJECTS: Technology/Material culture • LOCATION: State of Pará • POPULATION: Ribeirinhos/Caboclos/Seringueiros/Castanheiros.

142 PUBLICATION: Furtado, L. G.; Nascimento, I. H. Pescadores de linha no litoral paraense: uma contribuição aos estudos de campesinato na Amazônia. In: *Bol. Mus. Paraense Emílio Goeldi, Antropologia*, n. 82, MCT/CNPq, 1982, p. 1-49.

TRADITIONAL KNOWLEDGE: No • ENVIRONMENTAL MANAGEMENT: No • Non-indigenous • RELEVANCE: Fair • SUBJECTS: Icthyology/Fishing techniques/Technology/Material culture • LOCATION: Marapanim, Pará • POPULATION: Ribeirinhos/Caboclos/Seringueiros/Castanheiros.

143 PUBLICATION: Furtado, L. G. et al. Notas sobre uso terapêutico de plantas pela Population cabocla de Marapanim, Pará. *Bol. Mus. Paraense Emílio Goeldi, Antropologia*, n. 70, CNPq/INPA, 1978, p. 1-31.

TRADITIONAL KNOWLEDGE: Yes • ENVIRONMENTAL MANAGEMENT: No • Non-indigenous • RELEVANCE: High • SUBJECTS: Pharmacology/Medicine • LOCATION: Marapanim (Northeastern Pará) • POPULATION: Praieiros.

144 PUBLICATION: Furtado, L. G. Antropologia das sociedades marítimas, ribeirinhas e lacustres da Amazônia. In: POP. HUMANAS RIOS E MARES DA AMAZ. VI ENCONTRO DE CS. SOCIAIS E O MAR NO BRASIL. São Paulo: PPCAUB-USP/UFPA, 1992, p. 18-30.

TRADITIONAL KNOWLEDGE: No • ENVIRONMENTAL MANAGEMENT: No • Non-indigenous • RELEVANCE: Fair • SUBJECTS: Icthyology/Fishing techniques/Technology/Material culture • LOCATION: Quatipuru District, Pará; Cachoeira do Arari, Pará; Marapanim, Pará; Muaná/Pará • POPULATION: Ribeirinhos/Caboclos/Seringueiros/Castanheiros.

145 PUBLICATION: Furtado, L. G. *Pescadores do rio Amazonas*: um estudo antropológico da pesca ribeirinha numa área amazônica. Belém: Museu Paraense Emílio Goeldi, 1993, p. 486.

TRADITIONAL KNOWLEDGE: No • ENVIRONMENTAL MANAGEMENT: Yes • Non-indigenous • RELEVANCE: High • SUBJECTS: Botany of cultivated species/Botany of collected species/Icthyology/Fishing techniques • LOCATION: Óbidos (Lower Amazon) • POPULATION: Ribeirinhos/Caboclos/Seringueiros/Castanheiros.

152 PUBLICATION: Gentil, J. M. L. A juta na agricultura de várzea na área de Santarém, Médio Amazonas, *Bol. Mus. Paraense Emílio Goeldi, Antropologia,* v. 4, n. 2, SCT/CNPq/FINEP, 1988, p. 118-199.

TRADITIONAL KNOWLEDGE: No • ENVIRONMENTAL MANAGEMENT: No • Non-indigenous • RELEVANCE: Fair • SUBJECTS: Botany of cultivated species/Technology/Material culture • LOCATION: Santarém, Pará • POPULATION: Ribeirinhos/Caboclos/Seringueiros/Castanheiros.

165 PUBLICATION: Hébette, J. A agropecuária. In: _____. *Natureza, Technology e sociedades: a experiência brasileira de povoamento do trópico úmido.* Belém: UFPA/NAIA, 1998, p. 34-51. (Série Documentos do GIPCT)

TRADITIONAL KNOWLEDGE: No • ENVIRONMENTAL MANAGEMENT: No • Non-indigenous • RELEVANCE: Fair • SUBJECTS: Botany of cultivated species/Botany of collected species • LOCATION: Amazon region • POPULATION: Ribeirinhos/Caboclos/Seringueiros/Castanheiros.

168 PUBLICATION: Hiraoka, M. Mudanças nos padrões econômicos de uma Population ribeirinha do estuário do Amazônas. In: Furtado, L. G. *Povos das águas, realidades e perspectivas na Amazônia.* Belém: MCT/CNPq/Museu Goeldi, 1993, p. 133-157.

TRADITIONAL KNOWLEDGE: No • ENVIRONMENTAL MANAGEMENT: Yes • Non-indigenous • RELEVANCE: High • SUBJECTS: Botany of cultivated species/Botany of collected species/Icthyology/Fishing techniques • LOCATION: Abaetetuba island (Confluence of Tocantins and Pará rivers, Pará) • POPULATION: Fishers/Ribeirinhos/Caboclos/Seringueiros/Castanheiros.

169 PUBLICATION: Hiraoka, M.; Rodrigues, D. L. Porcos, palmeiras e ribeirinhos na várzea do estuário do Amazonas. In: Furtado, L. G. *Amazônia, desenvolvimento, sociodiversidade e qualidade de vida. Universidade e meio ambiente,* 9. Belém: Universidade Federal do Pará, 1997, p. 70-101.

TRADITIONAL KNOWLEDGE: No • ENVIRONMENTAL MANAGEMENT: Yes • Non-indigenous • RELEVANCE: High • SUBJECTS: Botany of cultivated species/Botany of collected species/Technology/Material culture/Zoology • LOCATION: Abaetetuba island (Confluence of Tocantins and Pará rivers, Pará) • POPULATION: Ribeirinhos/Caboclos/Seringueiros/Castanheiros.

170 PUBLICATION: Homma, A. K. O. *Extrativismo vegetal na Amazônia:* limites e oportunidades. Brasília: EMBRAPA/SPI/CPATU, 1993, p. 202.

TRADITIONAL KNOWLEDGE: No • ENVIRONMENTAL MANAGEMENT: No • Non-indigenous • RELEVANCE: Fair • SUBJECTS: Botany of cultivated species/Botany of collected species/Technology/Material culture • LOCATION: Amazon region • POPULATION: Ribeirinhos/Caboclos/Seringueiros/Castanheiros.

176 PUBLICATION: Imaflora. *Plano diretor e zoneamento comunitário da margem direita do Tapajós.* MMA-Ibama-Imaflora, 1996, p. 100.

TRADITIONAL KNOWLEDGE: Yes • ENVIRONMENTAL MANAGEMENT: Yes • Non-indigenous • RELEVANCE: High • SUBJECTS: Botany of cultivated species/Botany of collected species/Icthyology/Fishing techniques/Pedology • LOCATION: Tapajós National Forest (right bank of the Tapajós river) • POPULATION: Ribeirinhos/Caboclos/Seringueiros/Castanheiros.

177 PUBLICATION: Barthem, R.; Isaac, V. J. Os recursos pesqueiros da Amazônia brasileira. In: *Bol. Mus. Paraense Emílio Goeldi,* Antropologia, v. 11, n. 2, MCT/CNPq, 1995, p. 295-339.

TRADITIONAL KNOWLEDGE: No • ENVIRONMENTAL MANAGEMENT: Yes • Non-indigenous • RELEVANCE: Fair • SUBJECTS: Icthyology/Fishing techniques/Technology/Material culture • LOCATION: Amazon region • POPULATION: Ribeirinhos/Caboclos/Seringueiros/Castanheiros.

181 PUBLICATION: Jardim, M. A. G.; Stewart, P. J. Aspectos etnobotânicos e ecológicos de palmeiras no município de Novo Airão, Estado do Amazonas, Brasil. In: *Bol. Mus. Paraense Emílio Goeldi, Botânica,* v. 10, n. 1, MCT/CNPq, 1994, p. 69-76.

TRADITIONAL KNOWLEDGE: Yes • ENVIRONMENTAL MANAGEMENT: No • Non-indigenous • RELEVANCE: High • SUBJECTS: Botany of collected species • LOCATION: Novo Airão, Amazonas (2°40' S - 61°5' W) • POPULATION: Ribeirinhos/Caboclos/Seringueiros/Castanheiros.

184 PUBLICATION: Junk, W. J. Ecology of the várzea, floodplain of amazonian whitewater rivers. In: Sioli, H. *The Amazon Limnology and Landscape Ecology of a Mighty Tropical River and its Basin.* Netherlands, Dr. W. Junk Publishers, Dordrecht, Boston, 1984, p. 215-243.

TRADITIONAL KNOWLEDGE: No • ENVIRONMENTAL MANAGEMENT: No • Non-indigenous • RELEVANCE: Fair • SUBJECTS: Botany of cultivated species/Botany of collected species/Icthyology/Fishing techniques/Zoology • LOCATION: Amazon region - white-water rivers • POPULATION: Ribeirinhos/Caboclos/Seringueiros/Castanheiros.

190 PUBLICATION: Leeuwenberg, S. de M. L. R. *Treinamento para o desenvolvimento de um sistema de florestas nacionais.* FAO/Ibama, 1996.

TRADITIONAL KNOWLEDGE: No • ENVIRONMENTAL MANAGEMENT: Yes • Non-indigenous • RELEVANCE: Fair • SUBJECTS: Zoology • LOCATION: Tapajós National Forest. • POPULATION: Ribeirinhos/Caboclos/Seringueiros/Castanheiros.

191 PUBLICATION: Lescure, J. P. et al. Povos e produtos da floresta na Amazônia Central: o enfoque multidisciplinar do extrativismo. In: Vieira, P. F.; Weber, J. *Gestão de recursos naturais renováveis e desenvolvimento:* novos desafios para a pesquisa ambiental. São Paulo: Cortez, 1996, p. 433-468.

TRADITIONAL KNOWLEDGE: Yes • ENVIRONMENTAL MANAGEMENT: No • Non-indigenous • RELEVANCE: Fair • SUBJECTS: Botany of collected species • LOCATION: Amazon region • POPULATION: Ribeirinhos/Caboclos/Seringueiros/Castanheiros.

194 PUBLICATION: Jardim, M. A. G.; Lima, R. M. de S.; Santos, A. M. N. dos. Levantamento de plantas tóxicas em duas comunidades caboclas do estuário amazônico. *Bol. Mus. Paraense Emílio Goeldi, Botânica,* v.11, n. 2, MCT/CNPq, 1995, p. 255-263.

TRADITIONAL KNOWLEDGE: Yes • ENVIRONMENTAL MANAGEMENT: No • Non-indigenous • RELEVANCE: Fair • SUBJECTS: Botany of collected species • LOCATION: Combu island (Pará), Boa Vista island (Acará, Pará) • POPULATION: Ribeirinhos/Caboclos/Seringueiros/Castanheiros.

197 PUBLICATION: Lima, R. R. *Registro de introduções de plantas de cultura pré-colombiana coletadas na Amazônia brasileira.* Belém: Embrapa-CPATU, 1991, p. 210.

TRADITIONAL KNOWLEDGE: No • ENVIRONMENTAL MANAGEMENT: No • Non-indigenous • RELEVANCE: Fair • SUBJECTS: Botany of cultivated species/Botany of collected species • LOCATION: Amazon region • POPULATION: Outros/Ribeirinhos/Caboclos/Seringueiros/Castanheiros.

198 PUBLICATION: Lira, S. R. B. *Pólo oleiro-cerâmico de Abaetetuba:* expansão e crise. Belém: UFPA/NUMA/Poema/Idesp, 1998, p. 88.

TRADITIONAL KNOWLEDGE: No • ENVIRONMENTAL MANAGEMENT: No • Non-indigenous • RELEVANCE: High • SUBJECTS: Botany of cultivated species/Botany of collected species/Pharmacology/Medicine/Pedology/Technology/Material culture • LOCATION: Abaetetuba, Pará • POPULATION: Ribeirinhos/Caboclos/Seringueiros/Castanheiros.

204 PUBLICATION: Ferreira, C. A.; Machado, C. J. S. Levantamento de áreas extrativista das microbacias dos rios Cautário e São Miguel, Vale do Guaporé, Rondônia. *Relatório Socioeconômico do extrativismo da borracha no rio São Miguel e da coleta de castanha na localidade de Pedras Negras.* Porto Velho: IEF/RO, 1987, p. 70.

TRADITIONAL KNOWLEDGE: Yes • ENVIRONMENTAL MANAGEMENT: No • Non-indigenous • RELEVANCE: Fair • SUBJECTS: Botany of cultivated species/Botany of collected species/Pharmacology/Medicine/Technology/Material culture/Zoology • LOCATION: Pedras Negras vilalge, Rondônia; São Miguel river, Rondônia • POPULATION: Ribeirinhos/Caboclos/Seringueiros/Castanheiros.

206 PUBLICATION: Magalhães, S. B. Passados uns tempos... In: POPULAÇÕES HUMANAS RIOS E MARES DA AMAZÔNIA. IV ENCONTRO DE CIÊNCIAS SOCIAIS E O MAR NO BRASIL. São Paulo: PPCAUB/UFPA, 1990, p. 205-220.

TRADITIONAL KNOWLEDGE: Yes • ENVIRONMENTAL MANAGEMENT: No • Non-indigenous • RELEVANCE: Fair • SUBJECTS: Botany of cultivated species/Technology/Material culture • LOCATION: Moju, Pará • POPULATION: Ribeirinhos/Caboclos/Seringueiros/Castanheiros.

207 PUBLICATION: Magalhães, S. B. – O desencantamento da beira: reflexões sobre a transferência compulsória provocada pela Usina

Hidrelétrica de Tucuruí. *Energia na Amazônia*. vol. II. Magalhães, S. B.; Britto, R. de C.; Castro, E. R., Belém, Brasil, Museu Paraense. Emílio Goeldi/UFPA/Associação de Univers. Amaz., 1996, 697-746.

TRADITIONAL KNOWLEDGE: Yes • ENVIRONMENTAL MANAGEMENT: No • Non-indigenous • RELEVANCE: Fair • SUBJECTS: Botany of cultivated species/Technology/Material culture • LOCATION: Moju, Pará • POPULATION: Ribeirinhos/Caboclos/Seringueiros/Castanheiros.

208 PUBLICATION: Magee, P. *People, Forests and Rivers*: Development in the Tocantins River, Brazil.

TRADITIONAL KNOWLEDGE: No • ENVIRONMENTAL MANAGEMENT: No • Non-indigenous • RELEVANCE: Fair • SUBJECTS: Botany of collected species/Icthyology/Fishing techniques/Technology/Material culture • LOCATION: Tocantins river (Paruru island) • POPULATION: Ribeirinhos/Caboclos/Seringueiros/Castanheiros.

210 PUBLICATION: Maneschy, M. C. A arte do pescador artesanal. *Bol. Mus. Paraense Emílio Goeldi, Antropologia*, v. 6, n. 1, MCT/CNPq, 1990, p. 95-105.

TRADITIONAL KNOWLEDGE: No • ENVIRONMENTAL MANAGEMENT: No • Non-indigenous • RELEVANCE: High • SUBJECTS: Astronomy/Icthyology/Fishing techniques/Technology/Material culture • LOCATION: Bragança (Ajuruteua village), Pará • POPULATION: Praieiros.

212 PUBLICATION: Maneschy, M. C. *Ajurutema, uma comunidade pesqueira ameaçada*. Belém: UFPACFCH, 1993, p.167.

TRADITIONAL KNOWLEDGE: No • ENVIRONMENTAL MANAGEMENT: No • Non-indigenous • RELEVANCE: Fair • SUBJECTS: Icthyology/Fishing techniques/Technology/Material culture • LOCATION: Bragança (Ajuruteua village), Pará • POPULATION: Praieiros.

213 PUBLICATION: Maneschy, M. C. Pescadores nos manguezais: estratégias técnicas e relações sociais de produção na captura de caranguejo. In: Furtado, L. G. et al. *Povos das águas, realidades e perspectivas na Amazônia*. Belém: MCT/CNPq/, 1993, p. 19-61.

TRADITIONAL KNOWLEDGE: No • ENVIRONMENTAL MANAGEMENT: Yes • Non-indigenous • RELEVANCE: Fair • SUBJECTS: Zoology • LOCATION: São Caetano de Odivelas, Pará • POPULATION: Fishers.

216 PUBLICATION: Marin, R. E. A. *Nascidos no Curiaú*: relatório de identificação apresentado à Fundação Cultural Palmares. Belém: NAEA/UFPA, 1997, p. 84.

TRADITIONAL KNOWLEDGE: Yes • ENVIRONMENTAL MANAGEMENT: No • Non-indigenous • RELEVANCE: Fair • SUBJECTS: Botany of cultivated species/Botany of collected species/Zoology • LOCATION: Macapá, Amapá • POPULATION: Quilombolas.

220 PUBLICATION: Matos, G. C. G. *Atividades corporais:* uma estratégia de adaptação Biocultural numa comunidade rural do Amazonas. Unicamp, Faculdade de Educação Física, 1996, p. 144.

TRADITIONAL KNOWLEDGE: Yes • ENVIRONMENTAL MANAGEMENT: No • Non-indigenous • RELEVANCE: High • SUBJECTS: Hidrology/Technology/Material culture/Zoology • LOCATION: Amazon region • POPULATION: Ribeirinhos/Caboclos/Seringueiros/Castanheiros.

221 PUBLICATION: Maués, R. H. *A ilha encantada:* Medicine e xamanismo numa comunidade de pescadores. Belém: UFPA, 1990, p. 271.

TRADITIONAL KNOWLEDGE: No • ENVIRONMENTAL MANAGEMENT: No • Non-indigenous • RELEVANCE: High • SUBJECTS: Astronomy/Botany of cultivated species/Botany of collected species • LOCATION: Vigia (Povoado de Itapúa), Pará • POPULATION: Praieiros.

222 PUBLICATION: Maué, M. A. M.; Maués, R. H. *O folclore a alimentação:* tabus alimentares da Amazônia: um estudo de caso numa Population de pescadores do litoral paraense. Belém: UFPA, 1980, p. 15-109.

TRADITIONAL KNOWLEDGE: Yes • ENVIRONMENTAL MANAGEMENT: No • Non-indigenous • RELEVANCE: Fair • SUBJECTS: Botany of collected species/Pharmacology/Medicine • LOCATION: Vigia, Pará • POPULATION: Praieiros.

223 PUBLICATION: Maué, M. A. M.; Maués, R. H. Pesca e agricultura na Amazônia: a integração de uma comunidade rural ao modo de produção capitalista. In: *Bol. Mus. Paraense Emílio Goeldi, Antropologia*, v. 6, n. 1, MCT/CNPq, 1990, p. 29-40.

TRADITIONAL KNOWLEDGE: Yes • ENVIRONMENTAL MANAGEMENT: No • Non-indigenous • RELEVANCE: High • SUBJECTS: Botany of cultivated species/Icthyology/Fishing techniques • LOCATION: Vigia (Povoado de Itapuá), Pará • POPULATION: Praieiros.

224 PUBLICATION: Anderson, A. B. W. et al. Babassu palm in the agroforestry Brazil's mid-North region. *Agroforestry Systems*, 3, Dr. W. Junk e Martinus Nijhoff Publishers, 1985, p. 275-295.

TRADITIONAL KNOWLEDGE: Yes • ENVIRONMENTAL MANAGEMENT: Yes • Non-indigenous • RELEVANCE: High • SUBJECTS: Botany of cultivated species • LOCATION: Maranhão (North 6°S, East 46°W) • POPULATION: Babaçueiros.

226 PUBLICATION: Maybury-Lewis, B. Terra e água: identidade camponesa como referência de organização política entre os ribeirinhos do Rio Solimões. In: Furtado, L. G. *Amazônia desenvolvimento, sociodiversidade e qualidade de vida*. Belém: UFPA, 1997, p. 31-69.

TRADITIONAL KNOWLEDGE: No • ENVIRONMENTAL MANAGEMENT: No • Non-indigenous • RELEVANCE: High • SUBJECTS: Botany of cultivated species/Botany of collected species • LOCATION: Careiro da Várzea, Iranduba, Manacapuru and Manaquiri (Solimões river) • POPULATION: Ribeirinhos/Caboclos/Seringueiros/Castanheiros.

228 PUBLICATION: McGrath, D. G. Manejo comunitário da pesca nos lagos de varzea do Baixo Amazonas. In: Furtado, L. G. et al. P*ovos das Águas:* realidade e perspectivas na Amazônia. Belém: MCT/ CNPq/ Museu Goeldi, 1993, p. 213-229.

TRADITIONAL KNOWLEDGE: No • ENVIRONMENTAL MANAGEMENT: Yes • Non-indigenous • RELEVANCE: High • SUBJECTS: Icthyology/Fishing techniques • LOCATION: Lower Amazon (Faro, Juriti, Óbidos, Oriximiná, Alenquer, Monte Alegre, Santarém, Almerim) • POPULATION: Praieiros/Ribeirinhos/Caboclos/Seringueiros/Castanheiros.

229 PUBLICATION: McGrath, D. G. et al. Fisheries and the evolution of resource management on the lower amazon floodplain. *Human Ecology*, v. 21, n. 2, Plenum Publishing, 1993, p. 167-195.

TRADITIONAL KNOWLEDGE: No • ENVIRONMENTAL MANAGEMENT: Yes • Non-indigenous • RELEVANCE: High • SUBJECTS: Icthyology/Fishing techniques/Technology/Material culture • LOCATION: Lower Amazon (Faro, Juriti, Óbidos, Oriximiná, Alenquer, Monte Alegre, Santarém, Almerim) • POPULATION: Ribeirinhos/Caboclos/Seringueiros/Castanheiros.

230 PUBLICATION: McGrath, D. G. et al. Manejo comunitário de lagos de várzea e o desenvolvimento sustentável da pesca na Amazônia. Paper do NAEA 58. NAEA/UFPA, Belém, 1996, p. 30.

TRADITIONAL KNOWLEDGE: No • ENVIRONMENTAL MANAGEMENT: Yes • Non-indigenous • RELEVANCE: Fair • SUBJECTS: Icthyology/Fishing techniques/Technology/Material culture • LOCATION: Amazon region • POPULATION: Ribeirinhos/Caboclos/Seringueiros/Castanheiros.

231 PUBLICATION: McGrath, D. G. et al. Reservas de lago e o manejo comunitário da pesca no baixo Amazonas: uma avaliação preliminar. Paper do NAEA 18. NAEA/UFPA, Belém, 1994, p. 16.

TRADITIONAL KNOWLEDGE: No • ENVIRONMENTAL MANAGEMENT: Yes • Non-indigenous • RELEVANCE: Fair • SUBJECTS: Icthyology/Fishing techniques/Technology/Material culture • LOCATION: Amazon region • POPULATION: Ribeirinhos/Caboclos/Seringueiros/Castanheiros.

232 PUBLICATION: McGrath, D. G. et al. Varzeiros, geleiros e o manejo dos recursos naturais na várzea do Baixo Amazonas, *Cadernos do NAEA*, n. 11, 1993, p. 91-125.

TRADITIONAL KNOWLEDGE: No • ENVIRONMENTAL MANAGEMENT: Yes • Non-indigenous • RELEVANCE: High • SUBJECTS: Icthyology/Fishing techniques/Technology/Material culture • LOCATION: Lower Amazon (Faro, Juriti, Óbidos, Oriximiná, Alenquer, Monte Alegre, Santarém, Almerim) • POPULATION: Ribeirinhos/Caboclos/Seringueiros/Castanheiros.

233 PUBLICATION: McGrath, D. G. et al. *A Traditional Floodplain Fishery of the Lower Amazon River, Brazil*. In: Naga, The ICLARM Quarterly, 1998, p. 4-11.

TRADITIONAL KNOWLEDGE: No • ENVIRONMENTAL MANAGEMENT: No • Non-indigenous • RELEVANCE: Fair • SUBJECTS: Icthyology/Fishing techniques/Technology/Material culture • LOCATION: Ituqui island (Santarém, Pará) • POPULATION: Ribeirinhos/Caboclos/Seringueiros/Castanheiros.

236 PUBLICATION: Mello, A. F. *A pesca sob o capital:* a Technology a serviço da dominação. Belém: UFPA, 1985, p. 296.

TRADITIONAL KNOWLEDGE: No • ENVIRONMENTAL MANAGEMENT: No • Non-indigenous • RELEVANCE: Fair • SUBJECTS: Icthyology/Fishing techniques/Technology/Material culture • LOCATION: Vigia, Pará • POPULATION: Praieiros.

239 PUBLICATION: Miranda, V. C. *Os campos de Marajó e a sua flora.*
TRADITIONAL KNOWLEDGE: No • ENVIRONMENTAL MANAGEMENT: No • Non-indigenous • RELEVANCE: Fair • SUBJECTS: Botany of cultivated species/Botany of collected species • LOCATION: Ilha de Marajó, Pará • POPULATION: Praieiros.

241 PUBLICATION: Moran, E. F. Estratégias de sobrevivência: o uso de recursos ao longo da rodovia Transamazônica, *Acta Amazônica,* v. VII, n. 3, 1977, p. 363-379.
TRADITIONAL KNOWLEDGE: Yes • ENVIRONMENTAL MANAGEMENT: No • Non-indigenous • RELEVANCE: Fair • SUBJECTS: Botany of cultivated species/Botany of collected species • LOCATION: Amazon region • POPULATION: Others.

242 PUBLICATION: Moran, E. F. Nurturing the forest: strategies of native amazonians. In: Ellen, R.; Fukui, K. *Redefining Nature-Ecology, Culture and Domestication.* Washington, USA, Oxford, 1996, p. 531-555.
TRADITIONAL KNOWLEDGE: No • ENVIRONMENTAL MANAGEMENT: Yes • Non-indigenous • RELEVANCE: High • SUBJECTS: Botany of cultivated species/Botany of collected species/Icthyology/Fishing techniques • LOCATION: Amazon region • POPULATION: Ribeirinhos/Caboclos/Seringueiros/Castanheiros.

243 PUBLICATION: Moran, E. F. Rich and poor ecosystems of amazonia: An approach to management. In: Nishizawa, T.; Uitto, J. I. *The Fragile Tropics of Latin America: Sustainable Management of Changing Environments.* Tokyo, New York, Paris, United Nations University Press, 1985, p. 45-67.
TRADITIONAL KNOWLEDGE: No • ENVIRONMENTAL MANAGEMENT: Yes • Non-indigenous • RELEVANCE: Fair • SUBJECTS: Botany of collected species • LOCATION: Amazon region rivers • POPULATION: Ribeirinhos/Caboclos/Seringueiros/Castanheiros.

244 PUBLICATION: Moran, E. F. *A ecologia humana das populações da Amazônia.* Petrópolis: Vozes, 1990, p. 158-252.
TRADITIONAL KNOWLEDGE: Yes • ENVIRONMENTAL MANAGEMENT: No • Non-indigenous • RELEVANCE: Fair • SUBJECTS: Botany of cultivated species/Botany of collected species/Icthyology/Fishing techniques/Technology/Material culture • LOCATION: Blackwater rivers in the Amazon region • POPULATION: Ribeirinhos/Caboclos/Seringueiros/Castanheiros.

246 PUBLICATION: Moreira, E. S.; Rocha, R. M. Pesca estuarina: uma contribuição ao estudo da organização social da pesca no Pará. *Bol. Mus. Paraense Emílio Goeldi, Antropologia,* v. 11, n. 1, MCT/CNPq, 1995, p. 57-86.
TRADITIONAL KNOWLEDGE: Yes • ENVIRONMENTAL MANAGEMENT: No • Non-indigenous • RELEVANCE: Fair • SUBJECTS: Icthyology/Fishing techniques/Technology/Material culture • LOCATION: Caratateua island (Pará), Abaetetuba (Pará) • POPULATION: Praieiros.

251 PUBLICATION: Murrieta, R. S. S. et al. Estratégias de subsistência de uma Population ribeirinha do Rio Marajó-Açu, Ilha de Marajó, Brasil. *Bol. Mus. Paraense Emílio Goeldi, Antropologia,* v. 5, n. 2, SCT/CNPq, 1989, p. 147-169.
TRADITIONAL KNOWLEDGE: Yes • ENVIRONMENTAL MANAGEMENT: Yes • Non-indigenous • RELEVANCE: High • SUBJECTS: Botany of cultivated species/Botany of collected species • LOCATION: Ponta de Pedras (1°22'54"S-48°50'10"W) • POPULATION: Ribeirinhos/Caboclos/Seringueiros/Castanheiros.

252 PUBLICATION: Murrieta, R. S. S. et al. Estratégias de subsistência da comunidade de Praia Grande, Ilha de Marajó, Pará, Brasil. *Bol. Mus. Paraense Emílio Goeldi, Antropologia,* v. 8, n. 2, MCT/CNPq, 1992, p. 185-201.
TRADITIONAL KNOWLEDGE: Yes • ENVIRONMENTAL MANAGEMENT: Yes • Non-indigenous • RELEVANCE: High • SUBJECTS: Botany of cultivated species/Botany of collected species/Technology/Material culture • LOCATION: Ponta de Pedras (1°22'54"S- 48°50'10"W) • POPULATION: Ribeirinhos/Caboclos/Seringueiros/Castanheiros.

257 PUBLICATION: Nacif, A. M. P. *Pesca artesanal:* aspectos ambientais, sócio-econômicos e culturais – o caso de Marudá/PA. Belém : NUMA, 1994.
TRADITIONAL KNOWLEDGE: Yes • ENVIRONMENTAL MANAGEMENT: No • Non-indigenous • RELEVANCE: Fair • SUBJECTS: Technology/Material culture • LOCATION: Vila de Marudá, Pará • POPULATION: Fishers.

258 PUBLICATION: Nascimento, I. H. Tempo da natureza e tempo do relógio: tradição e mudança em uma comunidade pesqueira. *Bol. Mus. Paraense Emílio Goeldi, Antropologia,* v. 11, n.1, MCT/CNPq, 1995 p. 5-19.
TRADITIONAL KNOWLEDGE: Yes • ENVIRONMENTAL MANAGEMENT: No • Non-indigenous • RELEVANCE: Fair • SUBJECTS: Technology/Material culture • LOCATION: Maracanã, Pará • POPULATION: Praieiros.

259 PUBLICATION: Nery, A. da C. Traços da Technology pesqueira de uma área de pesca tradicional na Amazônia – Zona do Salgado Pará. *Bol. Mus. Paraense Emílio Goeldi, Antropologia,* v.11, n 2, MCT/CNPq, 1995, p. 199-293.
TRADITIONAL KNOWLEDGE: No • ENVIRONMENTAL MANAGEMENT: Yes • Non-indigenous • RELEVANCE: High • SUBJECTS: Hidrologia/Technology/Material culture • LOCATION: Marapanim (Cajutuba and Marudá islands) 0°42'25"S-47°41'54"W. • POPULATION: Praieiros.

262 PUBLICATION: Neves, W. Sociodiversity and biodiversity, two sides of the equation. In: Clüsener-Godt, M.; Sachs, I. *Brazilian Perspectives on Sustainable Developmente of the Amazon Region.* Paris: The Parthenon Publishing Group, 1995, p. 91-124.
TRADITIONAL KNOWLEDGE: Yes • ENVIRONMENTAL MANAGEMENT: No • Non-indigenous • RELEVANCE: Fair • SUBJECTS: Botany of cultivated species/Botany of collected species/Icthyology/Fishing techniques • LOCATION: Amazon region • POPULATION: Ribeirinhos/Caboclos/Seringueiros/Castanheiros.

265 PUBLICATION: Noda, S. do N. et al. *Homem e natureza:* as agriculturas familiares nas várzeas do estado do Amazonas. FUA/Inpa/Embrapa/Ibama/GTZ/Fundação Oswaldo Cruz, dateless: 40.
TRADITIONAL KNOWLEDGE: Yes • ENVIRONMENTAL MANAGEMENT: Yes • Non-indigenous • RELEVANCE: High • SUBJECTS: Botany of cultivated species/Botany of collected species/Icthyology/Fishing techniques • LOCATION: Amazonas várzea • POPULATION: Ribeirinhos/Caboclos/Seringueiros/Castanheiros.

274 PUBLICATION: Silva, M. F. da; Corrêa, Y. M. B. Plantas ruderais de Manaus e seu potencial de utilização. *Bol. Mus. Paraense Emílio Goeldi, Botânica,* v. 11, n. 2, MCT/CNPq, 1995, p. 239-254.
TRADITIONAL KNOWLEDGE: No • ENVIRONMENTAL MANAGEMENT: No • Non-indigenous • RELEVANCE: Fair • SUBJECTS: Botany of collected species/Pharmacology/Medicine • LOCATION: Manaus, Amazonas • POPULATION: Ribeirinhos/Caboclos/Seringueiros/Castanheiros.

283 PUBLICATION: Peret, J. A. *Frutas da Amazônia.* Rio de Janeiro: Suframa, 1985, p. 107.
TRADITIONAL KNOWLEDGE: No • ENVIRONMENTAL MANAGEMENT: No • Non-indigenous • RELEVANCE: Fair • SUBJECTS: Botany of cultivated species/Botany of collected species • LOCATION: Amazon region • POPULATION: Ribeirinhos/Caboclos/Seringueiros/Castanheiros.

285 PUBLICATION: Petrere Jr., M. Pesca e esforço de pesca no Estado do Amazonas II – locais, aparelhos de capturas e estatística de desembarque. *Acta amazonica,* v. VIII, n. 3, supl. 2, CNPq/INPA, 1978, p. 54.
TRADITIONAL KNOWLEDGE: No • ENVIRONMENTAL MANAGEMENT: No • Non-indigenous • RELEVANCE: Fair • SUBJECTS: Icthyology/Fishing techniques/Technology/Material culture • LOCATION: State of Amazonas • POPULATION: Ribeirinhos/Caboclos/Seringueiros/Castanheiros.

286 PUBLICATION: Petrere Jr., M. As comunidades humanas ribeirinhas da Amazônia e suas transformações sociais. In: POPULAÇÕES HUMANAS RIOS E MARES DA AMAZÔNIA. IV ENCONTRO DE CIÊNCIAS SOCIAIS E O MAR NO BRASIL. São Paulo: PPCAUB/UFPA, 1990, p. 31-68.
TRADITIONAL KNOWLEDGE: No • ENVIRONMENTAL MANAGEMENT: No • Non-indigenous • RELEVANCE: Fair • SUBJECTS: Icthyology/Fishing techniques/Technology/Material culture • LOCATION: Amazon region • POPULATION: Ribeirinhos/Caboclos/Seringueiros/Castanheiros.

291 PUBLICATION: Delavaux, J.-J.; Pinton, F. *Côté forêt, côtè jardin notes sur les usages du végétal dans la région de Mauès.* 1993.
TRADITIONAL KNOWLEDGE: Yes • ENVIRONMENTAL MANAGEMENT: Yes • Non-indigenous • RELEVANCE: High • SUBJECTS: Botany of cultivated species/Botany of collected species/Pharmacology/Medicine • LOCATION: Maués, Amazonas • POPULATION: Ribeirinhos/Caboclos/Seringueiros/Castanheiros.

297 PUBLICATION: Rodrigues, E. Etnofarmacologia no Parque Nacional do Jaú. AM. *Revista brasileira de plantas Medicineis,* v. 1, n. 1. Instituto de Biociências de Botucatu, 1998, p.1-14.

TRADITIONAL KNOWLEDGE: Yes • ENVIRONMENTAL MANAGEMENT: No • Non-indigenous • RELEVANCE: High • SUBJECTS: Pharmacology/Medicine • LOCATION: Jaú National Park • POPULATION: Ribeirinhos/Caboclos/Seringueiros/Castanheiros.

298 PUBLICATION: Rodrigues, E. Moradores do Parque Nacional do Jaú, AM. *Espaço e Cultura USP,* FFLCH-Geografia Física, 1997, p. 147.

TRADITIONAL knowledge: Yes • ENVIRONMENTAL MANAGEMENT: Yes • Non-indigenous • RELEVANCE: High • SUBJECTS: Botany of cultivated species/Botany of collected species/Pharmacology/Medicine/Icthyology/Fishing techniques/Technology/Material culture • LOCATION: Jaú National Park • POPULATION: Ribeirinhos/Caboclos/Seringueiros/Castanheiros.

299 PUBLICATION: Rodrigues, E. Moradores do Parque Nacional do Jaú, AM. *Espaço e Cultura USP,* FFLCH, São Paulo, 1996, p. 44.

TRADITIONAL KNOWLEDGE: Yes • ENVIRONMENTAL MANAGEMENT: No • Non-indigenous • RELEVANCE: High • SUBJECTS: Botany of cultivated species/Botany of collected species/Pharmacology/Medicine • LOCATION: Jaú National Park • POPULATION: Ribeirinhos/Caboclos/Seringueiros/Castanheiros.

300 PUBLICATION: Rodrigues, R. M. R. *A flora da Amazônia.* Belém: CEJUP, 1989, p. 463.

TRADITIONAL KNOWLEDGE: No • ENVIRONMENTAL MANAGEMENT: No • Non-indigenous • RELEVANCE: Fair • SUBJECTS: Botany of cultivated species/Botany of collected species/Technology/Material culture • LOCATION: State of Pará • POPULATION: Ribeirinhos/Caboclos/Seringueiros/Castanheiros.

315 PUBLICATION: Martel, J. H. I.; Ribeiro, G. A.; Saragoussi, M. Comparação na composição de quintais de três localidades de terra firme do Estado do Amazonas. In: ETHNOBIOLOGY: IMPLICATIONS AND APPLICATIONS PROCEEDINGS OF THE FIRST INTERNATIONAL CONGRESS OF ETHNOBIOLOGY. Belém: SCT/CNPq/Museu Paraense Emílio Goeldi, 1990, p. 295-309.

TRADITIONAL KNOWLEDGE: Yes • ENVIRONMENTAL MANAGEMENT: Yes • Non-indigenous • RELEVANCE: High • SUBJECTS: Botany of cultivated species/Technology/Material culture • LOCATION: Bela Vista region, Amazonas; Juma region, Amazonas; Rio Preto da Eva, Amazonas • POPULATION: Sitiantes.

321 PUBLICATION: Shanley, P. et al. Frutíferas da mata na vida amazônica. Belém, IUCN, ICRW, USAID/WID, Embrapa/CPATU, EFA, USAID/GCC/BSP, 1998: 127.

TRADITIONAL KNOWLEDGE: No • ENVIRONMENTAL MANAGEMENT: No • Non-indigenous • RELEVANCE: Fair • SUBJECTS: Botany of collected species • LOCATION: State of Pará • POPULATION: Ribeirinhos/Caboclos/Seringueiros/Castanheiros.

332 PUBLICATION: Silveira, I. M. da. Quatipuru: agricultores, pescadores e coletores em uma vila amazônica. *Publicações avulsas,* n. 34 Belém: CNPq/INPA/Museu Paraense Emílio Goeldi, 1979, p. 72.

TRADITIONAL KNOWLEDGE: Yes • ENVIRONMENTAL MANAGEMENT: No • Non-indigenous • RELEVANCE: Fair • SUBJECTS: Botany of cultivated species/Botany of collected species/Icthyology/Fishing techniques/Technology/Material culture • LOCATION: Quatipuru District (Primavera, Pará) • POPULATION: Ribeirinhos/Caboclos/Seringueiros/Castanheiros.

333 PUBLICATION: Yesonian, L. T. L. *Devastação e impasses para a sustentabilidade dos açaizais no Vale do Rio Maracá, AP* (belongs to the Project Political Economy of the Vale do Rio Maracá). Belém: NAEA/UFPA, s/d: 28.

TRADITIONAL KNOWLEDGE: No • ENVIRONMENTAL MANAGEMENT: No • Non-indigenous • RELEVANCE: Fair • SUBJECTS: Botany of collected species/Technology/Material culture • LOCATION: Vale do Rio Maragá/Pará. • POPULATION: Ribeirinhos/Caboclos/Seringueiros/Castanheiros.

335 PUBLICATION: Siqueira, A. D. et al. Estratégias de subsistência da Population ribeirinha do Igarapé Paricatuba, Ilha de Marajó. *Bol. Mus. Paraense Emílio Goeldi, Antropologia,* v. 9, n. 2, MCT, CNPq, FINEP, 1993, p. 153-170.

TRADITIONAL KNOWLEDGE: Yes • ENVIRONMENTAL MANAGEMENT: Yes • Non-indigenous • RELEVANCE: High • SUBJECTS: Botany of cultivated species/Botany of collected species • LOCATION: Ponta de Pedras 1°22'54"S - 48°50'10"W. • POPULATION: Ribeirinhos/Caboclos/Seringueiros/Castanheiros.

336 PUBLICATION: Fidalgo, O.; Hirata, J. M. Etnomicologia Caiabi, Txicão e Txucarramãe. *Rickia,* 8, Instituto de Botânica, 1979: 1-5.

TRADITIONAL KNOWLEDGE: Yes • ENVIRONMENTAL MANAGEMENT: No • Indigenous People • RELEVANCE: High • SUBJECTS: Botany of collected species • LOCATION: Xingu Park - 346. • POPULATION: 178. Txikão/Txicão/Ikpeng (MT)/ 90. Kayabi/Caiabi/Kaiabi (MT/PA)/ 91. Kayapó/Kaiapó/Caiapó/Mebegnokre/A'Ukre/Gorotire/Kriketum/Mekragnoti/Kuben-kran-Ken/Kokraimoro/Kubenkokre/Metuktire/Pukanu/Xikrin do Bacajá/Xikrin do Cateté/Kararaô (MT/PA).

337 PUBLICATION: Sizer, N. C. *Parque Nacional do Jaú*: sugestões para integração da população humana local com a conservação da biodiversidade. Manaus: Instituto Nacional de Pesquisas da Amazônia, dateless: 23.

TRADITIONAL KNOWLEDGE: Yes • ENVIRONMENTAL MANAGEMENT: No • Non-indigenous • RELEVANCE: Fair • SUBJECTS: Botany of collected species/Icthyology/Fishing techniques • LOCATION: Jaú National Park • POPULATION: Ribeirinhos/Caboclos/Seringueiros/Castanheiros.

338 PUBLICATION: Smith, N. J. H. *Man, fishes, and the Amazon.* Nova Iorque: Columbia University Press, 1981, p. 1-133.

TRADITIONAL KNOWLEDGE: Yes • ENVIRONMENTAL MANAGEMENT: No • Non-indigenous • RELEVANCE: Fair • SUBJECTS: Botany of collected species/Icthyology/Fishing techniques/Technology/Material culture • LOCATION: Itacoatiara, Amazonas • POPULATION: Ribeirinhos/Caboclos/Seringueiros/Castanheiros.

339 PUBLICATION: Smith, N. J. H. *A pesca no rio Amazonas.* Manaus: CNPq/INPA, 1979, p. 154.

TRADITIONAL KNOWLEDGE: No • ENVIRONMENTAL MANAGEMENT: No • Non-indigenous • RELEVANCE: High • SUBJECTS: Icthyology/Fishing techniques • LOCATION: Itacoatiara, Amazonas • POPULATION: Ribeirinhos/Caboclos/Seringueiros/Castanheiros.

340 PUBLICATION: Smith, N. J. H. et al. *Amazonia*: resiliency and dynamism of the land and its people, UNU Studies on critical environmental regions. Tokyo/ New York/ Paris, Brazil, United Nations University Press, 1995: 208.

TRADITIONAL KNOWLEDGE: No • ENVIRONMENTAL MANAGEMENT: Yes • Non-indigenous • RELEVANCE: Fair • SUBJECTS: Botany of cultivated species/Botany of collected species/Technology/Material culture/Zoology • LOCATION: Amazon Region. • POPULATION: Others/Ribeirinhos/Caboclos/Seringueiros/Castanheiros.

343 PUBLICATION: Souza, B. P. *Peixe e pesca no Pará.* Belém: Museu Paraense Emilio Goeldi, 1987, p. 19.

TRADITIONAL KNOWLEDGE: Yes • ENVIRONMENTAL MANAGEMENT: No • Non-indigenous • RELEVANCE: Fair • SUBJECTS: Icthyology/Fishing techniques/Technology/Material culture • LOCATION: State of Pará • POPULATION: Praieiros.

349 PUBLICATION: Tenório, M. A. R. de O. Fitoterapia: uma estratégia terapêutica natural do Amapá. In: Buchillet, D. *Medicines tradicionais e Medicine ocidental na Amazônia.* Belém: MPEG/CNPq/SCT/PR/CEJUP/UEP, 1991, p. 413-461.

TRADITIONAL KNOWLEDGE: Yes • ENVIRONMENTAL MANAGEMENT: No • Non-indigenous • RELEVANCE: Fair • SUBJECTS: Botany of cultivated species/Botany of collected species • LOCATION: State of Amapá • POPULATION: Ribeirinhos/Caboclos/Seringueiros/Castanheiros.

355 PUBLICATION: Trajber, R. *Tropes and Tribulations:* discourse strategies in an Amazon peasant comunit. *Purdue University,* Philosophy, 1988, p. 205.

TRADITIONAL KNOWLEDGE: No • ENVIRONMENTAL MANAGEMENT: No • Non-indigenous • RELEVANCE: Fair • SUBJECTS: Arte/Cosmology • LOCATION: Amazon region • POPULATION: Ribeirinhos/Caboclos/Seringueiros/Castanheiros.

357 PUBLICATION: Van den Berg, M. E. Plantas de origem africana de valor sócio-econômico atual na região amazônica e no meio norte do Brasil. *Bol. Mus. Paraense Emílio Goeldi, Botânica,* v. 7, n 2, SCT/CNPq, 1991, p. 499-504.

TRADITIONAL KNOWLEDGE: Yes • ENVIRONMENTAL MANAGEMENT: No • Non-indigenous • RELEVANCE: Fair • SUBJECTS: Botany of collected species/Pharmacology/Medicine • LOCATION: Amazon region • POPULATION: Praieiros.

358 PUBLICATION: Van den Berg, M. E. Aspectos botânicos do culto afro-brasileiro da Casa das Minas do Maranhão. *Bol. Mus. Paraense Emílio Goeldi, Botânica*, v. 7, n. 2, SCT/CNPq, 1991, p. 485-499.

TRADITIONAL KNOWLEDGE: Yes • ENVIRONMENTAL MANAGEMENT: No • Non-indigenous • RELEVANCE: High • SUBJECTS: Botany of cultivated species/Botany of collected species/Pharmacology/Medicine • LOCATION: São Luís, Maranhão • POPULATION: Praieiros.

360 PUBLICATION: Vaz, F. A. Ribeirinhos da Amazônia: identidade e magia na floresta. *Cultura Vozes*, n. 2, 1996, p. 47-65.

TRADITIONAL KNOWLEDGE: No • ENVIRONMENTAL MANAGEMENT: No • Non-indigenous • RELEVANCE: Fair • SUBJECTS: Botany of collected species/Technology/Material culture • LOCATION: Amazon region • POPULATION: Ribeirinhos/Caboclos/Seringueiros/Castanheiros.

363 PUBLICATION: Vieira, I. J. A. *Lago Grande de Monte Alegre:* por uma administração de recursoso pesqueiros em águas interiores da Amazônia. Belém: IBAMA/Superint. do Estado do Pará, 1989, p. 17.

TRADITIONAL KNOWLEDGE: No • ENVIRONMENTAL MANAGEMENT: Yes • Non-indigenous • RELEVANCE: Fair • SUBJECTS: Icthyology/Fishing techniques/Technology/Material culture • LOCATION: Lake Grande de Monte Alegre, Pará (54°30' and 54°30'W-2°30' and 2°00'S) • POPULATION: Ribeirinhos/Caboclos/Seringueiros/Castanheiros.

366 PUBLICATION: Bruneau, T.; Wesche, R. *Integration and Change in Brazil's Middle Amazon*. UFMG/University of Ottawa, Centro de Desenvolvimento e Planejamento Regional, 1990, p. 144.

TRADITIONAL KNOWLEDGE: No • ENVIRONMENTAL MANAGEMENT: No • Non-indigenous • RELEVANCE: Fair • SUBJECTS: Botany of cultivated species/Botany of collected species/Technology/Material culture • LOCATION: Itacoatiara, Amazonas • POPULATION: Ribeirinhos/Caboclos/Seringueiros/Castanheiros.

373 PUBLICATION: Ximenes, T. O barco na vida do ribeirinho. In: *Embarcações, homens e rios na Amazônia*. Belém: UFPA, 1992, p. 53-72.

TRADITIONAL KNOWLEDGE: No • ENVIRONMENTAL MANAGEMENT: No • Non-indigenous • RELEVANCE: Fair • SUBJECTS: Botany of collected species/Technology/Material culture/Cosmology • LOCATION: Amazon region • POPULATION: Ribeirinhos/Caboclos/Seringueiros/Castanheiros.

378 PUBLICATION: Almeida, M. W. B. de. *Rubber Tappers of the Upper Juruá River*. The Making of a Forest Peasantry. University of Cambridge, Darwin College, 1992, p. 257-260.

TRADITIONAL KNOWLEDGE: Yes • ENVIRONMENTAL MANAGEMENT: No • Non-indigenous • RELEVANCE: High • SUBJECTS: Botany of cultivated species/Botany of collected species/Technology/Material culture • LOCATION: Upper Juruá River - Next to the Farm Foz do Riozinho • POPULATION: Ribeirinhos/Caboclos/Seringueiros/Castanheiros.

380 PUBLICATION: Anderson, A. B. W. The Names and Uses of Palms Among a Tribe of Yanomama Indians. *Principes - Journal of the Palm Society*, v. 22, n. 1, 1978, p. 30-41.

TRADITIONAL KNOWLEDGE: Yes • ENVIRONMENTAL MANAGEMENT: No • Indigenous People • RELEVANCE: High • SUBJECTS: Botany of collected species • LOCATION: AI Yanomami - 585 • POPULATION: 200 Yanomami/Ianomâmi/Xiririá (Roraima/Amazonas); Yanoman/Sunumá/Ninam (Venezuela).

390 PUBLICATION: Balée, W. A etnobotânica quantitativa dos índios Tembé Rio Gurupi, Pará. *Bol. Mus. Paraense Emílio Goeldi, Botânica*, v. 3, n. 1, 1987, p. 29-50.

TRADITIONAL KNOWLEDGE: Yes • ENVIRONMENTAL MANAGEMENT: Yes • Indigenous People • RELEVANCE: High • SUBJECTS: Botany of cultivated species/Botany of collected species/Pharmacology/Medicine/Technology/Material culture • LOCATION: AI Tembé-306 • POPULATION: 161. Tembé (Pará/Maranhão).

391 PUBLICATION: Balée, W. Análise preliminar do inventário florestal e a etnobotânica Ka, apor. *Bol. Mus. Paraense Emílio Goeldi, Botânica*, v. 2, n. 2, MCT/CNPq, 1986, p. 141-218.

TRADITIONAL KNOWLEDGE: Yes • ENVIRONMENTAL MANAGEMENT: No • Indigenous People • RELEVANCE: High • SUBJECTS: Botany of collected species • LOCATION: AI Alto Turiaçu – • POPULATION: 56. Kaapor/Urubu-Kaapor/Ka'apor/Kaaporté (Maranhão).

401 PUBLICATION: Brunelli, G. *De los Espíritus a los Microbios:* salud y sociedad en transformación entre los Zoró de la Amazonia Brasileña. Quito: Ediciones Abya-Ayala, dateless.

TRADITIONAL KNOWLEDGE: Yes • ENVIRONMENTAL MANAGEMENT: No • Indigenous People • RELEVANCE: High • SUBJECTS: Botany of collected species/Pharmacology/Medicine/Cosmology • LOCATION: AI Zoró-350 • POPULATION: 205. Zoró (Mato Grosso).

404 PUBLICATION: Campos, M. D. C. et al. Kuikúru: integração céu e terra na economia e no ritual. In: Greiff, J. A. de; Reichel, E. *Etnoastronomy americanas*. Bogota: Ediciones de la Universidad nacional de Colombia, 1987.

TRADITIONAL KNOWLEDGE: Yes • ENVIRONMENTAL MANAGEMENT: No • Indigenous People • RELEVANCE: High • SUBJECTS: Astronomy/Pedology • LOCATION: Xingu Park - 350 • POPULATION: 101. Kuikuro/Kuikuru (Mato Grosso).

407 PUBLICATION: Carneiro, R. L. Uso do solo e classificação da floresta (Kuikúro). In: Ribeiro, D. et al. (Ed.); Ribeiro, B. (Coord.). *Suma etnológica brasileira*. New edition of the Handbook of South American Indians, Etnobiologia v. 1, 2. ed. Petrópolis: FINEP/Vozes, 1987, p. 47-56.

TRADITIONAL KNOWLEDGE: Yes • ENVIRONMENTAL MANAGEMENT: No • Indigenous People • RELEVANCE: High • SUBJECTS: Botany of cultivated species/Pedology/Technology/Material culture • LOCATION: Xingu Park - 350 • POPULATION: 101. Kuikuro/Kuikuru (Mato Grosso).

413 PUBLICATION: Chernela, J. M. Os cultivares de mandioca na área do Uaupés Tukâno. In: Ribeiro, D. et al. (Ed.); Ribeiro, B. (Coord.). *Suma Etnológica Brasileira*. New edition of the Handbook of South American Indians, Etnobiologia v. 1, 2. ed. Petrópolis: FINEP/Vozes, 1987, p. 151-158.

TRADITIONAL KNOWLEDGE: Yes • ENVIRONMENTAL MANAGEMENT: Yes • Indigenous People • RELEVANCE: High • SUBJECTS: Botany of cultivated species • LOCATION: AI Upper Rio Negro - 766 • POPULATION: 172. Tukano/Tucano (Amazonas/Colombia).

414 PUBLICATION: Chernela, J. M. Pesca e hierarquização tribal no Alto Uaupés. In: Ribeiro, D. et al. (Ed.); Ribeiro, B. (Coord.). *Suma etnológica brasileira*. New edition of the Handbook of South American Indians, Etnobiologia v. 1, 2. ed. Petrópolis: FINEP/Vozes, 1987, p. 235-249.

TRADITIONAL KNOWLEDGE: Yes • ENVIRONMENTAL MANAGEMENT: No • Indigenous People • RELEVANCE: High • SUBJECTS: Botany of cultivated species/Botany of collected species/Icthyology/Fishing techniques/Technology/Material culture/Cosmology • LOCATION: AI Yauareté - 119 • POPULATION: 184. Wanano/Uanano (Amazonas/Colombia).

420 PUBLICATION: Coimbra Jr., C. E. A. Estudos de ecologia humana entre os Suruí do Parque Aripuanã. Plantas de importância econômica. In: *Bol. Mus. Paraense Emílio Goeldi, Antropologia*, 2(1), MCT/CNPq/MPEG, 1985, p. 37-55.

TRADITIONAL KNOWLEDGE: Yes • ENVIRONMENTAL MANAGEMENT: No • Indigenous People • RELEVANCE: High • SUBJECTS: Botany of cultivated species/Botany of collected species • LOCATION: Aripuaná Park - 38 • POPULATION: 153. Suruí/Paíter (Rondônia).

421 PUBLICATION: Coimbra Jr., C. E. A . Estudos de ecologia humana entre os suruí do Parque Aripuanã. Rondônia. Aspectos Alimentares. *Bol. Mus. Paraense Emílio Goeldi., Antropologia*, 2(1), MCT/CNPq/MPEG, 1985, p. 57-87.

TRADITIONAL KNOWLEDGE: Yes • ENVIRONMENTAL MANAGEMENT: Yes • Indigenous People • RELEVANCE: High • SUBJECTS: Botany of cultivated species/Botany of collected species/Icthyology/Fishing techniques/Zoology • LOCATION: Aripuanã Park - 38 • POPULATION: 153. Suruí/Paíter (Rondônia).

422 PUBLICATION: Coimbra Jr., Carlos Everaldo A. - Estudos de ecologia humana entre os Suruí do Parque Aripuanã. Rondônia. Elementos de etnozoology. *Bol. Mus. Paraense Emílio Goeldi, Antropologia*, 2, n.1, MCT/CNPq/MPEG, 1985: 9-36.

TRADITIONAL KNOWLEDGE: Yes • ENVIRONMENTAL MANAGEMENT: No • Indigenous People • RELEVANCE: High • SUBJECTS: Botany of collected species/Technology/Material culture/Zoology • LOCATION: Aripuanã Park - 38 • POPULATION: 153. Suruí/Paíter (Rondônia).

423 PUBLICATION: Conklin, Beth A.- O sistema médico Warí Pakaanóva. SANTOS, Ricardo V.; Coimbra Jr. C. E. A., Saúde e povos indígenas, Rio de Janeiro: Fiocruz, 1994: 161-186.

TRADITIONAL KNOWLEDGE: Yes • ENVIRONMENTAL MANAGEMENT: No • Indigenous People • RELEVANCE: High • SUBJECTS: Botany of cultivated species/Botany of collected species/Pharmacology/Medicine/Cosmology • LOCATION: AI Igarapé Lage - 127, AI Igarapé Ribeirão - 130, AI Pacaas-Novas - 226, AI Rio Negro/Ocaia - 271, AI Sagarana - 277 • POPULATION: 130. Pakaa Nova/Wari/Pacaás Novos (RO).

425 PUBLICATION: Universidade Federal do Mato Grosso; Gera. Centro de Estudos e Pesquisas da Amazônia Pantanal e Cerrado. *Estudo das Technologys empregadas no manejo de recursos para a formação de roças indígenas* - Diagnóstico Ambiental. Universidade Federal do Mato Grosso, Cuiabá, 1992: 198.

TRADITIONAL KNOWLEDGE: Yes • ENVIRONMENTAL MANAGEMENT: Yes • Indigenous People • RELEVANCE: High • SUBJECTS: Botany of cultivated species/Botany of collected species/Entomology/Pharmacology/Medicine/Icthyology/Fishing techniques • LOCATION: RI Pareci - 237 • POPULATION: 137. Pareci/Paresi/Haliti (Mato Grosso).

427 PUBLICATION: Costa Júnior, P.; Santos, G. M. dos. *Subsistência e alternativas econômicas na sociedade* (Enawene-Nawe Relatório). Opan, Gera/ICHS/UFMT, Cuiabá, 1995: 87.

TRADITIONAL KNOWLEDGE: Yes • ENVIRONMENTAL MANAGEMENT: No • Indigenous People • RELEVANCE: High • SUBJECTS: Botany of cultivated species/Botany of collected species/Pharmacology/Medicine/Hidrology/Icthyology/Fishing techniques/Technology/Material culture/Zoology • LOCATION: AI Enawene-Nawe - 279 • POPULATION: 34. Enawenê-Nawê/Salumã (Mato Grosso).

436 PUBLICATION: Elisabetsky, Elaine; Posey, Darrell Addison - Conceito de animais e seus espíritos em relação a doenças e curas entre os índios Kayapó da Aldeia Gorotire, Pará. In: *Bol. Mus. Paraense Emílio Goeldi., Antropologia*, 7(1), MCT/CNPq/MPEG, 1991: 21-36.

TRADITIONAL KNOWLEDGE: Yes • ENVIRONMENTAL MANAGEMENT: No • Indigenous People • RELEVANCE: High • SUBJECTS: Botany of cultivated species/Pharmacology/Medicine/Icthyology/Fishing techniques • LOCATION: Gorotire Village, Pará (7°52'S - 51°13'W) • POPULATION: 91. Kayapó/Kaiapó/Caiapó/Mebegnokre/A'Ukre/Gorotire/Kriketum/; Mekragnoti/Kuben-kran-Ken/Kokraimoro/Kubenkokre/Metuktire/; Pukanu/Xikrin do Bacajá/Xikrin do Cateté/Kararaô (Mato Grosso/Pará).

442 PUBLICATION: Ferraz, Cecília; Futemma, Célia Regina - *Uso e percepção dos recursos naturais pelos índios Tenharim da região de Humaitá/AM*. Instituto de Biociências/UNESP, Rio Claro, 1988, p. 31.

TRADITIONAL KNOWLEDGE: Yes • ENVIRONMENTAL MANAGEMENT: Yes • Indigenous People • RELEVANCE: High • SUBJECTS: Botany of cultivated species/Botany of collected species/Technology/Material culture • LOCATION: AI Tenharim/Marmelos - 307 • POPULATION: 162. Tenharim (Amazonas).

446 PUBLICATION: Fortune, Gretchen. The Importance of Turtle Months in the Karajá World, With a Focus on Ethnobiology in Indigenous Literary education. In: Posey, Darrell A.; Overal, W. L. *Ethnobiology*: Implications and Applications Proceedings of the First International Congress of Ethnobiology. v. 1. Belém: SCT/CNPq/MPEG, 1988, p. 89-97.

TRADITIONAL KNOWLEDGE: Yes • ENVIRONMENTAL MANAGEMENT: No • Indigenous People • RELEVANCE: High • SUBJECTS: Astronomy/Zoology/Cosmology • LOCATION: Ilha do Bananal, Tocantins • POPULATION: 75. Karajá/Carajá (Mato Grosso/Tocantins/Pará); Karajá/Javaé (Tocantins); Karajá/Xambioá/K. do norte (Tocantins).

462 PUBLICATION: Aquino, Txai Terri Valle de; Iglesias, Marcelo. *Kaxinawá do Rio Jordão*: Histórias, território, economia e desenvolvimento sustentado. Rio Branco: Coica/OXFAM-América, 1993, p. 302.

TRADITIONAL KNOWLEDGE: Yes • ENVIRONMENTAL MANAGEMENT: Yes • Indigenous People • RELEVANCE: High • SUBJECTS: Botany of cultivated species/Botany of collected species/Icthyology/Fishing techniques • LOCATION: AI Kaxinawã do Rio Jordão - 171 • POPULATION: 87. Kaxinawá/Cashinauá/Caxinauá (Acre) Cashinahua (Peru).

465 PUBLICATION: Jensen, Allen Arthur. Sistemas indígenas de classificação de aves: aspectos comparativos, ecológicos e evolutivos. Belém, MCT/CNPq - Museu Paraense Emílio Goeldi, col. Eduardo Galvão, 1988, p. 87.

TRADITIONAL KNOWLEDGE: Yes • ENVIRONMENTAL MANAGEMENT: No • Indigenous People • RELEVANCE: High • SUBJECTS: Botany of collected species/Zoology • LOCATION: AI Alto Turiaçu - 8, AI Andirá-Marau - 13, AI Waiãpi - 339 • POPULATION: 182. Waiãpi/Wayampi/Oyampi/Wayãpy (Amapá/French Guiana).

484 PUBLICATION: Lukesch, Anton - Bearded Indians of the Tropical Forest: The Assuríni of the Ipiaçaba. Notes and observations on the first contact and living together. Graz,, Austria, Akademische Druck - u. Verlagsanstalt, dateless: 133.

TRADITIONAL KNOWLEDGE: Yes • ENVIRONMENTAL MANAGEMENT: No • Indigenous People • RELEVANCE: High • SUBJECTS: Botany of cultivated species/Botany of collected species/Technology/Material culture • LOCATION: RI Piaçaba Asurini (3°25'S -52°20'W) • POPULATION: 19. Asuríni do Xingu/Awaeté (Pará).

485 PUBLICATION: Magalhães, Antonio Carlos- Pyrá - Atividade pesqueira entre os Parakanã. In: Furtado, Lourdes G.; Leitão, Wilma; Mello, A. F. de, Belém, *Povos das Águas*. Museu Paraense Emílio Goeldi. col. Eduardo Galvão, 1993: 101-117.

TRADITIONAL KNOWLEDGE: Yes • ENVIRONMENTAL MANAGEMENT: No • Indigenous People • RELEVANCE: High • SUBJECTS: Botany of collected species/Technology/Material culture • LOCATION: AI Paracanã - 236 • POPULATION: 136. Parakanã/Paracanã/Apiterewa (Pará).

487 PUBLICATION: Teixeira, D. L. M. Um estudo da etnozoology Karajá: o exemplo das máscaras de Aruanã. In: Ribeiro, B. et al. *O artesão tradicional e seu papel na sociedade contemporânea*. Rio de Janeiro: Funarte, Instituto Nacional do Folclore, 1983, p. 213-53.

TRADITIONAL KNOWLEDGE: Yes • ENVIRONMENTAL MANAGEMENT: No • Indigenous People • RELEVANCE: High • SUBJECTS: Art/Botany of collected species/Technology/Material culture/Zoology • LOCATION: Ilha do Bananal, Tocantins • POPULATION: 75. Karajá/Carajá (Mato Grosso/Tocantins/Pará); Karajá/Javaé (Tocantins); Karajá/Xambioá/K. do Norte (Tocantins).

489 PUBLICATION: Montagner, D. A cozinha marubo: a arte de comer e beber. *Revista do Museu Paulista*, Nova Série, 32, USP, 1987: 29-72.

TRADITIONAL KNOWLEDGE: Yes • ENVIRONMENTAL MANAGEMENT: No • Indigenous People • RELEVANCE: High • SUBJECTS: Cosmology • LOCATION: AI Vale do Javari - 333 • POPULATION: 112. Marubo (Amazonas).

497 PUBLICATION: Montagner, D. Mani Pei Rao: remédios do mato dos marubo In: Buchillet, D. Medicines tradicionais e Medicine ocidental na Amazônia, Belém: Museu Paraense Emílio Goeldi, CNPq, SCT/PR, Edições Cejup, Universidade do Estado do Pará, 1991, p. 463-487.

TRADITIONAL KNOWLEDGE: Yes • ENVIRONMENTAL MANAGEMENT: No • Indigenous People • RELEVANCE: High • SUBJECTS: Botany of collected species/Pharmacology/Medicine • LOCATION: AI Vale do Javari - 333 • POPULATION: 112. Marubo (Amazonas).

498 PUBLICATION: Montagner, D. Receitas da culinária marubo. *Bol. Mus. Paraense Emílio Goeldi, Antropologia*, 5(1), SCT/MPEG, 1989, p. 3-64.

TRADITIONAL KNOWLEDGE: Yes • ENVIRONMENTAL MANAGEMENT: No • Indigenous People • RELEVANCE: High • SUBJECTS: Technology/Material culture • LOCATION: AI Vale do Javari - 333 • POPULATION: 112. Marubo (Amazonas).

516 PUBLICATION: Universidade Federal do Mato Grosso; Gera - Centro de Estudos e Pesquisas da Amazônia, Pantanal e Cerrado; Opan. *Estudo das potencialidades e do manejo dos recursos naturais Indígena Enawene - Nawe*. Opan/Gera/UFMT, Cuiabá, 1995: 162.

TRADITIONAL KNOWLEDGE: Yes • ENVIRONMENTAL MANAGEMENT: Yes • Indigenous People • RELEVANCE: High • SUBJECTS: Botany of cultivated species/Botany of collected species/Hidrology/Icthyology/Fishing techniques/Pedology • LOCATION: AI Enawene-Nawê - 279 • POPULATION: 34. Enawenê-Nawê/Salumã (Mato Grosso).

518 PUBLICATION: Pedreira, R. *A lição indígena*. As técnicas de preservação do meio ambiente usadas pelos índios há centenas de anos podem ser aproveitadas pelo Brasil contemporâneo. *Meio Ambiente*, 1988, p. 51-54.

TRADITIONAL KNOWLEDGE: Yes • ENVIRONMENTAL MANAGEMENT: Yes • Indigenous People • RELEVANCE: High • SUBJECTS: Botany of cultivated species/Entomology/Pharmacology/Medicine/Pedology • Location: Gorotire Village, Pará (7°52'S - 51°13'W) • Population: 91. Kayapó/Kaiapó/Caiapó/Mebegnokre/A'Ukre/Gorotire/Kriketum; Mekragnoti/Kuben-kran-Ken/Kokraimoro/Kubenkokre/Metuktire; Pukanu/Xikrin do Bacajá/Xikrin do Cateté/Kararaô (Mato Grosso/Pará).

519 Publication: Petrere Jr., M. Notas sobre a pesca dos índios Kayapó da Aldeia Gorotire, Rio Fresco, Pará. *Bol. Mus. Paraense Emílio Goeldi, Antropologia*, 6(1), SCT/CNPq/MPEG, 1990: 5-27.

Traditional knowledge: Yes • Environmental management: Yes • Indigenous People • Relevance: High • Subjects: Hidrologia/Icthyology/Fishing techniques • Location: Gorotire Village, Pará (7°52'S - 51°13'W) • Population: 91. Kayapó/Kaiapó/Caiapó/Mebegnokre/A'Ukre/Gorotire/Kriketum; Mekragnoti/Kuben-kran-Ken/Kokraimoro/Kubenkokre/Metuktire; Pukanu/Xikrin do Bacajá/Xikrin do Cateté/Kararaô (Mato Grosso/Pará).

526 Publication: Posey, D. A. Manejo da floresta secundária, capoeiras, campos e cerrados (Kayapó). In: Ribeiro, D. (Ed.); Ribeiro, B. (Coord.). *Suma Etnológica Brasileira*. New edition of the Handbook of South American Indians. Etnobiologia, v. 1, 2 edição, Petrópolis, FINEP/Vozes, 1987, p. 173-185.

Traditional knowledge: Yes • Environmental management: Yes • Indigenous People • Relevance: High • Subjects: Botany of cultivated species • Location: Kayapó Indians of the State of Pará • Population: 91. Kayapó/Kaiapó/Caiapó/Mebegnokre/A'Ukre/Gorotire/Kriketum; Mekragnoti/Kuben-kran-Ken/Kokraimoro/Kubenkokre/Metuktire; Pukanu/Xikrin do Bacajá/Xikrin do Cateté/Kararaô (Mato Grosso/Pará).

529 Publication: Anderson, A. B. W.; Posey, D. A. Reflorestamento Indígena. In: *Ciência Hoje*, 6(31), SBPC, 1987, p. 44-51.

Traditional knowledge: Yes • Environmental management: Yes • Indigenous People • Relevance: High • Subjects: Botany of cultivated species/Botany of collected species • Location: Gorotire Village, Pará (7°52'S - 51°13'W) • Population: 91. Kayapó/Kaiapó/Caiapó/Mebegnokre/A'Ukre/Gorotire/Kriketum/ Mekragnoti/Kuben-kran-Ken/Kokraimoro/Kubenkokre/Metuktire/ Pukanu/Xikrin do Bacajá/Xikrin do Cateté/Kararaô (Mato Grosso/Pará).

530 Publication: Overal, W.; Posey, D. A. Uso de Formigas *Azteca spp*. Para controle biológico de pragas agrícolas entre os Índios Kayapó do Brasil. In: Posey, D.A.; Overal, W. *Ethnobiology*: Implications and Applications Proceedings of the First International Congress of Ethnobiology. Volume 1. Belém: SCT/CNPq/MPEG, 1988. p. 219-225.

Traditional knowledge: Yes • Environmental management: Yes • Indigenous People • Relevance: High • Subjects: Entomology • Location: Gorotire Village, Pará (7°52'S - 51°13'W) • Population: 91. Kayapó/Kaiapó/Caiapó/Mebegnokre/A'Ukre/Gorotire/Kriketum; Mekragnoti/Kuben-kran-Ken/Kokraimoro/Kubenkokre/Metuktire; Pukanu/Xikrin do Bacajá/Xikrin do Cateté/Kararaô (Mato Grosso/Pará).

531 Publication: Posey, D. A. Conseqüências ecológicas da presença do índio Kayapó na Amazônia: recursos antropológicos e direitos de recursos tradicionais. In: Cavalcanti, C. *Desenvolvimento e Natureza*: estudos para uma sociedade sustentável. São Paulo/Recife: Cortez / Fundação Joaquim Nabuco, 1995. p. 177-194.

Traditional knowledge: Yes • Environmental management: Yes • Indigenous People • Relevance: High • Subjects: Botany of cultivated species • Location: Gorotire Village, Pará (7°52'S - 51°13'W) • Population: 91. Kayapó/Kaiapó/Caiapó/Mebegnokre/A'Ukre/Gorotire/Kriketum/Mekragnoti/Kuben-kran-Ken/Kokraimoro/Kubenkokre/Metuktire; Pukanu/Xikrin do Bacajá/Xikrin do Cateté/Kararaô (Mato Grosso/Pará).

533 Publication: Posey, D. A. Etnobiologia e Ciência de Folk: sua importância para a Amazônia. *Tübinger Geographische Studien*, 95, 1987, p. 95-108.

Traditional knowledge: Yes • Environmental management: Yes • Indigenous People • Relevance: High • Subjects: Astronomy/Botany of cultivated species/Pharmacology/Medicine/Pedology/Zoology • Location: ALDEIA GOROTIRE/PA (7°52'S - 51°13'W) • Population: 91. Kayapó/Kaiapó/Caiapó/Mebegnokre/A'Ukre/Gorotire/Kriketum/Mekragnoti/Kuben-kran-Ken/Kokraimoro/Kubenkokre/Metuktire/Pukanu/Xikrin do Bacajá/Xikrin do Cateté/Kararaô (Mato Grosso/Pará).

534 Publication: Hecht, S. B.; Posey, D. A. Indigenuos soil management in the Latin American Tropics: Some Implications for the Amazon Basin. In: Posey, D. A.; Overal, W. L. *Ethnobiology*: Implications and Applications Proceedings of the First International Congress of Ethnobiology. v. 2. SCT/CNPq/MPEG, 1990, p. 73-86.

Traditional knowledge: Yes • Environmental management: Yes • Indigenous People • Relevance: High • Subjects: Pedology • Location: Kayapó Indians of the State of Pará • Population: 91. Kayapó/Kaiapó/Caiapó/Mebegnokre/A'Ukre/Gorotire/Kriketum/; Mekragnoti/Kuben-kran-Ken/Kokraimoro/Kubenkokre/Metuktire/ Pukanu/Xikrin do Bacajá/Xikrin do Cateté/Kararaô (Mato Grosso/Pará).

535 Publication: Kerr, W. E.; Posey, D. A. Informações adicionais sobre a agricultura dos Kayapó. *Interciência*, 9(6), 1984, p. 392-400.

Traditional knowledge: Yes • Environmental management: Yes • Indigenous People • Relevance: High • Subjects: Botany of cultivated species/Entomology/Pharmacology/Medicine • Location: Gorotire Village, Pará (7°52'S - 51°13'W) • Population: 91. Kayapó/Kaiapó/Caiapó/Mebegnokre/A'Ukre/Gorotire/Kriketum/; Mekragnoti/Kuben-kran-Ken/Kokraimoro/Kubenkokre/Metuktire/; Pukanu/Xikrin do Bacajá/Xikrin do Cateté/Kararaô (Mato Grosso/Pará).

536 Publication: Posey, D. A. *Kayapó controla inseto com uso adequado do ambiente*. 1979.

Traditional knowledge: Yes • Environmental management: Yes • Indigenous People • Relevance: High • Subjects: Botany of cultivated species/Botany of collected species/Entomology/Icthyology/Fishing techniques/Zoology • Location: Gorotire Village, Pará (7°52'S - 51°13'W) • Population: 91. Kayapó/Kaiapó/Caiapó/Mebegnokre/A'Ukre/Gorotire/Kriketum/; Mekragnoti/Kuben-kran-Ken/Kokraimoro/Kubenkokre/Metuktire; Pukanu/Xikrin do Bacajá/Xikrin do Cateté/Kararaô (Mato Grosso/Pará).

542 Publication: Posey, D. A. Os Kayapó e a natureza. In: *Ciência Hoje*, 2(12), SBPC, 1984, p. 35-41.

Traditional knowledge: Yes • Environmental management: Yes • Indigenous People • Relevance: High • Subjects: Botany of cultivated species • Location: Gorotire Village, Pará (7°52'S - 51°13'W) • Population: 91. Kayapó/Kaiapó/Caiapó/Mebegnokre/A'Ukre/Gorotire/Kriketum/; Mekragnoti/Kuben-kran-Ken/Kokraimoro/Kubenkokre/Metuktire; Pukanu/Xikrin do Bacajá/Xikrin do Cateté/Kararaô (Mato Grosso/Pará).

546 Publication: Anderson, A. B. W.; Posey, D. A. Manejo de Cerrado pelos Índios Kayapó. *Bol. Mus. Paraense Emílio Goeldi*, Botânica, 2(1), SCT/CNPq/MPEG, 1985, p. 77-98.

Traditional knowledge: Yes • Environmental management: Yes • Indigenous People • Relevance: High • Subjects: Botany of cultivated species/Botany of collected species/Pharmacology/Medicine • Location: Gorotire Village, Pará (7°52'S - 51°13'W) • Population: 91. Kayapó/Kaiapó/Caiapó/Mebegnokre/A'Ukre/Gorotire/Kriketum; Mekragnoti/Kuben-kran-Ken/Kokraimoro/Kubenkokre/Metuktire; Pukanu/Xikrin do Bacajá/Xikrin do Cateté/Kararaô (Mato Grosso/Pará).

547 Publication: Kerr, W. E.; Posey, D. A. "Kangàrà Kanê", Tanaecium nocturnum (Bignoneacea, um cipó usado pelos índios Kayapó como inseticida natural. *Bol. Mus. Paraense Emílio Goeldi*, Botânica, 7 (1), SCT/CNPq/MPEG, 1991, p. 23-26.

Traditional knowledge: Yes • Environmental management: Yes • Indigenous People • Relevance: High • Subjects: Botany of cultivated species/Botany of collected species/Pharmacology/Medicine • Location: Gorotire Village, Pará (7°52'S - 51°13'W) • Population: 91. Kayapó/Kaiapó/Caiapó/Mebegnokre/A'Ukre/Gorotire/Kriketum; Mekragnoti/Kuben-kran-Ken/Kokraimoro/Kubenkokre/Metuktire; Pukanu/Xikrin do Bacajá/Xikrin do Cateté/Kararaô (Mato Grosso/Pará).

549 Publication: Carvalho, M. R.; Reesink, E. B. Ecologia e Sociedade: uma breve introdução aos Kanamari. In: Magalhães, A. C. *Sociedades indígenas e transformações ambientais*. Belém: Universidade Federal do Pará. Núcleo de Meio Ambiente. Série Universidade e Meio Ambiente, 6, 1993, p. 113-153.

TRADITIONAL KNOWLEDGE: Yes • ENVIRONMENTAL MANAGEMENT: Yes • Indigenous People • RELEVANCE: High • SUBJECTS: Botany of cultivated species/Botany of collected species/Entomology/Icthyology/Fishing techniques/Technology/Material culture/Zoology/Cosmology • LOCATION: AI Vale do Javari - 333 • POPULATION: 68. Kanamari/Canamari (Amazonas).

555 PUBLICATION: Ribeiro, B. G. Cestos Armadilhas e outras técnicas de pesca dos índios Desâna. In: Diegues, A. C. Coletânea de trabalhos apresentados no VI ENCONTRO DE CIÊNCIAS SOCIAIS E O MAR NO BRASIL. São Paulo: Programa de Pesquisa e Conservação de Áreas Úmidas no Brasil, 1992, p. 93-106.

TRADITIONAL KNOWLEDGE: Yes • ENVIRONMENTAL MANAGEMENT: Yes • Indigenous People • RELEVANCE: High • SUBJECTS: Astronomy/Icthyology/Fishing techniques/Technology/Material culture/Cosmology • LOCATION: AI Pari Cachoeira I - 238 • POPULATION: 33. Dessano/Desâna/Desano/Wira (Amazonas/ Colombia).

556 PUBLICATION: Ribeiro, B. G. Classificação dos Solos e Horticultura Desâna. In: *Ethnobiology*: Implications and Applications Proceedings of the First International Congress of Ethnobiology. v. 2. Belém: SCT/CNPq/MPEG, 1990, p. 27-49.

TRADITIONAL KNOWLEDGE: Yes • ENVIRONMENTAL MANAGEMENT: Yes • Indigenous People • RELEVANCE: High • SUBJECTS: Botany of cultivated species/Botany of collected species/Pharmacology/Medicine/Pedology/Cosmology • LOCATION: AI Pari Cachoeira I - 238 • POPULATION: 33. Dessano/Desâna/Desano/Wira (Amazonas/Colombia).

560 PUBLICATION: Ribeiro, B. G. *Os índios das águas pretas*. Modos de produção e equipamentos produtivos. São Paulo: EDUSP/Companhia das Letras, 1995, p. 270.

TRADITIONAL KNOWLEDGE: Yes • ENVIRONMENTAL MANAGEMENT: Yes • Indigenous People • RELEVANCE: High • SUBJECTS: Astronomy/Botany of cultivated species/Botany of collected species/Entomology/Icthyology/Fishing techniques/Pedology/Technology/Material culture/Zoology • LOCATION: AI Pari Cachoeira I - 238 • POPULATION: 33. Dessano/Desâna/Desano/Wira (Amazonas/ Colombia).

573 PUBLICATION: Seeger, A. *Nature and Society in Central Brazil*: The Suya Indians of Mato Grosso. London, USA: Harvard University Press, 1981, p. 273.

TRADITIONAL KNOWLEDGE: Yes • ENVIRONMENTAL MANAGEMENT: Yes • Indigenous People • RELEVANCE: High • SUBJECTS: Arte/Astronomy/Botany of cultivated species/Botany of collected species/Pharmacology/Medicine/Icthyology/Fishing techniques/Technology/Material culture/Zoology/Cosmology • LOCATION: Xingu Park - 346 • POPULATION: 154. Suyá/Suiá (Mato Grosso).

574 PUBLICATION: Setz, E. Z. F. *Ecologia alimentar em um grupo indígena*: comparação entre aldeias nambiquara de floresta e de cerrado. Campinas: Unicamp, Instituto de Biologia, 1993, p. 209.

TRADITIONAL KNOWLEDGE: Yes • ENVIRONMENTAL MANAGEMENT: Yes • Indigenous People • RELEVANCE: High • SUBJECTS: Botany of cultivated species/Botany of collected species/Icthyology/Fishing techniques/Pedology/Technology/Material culture/Zoology • LOCATION: RI Nambiquara - 216 • POPULATION: 126. Nambikwara/Anunsu/Nhanbiquara (Mato Grosso/Rondônia); Nambikwara do Campo/Halotesu/Kithaulu/Wakalitesu/Sawentesu; Nambikwara do Norte/Negarotê/Mamaindê/Latundê/Sabanê e Manduka/Tawandê; Nambikwara do Sul/ Hahaintesu/Alantesu/Waikisu/Alaketesu/Wasusu/Sararé.

578 PUBLICATION: Silverwood-Cope, Peter L. *Os Maku*: povo caçador do noroeste da Amazônia. Brasília: Editora UnB, 1990, p. 205 (col. Pensamento Antropológico).

TRADITIONAL KNOWLEDGE: Yes • ENVIRONMENTAL MANAGEMENT: No • Indigenous People • RELEVANCE: High • SUBJECTS: Botany of cultivated species/Botany of collected species/Technology/Material culture/Cosmology • LOCATION: AI Maku - 540 • POPULATION: 109. Maku/Macu (Amazonas); Maku Yuhupde; Maku Hupdá; Maku Naded; Maku Dow; Maku Cacua e Nucak (Colombia).

580 PUBLICATION: Stout, M.; Txukarramãe, M. A expedição venatória dos Kayapó e animais importantes. In: Posey, D. A.; Overal, W. L. *Ethnobiology*: Implications and Applications Proceedings of the First International Congress of Ethnobiology. v. 1. Belém: SCT/CNPq/MPEG, 1988, p. 227-241.

TRADITIONAL KNOWLEDGE: Yes • ENVIRONMENTAL MANAGEMENT: Yes • Indigenous People • RELEVANCE: High • SUBJECTS: Botany of cultivated species/Botany of collected species/Entomology/Pharmacology/Medicine/Icthyology/Fishing techniques/Technology/Material culture/Zoology/Cosmology • LOCATION: AI Baú - 51, AI Kayapó - 173, AI Menkragnoti - 453 • POPULATION: 91. Kayapó/Kaiapó/Caiapó/Mebegnokre/A'Ukre/Gorotire/Kriketum; Mekragnoti/Kuben-kran-Ken/Kokraimoro/Kubenkokre/Metuktir; Pukanu/Xikrin do Bacajá/Xikrin do Cateté/Kararaô (Mato Grosso/Pará).

590 PUBLICATION: Velthem, Lucia Hussak van. Os Wayana, as águas, os peixes e a pesca. *Bol. Mus. Paraense Emílio Goeldi.*, Antropologia, 6(1), SCT/CNPq/MPEG.

TRADITIONAL KNOWLEDGE: Yes • ENVIRONMENTAL MANAGEMENT: No • Indigenous People • RELEVANCE: High • SUBJECTS: Icthyology/Fishing techniques/Technology/Material culture/Cosmology • LOCATION: Tumucumaque Park - 323 • POPULATION: 189. Wayana/Waiana/Uaiana (Pará/Suriname/French Guiana).

594 PUBLICATION: Posey, D. A. Kayapó Indian Natural Resources Management. In: Denslow, J. S.; Padoch, C. (Eds.). People of the Tropical Rain Forest. California: University of California Press, Institute Traveling Exhibition Service, 1988, p. 89-90.

TRADITIONAL KNOWLEDGE: Yes • ENVIRONMENTAL MANAGEMENT: Yes • Indigenous People • RELEVANCE: High • SUBJECTS: Botany of cultivated species/Botany of collected species • LOCATION: Kayapós from the State of Pará • POPULATION: 91. Kayapó/Kaiapó/Caiapó/Mebegnokre/A'Ukre/Gorotire/Kriketum; Mekragnoti/Kuben-kran-Ken/Kokraimoro/Kubenkokre/Metuktire; Pukanu/Xikrin do Bacajá/Xikrin do Cateté/Kararaô (Mato Grosso/Pará).

603 PUBLICATION: Milliken, W.; Wandelli, E. V.; Miller, R. P.; Pollard, S. R. *The Ethnobotany of the Waimiri Atroari Indians of Brazil*. Kew: Royal Botanic Gardens, 1992, p. 146.

TRADITIONAL KNOWLEDGE: Yes • ENVIRONMENTAL MANAGEMENT: No • Indigenous People • RELEVANCE: High • SUBJECTS: Art/Botany of cultivated species/Botany of collected species/Pharmacology/Medicine/Technology/Material culture • LOCATION: AI Waimiri-Atroari • POPULATION: 183. Waimiri Atroari/Kiña (Roraima/Amazonas).

608 PUBLICATION: Aires, J. do R. Produção e utilização de alimentos pelos Paresi. *Gerando Debates*, Ano I (1). UFMT/Gera, 1994, p. 47-70.

TRADITIONAL KNOWLEDGE: Yes • ENVIRONMENTAL MANAGEMENT: Yes • Indigenous People • RELEVANCE: High • SUBJECTS: Botany of cultivated species • LOCATION: AI Pareci - 237 • POPULATION: 137. Pareci/Paresi/Haliti (Mato Grosso).

612 PUBLICATION: Almeida, E. L. de. Sobre a vida Paresi: alguns dados censitários. *Gerando Debates*, Ano I (1), UFMT/Gera, 1994, p. 34-45.

TRADITIONAL KNOWLEDGE: Yes • ENVIRONMENTAL MANAGEMENT: No • Indigenous People • RELEVANCE: High • SUBJECTS: Pharmacology/Medicine • LOCATION: AI Pareci - 237. • POPULATION: 137. Pareci/Paresi/Haliti (Mato Grosso).

613 PUBLICATION: Anderson, A. B. W.; Posey, D. A. Management of a Tropical Scrub Savanna by the Gorotire Kayapó of Brazil. In: Posey, D.A.; Balée, W. *Resource Management in Amazonia*: Indigenous and Folks Strategies. New York: The New York Botanical Garden, 1989, p. 159-173.

TRADITIONAL KNOWLEDGE: Yes • ENVIRONMENTAL MANAGEMENT: Yes • Indigenous People • RELEVANCE: High • SUBJECTS: Botany of cultivated species/Botany of collected species/Entomology/Pedology • LOCATION: Gorotire Villare, Pará (7°52'S - 51°13'W) • POPULATION: 91. Kayapó/Kaiapó/Caiapó/Mebegnokre/A'Ukre/Gorotire/Kriketum; Mekragnoti/Kuben-kran-Ken/Kokraimoro/Kubenkokre/Metuktire; Pukanu/Xikrin do Bacajá/Xikrin do Cateté/Kararaô (Mato Grosso/Pará).

616 PUBLICATION: Balée, W.; Gély, A. Managed Forest Succession in Amazonia: The Ka'apor Case. In: Posey, D.A.; Balée, W. (Eds.) *Resource Management in Amazonia*: Indigenous and Folks Strategies. New York: The New York Botanical Garden, 1989, p. 129-158.

TRADITIONAL KNOWLEDGE: Yes • ENVIRONMENTAL MANAGEMENT: Yes • Indigenous People • RELEVANCE: High • SUBJECTS: Botany of cultivated species/Botany of collected species/Technology/Material culture • LOCATION: AI Alto Turiaçu/Kaapor - 8. • POPULATION: 56. Kaapor/Urubu-Kaapor/Ka'apor/Kaaporté (Maranhão).

618 PUBLICATION: Balée, W.; Daly. Resin Classification by the Ka'apor Indians. In: Prance, G.T.; Balick, M. J. (Eds) *New Directions in the Study of Plants and People*. Advances in Economic Botany, v. 8. New York: NYBG, 1990, p. 24-34.

TRADITIONAL KNOWLEDGE: Yes • ENVIRONMENTAL MANAGEMENT: No • Indigenous People • RELEVANCE: High • SUBJECTS: Botany of cultivated species/Botany of collected species • LOCATION: AI Alto Turiaçu - 8. • POPULATION: 56. Kaapor/Urubu-Kaapor/Ka'apor/Kaaporté (Maranhão).

620 PUBLICATION: Balick, M. J. The Use of Palms by the Apinayé and Guajajara Indians of Northeastern Brazil. In: Balick, M. J. (Ed.). *The Palm - Tree of Life*: Biology, Utilization and Conservation, Advances in Economy Botany, v. 6. New York: NYBG, 1988: 65-90.

TRADITIONAL KNOWLEDGE: Yes • ENVIRONMENTAL MANAGEMENT: Yes • Indigenous People • RELEVANCE: High • SUBJECTS: Botany of collected species • LOCATION: AI Apinayes - 17, AI Caru - 79, AI Rio Pindaré - 273 • POPULATION: 42. Guajajara/Tenethehara (Maranhão)/ 7. Apinayé/Apinajé/Apinaié (Tocantins).

627 PUBLICATION: Casagrande, H. C. *Representação em torno do domínio vegetal entre os Waiãpi do Amapari*. São Paulo: Humanitas, 1997, p. 119.

TRADITIONAL KNOWLEDGE: Yes • ENVIRONMENTAL MANAGEMENT: No • Indigenous People • RELEVANCE: High • SUBJECTS: Botany of cultivated species/Botany of collected species/Zoology/Cosmology • LOCATION: AI Waiãpi - 339. • POPULATION: 182. Waiãpi/Wayampi/Oyampi/Wayãpy (Amapá/French Guiana).

630 PUBLICATION: Chernela, J. M. Managing Rivers of Hunger: The Tukano of Brazil. In: Posey, D.A.; Balée, W. (Eds.). Resource Management in Amazonia: Indigenous and Folks Strategies. Advances in Economic Botany. New York: NYBG, 1989, p. 238-48.

TRADITIONAL KNOWLEDGE: No • ENVIRONMENTAL MANAGEMENT: Yes • Indigenous People • RELEVANCE: High • SUBJECTS: Icthyology/Fishing techniques • LOCATION: AI Alto Rio Negro - 766 • POPULATION: 172. Tukano/Tucano (Amazonas/Colombia).

631 PUBLICATION: Chernela, J. M. *Hierarchy and Economy of the Uanano (Kotiria Speaking Peoples of the Middle Uapes BaYes)*. New York: Columbia University, 1983, p. 180.

TRADITIONAL KNOWLEDGE: Yes • ENVIRONMENTAL MANAGEMENT: Yes • Indigenous People • RELEVANCE: High • SUBJECTS: Botany of collected species/Icthyology/Fishing techniques/Technology/Material culture • LOCATION: AI Yauareté - 119 • POPULATION: 184. Wanano/Uanano (Amazonas/Colombia).

634 PUBLICATION: Costa Filho, A. Análise dos sistemas econômicos da sociedade Paresi. *Gerando Debates*, Ano I (1). UFMT/Gera, 1994, p. 7-29.

TRADITIONAL KNOWLEDGE: Yes • ENVIRONMENTAL MANAGEMENT: Yes • Indigenous People • RELEVANCE: High • SUBJECTS: Botany of cultivated species/Botany of collected species/Icthyology/Fishing techniques/Technology/Material culture/Zoology • LOCATION: RI Pareci - 237 • POPULATION: 137. Pareci/Paresi/Haliti (Mato Grosso).

635 PUBLICATION: D'Angelis Filho, João Silveira. A classificação e o reconhecimento dos solos pelos Paresi. *Gerando Debates*, Ano I (1). UFMT/Gera, 1994, p. 83-95.

TRADITIONAL KNOWLEDGE: Yes • ENVIRONMENTAL MANAGEMENT: No • Indigenous People • RELEVANCE: High • SUBJECTS: Pedology • LOCATION: RI Pareci - 237 • POPULATION: 137. Pareci/Paresi/Haliti (Mato Grosso).

637 PUBLICATION: Doyle, M. A*spects of Baniwa Medicinel Flora and Ethno-Ecology*. Fundação Universidade Amazonas/Centro Ciências Biológicas, dateless.

TRADITIONAL KNOWLEDGE: Yes • ENVIRONMENTAL MANAGEMENT: No • Indigenous People • RELEVANCE: High • SUBJECTS: Botany of collected species/Pharmacology/Medicine • LOCATION: Tapira-Ponta Village (1°30'N - 68°20'W), Baniwa-Rio Içana • POPULATION: 25. Baniwá/Baniua/Baniva (Amazonas/Colombia/Venezuela).

640 PUBLICATION: Hecht, S. B.; Posey, D. A. Preliminary Results on Soil Management Techniques of the Kayapó Indians. In: Posey, D. A.; Balée, W. (Eds.) *Resource Management in Amazonia*: Indigenous and Folks Strategies. New York: Advances in Economic Botany/NYBG, 1989, p. 174-188.

TRADITIONAL KNOWLEDGE: Yes • ENVIRONMENTAL MANAGEMENT: Yes • Indigenous People • RELEVANCE: High • SUBJECTS: Botany of cultivated species/Botany of collected species/Pedology • LOCATION: Gorotire Village, Pará (7°52'S - 51°13'W) • POPULATION: 91. Kayapó/Kaiapó/Caiapó/Mebegnokre/A'Ukre/Gorotire/Kriketum; Mekragnoti/Kuben-kran-Ken/Kokraimoro/Kubenkokre/Metuktire; Pukanu/Xikrin do Bacajá/Xikrin do Cateté/Kararaô (Mato Grosso/Pará).

645 PUBLICATION: Leeuwenberg, F. *Diagnóstico de caça e manejo da fauna cinegética com os índios Xavante, aldeia Etenhiritipá*. 1991/1993 Report. Mato Grosso: Centro de Pesquisa Indígena, 1995, p. 45.

TRADITIONAL KNOWLEDGE: Yes • ENVIRONMENTAL MANAGEMENT: Yes • Indigenous People • RELEVANCE: High • SUBJECTS: Zoology • LOCATION: RI Pimentel Barbosa - 243 • POPULATION: 192. Xavante/Akwe/Awen/Akwen (Mato Grosso).

646 PUBLICATION: Leeuwenberg, Frans. *Etno-Zoological Analysis and Wildlife Management in the Xavante territory, Pimentel Barbosa, Mato Grosso State - december 1990 - december 1992 - Report of two years study*. Mato Grosso: Centro de Pesquisa Indígena - CPI/Brazil, 1993, p. 39.

TRADITIONAL KNOWLEDGE: Yes • ENVIRONMENTAL MANAGEMENT: Yes • Indigenous People • RELEVANCE: High • SUBJECTS: Technology/Material culture/Zoology • LOCATION: RI Pimentel Barbosa - 243 • POPULATION: 192. Xavante/Akwe/Awen/Akwen (Mato Grosso).

647 PUBLICATION: Leeuwenberg, Susana de M.L.R. *Manejo de fauna na Floresta Nacional do Tapajós*. Relatório de Consultoria em Manejo de Fauna. Treinamento para o desenvolvimento de um sistema de Florestas Nacionais. FAO/Ibama, 1992, p. 38.

TRADITIONAL KNOWLEDGE: No • ENVIRONMENTAL MANAGEMENT: No • Nonindigenous • RELEVANCE: Fair • SUBJECTS: Zoology • LOCATION: Tapajós National Forest • POPULATION: Ribeirinhos/Caboclos/Seringueiros/Castanheiros.

648 PUBLICATION: Luz, P. F. L. da. *O uso de plantas psicoativas entre os Hupda*. Comunicação apresentada na ABA. Salvador, April 1996.

TRADITIONAL KNOWLEDGE: Yes • ENVIRONMENTAL MANAGEMENT: Yes • Indigenous People • RELEVANCE: High • SUBJECTS: Botany of cultivated species/Botany of collected species • LOCATION: • POPULATION: 109. Maku/Macu (Amazonas); Maku Yuhupde; Maku Hupdá; Maku Naded; Maku Dow; Maku Cacua e Nucak (Colombia).

651 PUBLICATION: Albert, B.; Milliken, W. The Use of Medicinel Plants by the Yanomami Indians of Brazil. *Economic Botany*, 50. New York: NYBG, 1996, p. 10-25.

TRADITIONAL KNOWLEDGE: Yes • ENVIRONMENTAL MANAGEMENT: No • Indigenous People • RELEVANCE: High • SUBJECTS: Botany of cultivated species/Botany of collected species/Pharmacology/Medicine/Cosmology • LOCATION: AI Yanomami - 585 • POPULATION: 200. Yanomami/Ianomâmi/Xirianá (Roraima/Amazonas); Yanoman/Sunumá/Ninam (Venezuela).

652 PUBLICATION: Albert, B.; Milliken, W. Plantas medicinais dos Yanomami. Uma nova visão dentro da etnobotânica de Roraima. In: Barboza, R. I.; Ferreira, E. J. G.; Castellón, E. G. (Eds.) *Homem, Ambiente e Ecologia no Estado de Roraima*. Brasil: Inpa, 1997, p. 85-110.

TRADITIONAL KNOWLEDGE: Yes • ENVIRONMENTAL MANAGEMENT: No • Indigenous People • RELEVANCE: High • SUBJECTS: Pharmacology/Medicine • LOCATION: AI Yanomami - 585 • POPULATION: 200. Yanomami/Ianomâmi/Xirianá (Roraima/Amazonas); Yanoman/Sunumá/Ninam (Venezuela).

660 PUBLICATION: Posey, D. A. Etnobiologia y ciencia "folk": su importancia para la Amazonia. *Hombre y Ambiente*: el punto de vista indígena, Ano 1(4), p. 7-26.

TRADITIONAL KNOWLEDGE: Yes • ENVIRONMENTAL MANAGEMENT: Yes • Indigenous People • RELEVANCE: High • SUBJECTS: Entomology • LOCATION: Kayapó Indians of the State of Pará • POPULATION: 91. Kayapó/Kaiapó/Caiapó/Mebegnokre/A'Ukre/Gorotire/Kriketum;

Mekragnoti/Kuben-kran-Ken/Kokraimoro/Kubenkokre/Metuktire; Pukanu/Xikrin do Bacajá/Xikrin do Cateté/Kararaô (Mato Grosso/Pará).

661 PUBLICATION: Posey, D. A. Folk Apiculture of the Kayapó Indians of Brazil. *Biotropica*, 15(2), 1983, p. 154-158.

TRADITIONAL KNOWLEDGE: Yes • ENVIRONMENTAL MANAGEMENT: Yes • Indigenous People • RELEVANCE: High • SUBJECTS: Entomology • LOCATION: Gorotire Village, Pará (7°52'S - 51°13'W) • POPULATION: 91. Kayapó/Kaiapó/Caiapó/Mebegnokre/A'Ukre/Gorotire/Kriketum; Mekragnoti/Kuben-kran-Ken/Kokraimoro/Kubenkokre/Metuktire; Pukanu/Xikrin do Bacajá/Xikrin do Cateté/Kararaô (Mato Grosso/Pará).

662 PUBLICATION: Posey, D. A. Hierarchy and Utility in a Folk Biological Taxonomic System: Patterns in Classification of Arthropods by the Kayapó Indians of Brazil. *Journal of Ethnobiology*, 4(2), 1984, p. 123-39.

TRADITIONAL KNOWLEDGE: Yes • ENVIRONMENTAL MANAGEMENT: Yes • Indigenous People • RELEVANCE: High • SUBJECTS: Entomology • LOCATION: Gorotire Village, Pará (7°52'S - 51°13'W) • POPULATION: 91. Kayapó/Kaiapó/Caiapó/Mebegnokre/A'Ukre/Gorotire/Kriketum; Mekragnoti/Kuben-kran-Ken/Kokraimoro/Kubenkokre/Metuktire; Pukanu/Xikrin do Bacajá/Xikrin do Cateté/Kararaô (Mato Grosso/Pará).

663 PUBLICATION: Posey, D. A. Native and Indigenous Guidelines for New Amazonian Development Strategies: Understanding Biological Diversity Through Ethnoecology. Hamming, J. (Ed.). *Impact on Forests and Rivers*: Change in the Amazon Basin. Manchester: Manchester University Press, 1985, p. 156-80.

TRADITIONAL KNOWLEDGE: Yes • ENVIRONMENTAL MANAGEMENT: Yes • Indigenous People • RELEVANCE: High • SUBJECTS: Botany of cultivated species/Botany of collected species/Pharmacology/Medicine/Icthyology/Fishing techniques/Pedology/Technology/Material culture/Zoology/Cosmology • LOCATION: Gorotire Village, Pará (7°52'S - 51°13'W) • POPULATION: 91. Kayapó/Kaiapó/Caiapó/Mebegnokre/A'Ukre/Gorotire/Kriketum; Mekragnoti/Kuben-kran-Ken/Kokraimoro/Kubenkokre/Metuktire; Pukanu/Xikrin do Bacajá/Xikrin do Cateté/Kararaô (Mato Grosso/Pará).

664 PUBLICATION: Posey, D. A.; Camargo, J. M. F. de. Additional Notes on the Classification and Knoledge of Stingless Bees (Meliponinae, Apidae, Hymenoptera) by the Kayapó Indians of Gorotire, Pará, Brasil. *Annal of Carnegie Museum of Natural History*, 54 - Article 8, 1985, p. 247-73.

TRADITIONAL KNOWLEDGE: Yes • ENVIRONMENTAL MANAGEMENT: Yes • Indigenous People • RELEVANCE: High • SUBJECTS: Entomology • LOCATION: Gorotire Village, Pará (7°52'S - 51°13'W) • POPULATION: 91. Kayapó/Kaiapó/Caiapó/Mebegnokre/A'Ukre/Gorotire/Kriketum; Mekragnoti/Kuben-kran-Ken/Kokraimoro/Kubenkokre/Metuktire; Pukanu/Xikrin do Bacajá/Xikrin do Cateté/Kararaô (Mato Grosso/Pará).

665 PUBLICATION: Posey, D. A. Indigenous Ecological Knowledge and Development of the Amazon. In: Moran, E. (Ed.). *The Dilemma of Amazonian Development*. Boulder, Colorado: Westview Press, 1984, p. 225-57.

TRADITIONAL KNOWLEDGE: Yes • ENVIRONMENTAL MANAGEMENT: Yes • Indigenous People • RELEVANCE: High • SUBJECTS: Art/Botany of cultivated species/Botany of collected species/Entomology/Pharmacology/Medicine/Icthyology/Fishing techniques/Pedology/Technology/Material culture/Zoology/Cosmology • LOCATION: Kayapó Indians of the State of Pará • POPULATION: 91. Kayapó/Kaiapó/Caiapó/Mebegnokre/A'Ukre/Gorotire/Kriketum; Mekragnoti/Kuben-kran-Ken/Kokraimoro/Kubenkokre/Metuktire; Pukanu/Xikrin do Bacajá/Xikrin do Cateté/Kararaô (Mato Grosso/Pará).

666 PUBLICATION: Posey, D. A. *Wasps, Warrions and Fearless Men*: Ethnoentomology of the Kayapo Indians of Central Brazil. Georgia: University of Georgia, dateless, p. 24.

TRADITIONAL KNOWLEDGE: Yes • ENVIRONMENTAL MANAGEMENT: No • Indigenous People • RELEVANCE: High • SUBJECTS: Entomology • LOCATION: Gorotire Village, Pará (7°52'S - 51°13'W) • POPULATION: 91. Kayapó/Kaiapó/Caiapó/Mebegnokre/A'Ukre/Gorotire/Kriketum; Mekragnoti/Kuben-kran-Ken/Kokraimoro/Kubenkokre/Metuktire; Pukanu/Xikrin do Bacajá/Xikrin do Cateté/Kararaô (Mato Grosso/Pará).

668 PUBLICATION: Posey, D. A. A Preliminary Report on Diversified Management of Tropical Forest by the Kayapo Indians of the Brazilian Amazon. In: Prance, G. T.; Kallunki, J. A. *Ethnobotany in the Neotropics*. New York: NYBG, 1984, p. 112-26.

TRADITIONAL KNOWLEDGE: Yes • ENVIRONMENTAL MANAGEMENT: Yes • Indigenous People • RELEVANCE: High • SUBJECTS: Botany of cultivated species/Botany of collected species • LOCATION: AI Kayapó - 173. • POPULATION: 91. Kayapó/Kaiapó/Caiapó/Mebegnokre/A'Ukre/Gorotire/Kriketum; Mekragnoti/Kuben-kran-Ken/Kokraimoro/Kubenkokre/Metuktire; Pukanu/Xikrin do Bacajá/Xikrin do Cateté/Kararaô (Mato Grosso/Pará).

670 PUBLICATION: Posey, D. A. The Importance of Bees to Kayapó Indians of the Brazilian Amazon. *Florida Entomologist*, 65(4), 1982, p. 452-8.

TRADITIONAL KNOWLEDGE: Yes • ENVIRONMENTAL MANAGEMENT: Yes • Indigenous People • RELEVANCE: High • SUBJECTS: Zoology • LOCATION: Gorotire Village, Pará (7°52'S - 51°13'W) • POPULATION: 91. Kayapó/Kaiapó/Caiapó/Mebegnokre/A'Ukre/Gorotire/Kriketum; Mekragnoti/Kuben-kran-Ken/Kokraimoro/Kubenkokre/Metuktire; Pukanu/Xikrin do Bacajá/Xikrin do Cateté/Kararaô (Mato Grosso/Pará).

671 PUBLICATION: Posey, D. A. *Ethnoentomology of the Gorotire Kayapó of Central Brazil*. Georgia: University of Georgia, Philosophy, 1979, p. 177.

TRADITIONAL KNOWLEDGE: Yes • ENVIRONMENTAL MANAGEMENT: Yes • Indigenous People • RELEVANCE: High • SUBJECTS: Botany of cultivated species/Botany of collected species/Entomology/Icthyology/Fishing techniques/Technology/Material culture/Zoology/Cosmology • LOCATION: Gorotire Village, Pará (7°52'S - 51°13'W) • POPULATION: 91. Kayapó/Kaiapó/Caiapó/Mebegnokre/A'Ukre/Gorotire/Kriketum; Mekragnoti/Kuben-kran-Ken/Kokraimoro/Kubenkokre/Metuktire; Pukanu/Xikrin do Bacajá/Xikrin do Cateté/Kararaô (Mato Grosso/Pará).

673 PUBLICATION: Prance, G. T. The Use of Edible Fungi by Amazonian Indians. In: Prance, G. T.; Kallunki, J. A. *Ethnobotany in the Neotropics*. New York: NYBG, 1984, p. 127-39.

TRADITIONAL KNOWLEDGE: Yes • ENVIRONMENTAL MANAGEMENT: No • Indigenous People • RELEVANCE: High • SUBJECTS: Botany of collected species • LOCATION: AI Yanomami - 585 • POPULATION: 200. Yanomami/Ianomâmi/Xirianá (Roraima/Amazonas); Yanoman/Sunumá/Ninam (Venezuela).

675 PUBLICATION: Ribeiro, B. G. *A civilização da palha*: a arte do trançado dos índios do Brasil. v. 1 and 2. São Paulo: USP/FFLCH, 1980, p. 590.

TRADITIONAL KNOWLEDGE: Yes • ENVIRONMENTAL MANAGEMENT: No • Indigenous People • RELEVANCE: High • SUBJECTS: Art/Botany of cultivated species/Botany of collected species/Technology/Material culture • LOCATION: Indians of Brazil • POPULATION: General Indians.

676 PUBLICATION: Ribeiro, B. G. Araweté: a índia vestida. In: *Revista de Antropologia*, 26 - Separata. São Paulo: USP/FFLCH, 1983, p. 38.

TRADITIONAL KNOWLEDGE: Yes • ENVIRONMENTAL MANAGEMENT: Yes • Indigenous People • RELEVANCE: High • SUBJECTS: Botany of cultivated species/Botany of collected species/Technology/Material culture • LOCATION: TI Awaweté, Igarapé Ipixuna • POPULATION: 14. Araweté/Arauété (Pará).

677 PUBLICATION: Kenhíri, T.; Ribeiro, B. G. Rainy Seasons and Constellations: The Desâna Economic Callendar. In: Posey, D. A.; Balée, W. (Eds.). *Resource Management in Amazonia*: Indigenous and Folks Strategies. New York: NYBG, 1989, p. 97-114.

TRADITIONAL KNOWLEDGE: Yes • ENVIRONMENTAL MANAGEMENT: Yes • Indigenous People • RELEVANCE: High • SUBJECTS: Astronomy/Botany of cultivated species/Botany of collected species/Entomology/Pharmacology/Medicine/Icthyology/Fishing techniques/Technology/Material culture/Zoology/Cosmology • LOCATION: AI Pari Cachoeira I - 238 • POPULATION: 33. Dessano/Desâna/Desano/Wira (Amazonas/Colombia).

678 PUBLICATION: Rolim, S. G. *Terra Indígena Panará*: perspectivas de manejo sustentado dos recursos naturais. Field report (version 1.0). 1997.

TRADITIONAL KNOWLEDGE: Yes • ENVIRONMENTAL MANAGEMENT: Yes • Indigenous People • RELEVANCE: High • SUBJECTS: Botany of cultivated species/Botany of collected species/Technology/Material culture • LOCATION: AI Panará - 813 • POPULATION: 132. Panará/Krenhakarore/Krenakore; Krenakarore/Índios Gigantes; Kreen-Akarore (Mato Grosso).

681 PUBLICATION: Santos, A. C. M. L. dos. Os Parakanã: quando o rumo da estrada e o cuso das águas perpassam a vida de um povo. São Paulo: USP/FFLCH, Antropologia Social, 1982, p. 177.

TRADITIONAL KNOWLEDGE: Yes • ENVIRONMENTAL MANAGEMENT: No • Indigenous People • RELEVANCE: High • SUBJECTS: Botany of cultivated species/Botany of collected species/Icthyology/Fishing techniques/Technology/Material culture/Zoology • LOCATION: AI Paracanã - 236 • POPULATION: 136. Parakanã/Paracanã/Apiterewa (Pará).

682 PUBLICATION: Santos, G. M. dos. Caracterização das espécies e variedades vegetais cultivadas pelos Paresi. *Gerando Debates*, Ano I (1). Belo Horizonte: UFMT/Gera, 1994, p. 71-82.

TRADITIONAL KNOWLEDGE: Yes • ENVIRONMENTAL MANAGEMENT: Yes • Indigenous People • RELEVANCE: High • SUBJECTS: Botany of cultivated species • LOCATION: RI Pareci - 237 • POPULATION: 137. Pareci/Paresi/Haliti (Mato Grosso).

686 PUBLICATION: Serpa, P. M. N. *Boé Épa*: o cultivo de roça entre os Bororo do Mato Grosso. São Paulo: USP/FFLCH, Antropologia, 1988, p. 392.

TRADITIONAL KNOWLEDGE: Yes • ENVIRONMENTAL MANAGEMENT: Yes • Indigenous People • RELEVANCE: High • SUBJECTS: Botany of cultivated species/Botany of collected species/Icthyology/Fishing techniques/Pedology/Technology/Material culture/Cosmology • LOCATION: AI Tadarinama • POPULATION: 28. Bororo/Boe (Mato Grosso).

689 PUBLICATION: Smole, W. J. Yanoama Horticulture in the Parima Highlands of Venezuela and Brazil. In: Posey, D. A.; Balée, W. (Eds.) *Resource Management in Amazonia*: Indigenous and Folks Strategies. New York: NYBG, 1989, p. 115-28.

TRADITIONAL KNOWLEDGE: Yes • ENVIRONMENTAL MANAGEMENT: Yes • Indigenous People • RELEVANCE: High • SUBJECTS: Botany of cultivated species/Entomology/Hidrologia/Pedology/Technology/Material culture/Zoology • LOCATION: AI Yanomami - 585 • POPULATION: 200. Yanomami/Ianomâmi/Xirianá (Roraima/Amazonas); Yanoman/Sunumá/Ninam (Venezuela).

694 PUBLICATION: Ziegler-Birraux, P. *Ashaninca Shamanic Healing Ritual and Song*. Austin: The University of Texas, Arts, 1991, p. 113.

TRADITIONAL KNOWLEDGE: Yes • ENVIRONMENTAL MANAGEMENT: No • Indigenous People • RELEVANCE: High • SUBJECTS: Botany of cultivated species/Botany of collected species/Pharmacology/Medicine • LOCATION: Ai Kampa do Rio Amônea - 158, AI Kampa do Rio Envira - 159, AI Kaxinawã do Rio Breu - 431 • POPULATION: 66. Kampa/Campa/Asháninka (Acre)/Ashaninka (Peru).

696 PUBLICATION: D'Antona, A. de O. *O verão, o inverno e o inverso*. Sobre o modo de vida de comunidades residentes na região do Parque Nacional dos Lençóis Maranhenses. Campinas: Unicamp, Antropologia Social, 1997, p. 244.

TRADITIONAL KNOWLEDGE: No • ENVIRONMENTAL MANAGEMENT: No • Non-indigenous • RELEVANCE: High • SUBJECTS: Botany of cultivated species/Icthyology/Fishing techniques/Technology/Material culture • LOCATION: Lençóis Maranhenses National Park • POPULATION: Fishers/Praieiros.

697 PUBLICATION: Posey, D. A.; Santos, P. B. dos. *Concepts of Health, Illness, Curing and Death Relation to Medicinal Plants and Appearance of the Messianic King of the Island of Lençóis, Maranhão, Brazil*. Brazil/USA: Universidade Federal do Maranhão/Carnegie Museum of Natural History, dateless, p. 27.

TRADITIONAL KNOWLEDGE: Yes • ENVIRONMENTAL MANAGEMENT: Yes • Non-indigenous • RELEVANCE: High • SUBJECTS: Pharmacology/Medicine • LOCATION: Island of Lençóis, Maranhão (1°22'S 44°54'W) • POPULATION: Praieiros.

698 PUBLICATION: Barthem, R. Pesca experimental e seletividade de redes de espera para espécies de peixes amazônicos. In: *Bol. Mus. Paraense Paraense Emílio Goeldi*, Zoology, 1 (1), CNCT, 1984, p. 57-88.

TRADITIONAL KNOWLEDGE: No • ENVIRONMENTAL MANAGEMENT: No • Non-indigenous • RELEVANCE: Fair • SUBJECTS: Icthyology/Fishing techniques • LOCATION: Central Amazon (lakes through the Amazon, Solimões, Japurá, Negro and Branco rivers) • POPULATION: Ribeirinhos/Caboclos/Seringueiros/Castanheiros.

699 PUBLICATION: Frazão, J. M. F.; Pinheiro, C. U. Integral Processing of Babassu Palm (*Orbignya phalerata*, Arecaceae) Fruts: village level production in Maranhão, Brazil. In: *Economic Botany*, 49 (1). New York: NYBG, 1995, p. 31-9.

TRADITIONAL KNOWLEDGE: No • ENVIRONMENTAL MANAGEMENT: No • Non-indigenous • RELEVANCE: High • SUBJECTS: Botany of cultivated species/Technology/Material culture • LOCATION: São Luiz Gonzaga, Maranhão • POPULATION: Babaçueiros.

700 PUBLICATION: Van den Berg, M. E.; Silva, M. H. L. Ethnobotany of a traditional ablution in Pará, Brazil. In: *Bol. Mus. Paraense Emílio Goeldi*, Botânica, 2 (2), MCT/CNCT, 1986, p. 213-8.

TRADITIONAL KNOWLEDGE: Yes • ENVIRONMENTAL MANAGEMENT: No • Non-indigenous • RELEVANCE: High • SUBJECTS: Pharmacology/Medicine • LOCATION: Belém, Pará • POPULATION: Ribeirinhos/Caboclos/Seringueiros/Castanheiros.

701 PUBLICATION: Van den Berg, M. E. Ver-o-peso: The ethnobotany of an Amazonian Market. In: Prance, G. T.; Kallunki, J. A. *The Neotropics*, Advances in Economic Botany 1. New York: NYBG, 1984, p. 140-9.

TRADITIONAL KNOWLEDGE: No • ENVIRONMENTAL MANAGEMENT: No • Non-indigenous • RELEVANCE: High • SUBJECTS: Botany of collected species/Pharmacology/Medicine/Technology/Material culture • LOCATION: Belém, Pará • POPULATION: Ribeirinhos/Caboclos/Seringueiros/Castanheiros.

702 PUBLICATION: Strudwick, J.; Sobel, G. Uses of *Euterpe oleracea* Mart. in the Amazon Estuary, Brazil. In: Ballick, M. J. *The Palm-Tree of Life: Biology, Utilization and Conservation*, Advances in Economic Botany 6. New York: NYBG, 1988, p. 225-53.

TRADITIONAL KNOWLEDGE: Yes • ENVIRONMENTAL MANAGEMENT: Yes • Non-indigenous • RELEVANCE: High • SUBJECTS: Botany of collected species • LOCATION: State of Pará • POPULATION: Ribeirinhos/Caboclos/Seringueiros/Castanheiros.

703 PUBLICATION: Posey, D. A.; Frechione, J.; Coirolo, A. D. The perception of ecological zone and natural resources in the Brazilian Amazon: an ethnoecology of Lake Coari. In: Posey, D. A.; Ballé. *Amazonia: Indigenous and Folk Strategies*. New York: NYBG, 1989, p. 260-82.

TRADITIONAL KNOWLEDGE: Yes • ENVIRONMENTAL MANAGEMENT: Yes • Non-indigenous • RELEVANCE: High • SUBJECTS: Botany of collected species/Icthyology/Fishing techniques/Pedology/Technology/Material culture • LOCATION: Lake Coari microregion, Amazonas • POPULATION: Ribeirinhos/Caboclos/Seringueiros/Castanheiros.

704 PUBLICATION: Silva, L. F. Atividades e tradições dos grupos ceramistas do Maruanum, Amapá. *Bol. do Mus. Paraense Emílio Goeldi*, Antropologia, 7(1), SCT/CNCT, 1991, p. 73-94.

TRADITIONAL KNOWLEDGE: No • ENVIRONMENTAL MANAGEMENT: No • Non-indigenous • RELEVANCE: High • SUBJECTS: Pedology/Technology/Material culture • LOCATION: Maruanum Village, Amapá (0°15'N 51°20'W) • POPULATION: Ribeirinhos/Caboclos/Seringueiros/Castanheiros.

716 PUBLICATION: Figueiredo, N. Os "bichos" que curam: os animais e a medicina de "folk" em Belém do Pará. *Bol. Mus. Paraense Emílio Goeldi*, Antropologia, 10(1), 1994, p. 75-91.

TRADITIONAL KNOWLEDGE: Yes • ENVIRONMENTAL MANAGEMENT: No • Non-indigenous • RELEVANCE: Fair • SUBJECTS: Pharmacology/Medicine/Zoology • LOCATION: Belém, Pará • POPULATION: Ribeirinhos/Caboclos/Seringueiros/Castanheiros.

720 PUBLICATION: Jardim, M. A. G.; Mesquita, S. A. J. Avaliação das populações nativas de açaizeriro (*Euterpe oleracea*) na comunidade do Rio Marajoí, Município de Gurupá (PA). *Bol. Mus. Paraense Emílio Goeldi*, Botânica, 12(2), MCT/CNCT, 1996, p. 265-9.

TRADITIONAL KNOWLEDGE: No • ENVIRONMENTAL MANAGEMENT: Yes • Non-indigenous • RELEVANCE: Fair • SUBJECTS: Botany of collected species/Technology/Material culture • LOCATION: Marajoí river, in Gurupá, Pará • POPULATION: Ribeirinhos/Caboclos/Seringueiros/Castanheiros.

721 PUBLICATION: Acevedo, R.; Castro, E. Práticas agro-extrativistas de grupos negros do Trombetas. In: Castro, E.; Pinton, F. *Faces do trópico úmido, conceitos e questões sobre desenvolvimento e meio ambiente*. Belém: UFPA/NAEA, Cejup, 1997, p. 375-420.

TRADITIONAL KNOWLEDGE: No • ENVIRONMENTAL MANAGEMENT: No • Non-indigenous • RELEVANCE: Fair • SUBJECTS: Botany of cultivated species/Icthyology/Fishing techniques • LOCATION: Trombetas river/Pará • POPULATION: Ribeirinhos/Caboclos/Seringueiros/Castanheiros.

722 PUBLICATION: Parker, E. P. A Neglected Human Resource in Amazonia: The Amazon Caboclo. In: Posey, D. A.; Ballée, W. *Amazonia: Indigenous and Folk Strategies*, Advances in Economic Botany 7. New York: NYBG, 1989, p. 249-59.

TRADITIONAL KNOWLEDGE: No • ENVIRONMENTAL MANAGEMENT: No • Non-indigenous • RELEVANCE: Fair • SUBJECTS: Botany of cultivated species • LOCATION: Amazon Region • POPULATION: Ribeirinhos/Caboclos/Seringueiros/Castanheiros.

723 PUBLICATION: Giugliano, L. G.; Giugliano, R.; Shrimpton, R. Estudos nutricionais das populações rurais da Amazônia. *Acta Amazônica*, 11 (4), 1981, p. 773-88.

TRADITIONAL KNOWLEDGE: No • ENVIRONMENTAL MANAGEMENT: No • Non-indigenous • RELEVANCE: Fair • SUBJECTS: Botany of cultivated species • LOCATION: Families through the Solimões river, Amazonas • POPULATION: Ribeirinhos/Caboclos/Seringueiros/Castanheiros.

730 PUBLICATION: Schwartzman, S. *The Panara of the Xingu National Park*: The Transformation of a Society. Chicago: University of Chicago, Departament of Anthropology, 1988, p. 484.

TRADITIONAL KNOWLEDGE: Yes • ENVIRONMENTAL MANAGEMENT: Yes • Indigenous People • RELEVANCE: High • SUBJECTS: Botany of cultivated species/Botany of collected species/Entomology/Pharmacology/Medicine/Icthyology/Fishing techniques/Technology/Material culture/Zoology/Cosmology • LOCATION: AI Panará - 813 • POPULATION: 132. Panará/Krenhakarore/Krenakore; Krenakarore/Índios Gigantes; Kreen-Akarore (Mato Grosso): 91. Kayapó/Kaiapó/Caiapó/Mebegnokre/A'Ukre/Gorotire/Kriketum; Mekragnoti/Kuben-kran-Ken/Kokraimoro/Kubenkokre/Metuktire; Pukanu/Xikrin do Bacajá/Xikrin do Cateté/Kararaô (Mato Grosso/Pará).

731 PUBLICATION: Turner, T. *Environment and Cultural Classification: A Study of the Northern Kayapó*. Harvard University, Department of Anthropology, 1967, p. 190.

TRADITIONAL KNOWLEDGE: Yes • ENVIRONMENTAL MANAGEMENT: Yes • Indigenous People • RELEVANCE: High • SUBJECTS: Botany of cultivated species/Botany of collected species/Pharmacology/Medicine/Zoology/Cosmology • LOCATION: Gorotire Village (Pará) (7°52'S - 51°13'W) • POPULATION: 91. Kayapó/Kaiapó/Caiapó/Mebegnokre/A'Ukre/Gorotire/Kriketum; Mekragnoti/Kuben-kran-Ken/Kokraimoro/Kubenkokre/Metuktire; Pukanu/Xikrin do Bacajá/Xikrin do Cateté/Kararaô (Mato Grosso/Pará).

732 PUBLICATION: Giannini, I. V. *A ave resgatada*: a impossibilidade da leveza do ser. São Paulo: USP/FFLCH, Antropologia, 1991, p. 205.

TRADITIONAL KNOWLEDGE: Yes • ENVIRONMENTAL MANAGEMENT: No • Indigenous People • RELEVANCE: High • SUBJECTS: Astronomy/Botany of collected species/Pharmacology/Medicine/Cosmology • LOCATION: AI Xikrin do Cateté - 80. • POPULATION: 91. Kayapó/Kaiapó/Caiapó/Mebegnokre/A'Ukre/Gorotire/Kriketum; Mekragnoti/Kuben-kran-Ken/Kokraimoro/Kubenkokre/Metuktire; Pukanu/Xikrin do Bacajá/Xikrin do Cateté/Kararaô (Mato Grosso/Pará).

733 PUBLICATION: Posey, D. A. Indigenous Knowledge and Development: An Ideological Bridge to the Future. *Ciência e Cultura*, 35 (7), SBPC, 1983, p. 877-95.

TRADITIONAL KNOWLEDGE: Yes • ENVIRONMENTAL MANAGEMENT: Yes • Indigenous People • RELEVANCE: High • SUBJECTS: Botany of cultivated species/Botany of collected species/Pharmacology/Medicine/Cosmology • LOCATION: Gorotire Village, Pará (7°52'S - 51°13'W) • POPULATION: 91. Kayapó/Kaiapó/Caiapó/Mebegnokre/A'Ukre/Gorotire/Kriketum; Mekragnoti/Kuben-kran-Ken/Kokraimoro/Kubenkokre/Metuktire; Pukanu/Xikrin do Bacajá/Xikrin do Cateté/Kararaô (Mato Grosso/Pará).

734 PUBLICATION: Posey, D. A.; Camargo, J. M. F. de. O conhecimento dos Kayapó sobre as abelhas sociais sem ferrão (Meliponidae, Apidae, Hymenopetera): notas adicionais. *Bol. Mus. Paraense Paraense Emílio Goeldi*, Zoology, 6 (1), SCT/CNPq/MPEG, 1990, p. 17-42.

TRADITIONAL KNOWLEDGE: Yes • ENVIRONMENTAL MANAGEMENT: No • Indigenous People • RELEVANCE: High • SUBJECTS: Entomology • LOCATION: Gorotire Village, Pará (7°52'S - 51°13'W) • POPULATION: 91. Kayapó/Kaiapó/Caiapó/Mebegnokre/A'Ukre/Gorotire/Kriketum; Mekragnoti/Kuben-kran-Ken/Kokraimoro/Kubenkokre/Metuktire; Pukanu/Xikrin do Bacajá/Xikrin do Cateté/Kararaô (Mato Grosso/Pará).

735 PUBLICATION: Castro, E. V.; Teixeira, C. S. *Fitofisionomia da Área Indígena Arawaté-igarapé Ipixuna, Médio Xingu, Pará* (Preliminary study, with anthropologic commentaries). São Paulo: CEDI, 1992, p. 125.

TRADITIONAL KNOWLEDGE: Yes • ENVIRONMENTAL MANAGEMENT: No • Indigenous People • RELEVANCE: High • SUBJECTS: Art/Botany of cultivated species/Botany of collected species/Cosmology • LOCATION: AI Araweté do Igarapé Ipixuna • POPULATION: 14. Araweté/Araueté (Pará).

736 PUBLICATION: Posey, D. A. Apicultura popular dos Kayapó. *Atualidade Indígena*, n. 20, Funai, 1981, p. 36-41.

TRADITIONAL KNOWLEDGE: Yes • ENVIRONMENTAL MANAGEMENT: No • Indigenous People • RELEVANCE: High • SUBJECTS: Entomology • LOCATION: Kayapó Indians of the State of Pará • POPULATION: 91. Kayapó/Kaiapó/Caiapó/Mebegnokre/A'Ukre/Gorotire/Kriketum; Mekragnoti/Kuben-kran-Ken/Kokraimoro/Kubenkokre/Metuktire; Pukanu/Xikrin do Bacajá/Xikrin do Cateté/Kararaô (Mato Grosso/Pará).

738 PUBLICATION: Morais, R. M. G. G. *Os Paresí-Wáimare e o uso de plantas medicinais, Mato Grosso (Brasil)*. Cuiabá: Universidade Federal do Mato Grosso, Instituto Saúde Coletiva, Programa de Pós-Graduação Saúde e Ambiente, Área Etnobotânica, 1998.

TRADITIONAL KNOWLEDGE: Yes • ENVIRONMENTAL MANAGEMENT: No • Indigenous People • RELEVANCE: High • SUBJECTS: Botany of cultivated species/Botany of collected species/Pharmacology/Medicine/Technology/Material culture/Cosmology • LOCATION: AI Tirecatinga - 315, AI Utiariti - 331 • POPULATION: 137. Pareci/Paresi/Haliti (Mato Grosso).

746 PUBLICATION: Frikel, P. *Os Tiriyó*: seu sistema adaptativo. Hannover: Völkerkundliche Abhandlungen, Band V, 1973, p. 243.

TRADITIONAL KNOWLEDGE: Yes • ENVIRONMENTAL MANAGEMENT: No • Indigenous People • RELEVANCE: High • SUBJECTS: Art/Botany of cultivated species/Botany of collected species/Pharmacology/Medicine/Icthyology/Fishing techniques/Technology/Material culture/Zoology/Cosmology • LOCATION: PQ Tumucumaque Park - 323 • POPULATION: 166. Tiryó/Trio/Torona/Yawi/Pianokoto; Piano (Pará/Suriname).

750 PUBLICATION: Montagner, D. *O mundo dos espíritos*: estudo etnográfico dos ritos de cura Marubo. v. I and II. Brasília: Universidade de Brasília, Instituto de Ciências Humanas, Departamento de Ciências Sociais, 1985, p. 601.

TRADITIONAL KNOWLEDGE: Yes • ENVIRONMENTAL MANAGEMENT: No • Indigenous People • RELEVANCE: High • SUBJECTS: Botany of cultivated species/Botany of collected species/Pharmacology/Medicine/Icthyology/Fishing techniques/Technology/Material culture/Zoology • LOCATION: AI Vale do Javari • POPULATION: 112. Marubo (Amazonas).

755 PUBLICATION: Carrara, E. *Tsi Tewara*: um vôo sobre o cerrado Xavante. v. I and II. São Paulo: USP/FFLCH, Departamento de Antropologia, 1997, p. 323.

TRADITIONAL KNOWLEDGE: Yes • ENVIRONMENTAL MANAGEMENT: No • Indigenous People • RELEVANCE: High • SUBJECTS: Arte/Botany of cultivated species/Botany of collected species/Entomology/Technology/Material culture/Zoology/Cosmology • LOCATION: Xavante Indians of the State of Mato Grosso • POPULATION: 192. Xavante/Akwe/Awen/Akwen (Mato Grosso).

756 PUBLICATION: Velthem, L. H. van. *A pele de Tulupere*: estudos dos trançados Wayana-Aparai. São Paulo: USP/FFLCH, Antropologia Social, 1984, p. 307.

TRADITIONAL KNOWLEDGE: Yes • ENVIRONMENTAL MANAGEMENT: Yes • Indigenous People • RELEVANCE: High • SUBJECTS: Arte/Botany of cultivated species/Botany of collected species/Icthyology/Fishing techniques/Technology/Material culture/Cosmology • LOCATION:

Tumucumaque Park - 323 • POPULATION: 189. Wayana/Waiana/Uaiana (Pará/Suriname/French Guiana)/5. Aparai (Pará) 6. Apiaká (Mato Grosso) 7. Apinayé/Apinajé/Apinaié (Tocantins).

758 PUBLICATION: Hartamann, T. *A nomenclatura botânica dos Borôro*: materiais para um ensaio atno-botânico. São Paulo: IEB/USP, 1967, p. 81.

TRADITIONAL KNOWLEDGE: Yes • ENVIRONMENTAL MANAGEMENT: No • Indigenous People • RELEVANCE: High • SUBJECTS: Botany of cultivated species/Botany of collected species • LOCATION: Bororo Indians of the State of Mato Grosso • POPULATION: 28. Bororo/Boe (Mato Grosso).

759 PUBLICATION: Galvão, E.; Oliveira, A. E. de. A cerâmica dos índios Juruna (Rio Xingu). *Bol. Mus. Paraense Emílio Goeldi*, Antropologia, n. 41, SCT/CNPq/MPEG, 1969, p. 1-23.

TRADITIONAL KNOWLEDGE: Yes • ENVIRONMENTAL MANAGEMENT: No • Indigenous People • RELEVANCE: High • SUBJECTS: Arte/Botany of collected species/Technology/Material culture • LOCATION: Xingu Park - 346 • POPULATION: 55. Juruna/Yuruna/Yudjá (Pará).

760 PUBLICATION: No data.

TRADITIONAL KNOWLEDGE: Yes • ENVIRONMENTAL MANAGEMENT: No • Indigenous People • RELEVANCE: High • SUBJECTS: Pharmacology/Medicine/Cosmology • LOCATION: Wayana-Aparai (0°30' and 3°30'N - 54° and 55°30'W) • POPULATION: 189. Wayana/Waiana/Uaiana (Pará/Suriname/French Guiana).

765 PUBLICATION: Dufour, D. L. Insects as Food: a case study from the Northwest Amazon. *American Anthropologist*, 89(2), 1987, p. 383-97.

TRADITIONAL KNOWLEDGE: Yes • ENVIRONMENTAL MANAGEMENT: No • Indigenous People • RELEVANCE: High • SUBJECTS: Entomology • LOCATION: Ai Yaureté - 119 • POPULATION: 172. Tukano/Tucano (Amazonas/Colombia).

768 PUBLICATION: Anderson, A. B. W.; Posey, D. A. Reforestacion Indigena. dateless, p. 66-78.

TRADITIONAL KNOWLEDGE: Yes • ENVIRONMENTAL MANAGEMENT: Yes • Indigenous People • RELEVANCE: High • SUBJECTS: Botany of cultivated species • LOCATION: Gorotire Village, Pará (7°52'S - 51°13'W) • POPULATION: 91. Kayapó/Kaiapó/Caiapó/Mebegnokre/A'Ukre/Gorotire/Kriketum; Mekragnoti/Kuben-kran-Ken/Kokraimoro/Kubenkokre/Metuktire; Pukanu/Xikrin do Bacajá/Xikrin do Cateté/Kararaô (Mato Grosso/Pará).

775 PUBLICATION: Reichel-Dolmatoff, G. O contexto cultural de um alucinógeno aborígine. In: Coelho, V. P. Os alucinógenos e o mundo Yesbólico. São Paulo: EPU/EDUSP, 1976, p. 59-103.

TRADITIONAL KNOWLEDGE: Yes • ENVIRONMENTAL MANAGEMENT: No • Indigenous People • RELEVANCE: High • SUBJECTS: Pharmacology/Medicine/Cosmology • LOCATION: Amazon • POPULATION: General Indians.

780 PUBLICATION: Posey, D. A.; Frechione, J.; Silva, L. F. et al. Ethnoecology as applied anthropology in Amazonian development. In: *Human Organization, Journal of the Society for Applied Anthropology*, 43(2), 1984, p. 95-107.

TRADITIONAL KNOWLEDGE: Yes • ENVIRONMENTAL MANAGEMENT: Yes • Indigenous People • RELEVANCE: High • SUBJECTS: Botany of cultivated species/Botany of collected species/Entomology/Pharmacology/Medicine/Icthyology/Fishing techniques/Technology/Material culture/Zoology/Cosmology • LOCATION: Amazon • POPULATION: General Indians.

800 PUBLICATION: Frikel, P.; Cavalcante, P. B. *A farmacopéia Tiriyó*. Belém: CNP/Inpa/ MPEG. Publicações Avulsas n. 24, 1973: 145.

TRADITIONAL KNOWLEDGE: Yes • ENVIRONMENTAL MANAGEMENT: No • Indigenous People • RELEVANCE: High • SUBJECTS: Botany of cultivated species/Botany of collected species/Pharmacology/Medicine/Technology/Material culture • LOCATION: Tumucumaque Park - 323 • POPULATION: 166. Tiryó/Trio/Torona/Yawi/Pianokoto; Piano (Pará/Suriname).

802 PUBLICATION: Frikel, P. *Os Xikrin*: equipamentos e técnicas de subsistência. Belém: CNP/INPA/Museu Paraense Emílio Goeldi. Publicações Avulsas n. 7, 1968.

TRADITIONAL KNOWLEDGE: Yes • ENVIRONMENTAL MANAGEMENT: Yes • Indigenous People • RELEVANCE: High • SUBJECTS: Botany of cultivated species/Botany of collected species/Icthyology/Fishing techniques/Technology/Material culture/Zoology • LOCATION: AI Xikrin do Cateté • POPULATION: 91. Kayapó/Kaiapó/Caiapó/Mebegnokre/A'Ukre/Gorotire/Kriketum; Mekragnoti/Kuben-kran-Ken/Kokraimoro/Kubenkokre/Metuktire; Pukanu/Xikrin do Bacajá/Xikrin do Cateté/Kararaô (Mato Grosso/Pará).

808 PUBLICATION: Figueiredo, N. *Rezadores, pajés & puçangas*. Belém: Boitempo/UFPA, 1979, p. 96.

TRADITIONAL KNOWLEDGE: Yes • ENVIRONMENTAL MANAGEMENT: No • Non-indigenous • RELEVANCE: High • SUBJECTS: Botany of cultivated species/Botany of collected species/Pharmacology/Medicine • LOCATION: Belém, Pará • POPULATION: Ribeirinhos/Caboclos/Seringueiros/Castanheiros.

816 PUBLICATION: Alho, C. J. R. Maneje com cuidado: frágil. In: *Ciência Hoje*, 8 (46), SBPC, 1988, p. 40-7.

TRADITIONAL KNOWLEDGE: No • ENVIRONMENTAL MANAGEMENT: No • Non-indigenous • RELEVANCE: Fair • SUBJECTS: Botany of cultivated species/Zoology • LOCATION: Amazon region • POPULATION: Ribeirinhos/Caboclos/Seringueiros/Castanheiros.

817 PUBLICATION: Ribeiro, C. Mamirauá: preservar a natureza e integrar o homem. In: *Ecologia e desenvolvimento*, ano 2, n. 33, 1993, p. 4-9.

TRADITIONAL KNOWLEDGE: Yes • ENVIRONMENTAL MANAGEMENT: No • Non-indigenous • RELEVANCE: Fair • SUBJECTS: Icthyology/Fishing techniques/Technology/Material culture • LOCATION: Mamirauá Ecological Station, Amazonas • POPULATION: Ribeirinhos/Caboclos/Seringueiros/Castanheiros.

821 PUBLICATION: Comissão Pastoral da Terra. *Os ribeirinhos. Preservação dos lagos, defesa do meio ambiente e a pesca comercial.* Comissão Pastoral da Terra, Regional AM/RR, 1991. 19 p.

TRADITIONAL KNOWLEDGE: Yes • ENVIRONMENTAL MANAGEMENT: No • Non-indigenous • RELEVANCE: Fair • SUBJECTS: Icthyology/Fishing techniques/Technology/Material culture • LOCATION: Amazon region • POPULATION: Ribeirinhos/Caboclos/Seringueiros/Castanheiros.

822 PUBLICATION: Maués, R. H. Aplicação combinada dos modelos etnocientíficos e de tomada de decisão ao estudo da medicina popular. *Ciência e Cultura*, 31 (10), SBPC, 1979, p. 1155-1160.

TRADITIONAL KNOWLEDGE: Yes • ENVIRONMENTAL MANAGEMENT: No • Non-indigenous • RELEVANCE: Fair • SUBJECTS: Botany of collected species/Pharmacology/Medicine • LOCATION: State of Pará coast (Itapuá Village) • POPULATION: Ribeirinhos/Caboclos/Seringueiros/Castanheiros.

824 PUBLICATION: Couto, C. P.; Uchoa, P. *Comunidades da Flona Tapajós*: estudo sócio-econômico. Santarém: Ibama-MMA/Dirped/Depes/Dipen, 1994. 39 p.

TRADITIONAL KNOWLEDGE: Yes • ENVIRONMENTAL MANAGEMENT: No • Non-indigenous • RELEVANCE: Fair • SUBJECTS: Botany of cultivated species/Botany of collected species/Icthyology/Fishing techniques/Technology/Material culture • LOCATION: Tapajós National Forest • POPULATION: Ribeirinhos/Caboclos/Seringueiros/Castanheiros.

836 PUBLICATION: Prance, G. T.; Lisboa, P. L. B.; Maciel, U. N. Perdendo Rondônia. *Ciência Hoje*, 6 (36), SBPC, 1987, p. 48-56.

TRADITIONAL KNOWLEDGE: Yes • ENVIRONMENTAL MANAGEMENT: No • Non-indigenous • RELEVANCE: Fair • SUBJECTS: Botany of collected species • LOCATION: State of Rondônia • POPULATION: Ribeirinhos/Caboclos/Seringueiros/Castanheiros.

837 PUBLICATION: Prance, G. T. An ethnobotanical comparison of four tribes of Amazonian indians. *Acta Amazônica*, 2(2), s/d, p. 7-27.

TRADITIONAL KNOWLEDGE: Yes • ENVIRONMENTAL MANAGEMENT: No • Indigenous People • RELEVANCE: High • SUBJECTS: Botany of cultivated species/Botany of collected species • LOCATION: AI Paraná Boá-Boá - 468, AI Yanomami - 585, Deni of Tapauá River (6°21'S - 67°40'W), TI Caititu - 67 • POPULATION: 109. Maku/Macu (Amazonas); Maku Yuhupde; Maku Hupdá; Maku Naded; Maku Dow; Maku Cacua e Nucak (Colombia)/200. Yanomami/Ianomâmi/Xirianá (Roraima/Amazonas); Yanoman/Sunumá/Ninam (Venezuela)/32. Deni (Amazonas)/49. Jamamadi/Yamamadi/Djeoromitxi (Amazonas).

838 PUBLICATION: No data.

TRADITIONAL KNOWLEDGE: Yes • ENVIRONMENTAL MANAGEMENT: Yes • Indigenous People • RELEVANCE: High • SUBJECTS: Arte/Botany of cultivated species/Botany of collected species/Entomology/Pharmacology/Medicine/Icthyology/Fishing techniques/Pedology/Technology/Material culture/Zoology/Cosmology • LOCATION: Amazonia • POPULATION: 181. Wai-Wai/Waiwai (Roraima/Amazonas/Pará)/62. Kamayurá/Camaiurá (Mato Grosso)/91. Kayapó/Kaiapó/

Caiapó/Mebegnokre/A'Ukre/Gorotire/Kriketum/; Mekragnoti/Kuben-kran-Ken/Kokraimoro/Kubenkokre/Metuktire; Pukanu/Xikrin do Bacajá/Xikrin do Cateté/Kararaô (Mato Grosso/Pará).

840 PUBLICATION: Prance, G. T. et al. The Ethnobotany of the Paumarí indians. *Economic Botany*. New York: NYBG, dateless, p. 129-39.
TRADITIONAL KNOWLEDGE: Yes • ENVIRONMENTAL MANAGEMENT: No • Indigenous People • RELEVANCE: High • SUBJECTS: Botany of cultivated species/Botany of collected species/Pharmacology/Medicine • LOCATION: AI Parimari do Lago Marahã - 472 • POPULATION: 142. Paumari/Palmari (Amazonas).

842 PUBLICATION: Brewer-Carias, C.; Steyermark, J. A. Hallucinogenic Snuff Drugs of the Yanomamo Caburiwe-Teri in the Cauaburi River, Brazil. *Economic Botany*, 30. New York: NYBG, 1976, p. 57-66.
TRADITIONAL KNOWLEDGE: No • ENVIRONMENTAL MANAGEMENT: No • Indigenous People • RELEVANCE: High • SUBJECTS: Botany of cultivated species/Botany of collected species • LOCATION: AI Yanomami - 585 • POPULATION: 200. Yanomami/Ianomâmi/Xirianá (Roraima/Amazonas); Yanoman/Sunumá/Ninam (Venezuela).

843 PUBLICATION: Chagnon, N. A.; Le Quessne, P.; Cook, J. M. Yanomamö Hallucinogens: Anthropological, Botanical, and Chemical Findings. *Current Anthropology*, 12(1), 1971, p. 72-74.
TRADITIONAL KNOWLEDGE: Yes • ENVIRONMENTAL MANAGEMENT: No • Indigenous People • RELEVANCE: High • SUBJECTS: Botany of cultivated species/Botany of collected species/Pharmacology/Medicine • LOCATION: AI Yanomami - 585 • POPULATION: 200. Yanomami/Ianomâmi/Xirianá (Roraima/Amazonas); Yanoman/Sunumá/Ninam (Venezuela).

845 PUBLICATION: Dufour, D. L. Use of Tropical Rainforests by Native Amazonians. *Bioscience*, 4(9), 1990, p. 652-9.
TRADITIONAL KNOWLEDGE: Yes • ENVIRONMENTAL MANAGEMENT: Yes • Indigenous People • RELEVANCE: High • SUBJECTS: Botany of cultivated species/Botany of collected species/Entomology/Pharmacology/Medicine/Icthyology/Fishing techniques/Technology/Material culture/Zoology • LOCATION: AI Upper Rio Negro - 766 • POPULATION: 172. Tukano/Tucano (Amazonas/Colombia).

847 PUBLICATION: Balée, William. *Footprints of the Forest - Kaapor Etnobotany: The Historical Ecology of Plants Utilization by an Amazoniam People*. New York: Columbia University Press, 1993, 396 p.
TRADITIONAL KNOWLEDGE: Yes • ENVIRONMENTAL MANAGEMENT: Yes • Indigenous People • RELEVANCE: High • SUBJECTS: Art/Botany of cultivated species/Botany of collected species/Pharmacology/Medicine/Hidrology/Icthyology/Fishing techniques/Pedology/Technology/Material culture/Cosmology • LOCATION: AI Alto Turiaçu - 8 • POPULATION: 56. Kaapor/Urubu-Kaapor/Ka'apor/Kaaporté (Maranhão).

864 PUBLICATION: Andrade, J. de. F*olclore na região do Salgado, Pará*: Teredos na alimentação, profissões ribeirinhas. São Paulo: Escola de Folclore, 1979, p. 9-69.
TRADITIONAL KNOWLEDGE: Yes • ENVIRONMENTAL MANAGEMENT: No • Non-indigenous • RELEVANCE: Fair • SUBJECTS: Pharmacology/Medicine/Pedology/Technology/Material culture/Cosmology • LOCATION: Vigia, Pará • POPULATION: Praieiros.

875 PUBLICATION: Viana, V. M. et al. *Deforestation, Decay of Brazilnut Populations in Pastures and Forest Policies in the Amazon: the Case of Xapuri*. Draft, 1998. ESALQ/FEALQ/CAEX.
TRADITIONAL KNOWLEDGE: No • ENVIRONMENTAL MANAGEMENT: No • Non-indigenous • RELEVANCE: Fair • SUBJECTS: Botany of cultivated species/Botany of collected species/Technology/Material culture • LOCATION: Xapuri (10°40'S - 68°30'W), Acre. • POPULATION: Ribeirinhos/Caboclos/Seringueiros/Castanheiros.

876 PUBLICATION: Dubois, J. C. L. et al. *Manual agroflorestal para a Amazônia*. Rio de Janeiro: Rebraf, 1996, 27 p.
TRADITIONAL KNOWLEDGE: No • ENVIRONMENTAL MANAGEMENT: No • Non-indigenous • RELEVANCE: Fair • SUBJECTS: Botany of cultivated species/Botany of collected species/Technology/Material culture • LOCATION: Amazon region • POPULATION: Ribeirinhos/Caboclos/Seringueiros/Castanheiros.

877 PUBLICATION: Viana, V. M. Ecologia e manejo de populações de castanha-do-Pará em reservas extativistas Xapuri, Estado do Acre. In: Gascon, C.; Montinho, P. (Eds.). *Floresta Amazônica*: dinâmica, regeneração e manejo. INPA, 1998.
TRADITIONAL KNOWLEDGE: No • ENVIRONMENTAL MANAGEMENT: Yes • Non-indigenous • RELEVANCE: Fair • SUBJECTS: Botany of cultivated species/Botany of collected species/Technology/Material culture • LOCATION: Xapuri, Acre • POPULATION: Ribeirinhos/Caboclos/Seringueiros/Castanheiros.

882 PUBLICATION: Hutter, L. M. O emprego da madeira e outras matérias-primas do Brasil na construção naval. *Revista da SBPH*, n. 2, 1984/5, p. 15-52.
TRADITIONAL KNOWLEDGE: No • ENVIRONMENTAL MANAGEMENT: No • Non-indigenous • RELEVANCE: High • SUBJECTS: Botany of collected species/Technology/Material culture • LOCATION: Amazonia • POPULATION: Jangadeiros/Praieiros.

885 PUBLICATION: Peret, J.A. Amazonas: história, gente, costumes. Brasília/Manaus: Senado Federal, Centro Gráfico, 1985. 218 p.
TRADITIONAL KNOWLEDGE: No • ENVIRONMENTAL MANAGEMENT: No • Non-indigenous • RELEVANCE: Fair • SUBJECTS: Art/Pharmacology/Medicine/Technology/Material culture • LOCATION: State of Amazonas • POPULATION: Ribeirinhos/Caboclos/Seringueiros/Castanheiros.

902 PUBLICATION: Diegues, A. C. S. Povos e mares. São Paulo: Nupaub-USO, 1995. 269 p.
TRADITIONAL KNOWLEDGE: No • ENVIRONMENTAL MANAGEMENT: No • Non-indigenous • RELEVANCE: Fair • SUBJECTS: Hidrologia/Icthyology/Fishing techniques • LOCATION: Amazon region • POPULATION: Ribeirinhos/Caboclos/Seringueiros/Castanheiros.

903 PUBLICATION: Schmink, M. O desafio do desenvolvimento sustentável e as comunidades locais da Amazônia brasileira. *Anais Conf.: Abordagens interdisciplinares para a conservação da biodiversidade e dinâmica do uso da terra no novo mundo*. Belo Horizonte: UFMG/University of Florida, 1995, p. 79-88.
TRADITIONAL KNOWLEDGE: Yes • ENVIRONMENTAL MANAGEMENT: Yes • Non-indigenous • RELEVANCE: Fair • SUBJECTS: Botany of cultivated species/Botany of collected species • LOCATION: State of Acre • POPULATION: Ribeirinhos/Caboclos/Seringueiros/Castanheiros.

904 PUBLICATION: Ayres, D. L.; Moura, E. Mamirauá: ribeirinhos e a preservação da biodiversidade da várzea amazônica. *Anais Conf.: Abordagens interdisciplinares para a conservação da biodiversidade e dinâmica do uso da terra no novo mundo*. Belo Horizonte: UFMG/University of Florida, 1995, p. 169-82.
TRADITIONAL KNOWLEDGE: Yes • ENVIRONMENTAL MANAGEMENT: Yes • Non-indigenous • RELEVANCE: Fair • SUBJECTS: Botany of cultivated species/Botany of collected species/Icthyology/Fishing techniques • LOCATION: Mamirauá Ecological Station, Amazonas • POPULATION: Ribeirinhos/Caboclos/Seringueiros/Castanheiros.

905 PUBLICATION: Viana, V. M. Conservação da biodiversidade de fragmentos de florestas tropicais em paisagens intensivamentes cultivadas. *Anais Conf.: Abordagens interdisciplinares para a conservação da biodiversidade e dinâmica do uso da terra no novo mundo*. Belo Horizonte: UFMG/University of Florida, 1995, p. 135-54.
TRADITIONAL KNOWLEDGE: No • ENVIRONMENTAL MANAGEMENT: Yes • Non-indigenous • RELEVANCE: Fair • SUBJECTS: Botany of cultivated species/Botany of collected species • LOCATION: Amazon region • POPULATION: Caiçaras/Ribeirinhos/Caboclos/Seringueiros/Castanheiros.

907 PUBLICATION: Moran, E. F. Coping with a New Environment. In: Margolis, M.; Carter, W. (Eds.). *Brazil: Antropological Perpectives*. New York: Columbia University Press, 1979. 47 p.
TRADITIONAL KNOWLEDGE: Yes • ENVIRONMENTAL MANAGEMENT: Yes • Non-indigenous • RELEVANCE: High • SUBJECTS: Botany of cultivated species/Botany of collected species/Pharmacology/Medicine/Icthyology/Fishing techniques/Technology/Material culture/Zoology • LOCATION: Settlements along the Transamazonica Highway • POPULATION: Others.

910 PUBLICATION: Albert, B.; Milliken, W. The Use of Medicinal Plants by the Yanomami Indians of Brazil, Part II. *Economic Botany*, 51 (3), New York: NYBG, 1997, p. 264-78.
TRADITIONAL KNOWLEDGE: Yes • ENVIRONMENTAL MANAGEMENT: No • Indigenous People • RELEVANCE: High • SUBJECTS: Botany of cultivated species/Botany of collected species/Pharmacology/Medicine • LOCATION: AI Yanomami - 585 • POPULATION: 200. Yanomami/Ianomâmi/Xirianá (Roraima/Amazonas); Yanoman/Sunumá/Ninam (Venezuela).

913 PUBLICATION: Kenhíri, T.; Ribeiro, B. G. Chuvas e constelações: calendário econômico dos índios Desâna. In: *Ciência Hoje* - Amazônia, SBPC, dateless, p. 14-23.

TRADITIONAL KNOWLEDGE: Yes • ENVIRONMENTAL MANAGEMENT: No • Indigenous People • RELEVANCE: High • SUBJECTS: Astronomy/Botany of cultivated species/Botany of collected species/Entomology/Pharmacology/Medicine/Technology/Material culture/Zoology/Cosmology • LOCATION: AI Pari Cachoeira - 238 • POPULATION: 33. Dessano/Desâna/Desano/Wira (Amazonas/Colombia).

929 PUBLICATION: Redford, K. H.; Robinson, J. G. Subsistence and Commercial Uses of Wildlife in Latin America. *Subsistence and Commercial Uses of Wildlife*. Brasil, dateless, p. 6-23.

TRADITIONAL KNOWLEDGE: No • ENVIRONMENTAL MANAGEMENT: No • Non-indigenous • RELEVANCE: Fair • SUBJECTS: Technology/Material culture/Zoology • LOCATION: Amazon region • POPULATION: Ribeirinhos/Caboclos/Seringueiros/Castanheiros.

933 PUBLICATION: Arruda, R. S. V. *Os Ririkbaktsa do rio Juruena, frentes de expansão e meio ambiente na Amazônia*. São Paulo: PUC, 1997.

TRADITIONAL KNOWLEDGE: Yes • ENVIRONMENTAL MANAGEMENT: Yes • Indigenous People • RELEVANCE: High • SUBJECTS: Botany of cultivated species/Botany of collected species/Technology/Material culture/Zoology • LOCATION: AI Erikpatsa - 262, AI Japuíra - 145 • POPULATION: 149. Rikbaktsa/Canoeiros/Erigpaktsa (Mato Grosso).

934 PUBLICATION: Arruda, R. S. V. *Os Ririkbaktsa: mudança e tradição*. São Paulo: PUC, Programa de Pós-Graduação em Ciências Sociais, 1992.

TRADITIONAL KNOWLEDGE: Yes • ENVIRONMENTAL MANAGEMENT: Yes • Indigenous People • RELEVANCE: High • SUBJECTS: Arte/Botany of cultivated species/Botany of collected species/Entomology/Icthyology/Fishing techniques/Technology/Material culture/Zoology/Cosmology • LOCATION: AI Erikpatsa - 262, AI Japuíra - 145 • POPULATION: 149. Rikbaktsa/Canoeiros/Erigpaktsa (Mato Grosso).

954 PUBLICATION: Cavalcante, P. B. *Frutas comestíveis da Amazônia*. Belém: CEJUP/CNPq/Museu Paraense Emílio Goeldi, 1991. 279 p.

TRADITIONAL KNOWLEDGE: No • ENVIRONMENTAL MANAGEMENT: No • Non-indigenous • RELEVANCE: Fair • SUBJECTS: Botany of cultivated species/Botany of collected species • LOCATION: Amazon region • POPULATION: Ribeirinhos/Caboclos/Seringueiros/Castanheiros.

955 PUBLICATION: Moran, E. F. The Adaptive System of the Amazonian Caboclo. In: WAGLEY, C. *Man in the Amazon*. The University Presses of Florida, 1974, p. 136-59.

TRADITIONAL KNOWLEDGE: No • ENVIRONMENTAL MANAGEMENT: No • Non-indigenous • RELEVANCE: Fair • SUBJECTS: Botany of cultivated species/Botany of collected species/Technology/Material culture/Cosmology • LOCATION: Amazon region • POPULATION: Ribeirinhos/Caboclos/Seringueiros/Castanheiros.

956 PUBLICATION: Lins e Silva, T. *Os Curupiras foram embora*: economia, política e ideologia numa comunidade amazônica. Rio de Janeiro: Universidade do Rio de Janeiro, Museu Nacional, 1980. 188 p.

TRADITIONAL KNOWLEDGE: Yes • ENVIRONMENTAL MANAGEMENT: No • Non-indigenous • RELEVANCE: High • SUBJECTS: Botany of cultivated species/Botany of collected species/Pharmacology/Medicine/Icthyology/Fishing techniques/Technology/Material culture/Cosmology • LOCATION: Santarém, Amazonas • POPULATION: Ribeirinhos/Caboclos/Seringueiros/Castanheiros.

957 PUBLICATION: Chaves, M. do P. S. R. *De "cativo" a "liberto"*: o processo de constituição sócio-histórica do seringueiro no Amazônas. UFPB, Sociologia, 1994. 171 p.

TRADITIONAL KNOWLEDGE: No • ENVIRONMENTAL MANAGEMENT: No • Non-indigenous • RELEVANCE: Fair • SUBJECTS: Botany of cultivated species/Botany of collected species/Technology/Material culture/Cosmology • LOCATION: Novo Aripuanã, Amazonas • POPULATION: Ribeirinhos/Caboclos/Seringueiros/Castanheiros.

965 PUBLICATION: Nogueira, A. L. E. L. *Jamamadi, Acre: História e Etnologia*. Rio de Janeiro: Núcleo de Etnologia Indígena, LPS/IFCS/UFRJ, Fundação Univesitária José Bonifácio, 1991, p. 183-9

TRADITIONAL KNOWLEDGE: Yes • ENVIRONMENTAL MANAGEMENT: No • Indigenous People • RELEVANCE: High • SUBJECTS: Botany of cultivated species/Botany of collected species/Pharmacology/Medicine/Icthyology/Fishing techniques/Technology/Material culture/Zoology • LOCATION: AI Caititu - 67, AI Igarapé Capana - 393, AI Inauini/Teuini - 539, AI Jamamadi - 415 • POPULATION: 49. Jamamadi/Yamamadi/Djeoromitxi (Amazonas).

974 PUBLICATION: Ribeiro, D. Os índios Urubus: ciclo anual das atividades de subsistência de uma tribo da floresta tropical. In: Ribeiro, D. *Uirá sai à procura de Deus. Ensaios de Etnologia e Indigenismo*. Rio de Janeiro: Paz & Terra, 1976, p. 31-59.

TRADITIONAL KNOWLEDGE: Yes • ENVIRONMENTAL MANAGEMENT: No • Indigenous People • RELEVANCE: High • SUBJECTS: Botany of cultivated species/Botany of collected species/Icthyology/Fishing techniques/Technology/Material culture/Zoology • LOCATION: AI Alto Turiaçu • POPULATION: 56. Kaapor/Urubu-Kaapor/Ka'apor/Kaaporté (Maranhão).

976 PUBLICATION: Comissão Pró-Índio do Acre. *Chegou o tempo de plantar as frutas*. Acre: CPI, Setor de Agricultura e Meio Ambiente, 1998. 108 p.

TRADITIONAL KNOWLEDGE: Yes • ENVIRONMENTAL MANAGEMENT: Yes • Indigenous People • RELEVANCE: High • SUBJECTS: Botany of cultivated species/Botany of collected species/Technology/Material culture/Zoology/Cosmology • LOCATION: Acre (Kaxinawa/Jaminawa/Katukina/Manchineri Indians) 7 TI/4 ethnic groups. • POPULATION: 107. Machineri/Manchineri (Acre)/50. Jaminawa/Iamináua/Yaminahua (Acre/Peru)/8. Apurinã (Amazonas)/84. Katukina/Pedá Djapá (Amazonas)/87. Kaxinawá/Cashinauá/Caxinauá (Acre) Cashinahua (Peru).

983 PUBLICATION: Balée, W. *Relatório final: pesquisa etnobotânica entre quatro grupos Tupi - Guarani, 1984 - 1986*. Funai/CNPq, 1986.

TRADITIONAL KNOWLEDGE: Yes • ENVIRONMENTAL MANAGEMENT: No • Indigenous People • RELEVANCE: High • SUBJECTS: Botany of collected species/Technology/Material culture/Zoology • LOCATION: AI Alto Turiaçu (3°20'S - 46°10'W), AI Alto Turiaçu (2°20'S - 46°30'W), AI Igarapé Ipixuna (4°49'S - 52°31'W), Asurini Indians (4°S - 52°W) • POPULATION: 14. Araweté/Arauété (Pará)/161. Tembé (Pará/Maranhão)/19. Asurini do Xingu/Awaeté (Pará)/56. Kaapor/Urubu-Kaapor/Ka'apor/Kaaporté (Maranhão).

986 PUBLICATION: Velthem, L. H. van. "Comer verdadeiramente": Produção e preparação de alimentos entre os Wayana. *Horizontes Antropológicos - Comida*, Ano 2, n. 4, Prog. Pós-Graduação em Antropologia Social da UFRGS, 1996, p. 10-26.

TRADITIONAL KNOWLEDGE: Yes • ENVIRONMENTAL MANAGEMENT: Yes • Indigenous People • RELEVANCE: High • SUBJECTS: Botany of cultivated species/Botany of collected species/Icthyology/Fishing techniques/Pedology/Technology/Material culture/Zoology/Cosmology • LOCATION: AI Rio Paru D'Este - 272, Tumucumaque Park - 323. • POPULATION: 189. Wayana/Waiana/Uaiana (Pará/Suriname/French Guiana).

991 PUBLICATION: Frikel, P. Agricultura dos índios Munduruku. *Bol. Mus. Paraense Emílio Goeldi*, Antropologia, n. 4, SCT/CNPq/MPEG, 1959, p. 1-35.

TRADITIONAL KNOWLEDGE: Yes • ENVIRONMENTAL MANAGEMENT: Yes • Indigenous People • RELEVANCE: High • SUBJECTS: Botany of cultivated species/Technology/Material culture • LOCATION: Mundukuru Indians of the Amazon • POPULATION: 123. Mundukuru/Mundurucu (Pará).

995 PUBLICATION: Balée, W. Indigenous Adaptation to Amazonian Palm Forest. *Principes*, 32(2), Journal of the International Palm Society, 1988, p. 47-54.

TRADITIONAL KNOWLEDGE: Yes • ENVIRONMENTAL MANAGEMENT: No • Indigenous People • RELEVANCE: High • SUBJECTS: Botany of cultivated species/Botany of collected species/Technology/Material culture • LOCATION: AI Rio Pindaré, AI Alto Rio Turiaçu, AI Igarapé Ipixuna, AI Koatinemo • POPULATION: 14. Araweté/Arauété (Pará)/19. Asurini do Xingu/Awaeté (Pará)/41. Guajá/Awá/Avá (Maranhão)/56. Kaapor/Urubu-Kaapor/Ka'apor/Kaaporté (Maranhão).

997 PUBLICATION: Chagnon, N. A. Yanomamö: the Fierce People. In: Splinder, G. *Cases in Cultural Anthropology*. New York: Hoelt, Rineart and Winston Inc., 1968.

TRADITIONAL KNOWLEDGE: Yes • ENVIRONMENTAL MANAGEMENT: No • Indigenous People • RELEVANCE: High • SUBJECTS: Botany of cultivated species/Botany of collected species/Pharmacology/Medicine/Technology/Material culture/Zoology/Cosmology • LOCATION: AI Yanomami - 585 • POPULATION: 200. Yanomami/Ianomâmi/Xiriana (Roraima/Amazonas); Yanoman/Sunumá/Ninam (Venezuela).

998 PUBLICATION: Balée,W.; Boom, B. M.; Prance, G. T. Quantitative Ethnobotany and the Case for Conservation in Amazonia. In: *Conservation Biology*, 1(4), 1897, p. 296-310.

TRADITIONAL KNOWLEDGE: Yes • ENVIRONMENTAL MANAGEMENT: No • Indigenous People • RELEVANCE: High • SUBJECTS: Botany of collected species/Pharmacology/Medicine/Technology/Material culture • LOCATION: AI Alto Turiaçu - 8 • POPULATION: 161. Tembé (Pará/Maranhão)/ 56. Kaapor/Urubu-Kaapor/Ka'apor/Kaaporté (Maranhão).

999 PUBLICATION: Posey, D. A. Ethnomethodology as an Amic Guide to Cultural Systems: the Case of the Insects and the Kayapó Indians of Amazonia. In: *Revista Brasileira de Zoology*, 1(3), Departamento de Zoology/Instituto de Biociências/USP, 1983, p. 135-44.

TRADITIONAL KNOWLEDGE: Yes • ENVIRONMENTAL MANAGEMENT: No • Indigenous People • RELEVANCE: High • SUBJECTS: Entomology/Zoology/Cosmology • LOCATION: Gorotire Village, Pará (7°52'S - 51°13'W) • POPULATION: 91. Kayapó/Kaiapó/Caiapó/Mebegnokre/A'Ukre/Gorotire/Kriketum; Mekragnoti/Kuben-kran-Ken/Kokraimoro/Kubenkokre/Metuktire; Pukanu/Xikrin do Bacajá/Xikrin do Cateté/Kararaô (Mato Grosso/Pará).

1018 PUBLICATION: Almeida, R. Al. de. *O saber camponês*. Brasília: UnB, Antropologia, 1988, p. 67.

TRADITIONAL KNOWLEDGE: Yes • ENVIRONMENTAL MANAGEMENT: Yes • Non-indigenous • RELEVANCE: Fair • SUBJECTS: Astronomy/Botany of collected species/Technology/Material culture • LOCATION: Santa Terezinha, Mato Grosso • POPULATION: Sitiantes.

1021 PUBLICATION: Figueiredo, N. Los bichos que curan. Los animales y la Medicine popular en Belém do Pará (Brasil). *Revista Good Year*, Montalban, 1991, p. 135-150.

TRADITIONAL KNOWLEDGE: Yes • ENVIRONMENTAL MANAGEMENT: No • Non-indigenous • RELEVANCE: High • SUBJECTS: Zoology • LOCATION: Belém, Pará • POPULATION: Ribeirinhos/Caboclos/Seringueiros/Castanheiros.

1022 PUBLICATION: Anderson, A. B. W. People and the Palm Forest. *Biology and Utilization of Babassu Forest in Maranhão, Brazil*. University of Florida, Botany, 1983, 156 p.

TRADITIONAL KNOWLEDGE: Yes • ENVIRONMENTAL MANAGEMENT: Yes • Non-indigenous • RELEVANCE: High • SUBJECTS: Botany of cultivated species/Botany of collected species/Technology/Material culture • LOCATION: State of Maranhão • POPULATION: Babaçueiros.

1028 PUBLICATION: Begossi, A.; Silvano, R. A.; Amaral, B. D. do. Reserva extrativista do Alto Juruá: aspéctos de etnoecologia In: *A questão ambiental: cenários de pesquisa*. A experiência do Ciclo de Seminários do NEPAM. Campinas: Nepam, 1995, p. 95-105.

TRADITIONAL KNOWLEDGE: Yes • ENVIRONMENTAL MANAGEMENT: No • Non-indigenous • RELEVANCE: Fair • SUBJECTS: Icthyology/Fishing techniques • LOCATION: Upper Juruá Extractivist Reserve • POPULATION: Ribeirinhos/Caboclos/Seringueiros/Castanheiros.

1029 PUBLICATION: Saragoussi, M. et al. A *gênese de um plano de manejo*: o caso do Parque Nacional do Jaú. Manaus: Fundação Vitória Amazônica, 1998. 114 p.

TRADITIONAL KNOWLEDGE: Yes • ENVIRONMENTAL MANAGEMENT: No • Non-indigenous • RELEVANCE: Fair • SUBJECTS: Botany of cultivated species/Icthyology/Fishing techniques/Technology/Material culture • LOCATION: Jaú National Park, Amazonas • POPULATION: Ribeirinhos/Caboclos/Seringueiros/Castanheiros.

1037 PUBLICATION: Ming, Lin; Gaudêncio, P.; Santos, V. P. dos. *Plantas medicinais*: uso popular na Reserva Extrativista Chico Mendes - Acre. Botucatu: Ceplam-Unesp, 1997. 165 p.

TRADITIONAL KNOWLEDGE: Yes • ENVIRONMENTAL MANAGEMENT: No • Non-indigenous • RELEVANCE: Fair • SUBJECTS: Botany of cultivated species/ Botany of collected species • LOCATION: Chico Mendes Extraction Reserve • POPULATION: Ribeirinhos/Caboclos/Seringueiros/Castanheiros.

1041 PUBLICATION: Prance, G. T. Botânica econômica, uma ciência importante para a região amazônica. In: *Botânica Brasileira*, 2(1), 1989, p. 279-286.

TRADITIONAL KNOWLEDGE: No • ENVIRONMENTAL MANAGEMENT: No • Non-indigenous • RELEVANCE: Fair • SUBJECTS: Botany of cultivated species/Botany of collected species • LOCATION: Amazon region • POPULATION: Ribeirinhos/Caboclos/Seringueiros/Castanheiros.

1046 PUBLICATION: Coelho, V. P. A festa do Pequi e os zunidor entre os índios Waurá. In: *Schweizerisch Amerikanisten* - Gesellshaft, 55-56, 1991/92, p. 37-54.

TRADITIONAL KNOWLEDGE: Yes • ENVIRONMENTAL MANAGEMENT: No • Indigenous People • RELEVANCE: High • SUBJECTS: Botany of cultivated species/Zoology/Cosmology • LOCATION: Xingu Park • POPULATION: 188. Waurá/Uará/Wauja (Mato Grosso).

1047 PUBLICATION: Setz, E. Z. F. Animals in the Nambikwara diet methods of collection and processing. In: *J. Ethinobiol*, 11(1), 1991, p. 1-22.

TRADITIONAL KNOWLEDGE: Yes • ENVIRONMENTAL MANAGEMENT: No • Indigenous People • RELEVANCE: High • SUBJECTS: Icthyology/Fishing techniques/Zoology • LOCATION: AI Vale do Guaporé - 332, RI Nambiquara - 216. • POPULATION: 126. Nambikwara/Anunsu/Nhanbiquara (Mato Grosso/Rondônia); Nambikwara do Campo/Halotesu/Kithaulu/ Wakalitesu/Sawentesu; Nambikwara do Norte/Negarotê/Mamaindê/ Latundê/Sabanê and Manduka/Tawandê; Nambikwara do Sul/ Hahaintesu/Alantesu/Waikisu/Alaketesu/Wasusu/Sararé.

1048 PUBLICATION: Schmidt, M. *Etnisilvicultura Kaiabi no Parque Nacional do Xingu*: subsídios ao manejo de recursos naturais. Departamento de Floresta/ESALQ, 1998.

TRADITIONAL KNOWLEDGE: Yes • ENVIRONMENTAL MANAGEMENT: No • Indigenous People • RELEVANCE: High • SUBJECTS: Botany of cultivated species/Botany of collected species • LOCATION: Xingu Park - 346. • POPULATION: 90. Kayabi/Caiabi/Kaiabi (Mato Grosso/Pará).

1052 PUBLICATION: Kroemer, G. *Kunahã Made*: o povo do veneno sociedade e cultura do povo Juruahá. Belém: Mensageiro, 1994. 197 p.

TRADITIONAL KNOWLEDGE: Yes • ENVIRONMENTAL MANAGEMENT: No • Indigenous People • RELEVANCE: High • SUBJECTS: Arte/Astronomy/ Botany of cultivated species/Botany of collected species/Zoology • LOCATION: AI Zuruahã - 351 • POPULATION: 206. Zuruahã/Sorowaha/ Suruwaha (Amazonas).

1057 PUBLICATION: Ribeiro, B. G.; Kenhiri, T. EtnoIcthyology Desâna. In: Pavan, C. *Uma estratégia latino americana para a Amazônia*. São Paulo: Memorial da América Latina/Unesp, 1996, p. 201-31.

TRADITIONAL KNOWLEDGE: Yes • ENVIRONMENTAL MANAGEMENT: No • Indigenous People • RELEVANCE: High • SUBJECTS: Botany of collected species/Icthyology/Fishing techniques/Technology/Material culture • LOCATION: AI Pari Cachoeira I - 238 • POPULATION: 33. Dessano/ Desâna/Desano/Wira (Amazonas/Colombia).

1058 PUBLICATION: Emmerich, M.; Valle, L. Estudos de etnobotânica no Parque indígena do Xingu. Plantas abortivas, anticoncepcionais, conceptivas e sexo-determinantes. In: *Bradea*, 6 (2), 1991, p. 13-20.

TRADITIONAL KNOWLEDGE: Yes • ENVIRONMENTAL MANAGEMENT: No • Indigenous People • RELEVANCE: High • SUBJECTS: Botany of cultivated species/Botany of collected species • LOCATION: Xingu Park - 346. • POPULATION: 201. Yawalapiti/Iaualapiti (Mato Grosso).

1059 PUBLICATION: Emmerich, M.; Valle, L. Estudos de etnobotânica no parque indígena do Xingu: os fortificantes. In: *Bradea*, 5 (37), 1990, p. 364-75.

TRADITIONAL KNOWLEDGE: Yes • ENVIRONMENTAL MANAGEMENT: No • Indigenous People • RELEVANCE: High • SUBJECTS: Botany of cultivated species/Botany of collected species • LOCATION: Xingu Park - 346. • POPULATION: 201. Yawalapiti/Iaualapiti (Mato Grosso).

1060 PUBLICATION: Marimon, B. *Estrutura, composição florística e etnobotânica de floresta monodominante no Vale do Araguaia - Mato Grosso*. Brasília: UnB, Instituto de Ciências Biológicas, 1998, 215 p.

TRADITIONAL KNOWLEDGE: Yes • ENVIRONMENTAL MANAGEMENT: No • Indigenous People • RELEVANCE: High • SUBJECTS: Botany of cultivated species/Botany of collected species • LOCATION: Eldorado Farm, in Nova Xavantina, Mato Grosso (14°50'S - 52°08'W), RI Areões - 36 • POPULATION: 192. Xavante/Akwe/Awen/Akwen (Mato Grosso).

1061 PUBLICATION: Comissão Pró-Índio do Acre. *Legumes, frutas, bichos e os índios*: a ecologia da floresta. Rio Branco: Comissão Pró-Índio do Acre, 1996, 74 p.

TRADITIONAL KNOWLEDGE: Yes • ENVIRONMENTAL MANAGEMENT: No • Indigenous People • RELEVANCE: High • SUBJECTS: Botany of cultivated species/Botany of collected species/Icthyology/Fishing techniques/ Technology/Material culture/Cosmology • LOCATION: AI Mamoadate - 195 • POPULATION: 107. Machineri/Manchineri (Acre)/87. Kaxinawá/ Cashinauá/Caxinauá (Acre) Cashinahua (Peru).

Elements for a discussion on the conservation of agrobiodiversity: the example of manioc (*Manihot esculenta* Crantz) in the Brazilian Amazon

Laure Emperaire[*] *Institut Français de Recherche Scientifique pour le Dévéloppement en Coopération*

Introduction

Given the widespread interest in the conservation of native biodiversity, action aimed at the preservation of agrobiodiversity has been less noticeable. Cultivated species are mainly the object of *ex situ* conservation by means of germplasm collections. In Brazil, such germplasm collections contain approximately 200,000 accessions. Of these, only 24% are native to Brazil (Brazil, MMA 1998). Embrapa[1], with forty units carrying out work on conservation, research, and improvement, is the main institution responsible for these collections.

Ex situ conservation as a modality partially meets the needs of maintaining a broad genetic base of the range of cultivated plants for the purposes of improvement; however, it impedes our perception of the unique biological dimension of plants. Domesticated or cultivated resources are essentially the result of interaction between the biological characteristics of the species, ecological conditions, selective pressures, and the agricultural practices of one or more cultural groups. The continued existence of plant genetic resources is therefore associated with the cultural continuity of the human groups who produce them and with their associated agricultural systems. This biological material, whose future existence is presently at stake, results from a cumulative learning process and its transmission through the generations, elements that give it its unique value. This value is thus also a heritage value. These topics are the subject of a brief analysis of the example of manioc.

Why is manioc important?

Manioc (*Manihot esculenta* Crantz) is the most important cultivated species in the Amazon region and constitutes one of the main sources of carbohydrates. Its consumption can supply 80% of a person's daily calorific needs. Despite its low protein content, it accounts for an important part of protein needs (up to 20% in the Rio Negro region, where sources of animal protein are scarce).

This crop, of Neotropical origin, can be found in various ecological and cultural contexts: in terra firme, floodplains, the central Amazon region, the Amazon; among indigenous groups, mestiço (mixed-race) populations, caboclos (of mixed European and indigenous descent), or colonos (settlers, homesteaders). It is a dietary staple in urban and rural areas. While noting this almost universal presence of manioc in the Amazon basin, we should not ignore the fact that various indigenous groups base their diet on other crops such as maize, sweet potato, banana, or, in rare cases, on hunting, fishing, and forest resources.

For rural populations, growing manioc represents a degree of dietary autonomy. However, for these populations it has increasingly developed into one of the few trade options. The trade in manioc by-products is not new: the sale or supply of manioc flour to missions, reductions[2], military expeditions and landowners began during the colonial period. Consequently, today it is one of the few options for these populations to gain access to industrial goods. The increase of the urban population, partly the result of migration flows to regional towns, has contributed to the existence of an active, albeit poorly remunerated, market.

Due to its key role in material, cultural, and economic daily life, manioc is a plant genetic resource of the utmost importance to Amazonian populations. Within traditional agricultural systems this crop is characterized by high varietal diversity, and the scope and structure of this diversity may be considered to be an indicator of the state of such systems.

Studies on varietal diversity

Scientific studies on manioc diversity are scarce when we consider the high ethnic and territorial diversity of the traditional groups who cultivate the species. The leading ethno-biological studies are those of Chernela 1986, Kerr 1986, Ribeiro 1995, Sodero Matins 1994, Grenand 1996, and Emperaire et al. 1998 for the Brazilian Amazon region, Amorozo for Mato Grosso, and Boster 1984, Salick et al. 1997 for the Amazon region of Peru. While ethnological monographs provide much information on the diversity of manioc varieties, their uses, and symbolic

---

[*] Project *Manejo dos recursos biológicos na Amazônia: a diversidade varietal da mandioca e sua integração nos sistemas de produção* [Management of biological resources in Amazonia: varietal diversity of manioc and its integration into production systems], a research project under the auspices of the ISA/CNPq-IRD 1998- 2000 agreement; coordinators L. Emperaire (IRD) and G. Andrello (ISA), financial support from IRD, CNPq, BRG, and CNRS.

1. *Empresa Brasileira de Pesquisa Agropecuária* (Brazilian Agricultural Research Company).
2. Jesuit mission settlements of the seventeenth and eighteenth centuries (Editor's note).

aspects associated with their cultivation (Carneiro 1973, Ribeiro 1976, Grenand & Haxaire 1977), the interpretation of much of the data is difficult due to the lack of methodological references – for example, the research scale (individual, family, village) or the level of depth of interviews or field surveys. Table 1 presents a preliminary synthesis of the data derived from these bibliographical sources.

The germplasm collections constitute a third data source. However, the institutional surveys were mainly carried out among communities of non-indigenous small farmers, reflecting only a portion of the cultivated diversity (cf. Cordeiro et al. s/d, Burle et al. s/d). Another important point is that, in addition to the collection of the manioc varieties present within a location and a cultural group (the basis for this diversity), the object of interest of researchers has been the plant as a representative of a variety, as a future clone for the geneticist.

In Brazil, manioc collections in agronomy research institutions contain around 5,000 cultivated accessions and approximately 1,000 samples conserved *in vitro* (as well as, respectively, 79 and 34 wild species of *Manihot*). 30% of these accessions are located at CNPMF/Embrapa.[3] The important regional Amazonian collections (CPAA/Embrapa in Manaus and CPATU/Embrapa in Belém[4]) represent 5% of the total (Costa and Morales 1992).

Variety: a concept with multiple meanings

The concept of variety varies depending on the cultural practices and backgrounds of the actors involved, from traditional populations to geneticists or agronomists. This heterogeneity of perceptions is reflected in the definition of 'cultivar' (from cultivated variety) in the International Code of Nomenclature for Cultivated Plants (1980). A variety is '…a set of cultivated plants, clearly differentiated by morphological, physiological, cytological, chemical or other characteristics, which, when reproduced by sexual or asexual multiplication, conserve these distinct characteristics'. This means that, from a taxonomic point of view, the concept of variety can comprise different biological units: it can refer simply to a clone, to a set of clones regarded as homogeneous, or even to a set of individuals reconstituted in each generation. It is the *basic unit of identification and of local management of biological diversity*. It is important to stress that, in the case of manioc, a plant principally reproduced by vegetative means, the notion of variety does not necessarily override that of the clone.

In this study a variety will be taken to mean a set of plants whose characteristics are considered at a local level to be sufficiently homogeneous, that is, distinct from others, to be grouped into a category recognized by a name. The concept of variety derives from the cognitive criteria specific to each cultural group, and it does not override the botanical definition of variety.

Thus, the examples of 'wild' and 'tame' maniocs[5], both belonging to the species *Manihot esculenta*, illustrate these differences of perception. In a community on the middle Rio Negro, the former belong to the manioc (*spp*) category, while the latter belong to the category of fruta ('fruit'), which includes yams, sweet potatoes, taros, etc. At the other extreme of the classification process, genetic analysis of 'wild' manioc varieties has shown individuals with the same name to be genetically related (Colombo 1997, Second et al. 1997, Emperaire et al. 1998). The concept of variety applies here to a set of genetically related clones. Therefore, the result of this analysis cannot be applied to all cultural contexts. In the Rio Negro case we can observe a deep and subtle knowledge of varietal diversity, whereas in recently colonized areas, such as Altamira, such knowledge is less common. The names seem to apply to a wider diversity of morphotypes (and probably of genotypes). The cultural context influences the way biological diversity is perceived.

Distribution and breadth of varietal diversity in the Amazon region

Mapping the data on varietal diversity only gives a first estimate of the quantitative and qualitative importance of the varieties of *Manihoc esculenta* – tame (*macaxeira* or *aipim*) or wild – cultivated in the Amazon basin. It brings together on an equal footing data that is heterogeneous in respect of both the conditions under which it was collected (see above) and the historical background. Situations of recent contact and of existing insertion into national society are juxtaposed. Another element, the diversity cited, by no means gives a true picture of the relative importance of the varieties in swidden cultivation. In general, two or three varieties occupy 70 or 80% of the cultivated area. Lastly, we should stress that a high number of varieties does not necessarily imply a wide genetic base; it should only be considered as a possible indicator of one.

Despite these reservations on its interpretation, Table 1 and Map 1 reveal:
• important spatial variety regarding knowledge of diversity;
• high varietal diversity in different cultural contexts;
• few differences between the number of varieties cultivated by traditional populations, indigenous or non-indigenous, but a far smaller diversity among recently arrived groups (see the case of the colonization settlements along the Transamazonica highway);
• an average diversity per population group of around fifteen varieties, but a great variety of situations;
• centers of high diversity in the upper Rio Negro region and in the Peruvian and Ecuadorian Amazon. However, the presence of such centers matches those regions where more detailed studies have been carried out. It is likely that other ethno-biological studies will reveal the existence of new centers in other regions or confirm the breadth of diversity in areas already studied;
• an unequal distribution of 'wild' and 'tame' manioc varieties in the Amazon basin. The former are found principally in central and northern Amazonia, while the latter are predominant from southeastern Amazonia as far as the Andean foothills;
• the overlap between areas of 'wild' and 'tame' manioc varieties appears to have resulted from processes of human contact.

---

3. *Centro Nacional de Pesquisa de Mandioca e Fruticultura da Embrapa* (Embrapa National Center for Research on Manioc and Fruit Crops).
4. *Centro de Pesquisa Agroflorestal da Amazonia/Embrapa* (Embrapa Agroforestry Research Center of Amazonia) and *Centro de Pesquisa Agropecuária do Trópico Humido/Embrapa* (Embrapa Agricultural Research Center of the Humid Tropics).
5. In other words, those that can simply be cooked prior to consumption (*mandioca mansa* – tame manioc) and those that require detoxification before they can be consumed (*mandioca brava* – wild manioc). This single criterion does not cover other categories, such as manioc for the preparation of *caxiri* (indigenous beer made of fermented manioc), or those kinds renowned for their high sugar content.

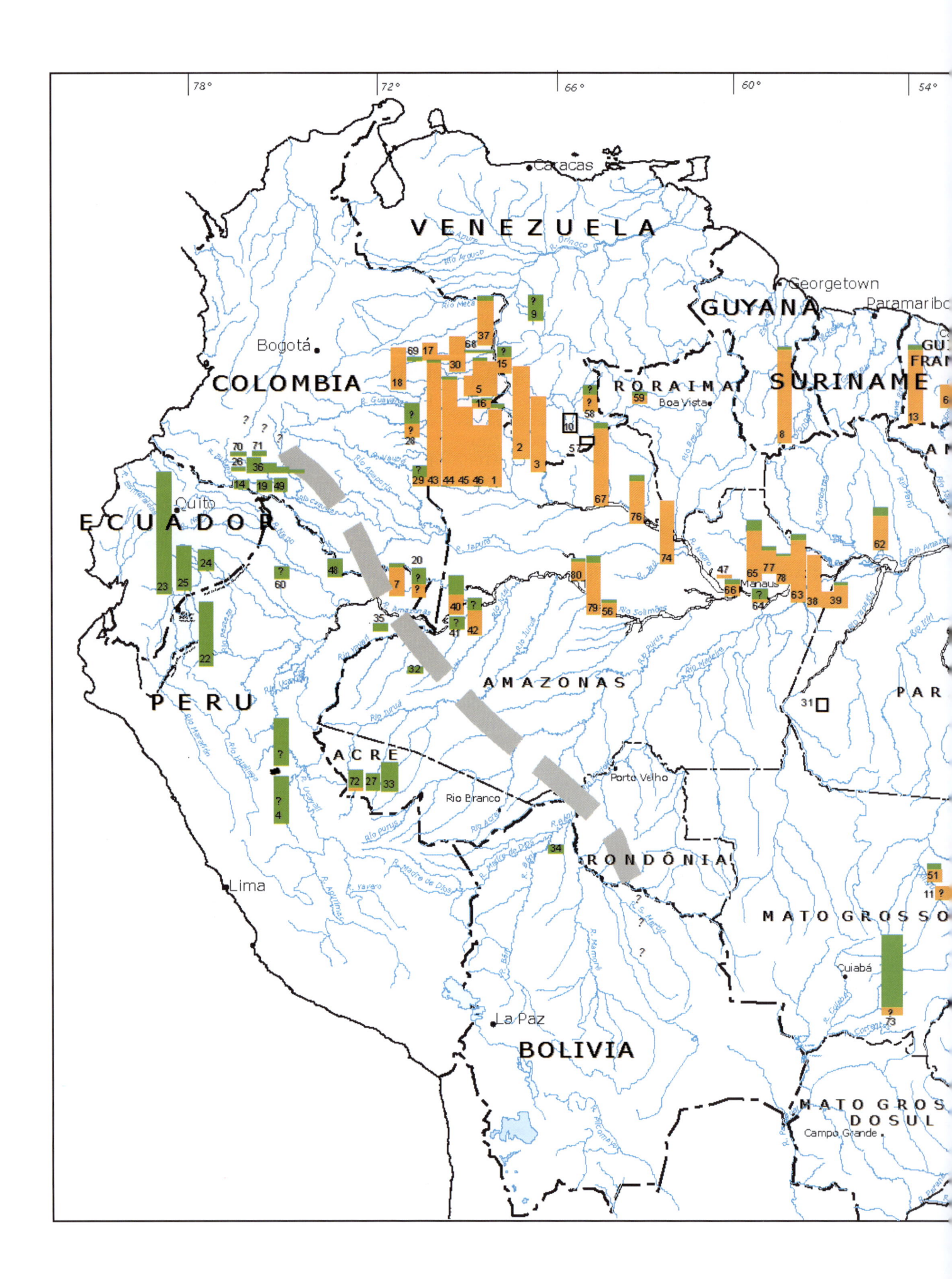

226 THEMATIC DOCUMENTS 2

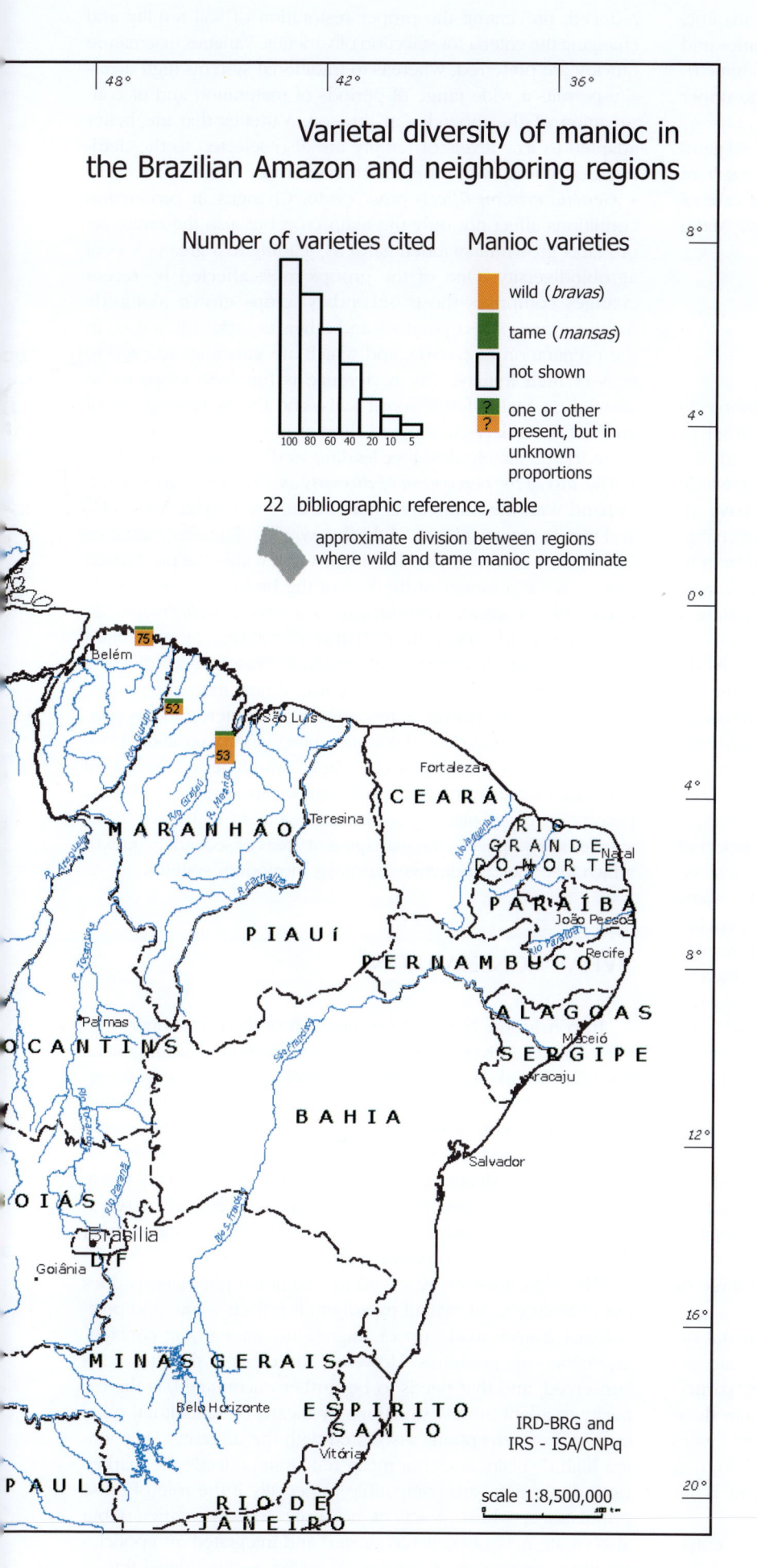

Varietal diversity of manioc in the Brazilian Amazon and neighboring regions

Number of varieties cited: 100, 80, 60, 40, 20, 10, 5

Manioc varieties:
- wild (*bravas*)
- tame (*mansas*)
- not shown
- ? one or other present, but in unknown proportions

22 bibliographic reference, table

approximate division between regions where wild and tame manioc predominate

IRD-BRG and IRS - ISA/CNPq

scale 1:8,500,000

Figure 1. South America – Antarctica maps, IGN France (1968). IRD Applied Cartographic Laboratory, Bondy, France.

In the Rio Negro region, for example, varieties of 'tame' manioc, previously in the minority, were introduced by missionaries and traders at the beginning of the nineteenth century. In symmetrical opposition, 'tame' manioc crops predominate in the upper Juruá region;

• among groups living basically from hunting, fishing, and gathering, varietal diversity is low and is, above all, the result of varieties introduced by neighboring groups. This is the case of the Huaorani in Ecuador (Rival, pers. com.) and the Maku (Silverwood-Cope 1990).

GENETIC EROSION

One of the functions of varietal diversity is to contribute to the stability of production systems, which now find themselves exposed to a wide range of pressures. On the one hand, the diversity of manioc varieties in the Amazon basin as a whole remains high, while on the other the conditions that have allowed the creation and conservation of this diversity are changing drastically. The reasons for such changes are linked both to the internal evolution of the societies in question as well as to direct external pressures. A comparative analysis of the different situations shows that:

• The *disintegration of traditional social exchange* leads to modification of systems for managing diversity, moving from the social management of varieties – based, for example, on exchanges within a wide area (Chernela 1986), or even on the existence within a community of a key individual who conserves these assets (Salick et al. 1987, Emperaire et al. 1998) – to an individualized system in which exchanges are based on the immediate needs of obtaining propagation material. The collective aspect of this heritage becomes lost, as does the notion of a common asset;

• The *evolution of dietary habits* leads to preference for some varieties. Generally speaking, we can observe the broad penetration of 'tame' manioc varieties (*macaxeira*) into 'wild' manioc areas. In regions of bitter manioc such as the Rio Negro, there is also a relative disappearance of white varieties, linked to the decline in the consumption of traditional *beijú* (manioc bread), and their replacement by the yellow varieties used to produce manioc flour for sale. Those varieties with specific uses linked to local dietary habits are in an even more vulnerable situation;

• The *production of manioc flour for sale* is growing. In general, the yellow varieties are preferred. The role of the market, however, is not automatically negative. In a region of low diversity, such as that of Altamira, the demand of the local market for manioc by-products (white and yellow manioc flour, *polvilho* (starch), *tucupi* (seasoned manioc juice), *macaxeira* (sweet cassava)) helps to maintain a level of diversity of around three or four varieties per farmer;

• There are *recent introductions*. The structure of varietal diversity, which results from countless inter- or intra-ethnic exchanges, continues to be modified with the entry of new participants. Action by rural extension agencies tends to introduce new varieties on the basis of their productive value and favors models of production involving few varieties. It is well-known that the primary reason worldwide for the loss of diversity is the expansion of modern agriculture;

• Due to *global changes in production systems*, the concentration of a portion of traditional populations in urban areas leads to increasing pressure on arable lands. Periods of fallow are reduced, preventing the proper restoration of soil fertility and changing the criteria for selection of varieties. Varieties that mature quickly are preferred, whereas in traditional systems high diversity permits a wide range of periods of maturation and of conservation of the tubercles in the soil. Varieties that are better adapted to low levels of fertility are also selected to the detriment of others, with different characteristics;

• *Genetic erosion affects other crops*. Changes in production conditions affect not only the main crop but also the entire set of plants grown in swidden gardens, leading to a greater loss of agrobiodiversity. One of the groups most affected by recent changes comprises those 'secondary' crops grown alongside manioc (yams, sweet potatoes and other tubercles often used in the preparation of *caxiri*), and which are generally adapted to soils of high fertility. The preference is for these crops to be planted on highly fertile forest soils, and the increasing use of areas of secondary growth and short crop cycles does not allow them to adequately develop, leading to their abandonment;

• The *loss of the perception of diversity* as a resource goes hand-in-hand with the impoverishment of the knowledge, practices, and means of transmission of this knowledge. The disappearance of the name of a variety and of interest in it within the production system is a forerunner of the loss of the biological object itself;

• The role of *sexual reproduction as a source of diversity* is diminishing. In addition to the exchange of cuttings among families or ethnic groups leading to high levels of diversity, such diversity is maintained and increased by the use of new morphotypes derived from seeds. However, recognition of or interest in this phenomenon becomes diluted with the integration of traditional systems into agricultural models where spontaneous biological phenomena are controlled rather than taken advantage of. This perception of spontaneity in the management of biological resources also applies to the managing of areas of secondary growth which lose their productive functions in modern systems.

WHAT CONSERVATION?

In conclusion, this brief presentation of the evolutionary factors of varietal diversity shows that conservation of plant genetic resources is linked to the global, cultural and material workings of the society that created them. In traditional societies, whether indigenous or not, diversity is a source of collective wealth, individually managed. These assets and their associated knowledge incorporate an identity value, and to reduce this diversity solely to its productive aspect makes it more fragile. National conservation guidelines, which respond to other economic and cultural drivers, must also incorporate local perspectives.

The high diversity observed in traditional populations does not characterize an overall paradigm. It reflects a pre- and post-colonial history made up of migrations, inter-ethnic contacts, and economic pressures. However, the element that has been conserved, and that needs to be further encouraged, is the capacity to adapt to new situations by means of agricultural practices and of perceptions associated with the diversity. Maintaining high diversity does not mean remaining outside the market. Both dimensions are compatible, especially if the role of these populations, whose practices not only conserve varieties but also create new ones, is recognized and integrated into policies for the conservation of genetic resources, within a legal framework that guarantees their rights over the biological material.

TABLE 1 - MAIN SOURCES OF INFORMATION ON VARIETAL DIVERSITY OF MANIOC IN THE AMAZON BASIN AND NEIGHBORING REGIONS (B = BRAVA (WILD), M = MANSA (TAME))								
no.	Language (language group)*	Ethnic group	Location	Number of varieties			Sample	Source
				Total	B	M		
1	Arawak	Tariano	Uaupés river, Upper Rio Negro, Amazonas, Brazil	62	62	0	1 village	Chernela 1980
2		Baniwa	Içana river, Upper Rio Negro, Amazonas, Brazil	74	74	0	6 informants, in 2 villages	Emperaire, Pinton & Velthem, in course
3		Baré	Upper Rio Negro, Amazonas, Brazil	60	60	0	9 farmers of 1 village	Emperaire, Pinton & Velthem, in course
4		Amuesha	Palcazu river, Amazonia, Peru	204	?	+++	16 communities	Salick et al. 1997, p. 7
5		Curripaco	Guaviare river, Vichada, Colombia	16 / 32 (+4?) / 28	16 / 26 / 27 (+1?)	0 / 2 / 0	2 informants [a] / Not shown / Not shown	Gutierrez 1991, p. 43 et seq.
6		Palikur	Lower Oiapoque, French Guiana	18	18	0	9 swidden gardens	Ouhoud-Renoux 1999, p. 5
7	Bora	Bora	Putumayo river, Amazonia, Peru	23	20	3		Guyot 1975
8	Caribe	Makushi	Southeastern Guiana	77	76	1	1 village of 26 Makuxi and 4 Wapixuna families (Arawak family)	Elias et al. forthcoming
9		Eñepa (Panare)	Middle Orinoco river, Venezuela	?	0	?	1 community of 30 people	Boom 1990, p. 70
10		Yekuana	Padamo river, Southern Venezuela	15	?	?	Not shown	Hames 1983
11		Kuikuro	Upper Xingu river, Mato Grosso, Brazil	?	+	0	Not shown	Dole 1978
12		Kuikuro	Upper Xingu river, Mato Grosso, Brazil	11	?	?	Not shown	Carneiro 1973
13		Wayana	Elahé village	65	5	60	1 village	Fleury pers. com.
14	Cofán	Cofán	Upper Putumayo river, Colombia (300-600 m alt.)	7	0	7	2 farm units	Gutierrez 1991, p. 108
15	Guahibo	Guahibo	Vichaya, Colombia	>= 13	13	?	Not shown	Morey 1974, p. 999
16		Guahibo	Guaviare, Vichaya, Colombia	5 / 6 / 1	4 / 5 / 0	1 / 1 / 1	Not shown / Not mentioned / 1 informant	Gutierrez 1991, p. 45
17		Guahibo	Planas river, Vichaya, Colombia	4 / 14	4 / 14	0 / 0	1 couple / 1 informant	Gutierrez 1991, p. 74
18		Sikuani	Meta river, Vichaya, Amazonia, Colombia	34	34	0	Not indicated	Rojas 1994
19	Huitoto	Huitoto	Upper Putumayo river, Colombia (250 m alt.)	9	0	9	1 farm units	Gutierrez 1991, p. 108
20		Huitoto	Iquitos region, Loreto, Peru	22	+	+	1 community of 43 families	Denevan & Treacy 1987, p. 9
21	Jê (Macro-Jê)	Gorotire (Kayapó)	Fresco river, Pará, Brazil	22	?	?	Not shown	Kerr & Posey 1984 in Hecht, Posey 1989, p. 75
22	Jivaro	Aguaruna	Upper Marañon river Amazonia, Peru	50	0	50	70 women of 1 community	Boster 1984, p. 38

continues

no.	Language (language group)*	Ethnic group	Location	Number of varieties			Sample	Source
				Total	B	M		
23	Jivaro	Huambisa	Santiago river, Amazonia, Peru	±100	?	prob. +++	4 villages	Boster 1983, p. 61
24		Achuar	Huosage and Pastazas rivers, Amazonia, Ecuador	17		17	Not shown	Descola 1988
25		Shuar	Upano river, Amazonia, Ecuador	36	0	36	1 informant	Mashinkiash & Tentets 1986, p. 100
26	Kamensa	Kamensa	Upper Putumayo river, Colombia (2.100 m alt.)	1	0	1	2 farm units	Gutierrez 1991, p. 109
27	Katukina	Katukina	Upper Juruá river, Acre, Brazil	14	0	14	Not shown	Pantoja et al. (forthcoming)
28	Maku-Puinave	Nukak	Upper Uaupés river, Colombia	?	?	? dom.	Not shown	Politis 1996, p. 190, 316
29		Maku	Upper Uaupés river, Rio Negro, Amazonas, Brazil	7	7 prob.	?	Not shown	Silverwood-Cope 1990, p. 45
30		Puinave	Inírida river, Amazonia, Colombia	28	28	0	Not shown	Triana 1985, p. 56
31	Munduruku (Tupi)	Munduruku	Pará/Amazonas border, Brazil	10	?	?	Not shown	Frikel 1959
32	Pano	Matis	Jutaí and Javari rivers, Amazonas, Brazil	5	0	5	Not shown	Erikson 1994, p. 51
33		Kashinawa	Upper Juruá river, Acre, Brazil	22	0	22	Not shown	Pantoja et al. (forthcoming)
34		Chacobó	Upper Ivón river, Beni, Bolivia	7	0	7	1 village	Boom 1987, p. 23
35	Peba Yagua	Yagua	Putumayo Javari river, Peru	>=6	0	>=6	Not shown	Chaumeil 1994, p. 235
36	Quechua	Inga	Upper Putumayo river, Colombia (300-600 m alt.)	11 2 12 4	0 0 0 0	11 2 12 4	4 farm units 1 farm unit 2 farm units 2 farm units	Gutierrez 1991, p. 108
37	Saliba-Piaroa	Piaroa	Orinoco river, Colombia	39	36	3	Not shown	Gutierrez 1991, p. 50
38	Sateré-Mawe (Tupi)	Sateré-Mawé [b]	Middle Amazon river, Pará/Amazonas border	40	40	0	5 informants	Figueroa 1997
39		Sateré-Mawé	Middle Amazon river, Pará/Amazonas border	12	12	0	4 farmers	Emperaire 2000a
40	Tikuna	Tikuna	Upper Solimões river, Amazonas, Brazil	31	16	15	Not shown	Cordeiro 1988
41		Tikuna	Upper Solimões river, Amazonas, Brasil	?	0	+	Not shown	Goulard 1994, p. 352
42		Tikuna	Same group, selling manioc flour	?	20	?	Not shown	Goulard 1994, p. 354
43	Tukano	Tatuyo (Tuk. or.)	Uaupés river, Colombia	± 100	± 100	2	1 village	Dufour 1993, p. 51
44		Tukano / Desana	Uaupés river, Upper rio Negro, Amazonas, Brazil	89	88	1	12 informants	Emperaire 2000b
45		Arapaso (Tuk. or.)	Uaupés river, Upper rio Negro, Amazonas, Brazil	64	64	0	1 village	Chernela 1980, 1986

continues

no.	Language (language group)*	Ethnic group	Location	Number of varieties			Sample	Source
				Total	B	M		
46	Tukano	Uanano	Uaupés river, Upper Rio Negro, Amazonas, Brazil	49	49	0	1 village	Chernela 1980, 1986
47		Tukano aculturados (tuk. or.)	Cueiras river, Lower Rio Negro, Amazonas, Brazil	3	3	0	6 swidden gardens	Grenand 1996, p. 706
48		Orejón - Mai huna (tuk. oc.)	Napo river, Amazonia, Peru	>=15	0	>=15	Not shown	Bellier 1994, p.71
49		Siona (tuk. or.).	Upper Putumayo river, Colombia (300-600 m alt.)	11	0	11	4 farm units	Gutierrez 1991, p. 108
50	Tupi-guarani (Tupi)	Araweté	Ipixuna river, Xingu river, Pará, Brazil	+	+	+	Not shown	Castro 1992, p. 41
51		Kayabi	Upper Xingu river, Mato Grosso, Brazil	12	9	3	Not shown	Silva 1999, p. 46
52		Urubu (Urubu Kaapor)	Gurupi river, Maranhão, Brazil	8	7	1	Not shown	Ribeiro 1976, p. 38
53		Ka'apor	Northern Maranhão, Brazil	19	17	2	2 villages of 5 and 13 families	Balee & Gely 1989, p. 138
54		Wayãpi	Upper Oiapoque river, French Guiana	26	26	1	31 swidden gardens	Grenand 1996, p. 706
55		Wayãpi	Upper Oiapoque river, French Guiana	30	30	0	1 swidden garden	Grenand & Haxaire 1977, p. 309
56		Kokama	Tefé, Middle Solimões river, Amazonas, Brazil	>11	>10	1	1 community of 35 families	Pereira 1992 com. pess
57	Yanomami	Yanomami	Padamo river, Southern Venezuela	6	?	?	Not shown	Hames 1983, p. 17
58		Yanomami	Parima river, Venezuela	?	?	? dom.	Not shown	Smole 1989, p. 116
59		Yanomami	Tootobi, Roraima, Brazil	9	6	3	1 village	Milliken et al. 1999, p. 23
60	Wao (Huaorani)	Wao (Huaorani)	Between the Napo and Curaray rivers, Amazonia, Ecuador	+	0	+	Not shown	Rival 1993, p. 644
61	Non-indigenous Spanish or Portuguese speaking farmers	Farmers originating outside the region (settlers from the 1970s-1990s and from the beginning of the 20th century	Altamira, Xingu river, Pará, Brazil	41	27	14	26 farmers	Pinton & Emperaire 2000, p. 351
62		Traditional farmers	Óbidos region, Middle Amazonas river, Pará, Brazil	31	<= 28	>= 3	1 swidden garden of 1 farmer	Santos Mühlen com. pess.
63		Traditional farmers	Maués region, Amazonas, Brazil	51	49	2	15 informants	Emperaire & Pinton 2000
64		Traditional farmers (*caboclos*)	Careiro island, Amazonas, Brazil	2	2	?	3 swidden gardens	Grenand 1996, p. 706
65		Terra firme farmers of various origins	Manaus region, Amazonas, Brazil	48	40	8	30 farmers	Lourd 1981
66		Floodplain farmers of various origins	Manaus region, Amazonas, Brazil	13	8	5	12 farmers	Lourd 1981
67		*Caboclos* of tukano and aruak origin	Medium Rio Negro, Amazonas, Brazil	64	62	2	5 farmers of 1 village	Emperaire et al. 1998
68		Agricultural colonists	Guaviare river, Vichada, Colombia	1 1	0 0	1 1	1 informant colon. 1 informant colon.	Gutierrez 1991, p. 45
69		Agricultural colonists	Planas river, Vichada, Colombia	2	0	2	1 informant	Gutierrez 1991, p. 74
70		Agricultural colonists	Upper Putumayo river, Colombia (2100 m alt.)	2	0	2	2 farm units	Gutierrez 1991, p. 109

continues

no.	Language (language group)*	Ethnic group	Location	Number of varieties			Sample	Source
				Total	B	M		
71	Non-indigenous Spanish or Portuguese speaking farmers	Agricultural colonists	Upper Putumayo river, Colombia (300-600 m alt.)	3	0	3	1 farm unit	Gutierrez 1991, p. 108
72		*Seringueiros* (rubber tappers)	Upper Juruá river, Acre, Brazil	16	1	15	29 informants	Emperaire & Pinton (this doc.)
73		Traditional farmers	Santo Antônio do Leverger, Mato Grosso, Brazil	60	+	+++	49 farm units	Amorozo 2000, p. 73
74		Traditional farmers	Upper Rio Negro, Floresta, Jaú National Park, Amazonas, Brazil	53	53	0	154 families	Oliveira pers. com.
75		Traditional farmers	Benjamin Constant community, Bragantina region, Pará, Brazil	11	9	2	2 farmers	Rios pers. com.
76		Traditional caboclo farmers	Lower Rio Negro, Barcelos, Amazonas, Brazil	38	33	5	6 informants	Desmoulière 2001
77		Traditional caboclo farmers	Manaus region, Manápoles, Amazonas, Brazil	22	18	4	7 informants	Desmoulière 2001
78		Traditional caboclo farmers	Manaus region, Rio Preto da Eva	26	24	2	6 informants	Desmoulière 2001
79		Traditional caboclo farmers	Middle Solimões, Tefé, Amazonas, Brazil	37	29	8	9 informants	Desmoulière 2001
80		Traditional caboclo farmers	Middle Solimões, Uarini, Amazonas, Brazil	15	13	2	6 informants	Desmoulière 2001

* According to Queixalós, Renault-Lescure, 2000; a: one is Curipaco and the other Puinave (of the Maku-Puinave family), however the varieties cited are all considered as belong to the Curipaco; b: isolated language of the Tupi family (Queixalós and Renault-Lescure 2000).

Bibliography

AMOROZO, M. C. de M. Management and Conservation of *Manihot esculenta Crantz* Germ Plasm by Traditional Farmers in Santo Antonio do Leverger, Mato Grosso State, Brazil. *Etnoecológica*, 4(6). 2000, p. 69-83.

BALEE, W. & GELY, A. Managed Forest Succession in Amazonia: the Ka'apor Case. *Advances in Economic Botany*, 7. 1989, p. 129-58.

BELLIER, I. Los Mai huna. In: Santos, F & Baraclay, F. (Eds.). *Guía etnográfica de la Alta Amazonia*, v. 1. Quito: Flacso/IFEA, 1994, p. 1-179.

BOOM, B. M. Ethnobotany of the Chácobo Indians, Beni, Bolivia. *Advances in Economic Botany*, 4. 1987.

_____. Useful Plants of the Panare Indians of the Venezuelan Guyana. *Advances in Economic Botany*, 8. 1990, p. 57-76.

BOSTER, J. S. A Comparison of the Diversity of Jivaroan Gardens with that of the Tropical Forest. *Human Ecology*, 2 (1). 1983, p. 47-67.

_____. Classification, Cultivation, and Selection of Aguaruna Cultivars of *Manihot esculenta* (Euphorbiaceae). *Advances in Economic Botany*, 1. 1984, p. 34-47.

BURLE, M. L.; ALLEM, A. C.; ABADIE, T.; COSTA, I. S.; FUKUDA, W. M. G. *The Use of Environmental Maps in GIS as a Tool for Cassava Genetics Resources Classification*, poster. Brasília: Embrapa/Cenargen.

CARNEIRO, R. L. Slash and Burn Cultivation Among the Kuikuru and its Implications for Cultural Development in the Amazon Basin. In Gross, D. R. (Ed.). *Peoples and Cultures of Native South America*. New York: American Museum of Natural History, 1973, p. 98-123.

CASTRO, E. V. de. *Araweté: o povo do Ipixuna*. São Paulo: CEDI, 1992.

CHAUMEIL, J.-P. Los Yagua. In: Santos, F & Baraclay, F. (Eds.). *Guía etnográfica de la Alta Amazonia*, v. 1. Quito: Flacso / IFEA, 1994, p. 121-307.

CHERNELA, J. M. *Diversity and Selection in Manioc Cultivation in Three Amazonian Indigenous Populations – A Report of Research in Progress*. Field report, INPA, 1980.

_____. Os cultivares de mandioca na área do Uapês (Tukâno). In: Ribeiro, B. G. (Ed.). *Suma Etnológica Brasileira*, v. 1, Etnobiologia. Petrópolis: Vozes/Finep, 1986, p. 151-8.

COLOMBO, C. *Etude de la diversité génétique de maniocs américains (Manihot esculenta Crantz) par les marqueurs moléculaires (RADP et AFLP)*. Ph.D. Montpellier: ENSAM, 1997, 144 p.

CORDEIRO, C. M. T. et al. *The Brazilian Core Collection of Cassava*, poster. Brasília: Cenargen/Embrapa, s/d.

CORDEIRO, L. B. *Plano de investigação sobre utilização de recursos naturais em áreas de ocupação ticuna – Relatório de trabalho de campo*. multigr. 1988.

COSTA, I. R. S. & MORALES, E. A. V. *Cassava Genetic Resources in South America*, in International Network for Cassava Genetic Resources. Rome: IPGRI, 1994, p. 16-20.

DENEVAN, W. M. & TREACY, J. M. Young Managed Fallows at Brillo Nuevo. *Advances in Economic Botany*, 5. 1987, p. 8-46.

DESCOLA, P. *La selva culta simbolismo y praxis en la ecología de los Achuar*. Quito: Abya-Yala y Instituto Francés de Estudios Andinos, 1988.

DOLE, G. E. The Use of Manioc among the Kuikuru: Some Interpretations. In Ford, R. I; Arbor, A. (Eds.). *The Nature and Status of Ethnobotany*. Michigan: University of Michigan Anthropological Papers, nº 67, 1978, p. 215-47.

DUFOUR, D. L. Manioc as a Dietary Staple: Implications for the Budgeting of Time and Energy in the Northwest Amazon. In: Cattle, D. & Schwerin, K. H. (Eds.). *Food Energy in Tropical Ecosystems*. New York: Gordon and Breach Science Publishers, 1985, p. 1- 20.

_____. Uso de la selva tropical por los indígenas Tukano del Vaupés. In: Correa, F. (Ed.). *La selva humanizada. Ecología alternativa en el trópico húmedo colombiano*. Bogotá: Instituto Colombiano de Antropologia, 1993, p. 47-62.

ELIAS, M.; MCKEY, D.; RIVAL, L. Perception and Management of Cassava (*Manihot esculenta Crantz*) Diversity among Makushi Amerindians of Guyana (South America). *Journal of Ethnobiology*. Submitted.

EMPERAIRE, L.; PINTON, F.; VAN VELTHEM, L. *Approche ethnobiologique et socio-économique de la gestion de la diversité variétale du manioc, le cas dans l'aire indigène du haut Rio Negro*. Paris/Brasília: IRD/ISA, submitted.

EMPERAIRE, L. *Approche ethnobiologique et socio-économique de la gestion de la diversité variétale du manioc, rapport sur la mission réalisée dans l'aire indigène Sateré-Mawé (zone du Marau)*. Paris/Brasília: IRD/ISA, 2000a, 15 p. (multigr.).

_____. *Approche ethnobiologique et socio-économique de la gestion de la diversité variétale du manioc, rapport sur la mission réalisée dans l'aire du haut rio Negro (régio de Yauareté)*. Paris/Brasília: IRD/ISA, 2000b, 20 p. (multigr.).

EMPERAIRE, L. & PINTON, F. *Approche ethnobiologique et socio-économique de la gestion de la diversité variétale du manioc, le cas d'Altamira*. Paris/Brasília: IRD/ISA, multigr., 1999.

EMPERAIRE, L.; PINTON, F.; SECOND, G. Gestion dynamique de la diversité variétale du manioc (*Manihot esculenta*) en Amazonie du nord-ouest. *Natures, Sciences et Sociétés*, 6 (2). 1998, p. 27-42.

ERIKSON, P. Los Mayoruna. In Santos, F. & Barclay, F. (Eds.). *Guía etnográfica de la Alta Amazonia*, v. 2. Quito: Flacso / IFEA, 1994, p. 1-128.

FIGUEROA, A. L. G. *Guerriers de l'écriture et commerçants du monde enchanté – Histoire, identité et traitement du mal chez les Sateré-Mawé (Amazonie centrale, Brésil)*. Ph. D. Paris: EHESS, 1997

FRIKEL, P. Agricultura dos índios munduruku. *Boletim do Museu Paraense Emílio Goeldi*, 4. 1959.

GOULARD, J.-P. Los Ticuna. Santos, F. & Barclay, F. (Eds.). *Guía etnográfica de la Alta Amazonia*, v. 1. Quito: Flacso/IFEA, 1994, p. 309-442.

GRENAND, F. Le Manioc Amer dans les basses terres d'Amérique tropicale, du mythe à la commercialisation. In: Hladik, M.-C. et al. in *L'Alimentation en forêt tropicale – Interactions bioculturelles et perspectives de développement*, v. 2: Bases culturelles des choix alimentaires et stratégies de développement. Paris: Unesco, MAB series, 1996, p. 699-716.

GRENAND, F. & HAXAIRE, C. Monographie d'un abattis Wayãpi. *Journal d'Agriculture Tropicale et de Botanique Appliquée*, 4. 1977, p. 285-310.

GUTIERREZ, M. M. *Diversidad de yuca,* Manihot esculenta Crantz *en Colombia, Visión geográfico-cultural*. Bogotá: Corporación Colombiana para la Amazonia, 1991, 169 p.

GUYOT, M. Agriculture Bora. In: Centlivre, P. (Ed.). *Culture sur Brulis et évolution du milieu forestier en Amazonie du Nord-Ouest*. Basel: Société Suisse d'ethnologie, 1975

HAMES, R. B. Monoculture, Polyculture and Polyvariety in Tropical Forest Swidden Cultivation. *Human Ecology*, 11 (1). 1983, p. 13-34.

HECHT, S. B. & POSEY, D. A. Preliminary Results on Soil Management Techniques of the Kayapó Indians. *Advances in Economic Botany*, 7. 1989, p. 174-188.

KERR, W. E. Agricultura e seleções genéticas de plantas. In: Ribeiro, B. G. (Ed.). *Suma Etnológica Brasileira*, v. 1, Etnobiologia. Petrópolis: Vozes/Finep, 1986, p. 159-172.

KERR, W. E. & POSEY, D. A. Informações adicionais sobre a agricultura dos Kayapo. *Interciência*, 9 (6): 1984, p. 392-400.

LOURD, M. *La Culture du manioc en Amazonie Centrale – Situation phytosanitaire et diversité variétale dans les plantations de la région de Manaus, Rapport de mission*. Manaus: INPA, 1981.

MASHINKIASH CHINKIAS, M. & AWAK TENTETS, M. *La selva, nuestra vida, sabiduría ecológica del pueblo Shuar*. Lima: Abya Yala, 1986.

MILLIKEN, W.; ALBERT, B.; GOODWIN, G. G. *Yanomami, a Forest People*. Kew: Royal Botanic Garden, 1999.

MINISTÉRIO DO MEIO AMBIENTE, BRASIL. *Relatório para a Convenção sobre Diversidade Biológica*. Brasília: MMA, 1998, 282 p.

MOREY, R. V. El cultivo de rotación entre los Guahibo de Colombia oriental. *América Indígena*, 35 (4). 1974, p. 993-1008.

OUHOUD-RENOUX, F. *Rapport d'activité synthétique sur les pratiques agricoles des Palikur de Saint Georges de l'Oyapock (Guyane française)*. Orléans: IRD, ERMES, Univ. Orléans, 9 p. multigr., 1999.

PANTOJA, M.; AQUINO, T.; ALMEIDA, M. Agricultura. In: Carneiro da Cunha, M. & Almeida, M. (Eds.). *Enciclopédia da floresta*. São Paulo: Companhia das Letras, 2002.

PEREIRA, H. dos S. *Extrativismo e agricultura: as escolhas de uma comunidade ribeirinha do Médio Solimões*. Master Degree in Ecology. Manaus: INPA, 1992.

PINTON, F. & EMPERAIRE, L. Pratiques agricoles et commerce du manioc sur un front de colonisation. In: Bahuchet, S.; Bley, D.; Pagezy, H; Vernazza-Licht, N. (Eds.). *L'homme et la forêt tropicale*. Marseille: éditions de Bergier, Châteuneuf-de-Grasse, 1999, p. 347-362.

POLITIS, G. *Nukak*. Bogotá: Sinchi, Instituto Amazônico de Investigaciones Científicas, 1996.

QUEIXALÓS, F. & RENAULT-LESCURE (Eds.). *As línguas amazônicas hoje*. São Paulo: IRD, ISA, MPEG, 2000.

RIBEIRO, B. G. *Os índios das águas pretas*. São Paulo: Companhia das Letras / Edusp, 1995.

RIBEIRO, D. Os índios Urubus – Ciclo anual das atividades de subsistência de uma tribo da floresta tropical. *Leituras de etnologia brasileira*. São Paulo: Companhia Editora Nacional, 1976, p. 127-155.

RIVAL, L. The Growth of Family Trees: Understanding Huaorani Perceptions of the Forest. *Man*, 28. 1993, p. 635-652.

ROJAS, J. *La yuca amarga de la cultura sikuano*. Bogotá: Fundación Etnollano, 1994.

SALICK, J.; CELINESE, N.; KNAPP, S. Indigenous Diversity of Cassava: Generation, Maintenance, Use and Loss Among the Amuesha, Peruvian Upper Amazon. *Economic Botany*, 51 (1). 1997, p. 6-19.

SILVA, G. M., *Agricultura Kaiabi e Yudja na paisagem norte do Parque Indígena do Xingu*. São Paulo: Instituto Socioambiental, Programa do Parque Indígena do Xingu, report, 1999.

SILVERWOOD-COPE, P. L. *Os Makú: povo caçador do noroeste da Amazônia*. Brasília: UnB, 1990.

SMOLE W. J. Yanoama Horticulture in the Parima Highlands of Venezuela and Brasil. *Advances in Economic Botany*, 7. 1989, p. 115-128.

SODERO MARTINS, P. Biodiversity and Agriculture: Patterns of Domestication of Brazilian Native Plant Species. *An. Acad. Bras. Ci.*, 66. 1994, p. 219-24.

TRIANA, G. *Los Puinaves del Inirida. Formas de subsistencia y mecanismos de adaptación*. Bogotá: Univ. Nac. de Colombia, 1985.

Biodiversity and traditional knowledge
Legal protection regimes and 'legislative piracy'[1]: Provisional measure violates indigenous rights and legitimizes biopiracy on their lands[2]

Juliana Santilli *Promotora de Justiça da 2ª Promotoria de Defesa do Meio Ambiente e do Patrimônio Cultural do Distrito Federal*[3]

The role of indigenous and other traditional communities in respect of the conservation of biodiversity is recognized in various international agreements, among them the Convention on Biological Diversity and Agenda 21. Brazilian legislation also enshrines and protects our rich socio-diversity. At the same time that civil society and the Congress are discussing legislative proposals to ensure the protection of traditional knowledge, innovations and practices relating to the conservation of biodiversity, and which would prohibit and punish its degradation or improper use, the government issues a Provisional Measure which directly violates indigenous rights and those of traditional communities by opening up their lands to biopiracy and the expropriation of their knowledge.

Legislative proposals under way in other countries in Latin America and Asia seek to create *sui generis* legal regimes for the protection of traditional knowledge associated with biodiversity, regimes that are different from the Western system of intellectual property, based on a patent system and which exclude collective innovations and indigenous inventiveness.

Provisional measure 2,052/2000

The discussion on the creation of legal mechanisms for the protection of indigenous and traditional biodiversity-related knowledge, as well as for control by and compensation to the communities holding such knowledge, takes on particular importance in light of the government's Provisional Measure no. 2,052 of 30th June 2001[4] and the legislative proposals under consideration in the National Congress.

While different sectors of government and civil society discuss the development of legislative proposals aimed at implementing the Convention on Biological Diversity, the Executive simply overrides the legislative process and issues a Provisional Measure designed to address the question by means that are clearly unconstitutional.

The Provisional Measure was drawn up in haste in order to 'legitimize' the agreement signed on 5th September 2000 between Bioamazônia, a non-governmental public organization, and the multinational company Novartis Pharma, under which ten thousand bacteria and fungi from the Amazon region would be sent to the Novartis laboratory in Switzerland. Bioamazônia was set up by the federal government itself to coordinate implementation of the Brazilian Program of Molecular Ecology for the Sustainable Use of the Biodiversity of Amazonia (Probem). Faced with the negative repercussions to the agreement[5], the government decided to issue a Provisional Measure that would regulate, albeit casuistically, access to genetic resources and to traditional biodiversity-related knowledge.

The Provisional Measure contained a series of unconstitutional elements and several of its provisions violated rights guaranteed to indigenous and traditional communities. These comments will address only the most serious aspects.

Its underlying casuistry was clearly expressed in article 10, which provided that: 'A person who in good faith, prior to 30th June 2000, commercially used or exploited any type of traditional knowledge in the country, is guaranteed the right to continue such use or exploitation, freely, under the same forms and conditions.' In other words, in order to 'legitimize' the agreement between Bioamazônia and Novartis (signed approximately a month before the Provisional Measure was issued), the government not only legalized each and every act of biopiracy and of plunder of traditional knowledge carried out in the country prior to 30th June 2000, but also guaranteed to biopirates the right to continue pirating our genetic resources and the knowledge of our traditional communities, 'freely, under the same forms and conditions.'

---

1. A few days after Provisional Measure 2.052/2000 was issued, senator Marina Silva (PT-Acre) spoke in the Senate denouncing the government for 'legislative piracy'. 'The government is resorting to 'legispiracy', a mechanism for taking over Congressional initiatives and transforming them into Provisional Measures', the senator claimed.
2. Information on Provisional Measure 2.052 was updated in November 2001.
3. Public Prosecutor, Second Public Prosecutor's Office for the Defense of the Environment and Cultural Heritage of the Federal District.
4. This Provisional Measure was successively re-issued; Provisional Measure 2.186-15 of 26th July 2001, currently in force, introduced alterations which are discussed below.
5. According to the Instituto Socioambiental, on 28th June 2000 sixteen Brazilian civil society organizations released a public statement condemning the decision of the federal government to regulate access to the genetic resources of the country by means of a Provisional Measure. According to the statement, 'the use of a Provisional Measure in this case is absolutely undemocratic, as it ignores the whole debate that has been going on for more than eight years between all the interested sectors of Brazilian society and the National Congress. To regulate an economic and environmental activity of strategic importance for the country by means of a Provisional Measure creates a situation of legal uncertainty for the negotiations on genetic resources in Brazil that have already taken place. Provisional Measures are weak and precarious, as they are a hostage to political pressure and can be altered each time they are re-issued.'

In spite of devoting a section of vague and generic principles to the 'protection of associated traditional knowledge' (articles 8, 9 and 10), the Provisional Measure directly violates the rights of indigenous communities to the permanent possession and exclusive use of the natural riches found on their traditional lands, as guaranteed by the Constitution. Article 14 states: 'In cases of relevant public interest, as determined by the competent authority, access to indigenous lands, public or private areas, for the purpose of obtaining access to genetic resources, will be exempt from the prior approval of indigenous and local communities and of owners'.

It is clear that this article, which allows access to genetic resources situated on indigenous lands without prior approval of the respective communities, violates the rights guaranteed in article 231, paragraph 2 of the Federal Constitution, which states: 'The lands traditionally occupied by indians are destined for their permanent possession, and the exclusive use of the riches of the soil, rivers and lakes existing there belongs to them'. The exceptions to the exclusive use that indigenous communities have over the natural resources present on their lands are those laid down in the Constitution itself: water resources (including their energy potential) and mining. Article 231, paragraph 6 of the Constitution, already provides for an exception to the exclusive use by indigenous communities of the natural resources present on their lands in cases of 'relevant public national interest, in accordance with the provisions of complementary law'. Thus any other exceptions to the right of exclusive use by indigenous communities of their traditional lands can only be established by means of a complementary law (the approval of which by the National Congress requires a special quorum – an absolute majority) and never by means of a Provisional Measure, issued by the Executive.

Contag (the National Confederation of Agricultural Workers), with the assistance of lawyers from the Instituto Socioambiental, took legal action alleging the unconstitutionality of articles 10 and 14 of the Provisional Measure. Although the Federal Supreme Court has not ruled on this case, the subsequent reissues of the Provisional Measure have excluded these articles. More recently, the Federal Government has issued Decree no. 3.945/2001, which defines the membership of the *Conselho de Gestão do Patrimônio Genético* (Council for the Management of Genetic Assets) and excludes any participation by civil society or traditional communities.

It should be emphasized that both indigenous communities[6] and black communities descended from quilombos benefit from special land and cultural rights guaranteed by the Constitution.[7] Furthermore, the Constitution protects the 'expressions of popular, indigenous and African-Brazilian cultures, and those of other groups participating in the process of national advancement' (article 215, paragraph 1), as well as the 'diversity and integrity of the genetic assets of the country' (article 225, paragraph 1, II). Thus our legal system protects both bio- and socio-diversity.

The Convention on the Biological Diversity

On the international level, the Convention on Biological Diversity[8] recognizes straight away in its preamble the 'close and traditional dependency of many indigenous and local communities embodying traditional life-styles on biological resources'. Article 8 (j) establishes that Parties should 'respect, preserve and maintain the knowledge, innovations and practices of indigenous and local communities embodying traditional life-styles relevant for the conservation and sustainable use of biological diversity', 'promote their wider application with the approval and involvement of the holders of such knowledge', and 'encourage the equitable sharing of the benefits arising from the utilization of this knowledge, innovations and practices'.

Agenda 21, in its chapter 26 'Recognizing and strengthening of the role of indigenous peoples and their communities', also identifies as part of the measures to be taken by national governments for the purpose of ensuring greater control by indigenous people over their lands and resources, the adoption and strengthening of 'appropriate policies and/or legal instruments that will protect indigenous intellectual and cultural property and the right to preserve customary and administrative systems and practices'.

It is clear that the need to protect socio-diversity, intrinsically linked to biodiversity, is not only enshrined in Brazilian legislation, but also in international agreements.

Nevertheless, the rights of traditional communities – indians, seringueiros (rubber tappers), ribeirinhos (riparian communities), small farmers and others – that have over the course of generations discovered, selected and managed species with pharmaceutical, dietary and agricultural properties[9], are not guaranteed by existing systems of intellectual property protection, through patent systems that accord special privileges to so-called 'new knowledge', which is individually generated, and not to traditional knowledge, generated collectively and informally and orally transmitted from one generation to the next. Such knowledge is considered to belong in the public domain, without any kind of patent protection.

The absence of any kind of legal protection for traditional biodiversity-related knowledge has led to the most varied forms of plunder and misappropriation. Among the best-known cases are those of the granting of patents to the American Loren Miller on *ayahuasca* (a medicinal plant from Amazonia used by various indigenous communities and of high spiritual importance to

---

6. There are 206 indigenous peoples in Brazil, the majority made up of micro-societies (34% of these peoples comprise fewer than 200 individuals), speaking approximately 170 different languages. Moreover, 98% of the total extent of indigenous lands is located in the Amazon region, where roughly 60% of the indigenous population lives (data from the study 'A sociodiversidade nativa contemporânea no Brasil' by the anthropologist Carlos Alberto Ricardo, published in *Povos indígenas no Brasil: 1991/1995*, São Paulo: Instituto Socioambiental, 1996).

7. See articles 231 and 232 of the Constitution, which deal with indigenous rights, as well as article 68 of the Transitory Constitutional Provisions, which guarantee rights to the permanent ownership of the lands they occupy to those black communities that are descended from 'quilombos'.

8. This article will restrict its comments to the Convention on Biological Diversity; however, there are other instruments which recognize the cultural rights of indigenous communities and guarantee the protection of their cultural diversity: Convention 169 of the International Labor Organization and Resolution 1990/27 of the Working Group on Indigenous Populations created in 1982 by the Economic and Social Council of the United Nations are among the most important.

9. As noted by Ricardo Arnt in his article 'Perspectivas do futuro: biotecnologia e direitos indígenas' (Prospects for the future: biotechnology and indigenous rights); presented at the international meeting 'Diversidade Eco-Social e Estratégias de Cooperação entre ONGs na Amazônia' (Eco-Social Diversity and Strategies for Co-operation among NGOs in the Amazon Region), Belém, 13th June 1994.

them)[10] and to two researchers from the University of Colorado, Duane Johnson and Sara Ward, on *quinua* (a plant of high nutritious value, commonly used in the diets of traditional communities in Bolivia and other Andean countries).[11]

Vandana Shiva[12] draws our attention to the prejudices and distortions contained in the very definition of knowledge, whereby Western knowledge is considered as 'scientific' and non-Western traditions as 'non-scientific', and argues that traditional knowledge systems have their own scientific and epistemological foundations, which distinguish them from the reductionist and Cartesian systems of Western knowledge. For this reason, Shiva and Gurdial Singh Nijar warn of the urgent need to protect traditional knowledge through legal regimes that take into account the specific cultural contexts that generate such systems.

Legislative proposals under consideration in the National Congress

In addition to the Provisional Measure referred to above, there are four draft legal proposals relating to these matters currently being considered by the National Congress: 1) a draft constitutional amendment submitted to Congress by the Executive which proposes to include genetic resources among those federal assets listed in article 20 of the Constitution; 2) a bill introduced by the Executive addressing 'access to genetic assets and associated traditional knowledge, and the distribution of benefits deriving from their utilization'; 3) a bill introduced by senator Marina Silva (PT-Acre[13]), already approved by the Senate in the form of a substitute bill submitted by the rapporteur of the Senate Social Affairs Committee, senator Osmar Dias (PSDB-Paraná[14]); and 4) a bill introduced by congressman Jacques Wagner (PT-Bahia), still under consideration in the Chamber of Deputies.[15] A special committee of the Chamber has been established to analyze these bills.

We will analyze these legislative proposals from the point of view of the protection of traditional biodiversity-related knowledge and of the implementation of the Convention on Biological Diversity.

Constitutional amendment

The constitutional amendment introduced by the government proposes to include genetic resources among the assets of the Union[16], making their ownership public, regardless of who is the holder of the property right to the soil and the natural resources where they are to be found. It thus establishes a legal regime for genetic resources analogous to that for mineral resources, which also constitute property distinct from the soil and belonging to the Union.

The negative consequences of such a legal regime for traditional communities in general, and for indians in particular, has already been stressed. If the right of indigenous communities to the exclusive use of such genetic resources as may be found on their traditional lands – regardless of who has the ownership rights to those resources – is not respected, indians will suffer yet another restriction on the exercise of their land and cultural rights, which are so fundamental for their survival as distinct populations.

It is understood that genetic resources – like environmental goods generally – need to have the access to them and their utilization limited by and subject to rules of public interest, irrespective of whether they belong to the private or public domain (in accordance with the ownership of the natural resources that contain them). This does not mean, however, that they are required to be considered as public assets. They are assets of public interest regardless of whether they are public or private property.

On this point, Vandana Shiva's comment[17] is well taken. She observes that the sovereignty over the genetic resources found within their national territories guaranteed to countries that are parties to the CBD should not be thought of as state sovereignty, but as sovereignty of the people, that is as sovereignty to be exercised by the civil society of each country. The constitutional amendment proposed by the government appears to commit precisely this mistake: it confuses the right of sovereignty over our genetic resources with public or state ownership. State protection does not necessarily signify public property.

---

10. Cancellation of patent no. 5,751, granted to Loren Miller, was requested of the Patent and Trademark Office, the US agency responsible for the registration of patents and trademarks, by the non-governmental organization Center for International Environmental Law (CIEL), on behalf of the Coordination of the Indigenous Organizations in the Amazon Basin (COICA) and of the Amazon Coalition, according to information provided by CIEL itself.

11. Patent no. 5,304,718, according to the newsletter IPR - Information about Intellectual Property Rights, n. 19, of July 97, published by IATP - Institute for Agriculture and Trade Policy.

12. Shiva, V. *The Politics of Knowledge at the CDB*. New Delhi: The Research Foundation for Science, Technology and Natural Resource Policy.

13. PT = Partido dos Trabalhadores (Workers' Party).

14. PSDB = Partido da Social Democracia Brasileira (Brazilian Social Democracy Party).

15. It should not be forgotten that the bill establishing the new *Estatuto das Sociedades Indígenas* (Statute of Indigenous Societies) is also currently under consideration in the National Congress. This bill provides that: 'The access and utilization, by third parties, of biogenetic resources on indigenous lands shall respect the rights of the indigenous communities to exclusive usufruct and will depend on their prior authorization, as well as on prior communication with the federal indigenous affairs agency.' Article 157 of the bill considers it a crime 'to commercially or industrially utilize genetic or biological resources existent on indigenous lands for the development of biotechnological processes or products without the prior written consent of the indigenous community or society who holds permanent property rights to them'. Such a crime would be subject to a fine of at least twice the amount of the financial gain obtained by the agent or to a minimum of twenty-five fine days. The Office of the Presidency, however, is negotiating the submission of a new draft of the Statute of Indigenous Societies to the National Congress.

16. I.e the Federal Republic of Brazil.

17. Shiva, V. *Protecting our Biological and Intellectual Heritage in the Age of Biopiracy*. New Delhi: Research Foundation for Science, Technology and Natural Resource Policy.

The government bill

The Provisional Measure issued by the Government reproduces various provisions of a bill previously submitted by the Executive to the National Congress, and contains various errors and direct violations of indians' guaranteed rights to exclusive use. The most serious are as follows. The government bill establishes that the authorization for entry to indigenous lands for access to the 'example of the component of the genetic assets and the associated traditional knowledge will be subject to approval by the official indigenous affairs agency, having heard the indigenous community involved'. In other words, it is the one who authorizes, and not the indians. This is a clearly unconstitutional provision, since it deprives indians of the right to use and benefit from the natural resources found on their lands, including genetic resources. Even more serious is the provision establishing the need for a prior hearing before the *Conselho de Defesa Nacional* (National Defense Council) in order to obtain 'authorization for admission to those areas indispensable to national security, in order to obtain access to the example of the component of the genetic assets and the associated traditional knowledge'. The power of decision over access to traditional biodiversity-related knowledge has to be recognized as belonging to the indigenous communities, who will be able to refuse access whenever they feel this violates their cultural integrity. Such decisions should be reached in conformity with a community's uses, customs and traditions, and the removal of the power to do so is inadmissible.

On the pretext of 'tidying up' the bills under consideration, the government proposal simply postpones to future 'regulations' the question of compensation mechanisms and benefits to be awarded to indigenous communities for the commercial use of genetic resources found on their traditional lands or of related traditional knowledge. Deferring these questions to future 'regulations' means that questions that are essential for indigenous communities, such as the fair and equitable distribution of the benefits derived from the utilization of their resources and knowledge, will depend on regulations to be issued by the Executive itself.

Recursos Genéticos (Genetic Resources Committee), comprising representatives of government, the scientific community, local and indigenous communities, non-governmental organizations, and private corporations, with the task of endorsing decisions made by the Executive under the national policy on genetic resources. According to the bill, access will be dependant upon a contract between the competent authority designated by the Executive and the interested party, and identifies the parties and the conditions for signing the contract.

The bill devotes a chapter (articles 44, 45, and 46, and their several paragraphs) to the 'Protection of Traditional Knowledge Associated with Genetic Resources', in which it determines that the 'Public Power recognizes and defends the rights of local communities and indigenous populations to benefit collectively from their traditional knowledge and to be compensated for the conservation of genetic resources by means of monetary payment, goods, services, intellectual property rights or other means'. It provides for the creation of a national register where local and indigenous communities will record their knowledge of genetic resources, and establishes that local and indigenous communities retain exclusive rights over their traditional knowledge, and that only they can cede these, by means of contracts.

It also determines that the proposal for a contract to obtain access to genetic resources, when these are situated on indigenous lands, 'will only be accepted if it is preceded by the prior informed consent of the local community or indigenous population, obtained in accordance with clear and precise norms to be defined for this purpose by the competent authority' (articles 44 and 45).

According to article 46 of the bill, 'the right to the benefits that arise from access to genetic resources is guaranteed to the local communities and indigenous populations of the areas where they are found, to be defined in the form of a related contract as provided for in this law, and following prior informed consent.' According to the sole paragraph of this article, 'local communities and indigenous populations will be able to request that the competent authority refuse access to genetic resources in the areas they occupy when they believe that these activities threaten the integrity of their natural or cultural heritage'. These are essentially the provisions of the bill.

Senator Marina Silva's bill

Bill no. 306/95, introduced by Senator Marina Silva (PT-AC), addresses access to genetic resources and products derived from these. It has already been approved by the Senate, in the form of a substitute bill introduced by Senator Osmar Dias, and is now in the Chamber of Deputies.

The current version of the (substitute) bill states in article 1 its intention to regulate 'rights and obligations related to the access to genetic resources, genetic material and products deriving from these, in *ex situ* or *in situ* situations, present within the national territory or of which Brazil is the country of origin; the traditional knowledge of indigenous populations and local communities associated with genetic resources or products deriving from these; and domesticated and semi-domesticated agricultural crops in Brazil'.

The bill sets out the conditions for the approval of access to national genetic resources, which are to be granted by the Executive, and provides for the establishment of a *Comissão de*

Congressman Jacques Wagner's bill

The bill introduced by Congressman Jacques Wagner (PT-Bahia) contains a few, positive, differences in relation to the substitute bill already approved by the Senate, and these are worth mentioning because they specifically concern traditional communities.

First, this bill alters the definitions of 'local community' and 'indigenous population' employed in the substitute bill and replaces them with two separate definitions, one for society and the other for indigenous community, as follows.

Indigenous societies are collectivities distinct from each other and from society as a whole because of their historical links to populations of pre-Colombian origin. *Indigenous community* is used to designate a local human group that is part of a wider indigenous society.

A *traditional population* is one who lives in a close relationship with the natural environment, depending on its natural resources for its social and cultural reproduction, by means of activities of low environmental impact. These are the terms and definitions used in the bills regulating the Statute of Indigenous Societies, and instituting the *Sistema Nacional de Unidades de Conservação* (SNUC, National System of Conservation Areas), both under consideration by the National Congress. A bill to regulate access to genetic resources should use the same terms and concepts as these bills in order to consolidate these legal concepts and to enhance conformity among different laws, avoiding conflicts, divergent interpretation and legislative confusion.

The bill introduced by Congressman Wagner also adds the following wording to paragraph 1 of article 44 of Senator Dias' substitute bill: 'without prejudice to the legitimization of legally constituted civil associations and of other entities with legal personality listed in law 7,347/85, together with the legitimization of indians, their communities and organizations, as provided for in article 232 of the Constitution'. This addition is highly commendable. The legitimate right of civil associations (non-governmental organizations) to promote the legal defense of the country's biogenetic assets and its socio-cultural diversity should be specifically safeguarded. The same needs to be said in relation to the legitimization of indians themselves, their communities and organizations for the promotion of the judicial and extrajudicial defense of their rights and interests, as recognized by the Constitution itself.

Also praiseworthy is the addition of the sole paragraph to article 46 of the substitute bill approved by the Senate, which contains the following wording: 'Local communities and indigenous populations will be able to deny access to genetic resources found in the areas they occupy, or access to traditional knowledge associated with these, when they have reason to believe that such activities threaten the integrity of their natural and cultural heritage.' The original text of the substitute bill merely allows for the possibility of communities 'requesting' that the competent authorities refuse access to genetic resources situated on their traditional lands.

Conclusion
A *SUI GENERIS* REGIME TO PROTECT COLLECTIVE INTELLECTUAL RIGHTS

Although the above bills contain some provisions for recognizing and protecting the biodiversity-related rights of traditional communities, which is a positive step forward, these initiatives are still timid and imprecise in establishing compensation mechanisms for traditional communities.

A *sui generis* legal regime for the protection of collective intellectual rights of traditional communities should start from the following premises:

1) An explicit provision that patents or any other intellectual property rights (such as trademarks) granted for processes or products that directly or indirectly result from the utilization of the knowledge of indigenous or traditional communities[18] are null and void and have no legal standing, as a way of preventing monopolies in such processes or products;

2) The reversal of the burden of proof in favor of traditional communities in legal actions against patents granted on processes or products resulting from their knowledge, such that it would up to the defendant to prove their case;

3) The explicit provision that traditional knowledge is incapable of being patented would allow the free exchange of information among different communities that is essential to the very creation of such knowledge;

4) The legal requirement for a) prior informed consent by traditional communities, including an explicit right of veto, in order to access any type of genetic resources situated on their lands or to utilize or divulge their traditional knowledge for any purpose; and b) in cases of commercial ventures, establishment of the forms of sharing profits from processes or products resulting from such resources and knowledge, by means of contracts signed directly with the indigenous communities, who will be entitled if they so wish to receive legal counsel from the official indigenous affairs agency, non-governmental organizations and the Federal Prosecution Service. The granting of exclusive rights to specific individuals or companies should be prohibited;

5) The creation of a national registry of traditional biodiversity-related knowledge as a means of guaranteeing the rights associated with such knowledge. Such a registry should be free of charge, optional and merely declaratory, a simple means of proof and not a condition for the exercise of any rights;[19]

6) Such a national registry system should be administered by a council with equal representation of government agencies, non-government organizations, and representative indigenous associations, as well as a team of ad hoc consultants capable of giving technical advice when necessary.

Proposals from other countries

Other countries have enacted domestic legislation to regulate the conservation of biodiversity and the fair and equitable distribution of benefits derived from the sustainable use of its resources. We will consider some initiatives aimed at protecting the knowledge, practices and innovations of traditional communities relevant to the conservation of biodiversity, in accordance with article 8 (j) of the Convention on Biological Diversity.

Costa Rica

On 23 April 1998, Costa Rica passed its 'Biodiversity Law', with a whole chapter dedicated to the 'Protection of intellectual and industrial property rights' (articles 77 to 85). The chapter begins with the recognition by the State of the 'existence and validity of the forms of knowledge and innovation' and of the 'need to protect them by means of legal mechanisms appropriate to each particular case'. It further affirms that the State grants

---

18. This diverges from article 47 of the bill introduced by Senator Marina Silva (in the substitute version), and reproduced in the bill of Congressman Jacques Wagner, which states that 'rights to intellectual property over products or processes related to traditional knowledge associated with genetic resources or derived products, where access has not been obtained in conformity with this law, will not be recognized'. In other words, if the access has been realized in conformity with the law, the granting of a patent for processes and products resulting from traditional indigenous knowledge is permitted.

19. The bills introduced by Marina Silva and Jacques Wagner provide for such a registry without defining its functioning, something that can be done by Executive decree. Professor Manuela Carneiro da Cunha, in a presentation during the International Seminar on Biodiversity Law, held in Brasilia in August 1999 by the Judicial Studies Center of the Federal Justice Council, proposed the creation of registries which 'are a kind of national library of traditional knowledge and which could be located, for example, at Iphan (*Instituto do Patrimônio Histórico e Artístico Nacional* – the National Historical and Artistic Heritage Institute).'

such protection 'among other forms, by means of patents, commercial secrets, plant breeding rights, *sui generis* community intellectual rights, author's rights, and farmers' rights'. In other words, Costa Rica opted for a hybrid system of protection, merging traditional intellectual property rights (patents, etc.) with a *sui generis* protection regime.

Explicitly excluded from the legal protection regime in Costa Rica are 'DNA sequences per se, plants and animals, non-genetically modified microorganisms, essentially biological procedures for the production of plants and animals, natural processes or cycles, inventions essentially derived from knowledge associated with traditional biological or cultural practices in the public domain, and inventions which, if commercially exploited as a monopoly, might affect the agricultural and livestock processes or products considered to be essential for food and health' (article 78). According to the Costa Rican law, the Registry of Intellectual and Industrial Property is obliged to consult the Technical Office of the National Commission for Biodiversity Management[20] before granting intellectual or industrial property rights over innovations which involve biodiversity resources.

From the perspective of seeking an alternative legal regime to protect the collective intellectual rights of indigenous communities, the most interesting mechanisms appear to be those which deal with '*sui generis* community intellectual rights'. These rights are so entitled in article 82 of the Costa Rican law, according to which the State recognizes and protects the knowledge, practices and innovations of indigenous populations and local communities related to the utilization of biodiversity resources and associated knowledge.

'These [*sui generis* community intellectual] rights exist and are legally recognized by the simple existence of cultural practice or of knowledge related to genetic and biochemical resources; they do not require prior declaration, explicit recognition, or official registration. They can, therefore, comprise practices which will fall under this category in the future. Such recognition implies that no form of protection of industrial or properties rights will be able to affect such historical practices'[21]. This is what article 82 of the Costa Rican law states, providing for the definition of a 'participatory process' involving indigenous and rural communities in order to arrive at the harmonization of such rights.

The Costa Rican law also provides for a system of registration of *sui generis* community intellectual rights and for an inventory of the knowledge, innovations and practices relevant to the conservation of biodiversity which these communities intend to protect, thus creating the possibility that, in the future, further knowledge with the same characteristics can be registered and recognized. Such registration is voluntary and free of charge, and may be performed by the interested parties in the form of an application, with no formalities. The existence of this registry will oblige the Technical Office of the National Commission for Biodiversity Management to give a negative response to any consultation regarding recognition of intellectual or industrial property rights over the particular resource or knowledge. Such a negative response, if well founded, can be given even when the sui generis right is not registered.

We can see that the Costa Rican law confers a simple declaratory effect to the registration of *sui generis* community intellectual rights, which is optional and confined to offering a higher level of legal protection. The nonexistence of official registration does not affect the recognition of such rights, nor does it exempt the Technical Office from the duty of examining whether any formal applications for patents, trademarks or other forms of intellectual property involve such knowledge, innovations or traditional practices and, if they do, of refusing the application on a secure basis.

Seen from this perspective, such a position is welcome since the collective intellectual rights of indigenous and traditional communities should always be recognized as being of a status equivalent to their land rights, to which they are intimately attached. The land rights are original and do not depend on any act of legitimization on the part of the State. Any act of registration can only be voluntary and cannot be imposed as a condition for the exercise of these rights.

Andean Pact[22]

This is a regional trade agreement between Colombia, Ecuador, Venezuela, Peru and Bolivia, countries that make up the northern Andean region of South America. The Common Andean Regime on Access to Genetic Resources was adopted by Resolution 391/1996, which gave responsibility for its regularization and implementation to each individual country. Excluded from scopes of Resolution 391 are: human genetic resources and products derived from these, the exchange of genetic resources and their derivatives and of biological products containing these; and the exchange of their intangible associated components undertaken by indigenous, African-American, and local communities of the member countries, among themselves and for their own consumption, based on their customary practices.

One of the objectives of Andean Pact Resolution 391 is to provide the foundation for the recognition and valuation of the intangible components associated with genetic resources. It considers that recognition of the historical contribution of indigenous, African-American and local communities to the conservation of biological diversity and to the sustainable use of its components is necessary. As a report published in the Colombian magazine *Semillas en la Economía Campesina* points out[23], Resolution 391 distinguishes between the genetic resource and the intangible component by defining the latter as 'any knowledge, innovation or individual or collective practice of real or potential value associated with the genetic resource, its derivations or the biological resource containing them, whether protected or not by forms of intellectual property rights'. Resolution 391 defines indigenous, African-American or local community as 'the human group whose social, cultural and economical situation distinguishes it from other sectors of the national society; which is ruled by its own customs or traditions and by special legislation; and which, whatever its legal situation might be, conserves its own social, economical, cultural and political institutions or parts of these'. Although the idea behind a common

---

20. An executive agency of the Costa Rican Ministry of the Environment and Energy responsible for formulating national policies for biodiversity conservation.
21. Author's translation.
22. Or Andean Community.
23. No. 11, November 1997. This report is entitled 'Aportes para la elaboración de estudios nacionales o propuestas sobre regímenes de protección del conocimiento e innovaciones tradicionales' (Contributions to the elaboration of national studies or proposals on regimes for the protection of traditional knowledge and innovations).

Andean regime is to provide a uniform set of judicial norms related to the access to genetic resources within the scope of the Andean Pact, each country will have to approve its own domestic laws.

The Common Andean Regime requires the access contract, when dealing with intangible components associated with genetic resources, to contain, as an integral part of the contract, an annex providing for the fair and equitable sharing of the benefits derived from their use.

Bolivia

Andean Pact Resolution 391 was incorporated into domestic law by Decree 24,676/97, which addresses genetic resources for which Bolivia is the country of origin, their derivations, their associated intangible components, and the biological resources which are naturally found within the Bolivian territory.

In relation to traditional knowledge, it provides for the signing of accessory contracts between the providers of the intangible components and the party requesting access. The State must ensure the 'legality of the obligations and rights arising from the accessory contract'.

Ecuador

In September 1996, Ecuador approved a short law for the protection of biodiversity, which does no more than declare that: 'The Ecuadorian State is the titleholder of the property rights over the species which make up the biodiversity of the country, and which are considered to be national assets and of public utility. Their commercial exploitation shall be subject to special regulation to be determined by the President of the Republic, guaranteeing the ancestral rights of indigenous communities over the knowledge and intangible components of such biodiversity and genetic resources, and the control over these.' There is still no regulation in the country regarding access to genetic resources, although a study group on biodiversity has already been formed.

The Confederation of Indigenous Nations of Ecuador[24], together with other local indigenous organizations (Ecuarunari and Fenocin[25]), and the Ecuadorian non-governmental organization *Acción Ecológica*, have drawn up a proposal for the regulation of collective rights and biodiversity. According to the report in the Colombian magazine *Semillas en la Economía Campesina* previously referred to, this proposal starts from the following principles:

1) Traditional knowledge is generally produced in a collective manner, and has an inter-generational (i.e. it transcends generations) and accumulative character; it is produced and maintained within a given cultural and biological context;

2) It is necessary to recognize all informal, collective and accumulative systems, as innovative. This therefore requires the recognition of the people's traditional knowledge. Different types of innovations need to be recognized, not only those at the biotechnological level;

3) Such traditional systems of knowledge are the heritage of indigenous populations and local communities, who have inalienable rights over them. They cannot therefore be subject to any kind of intellectual property right. One cannot refer to collective intellectual rights as long as the possibility exists that intellectual property rights over traditional knowledge and tangible components associated with knowledge could be granted. For this reason, a review of the entire legislation regarding intellectual property, which currently permits the granting of patents on traditional knowledge, is needed.

4) In addition to the informed consent of all the communities sharing the knowledge, the protection of traditional knowledge must also include the right to object on cultural grounds and to impose restrictions on activities carried out in a given ancestral territory;

5) A system of registration of collective innovations should be established, in accordance with the uses and customs by which these innovations are produced;

6) In order to ensure that such rights to protection are effective, the following rights must be guaranteed to the communities: the right to land; to territory; to the maintenance of their traditional mechanisms of internal control and of all practices concerning the management of biodiversity; the right to the preservation of their culture and world view, and to the conservation of their ancestral way of life.

Peru

The Peruvian government designated a group consisting of indigenous representatives, non-governmental organizations, and official of the ministries of health, industry and agriculture and of the National Institute for the Defense of Competition and Protection of Intellectual Property[26] to draft a bill regulating access to genetic resources and protecting traditional indigenous biodiversity-related knowledge. The bill should set rules for the signing of contracts between indigenous communities and parties interested in gaining access to these resources, and determine the percentage of the profits generated from processes or products based on traditional indigenous knowledge to be paid into the Indigenous Peoples Development Fund. It should be pointed out that the Peruvian industrial property law (Legislative Decree 823) is one of the few which (in its article 63) explicitly requires the State to enact special regulations to protect and register the knowledge of indigenous and rural communities.[27]

Colombia

The Colombian Constitution is one of the few in the Americas which expressly recognize the multiethnic and multicultural character of the nation, and, as a consequence, the different forms of indigenous authority and jurisdiction within the territories of these populations. In Colombia there is a clear distinction between the indigenous peoples who inhabited

---

24. *Confederación de Nacionalidades Indígenas del Ecuador* (CONAIE).

25. Ecuarunari = *Confederación de Pueblos de la Nacionalidad Kichwa del Ecuador* (Federation of Peoples of the Quichua Nationality of Ecuador); Fenocin = *Federación Nacional de Organizaciones Campesinas, Indígenas y Negras del Ecuador* (National Federation of Peasant, Indigenous and Black Organizations of Ecuador).

26. Instituto Nacional de la Defensa de la Competencia y de la Protección de la Propriedad Intelectual (Indecopi).

27. Source: Peru: Industrial Property Law (Legislative Decree, no. 823), in *Industrial Property and Copyright*, WIPO, Geneva, September 1996, cited in *Signposts to Sui Generis Rights: Background Discussion Papers for the International Seminar on Sui Generis Rights*. GRAIN, BIOTHAI, Bangkok: 1997.

Colombian territory before the arrival of the Spanish, and the African-American or black communities, who gained recognition under the Constitution approved in 1991.[28] Both have rights over their collective territories and control of their natural resources.

The Colombian Ad Hoc Biodiversity Group[29] was responsible, as far back as 1995, for the elaboration of a bill aimed at regulating the protection, conservation and use of biological diversity and genetic resources, and including a number of provisions addressing traditional knowledge and collective intellectual rights. The bill expressly excludes from its scope human beings, their cells, and human genetic resources, as well as the exchange of biological resources containing genetic resources or intangible components associated with these between local communities in order to meet their own needs and based on their customary practices.

The Colombian proposal establishes two different regimes for considering requests for access to genetic resources: 1) a special access regime, which considers the requests and sets out the conditions for access to resources associated with traditional knowledge. This regime represents a form of *sui generis* intellectual property; 2) a general access regime, which considers requests for access to resources that do not involve traditional knowledge. This system forms part of the system of individual intellectual property (such as patents and plant breeders' rights).

The requests that fall under the special access regime include those submitted by local communities intending to research or compile inventories of the resources on their lands, requests from those seeking access to resources situated on the lands of indigenous or black communities, or from those intending to investigate resources associated with collective knowledge. In accordance with the special regime (and in addition to the requirements laid out in the general regime), the request must at a minimum include: a) the identification of the parties (the State and the applicant for access, as well of the person or community providing the resource, with the consent of this last party attached, together with the identification of the mechanisms guaranteeing the protection of the cultural integrity and knowledge of the community involved); b) the general obligations of the receiver and of the providers (country and communities), including the obligation on the former to inform the providers about future uses and the prohibition on transfer to third parties; c) the acknowledgement that the contract complies with the system of collective intellectual property rights, of sharing of benefits between the receiver and the provider in exchange for access to the resource, as well as of any benefits that may arise subsequently, and of the right of the communities to restrict access should cultural objections emerge.

In chapter IX, which deals with the protection of knowledge, the government recognizes and accepts responsibility for the promotion and defense of the rights of traditional communities to collectively benefit from their traditions and customs, and to be compensated for their continual task of conserving and creating useful biological materials. In this context, it 'recognizes and commits itself to defending the rights of such communities to protect their traditional and collective knowledge, either by means of intellectual property rights or by other means'.

The Philippines

This was one of the first developing countries to enact domestic legislation to implement the Convention on Biological Diversity. Presidential Executive Order 247, of 18 May 1995, establishes norms for bio-prospecting activities in the country. In June 1996, the Department of the Environment and Natural Resources issued Administrative Order 96-20, which regulates the implementation of the Executive Order and specifies the procedures to be followed by parties wishing to obtain access to genetic resources. In addition to the representation of various government agencies, it also provides for the participation of one representative of an indigenous organization and one of a non-governmental organization in the Genetic and Biological Resources Committee, charged with reviewing access requests.

The Order makes a distinction between access permits for academic or scientific research (called 'academic research agreements'), granted to universities, academic institutions, and governmental and intergovernmental agencies, and permits for commercial research (called 'commercial research agreements'), carried out by individuals and by private or international corporations. It also requires that the 1997 Indigenous Peoples' Rights Act be obeyed as well.[30]

The Indigenous Peoples' Rights Act[31] recognizes and protects the rights of indigenous communities to their 'ancestral domains', cultural integrity, self-government (including the implementation of their own judicial system), collective ownership of the lands they occupy, as well as to the practice and preservation of indigenous knowledge systems. The Indigenous Peoples' Rights Act also guarantees indigenous communities the right to control access to their own genetic resources, which have been the object of collection by means of blood, hair and saliva samples. Interestingly, it guarantees indigenous communities the right to the 'restitution of their spiritual, cultural, intellectual and religious assets, taken from them without their prior informed consent and in violation of their laws, traditions and customs'.

The Order recognizes the rights of indigenous populations and other communities of the Philippines over their traditional knowledge and commits itself to protecting this knowledge when it is 'used, directly or indirectly, for commercial purposes'. Both the Order and the Indigenous Peoples' Rights Act provide for access to indigenous knowledge related to the conservation, utilization and improvement of genetic and biological resources to be permitted within ancestral indigenous lands only with the prior informed consent of these communities, to be obtained in accordance with the customary laws and traditions of the community in question.

---

28. See *Signposts to Sui Generis Rights: Background Discussion Papers for the International Seminar on Sui Generis Rights*. GRAIN, BIOTHAI, Bangkok: 1997.
29. The Ad Hoc Biodiversity Group of Colombia includes the *Instituto Latinoamericano de Servicios Legales Alternativos* (ILSA) (Latin-American Institute for Alternative Legal Services), the *Grupo Semillas*, the *Instituto de Gestión Ambiental* (IGEA) (Institute of Environmental Management) and the project for the implementation of the Convention on Biological Diversity of the World Wildlife Fund (WWF).
30. 'Access to Genetic Resources: Evaluation of the Development and Implementation of Recent Regulation and Access Agreements', Working Paper # 4, prepared for the Biodiversity Action Network by the Environmental Policy Studies Workshop, 1999. Columbia University, School of International and Public Affairs.
31. The main author and negotiator of the Indigenous Peoples' Rights Act was senator Juan Flavier, president of the Cultural Communities Committee of the Philippine Senate.

Thailand

Although the country has not ratified the Convention on Biological Diversity, the Ministry of Public Health has proposed the publication of norms for the registration of traditional Thai medicine. According to the bill introduced, and which will depend on the Parliament in order to become law, traditional Thai healers would be able to register their medical knowledge with a view to ensuring compensation for its commercial use. In April 1997, the U.S. State Department wrote to the Thai government claiming that such a registry system was a violation of the TRIPs Agreement.[32]

Another important legislative proposal under discussion in the Thai Parliament is the Community Forestry Bill, which recognizes the rights of traditional communities living in or around the Thai forest reserves to protect and manage these in cooperation with the Forestry Department.

India

A bill addressing access to biological resources, their sustainable use, and the equitable sharing of benefits with the country of origin and the local communities, in accordance with the Convention on Biological Diversity, is under consideration in Parliament. Human genetic resources are excluded from the scope of the bill. The bill states that it will have no negative effect on the rights of local communities over non-timber forest products, rights that are assured to them in accordance with the practices, codes and regulations of the country's different states. Local communities will be able to freely exchange intangible components of biological resources for their own purposes. In 1995, the Peoples' Biodiversity Registry was established in order, among other things, to create decentralized databases on the *status* of biodiversity resources and local knowledge about their properties and use. The bill provides for the benefits resulting from the use of traditional knowledge to be directly passed on to the community or individual, when these are clearly identifiable. When they are not identifiable, the benefits will be deposited in the National Biodiversity Fund. One of the most polemical aspects of the Indian bill is precisely the recognition of indigenous knowledge and the division of power between the State and the communities.[33]

India has stood out in its defense of farmers rights in the international community and, in particular, in the TRIPs Council of the World Trade Organization.

Malaysia

We cannot fail to mention the draft Community Intellectual Rights Act prepared by the Third World Network, the network of non-governmental organizations coordinated by one of the greatest specialists in this matter worldwide, Dr. Gurdial Singh Nijar. In numerous articles, Nijar[34] was one of the first to point out the absence of legal instruments or frameworks for the protection of indigenous and local communities against the biopirating of their knowledge. Nijar points out that the knowledge systems of indigenous communities are denied any type of recognition, and that only the Western industrial model of innovation is recognized. It is therefore necessary to redefine the concept of 'innovation', in such a way as to provide for the protection of the creativity of indigenous and local communities. The proposal drawn up by the Third World Network is based on the following concepts: 1) local and indigenous communities are the custodians of their innovations; 2) any exclusive monopoly rights to such innovations must be prevented, and any transactions which violate such a prohibition are invalid and have no legal effect; 3) the free exchange and transmission of knowledge between communities and across generations must be respected; 4) anyone interested in the commercial utilization of the innovation or part of it must obtain the written consent of the community and pay them an amount representing a minimum percentage of the profits arising from the utilization of the knowledge; 5) concessions granting exclusive commercial utilization to individuals or corporations should be prohibited; 6) reversal of the burden of proof in favor of the community who declares ownership of the knowledge, while the individual or company using it shall be obliged to prove the contrary.

Bibliography

Access to Genetic Resources: Evaluation of the Development and Implementation of Recent Regulation and Access Agreements. Working Paper 4. BIODIVERSITY ACTION NETWORK, BY THE ENVIRONMENTAL POLICY STUDIES WORKSHOP, 1999. Columbia University, School of International and Public Affairs.

Aportes para la elaboración de estudios nacionales o propuestas sobre regimenes de protección del conocimiento e innovaciones tradicionales. *Semillas en la Economía Campesina*, Colombia, n. 11, November 1997.

ARNT, R. *Perspectivas de futuro: biotecnologia e direitos indígenas*. Presentation to the internal workshop on 'Diversidade Eco-Social e Estratégias de Cooperação entre Ongs na Amazônia' (Eco-Social diversity and strategies for cooperation among NGOs in Amazonia), Belém, 13 June 1994.

Biological and Cultural Diversity: Challenges and Proposals from Latin America, *Mas Allá del Derecho*, v. 6, n. 8-19, July 1998, Instituto Latinoamericano de Servicios Legales Alternativos (ILSA), Colombia.

From Principles to Practice: Indigenous Peoples and Biodiversity Conservation in Latin America. Proceedings of the Pucallpa Conference. Peru, 1997.

INSTITUTE FOR AGRICULTURE AND TRADE POLICY. *IPR – Information about Intellectual Property Rights* (briefing), no. 19, July 1997.

---

32. Agreement on Trade-Related Intellectual Property Rights, one of the international agreements administered by the World Trade Organization and which contains provisions relating to the protection of intellectual property rights - patents, trademarks, etc..

33. According to *Signposts to Sui Generis Rights: Background Discussion Papers for the International Seminar on Sui Generis Rights*, Grain, Biothai, Bangkok; and the report *Contributions for the Elaboration of National Studies or Proposals on Traditional Knowledge and Innovations Protection Regimes*, also referred to previously. The Research Foundation for Science, Technology and Ecology, a non-governmental organization headed by one of the greatest specialists in this matter (Dr. Vandana Shiva) and based in New Delhi, is one of the main proponents of measures aimed at protecting Indian biodiversity and the knowledge of traditional indigenous and farming communities.

34. Nijar, Gurdial. *Protecting Local Community Knowledge: What Next?* and *In Defence of Local Community Knowledge and Biodiversity: a Conceptual Framework and Essential Elements of a Rights Regime*, Penang: Third World Network.

NIJAR, G. S. Protecting Local Community Knowledge: What Next? *Third World Network*, Penang.

_____. In Defence of Local Community Knowledge and Biodiversity: a Conceptual Framework and Essential Elements of a Rights Regime. *Third World Network*, Penang.

RICARDO, C. A. A sociodiversidade nativa contemporânea no Brasil, *Povos indígenas no Brasil – 1991/1995*. São Paulo: Instituto Socioambiental, 1996.

RURAL ADVANCEMENT FOUNDATION INTERNATIONAL (RAFI). *Conservación de Conocimientos autóctonos: integración de dos sistemas de inovación*. Independent study undertaken for the United Nations Development Programme.

Signposts: to *Sui Generis Rights: Background Discussion Papers for the International Seminar on Sui Generis Rights*, co-organised by the Thai Network on Community Rights and Biodiversity (BIOTHAI) and Genetic Resources Action International (GRAIN). Bangkok: 1997.

SHIVA, V. *The Politics of Knowledge at the CDB*. New Delhi: The Research Foundation for Science, Technology and Natural Resource Policy.

_____. *Protecting our Biological and Intellectual Heritage in the Age of Biopiracy*. New Delhi: Research Foundation for Science, Technology and Natural Resource Policy.

TORRES, R. (Ed.). *Entre lo propio y lo ajeno: derechos de los pueblos indigenas y propiedad intelectual*. Coordinadora de las Organizaciones Indígenas de la Cuenca Amazónica (COICA), 1997.

Thematic documents 3

Conservation areas and indigenous lands

Conservation areas in Legal Amazonia*

Fany Ricardo *Instituto Socioambiental*
João Paulo R. Capobianco *Instituto Socioambiental*

The present document provides a list of the 236 conservation areas existent in Legal Amazonia in April 2004. On the basis of the information contained in the legal instruments creating them, these cover an area of 74,539,140 hectares and correspond to 14.88% of the total area of Legal Amazonia.

Fewer than half of these areas, 91 (38.56%) of the 236, are strict conservation areas (full protection), while 145 (61.44%) are direct use conservation areas (sustainable use).

Of these 236 areas, 103 fall within the jurisdiction of the Federal Government, corresponding to little under half of the total (43.64%), and 133 (56.35%) are under the control of state governments.

It is important to stress, however, that simply adding up the total dimensions of federal and state conservation areas gives a misleading impression of the geographical size of the overall area under protection in Legal Amazonia. This is because there is an enormous degree of overlap between the areas themselves, and also between these areas and other categories of lands with special functions defined by the State, such as indigenous lands, prospecting reserves, and military land.

After discounting these overlaps, the percentage of Legal Amazonia under protection in the form of conservation areas at the moment falls from the 14.88% suggested by the official figures to approximately 11.39%.

Table 1 – Conservation areas in Legal Amazonia Overall total by category (april/2004)

Conservation Areas	Quantity	Area (as officially given)[1]	
		(ha)	%[2]
Legal Amazonia	236	74,539,140	14.88
Strict (full protection) conservation area	91	25,642,786	5.12
Federal	38	19,816,023	3.96
State	53	5,826,763	1.16
Direct use (sustainable use) conservation areas	145	48,896,354	9.76
Federal	65	22,592,922	4.51
State	80	26,303,432	5.25

Table 2 - Conservation areas in Legal Amazonia Overall total by category (april/2004)

Conservation Areas	Number	Area (as officially given)[1]	
		ha	%[2]
Legal Amazonia	236	74,539,140	14.88
Federal Conservation Areas	103	42,408,945	8.47
Strict	38	19,816,023	3.96
National parks	15	13,372,271	2.67
Biological reserves	9	3,510,284	0.70
Ecological stations	13	2,933,359	0.59
Ecological reserves	1	109	0.00
Direct use	65	22,592,922	4.51
National forests	36	17,282,057	3.45
Extractive reserves	23	4,950,048	0.99
Environmental protection areas	3	339,741	0.07
Areas of special ecological importance	3	21,076	0.00
State Conservation Areas	133	32,130,195	6.41
Strict	53	5,826,763	1.16
State parks	36	5,096,744	1.02
Biological reserves	5	106,183	0.02
Ecological stations	6	387,634	0.08
Ecological reserves	2	103,900	0.02
Natural monuments	1	32,152	0.01
Wildlife refuges	2	100,000	0.02
Ecological parks	1	150	0.00
Direct use	80	26,303,432	5.25
Sustainable production forests	18	1,470,762	0.29
Extractive forests	3	1,438,907	0.29
State forests	1	76,832	0.02
Environmental protection areas	28	14,306,889	2.86
Extractive reserves	23	1,243,132	0.25
Sustainable development reserves	7	7,766,910	1.55

Notes to Tables 1 and 2

1. Marine areas and areas outside Legal Amazonia are not included in these figures.
2. In relation to the total area of Legal Amazonia (500,631,680 ha.).

---

* Figures updated in April 2004.

LIST OF FEDERAL AND STATE CONSERVATION AREAS IN LEGAL AMAZONIA					
Federal strict conservation areas		State	Area (ha)	Created by
National parks	Amazonia (AM)	PA	864,047	Decree no. 73,683 of 02/19/1974
	Araguaia	TO	557,714	Decree no. 47,570 of 12/31/1959
	Cabo Orange	AP	619,000	Decree no. 84,913 of 07/15/1980
	Chapada dos Guimarães	MT	33,000	Decree no. 97,656 of 04/12/1989
	Jaú	AM	2,272,000	Decree no. 85,200 of 09/24/1980
	Montanhas do Tumucumaque	AP	3,867,000	Decree of 08/22/2002
	Monte Roraima	RR	116,000	Decree no. 97,887 of 06/28/1989
	Nascentes do rio Paranaíba (MA, PI, BA)	TO	729,814	Decree of 07/17/2002
	Pacaás Novos	RO	764,801	Decree no. 84,019 of 09/21/1979
	Pantanal Matogrossense	MT	135,000	Decree no. 86,392 of 09/24/1981
	Pico da Neblina	AM	2,200,000	Decree no. 83,550 of 06/05/1979
	Serra da Cotia	RO	283,611	Decree of 08/01/2001
	Serra do Divisor	AC	846,633	Decree no. 97,839 of 06/16/1989
	Serra da Mocidade	RR	350,960	Decree of 04/29/1998
	Viruá	RR	227,011	Decree of 04/29/1998
Biological reserves	Abufari	AM	288,000	Decree no. 87,585 of 09/20/1982
	Guaporé	RO	600,000	Decree no. 87,587 of 09/20/1982
	Gurupi	MA	341,650	Decree no. 95,614 of 01/12/1988
	Jari (PA)	AP	227,126	Decree no. 87,092 of 04/12/1982
	Jaru	RO	268,150	Decree no. 83,716 of 07/12/1979
	Lago Piratuba	AP	357,000	Decree no. 84,914 of 07/16/1980
	Rio Trombetas	PA	385,000	Decree no. 84,018 of 09/21/1979
	Tapirapé	PA	103,000	Decree no. 97,719 of 05/05/1989
	Uatumã	AM	940,358	Decree no. 99,277 of 06/06/1990
Ecological stations	Anavilhanas	AM	350,018	Decree no. 86,061 of 06/02/1981
	Caracaraí	RR	80,560	Decree no. 87,222 of 05/31/1982
	Cuniã	RO	53,221	Decree of 09/27/2001
	Iquê	MT	200,000	Decree no. 86,061 of 06/02/1981
	Juami-Japurá	AM	745,830	Decree no. 91,307 of 06/03/1985
	Jutaí-Solimões	AM	288,187	Decree no. 88,541 of 07/21/1983
	Maracá	RR	101,312	Decree no. 86,061 of 06/02/1981
	Maracá Jipioca	AP	72,000	Decree no. 86,061 of 06/02/1981
	Niquiá	RR	286,600	Decree no. 91,306 of 06/03/1985
	Rio Acre	AC	77,500	Decree no. 86,061 of 06/02/1981
	Serra das Araras	MT	28,700	Decree no. 87,222 of 05/31/1982
	Serra Geral dos Tocantins (BA)	TO	716,306	Decree of 09/27/2001
	Taiamã	MT	11,200	Decree no. 86,061 of 06/02/1981
Ecological reserves	Sauim-Castanheiras	AM	109	Decree no. 87,455 of 08/12/1982

Federal direct use conservation areas		State	Area (ha)	Created by
National forests	Altamira	PA	689,012	Decree no. 2,483 of 02/02/1998
	Amapá	AP	412,000	Decree no. 97,930 of 04/10/1989
	Amazonas	AM	1,573,100	Decree no. 97,546 of 03/01/1989
	Bom Futuro	RO	280,000	Decree no. 96,188 of 06/21/1988
	Carajás	PA	411,949	Decree no. 2,486 of 02/02/1998
	Caxiuanã	PA	200,000	Decree no. 239 of 11/28/1961
	Cubaté	AM	416,533	Decree no. 99,105 of 03/09/1990
	Cuiari	AM	109,519	Decree no. 99,109 of 03/09/1990
	Humaitá	AM	468,790	Decree no. 2,485 of 02/02/1998
	Içana	AM	200,562	Decree no. 99,110 of 03/09/1990
	Içana Aiari	AM	491,401	Decree no. 99,108 of 03/09/1990
	Itacaiúnas	PA	141,400	Decree no. 2,480 of 02/02/1998
	Itaituba I	PA	220,035	Decree no. 2,481 of 02/02/1998
	Itaituba II	PA	440,500	Decree no. 2,482 of 02/02/1998
	Jamari	RO	215,000	Decree no. 90,224 of 09/25/1984
	Jatuarana	AM	837,100	Decree of 09/19/2002
	Macauã	AC	173,475	Decree no. 96,189 of 06/21/1988
	Mapiá-Inauini	AM	311,000	Decree no. 98,051 of 08/14/1989
	Mulata	PA	212,752	Decree of 08/01/2001
	Pari Cachoeira I	AM	18,000	Decree no. 98,440 of 11/23/1989
	Pari Cachoeira II	AM	654,000	Decree no. 98,440 of 11/23/1989
	Pau-Rosa	AM	827,877	Decree of 08/07/2001
	Pirauiara	AM	631,437	Decree no. 99,111 of 03/09/1990
	Purus	AM	256,000	Decree no. 96,190 of 06/21/1988
	Roraima	RR	2,664,685	Decree no. 97,545 of 03/01/1989
	Santa Rosa do Purus	AC	230,257	Decree of 08/07/2001

continues

Federal direct use conservation areas		State	Area (ha)	Created by
National forests	São Francisco	AC	21,600	Decree of 08/07/2001
	Saracá-Taquera	PA	429,600	Decree no. 98,704 of 12/27/1989
	Tapajós	PA	600,000	Decree no. 73,684 of 02/19/1974
	Tapirapé Aquiri	PA	190,000	Decree no. 97,720 of 05/05/1989
	Taracuá I	AM	647,744	Decree no. 99,112 of 03/09/1990
	Taracuá II	AM	559,505	Decree no. 99,113 of 03/09/1990
	Tefé	AM	1,020,000	Decree no. 97,629 of 04/10/1989
	Urucu	AM	66,497	Decree no. 99,106 of 03/09/1990
	Xié	AM	407,936	Decree no. 99,107 of 03/09/1990
	Xingu	PA	252,790	Decree no. 2,484 of 02/02/1998
Extractive reserves	Alto Juruá	AC	506,186	Decree no. 98,863 of 01/23/1990
	Alto Tarauacá	AC	151,200	Decree of 11/08/2000
	Auati-Paraná	AM	146,950	Decree of 08/07/2001
	Baixo Juruá	AM	187,982	Decree of 08/01/2001
	Barreiro das Antas	RO	107,235	Decree of 08/07/2001
	Cazumba-Iracema	AC	750,795	Decree of 09/19/2002
	Chico Mendes	AC	970,570	Decree no. 99,144 of 03/12/1990
	Chocoaré-Mato Grosso	PA	2,786	Decree of 12/13/2002
	Ciríaco	MA	7,050	Decree no. 534 of 05/20/1992
	Extremo Norte do Tocantins	TO	9,280	Decree no. 535 of 05/20/1992
	Lago do Cuniã	RO	55,850	Decree no. 3,238 of 11/10/1999
	Mãe Grande do Curuçá	PA	37,062	Decree of 12/13/2002
	Maracanã	PA	30,019	Decree of 12/13/2002
	Marinha de Soure	PA	27,464	Decree of 11/22/2001
	Mata Grande	MA	10,450	Decree no. 532 of 05/20/1992
	Médio Juruá	AM	253,227	Decree of 03/04/1997
	Quilombo do Frexal	MA	9,542	Decree no. 536 of 05/20/1992
	Rio Cajari	AP	481,650	Decree no. 99,145 of 03/12/1990
	Rio Cautário	RO	73,818	Decree of 08/07/2001
	Rio Jutaí	AM	275,533	Decree of 07/16/2002
	Rio Ouro Preto	RO	204,583	Decree no. 99,166 of 03/13/1990
	São João da Ponta	PA	3,204	Decree of 12/13/2002
	Tapajós-Arapiuns	PA	647,611	Decree of 11/06/1998
Environmental protection areas	Igarapé Gelado	PA	21,600	Decree no. 97,718 of 05/06/1989
	Meandros do Rio Araguaia (GO, TO)**	MT	357,126	Decree of 10/02/1998
	Serra da Tabatinga	TO	32,297	Decree no. 99,278 of 06/06/1990
Areas of special ecological importance	Javari-Buriti	AM	15,000	Decree no. 91,886 of 11/05/1985
	PDBFF- Projeto Dinâmica Biológica de Fragmentos Florestais	AM	3,500	Decree no. 91,884 of 11/06/1985
	Seringal Nova Esperança	AC	2,576	Decree of 08/20/1999

State strict conservation areas		State	Area (ha)	Created by
State parks	Águas do Cuiabá	MT	10,600	Decree of 06/05/2002
	Águas Quentes	MT	1,488	Decree 1,240 of 01/13/1978
	Araguaia	MT	230,000	Decree no. 7,517 of 09/28/2001
	Belém	PA	1,340	Decree no. 1,552 of 05/03/1993
	Bacanga	MA	3,075	Decree no. 7,545 of 03/07/1980
	Candeias	RO	8,985	Decree no. 4,572 of 03/23/1990
	Cantão	TO	90,018	Law no. 996 of 07/14/1998
	Cristalino I	MT	66,900	Decree no. 7,518 of 09/28/2001
	Cristalino II	MT	118,000	Decree no. 2,628 of 05/30/2001
	Corumbiara	RO	384,056	Decree no. 4,576 of 05/23/1990
	Dom Osório Stoffel	MT	6,422	Decree no. 5,437 of 11/12/2002
	Gruta da Lagoa Azul	MT	12,513	Law no. 7,369 of 12/20/2000
	Guajará Mirim	RO	216,568	Decree no. 4,575 of 03/23/1990
	Guirá	MT	100,000	Law no. 7,625 of 01/15/2002
	Igarapés do Juruena	MT	227,817	Decree no. 5,438 of 11/12/2002
	Jalapão	TO	158,885	Law no. 1,203 of 01/12/2001
	Lajeado	TO	9,931	Law no. 1,224 of 05/11/2001
	Mãe Bonifácia	MT	78	Decree no. 1,470 of 09/28/2001
	Massairo Okamura	MT	54	Law no. 7,506 of 09/21/2001
	Mirador	MA	700,000	Decree no. 7,641 of 06/04/1980
	Monte Alegre	PA	5,800	Law no. 6,412 of 11/09/2001
	Nhamundá	AM	28,370	Decree no. 12,175 of 07/07/1989
	Rio Negro Setor Norte	AM	146,028	Decree no. 16,497 of 04/02/1995
	Rio Negro Setor Sul	AM	157,807	Decree no. 16,497 of 04/02/1995
	Saúde	MT	66	Decree no. 1,693 of 08/23/2000

continues

State strict conservation areas		State	Area (ha)	Created by
State parks	Serra do Araçá	AM	1,818,700	Decree no. 12,836 of 03/09/1990
	Serra Azul	MT	11,002	Decree no. 6,439 of 05/31/1994
	Serra de Santa Bárbara	MT	120,093	Law no. 7,165 of 08/23/1999
	Serra dos Martírios/Andorinhas	PA	24,897	Law no. 5,982 of 07/25/1996
	Serra dos Parecis	RO	38,950	Decree no. 4,570 of 03/23/1990
	Serra dos Reis	RO	36,443	Decree no. 7,027 of 08/08/1995
	Serra dos Reis (A)	RO	2,244	Decree no. 7,637 of 11/07/1996
	Serra Ricardo Franco	MT	158,621	Decree no. 1,796 of 11/04/1997
	Sumaúma	AM	51	Decree no. 23,721 of 09/05/2003
	Tucumã	MT	66,475	Decree no. 5,439 of 11/12/2002
	Xingu	MT	134,464	Decree no. 3,585 of 12/07/2001
Biological reserves	Fazendinha	AP	193	Decree no. 20 of 12/14/1984
	Morro dos Seis Lagos	AM	36,900	Decree no. 12,836 of 03/09/1990
	Parazinho	AP	112	Decree no. 5 of 01/21/1985
	Rio Ouro Preto	RO	46,438	Decree no. 4,580 of 03/28/1990
	Traçadal	RO	22,540	Decree no. 4,583 of 03/28/1990
Ecological stations	Antonio Mujica Nava	RO	18,281	Decree no. 7,635 of 11/07/1996
	Rio Madeirinha	MT	13,683	Decree no. 7,163 of 08/23/1999
	Rio Ronuro	MT	131,795	Decree no. 2,207 of 04/23/1998
	Rio Roosevelt	MT	53,001	Decree no. 7,162 of 08/23/1999
	Samuel	RO	71,061	Decree no. 4,247 of 07/18/1989
	Serra dos Três Irmãos	RO	99,813	Decree no. 4,584 of 03/28/1990
Ecological reserves	Apiacás	MT	100,000	Decree no. 1,357 of 03/27/1992
	Culuene	MT	3,900	Decree no. 1,387 of 01/18/1989
Natural monuments	Árvores Fossilizadas do Estado de Tocantins	TO	32,152	Law no. 1,179 of 10/04/2000
Wildlife refuges	Corixão da Mata Azul	MT	40,000	Law no. 7,519 of 09/28/2001
	Quelônios do Araguaia	MT	60,000	Law no. 7,520 of 09/28/2001
Ecological parks	Lagoa Jansen	MA	150	Decree no. 4,878 of 06/23/1988

State direct use conservation areas		State	Area (ha)	Created by
Sustainable production forests	Araras	RO	965	Decree no. 7,605 of 10/08/1996
	Cedro	RO	2,567	Decree no. 7,601 of 10/08/1996
	Gavião	RO	441	Decree no. 7,604 of 10/08/1996
	Mutum	RO	11,472	Decree no. 7,602 of 10/08/1996
	Periquito	RO	1,163	Decree no. 7,606 of 10/08/1996
	Rio Abunã	RO	62,219	Decree no. 4,577 of 03/23/1994
	Rio Machado	RO	175,781	Decree no. 4,571 of 03/23/1990
	Rio Madeira (A)	RO	63,812	Decree no. 4,547 of 03/23/1990
	Rio Madeira (B)	RO	51,856	Decree no. 7,600 of 10/08/1996
	Rio Madeira (C)	RO	30,000	Decree no. 4,697 of 06/06/1990
	Rio Mequéns	RO	425,844	Decree no. 4,573 of 03/23/1990
	Rio Roosevelt	RO	27,860	Decree no. 4,569 of 03/23/1990
	Rio São Domingos	RO	267,375	Decree no. 4,566 of 03/23/1990
	Rio Vermelho (A)	RO	38,688	Decree no. 4,581 of 03/28/1990
	Rio Vermelho (B)	RO	152,000	Decree no. 4,582 of 03/28/1990
	Rio Vermelho (C)	RO	20,215	Decree no. 4,567 of 03/23/1990
	Rio Vermelho (D)	RO	137,844	Decree no. 4,610 of 04/16/1990
	Tucano	RO	660	Decree no. 7,603 of 10/08/1996
Extractive forests	Laranjeiras	RO	30,688	Decree no. 4,568 of 03/23/1990
	Pacaás Novos	RO	353,219	Decree no. 4,591 of 04/03/1990
	Rio Preto-Jacundá	RO	1,055,000	Decree no. 4,245 of 07/17/1989
State forests	Antimari	AC	76,832	Decree no. 46 of 02/07/1997
Environmental protection areas	Algodoal-Maiandeua	PA	2,378	Decree no. 5,621 of 11/27/1990
	Arquipélago do Marajó	PA	5,500,000	Art. 13, par. 2 of the State Constitution
	Baixada Maranhense	MA	1,775,036	Decree no. 11,900 of 06/11/1991
	Cabeceiras do Rio Cuiabá	MT	473,411	Law no. 7,161 of 08/23/1999
	Caverna do Maroaga	AM	374,700	Decree no. 12,836 of 03/09/1990
	Chapada dos Guimarães	MT	251,848	Decree no. 537 of 11/21/1995
	Curiaú	AP	21,676	Law no. 431 of 09/15/1998
	Foz do Rio Santa Teresa	TO	50,784	Law no. 905 of 05/20/1997
	Ilha do Combú	PA	1,500	Law no. 6,083 of 11/13/1997
	Jalapão	TO	461,730	Law no. 1,172 of 07/31/2000
	Lago de Palmas	TO	50,370	Law no. 1,098 of 10/20/1999
	Lago de Peixe / Angical	TO	78,874	Decree no. 1,444 of 03/18/2002
	Lago de Tucuruí	PA	568,667	Law no. 6,451 of 04/08/2002
	Leandro (Ilha do Bananal / Cantão)	TO	1,678,000	Law no. 907 of 05/20/1997

continues

State direct use conservation areas		State	Area (ha)	Created by
Environmental protection areas	Mananciais de Abastecimento de Água de Belém	PA	7,500	Decree no. 1,551 of 05/03/1993
	Nascentes de Araguaína	TO	15,822	Law no. 1,116 of 12/09/1999
	Parintins - Nhamundá	AM	195,900	Decree no. 12,836 of 03/09/1990
	Paytuna	PA	56,129	Law no. 6,426 of 12/17/2001
	Pé da Serra Azul	MT	7,980	Decree no. 6,436 of 05/27/1994
	Região de Maracanã	MA	1,831	Decree no. 12,103 of 10/01/1991
	Reentrâncias Maranhenses	MA	2,680,911	Decree no. 11,901 of 06/11/1991
	Rio Madeira	RO	6,741	Decree no. 5,124 of 06/06/1991
	Rio Negro - left margin	AM	643,215	Decree no. 16,498 of 04/02/1995
	Rio Negro - right margin	AM	566,365	Decree no. 16,498 of 04/02/1995
	Salto Magessi	MT	7,847	Law no. 7,841 of 12/20/2002
	São Geraldo do Araguaia	PA	29,655	Law no. 5,983 of 07/25/1996
	Serra do Lajeado	TO	121,416	Decree no. 213 of 02/14/1989
	Upaon-Açu/Miritiba/Alto Preguiças	MA	1,535,310	Decree no. 12,428 of 06/05/1992
Extractive reserves	Angelim	RO	8,924	Decree no. 7,095 of 09/04/1995
	Aquariquara	RO	18,100	Decree no. 7,106 of 09/04/1995
	Castanheira	RO	10,200	Decree no. 7,105 of 09/04/1995
	Catuá-Ipixuna	AM	217,486	Decree no. 23,722 of 09/05/2003
	Curralinho	RO	1,758	Decree no. 6,952 of 07/14/1995
	Freijó	RO	601	Decree no. 7,097 of 09/04/1995
	Garrote	RO	803	Decree no. 7,109 of 09/04/1995
	Guariba-Roosevelt	MT	57,630	Law no. 7,164 of 08/23/1999
	Ipê	RO	816	Decree no. 7,101 of 09/04/1995
	Itaúba	RO	1,758	Decree no. 7,100 of 09/04/1995
	Jatobá	RO	1,136	Decree no. 7,102 of 09/04/1995
	Maracatiara	RO	9,504	Decree no. 7,096 of 09/04/1995
	Massaranduba	RO	5,567	Decree no. 7,103 of 09/04/1995
	Mogno	RO	2,451	Decree no. 7,099 of 09/04/1995
	Pedras Negras	RO	124,409	Decree no. 6,954 of 07/14/1995
	Piquiá	RO	1,449	Decree no. 7,098 of 09/04/1995
	Rio Cautário	RO	146,400	Decree no. 7,028 of 08/08/1995
	Rio Jaci Paraná	RO	191,325	Decree no. 7,335 of 01/17/1996
	Rio Pacaás Novos	RO	342,904	Decree no. 6,953 of 07/14/1995
	Rio Preto Jacundá	RO	95,300	Decree no. 7,336 of 01/17/1996
	Roxinho	RO	883	Decree no. 7,107 of 09/04/1995
	Seringueira	RO	538	Decree no. 7,108 of 09/04/1995
	Sucupira	RO	3,189	Decree no. 7,104 of 09/04/1995
Sustainable development reserves	Alcobaça	PA	36,128	Law no. 6,451 of 04/08/2002
	Amanã	AM	2,313,000	Decree no. 19,021 of 08/04/1998
	Cujubim	AM	2,450,382	Decree no. 23,724 of 09/05/2003
	Mamirauá	AM	1,124,000	Decree no. 12,836 of 03/09/1990
	Piagaçu-Purus	AM	1,008,167	Decree no. 23,723 of 09/05/2003
	Pucuruí-Ararão	PA	29,049	Law no. 6,451 of 04/08/2002
	Rio Iratapuru	AP	806,184	Law no. 392 of 12/11/1997

Indigenous lands in Legal Amazonia

Fany Ricardo *Instituto Socioambiental*

This document provides a compilation of the 400 indigenous lands in Legal Amazonia. These add up to an area of 104,367,705 ha (1,043,677 km²), corresponding to 20.85% of the overall region.

Overall total of indigenous lands in Legal Amazonia (situation as of 04/20/2004)			
Legal Situation	Number	Size	
		hectares	% (*)
Awaiting identification	21		
Being identified (10 being revised)	59	2,777,714	
Use restrictions applying to non-indians	2	221,000	
Subtotal	82	2,998,714	2.87%**
Identified/approved by Funai. Subject to appeal.	16	2,305,468	2.22%
Delimited	36	10,148,591	9.72%
Demarcated by Incra or owned in fee simple	4	15,232	
Ratified	29	4,760,662	
Registered in the CRI (local land registry) or the SPU (registry of federal assets)	233	84,139,038	
Subtotal	266	88,914,932	85.19%
Total in Legal Amazonia	400	104,367,705	100%

* In relation to the total area of indigenous lands in Legal Amazonia.
** Area in process of definition.

Of the total extent of indigenous lands in Brazil, 98.9% is concentrated in Legal Amazonia. The remaining 1.2% is spread across the northeast, southeast and southern regions, as well as in the state of Mato Grosso do Sul.

The indigenous population of the Brazilian Amazon is approximately 180,000 (not counting indians living outside indigenous lands), which represents less than 1% of the local population.

There are also indications of the existence of approximately 53 uncontacted indigenous groups, of which Funai has been able to confirm the existence of twelve.

Lists of indigenous lands in Legal Amazonia, classified by the stage of demarcation process (situation as of 04/20/2004)

List 1: Lands awaiting identification, including those occupied by 'isolated indians'

Indigenous lands awaiting identification are those where the indigenous communities inhabiting them have had no formal contact with Funai, even though they may have had long-standing relations with the local population. In other words, the federal indian agency has not yet sent a working group to the area to begin the process of official recognizing the indigenous area. Included in this category are those lands occupied by 'isolated indians' (those that live outside already recognized areas inhabited by 'contacted indians') for which Funai has information and an approximate location.

no.	Name of Land	People	State	Source
1.	Arama/Inauini	isolated	AM	Funai 1993
2.	Awá Guajá	Guajá	MA	Funai 1989
3.	Barreira Campo	Karajá	PA	Funai 1993
4.	Guajá	isolated	MA	Funai 1985
5.	Ig. Muriru e Pacutinga	isolated	MT	Funai 1988
6.	Jacareuba/Katawixi	isolated	AM	Funai 1993
7.	Karipuna II (Jaci-Paraná)	isolated	RO	Funai 1994
8.	Lago Grande	Karajá	MT	Funai 1995
9.	Parauari	isolated	AM	Funai 1988
10.	Piripicura	isolated	MT	Funai 1993
11.	Posto Fiscal	Macurap	RO	Funai 1993
12.	Pu'ro - Baixo Rio Curuá	isolated (Kayapó)	PA	Funai 1988
13.	Rio Bararati e Maracanã	isolated	AM	Funai 1987
14.	Rio Candeias	isolated	RO	Funai 1994
15.	Rio Liberdade	isolated	MT	Funai 1989
16.	Rio Merure	isolated (Kayapó)	PA	Verswijver
17.	Rio Tapirapé/Tuerê	isolated	PA	Funai 1988
18.	Rio Ximari/Rio Matrinxã	isolated (Apiaká)	MT	Funai 1988
19.	Tapauá	Katukina, Paumari	AM	Funai 1993
20.	Waiãpi do Alto Amapari	isolated (Waiãpi)	AP	Funai 1990
21.	Waiãpi do Alto Ipitinga	isolated (Waiãpi)	PA	Funai 1994

Sources:
FUNAI. *Listagem da situação das terras indígenas* (List of the situation of indigenous lands), published by Funai in 1985, 1987, 1988, 1989, 1990, 1993 and 1994.
VERSWIJVER, G. *Terras indígenas no Brasil* (Indigenous Lands in Brazil). Cedi/Museu Nacional, 1987, p. 109.

Notes on *lands awaiting identification*

Under the current system, *lands awaiting identification* are those awaiting the establishment of a Funai working group.

This category includes 'isolated indians' – indigenous groups that have not yet been officially contacted by the Indian agency.

There is evidence of approximately 53 indigenous groups with no contact with the national society. The existence of only twelve of these has been confirmed by Funai.

At least 31 of these groups inhabit indigenous lands that have either been demarcated or have received some type of recognition by federal agencies.

References to these groups, almost all of them in the Amazon region, can be found in Funai technical reports and are based on information given by other indians and local inhabitants. Other information has emerged at meetings of NGO representatives, Funai staff, missionaries, fieldworkers, and indians, when references have been compiled and the situation of these groups reviewed. Funai's Department of Isolated Indians, established in 1987, maintains a record of references to these isolated groups.

Lands inhabited by 'isolated indians' were listed in our previous report on lands where no measures have been taken, but areas were not calculated since the first step towards identifying their boundaries depends on determining the exact location of the villages, and obtaining information on the use the group makes of a given territory. This presupposes the existence of peaceful contacts between these groups and the government indian affairs agency. According to criteria currently used by Funai (in its Administrative Rule PP 1900/87), this will require a set of 'indications' on the part of an 'isolated group' that it is looking to make contact, as well the existence of circumstances that constitute a risk to its survival. Funai's policy is in fact not to contact 'isolated indians' unless these conditions are met.

List 2: Lands being identified

1. Indigenous lands being identified are those currently being studied by Funai, following the setting up of a working group which is sent to the region to identify the indigenous land in question.

2. A number of areas for which an administrative declaration of possession had been issued under Funai's previous administrative procedures for demarcation (i.e. procedures in effect prior to Decree 1,775) had not been ratified and registered at the time the procedures were modified.

3. Other lands where Funai has published a notice in the Diário Oficial da União (the official federal gazette) restricting their use by non-indians.

no.	Name of Land	People	State
1.	Amanayé	Amanayé	PA
2.	Arara do Alto Juruá	Arara	AC
3.	Anaro	Wapixana	RR
4.	Areões I **	Xavante	MT
5.	Arary ****	Mura	AM
6.	Areões II **	Xavante	MT
7.	Boca do Cano do Correio	Ticuna	AM
8.	Cacaia do Piquiá	Mura	AM
9.	Capana do Aracu ****	Mura	AM
10.	Capivara	Mura	AM
11.	Capitão Marcos/Uirapuru *	Parecí	MT
12.	Capoeira Grande	Mura	AM

continues

no.	Name of Land	People	State
13.	Castanha do Sapucaia	Mura	AM
14.	Colônia São João	Mura	AM
15.	Cué-Cué/Marabitanas	Baniwa, Baré, etc.	AM
16.	Estação	Kokama	AM
17.	Fortuna	Chiquitano	MT
18.	Guanabara	Kokama	AM
19.	Guapenu	Mura	AM
20.	Igarapé Açu ****	Mura	AM
21.	Igarapé Acurau	Mura	AM
22.	Igarapé do Anjo	Kaxinawá	AC
23.	Ig. Carioca	Apurinã	AM
24.	Ig. Joari	Apurinã	AM
25.	Ilha Jacaré Xipaca *	Sateré Mawé	AM
26.	Inajazinho	Mura	AM
27.	Juruá ***	Kulina	AM
28.	Jutaí/Igapó Açu	Mura	AM
29.	Kanela-Buriti Velho	Kanela	MA
30.	Kaxinawá do Seringal Curralinho	Kaxinawá	AC
31.	Kokama *	Kokama	AM
32.	Krahô-Kanela	Krahô-Kanela	TO
33.	Kulina do Médio Jutaí	Kulina	AM
34.	Lago Grande	Chiquitano	MT
35.	Manchineri Seringal Guanabara	Manchineri	AC
36.	Mapari	Kaixana	AM
37.	Muratuba	Mura	AM
38.	Murutinga	Mura	AM
39.	Naruvoto	Naruvoto	MT
40.	Nawa	Nawa	AC
41.	Onça	Mura	AM
42.	Onça II	Mura	AM
43.	Pacajá	Asurini	PA
44.	Pacovão ****	Mura	AM
45.	Pantaleão	Mura	AM
46.	Paraná do Maquira	Mura	AM
47.	Picina	Nambikwara	MT
48.	Porquinhos - Aldeia Chinela	Kanela	MA
49.	Porto Limoeiro	Ticuna	AM
50.	Riozinho	Ticuna	AM
51.	Salsal	Mura	AM
52.	Sapotal	Kokama	AM
53.	S. José	Ticuna	AM
54.	São Gabriel / São Salvador	Kokama	AM
55.	Sururuá	Kokama	AM
56.	Tracajá	Mura	AM
57.	Trombetas Mapuera	Wai Wai	RR/AM/PA
58.	Utaria Wyhyna / Hirari Berena	Karajá	TO
59.	Vila Real	Guajajara	MA

* Lands that have already been the subject of identification procedures. Many are cases being reexamined.

** Lands for which an administrative restriction has been issued and which are being investigated.

*** Lands granted an Administrative Declaration of Permanent Possession under previous procedures, but whose demarcation process was not finalized.

**** There are a number of areas occupied by the Mura indians which were classified as reserves in the 1920s by the old SPI (*Serviço de Proteção aos Índios* – Indian Protection Service) and whose current legal status is unknown even to Funai, due to the loss of the records over the years. They are small areas sub-divided into plots for groups of Mura families living along the rivers and streams in the region of the Tapajós and Madeira rivers. Funai has previously conducted a survey of these areas, classifying them as *under review*. As this term does not correspond to any existing term under the current demarcation procedures, we have decided to list them as *lands being identified*.

Three areas marked as **** are not included in the final calculation because a number of the names may refer to a single area, and because working groups have not been set up for some of them.

List 3: Lands where entry is restricted by the president of Funai by means of administrative orders issued under Decree no. 1,775:

1 - Rio Muqui: isolated indians in the municipalities of Urupá and Alvorada D'Oeste, Rondônia;
2 - Rio Pardo: isolated indians, 166,000 ha in the municipalities of Novo Aripuanã, Amazonas and Colniza, Mato Grosso.

List 4: Lands identified and approved by the president of Funai, subject to appeal

no.	Name of Land	People	State	Area (ha)	Date (DOU) *
1.	Tabocal	Mura	Amazonas	907	12/03/1999
2.	Cajuhiri-Atravessado	Miranha, Kambeba, Ticuna	Amazonas	12,500	10/23/2001
3.	Saraua	Amanayé	Pará	18,635	06/07/2002
4.	Banawá	Banawá	Amazonas	195,700	08/01/2002
5.	Balaio	Tukano, Baniwa, Baré among others	Amazonas	255,823	08/23/2002
6.	Apurinã do Igarapé Mucuim	Apurinã	Amazonas	73,000	10/24/2002
7.	Cacique Fontoura	Karajá	Mato Grosso	32,069	11/18/2002
8.	Manoki	Iranxe (Manoki)	Mato Grosso	252,000	11/18/2002
9.	Xipaia	Xipaia	Pará	199,640	04/08/2003
10.	Apyterewa	Parakanã	Pará	773,000	06/24/2003
11.	Baía dos Guató	Guató	Mato Grosso	19,164	07/17/2003
12.	São Domingos do Jacapari e Estação	Kokama	Amazonas	133,630	07/17/2003
13.	Batelão	Kaiabi	Mato Grosso	117,050	07/17/2003
14.	Itixi-Mitari	Apurinã	Amazonas	180,850	08/25/2003
15.	Las Casas	Kayapó	Pará	21,100	08/25/2003
16.	Matintin	Ticuna	Amazonas	20,400	10/07/2003

* Date of publication in the official federal gazette of the order by the president of Funai approving the land identification record, together with the supporting report and survey plans. The same documents are published in the *Diário Oficial do Estado*, the official gazette of the state where the land is located, and posted at the respective municipal offices.

List 5: Lands delimited by the Minister of Justice but not physically demarcated

no.	Name of Land	Year of delimitation	People	State
1.	Acupari de Cima	2000 (in demarcation)	Kokama	Amazonas
2.	Alto Tarauacá	2001 (in demarcation)	isolated	Acre
3.	Apurinã do Ig. São João	2000 (in demarcation)	Apurinã	Amazonas
4.	Arara do Igarapé Humaitá	2002	Arara Shawanawá	Acre
5.	Awá	1992 (being restudied)	Guajá	Maranhão
6.	Barreirinha	2004	Amanayé	Pará
7.	Baú	1991 and 1998 (in demarcation)	Kayapó Mekregnoti	Pará
8.	Cachoeira Seca	1993 (being restudied)	Arara	Pará
9.	Cunhã-Sapucaia	2002	Mura	Amazonas
10.	Diahui	2001 (demarcated)	Diahui	Amazonas
11.	Deni	2001 (in demarcation)	Deni	Amazonas
12.	Espírito Santo	1999 (in demarcation)	Kokama	Amazonas
13.	Estação Paresi	1996 (subjudice)	Pareci	Mato Grosso
14.	Hi-Merimã	2001 (in demarcation)	isolated	Amazonas
15.	Inãwebohona	2001 (demarcated)	Javaé, Karajá	Tocantins
16.	Kayabi	2002	Kaiabi, Apiacá, Munduruku	Pará
17.	Krikati	1992 (in demarcation)	Krikati	Maranhão
18.	Kumaru do Lago Ualá	2001 (demarcated)	Kulina	Amazonas
19.	Kuruaya	2002	Kuruaya	Pará
20.	Lago Jauari	1998 (in demarcation)	Mura	Amazonas
21.	Maraítá	2004	Ticuna	Amazonas
22.	Marambatuba	2002	Karajá	Pará
23.	Nova Esperança do Rio Jandiatuba	2001 (in demarcation)	Ticuna	Amazonas
24.	Lauro Sodré	2002 (demarcated)	Ticuna	Amazonas
25.	Paraná do Arauató	2000 (demarcated)	Mura	Amazonas
26.	Raposa Serra do Sol	1998 (demarcated)	Makuxi/Wapixana/Ingarikó and Patamona	Roraima
27.	Rio Jumas	2000 (demarcated)	Mura	Amazonas
28.	Rio Omerê	2002	Kanoê and Akuntsu	Rondônia
29.	Rio Urubu	2000 (demarcated)	Mura	Amazonas
30.	São Francisco do Canimari	2002	Ticuna	Amazonas
31.	São Sebastião	2001 (in demarcation)	Kaixana, Kokama	Amazonas

continues

no.	Name of Land	Year of delimitation	People	State
32.	Sepoti	2000 (demarcated)	Tenharim	Amazonas
33.	Tabalascada	2002	Wapixana and Makuxi	Roraima
34.	Tereza Cristina	1996 (sub judice)	Bororo	Mato Grosso
35.	Tora	2000 (in demarcation)	Torá	Amazonas
36.	Zo'é	2001 (in demarcation)	Zoé	Pará

List 6: Indigenous lands sub-divided and demarcated by Incra

no.	Name of Land	People	State
1.	Praia do Índio	Munduruku	Pará
2.	Praia do Mangue	Munduruku	Pará

List 7: Indigenous lands owned in fee simple

no.	Name of Land	People	State
1.	Nova Jacundá	Guarani Mbya	Pará
2.	Seringal Independência	Kaxinawá	Acre

List 8: Lands ratified but not registered

no.	Name of Land	People	State
1.	Apipica	Mura	Amazonas
2.	Ariramba	Mura	Amazonas
3.	Badjonkôre	Kayapó	Pará
4.	Barata Livramento	Makuxi and Wapixana	Roraima
5.	Boa Vista	Mura	Amazonas
6.	Boqueirão	Makuxi and Wapixana	Roraima
7.	Coatá	Munduruku and Sateré Mawé	Amazonas
8.	Cuiu Cuiu	Miranha	Amazonas
9.	Fortaleza do Castanho	Mura	Amazonas
10.	Fortaleza do Patauá	Apurinã	Amazonas
11.	Igarapé Grande	Kambeba	Amazonas
12.	Itaitinga	Mura	Amazonas
13.	Jacamim	Wapixana and some Makuxi	Roraima
14.	Jaminawa/Envira	Kulina and Ashaninka	Acre
15.	Jatuarana	Apurinã	Amazonas
16.	Juma	Juma	Amazonas
17.	Kwazá do Rio S.Pedro	Kwazá	Rondônia
18.	Lago Capana	Mura	Amazonas
19.	Moskow	Wapixana	Roraima
20.	Munduruku	Munduruku	Pará
21.	Muriru	Wapixana	Roraima
22.	Padre	Mura	Amazonas
23.	Patauá	Mura	Amazonas
24.	Pinatuba	Mura	Amazonas
25.	Porto Praia	Ticuna	Amazonas
26.	Rio Manicoré	Mura	Amazonas
27.	Tenharim do Igarapé Preto	Tenharim	Amazonas
28.	Tpã Supé	Ticuna	Amazonas
29.	Wai Wai	Wai Wai	Roraima

List 9: Indigenous lands registered in the CRI (*Cartório de Registro de Imóveis* – local land registry) or the SPU (*Serviço de Patrimônio da União* – registry of federal assets)

no.	Name of Land	People	State
1.	Alto Purus	Kaxinawá and Kulina	Acre
2.	Cabeceira do Rio Acre	Jaminawá	Acre
3.	Campinas	Katukina	Acre and Amazonas
4.	Jaminawa / Arara do Rio Bagé	Jaminawa and Arara	Acre
5.	Jaminawa do Igarapé Preto	Jaminawa	Acre
6.	Katukina/Kaxinawá de Feijó	Katukina and Kaxinawá	Acre / Amazonas
7.	Kampa do Rio Amonea	Ashaninka	Acre
8.	Kampa do Igarapé Primavera	Ashaninka	Acre
9.	Kampa and isolated people from the Rio Envira	Ashaninka and isolated	Acre
10.	Kaxinawá and Ashaninka do Rio Breu	Kaxinawá and Ashaninka	Acre
11.	Kaxinawá Colonia Vinte e Sete	Kaxinawá	Acre

continues

no.	Name of Land	People	State
12.	Kaxinawá Nova Olinda	Kaxinawá	Acre
13.	Kaxinawá do Baixo Jordão	Kaxinawá	Acre
14.	Kaxinawá da Praia do Carapanã	Kaxinawá	Acre
15.	Kaxinawá Rio Jordão	Kaxinawá	Acre
16.	Kaxinawá Igarapé do Caucho	Kaxinawá	Acre
17.	Kaxinawá Rio Humaitá	Kaxinawá and Ashaninka	Acre
18.	Kulina do Igarapé do Pau	Kulina	Acre
19.	Kulina do Rio Envira	Kulina	Acre
20.	Mamoadate	Jaminawa and Machineri	Acre
21.	Nukini	Nukini	Acre
22.	Poyanawa	Poyanawa	Acre
23.	Rio Gregório	Inauanawá, Katukina and Kanamanti	Acre
24.	Acimã	Apurinã	Amazonas
25.	Água Preta	Apurinã	Amazonas
26.	Alto Rio Negro	Tukano, Baniwa, Maku among others	Amazonas
27.	Alto Sepatini	Apurinã	Amazonas
28.	Andirá Marau	Sateré Mawé	Amazonas
29.	Apurinã Igarapé Tauamirim	Apurinã	Amazonas
30.	Apurinã KM 124 - BR 317	Apurinã	Amazonas
31.	Barreira da Missão	Miranha, Kambeba, Ticuna	Amazonas
32.	Betânia	Ticuna	Amazonas
33.	Boca do Acre	Apurinã	Amazonas
34.	Bom Intento	Ticuna	Amazonas
35.	Cacau do Tarauacá	Kulina	Amazonas
36.	Caititu	Apurinã	Amazonas
37.	Camadeni	Deni	Amazonas
38.	Camicuã	Apurinã	Amazonas
39.	Catipari / Mamoriá	Apurinã	Amazonas
40.	Cuia	Mura	Amazonas
41.	Estrela da Paz	Ticuna	Amazonas
42.	Évare I (Funai restudies to separate the Land of the Kokama)	Ticuna	Amazonas
43.	Évare II	Ticuna	Amazonas
44.	Gavião	Mura	Amazonas
45.	Guajahã	Apurinã	Amazonas
46.	Igarapé Capana	Jamamadi	Amazonas
47.	Ilha do Camaleão	Ticuna	Amazonas
48.	Inauini/Teuini	Jamamadi	Amazonas
49.	Ipixuna	Parintintin	Amazonas
50.	Jaquiri	Kambeba	Amazonas
51.	Jarawara / Jamamadi / Kanamanti	Jarawara, Jamamadi and Kanamanti	Amazonas
52.	Kanamari do Rio Juruá	Kanamari	Amazonas
53.	Kaxarari	Kaxarari	Amazonas
54.	Kulina do Médio Juruá	Kulina	Amazonas
55.	Lago do Aiapuá	Mura	Amazonas
56.	Lago Beruri	Ticuna	Amazonas
57.	Macarrão	Ticuna	Amazonas
58.	Maraã	Kanamari	Amazonas
59.	Marajaí	Matsé	Amazonas
60.	Mawetek	Kanamari	Amazonas
61.	Médio Rio Negro I	Tukano, Baré, Maku among others	Amazonas
62.	Médio Rio Negro II	Baré, Tukano among others	Amazonas
63.	Méria	Miranha, Mura, Uitoto, Karapanã	Amazonas
64.	Miguel / Josefa	Mura	Amazonas
65.	Miratu	Miranha, Mura, Uitoto, Karapanã	Amazonas
66.	Natal/Felicidade	Mura	Amazonas
67.	Nhamundá/Mapuera	Wai-Wai, Xexeu, Hyskariana	Amazonas
68.	Nove de Janeiro	Parintintin	Amazonas
69.	Paracuhuba	Mura	Amazonas
70.	Paraná Boá-Boá	Maku	Amazonas
71.	Paraná do Paricá	Kanamari	Amazonas
72.	Paumari do Cuniuá	Paumari	Amazonas
73.	Paumari do Lago Paricá	Paumari	Amazonas

continues

no.	Name of Land	People	State
74.	Paumari do Lago Marahã	Paumari	Amazonas
75.	Paumari do Rio Ituxi	Paumari	Amazonas
76.	Peneri / Tacaquiri	Apurinã	Amazonas
77.	Pirahã	Pirahã	Amazonas
78.	Porto Espiritual	Ticuna	Amazonas
79.	Recreio São Felix	Mura	Amazonas
80.	Rio Apapóris	Maku	Amazonas
81.	Rio Biá	Katukina	Amazonas
82.	Rio Tea	Maku	Amazonas
83.	São Leopoldo	Ticuna	Amazonas
84.	São Pedro	Mura	Amazonas
85.	São Pedro do Sepatini	Apurinã	Amazonas
86.	Seruini / Marienê	Apurinã	Amazonas
87.	Tenharim / Marmelos	Tenharim	Amazonas
88.	Terra Vermelha	Apurinã	Amazonas
89.	Ticuna Feijoal	Ticuna	Amazonas
90.	Ticuna Santo Antonio	Ticuna	Amazonas
91.	Trincheira	Mura	Amazonas
92.	Tukuna Umariaçu	Ticuna	Amazonas
93.	Tumiã	Apurinã	Amazonas
94.	Uati -Paraná	Ticuna	Amazonas
95.	Uneuixi	Maku Nadeb	Amazonas
96.	Vale do Javari	Marubo, Matis, Mayoruna, etc.	Amazonas
97.	Vui Uata In	Ticuna	Amazonas
98.	Waimiri-Atroari	Waimiri-Atroari	Amazonas / Roraima
99.	Yanomami	Yanomami	Amazonas / Roraima
100.	Zuruahã	Zuruahã	Amazonas / Roraima
101.	Galibi	Galibi	Amapá
102.	Juminá	Galibi do Uaçá	Amapá
103.	Uaçá	Galibi do Uaçá, Karipuna, Palikur	Amapá
104.	Waiãpi	Wayãpi	Amapá
105.	Alto Turiaçu	Urubu Kaapor, Tembé and Guajá	Maranhão
106.	Araribóia	Guajajara and Guajá	Maranhão
107.	Bacurizinho	Guajajara	Maranhão
108.	Cana Brava	Guajajara	Maranhão
109.	Caru	Guajajara and Guajá	Maranhão
110.	Geralda Toco Preto	Kokuiregatejê and Guajajara	Maranhão
111.	Governador	Gavião Pukobye. and Guajajara	Maranhão
112.	Kanela	Kanela Rankokamekra	Maranhão
113.	Lagoa Comprida	Guajajara	Maranhão
114.	Morro Branco	Guajajara	Maranhão
115.	Porquinhos	Kanela Apaniekra	Maranhão
116.	Rio Pindaré	Guajajara	Maranhão
117.	Rodeador	Guajajara	Maranhão
118.	Urucu Juruá	Guajajara	Maranhão
119.	Apiaká/Kayabi	Apiaká and Kayabi	Mato Grosso
120.	Areões	Xavante	Mato Grosso
121.	Aripuanã	Cinta Larga	Mato Grosso
122.	Bakairi	Bakairi	Mato Grosso
123.	Batovi	Waurá	Mato Grosso
124.	Capoto Jarina	Kayapó	Mato Grosso
125.	Chão Preto	Xavante	Mato Grosso
126.	Enawenê-Nawê	Enawenê-Nawê	Mato Grosso
127.	Erikpatsa	Rikbaktsa	Mato Grosso
128.	Escondido	Rikbaktsa	Mato Grosso
129.	Estivadinho	Pareci	Mato Grosso
130.	Figueiras	Pareci	Mato Grosso
131.	Irantxe	Irantxe	Mato Grosso
132.	Japuira	Rikbaktsa	Mato Grosso
133.	Jarudore	Bororo	Mato Grosso
134.	Juininha	Pareci	Mato Grosso
135.	Karajá do Aruanã I	Karajá	Mato Grosso

continues

no.	Name of Land	People	State
136.	Lagoa dos Brincos	Nambikwara Negarotê	Mato Grosso
137.	Maraiwatsede	Xavante	Mato Grosso
138.	Marechal Rondon	Xavante	Mato Grosso
139.	Menku	Menku	Mato Grosso
140.	Merure	Bororo	Mato Grosso
141.	Nambiquara	Nambikwara	Mato Grosso
142.	Parabubure	Xavante	Mato Grosso
143.	Pareci	Pareci	Mato Grosso
144.	Parque Indígena do Aripuanã	Cinta Larga	Mato Grosso
145.	Parque Indígena do Xingu	several	Mato Grosso
146.	Pequizal	Nambikwara	Mato Grosso
147.	Perigara	Bororo	Mato Grosso
148.	Pimentel Barbosa	Xavante	Mato Grosso
149.	Pirineus de Souza	Nambiquara Mamaindê, Manduca	Mato Grosso
150.	Rio Formoso	Pareci	Mato Grosso
151.	Roosevelt	Cinta Larga	Mato Grosso
152.	Sangradouro/Volta Grande	Xavante and Bororo	Mato Grosso
153.	Santana	Bakairi	Mato Grosso
154.	São Domingos	Karajá	Mato Grosso
155.	São Marcos	Xavante	Mato Grosso
156.	Sararé	Nambiquara Katitawlu	Mato Grosso
157.	Serra Morena	Cinta Larga	Mato Grosso
158.	Sete de Setembro	Suruí Paiter	Mato Grosso
159.	Tadarimana	Bororo	Mato Grosso
160.	Taihantesu	Nambiquara / Wasusu	Mato Grosso
161.	Tapirapé/Karajá	Tapirapé and Karajá	Mato Grosso
162.	Tirecatinga	Nambiquara Halotesu	Mato Grosso
163.	Ubawawe	Xavante	Mato Grosso
164.	Umutina	Umutina, Pareci among others	Mato Grosso
165.	Urubu branco	Tapirapé	Mato Grosso
166.	Utiariti	Pareci	Mato Grosso
167.	Wawi	Xavante	Mato Grosso
168.	Vale do Guaporé	Nambiquara	Mato Grosso
169.	Zoró	Zoró	Mato Grosso
170.	Alto Rio Guamá	Tembé, Urubu Kaapor, Guajá	Pará
171.	Anambé	Anambé	Pará
172.	Arara *	Arara	Pará
173.	Arawete	Arawete	Pará
174.	Karajá Santana do Araguaia	Karajá	Pará
175.	Kararaô	Kararaô	Pará
176.	Kayapó	Kayapó	Pará
177.	Koatinemo	Koatinemo	Pará
178.	Menkragnoti	Mekragnoti	Pará
179.	Paquiçambá	Juruna	Pará
180.	Parakanã	Parakanã	Pará
181.	Mãe Maria	Gavião Parkatejê	Pará
182.	Nova Jacundá	Guarani Mbya	Pará
183.	Panará	Panará	Pará
184.	Rio Paru de Este	Wayana aparai	Pará
185.	Sai Cinza	Munduruku	Pará
186.	Sororó	Surui Aikewara	Pará
187.	Tembé	Tembé Turiwara	Pará
188.	Trincheira Bacajá	Xikrin do Bacajá	Pará
189.	Trocará	Assurini do Tocantins	Pará
190.	Turé Mariquita	Tembé	Pará
191.	Tumucumaque	Tiriyó, Wayana among others	Pará
192.	Xicrin do Cateté	Xicrin	Pará
193.	Arara do Rio Branco	Arara	Rondônia
194.	Igarapé Lage	Pakaa Nova	Rondônia
195.	Igarapé Lourdes	Gavião e Arara	Rondônia
196.	Igarapé Ribeirão	Pakaa Nova	Rondônia
197.	Karipuna	Karipuna	Rondônia

continues

no.	Name of Land	People	State
198.	Karitiana	Karitiana	Rondônia
199.	Massaco	isolated	Rondônia
200.	Pacaas Novas	Pakaa Nova	Rondônia
201.	Rio Branco	Macurap, Tupari among others	Rondônia
202.	Rio Guaporé	Tupari among others	Rondônia
203.	Rio Mequéns	Macurap and Sakirabiap	Rondônia
204.	Rio Negro Ocaia	Pakaa Nova	Rondônia
205.	Sagarana	Pakaa Nova	Rondônia
206.	Tubarão Latundê	Aikaná, Namb. Latundê and Sabanê	Rondônia
207.	Uru-Eu-Wau-Wau	Uru-Eu-Wau-Wau	Rondônia
208.	Ananás	Makuxi	Roraima
209.	Aningal	Makuxi	Roraima
210.	Anta	Makuxi and Wapixana	Roraima
211.	Araçá	Makuxi and Wapixana	Roraima
212.	Bom Jesus	Makuxi and Wapixana	Roraima
213.	Cajueiro	Makuxi	Roraima
214.	Canauanim	Wapixana	Roraima
215.	Jaboti	Wapixana and Makuxi	Roraima
216.	Malacacheta	Makuxi and Wapixana	Roraima
217.	Mangueira	Makuxi and Wapixana	Roraima
218.	Manoá-Pium	Wapixana and Makuxi	Roraima
219.	Ouro	Makuxi	Roraima
220.	Pium	Makuxi and Wapixana	Roraima
221.	Ponta da Serra	Makuxi and Wapixana	Roraima
222.	Raimundão	Wapixana	Roraima
223.	Santa Inez	Makuxi	Roraima
224.	São Marcos	Taurepang, Wapixana and Makuxi	Roraima
225.	Serra da Moça	Wapixana	Roraima
226.	Sucuba	Makuxi and Wapixana	Roraima
227.	Truaru	Wapixana	Roraima
228.	Apinayé	Apinayé	Tocantins
229.	Araguaia	Karajá, Javaé and Avá-Canoeiro	Tocantins
230.	Funil	Xerente	Tocantins
231.	Kraolandia	Krahô	Tocantins
232.	Xambioá	Karajá do Norte	Tocantins
233.	Xerente	Xerente	Tocantins

Overlapping federal and state conservation areas, indigenous lands, military areas, and prospecting reserves in Legal Amazonia*

Fany Ricardo *Instituto Socioambiental*

This document provides statistics on overlapping federal and state conservation areas, indigenous lands, and military areas in Legal Amazonia. The analysis was carried out using the geographic information system (GIS) of the Instituto Socioambiental (ISA).

The GIS/ISA records 65 overlaps, totaling 17.504.905 hectares, between these different categories involving: 38 federal conservation areas, 17 state conservation areas, 26 indigenous lands, and 6 military areas. We have excluded from these calculations overlaps involving Environmental Protection Areas (APAs). This is a category included in the National System of Conservation Areas (SNUC), but one where the areas are mainly not publicly owned and in general comprise large areas with few problems of compatibility with other conservation area categories.

This high level of overlap among areas destined for differing, and mostly incompatible, purposes reveals the inability of the Brazilian State to carry out spatial planning that is appropriate for Amazonia and the need for urgent measures to provide solutions to the conflicts arising from this situation.

* Updated on April 30, 2004.

TABLE 1 - Overlaps among federal conservation areas

State	Federal Conservation Area	Federal Conservation Area	Area of overlap		
			ha	%[1]	%[2]
Pará/Amazonas	Amazônia National Park	Pau-Rosa National Forest	16,390	1.77	1.71
Pará	Tapirapé Aquiri National Forest	Itacaiúnas National Forest	82,417	42.20	60.05

1. Percentage of the federal conservation area in the second column.
2. Percentage of the federal conservation area in the third column.

TABLE 2 - Overlaps between federal and state conservation areas

State	Federal Conservation Area	State Conservation Area	Area of overlap		
			ha	%[1]	%[2]
Amazonas	Pico da Neblina National Park	Morro dos Seis Lagos Biological Reserve	37,517	1.67	100.00
Pará/Amapá	Jari Ecological Station	Rio Iratapu Sustainable Development Reserve	7,525	3.00	0.86
Amazonas	Amazonas National Forest	Serra do Araçá State Park	1,087,155	58.50	58.70

1. Percentage of the federal conservation area.
2. Percentage of the state conservation area.

TABLE 3 - Overlaps between federal conservation areas and indigenous lands

State	Federal Conservation Area	Indigenous Land	Area of overlap		
			ha	%[1]	%[2]
Mato Grosso	Iquê Ecological Station	Enawenê Nawê	187,826	98.34	25.54
Amazonas	Jutaí/Solimões Ecological Station	Betânia	5,186	1.80	63.45
Amazonas	Jutaí/Solimões Ecological Station	São Domingos do Jacapari and Station	31,117	10.79	23.29
Rondônia	Bom Futuro National Forest	Karitiana	31,299	11.53	34.92
Amazonas	Cubate National Forest	Alto Rio Negro	425,002	100.00	5.29
Amazonas	Cuiari National Forest	Alto Rio Negro	109,294	100.00	1.36
Amazonas	Humaitá National Forest	Diahui	29,314	6.07	61.31
Roraima	Roraima National Forest	Yanomami	2,786,523	95.82	28.98
Acre	Santa Rosa do Purus National Forest	Jaminauá/Envira	70,702	30.88	87.20
Amazonas	Amazonas National Forest	Yanomami	1,600,540	86.13	16.64
Amazonas	Purus National Forest	Inauini/Teuini	66,608	25.94	13.98
Amazonas	Içana National Forest	Alto Rio Negro	197,059	100.00	2.45
Amazonas	Içana-Aiari National Forest	Alto Rio Negro	497,205	100.00	6.19
Amazonas	Mapiá-Inauini National Forest	Inauini/Teuini	5,322	1.45	1.12
Amazonas	Pari Cachoeira II National Forest	Alto Rio Negro	617,631	100.00	7.69
Amazonas	Pari Cachoeira I National Forest	Alto Rio Negro	17,283	100.00	0.22
Amazonas	Piraiauara National Forest	Alto Rio Negro	630,566	100.00	7.85
Amazonas	Taracuá I National Forest	Alto Rio Negro	658,656	100.00	8.20
Amazonas	Taracuá II National Forest	Alto Rio Negro	561,495	100.00	6.99
Amazonas	Urucu National Forest	Alto Rio Negro	68,391	100.00	0.85
Amazonas	Xié National Forest	Alto Rio Negro	399,330	99.03	4.97

continues

State	Federal Conservation Area	Indigenous Land	Area of overlap		
			ha	%[1]	%[2]
Pará/Amazonas	Amazônia National Park	Andirá-Marau	90,593	9.78	11.45
Tocantins	Araguaia National Park	Inawebohona	364,356	66.25	100.00
Roraima	Monte Roraima National Park	Raposa/Serra do Sol	116,332	100.00	6.70
Amazonas	Pico da Neblina National Park	Balaio	240,523	10.71	93.25
Amazonas	Pico da Neblina National Park	Médio Rio Negro II	47,958	2.14	14.76
Amazonas	Pico da Neblina National Park	Yanomami	1,131,728	50.41	11.77
Rondônia	Pacaás Novos National Park	Uru-Eu-Wau-Wau	732,934	100.00	39.07
Rondônia	Guaporé Biological Reserve	Massaco	411,802	66.53	96.22
Rondônia	Jaru Biological Reserve	Igarapé Lourdes	14,021	4.77	6.91
Amazonas/Pará	Pau-Rosa National Forest	Andirá-Marau	20,105	2.10	2.54

1. Percentage of the federal conservation area.
2. Percentage of the indigenous land.

Table 4 - Overlaps between federal conservation areas and military areas

State	Federal Conservation Area	Military Area	Area of overlap		
			ha	%[1]	%[2]
Amazonas	Amazonas National Forest	Gleba Niquiá	6,268	0.34	3.80
Roraima	Caracaraí Ecological Station	Gleba Caracaraí	92,163	100.00	100.00
Pará	Itaituba II National Forest	Gleba Damião	424,565	100.00	100.00
Pará	Itaituba I National Forest	Gleba da Prata	221,367	100.00	100.00
Pará	Altamira National Forest	Gleba Limão	706,136	100.00	99.10
Pará	Xingu National Forest	Gleba Mossoró	242,180	100.00	100.00

1. Percentage of the federal conservation area.
2. Percentage of the military area.

Table 5 - Overlaps among state conservation areas

State	State Conservation Area	State Conservation Area	Area of overlap		
			ha	%[1]	%[2]
Rondônia	Rio Preto-Jacundá Extractive Forest	Samuel Ecological Station	47,164	4.46	85.43
Rondônia	Rio São Domingos Sustainable Development Forest	Rio Cautário Extractive Reserve	15,379	5.00	11.23
Rondônia	Pacaás Novos Extractive Forest	Rio Pacaás Novos Extractive Reserve	356,826	100.00	100.00
Rondônia	Corumbiara State Park	Rio Mequéns Sustainable Development Forest	50,799	12.52	11.92
Rondônia	Rio Preto-Jacundá Extractive Forest	Rio Preto-Jacundá Extractive Reserve	102,047	9.66	100.00

1. Percentage of the state conservation area in the second column.
2. Percentage of the state conservation area in the third column.

Table 6 - Overlaps between state conservation areas and indigenous lands

State	State Conservation Area	Indigenous Land	Area of overlap		
			ha	%[1]	%[2]
Rondônia	Rio Vermelho (D) Sustainable Development Forest	Kaxarari	5,229	3.63	3.59
Amazonas	Serra do Araçá State Park	Yanomami	1,517,123	81.91	15.78
Amazonas	Morro dos Seis Lagos Biological Reserve	Balaio	37,517	100.00	14.55
Amazonas	Amaná Sustainable Development Reserve	Cuiú-Cuiú	37,405	1.66	100.00
Amazonas	Mamirauá Sustainable Development Reserve	Uati-Paraná	13,370	1.01	11.74
Amazonas	Mamirauá Sustainable Development Reserve	Porto Praia	3,870	0.29	100.00
Amazonas	Mamirauá Sustainable Development Reserve	Jaquiri	1,883	0.14	100.00
Amazonas	Mamirauá Sustainable Development Reserve	Acapuri de Cima	19,783	1.50	100.00
Amazonas	Piagaçu-Purus Sustainable Development Reserve	Terra Vermelha	7,196	0.69	100.00
Amazonas	Piagaçu-Purus Sustainable Development Reserve	Lago Aiapoá	22,146	2.13	100.00
Amazonas	Piagaçu-Purus Sustainable Development Reserve	Itixi-Mirati	176,757	17.02	100.00

1. Percentage of the state conservation area.
2. Percentage of the indigenous land.

Table 7 - Overlaps between state conservation area and prospecting reserves

State	State Conservation Area	Prospecting Reserve	Area of overlap		
			ha	%[1]	%[2]
Rondônia	Rio Vermelho (C) Sustainable Development Reserve	Rio Madeira II	1,598	7.70	4.93
Rondônia	Rio Vermelho (A) Sustainable Development Reserve	Rio Madeira	1,318	3.25	5.60

1. Percentage of the state conservation area.
2. Percentage of the prospect reserve.

| TABLE 8 - OVERLAPS BETWEEN INDIGENOUS LANDS AND MILITARY AREAS ||||||
| State | Indigenous Land | Military Area | Area of overlap |||
			ha	%[1]	%[2]
Amazonas	Évare I	Gleba Tacana	101,238	18.63	98.74
Pará/Mato Grosso	Kayabi	Cachimbo	26	0.00	0.00
Amazonas	Médio Rio Negro I	Gleba do Exército	1,015,027	56.52	100.00
Amazonas	Rio Jumas	Gleba Juma	7,510	75.51	7.06
Mato Grosso	São Marcos (Xavante)	Gleba Matrinxã	5,506	2.88	95.46

1. Percentage of the indigenous land.
2. Percentage of the military area.

| TABLE 9 - OVERLAPS BETWEEN CONSERVATION AREAS AND OTHER FEDERAL AREAS ||
Overlaps	Area (ha)
between conservation areas and indigenous lands	14,008,998
between conservation areas and military areas	1,692,683

| TABLE 10 - OVERLAPS AMONG CONSERVATION AREAS ||
Overlaps	Area (ha)
among conservation areas	1,803,224

Representativity of Conservation Areas and Indigenous Lands in Relation to the Vegetation Types of Legal Amazonia

João Paulo R. Capobianco *Instituto Socioambiental*

The present document analyzes the representativity of the federal and state conservation areas and indigenous lands in Legal Amazonia in relation to the vegetation types present in the region.

Statistical analysis was carried out using the geographic information system (GIS) of the Instituto Socioambiental (ISA), taking into consideration: (i) 11 vegetation groups and their sub-classes, comprising the 30 vegetation types used in the IBGE 1:2,500,000 Vegetation Map of Legal Amazonia (1989); (ii) 154 strict (full protection) and direct use (sustainable use) conservation areas, 81 of which are federal and 73 state managed; and (iii) 369 indigenous lands.

The data show that, with the exception of ecological refuge areas, all vegetation types present in Legal Amazonia are underrepresented in the strict conservation areas (Table 1). Taking into consideration the low level of implementation of these areas, which has led to many of them suffering anthropogenic degradation, we can conclude that actual levels of protection are even lower than those shown.

TABLE 1 - Vegetation types of Legal Amazonia in federal and state conservation areas (total)

Vegetation type	Subclass		Total strict conservation areas		Total direct use conservation areas		Total conservation areas	
	ha	%	ha	%	ha	%	ha	%
Dense rainforest	200,501,263	40.04	9,690,921	4.83	19,472,964	9.71	29,163,885	14.55
Open rainforest	86,932,496	17.36	2,320,557	2.67	5,486,136	6.31	7,806,693	8.98
Semi-deciduous seasonal forest	4,741,031	0.95	290,458	6.13	72,202	1.52	362,660	7.65
Deciduous seasonal forest	769,016	0.15	-	-	-	-	-	-
Campinarana/campinas of the Rio Negro	10,416,787	2.08	842,581	8.09	1,677,525	16.10	2,520,106	24.19
Steppe-savanna/Roraima grasslands	1,212,365	0.24	10,353	0.85	-	-	10,353	0.85
Savanna	63,806,195	12.74	1,790,276	2.81	1,281,095	2.01	3,071,371	4.81
Ecological transition areas	76,141,962	15.20	3,011,803	3.96	3,580,822	4.70	6,592,625	8.66
Pioneer formations	10,125,392	2.02	1,069,904	10.57	1,797,727	17.75	2,867,632	28.32
Ecological refuge	105,661	0.02	32,979	31.21	45,807	43.35	78,786	74.56
Areas of anthropogenic impacts	47,259,290	9.44	99,380	0.21	2,891,760	6.12	2,991,140	6.33

Another aspect that deserves more detailed analysis is the significant increase in these rates when conservation areas and indigenous lands are calculated together (Table 2). Given the increasing difficulties of creating new strict conservation areas, and the weak institutional and financial capacity of both federal and state governments to implement those already existing, a proper assessment of the real potential of indigenous lands to contribute to the conservation of the region's biodiversity is needed.

It should be noted, however, that the figures for the extent of the vegetation types given in Table 2 are overestimates in some cases, a result of the high degree of overlap that exists between federal and state conservation areas, and between these and other State-defined land categories such as indigenous lands, prospecting reserves and military areas. When the overlaps are removed, the total area of conservation areas in Legal Amazonia falls to 42,872,115 ha, and the percentage of the area under protection in the region is reduced from the official 12.22% to approximately 8.56%.

TABLE 2 - Vegetation types of Legal Amazonia in indigenous lands and conservation areas (total)

Vegetation type	Subclass		Total indigenous lands		Total conservation areas		Total	
	ha	%	ha	%	ha	%	ha	%
Dense rainforest	200,501,263	40.04	42,150,768	21.00	29,163,885	14.55	71,314,653	35.57
Open rainforest	86,932,496	17.36	25,865,216	29.75	7,806,693	8.98	33,671,909	38.73
Semi-deciduous seasonal forest	4,741,031	0.95	564,801	11.91	362,660	7.65	927,461	19.56
Deciduous seasonal forest	769,016	0.15	328,825	42.76	-	-	328,825	42.76
Campinarana/campinas of the Rio Negro	10,416,787	2.08	3,798,284	36.46	2,520,106	24.19	6,318,390	60.66
Steppe-savanna/Roraima grasslands	1,212,365	0.24	1,163,881	96.00	10,353	0.85	1,174,234	96.85
Savanna	63,806,195	12.74	8,352,374	13.09	3,071,371	4.81	11,423,745	17.90
Ecological transition areas	76,141,962	15.20	18,275,746	24.00	6,592,625	8.66	24,868,371	32.66
Pioneer formations	10,125,392	2.02	1,724,492	17.03	2,867,632	28.32	4,592,124	45.35
Ecological refuge	105,661	0.02	70,671	66.88	78,786	74.56	149,457	99.00
Areas of anthropogenic impacts	47,259,290	9.44	976,966	2.07	2,991,140	6.33	3,968,106	8.40

continues

The following tables provide data by vegetation subclass, following the IBGE Vegetation Map of Legal Amazonia (1989) which uses the following classification:

Dense rainforest – D
Da   Alluvial
Db   Lowland
Dm   Montane
Ds   Submontane

Open rainforest – A
Ab   Lowland
As   Submontane

Semi-deciduous seasonal forest – F
Fa   Alluvial
Fb   Lowland
Fs   Submontane

Deciduous seasonal forest – C
Cs   Submontane

Woody oligotrophic swamp vegetation (*Campinarana* and *campina* swamps) – L
La   Open arboreal
Ld   Dense arboreal
Lg   Woody-grassy

Roraima Grasslands – T
Ta   Open arboreal
Td   Dense arboreal
Tp   Parkland

Savanna (cerrado) – S
Sa   Open arboreal
Sd   Dense arboreal
Sg   Grassy-woody
Sp   Steppe-savanna park

Areas of ecological transition (contacts)
LO   Campinarana/rainforest
ON   Rainforest/seasonal forest
SN   Savanna/seasonal forest
TN   Steppe-savanna/seasonal forest
SO   Savanna/rainforest
ST   Savanna/steppe-savanna

Area of pioneer formations – P
Pa   Fluvial influence
Pf   Tidal influence

Ecological refuge
Rm – Montane

Areas of anthropogenic impacts
AA – Agricultural, silvicultural and ranching activities

Table 3 - Vegetation types present in Federal conservation areas								
Vegetation type	Subclass			Federal strict conservation area		Federal direct use conservation area		Overlap
	code	ha	%	ha	%	ha	%	ha
Dense rainforest		200,501,263	40.04	7,323,042	3.65	10,637,263	5.31	52,138
	Da	40,364,915	8.06	1,060,638	2.63	730,885	1.81	-
	Db	78,726,719	15.72	3,364,921	4.27	3,849,104	4.89	-
	Ds	77,904,765	15.56	2,406,009	3.09	4,546,218	5.84	52,138
	Dm	3,504,865	0.70	491,475	14.02	1,511,056	43.11	-
Open rainforest		86,932,496	17.36	1,795,814	2.07	3,028,411	3.48	30,189
	Ab	33,980,839	6.79	1,087,528	3.20	1,426,185	4.20	-
	As	52,951,657	10.57	708,286	1.34	1,602,226	3.03	30,189
Semi-deciduous seasonal forest		4,741,031	0.95	125,492	2.65	-	-	-
	Fa	1,738,068	0.35	85,971	4.95	-	-	-
	Fb	754,543	0.15	-	-	-	-	-
	Fs	2,248,420	0.45	39,521	1.76	-	-	-
Deciduous seasonal forest		769,016	0.15	-	-	-	-	-
	Cs	196,696	0.04	-	-	-	-	-
	Cs	572,320	0.11	-	-	-	-	-
Campinarana/ campinas of the Rio Negro		10,416,787	2.08	817,659	7.85	1,597,647	15.34	-
	Ld	6,458,388	1.29	526,648	8.15	1,564,208	24.22	-
	La	1,568,664	0.31	121,927	7.77	7,435	0.47	-
	Lg	2,389,736	0.48	169,084	7.08	26,004	1.09	-
Roraima grasslands		1,212,365	0.24	10,353	0.85	-	-	-
	Ta	19,997	0.00	-	-	-	-	-
	Td	243,991	0.05	-	-	-	-	-
	Tp	948,377	0.19	10,353	0.85	-	-	-
Savanna		63,806,195	12.74	812,693	1.27	200,687	0.31	-
	Sa	37,716,441	7.53	216,544	0.57	15,211	0.04	-
	Sd	4,833,158	0.97	155,544	3.22	10,299	0.21	-
	Sg	3,542,096	0.71	64,771	1.83	25,328	0.72	-
	Sp	17,714,500	3.54	375,833	2.12	149,850	0.85	-
Ecological transition areas		76,141,962	15.20	2,569,292	3.37	2,655,539	3.49	3,504
	ON	18,086,593	3.61	15,461	0.09	173,755	0.96	-
	SN	26,537,185	5.30	425,834	1.60	135,427	0.51	-
	SO	13,341,323	2.66	237,592	1.78	174,585	1.31	-
	LO	18,176,860	3.63	1,890,406	10.40	2,171,772	11.95	3,504
Pioneer formations		10,125,392	2.02	958,371	9.47	132,017	1.30	-
	Pa	9,355,269	1.87	706,512	7.55	132,017	1.41	-
	Pf	770,123	0.15	251,859	32.70	-	-	-
Ecological refuge	Rm	105,661	0.02	10,451	9.89	45,807	43.35	-
Areas of anthropogenic impacts	AA	44,259,290	9.44	37,215	0.08	230,518	0.49	-

Table 4 - Vegetation types present in state conservation areas

Vegetation type	Subclass code	ha	%	State indirect use conservation area ha	%	State direct use conservation area ha	%	Overlap Total
Dense rainforest		200,501,263	40.04	2,367,878	1.18	8,835,701	4.41	61,945
	Da	40,364,915	8.06	81,573	0.20	4,688,667	11.62	54,617
	Db	78,726,719	15.72	370,538	0.47	2,701,592	3.43	7,328
	Ds	77,904,765	15.56	1,604,167	2.06	1,445,443	1.86	-
	Dm	3,504,865	0.70	311,601	8.89	-	-	-
Open rainforest		86,932,496	17.36	524,743	0.60	2,457,724	2.83	397,916
	Ab	33,980,839	6.79	279,455	0.82	1,424,996	4.19	244,634
	As	52,951,657	10.57	245,288	0.46	1,032,728	1.95	153,283
Semi-deciduous seasonal forest		4,741,031	0.95	164,967	3.48	72,202	1.52	-
	Fa	1,738,068	0.35	8,799	0.51	19,296	1.11	-
	Fb	754,543	0.15	131,288	17.40	44,704	5.92	-
	Fs	2,248,420	0.45	24,880	1.11	8,202	0.36	-
Deciduous seasonal forest		769,016	0.15	-	-	-	-	-
	Cs	196,696	0.04	-	-	-	-	-
	Cs	572,320	0.11	-	-	-	-	-
Campinarana/ campinas of the Rio Negro		10,416,787	2.08	24,922	0.24	79,878	0.77	-
	Ld	6,458,388	1.29	-	-	46,308	0.72	-
	La	1,568,664	0.31	-	-	33,569	2.14	-
	Lg	2,389,736	0.48	24,922	1.04	-	-	-
Roraima grasslands		1,212,365	0.24	-	-	-	-	-
	Ta	19,997	0.00	-	-	-	-	-
	Td	243,991	0.05	-	-	-	-	-
	Tp	948,377	0.19	-	-	-	-	-
Savanna		63,806,195	12.74	977,583	1.53	1,080,408	1.69	-
	Sa	37,716,441	7.53	484,663	1.29	275,819	0.73	-
	Sd	4,833,158	0.97	123,006	2.55	42,922	0.89	-
	Sg	3,542,096	0.71	17,780	0.50	-	-	-
	Sp	17,714,500	3.54	352,134	1.99	761,667	4.30	-
Ecological transition areas		76,141,962	15.20	442,511	0.58	925,283	1.22	19,985
	ON	18,086,593	3.61	137,805	0.76	14,713	0.08	-
	SN	26,537,185	5.30	45,305	0.17	134,410	0.51	-
	SO	13,341,323	2.66	208,498	1.56	268,238	2.01	19,985
	LO	18,176,860	3.63	50,902	0.28	507,923	2.79	-
Pioneer formations		10,125,392	2.02	111,533	1.10	1,665,710	16.45	-
	Pa	9,355,269	1.87	111,533	1.19	1,489,288	15.92	-
	Pf	770,123	0.15	-	-	176,422	22.91	-
Ecological refuge	Rm	105,661	0.02	22,528	21.32	-	-	-
Areas of anthropogenic impact	AA	47,259,290	9.44	62,164	0.13	2,661,242	5.63	2,556

Table 5 - Vegetation types present in federal and state conservation areas (total)

Vegetation type	Subclass code	ha	%	Strict conservation areas ha	%	Direct use conservation areas ha	%	Total conservation areas ha	%
Dense rainforest		200,501,263	40.04	9,690,921	4.83	19,472,964	9.71	29,163,885	14.55
	Da	40,364,915	8.06	1,142,210	2.83	5,419,552	13.43	6,561,762	16.26
	Db	78,726,719	15.72	3,735,459	4.74	6,550,695	8.32	10,286,154	13.07
	Ds	77,904,765	15.56	4,010,175	5.15	5,991,661	7.69	10,001,836	12.84
	Dm	3,504,865	0.70	803,076	22.91	1,511.056	43.11	2,314,132	66.03
Open rainforest		86,932,496	17.36	2,320,557	2.67	5,486,136	6.31	7,806,693	8.98
	Ab	33,980,839	6.79	1,366,983	4.02	2,851,181	8.39	4,218,164	12.41
	As	52,951,657	10.57	953,574	1.80	2,634,954	4.98	3,588,528	6.78
Semi-deciduous seasonal forest		4,741,031	0.95	290,458	6.13	72,202	1.52	362,660	7.65
	Fa	1,738,068	0.35	94,770	5.45	19,296	1.11	114,066	6.56
	Fb	754,543	0.15	131,288	17.40	44,704	5.92	175,991	23.32
	Fs	2,248,420	0.45	64,401	2.86	8,202	0.36	72,603	3.23
Deciduous seasonal forest		769,016	0.15	-	-	-	-	-	-
	Cs	196,696	0.04	-	-	-	-	-	-
	Cs	572,320	0.11	-	-	-	-	-	-
Campinarana/ campina of the Rio Negro		10,416,787	2.08	842,581	8.09	1,677,525	16.10	2,520,106	24.19
	Ld	6,458,388	1.29	526,648	8.15	1,610,517	24.94	2,137,165	33.09
	La	1,568,664	0.31	121,927	7.77	41,005	2.61	162,931	10.39
	Lg	2,389,736	0.48	194,006	8.12	26,004	1.09	220,010	9.21

continues

Vegetation type		Subclass		Strict conservation areas		Direct use conservation areas		Total conservation areas	
	code	ha	%	ha	%	ha	%	ha	%
Roraima grasslands		1,212,365	0.24	10,353	0.85	-	-	10,353	0.85
	Ta	19,997	0.00	-	-	-	-	-	-
	Td	243,991	0.05	-	-	-	-	-	-
	Tp	948,377	0.19	10,353	1.09	-	-	10,353	1.09
Savanna		63,806,195	12.74	1,790,276	2.81	1,281,095	2.01	3,071,371	4.81
	Sa	37,716,441	7.53	701,206	1.86	291,029	0.77	992,236	2.63
	Sd	4,833,158	0.97	278,550	5.76	53,221	1.10	331,771	6.86
	Sg	3,542,096	0.71	82,552	2.33	25,328	0.72	107,879	3.05
	Sp	17,714,500	3.54	727,968	4.11	911,517	5.15	1,639,485	9.26
Ecological transition areas		76,141,962	15.20	3,011,803	3.96	3,580,822	4.70	6,592,625	8.66
	ON	18,086,593	3.61	153,266	0.85	188,468	1.04	341,733	1.89
	SN	26,537,185	5.30	471,140	1.78	269,836	1.02	740,976	2.79
	SO	13,341,323	2.66	446,090	3.34	442,823	3.32	888,913	6.66
	LO	18,176,860	3.63	1,941,308	10.68	2,679,695	14.74	4,621,004	25.42
Pioneer formations		10,125,392	2.02	1,069,904	10.57	1,797,727	17.75	2,867,632	28.32
	Pa	9,355,269	1.87	818,045	8.74	1,621,305	17.33	2,439,350	26.07
	Pf	770,123	0.15	251,859	32.70	176,422	22.91	428,282	55.61
Ecological refuge	Rm	105,661	0.02	32,979	31.21	45,807	43.35	78,786	74.56
Areas of anthropogenic impacts	AA	47,259,290	9.44	99,380	0.21	2,891,760	6.12	2,991,140	6.33

Table 6 - Vegetation types present in indigenous lands and conservation areas (total)

Vegetation type		Subclass		Indigenous lands		Conservation areas		Total conservation areas	
	code	ha	%	ha	%	ha	%	ha	%
Dense rainforest		200,501,263	40.04	42,150,768	21.02	29,163,885	14.55	71,314,653	35.57
	Da	40,364,915	8.06	5,387,031	13.35	6,561,762	16.26	11,948,793	29.60
	Db	78,726,719	15.72	9,302,272	11.82	10,286,154	13.07	19,588,426	24.88
	Ds	77,904,765	15.56	24,551,003	31.51	10,001,836	12.84	34,552,839	44.35
	Dm	3,504,865	0.70	2,910,461	83.04	2,314,132	66.03	5,224,593	149.07
Open rainforest		86,932,496	17.36	25,865,216	29.75	7,806,693	8.98	33,671,909	38.73
	Ab	33,980,839	6.79	10,293,701	30.29	4,218,164	12.41	14,511,865	42.71
	As	52,951,657	10.57	15,571,515	29.41	3,588,528	6.78	19,160,043	36.18
Semi-deciduous seasonal forest		4,741,031	0.95	564,801	11.91	362,660	7.65	927,461	19.56
	Fa	1,738,068	0.35	302,102	17.38	114,066	6.56	416,168	23.94
	Fb	754,543	0.15	4,320	0.57	175,991	23.32	180,311	23.90
	Fs	2,248,420	0.45	258,380	11.49	72,603	3.23	330,983	14.72
Deciduous seasonal forest		769,016	0.15	328,825	42.76	-	-	328,825	42.76
	Cs	196,696	0.04	41,542	21.12	-	-	41,542	21.12
	Cs	572,320	0.11	287,283	50.20	-	-	287,283	50.20
Campinarana/ campina of the Rio Negro		10,416,787	2.08	3,798,284	36.46	2,520,106	24.19	6,318,390	60.66
	Ld	6,458,388	1.29	3,553,567	55.02	2,137,165	33.09	5,690,732	88.11
	La	1,568,664	0.31	218,847	13.95	162,931	10.39	381,778	24.34
	Lg	2,389,736	0.48	25,870	1.08	220,010	9.21	245,880	10.29
Roraima grasslands		1,212,365	0.24	1,163,881	96.00	10,353	0.85	1,174,234	96.85
	Ta	19,997	0.00	9,466	47.34	-	-	9,466	47.34
	Td	243,991	0.05	231,823	95.01	-	-	231,823	95.01
	Tp	948,377	0.19	922,593	97.28	10,353	1.09	932,946	98.37
Savanna		63,806,195	12.74	8,352,374	13.09	3,071,371	4.81	11,423,745	17.90
	Sa	37,716,441	7.53	3,485,783	9.24	992,236	2.63	4,478,019	11.87
	Sd	4,833,158	0.97	905,375	18.73	331,771	6.86	1,237,146	25.60
	Sg	3,542,096	0.71	760,909	21.48	107,879	3.05	868,788	24.53
	Sp	17,714,500	3.54	3,200,308	18.07	1,639,485	9.26	4,839,793	27.32
Ecological transition areas		76,141,962	15.20	18,275,746	24.00	6,592,625	8.66	24,868,371	32.66
	ON	18,086,593	3.61	3,227,591	17.85	341,733	1.89	3,569,324	19.73
	SN	26,537,185	5.30	3,843,160	14.48	740,976	2.79	4,584,136	17.27
	SO	13,341,323	2.66	4,172,625	31.28	888,913	6.66	5,061,538	37.94
	LO	18,176,860	3.63	7,032,370	38.69	4,621,004	25.42	11,653,374	64.11
Pioneer formations		10,125,392	2.02	1,724,492	17.03	2,867,632	28.32	4,592,124	45.35
	Pa	9,355,269	1.87	1,724,492	18.43	2,439,350	26.07	4,163,842	44.51
	Pf	770,123	0.15	-	-	428,282	55.61	428,282	55.61
Ecological refuge	Rm	105,661	0.02	70,671	66.88	78,786	74.56	149,457	98.00
Areas of anthropogenic impacts	AA	47,259,290	9.44	976,966	2.07	2,991,140	6.33	3,968,106	8.40

Identifying priority areas for biodiversity conservation by means of the representativity of conservation areas and vegetation types in the ecoregions of Brazilian Amazonia

Leandro V. Ferreira, Rosa Lemos de Sá, Robert Buschbacher, Garo Batmanian, José Maria Cardoso da Silva *World Wildlife Fund*
Moacyr B. Arruda, Edmar Moretti, Luís Fernando S. N. de Sá, Júlio Falcomer, Maria Iolita Bampi *Instituto Brasileiro do Meio Ambiente e dos Recursos Naturais Renováveis*

Introduction

The biological complexity of natural environments poses a challenge to biogeographical classification and causes serious difficulties for the definition of strategies and methodologies for the identification of priority areas for biodiversity conservation. The Convention on Biological Diversity recommends that, in their conservation strategies, countries adopt an approach that covers all possible scales: ecosystems, protected areas, species, and genetic resources, amongst others.

With almost one third of the world's remaining rainforests, Brazil is acknowledged as one of the most important countries for global biological diversity (Prance 1987). Despite this key position, federal strict conservation areas represent only 1.85% of the national territory, significantly below the world average for protected areas of 6% (Sales 1996). However, recent research has shown that the real situation in Brazil is even worse, since these conservation areas are poorly distributed between Brazilian biomes and ecotones and characterized by areas not yet implemented and/or of medium to high vulnerability. Effectively protected areas are scarce (Ferreira et al. 1999).

One of the most effective strategies for biodiversity conservation is the creation of a coherent national network of protected areas. In addition to preserving biological diversity *in situ* and accumulating environmental capital for the future, such networks directly contribute to maintaining a balanced and healthy environment by providing society with a wide range of environmental services. Nevertheless, for the system to achieve its conservation objectives, such protected areas need to be evenly distributed between the various biogeographical regions in order to ensure the preservation of a significant and representative sample of biodiversity and landscapes.

Urgent measures are therefore needed to expand and better implement the National System of Conservation Areas (SNUC). This calls for research on the representativity of conservation areas in Brazil, by means of examining the representativity of the current system of conservation areas, in order to identify gaps and priorities for the expansion of the system. However, the procedures adopted so far for selecting areas for the creation of new conservation areas have been severely limited by the lack of a systematic methodology for quantifying the representativity of the environments selected.

To summarize, this study intends to present a new overview of the ecoregions of the Amazon biome, and to analyze the representativity of the protected areas when compared against the ecoregions, as well as the representativity of the vegetation types in relation to the protected areas.

The objectives of this study are: 1) to describe the methodologies currently employed for selecting priority areas for biodiversity conservation in Amazonia, and to present a new methodology based on the concept of ecoregions; and 2) using this methodology, to analyze the representativity of conservation areas and other types of special areas found in Amazonia.

Historical background

Various studies have been suggested for selecting priority areas for biodiversity conservation in Amazonia. Some were carried out using methodologies based on species distribution, while others were based on ecosystem distribution.

Species distribution

Two studies based on species distribution have so far been applied to the selection of priority areas for biodiversity conservation in Amazonia. Wetterberger et al. (1976) proposed giving priority to areas with a high concentration of endemic species (centers of endemism), called 'refuge areas'. Thus, areas of high priority for the creation of new conservation areas would be those presenting high degrees of spatial agreement among refuges, considered centers of high biodiversity concentration, and one of the possible reasons for the region's high biodiversity. This theory is based on the hypothesis of global climate warming during the

Pleistocene epoch of the Quaternary period, which caused the forest cover to recede worldwide. The Amazon forest became a type of savanna, with drier vegetation and various forest enclaves distributed throughout the region. As a result, many animal and plant groups were isolated in the remaining forests, called refuges, and underwent processes of adaptive irradiation and speciation. When the global climate cooled, the forest returned to its original extent, and many species considered endemic or of restricted distribution coincide with the former isolated forest fragments. However, the main criticism of this methodology arises from recent research questioning the existence of such 'refuges' and arguing that endemism sites are related to collecting efforts; in other words, sites showing a high concentration of endemic species are in fact those sites with the greatest concentration of collecting activity (Nelson 1990). Other studies have also demonstrated that the concept of 'refuges' has not been borne out in most of the research undertaken in Amazonia among the widest possible range of biological groups (Colli 1996).

A second attempt to use species distribution was employed during the *Workshop 90*, held in Macapá, at which a large group of researchers and conservationists drew up a list of priority areas for biodiversity conservation in Amazonia based on criteria of endemism, species richness or rarity, or endangered species, and the presence of geological or geochemical phenomena of special interest. The specific maps related to each criterion were overlaid and, from this, 57 areas were identified as priority conservation areas in Amazonia, amounting to 50% of the region (Rylands 1991; IBAMA/INPA/CI 1991). The main criticism of this methodology is the absence of, or sometimes the uneven knowledge of, many biological groups. The final map produced by the Workshop is a map of our knowledge of Amazonian biodiversity, rather than a synthesis of the areas judged to be high priority areas for conservation (Rylands and Pinto 1998, Silva unpublished data).

In conclusion, the main criticism of methodologies based on species distribution is that they require excellent systematics and species distribution. This is not the case in relation to the most important tropical ecosystems, especially the Amazon biome, which suffers from a critical lack of basic information on biodiversity distribution (Silva, unpublished data).

Ecosystem distribution

A methodology based on ecosystem distribution has been proposed by many authors as an alternative for selecting priority conservation areas in Amazonia, where knowledge of species distribution is poor.

This methodology was used by Ayres and Best (1979), who suggested that the large Amazon interfluve regions should be used as biogeographical units for analysis aiming at biodiversity conservation. The major Amazon rivers are extremely important as biogeographical barriers for different groups of terrestrial organisms, and it is conjectured that each interfluve region houses a distinct biota, with significant functional, morphological, and genetic differences. The main advantage of this methodology is that of identifying biogeographical units with clear natural boundaries; one disadvantage is the very superficial scale of analysis.

A second methodology was proposed by Fearnside and Ferraz (1995), who carried out a gap analysis for Brazilian Amazonia in order to determine conservation priorities for the region. This method uses the vegetation map of Brazil produced by the *Projeto RadamBrasil* (1968-1978), and takes the states as the geographical units of analysis. Thus, the study identified in each state the vegetation types not included in the current system of conservation areas and considered these to be priority types for future protection by means of new conservation areas. The main criticism of this methodology is the use of states as the geographical units of analysis, given that they are political, and not biogeographical units. Nevertheless, the use of vegetation types as landscape units represented a significant advance in the scale of analysis.

A third methodology, proposed by da Silva (unpublished data), combines the methods proposed by Ayres and Best (1979) and Fearnside and Ferraz (1995). This study carries out a gap analysis to identify priority areas for the creation of new conservation areas in Amazonia based on the RadamBrasil vegetation type maps, but using the large interfluve regions as the biogeographical units of analysis, rather than the states used by Fearnside and Ferraz (1995). Silva (unpublished data) thus divided Legal Amazonia into 13 interfluve regions: Solimões-Japurá, Japurá-Solimões-Negro, Negro-Branco, Branco-Negro-Trombetas, Trombetas-Ocean, Marajó, Solimões-Javari-Juruá, Juruá-Purus, Purus-Madeira, Madeira-Tapajós, Tapajós-Xingu, Xingu-Tocantins-Araguaia, Tocantins-Araguaia-Maranhão. The main criticism of this methodology is the use of Legal Amazonia as a geographical unit of analysis. As in the case of Fearnside and Ferraz (1995), there is no biogeographical basis for this choice, since Legal Amazonia is a political unit. Another deficiency of this methodology is the exclusive use of the large interfluve regions as the sole criterion for the division of biogeographical units. Some studies have recorded that not all Amazonian rivers are important barriers for all groups of organisms, particularly those rivers with more unstable beds and located in the upper Amazon region or to the north of the river. This does not, however, weaken the case for the use of interfluve regions as units of analysis for conservation.

A new methodology was proposed during the *Workshop 94* held in Miami (USAID and the World Bank), at which a large group of scientists and conservationists drew up a list of priority areas for biodiversity conservation in Latin America and the Caribbean, taking into consideration the representation of the region's main ecosystems and habitat types on the basis of a biogeographical unit denominated as an 'ecoregion'. A biogeographical unit is therefore considered to be a fragment of the geographical space representing an environmental unit of analysis, defined by separating the biosphere elements into their biotic and abiotic dimensions, according to different criteria. The basic biogeographical unit in the present study is the ecoregion, defined as 'a group of geographically distinct natural communities which share most of their dynamic species and ecological processes, as well as similar environmental conditions, in which ecological interactions are crucial for their long-term survival' (Dinerstein et al. 1995).

This concept represents an advance in reaching strategic planning goals for biodiversity conservation, for the following reasons:

1. The ecoregion becomes a unit of landscape analysis;
2. Different biogeographical scales and long-term objectives are employed in biodiversity conservation planning;
3. The whole biota, from species to communities, is the object of the conservation approach;
4. Relatively rare components of biodiversity (unique habitats, communities or species) are covered by the change of biogeographical scale;
5. The importance of preserving the evolutionary phenomena and ecological processes responsible for maintaining biodiversity is emphasized.

Case study

Objectives

A. To assess the representativity of federal direct use and strict conservation areas and of indigenous areas in the Amazon biome by cross-reference to ecoregions;

B. To assess the representativity of federal strict conservation areas in relation to the vegetation types of the Amazon biome;

C. To identify the priority vegetation types in each ecoregion for protection in federal strict conservation areas in the Amazon biome.

Methods

The method employed in this study can be summarized in three stages:

1. The first stage deals with the discussion of adoption of the biogeographical unit of analysis, the ecoregion, and its refining in conceptual terms and spatial delimitation applicable to the Amazon biome, so as to systematize references in order to establish in a more objective way a hierarchy of priorities for *in situ* conservation;

2. The second stage presents a brief description of the gap analysis and its procedures for identifying the degree of representativity of the current set of federal conservation areas and indigenous areas in the ecoregions comprising the Amazon biome;

3. Finally, the third stage deals with the classification of the themes to be used for the cross-referencing of the biological attributes (vegetation types) found in the ecoregions and these themes or areas, by means of overlays.

Data Analysis

The data presented in this study were obtained using spatial analysis of digital cartographic data techniques. They were processed using Arcinfo and Arcview (ESRI) geo-processing software for the database compilation and spatial cross-reference stages, and the Microsoft Access relational database manager.

The following data were used:

- the *digital map of Brazilian biomes* developed by WWF Brazil (1999, Figure 1), based on the digital map of South America and the Caribbean ecoregions developed by WWF-US (1998), both at a scale of 1:5,000,000. The digital files of both maps were supplied in Arcinfo format and geographical projection.

- the *boundaries of federal conservation areas* supplied by the Ibama conservation areas information system. This database was created by digitizing the boundaries of the conservation areas, on the basis of the respective legal instruments for their establishment and, where necessary, additional field information from Ibama staff.

- the areas were for the most part drawn at a scale of 1:250,000; however, some boundaries were defined on the basis of 1:100,000 scale maps or reports from the process of physical demarcation. The data were supplied in Arcinfo format (coverage) and geographical projection.

- the *boundaries of indigenous lands* compiled from digital files supplied by Funai. These files correspond to the mapping of indigenous lands by state at different scales, but mainly 1:1,000,000. The files were originally supplied in DGN format and polyconic projection.

- the IBGE *digital map of vegetation types* developed jointly with the *Secretaria de Assuntos Estratégicos* (the federal agency for strategic affairs) for the Environmental Diagnosis of the Brazilian Legal Amazonia (IBGE 1997). The map was developed at a scale of 1:2,500,000 and supplied in DGN format and polyconic projection. The data received in DGN format were converted using Arcview (conversion DGN → shape file) and then processed using Arcinfo (conversion shape file → coverage).

In the case of indigenous lands, the original topology in the files was lost during conversion, and had to be reconstructed using Arcinfo. The main problem in this conversion was dealing with files using different projections and the overlapping of indigenous lands between the different states when putting the files together. Following the data conversion, each indigenous area was classified according to its legal and administrative status following the 1998 map of the Instituto Socioambiental.

The most complex conversion was that of the vegetation map. Due to the nature of the DGN files, which were digitalized with techniques based on CAD systems, the shape-file → coverage conversion could not be done directly using Arcinfo for fear that errors would occur when recovering the attributes related to the classification of each digitalized polygon. The problem was solved by developing a program in Avenue (Arcview's internal programming language) to first separate the various overlapping polygons, and then to join them later. Once this was done the files could be converted to coverage.

The cross-referencing of the themes was performed using the unite vector themes function ('union' function) in Arcinfo. Loss of data was avoided by specifying double numeric precision.

The cross-referencing resulted in a single file in coverage format containing a cross-referenced table. Following this, the overlapped areas were calculated by altering the original geographical projection to the sinusoidal projection (central meridian -54) and to the square meter as the unit of measurement. This projection was chosen to preserve the areas of the cross-referenced features (themes). The cross-referenced tables were exported to dBase format. Thanks to Access database software, data of interest could be extracted from the dBase table (queries and reports were created to obtain consolidated data). It should be noted that analysis of the final data should take into account the process used and the quality of the original data. As the ecoregions and vegetation themes were supplied at small scales, the final result, from a cartographic point of view, is conditioned by these scales. The conversion process adopted for the indigenous areas and vegetation also alters the original figures, causing some, though not significant, loss.

Results and Discussion

The ecoregions of the Amazon biome

The Amazon biome is composed of 23 ecoregions, corresponding to an area of 4,105,401 km² (48.1% of the Brazilian territory). These ecoregions represent various types of habitats, with different physiognomies, structures, and vegetation types (Figure 2).

One of the main criteria used to distinguish these ecoregions was the large interfluves (Figure 2). The important role of the major Amazon rivers as biogeographical barriers has been stressed ever since the first naturalists began scientific exploration of the region. This fact was first acknowledged by Wallace (1853), and was supported by the studies of Snethlage (1910) and Hellmayr (1910). Since then, the hypothesis that rivers act as barriers has received continuous support in studies on animal and plant distribution and differentiation in Amazonia (Sick 1967; Haffer 1974, 1978; Ayres and Clutton-Brock 1992; Caparella 1988, 1991). Based on these studies, the use of interfluve regions, especially in the lower and middle river valleys, as one of the criteria for separating the ecoregions of the Amazon biome to be used as biogeographical units for conservation analysis, is well established. These areas have well defined natural limits corresponding to differences in evolutionary history and, therefore, to the distribution of natural communities. Any other alternative biogeographical division (for example, the plant geographical regions of Ducke and Black 1953, Rizzini 1963, Hueck and Seibert 1981, Prance 1977) will be based on the distribution of species of only a few groups of organisms, whose distribution patterns are still not well known.

In the Amazon biome, the large interfluves are found mainly to the south of the Solimões-Amazonas river (Figure 2). The ecoregions in this area are formed by the interfluves of the main tributaries, such as the Juruá, Purus, Madeira, Tapajós, Xingu, Tocantins and Araguaia rivers. The main tributaries to the north of the Solimões-Amazonas river, such as the Rio Branco and the Trombetas, are not usually regarded as barriers to species distribution (Figure 2). Other important factors in the division of some ecoregions were height gradients (tepuis and the Andes), soil types (Rio Negro campinaranas), variation in river and tide levels (várzeas and igapós), and geological arcs (southwestern Amazonia, várzeas), among others (Figure 2).

The percentage of area occupied by each of the 23 ecoregions of the Amazon biome varies from 0.02% (tepuis) to 16.07% (Madeira-Tapajós interfluve) (Table 1, Figure 2). Three regions alone, the Madeira-Tapajós interfluve, the Uatumã-Trombetas interfluve, and the Mato Grosso dry forests, each occupy more than 10% of the Amazon biome each; the majority of the ecoregions, (15 or 65.2%), each occupy less than 5% of the biome (Table 1, Figure 2).

This partially supports the concept proposed by Prance (1987) that Amazonia is formed by a great mosaic of habitats with different evolutionary histories, resulting in a wide distribution of ecosystems. Consequently, the selection of priority areas for biodiversity conservation in the region, to ensure good representation of the majority of the region's habitats, is a difficult and delicate process.

Types of conservation areas and special areas in the Amazon biome

In the Amazon biome there are currently various types of federal conservation areas and indigenous areas, each with different degrees of representativity, as well as the problem of the overlaps between these areas.

Federal strict conservation areas occupy around 3.25% of the Amazon biome, ignoring the overlaps with indigenous areas (Figure 3). Taking the overlaps (20.66%) into account, the area of the Amazon biome in strict conservation areas drops to around 2.56%.

Federal direct use conservation areas occupy around 4.82% of the Amazon biome, ignoring the overlaps with indigenous areas (Figure 4). Taking the overlaps (53.17%) into account, the area of the Amazon biome in direct use conservation areas drops to around 2.26%.

Indigenous areas occupy approximately 22.52% of the Amazon Biome, ignoring the overlaps with strict and direct use conservation areas (Figure 5).

Twenty-nine strict conservation areas were found in the 23 ecoregions of the Amazon biome (ignoring the overlaps with indigenous areas), in the four use categories: ecological reserves (N = 3), biological reserves (N = 9), ecological stations (N = 8), and national parks (N = 9), adding up to an area of 3.25% (Figure 3).

The strict conservation areas are not evenly distributed among the 23 ecoregions that make up the Amazon biome. Five of these ecoregions (17.4%) contain no federal strict conservation areas, 11 (52.2%) have less than 5% of their area within federal strict conservation areas, 5 (21.7%) have between 5% and 20% of their area within federal strict consevation areas, and only 2 ecoregions have more than 20% of their area within federal strict conservation areas (Figure 3 and Table 1).

In conclusion, the federal system of conservation areas in the Amazon biome is still not sufficient to protect the broad ecosystem diversity found in the region (Table 1). This conclusion, however, is still provisional, as this report does not include state strict conservation areas, due to the fact that not all these data are available from a single agency, as is the case with the federal areas. The existing data are dispersed among the different state conservation agencies, which makes access to them more difficult. Nevertheless, the data presented in this study give us a fair picture of the representativity of conservation areas in the ecoregions of the Amazon biome. The ecoregions recommended as the most important for the creation of new conservation areas are those that: a) do not have any protected areas designated as federal strict conservation areas, and b) have less than 10% of their area in federal strict conservation areas. However, this percentage is arbitrary and should be applied only to those ecoregions with extensive areas in Amazonia. Ecoregions with smaller areas should have a higher proportion in conservation areas than the minimum area proposed above. Studies on the critical minimum size for conservation areas needed to maintain the ecological processes fundamental for the conservation of the biodiversity of the Amazon region remain unpublished or do not exist.

Vegetation types in the Amazon biome

Seventy primary (no human disturbance) and six secondary (resulting from human disturbance) vegetation types were recognized in the Amazon biome by the IBGE data (1997, Figure 6). Overall, the following vegetation types were recognized, according to their structure, physiognomy, topography, altitude, and floristic composition:

- Campinaranas (white-sand grasslands), comprising five types and one ecotone with rainforests, occupying around 4.10% and distributed among three to twelve ecoregions of the Amazon biome (Figure 7);
- Deciduous and semi-deciduous seasonal forests, comprising six types each, occupying around 4.67% and distributed among one to six ecoregions of the Amazon biome (Figure 8);
- Open rainforests, comprising eleven types, occupying around 25.48% and distributed among two to eighteen ecoregions of the Amazon biome (Figure 9);
- Dense rainforests, comprising twelve types, occupying around 53.63% and distributed among one to twenty-three ecoregions of the Amazon biome (Figure 10);

• Pioneer formations of fluvial and/or tidal influence, comprising nine types, occupying around 1.87% and distributed among one to twelve ecoregions of the Amazon biome (Figure 11);

• Montane refuges, comprising three types, occupying around 0.029% and distributed among one to four ecoregions of the Amazon biome (Figure 12);

• Amazonian savannas, comprising fifteen types and two ecotones with rainforests and seasonal forests, occupying around 6.07% and distributed among one to ten ecoregions of the Amazon biome (Figure 13);

Vegetation types in the ecoregions of the Amazon biome

The number of vegetation types in the twenty-three ecoregions comprising the Amazon biome varied between five (Caquetá forests) and forty (Mato Grosso dry forests), and the number of vegetation types within strict conservation areas varied from none in the Caquetá forests, Gurupá várzeas, Monte Alegre várzeas, and the Purus-Madeira interfluve to seventeen types in the Madeira-Tapajós interfluve (Table 2).

Of the seventy vegetation types existing in the twenty-three ecoregions of the Amazon biome, thirty one types (44.28%) are not represented in any of the strict conservation areas; for sixteen types (22.86%) less than 1% of their area is within strict conservation areas; for eleven types (15.71%) between 1% and 4.9% of their area is within strict conservation areas; for seven types (10%) between 5% and 9.9% of their area is within strict conservation areas, and only five types (7.14%) have more than 10% of their area within strict conservation areas (Table 3).

Therefore, as in the case of the ecoregions, the federal system of conservation areas is still not sufficient to protect the wide diversity of vegetation types existing in the twenty three ecoregions that make up the Amazon biome (Table 3).

In conclusion, the most important vegetation types for the creation of conservation areas in each of the twenty three ecoregions that make up the Amazon biome area those that: a) are still unprotected (see the vegetation types in bold in Table 4), and b) have less than 10% of their areas located within conservation areas.

Conclusion

The results of this study permit a quantitative assessment of the importance for biodiversity conservation of the areas within each of the twenty three ecoregions that make up the Amazon biome. This is important because these areas and, as a consequence, the priority actions for biodiversity conservation in the Amazon biome, need to be individually identified in each ecoregion, as each represents a distinct biological unit resulting from historical, evolutionary, and ecological processes, and thus presenting unique biotic and abiotic components.

This study has its limitations; when the databases of the state strict and direct use conservation areas have been integrated, it will be possible to have an overall picture of the conservation gaps within the Amazon biome. The vegetation types identified in this study can be subdivided, to also include their sub-formations, as described by IBGE (1992). This will allow a more detailed analysis of ecosystem diversity in each ecoregion, minimizing the possibility, when setting conservation priorities, of overlooking unique biotic communities that are poorly represented in territorial terms.

Improving the record so that Ibama can quickly and safely assess priority areas for the creation of new conservation areas will require investment in equipment and personnel to add missing information and to speedily carry out an assessment procedure for new areas based on the methodology proposed in this study.

As a goal for any efficient system of reserves for the Amazon biome, we propose a significant increase of protected areas within each ecoregion, to include all the vegetation types present in each and paying special attention to unique, small scale environments, as these are the ones that most probably contain unusual biotic elements. The areas created in each ecoregion can and should be connected by corridors including other categories of areas, such as direct use conservation areas and even indigenous areas, provided there is permanent monitoring of the environmental quality of these areas.

If one accepts the basis of the present analysis, corridors connecting conservation areas should be established parallel to the major tributaries of the Solimões-Amazonas, or be located on the boundaries of ecoregions not separated by interfluves. This would maximize the possibility of connecting the system's reserves by means of narrower stretches of rivers or other physical barriers, where the probability of gene flow between populations of different ecoregions is higher (Haffer 1992).

Another important point would be to incorporate socioeconomic processes into this analysis of the representativity of priority areas for biodiversity conservation in the Amazon biome. The main processes to be analyzed would include the location of main cities, highways, and waterways, types of soil use, location of areas of deforestation, the expanding frontier of human occupation, amongst others. These data can then be processed using spatial analysis techniques and spatially cross-referenced with the biogeographical data of this study, to obtain a true picture of the areas and of priority action for biodiversity conservation in the ecoregions of the Amazon biome. Another important element is public policies. The effective implementation of the results of this study requires the establishment of multi-level partnerships, through dialogue and information exchange, between the State and non-governmental organizations.

Acknowledgements

The first author thanks George Powell and Wesley Wettengel of WWF-US for a Geographic Information System (SIG) training course, and Ibama for providing the data in this study and for contributing to their analysis.

Bibliography

AYRES, J. M.; BEST, R. Estratégias para a conservação da fauna amazônica. *Acta Amazonica,* n. 9 (supplement), p. 81-102, 1979.

AYRES, J. M.; CLUTTON-BROCK, T. H. River Boundaries and Species Range Size in Amazonian Primates, *American Naturalist,* n. 140, p. 531-537, 1992.

CAPPARELLA, A. P. Genetic Variation in Neotropical Birds: Implications for the Speciation Process. *Acta Congressus Internationalis Ornithologici,* n. 19, p. 1658-1673, 1988.

_____. Neotropical Avian Diversity and Riverine Barriers. *Acta Congressus Internationalis Ornithologici,* 20. 1991. p. 307-316.

COLLI, G. R. *Amazonian Savanna Lizards and the Historical Biogeography of Amazonia,* 137 p. Doctoral thesis. University of California, 1996.

DINERSTEIN, E. et al. *A Conservation Assessment of the Terrestrial Ecoregions of Latin America and the Caribbean.* World Wildlife Fund Report to the World Bank/LATEN, 1995.

DUCKE, A.; BLACK, G. A. Phytogeographical Notes on the Brazilian Amazon. *Anais da Academia Brasileira de Ciências,* 25. 1953, p. 1-46.

FEARNSIDE, P. M.; FERRAZ, J. A Conservation Gap Analysis of Brazil's Amazonian Vegetation, *Conservation Biology,* n. 9, p. 1134-1147, 1995.

FERREIRA, L. V. et al. *Análise do grau de vulnerabilidade e implementação das unidades de conservação federais de uso indireto no Brasil:* uma proposta de criação do ranking das unidades brasileiras. Technical report. WWF, 1999.

HAFFER, J. Avian Speciation in South America. *Publications of the Nuttall Ornithological Club,* n. 14, p. 1-390, 1974.

_____. Distribution of Amazon Birds. *Bonner Zoologische Beiträge,* n. 29, p. 38-78, 1978.

_____. On the River Effect. Some Forest Birds of Southern Amazonia. *Bol. Mus. Paraense Emílio Goeldi, série Zoológia,* n. 8, p. 217-245, 1992.

HELLMAYR, C. E. The Birds of the Rio Madeira. *Novitates Zoologicae,* n. 17, p. 257-428, 1910.

HUECK, K.; SIEBERT, P. *Vegetationskarte von Südamaerika.* Stuttgart: Gustav Fischer Verlag, 1981.

IBAMA/INPA/CI. *Workshop 90: Biological Priorities for Conservation in Amazonia.* Map and Legend Prepared from January 1990 Conference in Manaus Sponsored by IBAMA, INPA, Conservation International, the New York Botanical Garden, the Smithsonian Institution, and the Royal Botanic Gardens. Washington D.C.: Conservation International, 1991.

IBGE. *Manual técnico da vegetação brasileira.* Rio de Janeiro: IBGE, 1992.

_____. *Diagnóstico ambiental da Amazônia Legal.* CD-ROM. Rio de Janeiro: IBGE, 1997.

NELSON, B. W. et al. Endemism Centres, Refugia and Botanical Collection Density in Brazilian Amazonia. *Nature,* n. 345, p. 714-716, 1990.

PRANCE, G. T. The Phytogeographic Subdivisions of Amazonia and their Influence on the Selection of Biological Reserves. In: PRANCE, G. T.; ELIAS, T. S. (Eds.). *Extinction is Forever.* New York: New York Botanical Garden, 1977, p. 195-212.

_____. Vegetation. In: WHITMORE, T. C.; PRANCE, G. T. (Eds.). *Biogeography and Quaternary History in Tropical America,* Oxford: Clarendon Press, 1987. p. 28-45. (Oxford Monographs on Biogeography, 3)

RADAMBRASIL. *Levantamento de recursos naturais,* v. 1-18. Ministério de Minas e Energia. Rio de Janeiro: Departamento Nacional de Produção Mineral, 1968-1978.

RIZZINI, C. T. Nota prévia sobre a divisão fitogeográfica do Brasil. *Revista Brasileira de Geografia,* n.1, p. 1-64, 1963.

RYLANDS, A. B.; PINTO L. P. S. Conservação da biodiversidade na Amazônia brasileira: uma análise do sistema de unidades de conservação. *Cadernos FBDS,* n. 1, p. 1-65, 1998.

RYLANDS, A. B. *The Status of Conservation Areas in the Brazilian Amazon.* Washington D.C.: World Wildlife Fund and Conservation International, 1991.

SALES, G. O sistema nacional de unidades de conservação: o estado atual. *Anais do seminário internacional sobre presença humana em unidades de conservação,* 1996, p. 14-20.

SICK, H. Rios e enchentes na Amazônia como obstáculo para a avifauna. *Atas do Simpósio sobre a Biota Amazônica, v. 5 (Zoologia),* 1967, 495-520.

SNETHLAGE, E. Sobre a distribuição da avifauna campestre na Amazônia. *Bol. Mus. Paraense Emílio Goeldi,* n. 6, p. 226-235, 1910.

WALLACE, A. R. *A Narrative of Travels on the Amazon and Rio Negro.* London: Reeves, 1853.

WETTERBERGER, G. B. et al. Uma análise de prioridades em conservação da natureza na Amazônia. *Projeto de Desenvolvimento e Pesquisa Florestal (PRODEPEF) PNUD/FAO/IBDF/BRA-45,* Série Técnica, n. 8, p. 1-63, 1976.

Table 1 - Percentage of the area occupied by the 23 ecoregions comprising the Amazon biome, and the area of the ecoregions found within federal strict and direct use conservation areas, and indigenous areas

no.	Ecoregions of Brazilian Amazonia	% of area of Amazonia	Indigenous areas	Conservation area Strict	Conservation area Direct use
1	Rio Negro campinarana	1.96	36	8.34	15.38
2	Caquetá Forests	0.31	96	0.00	28.99
3	Guiana highland forests	2.77	80	8.62	55.44
4	Mato Grosso dry forests	10.08	17	0.01	0.09
5	Guianan tropical forests	1.75	26	1.75	0.09
6	Japurá-Solimões-Negro interfluve	5.73	30	11.30	11.09
7	Juruá-Purus interfluve	5.92	16	0.57	5.41
8	Madeira-Tapajós interfluve	16.07	17	3.88	2.04
9	Negro-Branco interfluve	1.19	17	29.55	0.34
10	Purus-Madeira interfluve	4.24	9	0.00	0.00
11	Solimões-Japurá interfluve	0.90	11	19.77	0.00
12	Tapajós-Xingu interfluve	8.20	24	0.00	6.20
13	Tocantins-Araguaia-Maranhão interfluve	4.72	7	1.41	0.05
14	Uatumã-Trombetas interfluve	11.51	23	3.29	2.62
15	Xingu-Tocantins interfluve	6.56	26	0.37	3.66
16	Guiana savannas	1.90	50	1.14	0.01
17	Southwestern Amazonia	7.80	37	2.80	5.28
18	Tepuís	0.02	100	65.04	33.43
19	Iquitos várzeas	0.74	11	0.99	1.84
20	Monte Alegre várzeas	1.63	4	0.00	0.12
21	Gurupá várzeas	0.25	0	0.00	0.00
22	Marajó várzeas	1.99	2	6.96	1.73
23	Purus várzeas	3.48	13	3.24	1.84

Table 2 - Number of vegetation types protected in federal strict conservation areas in the 23 ecoregions of the Amazon biome

no.	Ecoregions of the Brazilian Amazonia	no. of vegetation types	no. of vegetation types in conservation areas
1	Rio Negro campinarana	18	8
2	Caquetá forests	5	0
3	Guiana highland forests	26	16
4	Mato Grosso dry forests	40	2
5	Guiana tropical forests	14	6
6	Japurá-Solimões-Negro interfluve	17	9
7	Juruá-Purus interfluve	12	3
8	Madeira-Tapajós interfluve	31	17
9	Negro-Branco interfluve	19	13
10	Purus-Madeira interfluve	22	0
11	Solimões-Japurá interfluve	10	5
12	Tapajós-Xingu interfluve	23	1
13	Tocantins-Araguaia-Maranhão interfluve	13	2
14	Uatumã-Trombetas interfluve	34	7
15	Xingu-Tocantins interfluve	30	5
16	Guiana savannas	30	9
17	Southwestern Amazonia	17	7
18	Tepuís	6	4
19	Iquitos várzeas	10	3
20	Monte Alegre várzeas	15	0
21	Gurupá várzeas	11	0
22	Marajó várzeas	18	6
23	Purus várzeas	13	5

Table 3 - Representativity of the area occupied by vegetation types and their distribution within the ecoregions of the Amazon biome

	Vegetation classes	% of biome	Occurrence in ecoregions
1	Alluvial buriti palme fluvial influence pioneer formation	0.0576	1
2	Alluvial dense rainforest	2.1615	20
3	Alluvial dense rainforest with emergents in canopy	4.7805	16
4	Alluvial dense rainforest with uniform canopy	3.1006	19
5	Alluvial herbaceous fluvial influence pioneer formation	1.1148	12
6	Alluvial herbaceous fluvial influence pioneer formation without palms	0.0993	8
7	Alluvial shrubby fluvial influence pioneer formation	0.1760	9
8	Alluvial shrubby fluvial influence pioneer formation with palms	0.0027	1
9	Alluvial shrubby fluvial influence pioneer formation without palms	0.3236	3
10	Alluvial semi-deciduous seasonal forest	0.0043	2
11	Alluvial semi-deciduous seasonal forest with emergents in canopy	0.1766	3
12	Campinarana/rainforest	0.5941	6
13	Forested moist campinarana	2.1439	12
14	Forested moist campinarana with palms	0.1455	4
15	Forested seasonal savanna	1.8908	10
16	Forested seasonal steppe-savanna	0.0575	2
17	Grassy-woody moist campinarana	0.1117	6
18	Grassy-woody seasonal savanna	0.3714	6
19	Grassy-woody seasonal savanna with gallery forest	0.0969	2
20	Grassy-woody seasonal savanna without gallery forest	0.0049	2
21	Herbaceous marine influence pioneer formation	0.0006	1
22	Herbaceous tidal influence pioneer formation	0.0198	2
23	High montane herbaceous refuge	0.0004	1
24	Lowland deciduous seasonal forest	0.0009	1
25	Lowland deciduous seasonal forest with emergents in canopy	0.0293	1
26	Lowland dense rainforest	0.1605	9
27	Lowland dense rainforest with emergents in canopy	22.2879	22
28	Lowland dense rainforest with uniform canopy	1.4369	17
29	Lowland open rainforest	0.0087	2
30	Lowland open rainforest with vines	0.5407	10
31	Lowland open rainforest with palms	4.1700	17
32	Lowland semi-deciduous seasonal forest with uniform canopy	0.0509	2
33	Montane deciduous seasonal forest	0.0038	2
34	Montane deciduous seasonal forest with emergents in canopy	0.0130	1
35	Montane dense rainforest	0.0009	1
36	Montane dense rainforest with emergents in canopy	0.3003	5
37	Montane dense rainforest with uniform canopy	0.2398	8
38	Montane herbaceous refuge	0.0004	2
39	Montane open rainforest	0.0044	2
40	Montane open rainforest with vines	0.0168	3
41	Montane open rainforest with palms	0.0068	2
42	Montane refuge	0.0206	4
43	Montane shrubby refuge	0.0080	3
44	Park seasonal savanna	0.4053	8
45	Park seasonal savanna with gallery forest	0.9107	8
46	Park seasonal savanna without gallery forest	0.0859	5
47	Park seasonal steppe-savanna	0.2150	1
48	Savanna/Seasonal forest	0.0137	2
49	Savanna/rainforest	0.1117	3
50	Submontane deciduous seasonal forest	0.0055	2
51	Submontane deciduous seasonal forest with emergents in canopy	0.3921	3
52	Submontane dense rainforest	0.0313	6
53	Submontane dense rainforest with emergents in canopy	14.9281	23
54	Submontane dense rainforest with uniform canopy	4.2051	18
55	Wooded moist campinarana	0.4592	6

continues

	Vegetation classes	% of biome	Occurrence in ecoregions
56	Wooded moist campinarana with palms	0.6268	6
57	Wooded moist campinarana without palms	0.0144	3
58	Wooded seasonal savanna	0.4492	9
59	Wooded seasonal savanna with gallery forest	0.8591	7
60	Wooded seasonal savanna without gallery forest	0.5995	4
61	Wooded seasonal steppe-savanna	0.0013	2
62	Wooded tidal influence pioneer formation	0.0803	4
63	Submontane open rainforest	0.0072	2
64	Submontane open rainforest with bamboo	1.3490	7
65	Submontane open rainforest with palms	12.0989	18
66	Submontane open rainforest with sororocas	0.1565	3
67	Submontane open rainforest with vines	7.1175	13
68	Submontane semi-deciduous seasonal forest	0.0272	1
69	Submontane semi-deciduous seasonal forest with emergents in canopy	3.8397	6
70	Submontane semi-deciduous seasonal forest with uniform canopy	0.1218	3
1	Agriculture-livestock raising	0.5204	18
2	Reforestation with fruit species	0.0005	2
3	Reforestation with pine	0.0056	2
4	Secondary vegetation	0.0728	8
5	Secondary vegetation with palms	0.3384	6
6	Secondary vegetation without palms	0.9951	8
1	Unmapped areas	2.2200	-

TABLE 4 - PERCENTAGE OF VEGETATION TYPES IN THE ECOREGIONS OF THE AMAZON BIOME AND THEIR REPRESENTATIVITY IN FEDERAL INDIRECT USE CONSERVATION AREAS (IN BRACKETS). FIGURES IN BOLD INDICATE THE VEGATION TYPES IN EACH ECOREGION NOT PRESENT IN CONSERVATION AREAS.

	Vegetation types (IBGE 1997) Ecoregions	Rio Negro campinaranas	Caquetá forests	Guiana highland forests	Guiana moist forests	Japurá-Solimões-Negro interfluve	Juruá-Purus interfluve	Madeira-Tapajós interfluve
1	Alluvial buriti palm fluvial influence pioneer formation							0.358 (38.2)
2	Alluvial dense rainforest	0.207 (0)		0.009 (0)		0.896 (0.05)	0.726 (0)	0.355 (0)
3	Alluvial dense rainforest with emerging canopy	0.633 (0)				3.306 (0.021)	11.485 (0.0001)	1.640 (0.15)
4	Alluvial dense rainforest with uniform canopy	0.130 (0)			0.55 (0.08)	4.725 (2.98)	11.148 (0.25)	1.503 (0.11)
5	Alluvial herbaceous fluvial influence pioneer formation				1.107 (0.37)			0.708 (2.43)
6	Alluvial herbaceous fluvial influence pioneer formation without palms							0.158 (0)
7	Alluvial shrubby fluvial influence pioneer formation					0.001 (0)	0.030 (0)	0.655 (0)
8	Alluvial shrubby fluvial influence pioneer formation with palms							
9	Alluvial shrubby fluvial influence pioneer formation without palms							0.0161 (0)
10	Alluvial semi-deciduous seasonal forest							
11	Alluvial semi-deciduous seasonal forest with emergents in canopy							0.064 (0)
12	Campinarana/rainforest	3.776 (1.98)		0.57 (0.75)				
13	Forested moist campinarana	47.715 (3.94)	24.03 (0)	1.74 (0.22)		14.307 (0.49)		

continues

	Vegetation types (IBGE 1997) Ecoregions	Rio Negro campinaranas	Caquetá forests	Guiana highland forests	Guiana moist forests	Japurá-Solimões-Negro interfluve	Juruá-Purus interfluve	Madeira-Tapajós interfluve
14	Forested moist campinarana with palms	6.073 (2.95)		0,035 (0)				
15	Forested seasonal savanna				0.133 (0)			1.409 (1.03)
16	Forested seasonal steppe-savanna			0.07 (0)				
17	Grassy-woody moist campinarana	3.052 (0)				0.669 (0)		
18	Grassy-woody seasonal savanna	0.082 (0.12)		0,14 (0)				0.055 (0)
19	Grassy-woody seasonal savanna with gallery forest							
20	Grassy-woody seasonal savanna without gallery forest							
21	Herbaceous marine influence pioneer formation							
22	Herbaceous tidal influence pioneer formation							
23	High montane herbaceous refuge							
24	Lowland deciduous seasonal forest							
25	Lowland deciduous seasonal forest with emergents in canopy							
26	Lowland dense rainforest	0.409 (0)		0.14 (0)		0.164 (0)		
27	Lowland dense rainforest with emergents in canopy	8.788 (0.02)	12.99 (0)	2.60 (0.05)	0.88 (0)	51.129 (1.67)	67.320 (0.12)	27.745 (0.66)
28	Lowland dense rainforest with uniform canopy	0.076 (0)		3.21 (0.91)	14.37 (7.14)	1.020 (0.31)		0.606 (0)
29	Lowland open rainforest						0.00001 (0)	
30	Lowland open rainforest with vines						0.1311 (0)	1.342 (0)
31	Lowland open rainforest with palms	0.681 (0.16)	0.48 (0)	1.93 (0.37)		5.696 (2.08)	4.880 (0)	6.293 (0.001)
32	Lowland semi-deciduous seasonal forest with uniform canopy			0.122 (4.24)				
33	Montane deciduous seasonal forest							
34	Montane deciduous seasonal forest with emergents in canopy							
35	Montane dense rainforest							
36	Montane dense rainforest with emergents in canopy			10.21 (0)	0.199 (0)			
37	Montane dense rainforest with uniform canopy			6.40 (6.75)	2.166 (0)			
38	Montane herbaceous refuge			0.007 (44.32)				
39	Montane open rainforest							
40	Montane open rainforest with vines			0.21 (0)				
41	Montane open rainforest with palms							
42	Montane refuge			0.55 (0)				
43	Montane shrubby refuge					0.035 (0)		
44	Park seasonal savanna							0.992 (3.18)
45	Park seasonal savanna with gallery forest			0.30 (0.03)	0.217 (0)			0.073 (0)

continues

	Vegetation types (IBGE 1997) Ecoregions	Rio Negro campinaranas	Caquetá forests	Guiana highland forests	Guiana moist forests	Japurá-Solimões-Negro interfluve	Juruá-Purus interfluve	Madeira-Tapajós interfluve
46	Park seasonal savanna without gallery forest							0.082 (5.29)
47	Park seasonal steppe-savanna			0.29 (0)	0.489 (0.68)			
48	Savanna/seasonal forest							0.003 (0.16)
49	Savanna/rainforest							0.465 (0)
50	Submontane deciduous seasonal forest							
51	Submontane deciduous seasonal forest with emergents in canopy							0.104 (0)
52	Submontane dense rainforest	0.148 (0)		0.62 (9.60)				0.017 (0)
53	Submontane dense rainforest with emergents in canopy	1.831 (0)	53.49 (0)	48.90 (0.31)	33.228 (0)	2.699 (0)	2.592 (0)	8.621 (0.50)
54	Submontane dense rainforest with uniform canopy	0.048 (0)		16.58 (2.59)	44.45 (0.03)	0.032 (0)		1.301 (0.15)
55	Wooded moist campinarana	15.982 (9.14)		1.70 (0.07)		0.678 (0.20)		
56	Wooded moist campinarana with palms	8.861 (1.55)	6.86 (0)			6.277 (5.41)		
57	Wooded moist campinarana without palms	0.591 (0)				0.01 (0)		
58	Wooded seasonal savanna							0.471 (6.19)
59	Wooded seasonal savanna with gallery forest				0.180 (0)			0.170 (0.86)
60	Wooded seasonal savanna without gallery forest							0.372 (2.18)
61	Wooded seasonal steppe-savanna							
62	Wooded tidal influence pioneer formation				0.013 (0.28)			
63	Submontane open rainforest							
64	Submontane open rainforest with bamboo						0.047 (0)	0.005 (0)
65	Submontane open rainforest with palms			1.56 (0.009)		3.513 (0)	1.037 (0)	26.558 (1.60)
66	Submontane open rainforest with sororocas							
67	Submontane open rainforest with vines			0.47 (0)	0.034 (0)		0.004 (0)	12.671 (0.81)
68	Submontane semi-deciduous seasonal forest							
69	Submontane semi-deciduous seasonal forest with emergents in canopy			0.55 (0.18)				2.892 (0)
70	Submontane semi-deciduous seasonal forest with uniform canopy			0.58 (2.60)				

Brazilian biomes

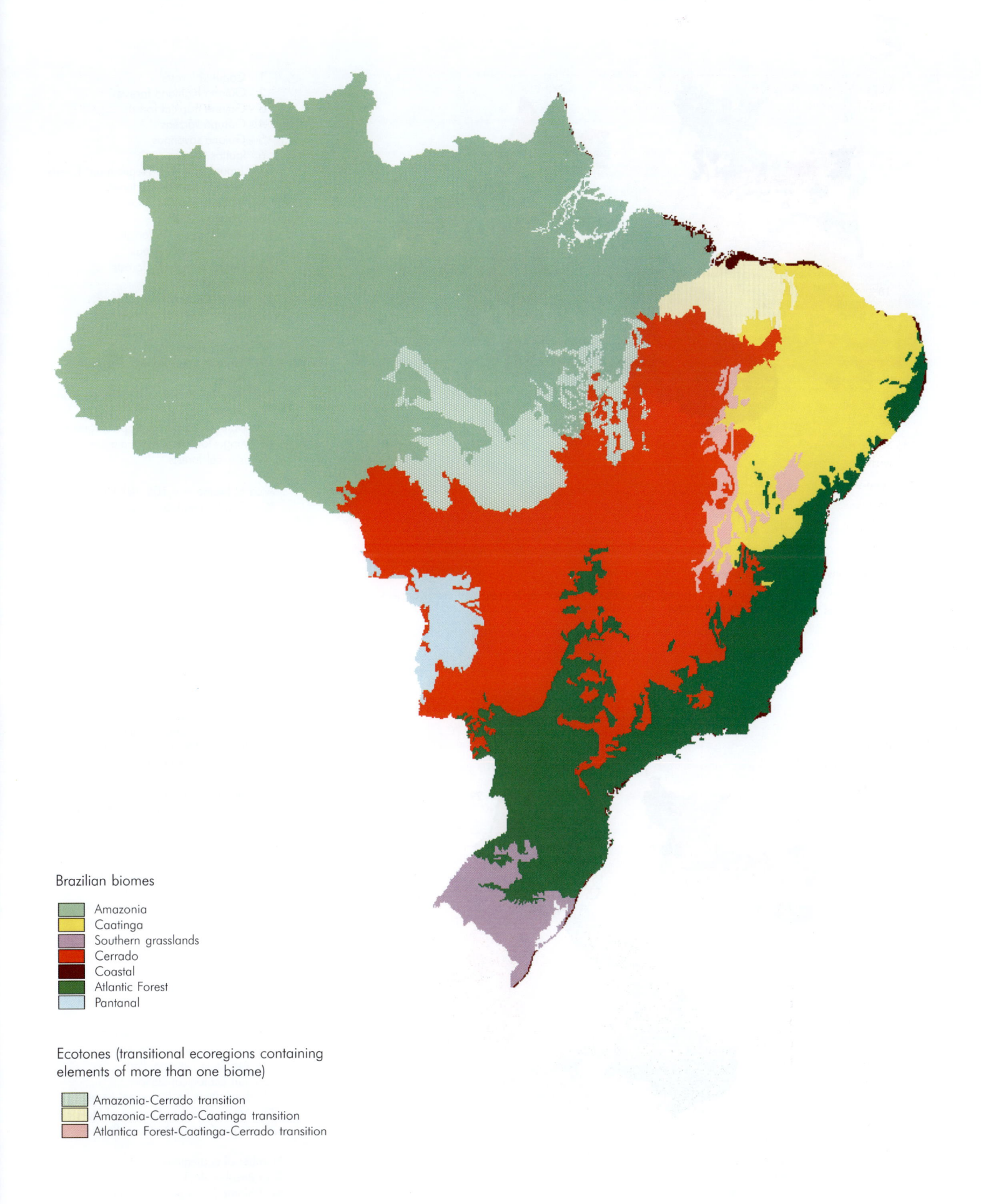

- Amazonia
- Caatinga
- Southern grasslands
- Cerrado
- Coastal
- Atlantic Forest
- Pantanal

Ecotones (transitional ecoregions containing elements of more than one biome)

- Amazonia-Cerrado transition
- Amazonia-Cerrado-Caatinga transition
- Atlantica Forest-Caatinga-Cerrado transition

Figure 1. Brazilian biomes* and ecotones

Sinusoidal projection, central meridian (-54 degrees). The area of the features is preserved in this projection.
Source: WWF 2000.

* Biome is understood as 'a group of similar ecoregions, fauna, flora, and ecological dymanics and processes'.

1 - Caquetá forests
2 - Guiana highland forests
3 - Guiana tropical forests
4 - Gurupá várzeas
5 - Guiana savannas
6 - Iquitos várzeas
7 - Japurá/Solimões-Negro moist forests
8 - Juruá-Purus tropical forests
9 - Madeira-Tapajós tropical forests
10 - Marajó várzeas
11 - Mato Grosso dry forests
12 - Monte Alegre várzeas
13 - Negro-Branco dry forests
14 - Purus várzeas
15 - Purus-Madeira tropical forests
16 - Upper Rio Negro campinaranas
17 - Solimões-Japurá tropical forests
18 - Southwestern Amazonia
19 - Tapajós-Xingu tropical forests
20 - Tepuís
21 - Tocantins-Araguaia-Maranhão tropical forests
22 - Uatumã-Trombetas tropical forests
23 - Xingu-Tocantins-Araguaia tropical forests

Area of biome = 4,105,401 km^2
% of Brazilian territory = 48.1

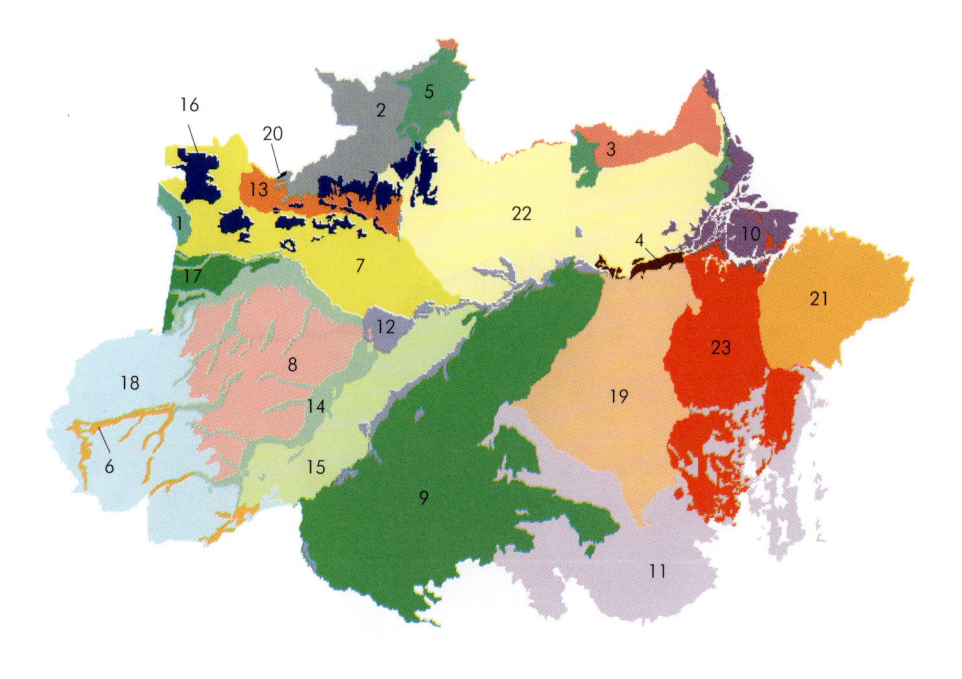

Figure 2. Ecoregions of the Amazon biome
Sinusoidal projection, central meridian (-54 degrees). The area of the features is preserved in this projection.
Source: Ecoregions of South America (WWF 1999).

1 - Monte Roraima National Park
2 - Maracá Ecological Station
3 - Caracaraí Ecological Station
4 - Niquiá Ecological Station
5 - Serra da Mocidade National Park
6 - Viruá National Park
7 - Pico da Neblina National Park
8 - Jaú National Park
9 - Juami/Japura Ecological Reserve
10 - Juami/Japura Ecological Station
11 - Jutaí/Solimões Ecological Reserve
12 - Abufari Biological Reserve
13 - Sauim/Castanheira Ecological Reserve
14 - Uatumã Biological Reserve
15 - Rio Trombetas Biological Reserve
16 - Serra do Divisor National Park
17 - Rio Acre Ecological Station
18 - Pacaás Novos National Park
19 - Guaporé Biological Reserve
20 - Jaru Biological Reserve
21 - Ique Ecological Station
22 - Amazonia Biological Reserve
23 - Tapirapé Biological Reserve
24 - Gurupi Biological Reserve
25 - Araguaia National Park
26 - Jari Ecological Station
27 - Lago Piratuba Biological Reserve
28 - Maracá-Jipioca Ecological Station
29 - Cabo Orange National Park

Number of ecoregions = 23
% of Brazil = 48.1
% of biome in conservation areas = 3.25

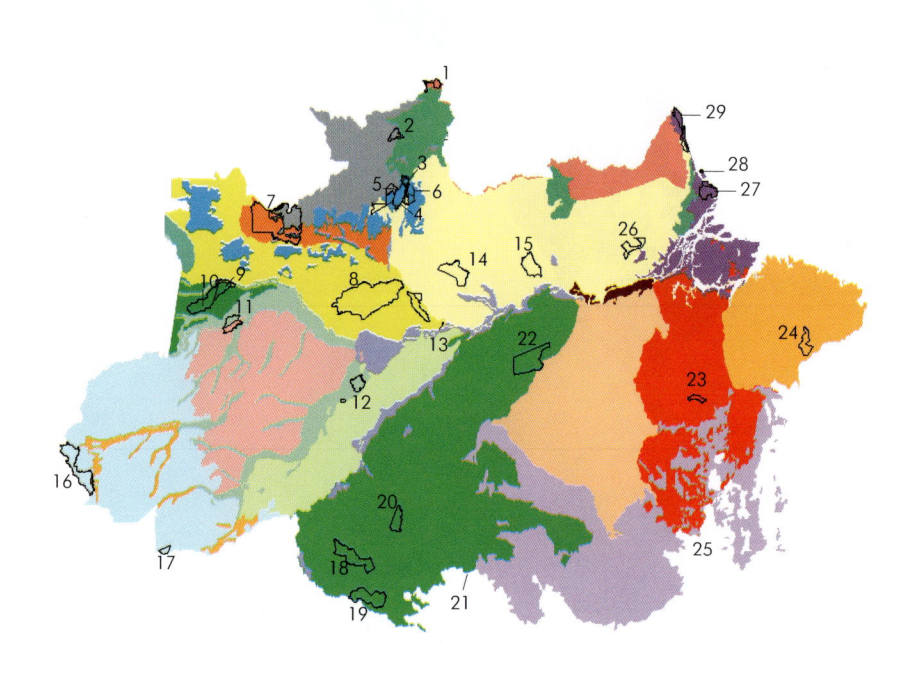

Figure 3. Ecoregions of the Amazon biome showing federal strict conservation areas.
Sinusoidal projection, central meridian (-54°). The area of the features is preserved in this projection.

REPRESENTATIVITY BY AREA

■ National Forests (4.22%)
■ Extractive Reserves (0.59%)
■ Environmental Protection Areas (0.006%)

Number of ecoregions = 23
Área of biome = 4,105,401 km^2
% of biome in conservation areas = 4.82

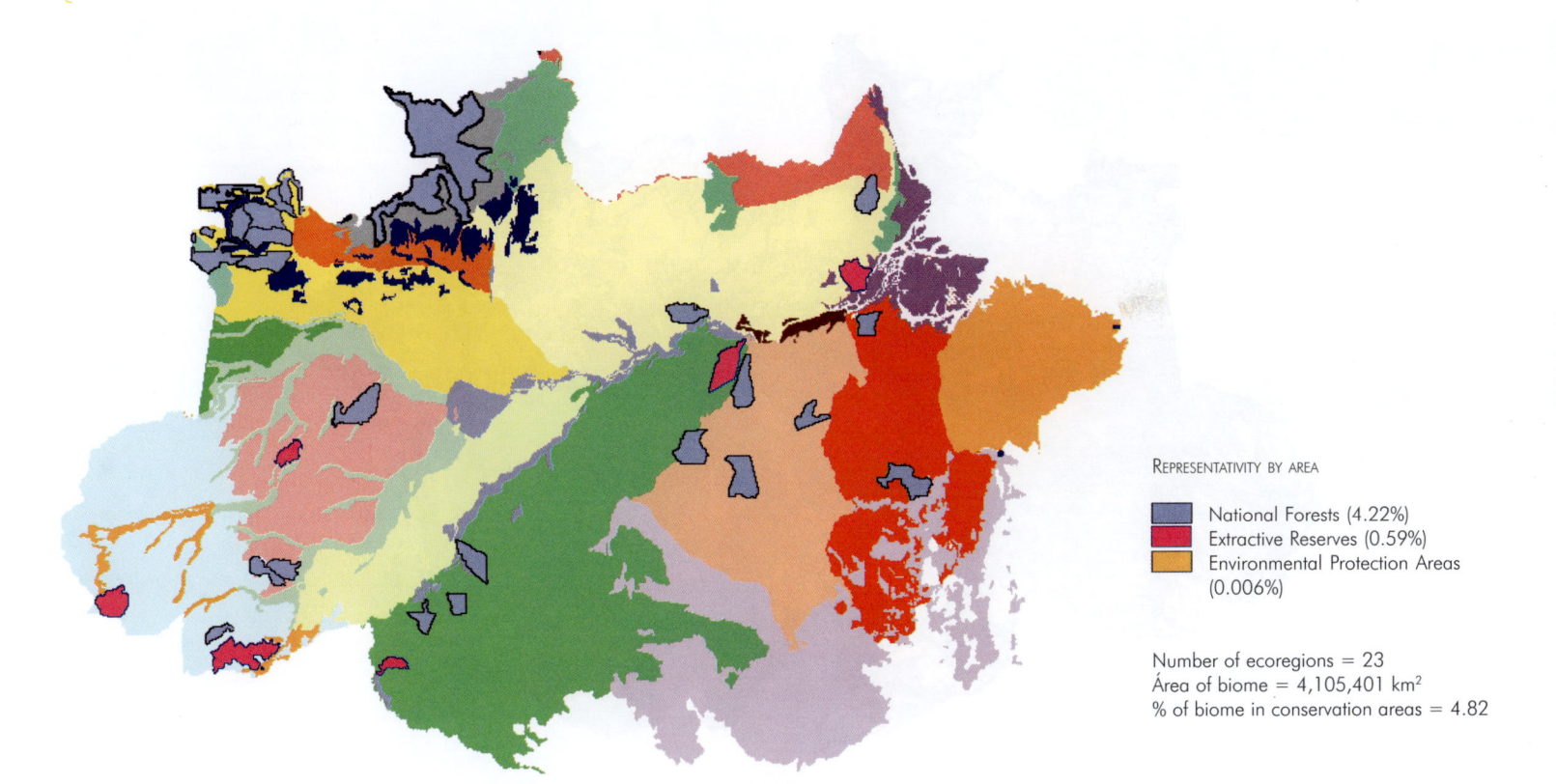

Figure 4. Ecoregions of the Amazon biome showing federal direct use conservation areas.
Sinusoidal projection, central meridian (-54 degrees). The area of features is preserved in this projection.
Source: Ecoregions of South America (WWF 1999)

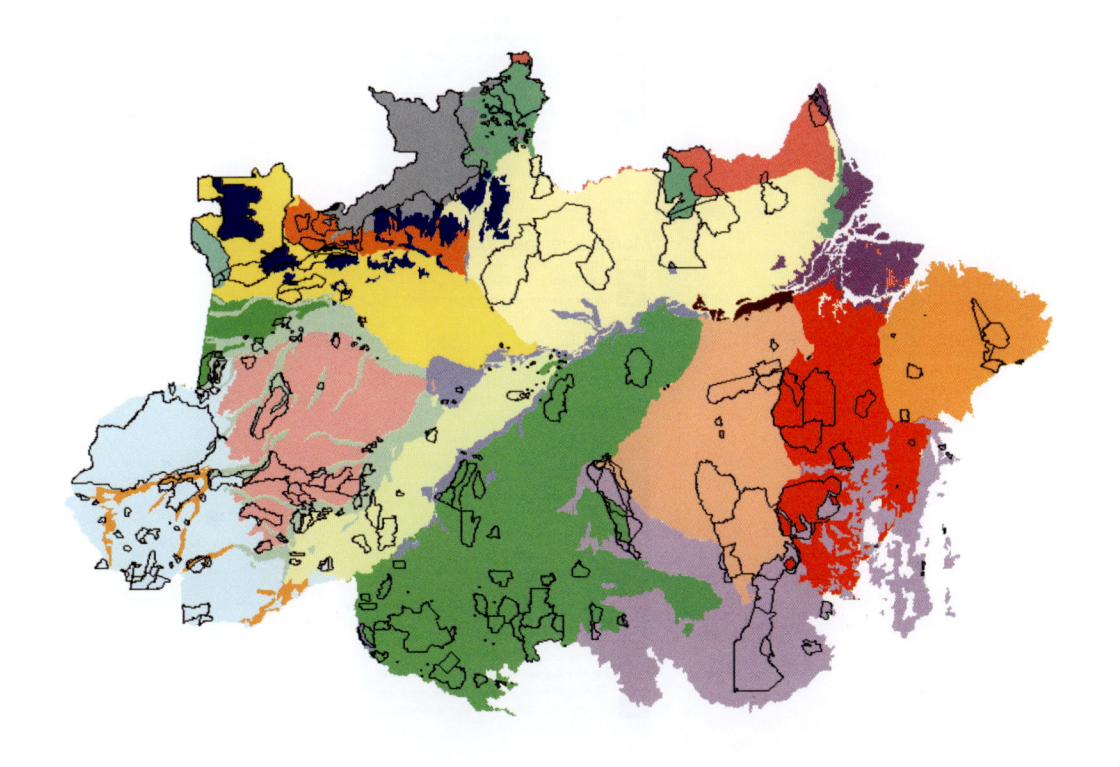

Number of ecoregions = 23
Area of biome = 4,105,401 km^2
% of biome in indigenous lands = 22.52

Figure 5. Ecoregions of the Amazon biome showing the distribution of indigenous lands.
Sinusoidal projection, central meridian (-54 degrees). The area of the features is preserved in this projection.
Source: Ecoregions of South America (WWF 1999).

CONSERVATION AREAS AND INDIGENOUS LANDS

Figure 6. Vegetation type classes in the ecoregions of the Amazon biome.
Sinusoidal projection, central meridian (-54 degrees). The area of the features is preserved in this projection.
Source: Ecoregions of South America (WWF 1999).

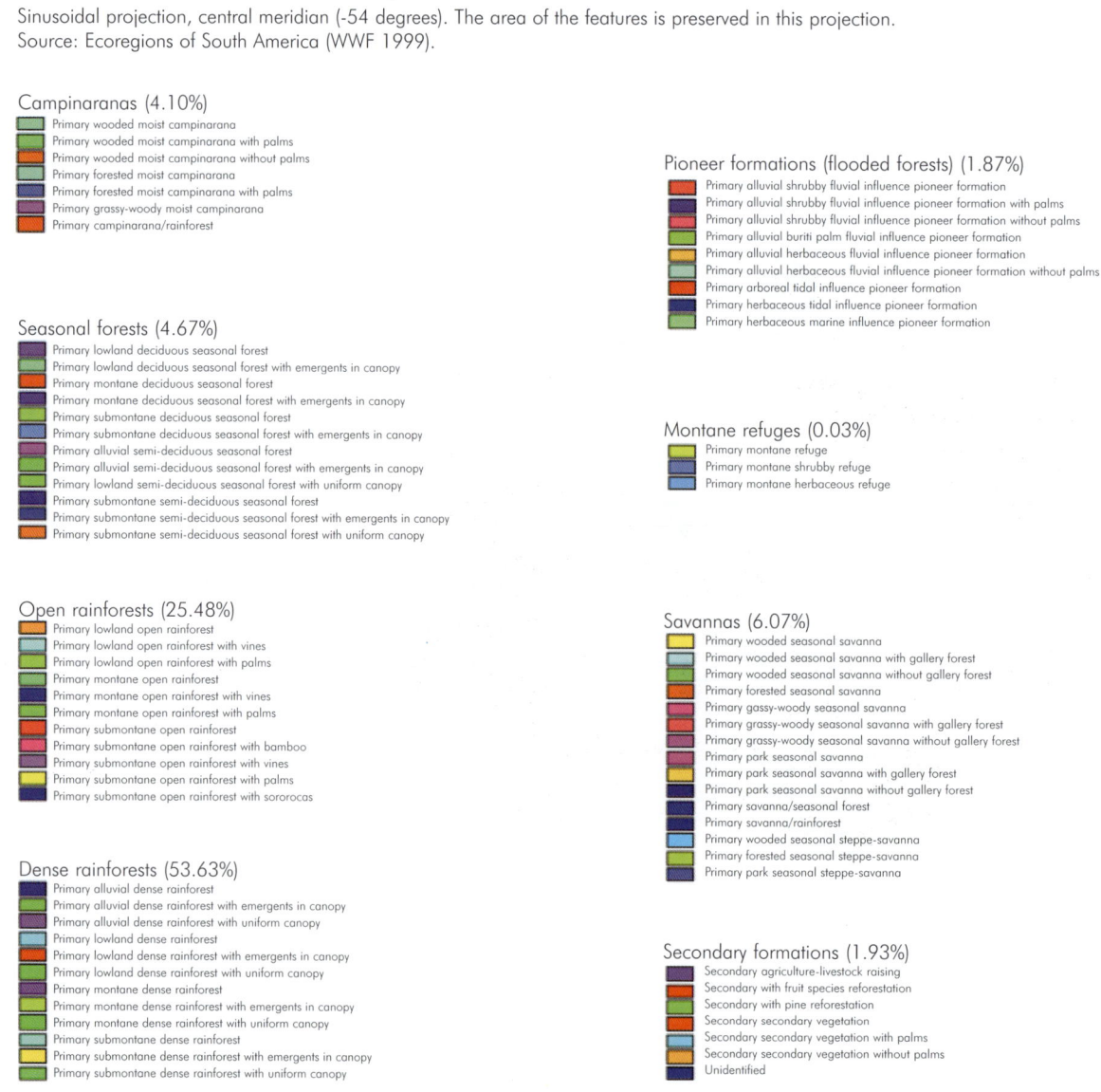

Campinaranas (4.10%)
- Primary wooded moist campinarana
- Primary wooded moist campinarana with palms
- Primary wooded moist campinarana without palms
- Primary forested moist campinarana
- Primary forested moist campinarana with palms
- Primary grassy-woody moist campinarana
- Primary campinarana/rainforest

Seasonal forests (4.67%)
- Primary lowland deciduous seasonal forest
- Primary lowland deciduous seasonal forest with emergents in canopy
- Primary montane deciduous seasonal forest
- Primary montane deciduous seasonal forest with emergents in canopy
- Primary submontane deciduous seasonal forest
- Primary submontane deciduous seasonal forest with emergents in canopy
- Primary alluvial semi-deciduous seasonal forest
- Primary alluvial semi-deciduous seasonal forest with emergents in canopy
- Primary lowland semi-deciduous seasonal forest with uniform canopy
- Primary submontane semi-deciduous seasonal forest
- Primary submontane semi-deciduous seasonal forest with emergents in canopy
- Primary submontane semi-deciduous seasonal forest with uniform canopy

Open rainforests (25.48%)
- Primary lowland open rainforest
- Primary lowland open rainforest with vines
- Primary lowland open rainforest with palms
- Primary montane open rainforest
- Primary montane open rainforest with vines
- Primary montane open rainforest with palms
- Primary submontane open rainforest
- Primary submontane open rainforest with bamboo
- Primary submontane open rainforest with vines
- Primary submontane open rainforest with palms
- Primary submontane open rainforest with sororocas

Dense rainforests (53.63%)
- Primary alluvial dense rainforest
- Primary alluvial dense rainforest with emergents in canopy
- Primary alluvial dense rainforest with uniform canopy
- Primary lowland dense rainforest
- Primary lowland dense rainforest with emergents in canopy
- Primary lowland dense rainforest with uniform canopy
- Primary montane dense rainforest
- Primary montane dense rainforest with emergents in canopy
- Primary montane dense rainforest with uniform canopy
- Primary submontane dense rainforest
- Primary submontane dense rainforest with emergents in canopy
- Primary submontane dense rainforest with uniform canopy

Pioneer formations (flooded forests) (1.87%)
- Primary alluvial shrubby fluvial influence pioneer formation
- Primary alluvial shrubby fluvial influence pioneer formation with palms
- Primary alluvial shrubby fluvial influence pioneer formation without palms
- Primary alluvial buriti palm fluvial influence pioneer formation
- Primary alluvial herbaceous fluvial influence pioneer formation
- Primary alluvial herbaceous fluvial influence pioneer formation without palms
- Primary arboreal tidal influence pioneer formation
- Primary herbaceous tidal influence pioneer formation
- Primary herbaceous marine influence pioneer formation

Montane refuges (0.03%)
- Primary montane refuge
- Primary montane shrubby refuge
- Primary montane herbaceous refuge

Savannas (6.07%)
- Primary wooded seasonal savanna
- Primary wooded seasonal savanna with gallery forest
- Primary wooded seasonal savanna without gallery forest
- Primary forested seasonal savanna
- Primary gassy-woody seasonal savanna
- Primary grassy-woody seasonal savanna with gallery forest
- Primary grassy-woody seasonal savanna without gallery forest
- Primary park seasonal savanna
- Primary park seasonal savanna with gallery forest
- Primary park seasonal savanna without gallery forest
- Primary savanna/seasonal forest
- Primary savanna/rainforest
- Primary wooded seasonal steppe-savanna
- Primary forested seasonal steppe-savanna
- Primary park seasonal steppe-savanna

Secondary formations (1.93%)
- Secondary agriculture-livestock raising
- Secondary with fruit species reforestation
- Secondary with pine reforestation
- Secondary secondary vegetation
- Secondary secondary vegetation with palms
- Secondary secondary vegetation without palms
- Unidentified

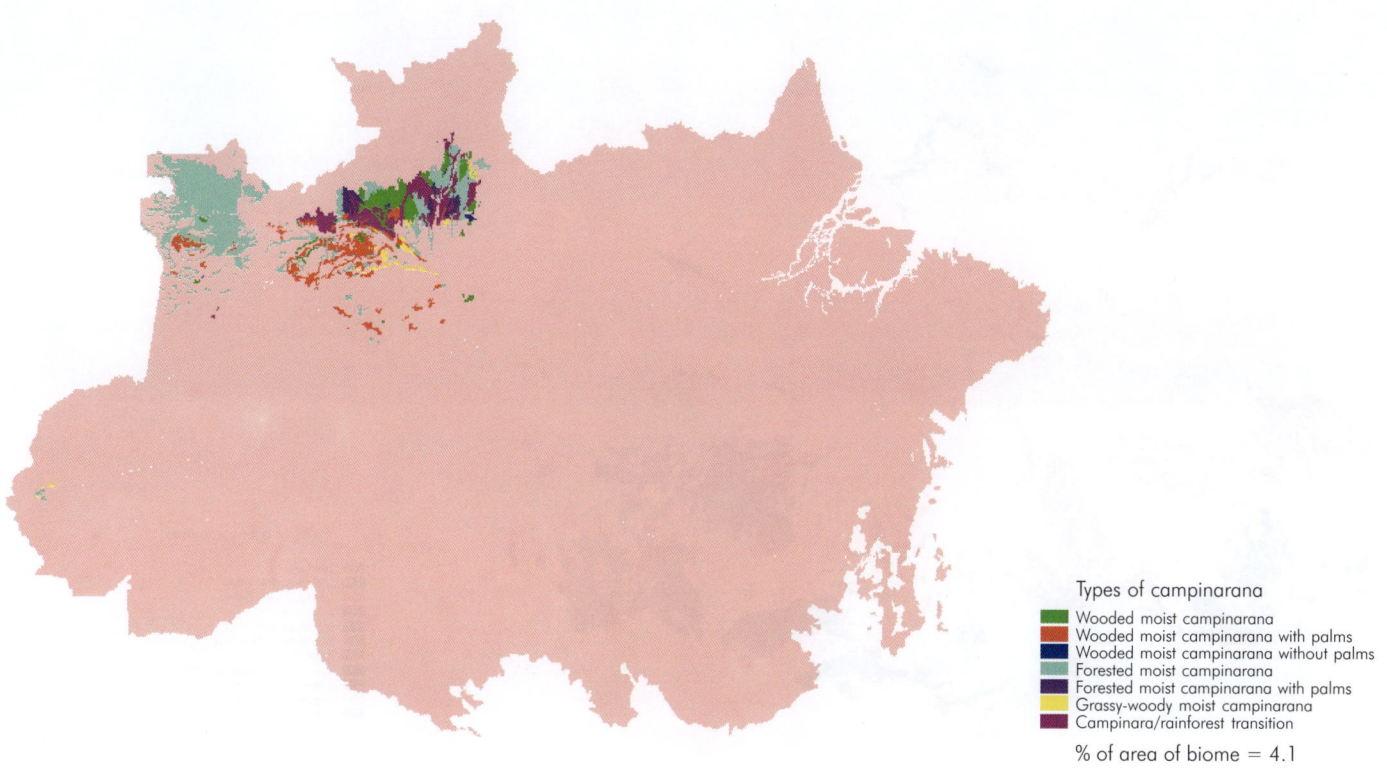

Figure 7. Distribution of campinarana in the Amazon biome.
Sinusoidal projection, central meridian (-54 degrees). The area of the features is preserved in this projection.

Types of campinarana
- Wooded moist campinarana
- Wooded moist campinarana with palms
- Wooded moist campinarana without palms
- Forested moist campinarana
- Forested moist campinarana with palms
- Grassy-woody moist campinarana
- Campinara/rainforest transition

% of area of biome = 4.1

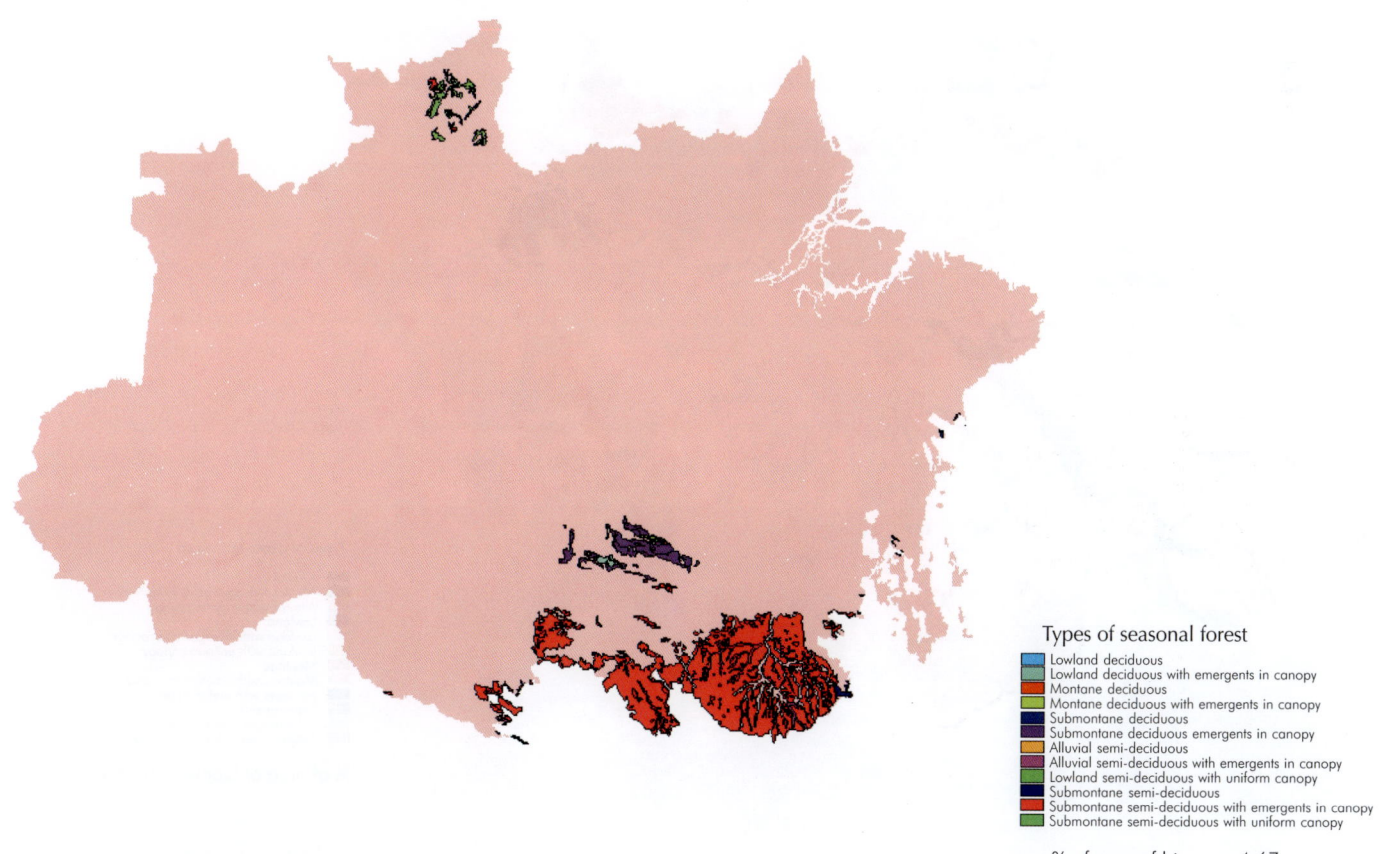

Figure 8. Distribution of seasonal forests in the Amazon biome.
Sinusoidal projection, central meridian (-54 degrees). The area of the features is preserved in this projection.

Types of seasonal forest
- Lowland deciduous
- Lowland deciduous with emergents in canopy
- Montane deciduous
- Montane deciduous with emergents in canopy
- Submontane deciduous
- Submontane deciduous emergents in canopy
- Alluvial semi-deciduous
- Alluvial semi-deciduous with emergents in canopy
- Lowland semi-deciduous with uniform canopy
- Submontane semi-deciduous
- Submontane semi-deciduous with emergents in canopy
- Submontane semi-deciduous with uniform canopy

% of area of biome = 4.67

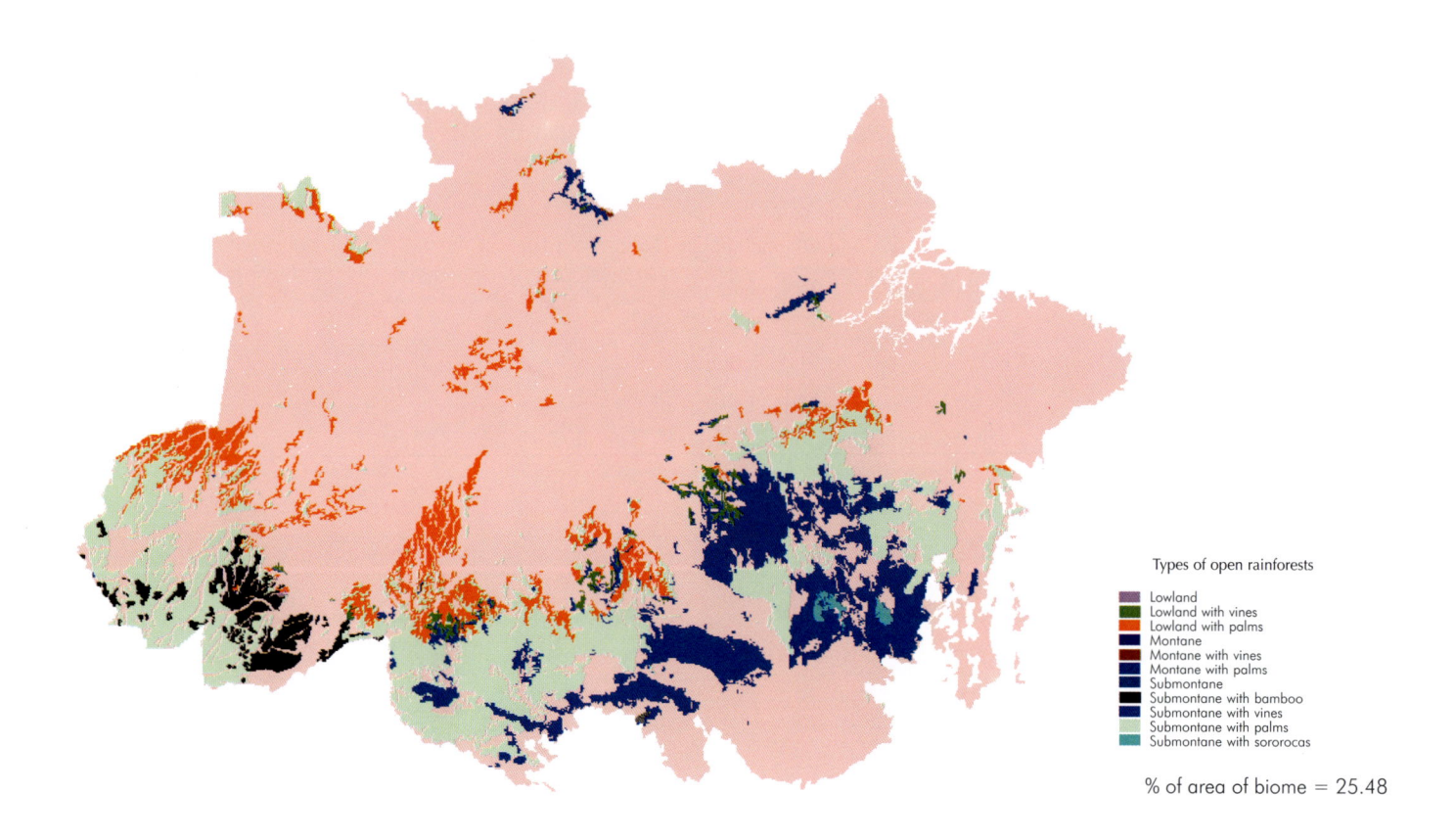

Figure 9. Distribution of open rainforests in the Amazon biome.
Sinusoidal projection, central meridian (-54 degrees). The area of the features is preserved in this projection.

Types of open rainforests
- Lowland
- Lowland with vines
- Lowland with palms
- Montane
- Montane with vines
- Montane with palms
- Submontane
- Submontane with bamboo
- Submontane with vines
- Submontane with palms
- Submontane with sororocas

% of area of biome = 25.48

Types of dense rainforests
- Alluvial
- Alluvial with emergents in canopy
- Alluvial with uniform canopy
- Lowland
- Lowland with emergents in canopy
- Lowland with uniform canopy
- Montane
- Montane with emergents in canopy
- Montane with uniform canopy
- Submontane
- Submontane with emergents in canopy
- Submontane with uniform canopy

% of area of biome = 53.63

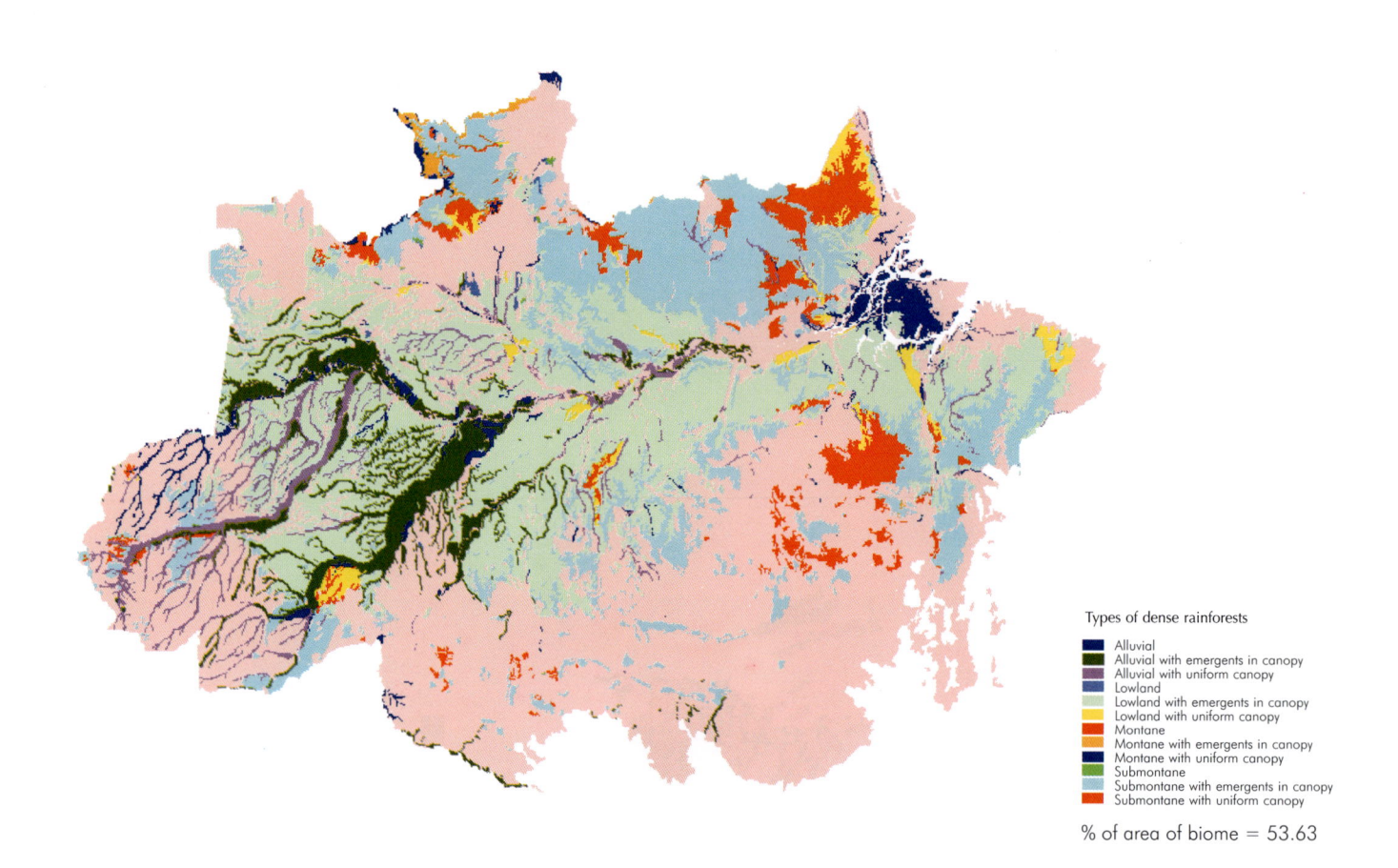

Figure 10. Distribution of dense rainforests in the Amazon biome.
Sinusoidal projection, central meridian (-54 degrees). The area of the features is preserved in this projection.

Types of pioneer formations
- Alluvial shrubby fluvial influence
- Alluvial shrubby fluvial influence with palms
- Alluvial shrubby fluvial influence without palms
- Alluvial buriti palm grove fluvial influence
- Alluvial herbaceous fluvial influence
- Alluvial herbaceous fluvial influence without palms
- Arboreal tidal influence
- Herbaceous tidal influence
- Herbaceous marine influence

% of area of biome = 1.87

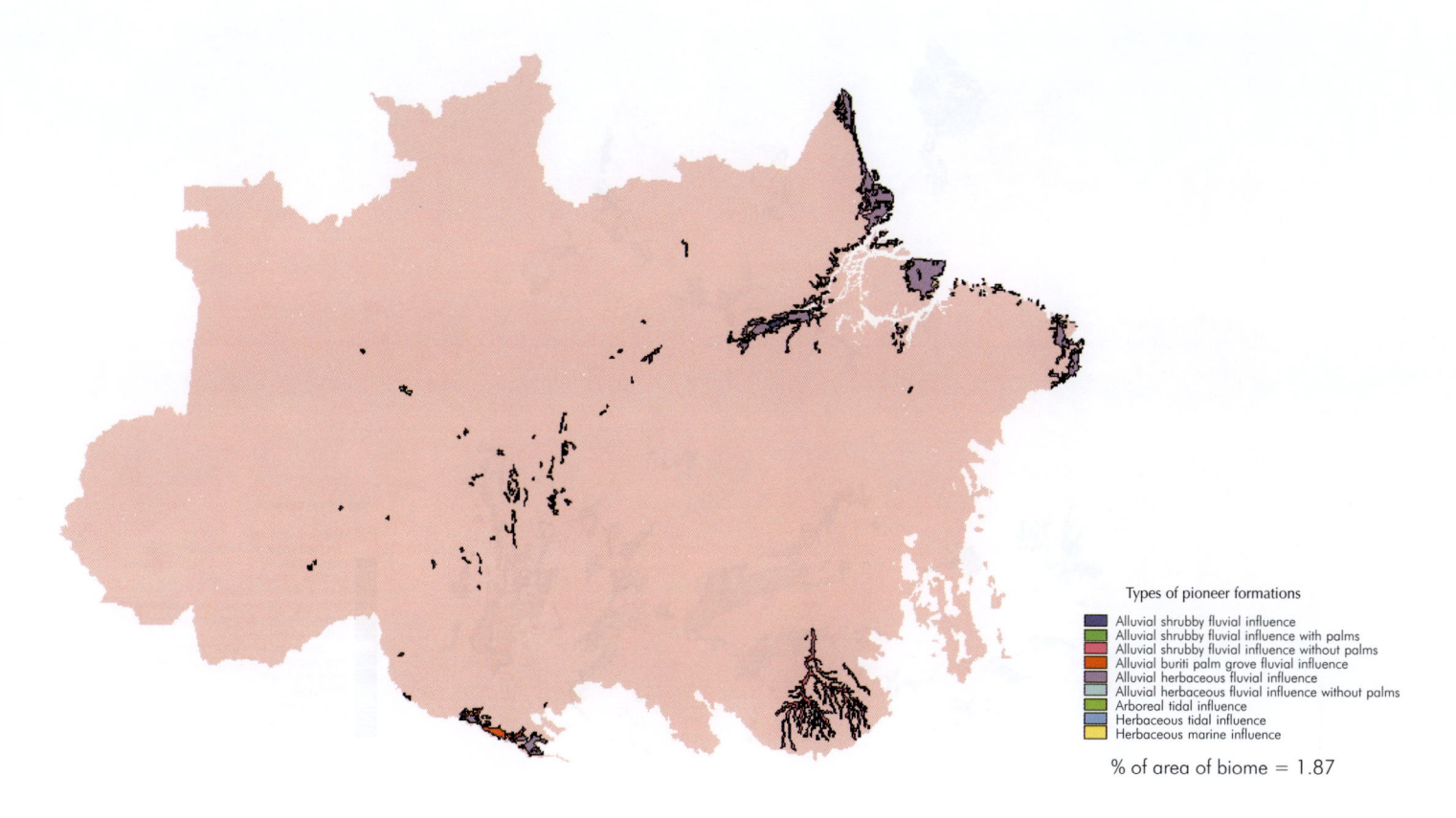

Figure 11. Distribution of pioneer formations (flooded forests) in the Amazon biome.
Sinusoidal projection, central meridian (-54 degrees). The area of the features is preserved in this projection.

Tipos of montane refuges
- Montane
- Montane shrubby
- Montane herbaceous

% of area of biome = 0.03

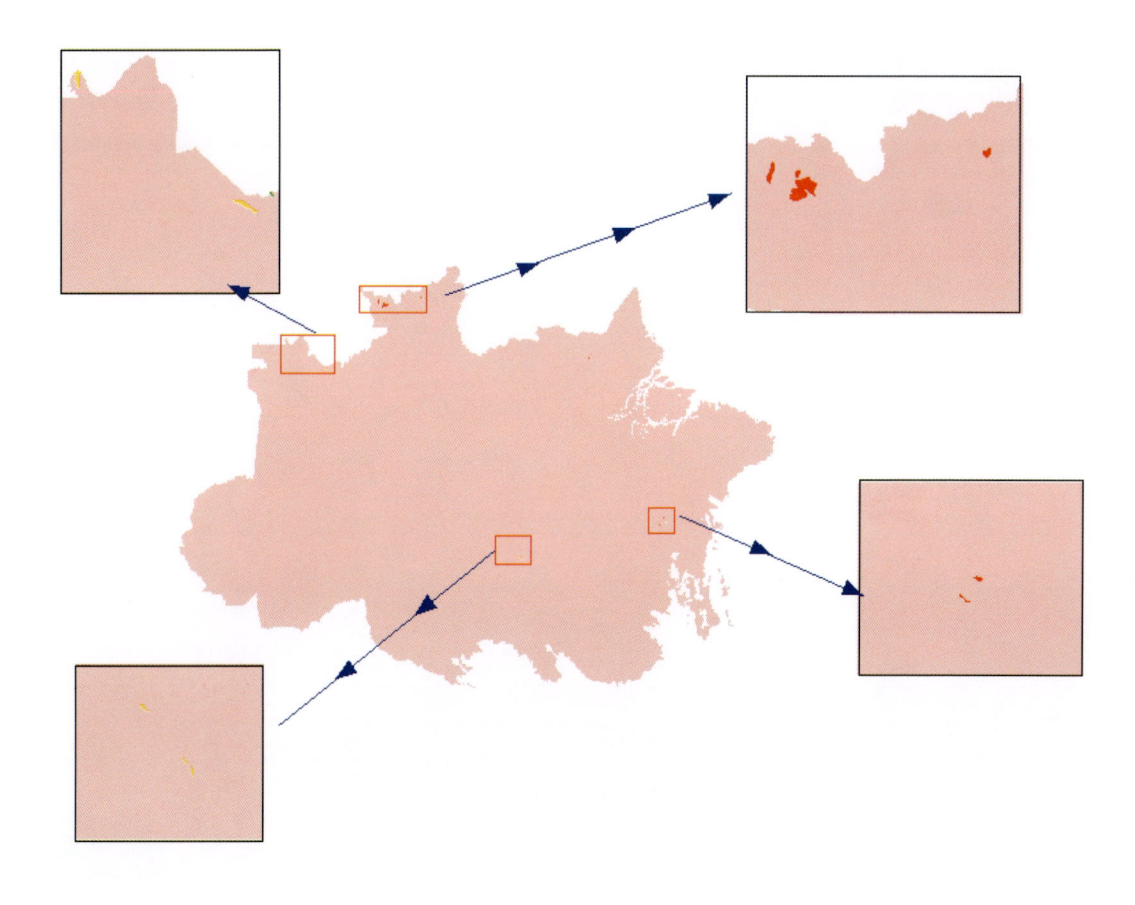

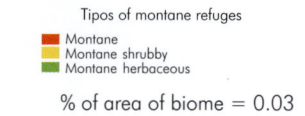

Figure 12. Distribution of montane refuges in the Amazon biome.
area = 4.67

CONSERVATION AREAS AND INDIGENOUS LANDS

Types of savanna

- ■ Wooded seasonal
- Wooded seasonal with gallery forest
- ■ Wooded seasonal without gallery forest
- ■ Forested seasonal
- ■ Grassy-woody seasonal
- ■ Grassy-woody seasonal with gallery forest
- ■ Grassy-woody seasonal without gallery forest
- ■ Park seasonal
- ■ Park seasonal with gallery forest
- ■ Park seasonal without gallery forest
- ■ Seasonal forest
- ■ Rainforest
- ■ Wooded seasonal steppe
- ■ Forested seasonal steppe
- ■ Park seasonal steppe

% of area of biome = 6.07

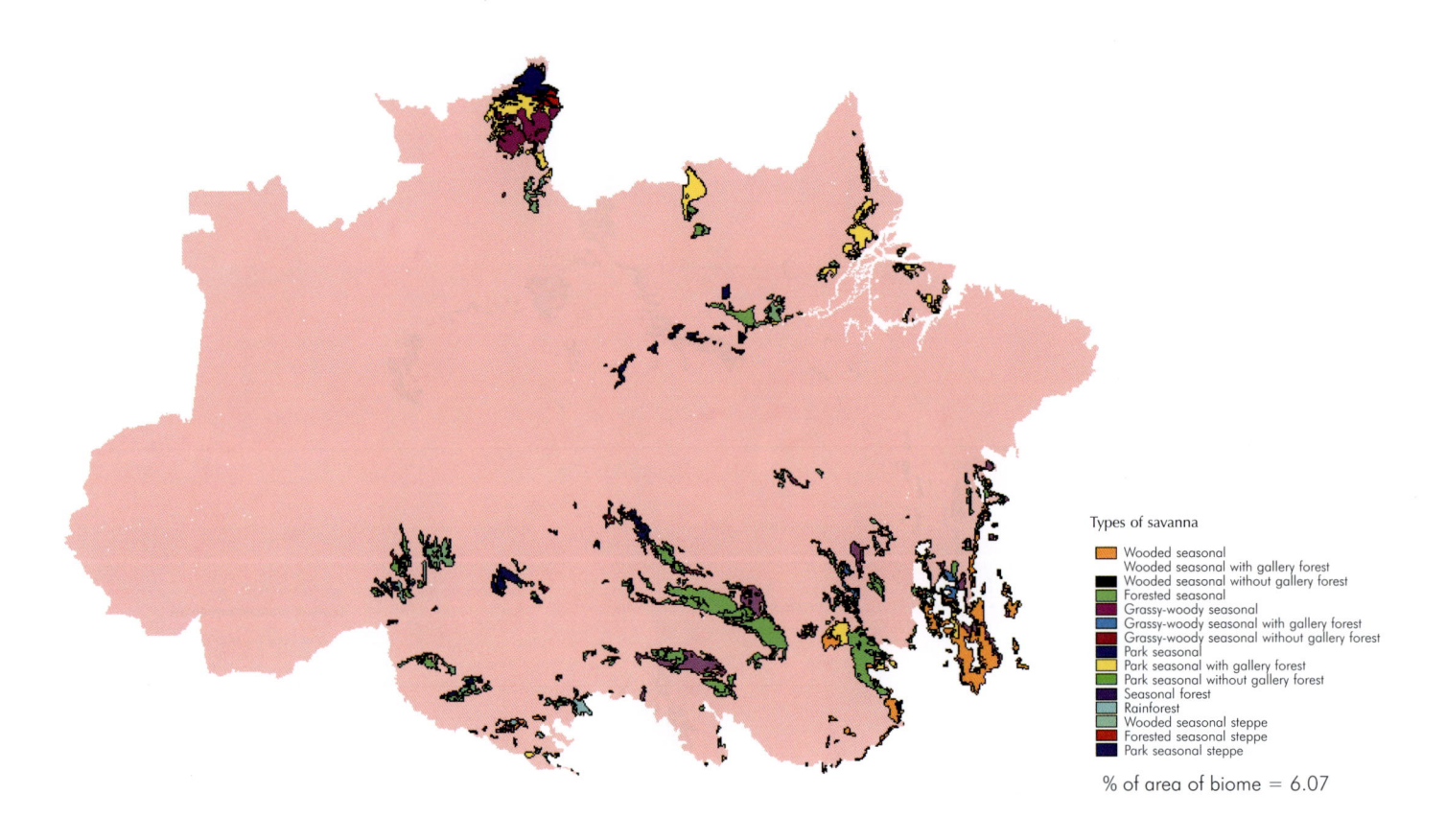

Figure 13. Distribution of savannas in the Amazon biome.
Sinusoidal projection, central meridian (-54 degrees). The area of the features is preserved in this projection.

Incidence of mining applications and titles in federal and state conservation areas in Legal Amazonia

Fany Ricardo *Instituto Socioambiental*

The Instituto Socioambiental has cross-referenced the information in its database with data on the geographically referenced perimeters of conservation areas, as described in their legal instruments of creation (LICs), held by the National Department of Mineral Production (DNPM) in February 1998. This has enabled the development of a table showing the incidence of mining titles in full-protection and sustainable use conservation areas in Amazonia, at both federal and state levels.

Of the 66 federal and state full-protection conservation areas, 44 reveal examples of mining interests in their subsoils. Eleven of these areas have more than 70% of their subsoil as the object of mining applications. The Tapirapé Biological Reserve, for example, has applications for 97.43% of its subsoil; in the Candeias State Park, the figure is 100%. All twelve national parks in Amazonia show overlapping mining interests.

The incidence of mining titles was calculated on the basis of the areas of the conservation areas calculated by the Geographic Information System of the Instituto Socioambiental (GIS/ISA). Because there are differences between the areas of the conservation areas described in their legal instruments of creation and the areas resulting from the digitalization of their perimeters, both figures have been included in the table below.

Conservation area		Area of the conservation area (ha)		Incidence of mining applications[1]		
		LIC	GIS/ISA	no.	Area	%[2]
National Park	Chapada dos Guimarães	33,000	38,151	13	7,872	20.63
	Amazônia	994,000	911,607	37	202,914	22.26
	Serra do Divisor	605,000	860,031	5	16,284	1.89
	Araguaia	562,312	549,600	12	12,501	2.27
	Cabo Orange	619,000	696,419	3	2,572	0.37
	Jaú	2,272,000	2,350,097	1	10,045	0.43
	Monte Roraima	116,000	106,169	14	39,653	37.35
	Pico da Neblina	2,200,000	2,251,923	22	64,012	2.84
	Viruá	227,011	222,106	17	155,645	70.08
	Pacaás Novos	764,801	704,354	75	375,857	53.36
	Pantanal Mato-Grossense	135,000	128,716	4	1,405	1.09
	Serra da Mocidade	350,960	375,399	47	328,737	87.57
Federal Ecological Station	Anavilhanas	350,018	345,604	4	4,926	1.43
	Caracaraí	80,560	90,662	3	16,215	17.88
	Maracá	101,312	101,396	14	68,323	67.38
	Jari	227,126	251,856	54	176,504	70.08
	Iquê	200,000	223,472	24	140,072	62.68
	Juami-Japurá	572,650	582,030	2	2,638	0.45
	Niquiá	286,600	28,833	25	149,099	52.35
Federal Biological Reserve	Gurupi	341,650	265,200	4	16,132	6.94
	Jaru	268,150	284,296	24	94,628	33.28
	Rio Trombetas	385,000	423,403	4	6,218	1.47
	Tapirapé	103,000	139,597	73	139,624	97.43
	Uatumã	560,000	593,810	13	43,296	7.29
Federal Area of Special Ecological Interest	PD Biológ. de Fragmentos Florestais	3,288	2,634	1	56	2.12
Federal Extractive Reserve	Cajari	501,771	535,412	51	377,058	70.42
	Extremo Norte do Tocantins	9,280	9,237	3	3,990	43.20
	Rio Ouro Preto	204,583	218,149	23	108,264	49.63

continues

Conservation area		Area of the conservation area (ha)		Incidence of mining applications[1]		
		LIC	GIS/ISA	no.	Area	%[2]
Federal Environmental Protection Areas	Igarapé Gelado	21,600	21,934	60	33,027	99.81
National Forest	Altamira	689,012	707,105	132	619,215	87.57
	Bom Futuro	280,000	282,338	34	117,948	41.78
	Carajás	411,948	389,442	257	385,536	99.73
	Cubate	416,532	432,645	5	18,103	4.18
	Cuiari	109,518	109,268	24	102,098	93.44
	Caxiuana	200,000	313,666	3	9,678	3.09
	Roraima	2,664,685	2,926,829	348	1,913,024	65.36
	Amapá	412,000	457,760	72	295,114	64.47
	Amazonas	1,573,100	1,479,808	165	1,017,127	68.53
	Jamari	225,000	229,309	63	222,511	97.04
	Tapajós	600,000	547,586	24	92,251	16.85
	Tapirapé AquiriI	190,000	141,926	86	137,703	97.02
	Xingu	252,790	251,501	38	194,867	80.69
	Humaitá	468,790	483,302	1	3,498	0.72
	Içana	200,561	198,581	36	177,442	89.36
	Içana-Aiari	491,400	486,668	45	192,754	39.61
	Itacaiúnas	141,400	63,516	95	57,733	90.89
	Itaituba I	220,034	223,667	144	223,279	99.83
	Itaituba II	440,500	419,647	183	362,951	86.49
	Pari Cachoeira II	654,000	636,316	66	361,569	5.82
	Piraiauara	631,436	636,941	11	33,130	5.20
	Saracataquera	429,600	476,028	41	116,119	24.39
	Taracuá I	647,744	655,385	25	145,604	22.22
	Taracuá II	559,504	562,582	11	48,425	8.61
	Uruçu	66,496	72,492	4	11,171	11.78
	Xié	407,935	405,738	36	201,689	49.71
State Parks	Águas Quentes	3,000	1,635	1	7	0.40
	Serra Azul	11,002	9,643	12	3,718	38.55
	Candeias	8,985	9,014	2	3,256	100.00
	Mirador	700,000	430,995	1	81	0.02
	Rio Negro Setor Norte	178,620	160,384	1	301	0.15
	Rio Negro Setor Sul	257,422	244,222	21	39,668	13.29
	Guajará Mirim	258,813	256,786	49	237,842	92.62
	Serra de Santa Barbara	157,151	159,299	48	127,849	80.26
	Serra do Araçá	1,818,700	1,860,058	275	1,444,259	77.65
	Serra dos Martírios/Andorinhas	24,897	28,272	9	5,820	20.59
	Serra Ricardo Franco	158,620	157,164	22	118,058	75.12
State Biological Reserve	Dos Seis Lagos	36,900	37,602	1	10,045	26.71
	Rio Ouro Preto	46,438	49,367	6	21,387	43.32
State Biological Station	Samuel	20,865	21,303	2	4,370	45.01
	Serra dos Três Irmãos	99,813	103,015	31	87,169	84.62
	Rio Roosevelt	80,915	61,431	15	60,863	99.07
State Ecological Reserve	Culuene	3,900	4,025	1	812	20.17
	Lageado	0	138,606	42	90,889	65.57
	Apiacás	100,000	119,308	25	76,814	64.38
State Sustainable Development Reserve	Amanã	2,350,000	2,250,841	1	640	0.03
	Mamirauá	1,124,000	1,301,654	3	13,384	1.03
	Rio Iratapuru	806,184	872,587	194	786,795	90.17
State Extractive Reserve	Dos Pacaas Novos	342,903	357,665	18	77,843	21.76
	Guariba-Roosevelt	57,630	61,996	14	61,995	100.00
	Rio Cautário	146,400	124,631	9	28,141	22.58
	Rio Jaci Paraná	205,000	206,686	15	86,708	41.95
	Rio Preto Jacundá	95,300	96,397	9	20,612	21.38

continues

Conservation area		Area of the conservation area (ha)		Incidence of mining applications[1]		
		LIC	GIS/ISA	no.	Area	%[2]
State Sustainable Development Reserve	Rio Vermelho (B)	152,000	140,889	67	80,726	57.30
	Rio Vermelho (D)	137,844	110,690	7	38,209	34.52
	Rio S. Domingos	267,375	308,938	38	162,836	52.71
	Rio Roosevelt	27,860	29,546	34	28,881	97.75
	Rio Vermelho (C)	20,215	20,742	11	19,997	96.41
	Rio Machado	175,781	77,334	1	1	0.00
	Rio Vermelho (A)	38,688	40,509	23	28,379	70.06
	Rio Abunã	62,219	65,071	7	15,124	23.24
State Extractive Forest	Dos Pacaás Novos	353,219	368,709	24	83,944	22.77
	Rio Preto/Jacundá	1,055,000	1,045,184	45	246,334	23.56
State Environmental Protection Area	São Geraldo do Araguaia	29,655	21,884	17	9,580	43.78
	Cuirau	23,000	22,701	5	22,113	97.41
	Baixada Maranhense	1,775,035	1,779,260	12	79,967	4.49
	Caverna do Moroaga	374,700	250,464	34	146,360	58.44
	Chapada dos Guimarães	251,847	272,430	63	85,678	31.45
	Maracanã region	1,831	1,085	1	2	0.19
	Rio Cuiabá Headwaters	264,029	477,831	9	31,536	6.60
	Das Reentrâncias Maranhenses	2,680,911	2,572,378	119	705,080	27.41
	Rio Madeira	6,741	8,464	7	8,045	95.04
	Right bank of the Rio Negro	554,334	646,999	18	1,101	0.20
	Left bank of the Rio Negro	740,757	743,076	52	187,124	25.41
	Lago do Cuniã	104,000	105,035	1	551	0.52

1. According to the National Department of Mineral Production (DNPM) in February 1998.
2. Of the total area of the conservation area.

Indigenous natural resources reserves

Márcio Santilli *Instituto Socioambiental*

In a blatant case of federal schizophrenia over land, Legal Amazonia alone contains 27 federal environmental conservation areas that totally or partially overlap 17 indigenous lands (which are also federal), to a total area of over 11 million hectares. Such overlaps are legally incompatible, given that the management categories of these conservation areas imply use restrictions that conflict with the exclusive rights held by indians to the use of the natural resources of their lands.

The current state of overlaps between conservation areas and indigenous lands in Brazilian Legal Amazonia can be summarized as follows:

Indigenous lands represent approximately 12% of the Brazilian territory, and a little over 20% of the total area of Brazilian Legal Amazonia. The majority of this area is made up of forests, which are thus significantly preserved from deforestation, burning and forest fires, even when under strong pressure from predatory selective logging or from prospecting. In order to succeed, any coherent forest conservation or sustainable management strategy must therefore begin with the active inclusion of the indigenous populations and the natural assets represented by their lands.

Historically, the federal environment agency Ibama (and the Ministry of the Environment), has behaved bureaucratically in relation to the conservation and management of natural resources in indigenous lands. It claims that these lands are under the jurisdiction of Funai, the federal Indian agency; however, the law does not set geographical limits to Ibama's responsibility for protecting the environment. If this were the case, it would have even less authority to monitor private, state or untitled areas, and no environmental protection would be possible at all. At the same time, it has done nothing to rectify the existing overlaps between conservation areas and indigenous lands, or to effectively administer such overlapping areas. As a result, that part of the national system of conservation areas (the SNUC) that overlaps indigenous lands is remiss in law and non-existent in practice; nor is there any political initiative or legal instrument to promote the linkages between indigenous lands and the SNUC (whose total area is between a quarter and a third of the total area of indigenous lands, depending on whether or not the overlaps are taken into account).

Given this absurd state of affairs, during the negotiations in the Environment Committee of the Chamber of Deputies over the bill creating the SNUC, the Instituto Socioambiental proposed the adoption of two clauses providing for: (a) the creation of a specific category of conservation area within the system – the Reserva Indígena de Recursos Naturais (indigenous natural resources reserves) or RIRN – to be created on the initiative of interested indigenous communities, by reserving part of their territories for the conservation or sustainable management of natural resources, in accordance with a specific management plan and prohibiting any mining or logging activities within the area; and (b) the introduction of means for the reclassification of conservation areas created prior to the approval of the SNUC law that overlap indigenous lands. Under these legal provisions, the federal government and indigenous communities would be able to definitively resolve the situations of conflict that had arisen with the overlapping areas and to advance the integration of indigenous lands into the SNUC and the efforts for forest conservation.

Unfortunately, the proposal was not accepted by the rapporteur, Congressman Fernando Gabeira (Green Party-Rio de Janeiro) during the debate on the SNUC bill. Despite agreeing with the merit and need, the rapporteur cut out of his report the text creating the RIRN at the request of Ibama, whose representatives opposed inclusion of this management category on the grounds that would force them into a difficult institutional relationship with Funai. They preferred to ignore the extent of the overlaps, thereby perpetuating their bureaucratic approach to the problem.

However, no coherent alternative proposal for a solution was submitted by Ibama, by the Chamber of Deputies or by any of the other parties to the negotiations. At the same time, new cases of overlaps between conservation areas and indigenous lands and of conflicts between indians and Ibama continue to arise – as in

Table 1 - Overlaps between conservation areas and indigenous lands in Legal Amazonia (summary)			
Conservation areas	Area	Overlaps with indigenous lands	
	ha[1]	ha[1]	%[2]
All conservation areas	59,441,718	13,251,516	22.29
All strict conservation areas	19,538,659	4,510,215	23.08
All sustainable use conservation areas	39,903,059	8,741,301	21.91
Federal strict conservation areas	14,784,400	2,971,311	20.10
State strict conservation areas	4,754,259	1,538,904	32.37
Federal sustainable use conservation areas	18,802,872	8,530,840	45.37
State sustainable use conservation areas	21,100,187	210,461	1.00

1. According to the Geographic Information System of the Instituto Socioambiental (GIS/ISA).
2. Of the total area of the category.

the recent case of the occupation of the headquarters of the Monte Pascoal national park in southern Bahia by Pataxó indians – and neither the federal government nor the indigenous communities are equipped to implement a policy of conservation and sustainable management of natural resource that is fully compatible with the rights of indigenous communities.

The Instituto Socioambiental stands by its proposed solution and calls on the public institutions responsible and interested non-governmental organizations (especially indigenous organizations) to broaden the debate on the participation of indigenous communities in strategies for the conservation of Brazilian forests.

TABLE 2 – OVERLAPS BETWEEN CONSERVATION AREAS AND INDIGENOUS LANDS IN LEGAL AMAZONIA

	Conservation Area	Indigenous Land	Area of overlap
Federal	Iquê Ecological Station	Enawenê Nawê	187,826
	Jutaí/Solimões Ecological Station	Betânia	5,186
	Jutaí/Solimões Ecological Station	São Domingos do Jacapari and Station	31,117
	Bom Futuro National Forest	Karitiana	31,299
	Cubate National Forest	Alto Rio Negro	425,002
	Cuiari National Forest	Alto Rio Negro	109,294
	Humaitá National Forest	Diahui	29,314
	Roraima National Forest	Yanomami	2,786,523
	Santa Rosa do Purus National Forest	Jaminauá/Envira	70,702
	Amazonas National Forest	Yanomami	1,600,540
	Purus National Forest	Inauini/Teuini	66,608
	Içana National Forest	Alto Rio Negro	197,059
	Içana-Aiari National Forest	Alto Rio Negro	497,205
	Mapiá-Inauini National Forest	Inauini/Teuini	5,322
	Pari Cachoeira II National Forest	Alto Rio Negro	617,631
	Pari Cachoeira I National Forest	Alto Rio Negro	17,283
	Piraiauara National Forest	Alto Rio Negro	630,566
	Taracuá I National Forest	Alto Rio Negro	658,656
	Taracuá II National Forest	Alto Rio Negro	561,495
	Urucu National Forest	Alto Rio Negro	68,391
	Xié National Forest	Alto Rio Negro	399,330
	Amazônia National Park	Andirá-Marau	90,593
	Araguaia National Park	Inawebohona	364,356
	Monte Roraima National Park	Raposa/Serra do Sol	116,332
	Pico da Neblina National Park	Balaio	240,523
	Pico da Neblina National Park	Médio Rio Negro II	47,958
	Pico da Neblina National Park	Yanomami	1,131,728
	Pacaás Novos National Park	Uru-Eu-Wau-Wau	732,934
	Guaporé Biological Reserve	Massaco	411,802
	Jaru Biological Reserve	Igarapé Lourdes	14,021
	Pau-Rosa National Forest	Andirá-Marau	20,105
State	Rio Vermelho(d) Sustainable Development Forest	Kaxarari	5,229
	Serra do Araçá State Park	Yanomami	1,517,123
	Morro dos Seis Lagos Biological Reserve	Balaio	37,517
	Amaná Sustainable Development Reserve	Cuiú-Cuiú	37,405
	Mamirauá Sustainable Development Reserve	Uati-Paraná	13,370
	Mamirauá Sustainable Development Reserve	Porto Praia	3,870
	Mamirauá Sustainable Development Reserve	Jaquiri	1,883
	Mamirauá Sustainable Development Reserve	Acapuri de Cima	19,783
	Piagaçu-Purus Sustainable Development Reserve	Terra Vermelha	7,196
	Piagaçu-Purus Sustainable Development Reserve	Lago Aiapoá	22,146
	Piagaçu-Purus Sustainable Development Reserve	Itixi-Mirati	176,757

AMENDMENTS PROPOSED BY ISA TO SNUC BILL 2,892/92, IN 1996

VIII - Indigenous natural resources reserves

Article 22 *(submitted as amendment)*
(new draft)

The Indigenous Natural Resources Reserve is a federal conservation area destined for the protection of the environmental resources present within indigenous lands.

Paragraph 1 – The RIRN shall be established by presidential decree, at the request of the indigenous community or communities holding occupation rights to the specific area to be protected, located within a given indigenous land, following approval by the federal environmental agency on the basis of the environmental importance of the area.

Paragraph 2 – The establishment of the RIRN shall be without prejudice to the fulfilment of the legal attributions of the federal indian agency over the area of the RIRN.

Paragraph 3 – The management plan for the RIRN shall be jointly formulated and executed by the indigenous community and by the indian and environmental agencies, who shall be able, when necessary, to call upon other public or private institutions with recognized expertise in the area.

Paragraph 4 – The management plan shall specify:
I. The monitoring, natural resources management, research and visiting activities which can or should take place in the area;
II. The possible land use restrictions that the resident indigenous community or communities may make use of;
III. The attributions of the federal environmental agency in respect of the area of the RIRN.

Paragraph 5 – The RIRN shall be administered by the resident indigenous community, who shall be able to call upon the support of the indian and environmental agencies for the undertaking of protection and monitoring activities.

Paragraph 6 – No works not foreseen in the management plan shall be carried out in the RIRN, nor any activities involving deforestation, logging or mining.

Paragraph 7 – The indigenous communities residing in lands in which RIRN are created shall have preferential access to lines of credit and other incentives for the development of activities for economic self-sufficiency and the protection of environmental assets.

Forms of access to land and the conservation of the Amazon forest: a legal analysis of the regularization of the lands of quilombolas and rubber tappers

José Heder Benatti *Núcleo de Altos Estudos Amazônicos e Instituto de Pesquisa Ambiental da Amazônia*

Summary

This is a study of the land tenure of descendants of quilombos[1] and by rubber tappers, called agro-ecological tenure, in which it is shown that the demarcation of quilombos and the creation of extractive reserves are contributing to forest conservation in the Brazilian Amazon region.

The study also argues that the recognition of the land tenure rights of traditional populations forms part of the demands of these social groups, who seek forms of regularization of their lands that take their circumstances into account. This means more than a redefinition of tenure rights; rather, it means expanding the prevailing concept in order to provide these categories of rural workers with greater security and, as a consequence, to increase support for environmental protection.

Introduction

Discussion of the conservation of renewable natural resources (particularly forests) and land reform is commonly presented as if there were a dichotomy: to conserve and protect the forest in order to guarantee a better quality of life, or to destroy it and thereby guarantee the subsistence of poor marginalized populations.

We believe that there is another way of understanding the issue and avoiding this apparently insuperable antagonism. This way is already guaranteed through constitutional principles and international conventions which uphold the rational exploitation of land so that future generations may have sufficient food for their subsistence whilst, at the same time, enjoying a healthy and ecologically balanced environment.

The demarcation of the lands of descendants of quilombos and the creation of extractive reserves in the Brazilian Amazon region are examples proving that human development and environment protection are two complementary constitutional principles, and that conservation implies development. These special forms of recognizing rights, through the regularization of land tenure, are also ways of preserving renewable natural resources.

Presenting the problem

The ideas in this article form part of the conclusions of research carried out between July 1995 and June 1999, in collaboration with community associations and non-governmental organizations (NGOs)[2] and financed by the Ford Foundation's Brazil program. The main objective of the research was to bring together the demands of traditional populations in Brazilian Amazonia fighting to achieve the same objective: the regularization of their lands on the basis of their specific circumstances.[3]

We have sought to study the question of land regularization of specific categories of rural workers with a view to understanding their particular forms of land tenure and thereby developing a proposal that would both respect their rights and secure forest protection. In fact, the land tenure of traditional populations, in the particular cases of quilombolas and of rubber tappers, combines both elements.

The areas occupied by traditional populations consist of those spaces where their houses and gardens are found, together with those used for hunting, fishing and plant extractive activities. The notion of area occupied thus corresponds to the lands used by their inhabitants to guarantee the reproduction of their way of life.[4]

Land policy for Amazonia

The land policy implemented in Amazonia by different Brazilian governments over the last forty years has followed two

---

1. Community originating from a settlement of fugitive slaves established prior to the abolition of slavery in 1888 (see Glossary).
2. The partner organizations were: *Fundação Vitória Amazônica* (Vitoria Amazonica Foundation, FVA) based in Manaus; *Associação de Remanescentes de Quilombos de Pacoval* (Association of Descendants of Quilombo Communities of Pacoval) in the municipality of Alenquer, Pará; *Centro de Defesa e Estudo do Negro no Pará* (Center for the Study and Defense of Black People in Pará, CEDENPA) based in Belém; *Núcleo de Alto Estudos da Amazônia* (Institute of Advanced Studies of Amazonia) based in the University of Pará, Belém; and *Instituto de Pesquisa Ambiental da Amazônia* (Institute for Amazonian Environmental Research, IPAM) based in Belém.
3. The *Centro Nacional do Desenvolvimento Sustentado das Populações Tradicionais* (National Center for the Sustainable Development of Traditional Populations, CNPT), based in Brasilia and established by Administrative Order 22/N/92 of February 16, 1992, defines traditional populations as 'all communities whose subsistence is traditionally and culturally based on the extraction of renewable natural resources, a concept sufficiently flexible to accommodate the diversity of Brazilian rural communities.' (Murrieta et al. 1995, p. 51)
4. For further information on land tenure by traditional populations, or agro-ecological tenure, see: Bennati, J. H. and Maués A. G. M., 'O pluralismo jurídico e as posses agrárias na Amazônia' in *Lições de direito civil alternativo*, São Paulo: Acadêmica, 1994; and Bennati, J. H., 'Posse coletiva da terra: um estudo jurídico sobre o apossamento de seringueiros e quilombolas' in *Revista CEJ/Conselho de Justiça Federal, Centro de Estudos Judiciários*, v. 1, n. 1 (1997). Brasília: CJF, 1997.

courses of action: one designed to reduce social tensions and the serious conflicts that have arisen as a result of disputes over land; and a second aimed at redistributing expropriated rural property among individual family units of production.

The first policy represents the extent of the understanding of the agrarian question; the second is a classic example of land reform, in which each family receives a plot and, through its individual action, aims for its subsistence and independence.

In practice, the access to land resulting from government action has been limited in political, social, and ecological terms, since it offers destruction of the forest as the only way of legitimatizing the plots. This is because the replacement of the forest cover by pasture or agriculture signifies improvement – an improvement that proves that the rural worker has demonstrated an ability to work the land and thus justifies the granting of full legal title.

These two official approaches have led to two scenarios in Amazonia:

a) On one hand, there is the government's priority of trying to settle conflicts caused principally by post-1960s land occupation, invariably through the conservative form of land regularization, under which each family receives an individual plot;

b) On the other hand, the regional land holdings of rubber tappers, quilombolas, and riverbank populations, with their specific forms of land tenure, were excluded from official policies until the end of the 1980s.

We carried out our study with this second group because we believed that with the support and pressure of community associations, and a well-founded proposal, we would manage to provoke legislative and administrative changes in the definition of the criteria that would allow traditional populations to legalize their tenure and maintain the system of land use that has to this day contributed to forest conservation in their areas.

In the Amazon region, land regularization in the traditional conservative manner is not enough. It is extremely important to consider the region's heterogeneity in terms of its fauna, flora, hydrology and climate; its regional populations and recently-arrived migrants; and an economy that is closely linked to the immediate natural environment.

Since our intention is to investigate legal rights in Amazonia for the purpose of considering the totality of social and legal relations that have arisen here, in our case the study of land possession by traditional populations in Amazonia, we need to remind ourselves that, as well as the formal legal concept, there are also the concepts of different ethnic groups and categories of rural workers that historically form what we may call agro-ecological tenure. The fact that these have not been recognized in the past by the State does not mean they are not integral components of a legal regime.

Land tenure of traditional populations

Traditional populations form what we may call 'small family-based rural producers', with a family economy based on agro-extractive activities. From viewpoint of agrarian law, they are squatters since they occupy land without third-party consent and, therefore, do not have legal titles that guarantee the ownership of the land they possess. The only 'title' they have is the labor invested in the land in order to maintain themselves and their families.

For a better understanding of land tenure of these inhabitants, let us consider three possible legal classifications, the last of which best fits the cases studied.

The civil law conception

The Brazilian Civil Code defines not possession, but the possessor. The definition is to be found in article 458: 'possessor is considered to be the person that actually exercises, fully or otherwise, the use of some of the powers inherent to ownership, or property'. In the civil law conception, possession is the outward expression of property, deriving from a right, an entitlement.

Articles 499 to 519 and 522 of the Civil Code prescribe the effects of possession. These include: entitlement to benefits arising, responsibility for damages, right to compensation and to retention of improvements, usucaption (acquisition by the lapse of time prescribed by law) and claims to ownership by possessors under judicial restraint.

The agrarian law conception

One of the fundamental principals of agrarian law is recognition of the labor of men or women on the land, in other words agrarian tenure. The social and economical function of agrarian tenure arises through the connection with the land, realized by means of the agrarian activity. To this end, '[...] agrarian law attributes a greater value to the agrarian activity (the labor) that people perform on the land. This is valued more than mere ownership. Thus, agrarian law is guided towards recognition of the tenure of whoever works the land, economically exploiting it' (Mattos Neto 1988, p. 45).

Agrarian activity can be classified as 'the action of the rural worker – undertaken by means of an agro-biological process – over a set of assets that make up the rural enterprise and to which he devotes himself professionally with a view to profit and to meeting basic human needs' (Sodero 1978, p. 406). It is therefore the combination of assets and of actions that make up the rational economic use of the rural area undertaken by the occupier.

The objective of agrarian activity is precisely to give land a specific purpose, 'whether by turning it into merchandise, with the aim of profit, whether by removing this attribute, with the aim of simply satisfying food or other needs, whether safeguarding it for a conservation need, whether by using it for scientific purposes in the strict sense' (Laranjeira 1988, p. 68).

Hence the mere fact of exploitation of the rural area is not sufficient, rather it is important that this happens in such a way as to respect the environment, in accordance with agro-environmental legislation.

Under agrarian tenure, the holder can be any physical or legal person who is apt, in other words able to assume rights and responsibilities. The important thing is that this agent has this capability and, in the case of physical persons, no distinction is made between men and women.

Under Brazilian agrarian law, the necessary prerequisites for agrarian tenure are effective cultivation and habitual residence. Effective cultivation occurs when the possessor works an area and derives family subsistence from it, where economic exploitation entails the necessary environmental conservation. The habitual residence on the land is the place where the occupier can normally be found to be working for the clear purpose of undertaking agrarian activity. This does not signify that the occupier's home is necessarily to be found in this area.

The effects of agrarian law tenure are the same as those under civil law.

The agro-environmental conception

Traditional populations enjoy a very particular tenure situation, which cannot be fully covered under civil and agrarian law. Given this specific state of affairs, we need to conduct a legal analysis that is capable of addressing this type of land tenure.

The prevailing conception of land tenure consists of reducing it to a 'quadrilateral'. This conception fails to address the totality of the legal and social relationships that have developed in the Amazon region. It is important to observe that, in addition to formal legal concepts, there are the concepts of those rural social categories that have over the course of history constituted agro-ecological tenure.

Even taking the single legal institution of tenure, its modalities have been constructed at different historical moments and reveal very different economic, legal, social, and environmental aspects.

Tenure under civil law entails the subjective element and that the occupier has title to the asset; whereas agrarian tenure is fulfilled simply by the objective fact of the exploitation of the land by the possessor. In agro-ecological tenure, the objective fact is the sustainable use of the land, because in order to 'hold' tenure it is necessary to interact with the environment.

It is important to point out that, for these categories of rural workers, land does not have a commercial character, nor is it an object to be traded; neither is it viewed as an asset subject to individual ownership, but only as a family asset making up a wider collective form.

This collective form of tenure of natural resources and the presence of family agro-extractive practices characterize agro-ecological tenure.

The delimitation of occupiers' rights over areas used for cultivation and family households, with other plots of land reserved for collective use (where extractive activities take place), happens in accordance with a spatial logic under which there is no need for these areas (collective and family uses) to be adjacent and permanent, or even for labor and household activities to be confined to fixed locations. Furthermore, the distribution of gardens, houses, and collective use areas, in accordance with a given spatial division, arises from group consensus, and not from individual behavior.

Within this context there are two types of tenure: communal, in other words where a system of collective land use can be observed; and family tenure, based on the family unit of labor (which may be understood as 'private').

Within the Brazilian agrarian structure, collective use systems have always been considered marginal, to the point where we have no legally consolidated concept of collective use areas, notwithstanding the fact that these are considered to be 'vital to the survival of the overall set of family units' that make use of them (Almeida 1989, p. 185).

The difficulty in defining collective use areas, also known as 'common land', lies in the fact that no single family or group of rural workers freely and individually exercises control over the basic resources and the norms that regulate these social relations extend beyond legal norms codified by the state. In fact, these areas are regulated by a set of concepts whose purpose is to control relations over the land and other natural resources.

A common use area is 'an asset that is not subject to permanent individual appropriation. These are areas where private property and collective tenure are combined and where a degree of social solidarity and cohesion can be observed, arising from consensual norms that guarantee the maintenance of such spaces' (Almeida 1989, p. 183). Resources in these areas are open, inalienable and indivisible. Access to land for strictly family-based activities in common use areas is only permitted by the community for the purposes of house building, planting gardens, or extractive activities, and not for the purpose of appropriation of the common use area itself.

Common use areas are thus rivers, lakes, trails, beaches, riverbanks and forests managed by a group of local inhabitants, where collective use activities are undertaken. They are open areas, without private ownership and unavailable for individual appropriation. However, such 'open areas' are linked to the market, for their products are sold on markets or traded with neighboring communities.

In physical terms, agro-ecological tenure is the sum of the family areas and the common use areas.

As ecological and social spaces, distinct but integrated, agro-ecological tenure appears in the form of three elements: house, garden[5] and forest.

The *house* is taken to mean the physical space used as the family residence, where domestic activities take place, including surrounding areas, such as vegetable gardens, orchards, and spaces dedicated to the preparation of *farinha* (manioc flour) and the raising of small domestic animals. In some cases, the *casa de farinha* fulfills a social function as it is used by more than one family and as a meeting place.

The *garden* is the physical space where the family carries out its agricultural production activities, usually for subsistence and distinct from extractive activities.

The areas considered to belong to a family are those related to the product of its labor, such as the house, gardens, rubber-tapping or Brazil nut collecting trails, and the secondary growth areas of old gardens. These areas are identified with a particular family, as a result of their labor.

Forest is taken to mean areas of uncultivated trees and fauna. The forest is where extractive activities, such as collecting fruits, nuts, vines and wood, and tapping rubber, take place. It is also where subsistence hunting takes place.

In the forest, there are also clearings, areas opened for sowing and planting over one or two years. Following this, the areas are left to rest for periods of time, which can be long enough for the forest to take them over again, allowing the recovery of soil nutrients. Occasionally, there may still be crops to be gathered in the clearings, usually manioc.

In this set of propositions we have pointed out the differences in relation to official models of land rights, including questioning the traditional models of settlement through standardized agriculture plots that fail to consider the specificity and diversity of the natural environment in the Amazon region, and proposing the collective use of land.

Furthermore, we have drawn attention to the fact that the coming together of agrarian and agro-ecological questions gives

---

5. 'Garden' here signifies the *roça*: the patch cleared, planted and subsequently left to regenerate by practioners of swidden ('slash and burn') agriculture.

rise to new criteria for land tenure, based on the sustainable use of natural resources. As a result, we arrive at different views concerning habitual residence, effective cultivation, improvements and rural modules.[6]

The areas occupied by these categories of rural producers are those where their houses and gardens are located, as well as those areas used for hunting, fishing, and plant extractive activities. The notion of area occupied thus corresponds to the lands used by their inhabitants to guarantee the reproduction of their way of life.

The legal effects of agro-ecological tenure are the same as those under civil and agrarian law tenure.

Any prospects for resolving agrarian conflicts and for forest conservation in Amazonia must therefore take the particular form of land tenure of these social categories into account. This is what is happening with the identification of quilombola areas and the creation of extractive reserves.

The identification of quilombola areas and environmental conservation

In the state of Pará, nineteen communities have already been demarcated, as shown in Table 1[7]:

Currently, in Pará the working group established by State Decree 2,246 of 1997 is responsible for identifying areas of descendants of quilombos.

The working group is composed of representatives of Sectam (Department of Science, Technology, and the Environment of the State of Pará), Iterpa (State Land Agency of Pará), Secult (Department of Culture of the State of Pará), Sagri (Department of Agriculture of the State of Pará), Fetagri (Federation of Agricultural Workers in the State of Pará), Arqmo (Association of Communities Descendents of Quilombos of the Municipality of Oriximiná), Cedenpa (Center for the Study and Defense of Black People in Pará), and CPT (Pastoral Land Commission), and coordinated by Sectam.

To support the state working group, a research project entitled 'Mapping of rural black communities in Pará: territorial occupation and resource use, descent and way of life' is being carried out under the coordination of researchers from NAEA/UFPA (Institute of Advanced Studies of Amazonia, Federal University of Pará) in Belém: Dr Rosa Acevedo Marin (historian) and Dr Edna Ramos de Castro (sociologist). The project aims to contribute to the mapping of black communities being undertaken by the working group. So far around 229 communities of descendents of quilombos have been identified in different municipalities of Pará.

As part of the process of titling quilombola areas, 'Titles of Recognition of Ownership' have been issued. Among the provisions of these documents there is one embodying the concern with ensuring conservation of renewable natural resources. The second clause states that 'the property shall be used for extractive, agricultural and livestock, and *environmental conservation* activities, in such a way as to ensure the self-sufficiency of the community, for the purpose of preserving its social, cultural and historical aspects in accordance with articles 215 and 216 of the Federal Constitution, and is therefore inalienable and must remain in the possession and for the use of the grantee'[8] (emphasis added).

In order that these groups can guarantee their physical and cultural reproduction in accordance with their traditions and customs, it is thus important to respect their particular systems of tenure and to select a process of land regularization that is different from present procedures based solely on the division of land into standard plots. Out of the legal instruments available, the most appropriate is collective title, since this not only secures the particular way of life of the quilombolas, but also ensures environmental conservation.

In order to comply with article 68 of the Transitory Constitutional Provisions Act[9], which acknowledges the historic rights acquired by descendents of black slaves, the regularization of these areas of land is taking place by means of collective titling. This is because, firstly, the Federal Constitution refers to descendants of quilombos as communities and not as individuals, thus guaranteeing their rights as an ethnic group (descendants of quilombo communities). Secondly, the criteria for delimitation of the land to be demarcated must respect the particular way of life of the group, in such a way that the land is sufficient for the community's physical, social and cultural reproduction.

Rural black quilombola communities are groups that have constructed their history on the basis of their own culture, transmitted and adapted from generation to generation. From the start, quilombos were made up not only of black slaves, but also of indians, people of mixed race, and white outlaws. The ethnic identity of such groups has been formed not just by biological reproduction; recognition of a common origin has also been important. Members identify themselves as belonging to this group by means of certain shared elements of culture and behavior, which in turn results in a common identity. Thus, descendants of quilombos are communities that are historically constructed and which identify themselves as having a common territory which must be respected.

---

6. The '*módulo rural*' (rural module) is the minimum area necessary not only for the subsistence of the rural family unit, but also for its advancement. It is therefore that family property size that will ensure the minimum established levels of economic return and social utility of the land. In Amazonia, the rural module varies between 50 and 100 hectares, depending on the region, or up to 240 hectares, depending on the type of economic activity, such as extractive activities.

7. All these areas of descendants of quilombos have been demarcated and granted collective titles, issued in the name of the associations that represent the quilombolas in their respective areas. The federal settlement and land reform agency - INCRA - has created a settlement project in each of these areas, denominated Special Quilombola Settlement Project.

8. The first title granted, to the quilombola community of Boa Vista, did not contain this clause and the second clause simply stated: 'In accordance with the statement of the representative of the GRANTEE in the above-mentioned administrative process, the property that is the object of the present Title shall be used principally for extractive, agricultural and livestock activities.' However, environmental conservation was a constant theme of the discussions around the demarcation of quilombos. The titles in question are issued by Incra.

9. Article 68 - Full ownership by descendants of quilombo communities who are occupying their lands is hereby recognized, titles for which shall be issued by the State.

TABLE 1 - DEMARCATED QUILOMBOLA COMMUNITIES IN THE STATE OF PARÁ					
Community	Municipality	Area (ha)	Year of demarcation	no. of families
Boa Vista	Oriximiná	1,125.0341	1995	112
Pacoval	Alenquer	7,472.8780	1996	115
Água Fria	Oriximiná	557.1355	1996	15
Itamauari	Viseu	5,377.6020	1998	33
Trombetas *	Oriximiná	80,877.0941	1998	138
Erepecuru **	Oriximiná	57,584.8505	1998	160

Sources: DOU (Official Federal Gazette) and INCRA/PA.
* Trombetas is the name of a Special Quilombola Settlement Program formed by seven communities (Bacabal, Aracuan de Cima, Aracuan do Meio, Aracuan de Baixo, Serrinha, Terra Preta II, and Jarauacá). These communities received a single joint title to an area common to all.
** Erepecuru is the name of a Special Quilombola Settlement Program formed by eight communities (Pancada, Araça, Espírito Santo, Jauari, Boa Vista do Cuminã, Varre Vento, Jarauacá, and Acapu). These communities received a single joint title to an area common to all.

THE CREATION OF EXTRACTIVE RESERVES

Extractive reserves arose as an alternative to the seringal (rubber estate), simultaneously allowing a type of land regularization appropriate to the particular forms of land use of rubber tappers and aiming at ending the economic exploitation they suffer and at improving their lives. Thus the reserve 'can be defined simultaneously as a conservation and a production area, since the exploitation of natural resources depends on an appropriate management plan' (Allegretti 1994, p. 20).

The extractive reserve was the first conservation area to reconcile two concepts that up to then had been seen as distinct: conservation and economic use. It combines the principles of the indigenous area, which respects traditional uses and tenure rights, and of the conservation area, under which special guarantees of protection of the area are granted. Previous experience had shown that division into plots did not lead to economically and ecologically sustainable use. Hence the idea of only delimiting the perimeter of the areas, thereby respecting the pre-existing internal limits and spatial divisions. (Allegretti 1994, p. 26)

This way, extractive reserves should be understood as part of the struggle for land reform in the Amazon region, a specific proposal for the solution of land conflicts in the rubber estates of the Rio Acre valley. It was, in other words, the alternative of the rubber tappers to the system of debt bondage and to the new forms of land occupation that were leading to deforestation.

The fight for land in this region thus meant not just the struggle for the expropriation of rubber estates, but the recognition of the rubber tappers' tenure rights and the defense of the forest with its rubber and Brazil nut trees - the basis of extractive activities. In this combination, the concept of agro-ecological tenure being formulated is thereby linked to the sustainable use of the forest.

This concept is very clear as to the definition of the extractive reserve, envisaged as an area where non-predatory and sustainable extractive activities are undertaken or which has the potential for such activities; in other words, where economic utilization does not lead to the exhaustion of the natural resources.

The idea of the extractive reserves also presupposes:
a) The regularization of areas for sustainable extractive activities through the concession of public land to local popula-

b) Support to populations that already live in areas of sustainable extractive activities, and to those that have abandoned these areas, but wish to return;
c) Environmental conservation and the development of scientific research aiming at increasing productivity and improving the living conditions of those rural social categories whose economy is based on agro-extractive activities;
d) That, as these are conservation areas, society as a whole is the party most interested in the fate and use of the area; the rubber tappers are the recipients who will ensure the execution of the legally prescribed goal of the 'sustainable use and conservation of renewable natural resources by the extractive population' (Gomes et al 1994, p. 79);
e) The creation of the reserves depends essentially on the initiative of the beneficiary extractive populations.

The coming together of agrarian and agro-ecological questions implies new criteria for land tenure, based on the sustainable use of natural resources. Extractive reserves may therefore be understood as 'areas endowed with extractive potential, incorporated into the process of production – or that are able to be incorporated into it – by means of the development by extractive communities of activities that are ecologically sustainable and economically profitable, and whose autonomy, rights to the use of the natural resources, and support for development of economic and social activities are guaranteed by the State' (Meneses 1994, p.53).

The main characteristic of the reserves is to reclaim the importance of the human in a new perspective on the use of space in Amazonia that involves environmental conservation, and where social, cultural, economical, legal, and ecological aspects are taken into consideration.

Since this proposal arose from the demands of the communities themselves, it respects the various forms of land tenure in the Amazon region (those of rubber tappers, quilombolas, and riverbank communities).

Today in Amazonia, extractive reserves represent a space where categories of rural workers can construct or reconstruct their socioeconomic and legal relations with their respective environments.

The institutional development of extractive reserves

The first regulation recognizing extractive activities as a possible form of economic activity by a specific group was INCRA's Administrative Regulation 627, of July 30, 1987, establishing what are known as 'Assentamentos Extrativistas' (extractive settle-

Extractive Reserve as an instrument of the PNMA (the National Environment Policy), making the demands of rubber tappers compatible with the provisions of the Constitution. As a result of this law, which referred specifically to extractive reserves, it became possible to establish reserves by means of an executive order, that is, by decree, thereby guaranteeing State protection. It came into effect on January 30, 1990, when the President of the Republic issued Decree 98,897.

The main characteristics of the Decree regulating extractive reserves are:

a) The areas with extractive potential should be conserved and the sustainable use of their resources by extractive populations should be guaranteed (article 1). The law recognizes the possibility of the coexistence of people and nature in a conservation area, while also recognizing that people and natural resources can suffer as a result and therefore the State has a duty to protect them;

b) The reason behind its creation is the ecological and social interest (article 2). The latter is understood as not just pertaining to society, but also that society's interests will be safeguarded when the land rights of the social groups that use these areas in a non-predatory way are also guaranteed;

c) The definition of the geographical boundaries and of the beneficiary population is required in order to give effect to the decree creating the reserve (article 3). The geographical boundary is taken to refer only to the perimeter, to the outline of the polygon, since the detailing of the area can be undertaken later, given that it is assumed that there are inhabitants within the protected area;

d) The extractive reserve will be in the federal domain, and the transfer of usufruct rights to the inhabitants of the conservation area will occur through a contract of concession of land use rights to the organizations that represent the residents of the reserve. Titles authorizing the use of the land will be granted to the residents of the reserve on the basis of article 7 of Decree-Law 271 of 1967 (article 4 of the Decree), and free of charge (article 4, §1). The beneficiaries will not receive definite titles, nor will there be any qualifying period prior to signing of the concession contract;

e) Compulsory rescission clauses will be established for cases of environmental damage or transfer of concession (article 4, §2). This same paragraph provides for the concession contract to include a Utilization Plan, which will set standards for use of the land and regulate non-predatory behavior, in accordance with prevailing environmental legislation;

f) The responsibility for the expropriation, implementation and monitoring of the protected area, ensuring compliance with the terms of the concession contract and the Utilization Plan, lies with the federal environmental agency Ibama, and not with the federal land reform agency Incra (articles 3 and 5);

g) Respect for the different forms of land tenure is guaranteed once the Utilization Plan becomes part of the concession contract, since this is means by which the communities will determine the rules by which they will manage the extractive reserve in a sustainable way;

h) It also recognizes that, as well as traditional forms of settlement by granting family plots, there are other forms of land tenure that have been constructed historically by different ethnic groups and categories of rural workers. This avoids the division of the reserves into family modules, which does not signify disrespect for the family unit, but rather an incentive to union and to associative forms of land use.

The extractive reserve is a sui generis legal instrument that combines environmental conservation and economic use, designed especially for traditional populations and managed by them. It differs from traditional concepts of fauna and flora conservation areas because it presupposes the sustainable use and conservation of renewable natural resources by extractive populations; in other words, it guarantees human presence and respects their rights, organization and culture.

The federal agency responsible for the implementation, consolidation, management and development of extractive reserves is the Centro Nacional de Desenvolvimento Sustentado das Populações Tradicionais (National Center for the Sustainable Development of Traditional Populations) based in Brasilia. The mandate of the CNPT is to 'promote the development, introduction and implementation of plans, programs, projects and actions sought by traditional populations, through their representative bodies and/or, indirectly, through government agencies established for such ends, or further, through non-governmental organizations' (Murieta Rueda 1995, p. 53).

Table 2 provides data on current extractive reserves.

Conclusions

In light of the above, we can see that ensuring the regularization of lands occupied by traditional populations in Amazonia on the basis of their particular forms of land tenure is a legal and social instrument for forest conservation. We may therefore conclude that:

a) regularization of lands occupied by traditional populations in Amazonia, in particular those of quilombolas and rubber tappers, supports forest conservation;

b) land regularization in Amazonia should be based on the notion that the area in question must correspond to the land used by traditional populations to guarantee their physical, social, and cultural reproduction.

Table 2 - Extractive reserves in Amazonia (created as of 1998)				
Extractive Reserve	State	Area (ha)	Year of creation	no. of inhabitants*
Alto Juruá	Acre	506,186	1990	5,821
Chico Mendes	Acre	970,570	1990	12,017
Rio Cajari	Amapá	481,650	1990	3,639
Rio Ouro Preto	Amapá	204,583	1990	775
Pirajubaé	Santa Catarina	1,444	1992	690
Ciriaco	Maranhão	7,050	1992	844
Quilombo do Frexal	Maranhão	9,542	1992	1,080
Mata Grande	Maranhão	10,450	1992	776
Extremo Norte do Tocantins	Tocantins	9,280	1992	320
Tapajós-Arapiuns	Pará	647,610	1998	15,380

Source: DOU (Official Federal Gazette) and Ibama/CNPT, 1998.
* Approximate figures.

Bibliography

ACEVEDO MARIN, R. E.; CASTRO, E. M. R. de. *Negros do Trombetas: guardiães de matas e rios.* Belém: UFPA, NAEA, 1993.

ALLEGRETTI, M. H. Reservas extrativistas: parâmetros para uma política de desenvolvimento sustentável na Amazônia. In: *O destino da floresta: reservas extrativistas e desenvolvimento sustentável na Amazônia.* Rio de Janeiro/Curitiba: Relume-Dumará/Instituto de Estudos Amazônicos e Ambientais, Konrad Adenauer Foundation, 1994.

ALMEIDA, A. W. B. de. Terras de preto, terras de santo, terras de índio: uso comum e conflitos. In: CASTRO, E. M.; HEBETT, J. (Eds.). *Na trilha dos grandes projetos.* Belém: NAEA/UFPA, 1989.

ALVES, J. C. M. *Posse, 1: evolução histórica.* Rio de Janeiro: Forense, 1985.

_____. *Posse, 2:* estudo dogmático. Rio de Janeiro: Forense, 1990.

BENATTI, J. H. Posse coletiva da terra: um estudo jurídico sobre o apossamento de seringueiros e quilombolas, *Revista CEJ/Conselho da Justiça Federal, Centro de Estudos Judiciários,* v. 1, n. 1, 1997.

_____. Constituição e cidadania: a demarcação das terras de quilombolas no Estado do Pará, *Cadernos de pós-graduação em Direito da UFPA.* Belém: Programa Pós-Graduação em Direito da UFPA, n. 8/9, 1999.

CÂMARA DOS DEPUTADOS. *Estratégia Mundial para a Conservação.* Brasília: Comissão de defesa dos consumidor, meio ambiente e minorias, September 1994, typescript.

_____. *Substitutivo ao Projeto de Lei nº 2.892/92.* Brasília: Comissão de defesa, do consumidor, meio ambiente e minorias, 1996, typescript.

CONSTITUIÇÃO DA REPÚBLICA FEDERATIVA DO BRASIL. Brasília: Senado Federal, Centro Gráfico, 1988.

FACHIN, L. E. *A função social da posse e a propriedade contemporânea.* Porto Alegre: Fabris, 1988.

_____. Posseiros e seringueiros: aspectos jurídicos, *Revista da Associação Brasileira de Reforma Agrária (ABRA).* Campinas: ano 20, April/December 1990.

GIL, A. H. *La función social de la posesión (ensaio de teorización socilógico-jurídica).* Madrid: Alianza Editorial, 1984.

GOMES, M. E. A. C.; FELIPE, L. D. Tutela jurídica sobre as reservas extrativistas. In: *O destino da floresta:* reservas extrativistas e desenvolvimento sustentável na Amazônia. Rio de Janeiro/Curitiba: Relume-Dumará/Instituto de Estudos Amazônicos e Ambientais, Konrad Adenauer Foundation, 1994.

GORENDER, J. *O escravismo colonial,* 4th ed. São Paulo: Ática, 1985.

LARANJEIRA, R. *Propedêutica do direito agrário,* 2th ed. São Paulo, 1988.

_____. *Meio ambiente e direito à terra no Brasil.* Macerata-Italy, 1991, typescript.

MACHADO, P. A. L. *Direito ambiental brasileiro,* 4th ed. revised. São Paulo: Malheiros, 1992.

MATTOS NETO, A. J. de. *A posse agrária e suas implicações jurídicas no Brasil.* Belém: CEJUP, 1988.

MENESES, M. A. As reservas extrativistas como alternativa ao desmatamento na Amazônia. In: *O destino da floresta: reservas extrativistas e desenvolvimento sustentável na Amazônia.* Rio de Janeiro/Curitiba: Relume-Dumará/Instituto de Estudos Amazônicos e Ambientais, Konrad Adenauer Foundation, 1994.

MURRIETA, J. R.; RUEDA, R. P. *Reservas extrativistas.* Gland, Switzerland and Cambridge, UK: IUCN, 1995.

SILVA, J. A. da. *Curso de direito contitucional positivo,* 6th ed. São Paulo: RTr., 1990.

_____. Direito ambiental constitucional. São Paulo: Malheiros, 1994.

SODERO, F. P. Atividade agrária. In: FRANÇA, R. L. (Ed.) *Enciclopédia Saraiva do direito,* v. 8. São Paulo: Saraiva, 1978.

_____. *Esboço histórico da formação do direito agrário no Brasil.* Rio de Janeiro: IAJUP/FASE, 1990.

Human presence in conservation areas: a scientific, legal or political impasse?

José Heder Benatti *Núcleo de Altos Estudos Amazônicos e Instituto de Pesquisa Ambiental da Amazônia*

Article 225 of the Brazilian Constitution states that 'everyone has the right to an ecologically balanced environment, which is a common use good of the people and essential to a healthy quality of life; its defense and preservation for present and future generations is a duty that falls to both the State and the community.' By stating that all have the right to an ecologically balanced environment, the Constitution confirms that this right is assured to individuals and to the community and that the responsibility for defending and preserving this right falls to the State, to individuals and to the community. It attributes the same degree of rights and obligations to both public and private spheres, thereby eliminating an old civil law dichotomy.

The object of the legal guardianship, that which the law aims to protect, is thus 'the quality of the environment as a function of the quality of life. It can be said that there are two objects of protection: an immediate object, the quality of the environment, and an indirect object, the health, wellbeing and security of the population, covered under the expression 'quality of life'.'[1]

This constitutional provision includes the concept of ecological conservation, which comprises the preservation[2], maintenance, sustainable use, restoration and improvement of the natural environment. Ecological conservation is defined as 'the management of the use of the biosphere by human beings, resulting in sustainable benefits for present generations, but also retaining its potential to meet the needs and aspirations of future generations.'[3]

Given that 'everyone has the right to an ecologically balanced environment', one of the legal instruments available to public authorities for the defense, protection and preservation of public assets is the creation of protected spaces.

A protected space is 'any location, with or without defined boundaries, which is by law under special protection. It is created by regulatory or administrative acts that allow the public authority to give special protection to particular assets because of their inherent qualities, by restricting or limiting the possibilities of their use or transfer.'[4]

The creation of such protected spaces is essential for ensuring the efficacy of the constitutional provision and of guaranteeing ecological balance.

Paragraph 4 of article 225 of the Federal Constitution refers to some of the environmental assets protected by the Constitution, identified as part of the national heritage: the Amazon Forest, the Atlantic Forest and the Serra do Mar. Since they are so defined, by law their use is subject to conditions that ensure their environmental preservation, including in respect of the use of their natural resources.

Other legally protected areas are described in the Provisional Measure that amends article 44 of Law 4,771, of September 15, 1965, which prohibits the increase in the conversion of forests to agriculture areas in the North and in the northern part of the Center-West regions. In its article 1, §1, a legal reserve is defined as the area constituting at least 80% of each rural property in these regions. In addition to this percentage, areas of permanent preservation, natural forests included under article 2 of the Forest Code, and conservation areas are also protected under other legislation.

When a public authority creates a national forest, an extractive reserve or a national park, it is creating a conservation area.[5] Each area has its specific purpose which is the protection and preservation of fauna and flora, or indeed any other reason envisaged by law. A conservation area is thus a specialized protected space, with its own rules of use, management, and legally defined procedures for its creation.

At present, 5.57% of the national territory comes under government protection in the form of national parks, biological reserves, ecological stations, areas of special ecological interest, national forests, extractive reserves and environmental protection areas.[6]

The constitutional provision in article 225 defines the principles that have to be followed. In §1, subparagraph III of this article we find one of the instruments of guarantee and effectiveness referred to in the chapeau:

'§1 In order to ensure the effectiveness of this right, it is incumbent upon the State to: (…)

III - identify in each of the states of the Federation, territorial spaces and their components to be specially protected, any alterations and suppressions being permitted only by means of the law, and any use which could affect the integrity of the attributes justifying their protection being forbidden'.

However, we should not consider specially protected territorial spaces as being synonymous with conservation areas, since the latter are a type of the former. According to the constitutional

---

1. Silva, J. A. da. *Curso de direito constitucional positivo*, p. 54.
2. Preservation is taken to mean all nature conservation actions aimed at ensuring the full protection of natural attributes.
3. Silva, J. A. da. *op. cit.*, p. 60.
4. Souza Filho, C .F. M. de. *Espaços ambientais protegidos e unidades de conservação*, p. 11.
5. Despite the international tendency to adopt the term 'protected area' to designate those areas created by the State, public environmental agencies have preferred to use the term 'unidade de conservação', and which was later adopted by the rest of the community. Both terms are used here with the same meaning. (Editor's note: 'Unidade de conservação' is translated as 'conservation area' throughout this publication.)
6. Cf. Ibama/Ministry of the Environment. *Unidades de conservação*. Brasília: folder, s/d. Overall, there are 94 strict protection areas totaling 15,621,734 ha; and 71 sustainable use areas totaling 32,141,280 ha, out of the total national territory of 851,196,500 ha.

expert José Afonso da Silva, 'a territorial space becomes a conservation area when this is expressly declared in order to provide it with a more restrictive and particular legal regime.'[7]

Specially protected territorial spaces are 'public or private geographical areas (part of the national territory) containing environmental attributes that require their subjection, under law, to a public interest legal regime that implies their relative exemption from modification and their sustainable use, with a view to the preservation and protection of the integrity of samples of the overall diversity of ecosystems, the protection of the process of evolution of species, the preservation and protection of natural resources'.[8] They are thus sensitive natural areas that require some form of legal protection (whether constitutional or not), but where there is no need to specify the exact location, which will be determined by the biome, by the characteristics of geographical location, or by ecological role performed. As examples of such territorial areas, we can cite the Amazon Forest, the Atlantic Forest, the Pantanal Mato-Grossense, the Serra do Mar, the coastal zone, mangrove forests, floodplains, dunes and those forests that are considered legal reserves[9] or under permanent preservation.[10]

Conservation units are 'territorial spaces and their components, including waters under national jurisdiction, containing important natural characteristics, which are legally established by the State, with defined conservation objectives and boundaries, under a special administrative regime, and to which specific guarantees of protection apply.'[11] These areas are therefore specific areas created by the State, under either public or private ownership, with total protection of their natural resources or otherwise, and, depending on the type, compatible with the presence of traditional populations in the area.

When Law 6,938 of August 31, 1981, concerning the National Environmental Policy, its objectives and the mechanisms for its formulation and implementation, as amended by Law 7,804 of July 18, 1989, states in its article 9, subparagraph VI that the instruments of the National Environmental Policy include 'the creation of territorial spaces specially protected by federal, state and municipal governments, such as Environmental Protection Areas, Areas of Special Ecological Interest and Extractive Reserves', this federal law is not implying that specially protected territorial spaces are the same as conservation areas; it is merely offering examples of a number of types of territorial spaces that have to be protected, amongst which are conservation areas.

There is no doubt that one of the main instruments of the National Environmental Policy for nature conservation, adopted worldwide, is the creation of protected natural areas, namely, conservation areas. The protection of such areas has three important aims:

a) conserving the life support systems that nature provides;
b) conserving the diversity of life on the planet;
c) ensuring the sustainable use of renewable natural resources.

The objectives described above are the prerequisites for ensuring the sustainable use, restoration and improvement of the environment, in order to benefit present generations, as well as guaranteeing the potential to meet the needs of future generations.

However, in order for protected areas to be able to achieve these desired objectives, they must firstly not be seen as 'islands of preservation' of the natural environment, isolated from regional and national contexts. Secondly, such protected natural spaces must not be created and managed without consulting the community, especially those populations directly affected. Thirdly, it is essential to combine the need to create environmental protection areas with the presence of traditional populations, an issue that will be discussed below.

Legal nature of conservation areas

In our opinion, conservation areas cannot be defined merely as public goods, following a classification that derives from article 66 of the Civil Code, which separates public goods into three categories: common use, special use and public domain.

According to Hely Lopes Meirelles, public goods, in the wider sense, 'are all things, tangible or intangible, fixed, movable or living creatures, credits, rights and stocks, which belong, under any form of title, to government entities, executive agencies, foundations, and semi-public bodies.'[12] Public goods enjoy prerogatives of inalienability[13], freedom from mortgage[14], and freedom from prescription.[15]

A public good is considered to be of common use when it is open to the public. It is of special use when its use by the public is restricted, because its use is intended for the execution of or support to public services. When it is not reserved for a particular purpose, either because it no longer retains its original purpose or has not yet been assigned one, the asset may be considered to be in the public domain. Therefore, to consider a good, irrespective of its use, as a public good is to affirm that it constitutes part of the set of national assets.

From this standpoint, environmental protection areas, natural monuments, wildlife refuges, reservoirs, and integrated ecological reserves are conservation areas that can include private property within their areas, and therefore cannot be considered public assets. In this case, we may consider that the State has public domain over these protected areas if we define 'public

---

7. Silva, J. A. da. *Direito ambiental constitucional*, p 161.

8. Ibid, p. 160-1.

9. The legal forest reserve is the forest cover of each rural property that cannot be cleared; depending on its location within Brazil, a minimum area of vegetation coverage to be retained is stipulated. In the North region, this is a minimum of 80%.

10. Permanent preservation forests are forest areas that cannot be cleared, in order to ensure amongst other things the physical protection of soils, water sources, riverbank vegetation, in accordance with articles 2; 3; 26a, b, and c; and 31b of the Forest Code.

11. Article 2, I of Substitute Bill 2,892 of 1992, establishing the National System of Conservation Areas and other measures (subsequently enacted as Law 9,985 of July 18, 2000).

12. Meirelles, H. L. *Direito administrativo brasileiro*, p. 428.

13. The asset cannot be sold, transferred, or donated to a third party.

14. The asset cannot be pledged or mortgaged.

15. The asset is protected against acquisition by adverse possession or usucaption. This principle is guaranteed under two constitutional provisions: article 183, §3 and article 191.

domain in a broad sense' as 'the power of dominance or regulation of the State over the goods that comprise its assets (public goods), or over the goods that comprise private assets (private goods of public interest), or over things that cannot be individually appropriated, but are of general benefit to the community (*res nullius*)'.[16] In respect of other categories, there is patrimonial domain[17], which can be considered a public asset.

The definition provided by the legal expert José Afonso da Silva is more precise, since it describes conservation areas as environmental goods of public interest, 'including not only assets belonging to public agencies, but also private assets subject to a specific discipline for the achievement of a public purpose. They become subject to a special legal regime as regards their use and availability, and also to a special regime of policing, intervention and public guardianship.'[18] Thus both conservation areas under public ownership and domain, and those which are characterized by private ownership and domain, thereby constituting private assets, share a common definition, that of environmental assets of public interest, not least because the regulatory power of the public authority is not confined to the internal area of the reserve, but also includes the buffer zone.

With regard to the interpretation of article 225 of the Federal Constitution, which states that, 'everyone has the right to an ecologically balanced environment, which is a *common use good of the people* and essential to a healthy quality of life; its defense and preservation for present and future generations is a duty that falls to both the State and the community' (emphasis added), this constitutional provision asserts that, in order to guarantee a healthy quality of life of the environment, to the benefit of the community present and future, it falls to all private and public bodies to protect the environment, and that the benefits attributed to the environment cannot be privately appropriated. Even if the asset has a private owner, the latter cannot make use of the environmental benefit in any way he chooses thereby putting the environmental benefit at risk. It is a public interest asset, whose enjoyment belongs to the common use of the population.[19]

When the Constitution refers to 'common use' (article 225), it is not using the same legal concept found in article 66 of the Brazilian Civil Code. To be considered as public assets of common use of the population (in accordance with the forms of access and use found in article 66 of the Civil Code), the conservation areas should have easy access and the ability to be used by any member of the public, since '[...] the use and enjoyment of these assets are available to any person, with no distinction made between nationals and foreigners, natural and legal persons, public and private persons. In return for this use and enjoyment, nothing is required in terms of authorization or permission, nor, at least in principle, is there any charge.'[20] However this is not what happens since, in order to obtain access to a protected area, it is necessary to obtain the permission of the environmental agency responsible for its management. In many cases, public visiting is forbidden and access is only permitted for the purposes of research, upon prior authorization by the area's management authority. Even then, access must obey the conditions and restrictions laid out in the conservation area's management plan.

INDIGENOUS AREAS AND CONSERVATION AREAS

This debate requires special care since some commentators argue that indigenous areas and conservation areas are legal constructs of a similar order. In our opinion, indigenous areas cannot be considered to be conservation areas.

The constitutional and legal basis of the lands traditionally occupied by indians is the *indigenato*, a legal instrument recognized by almost all successive Brazilian Constitutions and enshrined in the current Constitution in its own chapter (articles 231 and 232). Its origin goes back to the colonial warrant of April 1, 1680, in which the Portuguese Crown, in granting lands in Brazil to private persons, asserted that any land containing settlements, in other words under indian tenure, should be reserved for the indians, as the first and natural owners of the land. The origin of indigenous land is therefore linked to the existence of indian tenure which, as a consequence, gives rise to the emergence of state property. Although the protected area comes into being through an act of the State, not all protected areas are public assets, especially those that allow for the existence of private land within them, an issue previously addressed.

The motive that leads the State to recognize the rights of indigenous communities to their lands is the fact that they have traditionally occupied the area and need it in order to guarantee 'their productive activities, essential to the preservation of the natural resources necessary to their wellbeing and their physical and cultural reproduction, in accordance with their uses and customs' (Article 231, §1 of the Federal Constitution). The main objective in creating a protected natural area is to conserve nature and all its natural and cultural resources, an objective that is very different from that in the case of indigenous areas. Whilst the demarcation of indigenous areas entails the recognition of a right, a protected area arises as a 'necessity of modern times'.

Indigenous communities have the right to the exclusive use of the natural riches of their lands for their subsistence and for the preservation of their cultural identity. The land plays an important role in the group's ethnic identity. In the protected area, the forms of use of the land and natural resources have to be defined in the management plan, and these cannot run counter to the purposes for which the area was created.

The common feature of indigenous lands and conservation areas is that both have nature conservation as one of their objectives. Indigenous communities need the land in order to guarantee the conservation of natural resources for their wellbeing, that is for their physical and cultural survival. The creation of a protected area is intended to preserve and restore the essential ecological processes and to provide ecological management of the species and ecosystems.

---

16. Meirelles, H. L. *op. cit.*, p. 426.
17. Areas over which the State has patrimonial domain can be considered to be public assets, at least from a legal point of view. These are: biological reserves, ecological stations, national parks, national forests, extractive reserves, fauna reserves, cultural-ecological stations, in accordance with Law 9,985 of 2000. However, these protected areas do not fit exactly into any of the three categories of public goods identified under article 66 of the Civil Code.
18. Silva, J. A. *op. cit.*, p. 56
19. Idem, p. 56
20. Gasparini, Diogenes. *Direito administrativo*, p. 496.

The rights of traditional populations to their lands from a constitutional point of view

The definitions of conservation areas embody conservationist principles dating from the beginning of the twentieth century, when social and cultural values differed greatly from those of present-day Brazil. These therefore need changing and adapting to new times, so that they are updated and made more applicable to new paradigms.

When drawing up legal rules, the legislator allows himself, to a greater or lesser degree, to absorb the social and cultural values of the times. The spirit of the law thus reflects the social and cultural thinking in force at the time of its elaboration.

On the other hand, we should not forget that our 1988 Constitution categorically asserts that 'everyone has the right to an ecologically balanced environment, which is a common use good of the people and essential to a healthy quality of life; its defense and preservation for present and future generations is a duty that falls to both the State and the community' (article 225).

In another article, it similarly asserts that 'the Brazilian cultural heritage is made up of those tangible and intangible assets, considered individually or as a whole, which embody references to the identity, actions and memory of the different groups that constitute Brazilian society, including therein not only forms of expression, but also their means of creation and production and way of life' (Article 216, subparagraphs I and II).

In our view, defense of the environment extends beyond the mere defense of the fauna, flora and physical environment; it includes humans, with their cultural and material activities. 'The environment is thus the interaction of the sum of natural, artificial and cultural elements that favor the balanced development of life in all its forms. This interaction seeks to acquire a unified concept of the environment comprising its natural and cultural resources'.[21]

So it is no exaggeration to point out that the principles underlying the creation of conservation areas, as well as their operational concepts, predate the present Constitution and therefore need revising in order to be harmonized with the its provisions. If we fail to do this, we will face a situation of unconstitutionality: on one hand, a Constitution that safeguards the natural, artificial and cultural elements; while on the other, statutory environmental law which ignores the cultural aspects.

The collision of constitutional rights

When we analyze the environment from a constitutional point of view[22], we can see that there are at least three significant aspects that merit constitutional protection: a) natural; b) artificial, and c) cultural.

a) Natural or physical environment: this is 'the set of conditions, laws, influences and interactions of a physical, chemical and biological nature that permits, harbors and governs life in all its forms' (article 3 of Law 6,938 of 1981), made up of soil, water, air, biological resources or any other component of ecosystems;

b) Artificial environment: this includes constructions found in urban areas, the set of buildings that can be defined as closed urban spaces, as well as public assets of common use of the people, such as parks, roads, green areas, and so on, that we can call urban open spaces;

c) Cultural environment: this can be defined as 'the historical, artistic, archaeological, landscape, and tourist heritage that, although artificial and manmade, differs from the previous category (which is also cultural) because of the special value it has acquired or absorbed.'[23] These are therefore assets of a material or intangible nature created by man, which may be considered either individually or collectively, and which embody references to the identity, actions, and memory of the different groups that make up Brazilian society.

The 1988 Constitution emphasizes the importance of culture, taking this term in a broad sense, including the notion of identity and memory of the different groups that make up Brazilian society. This notion is referred to in various articles (23, III; 24, VII; 30, IX; 225; 261; and, with particular reference to ethnicity, 231). This concern with the question of culture is so clear that one could contemplate the existence of a specific cultural constitution, alongside the political, economic, social and environmental constitutions.

Having said this, when a protected area is created, all these aspects should be taken into consideration. However, government policy has so far only considered a few of them. To take an example, conservation areas that contain traditional populations could have their creation justified on at least two aspects worthy of protection: the natural and cultural. However by the manner in which they have so far been created, the natural has eclipsed the cultural. There have been cases where, in name of the defense of the natural, the cultural has been destroyed or broken. This has occurred when traditional populations have been violently and illegally removed from their areas.

This authoritarian policy of creating conservation areas in areas occupied by traditional populations has led to a collision between two fundamental rights guaranteed by the Constitution: cultural and natural rights (articles 215 and 225, respectively).

We can define a collision of fundamental rights as a situation in which 'the exercise of a fundamental right by one party collides with the exercise of a fundamental right by another party. This is not a case of a crossing or accumulation of rights (such as in a dispute for rights), but of a 'clash', an authentic conflict of rights.'[24] It is therefore a conflict between the fundamental rights and legal assets of traditional populations (cultural heritage), and the right to preserve an environmental asset (natural heritage).

The task of solving these conflicts is not easy, but we must in any case start from the constitutional assumption that all rights have, in principle, equal value, and that conflicts need to be solved, preferably by means of the principle of *agreement in*

---

21. Silva, J. A. da. *Direito ambiental constitucional*, p. 2 (emphasis added).
22. At an international level, Brazil is a signatory to the International Convention Concerning the Protection of the World Cultural and Natural Heritage whose main objective is to establish 'an effective system of collective protection of the cultural and natural heritage of outstanding universal value, organized on a permanent basis and in accordance with modern scientific methods'.
23. Silva, J. A. *op. cit.*, p. 3.
24. Canotilho, J. J. G. *Direito constitucional*, p. 495.

practice. In other words, the solution to the conflict must not lead to a (complete) sacrifice by one party in relation to the other. The conflicting constitutional rights are of equal constitutional value, and there is no hierarchical difference between them. It is therefore important to reach solutions that establish reciprocal limits and conditions in such a way as to reach an agreement in practice between the rights.[25]

If, on the one hand, one of the principles of conservation areas is a concern with protecting endangered ecosystems and species, with defining ecosystems that contribute to the conservation of biodiversity, and with maintaining the biological functions essential to the planet's balance, on the other hand traditional populations represent ethnicities or social groups that have constructed their territoriality within a specific environment. It then becomes a prerequisite to take the distinct forms of land tenure of these populations into consideration, together with their particular forms of use of natural resources, thereby safeguarding their activities and their way of life and cultural identity as communities.

Given that protected areas are important tools for Brazilian environmental conservation policy, their creation cannot be based solely on information concerning the physical environment, leading to decisions based only on information provided by the natural sciences and which ignore the social, economic and cultural processes that exist in the area to be protected. The environment is a unitary concept, made up of natural, artificial and cultural resources.

Traditional populations as beneficiaries of a public purpose

We have seen that we would be able to better define the legal nature of conservation areas by classifying them as environmental assets of public interest, because of the ecological and social interests which form the basis for their creation.

The purpose and use of the area cannot therefore conflict with the objectives of the act that establishes the area, just as it would be illegal or a misunderstanding to affirm that, when a protected area occupied by a traditional population is created, this area then belongs to that social group. A conservation area is protected because of its environmental and cultural characteristics, so the traditional population needs to be integrated with the physical environment, as these aspects constitute the basis for the creation of the area and the defense of the natural and cultural elements to be safeguarded by the State. The traditional population on its own does not justify the creation of the protected area, otherwise this would imply giving them differential legal treatment in relation to other individuals or social groups, which would result in unconstitutionality as all are equal before the law without distinction.

In this situation, the concession (but not the donation or sale) of a public area to traditional populations is based on the principle that the beneficiary population is 'the recipient of a public responsibility deriving from its background and *modus vivendi*, which qualifies it to fulfill the objectives of the law. This is the legal basis for dispensing with the prior public tendering provided for under Article 15, § 1 of Decree-law 2,300 of 1986[26] and obligatory for all contracts let by the State.'[27]

At the same time that the State recognizes the right of the traditional population to its land within a protected area, it is also asserting that this social group has a purpose of special public interest to fulfill. These purposes are laid out in the area's instrument of creation as contracts entered into by the public agency and the beneficiary population, and which will include the forms of use and management of the natural resources, which cannot conflict with the purposes of the act establishing the environmental area.

Legal provision for ceding parts of conservation areas to traditional populations

The first question that arises is whether it is legally possible for an environmental asset of public interest or a public asset to be used by private individuals or bodies. In other words, can traditional populations use areas in the public domain? Diogenes Gasparini, an expert in administrative law, argues that such assets 'can be used in a special way by anyone. The guidance is that, as long as the use satisfies the public interest, does not pervert the objectives, does not lead to alienation, and meets in advance all legal requirements […] private use, even when prolonged, does not alter the ownership of the asset. In fact, the Federal Constitution itself provides for this possibility in article 183, § 3, and article 191. The ownership, therefore, continues to belong to the State.'[28]

One of the administrative provisions regarding the use of public assets, and the most appropriate to this case, is the contract of concession of real right of use. It is the most appropriate for both parties because it offers greater stability in the relationship and because it is a real right. It is upheld and strengthened by the use of the asset, provided that this use respects the agreement reached between the parties.

The legal provision for the contract of concession of real right of use is in contained in Decree 271, of February 28, 1967, which establishes that the concession of real right of use of land is a formal contract transferring the temporary use of public or private land, in the form of real right, for a determined or undetermined period, for specific purposes of urban or industrial development, construction, cultivation, or *any other use in the social interest*.

Generally speaking, ownership of the conservation area belongs to the State, and the transfer of use to the inhabitants of the conservation area takes place by means of the contract of concession of real right of use. If the environmental interests of society are secure, the rights of the social groups that use

---

25. Idem, ibid.
26. Decree-law 2,300 of 1986, article 15, § 1 states: 'The Federal Government, when selling or disposing of property, will preferentially transfer use rights by means of public tender. Tendering may be dispensed with when use is granted to operators of public utilities, social services organizations, or is shown to be of *special public interest*, duly justified' (emphasis added).
27. Gomes, M. E. do A. C. et al. *Tutela jurídica sobre as reservas extrativistas*, p. 79.
28. Gasparini, D. *op. cit.*, p. 530.

these areas in a non-predatory way will also be secure. Therefore, as long as the land is appropriately used, in accordance with the contract, the real right to this use is maintained, and can be transferred to heirs. However, the moment the population fails to respect the agreed forms of use under the contract, or changes the legally defined objectives, the contract will be cancelled and the land will revert to the State.

However, if the reason for canceling the contract is not non-compliance with the contract, but the wish of the parties, the recipients of the concession are entitled to compensation for the improvements and work carried out on the asset, as in any possessory action.

The contract of concession will include a Utilization Plan[29] approved by the area's management authority, containing rescission clauses for cases of environmental damage.

It is the responsibility of the management authority to supervise agro-extractive areas and monitor compliance with the conditions laid down in the contract of concession and the Utilization Plan.

In order to regularize the agrarian law situation of the area, the contract of concession of real right of use should be signed by a legally constituted association representing all the residents of the protected area. The contract can therefore be either collective or individual for each family, as long as all the families agree on a single Utilization Plan.

The ecological Leviathan

The expression 'man is a wolf to man' is well known. This quotation summarizes the ideas of Thomas Hobbes (1588-1679) who argued that man in the natural state was individualistic, profoundly selfish, and with insatiable desires for power, which would only end at death. He would only participate in a social state when the preservation of his life was threatened. Thus he did not naturally live by cooperation; he was not a social being by nature. Life in society was a pact, artificial and precarious, and insufficient in itself to guarantee peace. For the pact to be honored and peace secured, it was necessary that individuals renounce their right to everything and transfer it to a sovereign with absolute powers. In this way, the social state and peace were guaranteed by the despotic State: the Leviathan.[30]

Retaining the central idea of Hobbes and simply changing the characters, we can conclude that man is a profoundly narrow-minded, individualistic destroyer of nature. Man and nature are unable to live 'naturally' in harmony – the former will always try to modify, change, or destroy the latter, disrupting the ecological balance and putting ecosystems at risk. Protected areas have to be created in order to ensure a 'peaceful' co-existence and the survival of nature. However such a pact of mutual respect will only be effective if there is a strong absolute State, which establishes protected areas and concentrates all power in its hands, to the point of not being obliged to justify its actions. We therefore need an ecological Leviathan.

This, in summary, has been the policy of the Brazilian State over all these years concerning the creation of conservation areas. We have come to the conclusion that this is not the best path to be followed. On the basis of our new assumptions, the conception offered in Law 9,985 establishing the National System of Conservation Areas and other measures manages to capture the present historical moment in Brazil. The law states very clearly the importance of protected areas in Brazil, while at the same time offering a proposed remedy to address the injustices suffered by communities who have been directly affected by the creation of the areas. It recognizes that the simple removal of traditional populations from their areas, where the encroachment of protected areas has occurred, is not just damaging from a social perspective, but also has serious consequences for nature conservation.

In this way, it separates the question of traditional populations into two distinct stages:

a) The discussion of the rights of traditional populations living in strict protection units established under past legislation, under which such areas were created and managed with no consultation with society and paying no attention to the rights of the communities directly affected.

In these cases Ibama will have a period of five years, with a further extension of five years subject to approval by Conama, in which to relocate such populations or to reclassify the area occupied by them as extractive reserves or cultural ecological reserves. However, the decision to reclassify or relocate will be taken by a working group created for this purpose and composed of representatives of the traditional population resident in the conservation area, the area's management authority and, if necessary, other public and private institutions with acknowledged expertise. The working group will review the situation and propose measures to overcome the problem whilst respecting the legislation in force.

The same procedure will occur in cases of total or partial overlaps between conservation areas created under previous legislation and indigenous areas. A working group will be formed in each case, composed of representatives of the resident indigenous community, the environmental and indian affairs agencies and, if necessary, other public and private institutions with acknowledged expertise and will analyze the matter and propose measures to solve the problem of boundaries between the conservation and indigenous areas. In cases where it proves impossible to reconcile the different objectives and interests, or in a case of total overlap, the instrument establishing the conservation area will be revoked.

b) The creation of new conservation units will be preceded by technical studies and full consultation between the population residing in the area and its surroundings, federal, state and municipal government agencies, research institutions and non-governmental organizations. This consultation will occur by means of public hearings and local meetings with the different social sectors directly involved in the selected area. The official environment agency is required to provide appropriate and comprehensible information to the local population and to other interested parties, allowing them sufficient time to prepare their own proposals. It should be noted that this whole discussion process will also help to better define the size and most appropriate boundaries of the area.

---

29. The Utilization Plan is a document drawn up, discussed and agreed by the resident population of the protected area, on the basis of their accumulated knowledge arising out of the contact with nature and the development of non-predatory forms of natural resource use that ensure forest conservation.
30. Hobbes, T. *Leviathan, or Matter, Form, and Power of a Commonwealth, Ecclesiastic and Civil*, p. XIV - XVI.

As a result, the creation of a new conservation area will be preceded by debates and clarification of the importance of the protected area. During the course of these discussions the legitimacy of the protected area at the regional level will be enhanced, since the final say on the establishment of the area, its type, size and boundaries will be a collective decision of society as opposed to one of an ecological Leviathan.

BIBLIOGRAPHY

ACSELRAD, H. Repensando o Conama: elementos para a discussão. In: *Projeto Meio Ambiente e Democracia*. Rio de Janeiro: Ibase, May 1995.

AGUIAR, R. A. R. de. *Direito do meio ambiente e participação popular*. Brasília: Ibama, 1994.

ALMEIDA, A. W. B. de. Terras de preto, terras de santo, terras de índio: uso comum e conflitos. In: CASTRO, E. M. & HEBETTE, J. (Eds.) *Na trilha dos grandes projetos*. Belém: Naea/UFPA, 1989.

ANTUNES, P. de B. *Curso de direito ambiental: doutrina, legislação e jurisprudência*. Rio de Janeiro: Renovar, 1990.

BENATTI, J. H. *Manual do plano de utilização para as reservas extrativistas*. Brasília: CNPT/Ibama, 1993. Typescript.

_____ & MAUES, A. G. M. O pluralismo jurídico e as posses agrárias na Amazônia. *Lições de direito civil alternativo*. São Paulo: Acadêmica, 1994.

_____. A posse agrária alternativa e a reserva extrativista. In: D'INCAO, M. A. & SILVEIRA, I. M. da (Eds.). *A Amazônia e a crise de modernização*. Belém: Museu Paraense Emílio Goeldi, 1994.

_____. *Posse agroecológica:* um estudo das concepções jurídicas de camponeses agroextrativistas na Amazônia. MA Thesis, 1996. Universidade Federal do Pará, Belém.

BRESSAN, D. *Gestão racional da natureza*. São Paulo: Hucitec, 1996.

CANDOTTI, E. Reflexões e refrações de uma Eco. *Revista Estudos Avançados*, v. 6, n. 15, 1992. São Paulo: USP.

CANOTILHO, J. J. G. *Direito constitucional*. Coimbra: Almedina, 4. ed., 1989.

CARDOSO, F. H. *Mãos à obra:* proposta de governo de Fernando Henrique Cardoso. Brasília: 1994.

CONSTITUIÇÃO DA REPÚBLICA FEDERATIVA DO BRASIL. Brasília: Senado Federal, Centro Gráfico, 1988.

DIEGUES, A. C. S. *O mito moderno da natureza intocada*. São Paulo: Nupaub/USP, 1994.

CÂMARA DOS DEPUTADOS. *Estratégia mundial para a conservação*. Brasília: Comissão de Defesa do Consumidor, Meio Ambiente e Minorias, Sept. 1994, typescript.

_____. *Substitutivo ao Projeto de Lei nº 2.892/92*. Brasília: Comissão de Defesa do Consumidor, Meio Ambiente e Minorias, 1996. Typescript.

FERNANDES, R. N. Da concessão de uso de bens públicos. *Revista de Direito Administrativo*, n. 118, Oct.-Dec. 1974, p. 1-11, Rio de Janeiro.

FERRAZ, G. C. Concessão de uso de terras públicas como direito real resolúvel. *Revista de Direito Agrário*, v. 9, n. 8, 2. sem. 1982, Brasília.

FERREIRA, I. S. Tutela penal do patrimônio cultural. *Revista dos Tribunais*, 1995, São Paulo.

FIGUEIREDO, L. V. *Curso de direito administrativo*. São Paulo: Malheiros, 1994.

FIORILLO, C. A. P. & RODRIGUES, M. A. *Direito ambiental e patrimônio genético*. Belo Horizonte: Del Rey, 1996.

GASPARINI, D. *Direito administrativo*. São Paulo: Saraiva, 1993.

GOMES, M. E. A. C. & FELIPE, L. D. Tutela jurídica sobre as reservas extrativistas. *O destino da floresta: reservas extrativistas e desenvolvimento sustentável na Amazônia*. Rio de Janeiro/Curitiba: Relume-Dumará/Instituto de Estudos Amazônicos e Ambientais/Fundação Konrad Adenauer, 1994.

HOBBES, T. *Leviatã ou matéria, forma e poder de um Estado eclesiático e civil*. São Paulo: Nova Cultural, 4ª ed., 1988.

KITAMURA, P. C. *Desenvolvimento sustentável: uma abordagem para as questões ambientais da Amazônia*. 1994. PhD Thesis. Campinas.

LIRA, R. P. A concessão do direito real de uso. *Revista de Direito Administrativo*, n. 163, p. 16-57, Jan./Mar. 1986, Rio de Janeiro.

MACHADO, P. A. L. *Direito ambiental brasileiro*. São Paulo: Malheiros, 4. ed., revised and expanded, 1992.

MEIRELLES, H. L. *Direito administrativo brasileiro*. São Paulo: Malheiros, 18th edition updated by Eurico de Andrade Azevedo, Délcio Balestero Aleixo and José Emmanuel Burle Filho, 1993.

MINISTÉRIO DO MEIO AMBIENTE E DA AMAZÔNIA LEGAL / IBAMA. *Roteiro técnico para elaboração/revisão de planos de manejo em áreas protegidas de uso indireto*. Brasília: 2nd version, 1994. Typescript.

_____. *Unidades de conservação*. Brasília: *folder*, n/d.

MOREIRA NETO, D. de F. *Curso de direito administrativo*. Rio de Janeiro: Forense, 1989.

MOTTA, N. J. *Breve resumo sobre unidades de conservação no direito brasileiro*. Curitiba: 1993. Typescript.

MURRIETA, J. R. & RUEDA, R. P. *Reservas extrativistas*. Gland, Switzerland and Cambridge, UK: IUCN, 1995.

RODRIGUES, J. E. R. Aspectos jurídicos das unidades de conservação. *Revista de Direito Ambiental*. São Paulo: Revista dos Tribunais, ano 1, Jan./Mar. 1996.

SCHUBART, H. O. R. O zoneamento ecológico-econômico como instrumento para o desenvolvimento sustentável da Amazônia. In: D'INCAO, M. A & SILVEIRA, I. M (Eds.). *A Amazônia e a crise de modernização*. Belém: Museu Paraense Emílio Goeldi, 1994.

SILVA, J. A. da. *Curso de direito constitucional positivo*. São Paulo: Revista dos Tribunais, 6. ed., 1990.

_____. Terras tradicionalmente ocupadas pelos índios. In: *Os direitos indígenas e a Constituição*. Porto Alegre: NDI/Fabris, 1993.

_____. *Direito ambiental constitucional*. São Paulo: Malheiros, 1994.

SOUZA, M. C. de. Das unidades de conservação criadas pelo Poder Público: conceito, classificação e possibilidade de cessão de uso a órgão público ou particular. *Revista de Direito Ambiental*. São Paulo: Revista dos Tribunais, ano 1, Jan./Mar. de 1996.

SOUZA FILHO, C. F. M. de. *Espaços ambientais protegidos e unidades de conservação*. Curitiba: Universitária Champagnat, 1993.

WWF. *Subsídios para discussão – Workshop 'Diretrizes políticas para unidades de conservação'*. Brasília: November 1994. Typescript.

Thematic documents 4

Socioeconomic and anthropogenic pressures

An analysis of the demography, socioeconomics and anthropogenic pressures in the Legal Amazon region

Maurício Pontes Monteiro and Donald Sawyer *Instituto Sociedade, População e Natureza*

Introduction

The present study will present a descriptive analysis of the results of demographic and socioeconomic indicators derived from secondary data for the Legal Amazon region. It is divided into three major parts. The first addresses the nature of the available information used for the analysis, its spatial distribution, and its quantification, with emphasis on the sources used and the selection of the principal indicators of the relevant subject matter. The second analyses the existing information and describes socioeconomic trends in the region. Finally we present a synthesis of the studies undertaken and some final considerations.

The nature of the available information

The main objective of the phase of describing the demographic and socioeconomic information on the area that comprises Legal Amazonia was to carry out a preliminary survey of the data and information with a view to developing indicators of anthropogenic pressure, as well as the production of cartographic outputs in the form of thematic maps of regional indicators. The information was initially drawn from municipal-level census data held, largely, by the Instituto Brasileiro de Geografia e Estatística (IBGE) and available through the Samba-Cabral system, complemented by data and reference information from other official sources. The municipality was adopted as the base mapping unit since it represents the smallest political and administrative unit for which the majority of the demographic and socioeconomic data have been made available.

The database for which indicators of anthropogenic pressure and of environmental sustainability, as well as for other socioeconomic studies, were created was derived from the following sources and/or institutions:
- 1980 and 1991 population censuses, IBGE;
- 1996 population count, IBGE;
- 1985 and 1995-96 agricultural and livestock censuses, IBGE;
- 1990 to 1994 agricultural production by municipality data, IBGE;
- 1990 to 1994 livestock production by municipality data, IBGE;
- 1993 plant extractive activities and forestry data, IBGE;
- 1997 Atlas of Human Development in Brazil, UNDP, IPEA and FJP;
- 1989 to 1995 National Treasury Secretariat data;
- 1993 to 1995 National Health Foundation data.

Quantifying the available information

During the phase of quantifying the information available from these sources, the development of indicators took place, as a means of permitting a better understanding of the demographic dynamics and of the overall evolution of regional economic development, human development and anthropogenic pressures. To allow a better understanding of the details of the chosen indicators, these have been arranged into three major groups: i) demographic, ii) socioeconomic and iii) human development and anthropogenic pressure.

Demographic indicators

Total population, rural and urban populations, and levels of urbanization

The variables for total population and for urban and rural population were selected for the years 1980, 1991 and 1996 on the basis of the IBGE census data and have been quantified by number of inhabitants. The 1996 population count took into account the creation of new municipalities, in such a way that the data is presented according to the municipalities in existence on January 1, 1997. For the spatial mapping, the total population data were represented by proportional symbols of different sizes and the level of urbanization (the ratio between urban and total population) was represented by different colors.

Rural and total demographic densities

Rural and total demographic densities, expressed in terms of inhabitants per square kilometer, were similarly quantified and mapped for the years 1980, 1991 and 1996, on the basis of the IBGE population censuses. Levels of population density constitute indicators of anthropogenic pressure, as they are related to the municipal area.

Rate of population growth between 1980 and 1991

Absolute and relative population growth constitutes a flux or trend indicator. The 1991 'Preliminary Synopsis of the Population Census' provided information on the total population in 1980 of the municipalities in existence in 1991 and this permits calculation of absolute growth and of annual averages. The same cannot be done for the period 1991 to 1996, as the IBGE did not publish comparative population data for this period. The following formula was used to quantify the figures for the period 1980 to 1991:

Rate8091 = {exp [ln (pop91/pop80) / (ny)] – 1}*100, where:
Rate8091 = Rate of population growth between 1980 and 1991
Pop91 = Total population 1991; Pop80 = Total population 1980
ny = Number of years

Socioeconomic indicators

Equity

The equity analysis used data drawn from the 1980 and 1991 population censuses. A comparative analysis of two main variables was undertaken: i) total number of people earning less than one minimum salary, and ii) total number of people earning more than twenty minimum salaries. The purpose of the analysis was to compare levels of income inequality, since the variables chosen were at opposite ends of the scale. The Gini Index was also used as an indicator of concentration of family income, using data from the 1991 population census.

Education

The main indicator of education used in the analysis was the total number of illiterates in 1991, also taken from the 1991 population census.

Health

For health indicators, the following variables were used in the study: i) life expectancy at birth (in years) and ii) infant mortality rate (number of deaths per thousand live births), with reference to 1980 and 1991 in both cases. The data sources are found in the 'Atlas of Human Development in Brazil' published by UNDP, IPEA and FJP. Another important indicator of anthropogenic pressure in the region concerns malaria, the data sources for which derive from the National Health Foundation data for 1993, 1994 and 1995. In this case two main variables were selected and mapped: i) number of patients testing positive and ii) the ratio of positive slides.

Public expenditures

The question of public expenditure for the Legal Amazon region was analyzed for the period 1989 to 1995 using data from the National Treasury Secretariat. For this the following indicators of the public expenditures were adopted: i) total current revenue, ii) domestic revenues (comprising the sum of tax revenues, revenue from property and assets, industrial revenues, revenues from the service sector and other current revenues) and iii) total current expenses.

Extractivism

Plant extractive production constitutes an indicator of the use, sustainable or otherwise, of biodiversity. For this case, the following products were mapped: i) rubber, by quantity (kg); ii) Brazil-nuts, by quantity (kg); iii) and wood, by extraction (cubic meters). The source of the data used was the IBGE data on plant extractive activities and forestry for 1993.

Indicators of human development and anthropogenic pressure

Human Development Index (HDI)

The Human Development Index, created in the 1990s by the United Nations Development Programme, combines three basic components of development:

- *Life expectancy*, which also reflects the health status of the population and is measured by life expectancy at birth;
- *Education*, measured by a combination of the adult literacy rate and the combined enrolment rate at primary, secondary, and tertiary levels; and
- *Income*, measured by the purchasing power of the population, based on GDP per capita adjusted to the local cost of living so as to allow comparison between countries, using the purchasing power parity (PPP) methodology.

The methodology for calculating the HDI involves transforming these three aspects into indices of life expectancy, education and income ranging from 0 (worst) to 1 (best), and combining these indices into a synthesis-indicator. The nearer the value of this indicator is to 1, the higher the level of human development of the country or the region will be. For this case the three components of the HDI (life expectancy, education and income) were quantified, together with a combined municipal index. The data from the PNUD/IPEA/FJP Atlas of Human Development in Brazil were mapped.

Index of Anthropogenic Pressure (IAP)

The Index of Anthropogenic Pressure constitutes an indicator that synthesizes the economic and demographic pressures exerted on the environment. It is made up of secondary data. The principal data sources were the following IBGE publications: population censuses, agriculture and livestock censuses, and municipal agricultural and livestock production data.

The methodological basis for developing the IAP consists of combining the stock (size or density) and the flow (speed or growth) sizes (Sawyer 1997). It is assumed that pressure is greater when the stock and the flow are higher, and less when both are lower. In the present study, stock and flow sizes were placed into one of three levels (low, medium and high) represented, respectively, by the values 0, 1 and 2. Overlaying two variables creates a 3 x 3 matrix, with nine data fields, and the sum of the values of the two variables gives a scale from 0 to 4, as shown in the following table:

Stock	Flow		
	0	1	2
0	0	1	2
1	1	2	3
2	2	3	4

For the purpose of developing an index of anthropogenic pressure index in the Amazon region in the present study, five levels were used: very low, low, medium, high and very high, represented by the values 1, 2, 3, 4 and 5. In this way, the overlay of two variables generated a 5 x 5 matrix, giving an index scale that ranges from 2 to 10, as shown below:

Stock	Flow				
	1	2	3	4	5
1	2	3	4	5	6
2	3	4	5	6	7
3	4	5	6	7	8
4	5	6	7	8	9
5	6	7	8	9	10

Given the availability of data, anthropogenic pressure can be calculated by means of two factors: i) anthropogenic population pressure (APP) and ii) anthropogenic agricultural pressure (AAP).

The population pressure can be calculated using the following sub-indices and their respective stock and flow variables:

UAP – *Urban anthropogenic pressure* (2-10), the result of combining:
  TSP: Total size of the urban population of the micro-region in 1996 (1-5)
  TGP: Total growth of the urban population of the micro-region between 1991 and 1996 (1-5)

RAP – Rural anthropogenic pressure (2-10), the result of combining:
  DRP: Density of the rural population of the municipality in 1996 (1-5)
  DGP: Density of the total growth of the rural population of the municipality between 1991 and 1996 (1-5).

The anthropogenic pressure due to agriculture and livestock can be calculated using the following secondary indices and their respective stock and flow variables:

APA – Anthropogenic pressure of arable farming (2-10), the result of combining:
  DAF: Density of arable farming (areas planted with rice, maize and soy beans) in 1996 (1-5)
  DGF: Density of the growth of arable farming (areas planted with rice, maize and soy beans) between 1991 and 1996 (1-5)

APC – Anthropogenic pressure of cattle (2-10), the result of combining:
  DCA: Density of cattle in 1996 (1-5)
  DGC: Density of the total growth of cattle herds between 1991 and 1996 (1-5)

Evaluation of the available information and socioeconomic tendencies

Demography

According to figures from the IBGE Population Count, in 1996 the Amazon region comprised a total of around eighteen million inhabitants, corresponding to about 11.5% of the total population of Brazil. The states of the Federation with the largest proportions of the regional population were: i) Pará with five and a half million inhabitants, ii) Maranhão, four and a half million, iii) Amazonas, 2.4 million and iv) Mato Grosso, 2.2 million. Together, these four states account for approximately 80% the total regional population (Table 1 and Figure 1).

The demographic portrait of the Legal Amazon Region is one of a region largely made up of municipalities with total populations of fewer than 100,000 inhabitants. There is a higher concentration of population in the eastern part of the region, in a north-south line along the eastern border of Pará and the western border of Maranhão, an area made up of a large number of municipalities with total populations of more than 40,000 inhabitants. There was an increase of 75% in the number of municipalities with populations greater than 100,000 during the period 1980 to 1996: in 1980 there were only 13, by 1991 there were 19, and by 1996 this number had reached 23.

The demographic density of the total population of the Amazon region is around 3.6 inhabitants per square kilometer according to data for 1996. Virtually all states showed indices equivalent to or fewer than five inhabitants per square kilometer, with the exception of Maranhão, which recorded the highest levels in the region for this year - around fifteen inhabitants per square kilometer. Spatial analysis of the indicator reveals the existence, from 1980 onwards, of a sub-region of higher population densities, with a significant concentration of municipalities with levels greater than fifteen inhabitants per square kilometer, in an area extending from the centre-north of Maranhão to northeastern Pará. In the period 1980 to 1996 we can see not only a higher density for municipalities in this sub-region in 1991, but also the formation of sub-regions with demographic densities of more than five inhabitants per square kilometer such as: i) the Rondônia-Acre corridor, ii) the area surrounding Manaus, eastern Amazonas and western Pará iii) the central-northern Tocantins corridor, and iv) the central part of Mato Grosso (Figure 4).

Analysis of urban population data indicates that the population size practically doubled during the period 1980 to 1996, reaching a total of approximately 11.2 million inhabitants by 1996. Levels of urbanization also changed during this period, increasing from 45% in 1980 to 61% in 1996 (Table 2). The Amazon states which showed the highest indices of urbanization levels in 1996 are: Amapá (87.1%), Goiás (79.3%) and Mato Grosso (75.8%) (Figure 2). In 1980 municipalities with an urban population of 50,000 and above were mainly concentrated in the regional state capitals. Their total number grew from 12 in 1980, to 25 in 1991, and to 31 municipalities in 1996. Analysis of levels of urbanization revealed that, generally speaking, there was a tendency in the period 1980 to 1996 towards the concentration of municipalities with high levels of urbanization (more than 80%) across Rondônia, southern Mato Grosso and along the corridor linking the central and northern parts of Tocantins (Figure 5).

The tendency towards increasing levels of urbanization in the region has led to the same problems as those which affect

TABLE 1 - POPULATION OVERVIEW OF THE LEGAL AMAZON						
State	Total population 1980	% 1980	Total population 1981	% 1991	Total population 1996	% 1996
Rondônia	491,025	4.38	1,132,692	6.91	1,231,007	6.80
Acre	301,276	2.68	417,718	2.55	483,726	2.67
Amazonas	1,430,528	12.75	2,103,243	12.84	2,389,279	13.20
Roraima	79,121	0.71	217,583	1.33	247,131	1.36
Pará	3,403,498	30.33	4,950,060	30.21	5,510,849	30.44
Amapá	175,258	1.56	289,397	1.77	379,459	2.10
Tocantins	739.049	6.59	919,863	5.61	1,048,642	5.79
Maranhão	3,379,814	30.12	4,233,997	25.84	4,487,272	24.78
Mato Grosso	1,138,918	10.15	2,027,231	12.37	2,235,832	12.35
Goiás	83,203	0.74	92,046	0.56	93,631	0.52
Total	11,221,690	100.00	16,383,830	100.00	18,106,828	100.00

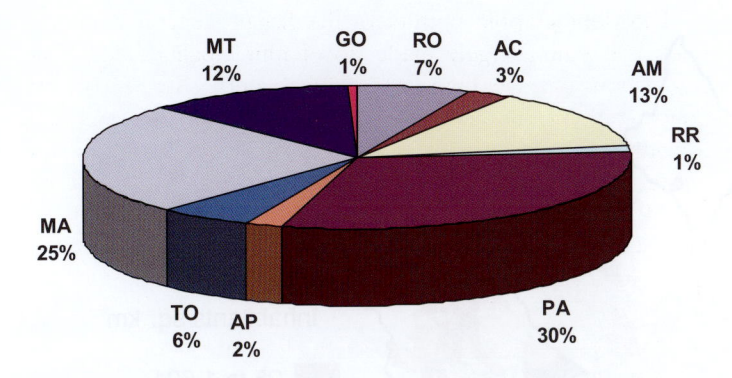

Figure 1. Population of the Legal Amazon region by state, 1996.

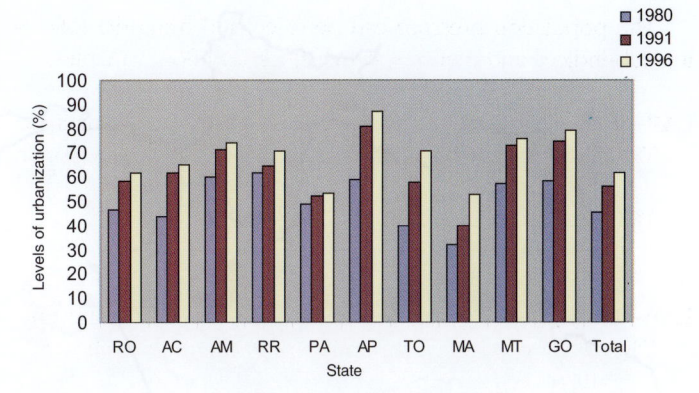

Figure 2. Levels of urbanization in Amazonia, 1980-1996.

the populations of large Brazilian cities and which result from a combination of different factors. Amongst these are high growth rates, the poverty of the migrating population, the lack of resources on the part of municipal and state governments, and tropical environmental factors, which consequently lead to more serious problems of environmental degradation than those found in the more developed urban areas, since a large part of the regional population has to make do with precarious infrastructural conditions, principally as regards sanitation (GTA/Amigos da Terra 1998).

As regards rural population, the percentage of the population living in rural areas varies between 77% and 87% in those regional municipalities with populations of fewer than 20,000. Spatial analysis of the rural population in 1980 identified four regions with higher concentrations of rural population: i) northwestern and central Maranhão, ii) northern Pará and southern Amapá; iii) central Amazonas and iv) northern Rondônia. As far as demographic density of the rural population is concerned, it can be clearly seen that the regions of higher density are those located along a corridor from northern Maranhão to northeastern Pará, which generally speaking have indices of more than ten inhabitants per square kilometer. As is the case with total population, rural population density reveals a predominance of municipalities, amounting to 70% of those in the region, with low population indices of fewer than five inhabitants per square kilometer.

Figure 3 presents the evolution of regional population growth for, respectively, total, urban and rural population for the years 1980, 1991 and 1996. Comparing the 1980-1991 and 1991-1996 periods it can be seen that the yearly average rate of population growth fell from 3.5 to 2%. The reduction in the rate of population growth was observed in almost all states, with Amapá and Tocantins as the only exceptions. When the periods 1980-1991 and 1991-1996 are compared, Rondônia and Roraima show significant reductions, in the order of 6 to 7 percentage points,

whilst the remaining states show gradual reductions, consistent with the regional average. As in the case of total population, urban population showed significant growth during recent years: 5.4% per year for the period 1980 to 1991 and 4.08% per year for 1991 to 1996. During the period 1980 to 1991, Rondônia and Roraima showed the highest indices of urban population growth, with annual rates of 10%, whilst in the period 1991 to 1996 other states showed growth tendencies, such as Tocantins and Amapá with annual rates of 6% to 7%. The rural population remained essentially unchanged during the period 1980 to 1996. It is worth pointing out that for the period 1991 to 1996 there was a fall of approximately 0.85%, a tendency that could be observed in almost every state, despite the fact that almost 86,000 families had been settled in the region during the period 1980 to 1995 as a result of state-sponsored agrarian reform programs, according to data from the MST and Incra (Stédile 1997). This can be seen in Table 3.

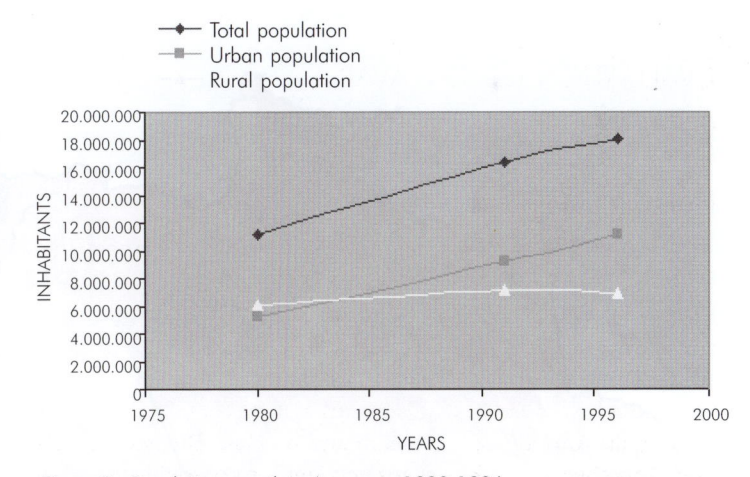

Figure 3. Population growth in Amazonia 1980-1996.

Table 2 - Urban population and level of urbanization for the Amazon region					
State	Urban population 1980	% 1980	Urban population 1981	% 1991	Urban population 1996	% 1996
Rondônia	228,539	46.54	659,327	58.21	762,864	61.97
Acre	132,169	43.87	258,520	61.89	315,404	65.20
Amazonas	856,617	59.88	1,502,754	71.45	1,766,166	73.92
Roraima	48,734	61.59	140,818	64.72	174,277	70.52
Pará	1,667,356	48.99	2,596,388	52.45	2,949,017	53.51
Amapá	103,735	59.19	234,131	80.90	330,590	87.12
Tocantins	293,442	39.71	530,636	57.69	741,009	70.66
Maranhão	1,083,768	32.07	1,684,048	39.77	2,377,735	52.99
Mato Grosso	654,952	57.51	1,485,110	73.26	1,695,548	75.84
Goiás	48,736	58.57	68,728	74.67	74,235	79.28
Total	5,118,048	45.61	9,160,460	55.91	11,186,845	61.78

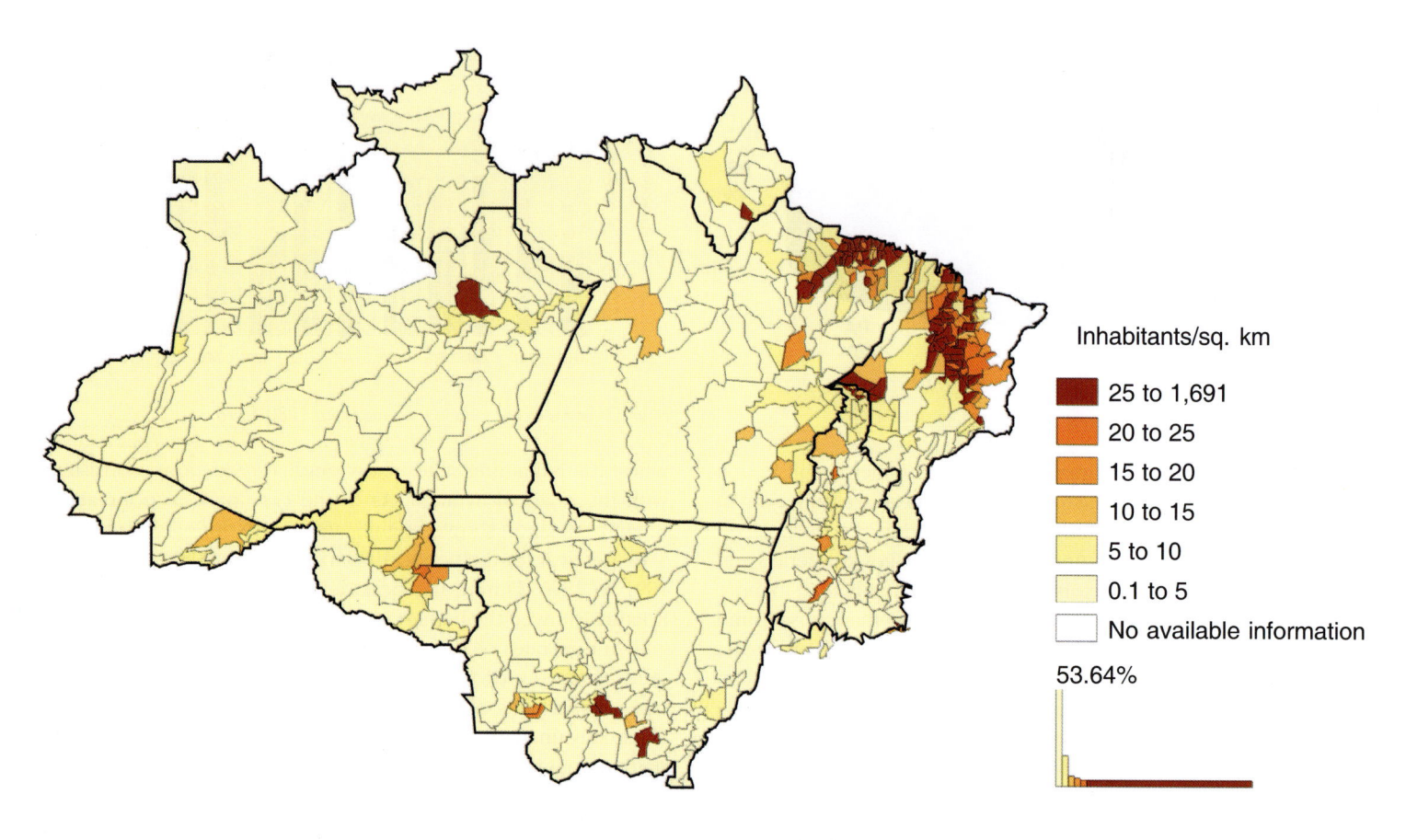

Figure 4. Total population density of Amazonia, 1991.
Source: 1991 population census

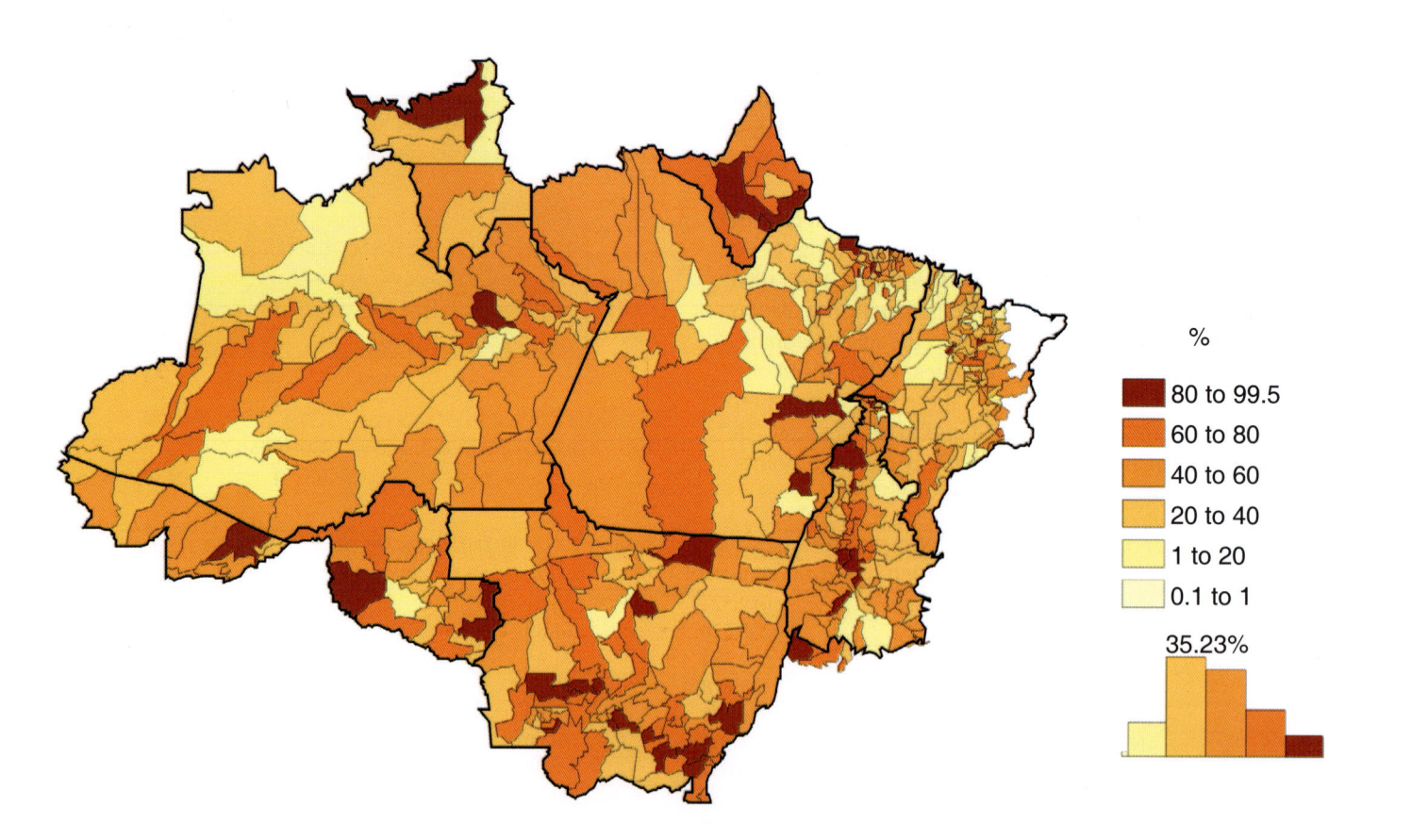

Figure 5. Level of urbanization in Amazonia, 1991.
Source: 1991 population census

TABLE 3 - AGRARIAN REFORM SETTLEMENTS IN AMAZONIAN STATES 1980-1995			
State	no. of settlements	no. of families	Total (ha)
Rondônia	33	13,324	720,080
Acre	3	1,104	326,500
Amazonas	10	5,847	461,514
Roraima	3	5,016	463,300
Pará	57	21,624	1,259,216
Amapá	13	1,696	254,277
Tocantins	62	5,606	326,318
Maranhão	51	12,847	1,104,582
Mato Grosso	119	18,646	956,562
Total	351	85,710	5,872,349
BRAZIL	1123	139,223	7,269,671

Spatial analysis of the annual rate of population growth was carried out for the period 1980 to 1991 (Figure 6) since, as previously mentioned, the 1991 IBGE preliminary synopsis of the population census gave the 1980 total population figures for the municipalities existing in 1991, thus permitting a comparative analysis of these years. Spatial analysis of this variable at the regional level revealed a population reduction throughout an area extending from eastern Mato Grosso to Maranhão, which showed negative rates of population growth. On the other hand, areas adjoining this sub-region, such as the centre-north of Mato Grosso, southwestern Pará and Rondônia, showed high rates of population growth, generally speaking above 3%, which suggests a tendency for a southwest-northeast migration within eastern Amazonia. Sub-regions with negative population growth rates can also be seen in the centre-east of Amazonas and in Acre, while there are sub-regions with higher population growth in northern Amazonas and in southern Roraima, which may also suggest another trend for migration flows within the region (Figure 3).

Socioeconomic indicators

Equity

As far as analysis of the index of concentration of family income, the Gini index, is concerned, the majority of municipalities (around 54%) showed an index varying from 0.45 to 0.60. Eastern Amazonia showed a tendency towards a higher level of equity in terms of family income, with a predominance of municipalities with indices of 0.45 to 0.60. However the highest inequalities can be found in the western part of the region. Some municipalities in western Amazonas exhibit the best indices in the region, greater than 0.75, whereas Gini index values in the northern and center-south regions of Amazonas are below 0.45.

As for the total number of households with incomes of less than one minimum salary, a considerable number of municipalities with more than 2,000 such households was found in the case of 1980. These stretched from southern Tocantins, through Maranhão, to northeastern Pará. Another important sub-region corresponds to the band extending from northwestern Pará to southern Mato Grosso and including Rondônia. For 1991, a gradual reduction in the number of municipalities with a high number of households with an income below one minimum salary could be seen in eastern Amazonia. It is possible that this is linked to two factors: i) improvements in the living standards of the local population in terms of income and ii) reduced population growth, with loss of dynamism of economic activities possibly leading to an outflow of population in search of areas of better opportunities. As regards the total number of household with incomes greater than twenty minimum salaries, in 1980 there was a preponderance (more than 90%) of municipalities with fewer than 500 households with such levels of income. Those municipalities not conforming to this pattern were largely confined to the larger regional state capitals. Figures for 1991 remain largely unchanged and comparable to those for 1980.

Education

As regards education, generally speaking the Amazon region has illiteracy rates of approximately 45%, according to data from the 1991 population census (Table 4). Among the states with the highest illiteracy rates are: Maranhão (54.8%), Acre (50.9%) and Tocantins (46.7%). The lowest rates are found in Mato Grosso (33.7%), Goiás (36.2%) and Roraima (37%). Spatial analysis of this indicator for 1991 shows that the situation varies widely within the region as a whole. In general, approximately 60% of municipalities have an illiterate population of between 1,000 and 15,000. These predominate above all in the southern (Mato Grosso and Tocantins) and northern (principally northern Amazonas and Roraima) parts of the region. Municipalities with the highest numbers of illiterates are generally concentrated in the central part of the region, in a band extending from Acre to Maranhão, including southern Amazonas and Pará. In this region municipalities with more than 15,000 illiterates are more frequent (Figure 7).

Health

Analysis of health indicators for the Amazon region found that, in the case of infant mortality, there was a majority of municipalities in 1980 with infant mortality rates of more than 50 deaths per thousand live births. This included an extreme situation in Maranhão, where virtually all municipalities showed rates of more than 90 deaths per thousand live births. Although of less relevance, southern Pará and Acre should be mentioned as having rates of more than 75 deaths per thousand live births. On the other hand, the region with the lowest infant mortality rates was found mainly in Mato Grosso, where municipalities with rates of fewer than 50 deaths per thousand live births predominated. A comparison with 1991 showed a sharp fall in the region as a whole, with a majority of municipalities showing rates of below 50 deaths per thousand live births. Maranhão

TABLE 4 - ILLITERATE POPULATION AND ILLITERACY LEVELS BY AMAZONIAN STATE			
State	Total pop. 1991	Illiterate pop. 1991	% illiterate pop. 1991
Rondônia	1,132,692	404,284	35.69
Acre	417,718	212,467	50.86
Amazonas	2,103,243	902,390	42.90
Roraima	217,583	80,592	37.04
Pará	4,950,060	2,151,911	43.47
Amapá	289,397	113.684	39.28
Tocantins	919,863	429.848	46.73
Maranhão	4,233,997	2,319,761	54.79
Mato Grosso	2,027,231	683,537	33.72
Goiás	92,046	33,295	36.17
Total	16,383,830	7,331,769	44.75

%

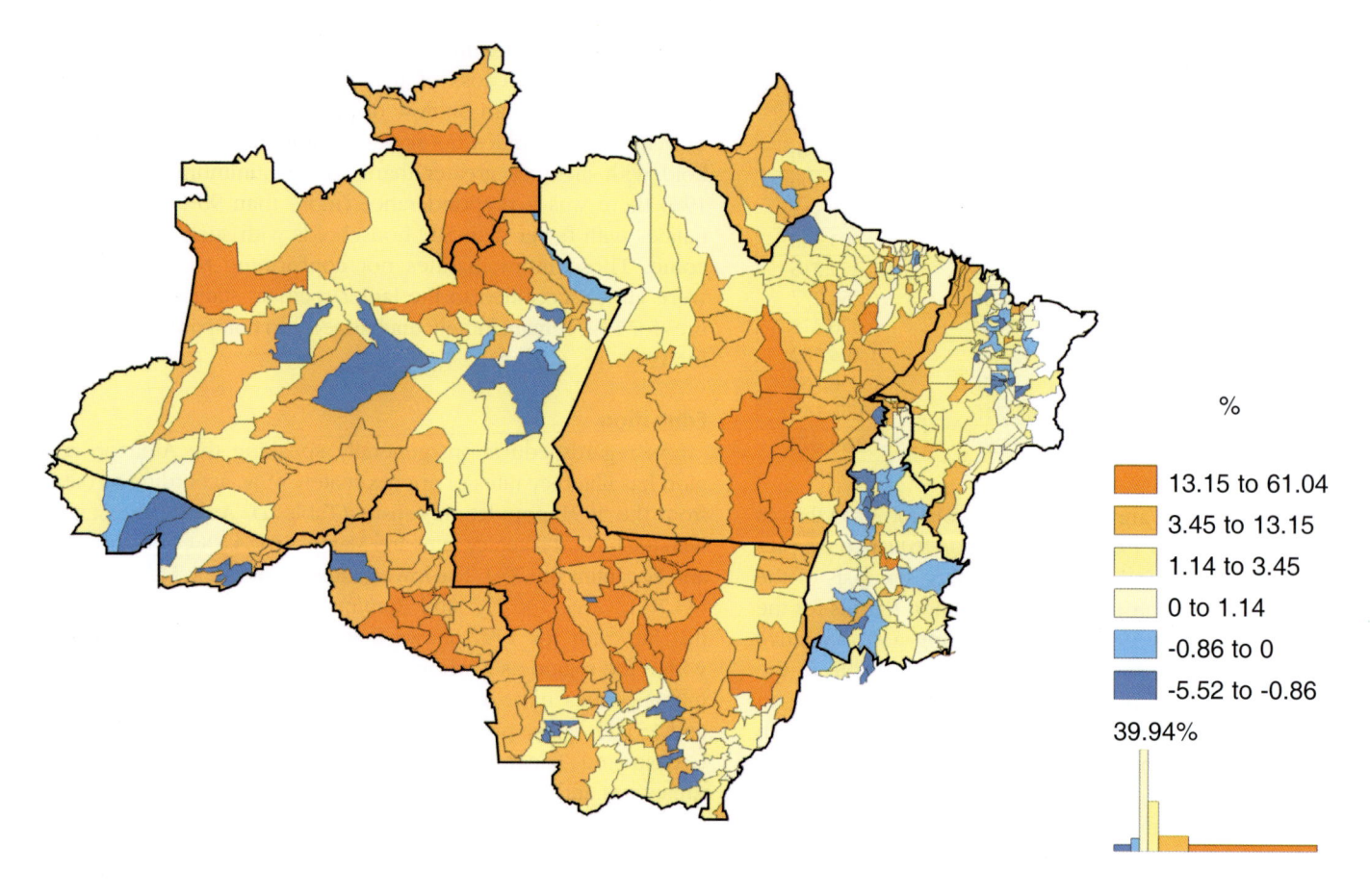

■ 13.15 to 61.04
■ 3.45 to 13.15
■ 1.14 to 3.45
□ 0 to 1.14
■ -0.86 to 0
■ -5.52 to -0.86

39.94%

Figure 6. Growth rate of total population 1980-1991.
Source: 1980 and 1991 population censuses

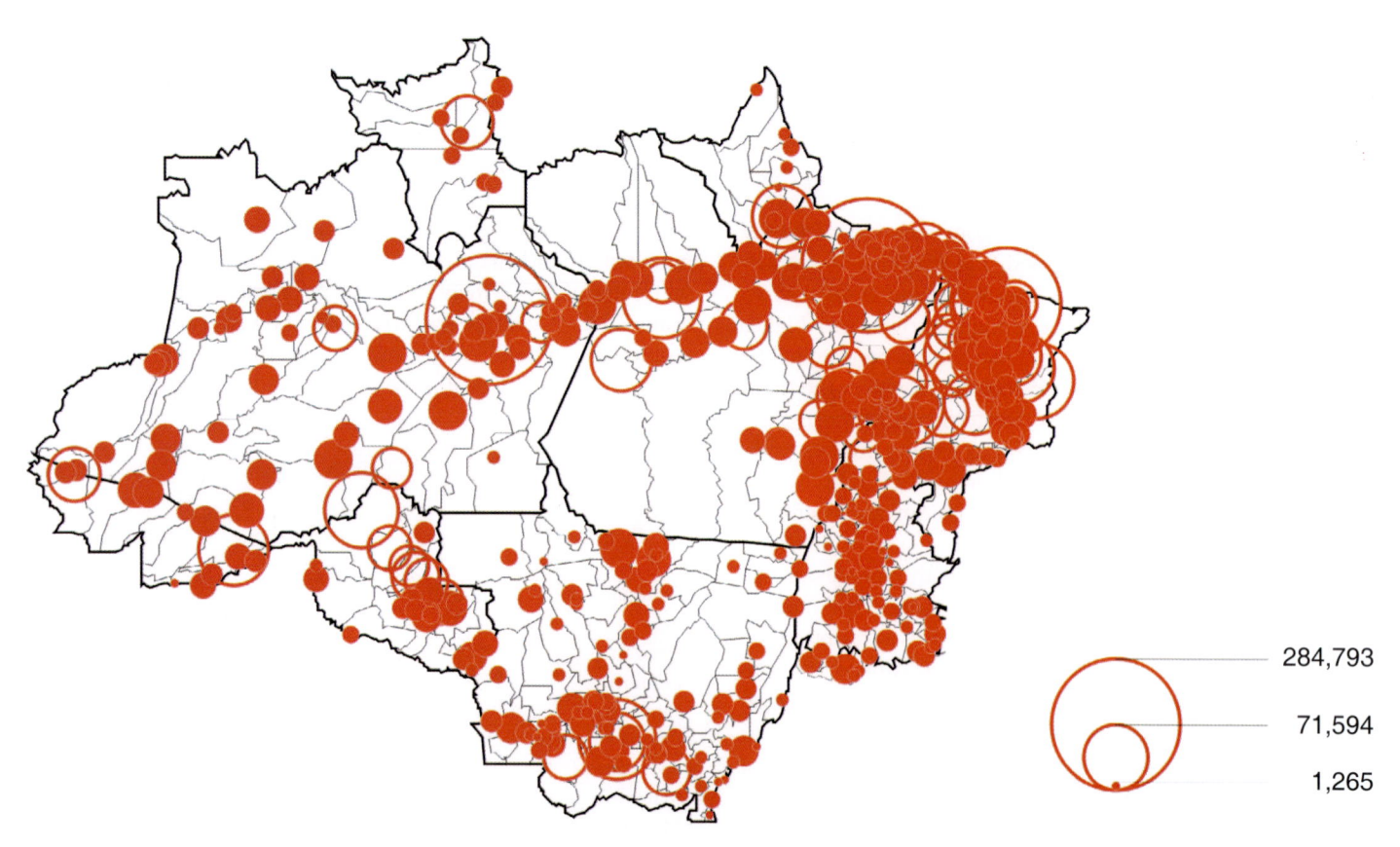

284,793
71,594
1,265

Figure 7. Total number of illiterates in Amazonia 1991.
Source: 1991 population census

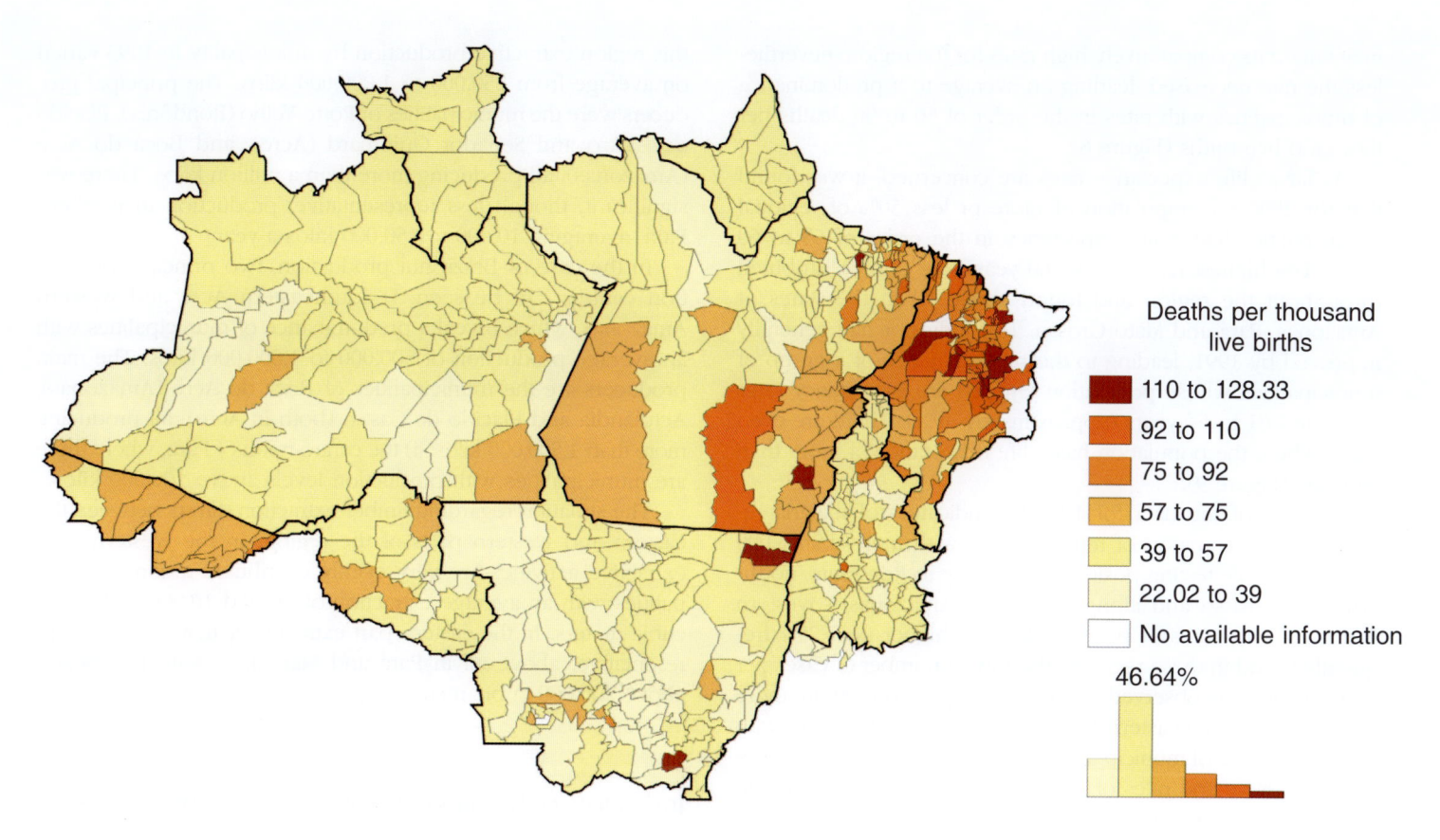

Figure 8. Total infant mortality in Amazonia 1991.
Source: Atlas of Human Development in Brazil - PNUD/IPEA/FIP.

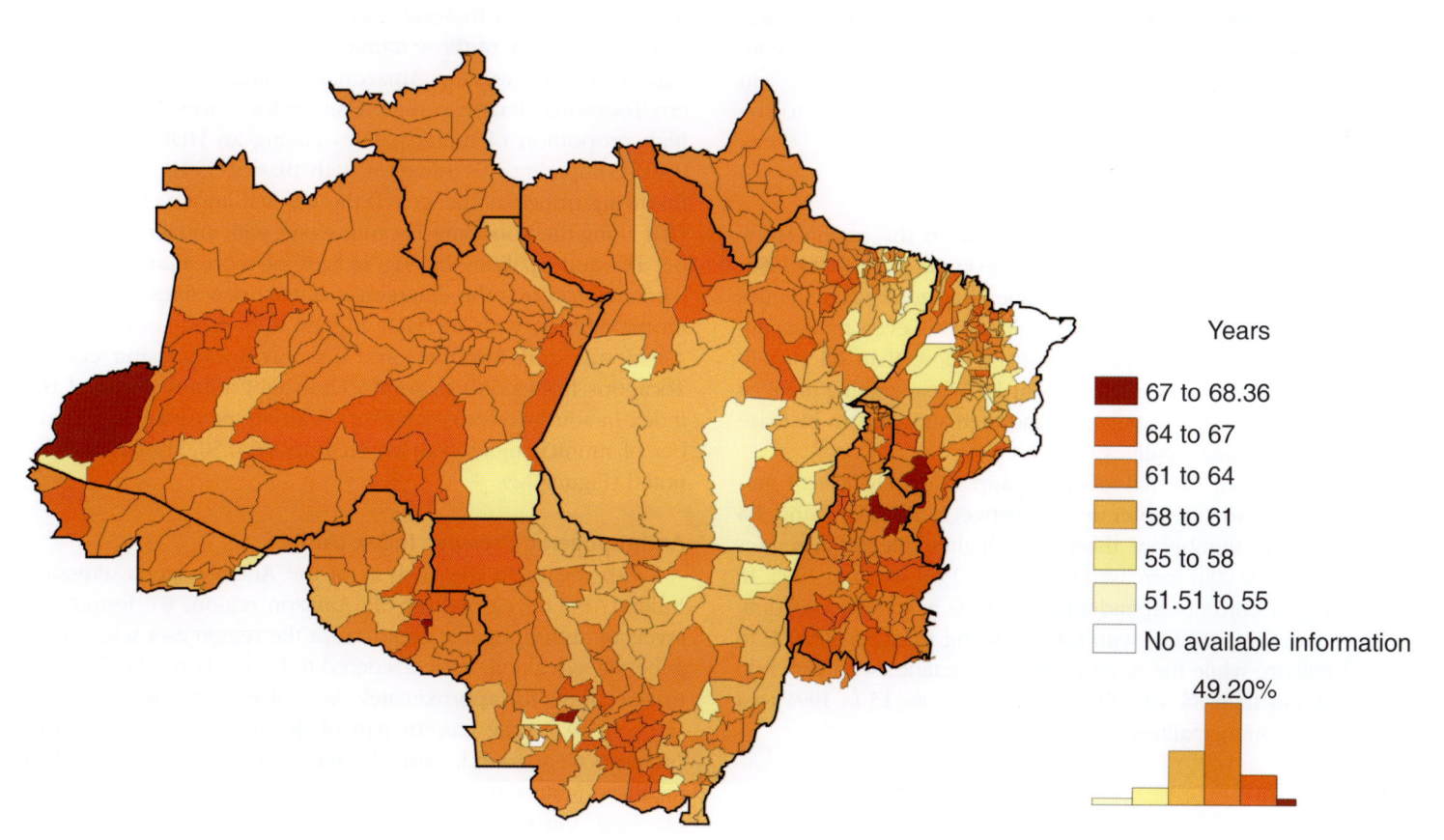

Figure 9. Life expectancy at birth (in years) for Amazonia 1991.
Source: Atlas of Human Development in Brazil - PNUD/IPEA/FIP.

SOCIOECONOMIC AND ANTHROPOGENIC PRESSURES

maintained its comparatively high rates for the region; nevertheless the rate decreased, leading on average to a predominance of municipalities with rates in the order of 50 to 90 deaths per thousand live births (Figure 8).

As far as life expectancy rates are concerned, it was found that for 1980 the population of more or less 50% of regional municipalities had a life expectancy in the order of 55 to 60 years. The highest rates (above 60 years) are thinly distributed throughout the region and found above all in the states of Amazonas, Pará and Mato Grosso. This indicator had generally improved by 1991, leading to the predominance of a group of municipalities whose population enjoyed life expectancy rates of around 61 to 64 years (approximately 49%). There are even some where the population has a life expectancy of more than 64 years (Figure 9).

Analysis of the data for 1993 for indicators of malaria revealed a concentration of municipalities with more than 5,000 cases of people testing positive, principally in Rondônia, northern Mato Grosso and along an eastern Amazonas – western Pará axis, with rates of positive slides of higher than 25% frequently found in these regions. The lowest number of cases per municipality was observed in the eastern Amazon region, more precisely along the eastern Mato Grosso to Maranhão axis, with a predominance of municipalities with approximately 150 people testing positive and rates of positive slides of less than 10%. In 1994 there were not very significant changes in relation to the current situation of the decline in public health caused by malaria, both in terms of the number of people testing positive and as regards rates of positive slides.

As far as the situation in 1995 is concerned, the figures in Rondônia show few alterations, with some municipalities showing a high number of people testing positive. A decrease can be seen in northern Mato Grosso and in the region covered by eastern Amazonas and western Pará. On the other hand there is an increasing trend in the number of cases in eastern Pará. There is a gradual increase in rates of positive slides of above 10% in eastern Mato Grosso and Pará, which may be related to the increasing occupation of these regions (Figure 10).

Public expenditures

Spatial analysis of public expenditure in the region show that, under the heading 'total current revenue' for 1991 to 1995, the majority of regional municipalities had total tax revenues ranging from R$ 500,000 to R$ 1 million. However, municipalities with higher tax revenues, generally more than R$ 10 million, varied from 15 municipalities in 1991, maintaining more or less the same number until 1994 and then showing an increase in 1995 to 26 municipalities.

In the case of internal revenues, approximately 70% of municipalities had tax revenues of between R$ 1,000 and R$ 100,000. The number of those with higher internal revenues (above R$ 500,000) increased from 41 in 1991 to 56 in 1995. In the case of current expenditures, there is a general predominance of municipalities with totals ranging from R$ 500,000 to R$ 2 million, while the number of municipalities with expenditure greater than R$ 10 million increased from 13 in 1991 to a total of 22 municipalities in 1995.

Extractivism

Evaluation of the data on extractive activities in the Amazon region shows that, in the case of rubber, this is heavily concentrated, above all in the Acre to northern Rondônia corridor. In this region extractive production by municipality in 1993 varied on average from 250,000 to 1,000,000 kilos. The principal producers were the municipalities of Porto Velho (Rondônia), Plácido de Castro and Senador Guiomard (Acre), and Boca do Acre (Amazonas), all producing more than a million kilos. There was significant, though less representative, production in northern Pará, averaging 10,000 to 150,000 kilos a year.

In the case of Brazil nut production, two principal production centers can be seen: i) southeastern Acre and western Amazonas, which reveal a predominance of municipalities with an average production of 500,000 to 1,000,000 kilos. The main producers are the municipalities of Boca do Acre (Amazonas), Acrelândia and Plácido de Castro (both in Acre), all producing more than 1,500,000 kilos; ii) the centre-north of Pará, where there are municipalities with production levels above 100,000 kilos.

The situation regarding timber extraction differs between the eastern and western parts of the region. In the western part, extractive activities are very evenly distributed among municipalities with an average extraction of around 10,000 to 100,000 cubic meters. In the eastern part extractive activity is more representative, above all in Pará and Maranhão, with production above 200,000 cubic meters (Figure 11).

Indicators of human development and anthropogenic pressure

Human Development Index (HDI)

Analysis by municipality of the Human Development Index (HDI) for the Amazon region in 1980 shows that around 40% of regional municipalities had an HDI of between 0.40 and 0.60. The main highlight is the group of municipalities extending from western Rondônia to southeastern Mato Grosso which represents the majority of those municipalities with an HDI of higher than 0.60. Southwestern Amazonas, central Acre and the eastern Tocantins-Maranhão region reveal the lowest HDIs, with a high proportion of municipalities having an HDI of less than 0.40. Comparing this situation with that of 1991 revealed the following principal changes: i) the gradual improvement of the HDI along the Rondônia-Tocantins axis, with an increased number of municipalities having indices of more than 0.60; ii) a tendency towards the emergence of two new axes comprising municipalities with an HDI higher than 0.60: northeastern Amazonas and Roraima, and an corridor crossing central Tocantins from north to south. The slight improvement of the index in southwestern Maranhão, with an increase in the number of municipalities with an HDI above 0.50, should also be noted (Figure 12).

Anthropogenic Pressure Index (API)

With regard to the analysis of the Anthropogenic Pressure Index (API) developed for the Amazon region, we found that levels of anthropogenic pressure for the region as a whole can, generally speaking, are considered to be medium, the category that accounts for approximately 48% of regional municipalities (Figure 13). In the eastern part of the region higher levels of pressure were found, normally medium or high, above all in southern Mato Grosso, northwestern Maranhão and northeastern Pará. On the basis of analysis of components of the API, the strong influence of urban anthropogenic pressures and of farming and ranching was observed in eastern and northeastern

Pará and in Maranhão and Tocantins. This can be linked to the development corridors implanted in the region, such as the Carajás railway and the Belém-Brasília highway. In Mato Grosso the main cause of anthropogenic pressure is farming and ranching, mainly in the eastern and southern regions. The areas of lowest anthropogenic pressures are located in northern Para and part of Amapá. There are also a few isolated nuclei of low anthropogenic pressure, mainly in municipalities in Mato Grosso where there are biodiversity conservation areas, such as the Chapada dos Guimarães national park, the northern part of the Pantanal Matogrossense and environmental protection areas along the Araguaia river.

The western part of the region reveals fewer anthropogenic impacts than the eastern part. Areas of low or very low pressure are found in the southern and the northern parts of Amazonas and in central Acre, while those with higher levels of anthropogenic pressure are confined to central Rondônia, eastern Acre and the area surrounding Manaus. In Rondônia there are two distinct situations concerning anthropogenic pressure in the northwestern and southeastern parts of the state. In the northwest the pressure is mainly demographic, whereas in the southeast the anthropogenic pressure mainly takes the form of agriculture and cattle raising. In the area around Manaus, as well as in a number of municipalities located along the Amazon river, anthropogenic pressure is above all urban, probably resulting from the migration of riverbank populations into urban centers in search of better living standards.

Final considerations

From the analysis of the results obtained, we can offer some considerations on demographic, socioeconomic and anthropogenic trends in the Legal Amazon region:

1) The demographic summary of the Amazon region shows a marked concentration of population in its eastern part, principally in eastern and northeastern Pará and in Maranhão, where population densities are higher than 15 inhabitants per square kilometer. In the western part the highest population pressures are to be found areas surrounding the principal cities, such as Manaus and Porto Velho. Rates of population growth, although falling over recent years, continue at levels above 2% per year.

2) In the case of the distribution of urban and rural population in the region, a trend towards urbanization can be observed. Over 60% of the population currently lives in urban areas, a fact which tends to aggravate environmental and social problems on the outskirts of large urban centers, compounding pre-existing local environmental problems. Some states which showed high urban population growth rates in the period 1980-1991, such as Rondônia and Roraima, have stabilized their rates and have been overtaken by other states such as Maranhão, Amapá and Tocantins. Notwithstanding the implementation of agricultural settlement projects, rural demographic trends have been stable over recent years, revealing a certain decline.

3) Generally speaking, there was a tendency for improvement of the health of the regional population during the period 1980 to 1991, according to analysis of the indices of infant mortality and life expectancy. In general, the lower life expectancy at birth indices of below 60 years seen in southern Pará and northern Mato Grosso can be linked to outbreaks of malaria in the region, both in terms of high case numbers and in terms of levels of those testing positive in these areas.

4) For extractive activities, principally timber, we can observe a correlation with areas of higher concentrations of population, indicating that the activity in question is related to issues of infrastructure and market. Areas of higher regional demographic concentration imply better availability of energy and as a consequence offer more favorable conditions that enable distribution, because of proximity to the principal development corridors.

5) Anthropogenic pressure in the Amazon region is shown to be strongly influenced by the factors of urban anthropogenic pressure, of farming and of stock raising, and is less the result of rural anthropogenic pressure. Given the concentration of population, economic activities and the major development corridors, the situation is more critical in the eastern part of the region where the areas of higher anthropogenic pressure are more intense and concentrated than in the western part where the areas of higher anthropogenic pressure are sparsely distributed. We should also note that some places in the region, such as Maranhão and eastern Pará, as well as showing higher levels of anthropogenic pressure, are also areas of low levels of human development, with an HDI of generally less than 0.40. From a socio-environmental viewpoint, these areas thus represent less sustainable conditions; leading, in other words, to the exhaustion of resources with no corresponding improvements in living standards. This is not seen in states such as Tocantins, Rondônia and Mato Grosso which, despite high levels of anthropogenic pressure, also reveal better levels of human development, with HDIs of over 0.60. On the other hand, from a social and environmental point of view, there are some scattered centers characterized by better social and environmental sustainability, such as northwestern Mato Grosso and southern Roraima, where levels of anthropogenic pressure are low and those of human development are comparatively high.

Bibliography

GTA/AMIGOS DA TERRA. *Políticas públicas coerentes. Para uma Amazônia sustentável, o desafio da inovação e o programa piloto.* 1998.

SAWYER, D. *Índice de pressão antrópica: uma proposta metodológica.* Brasília: ISPN, 1997.

STÉDILE, J. P. *Questão agrária no Brasil.* São Paulo: Atual, 1997.

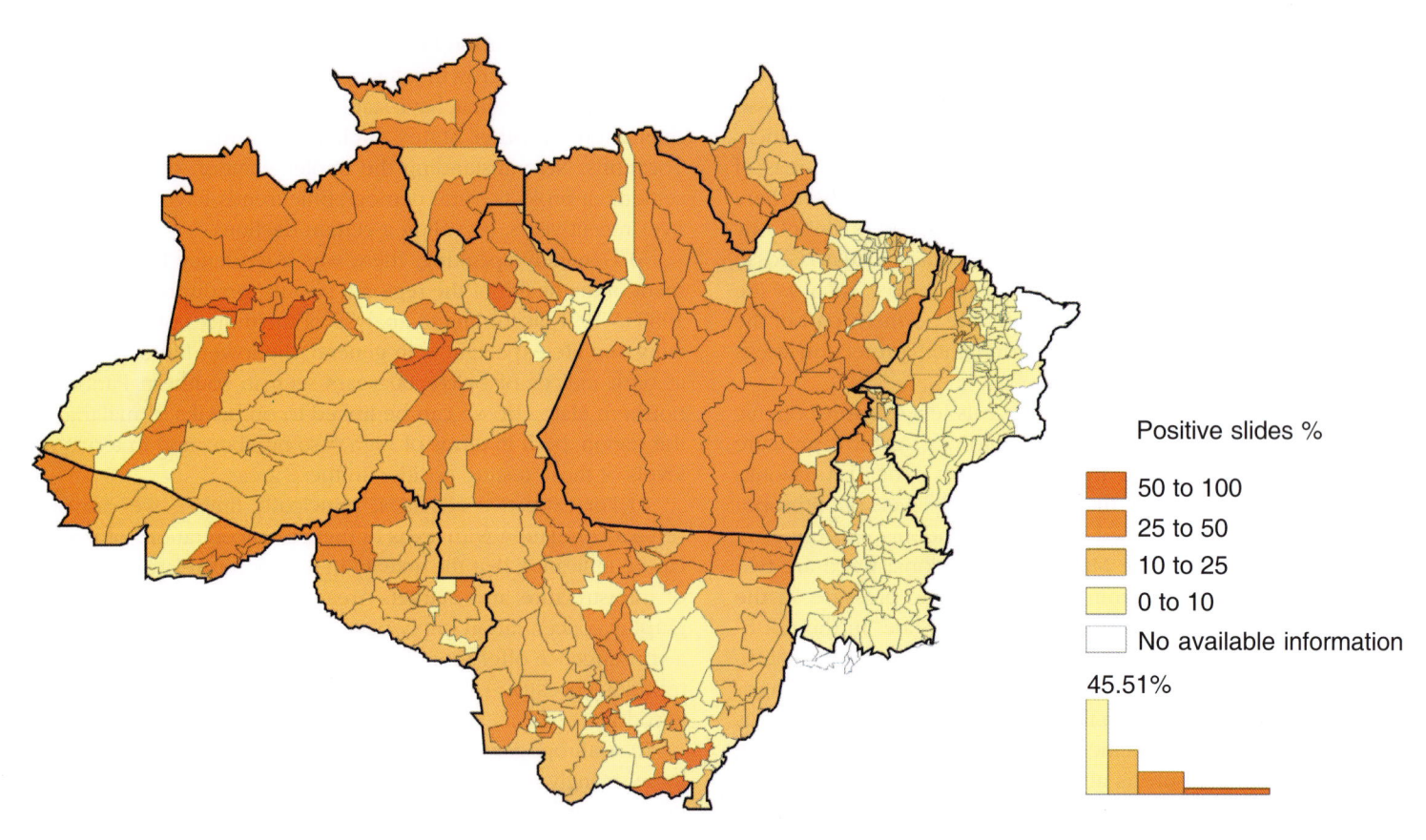

Figure 10. Malaria, index of positive slides, Amazonia, 1995.
Source: National Health Foundation 1995

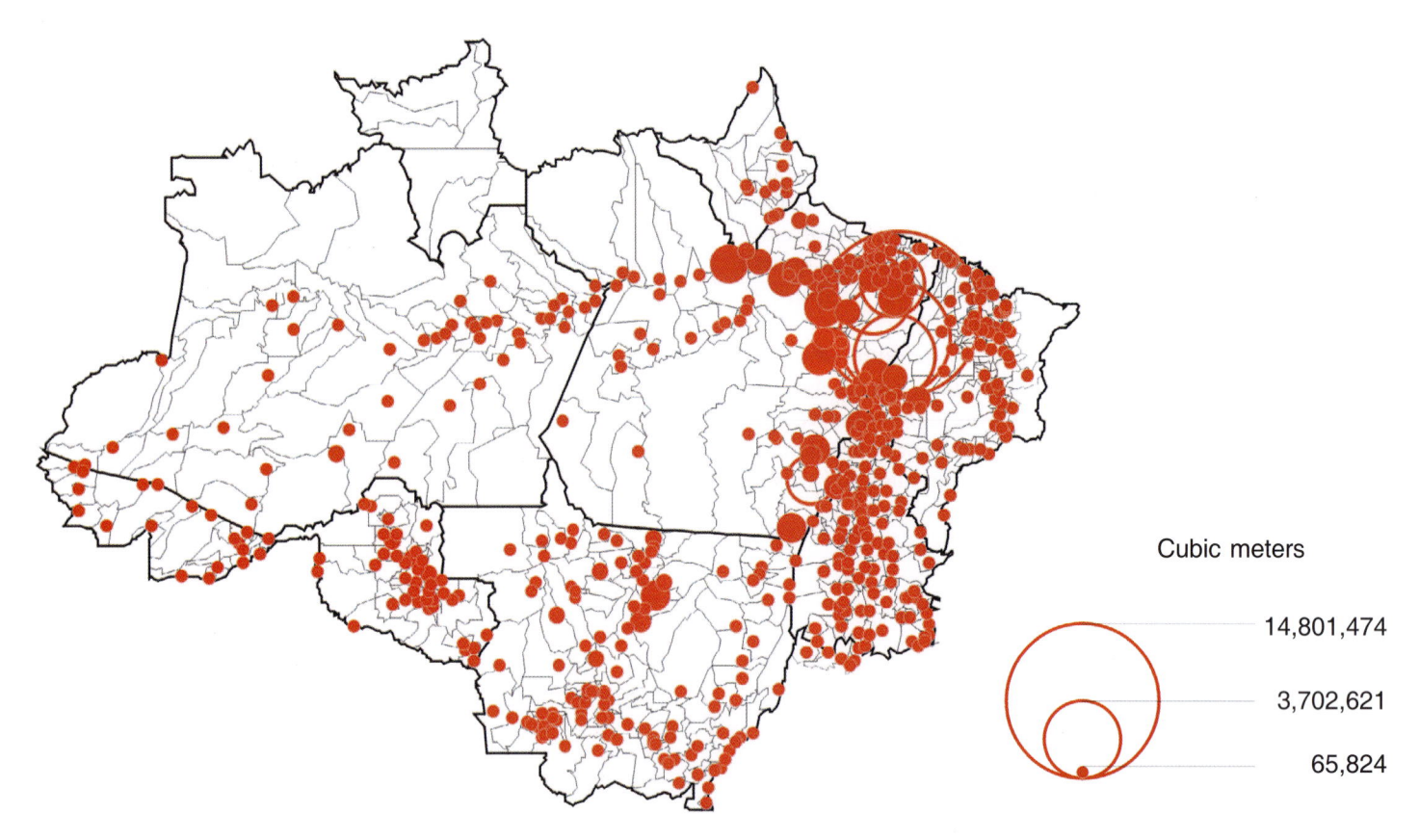

Figure 11. Timber extraction in Amazonia 1993.
Source: IBGE plant extractive activities and forestry data 1993

Figure 12. Human Development Index for Amazonia 1991.
Source: Atlas of Human Development in Brazil - PNUD/IPEA/FIP.

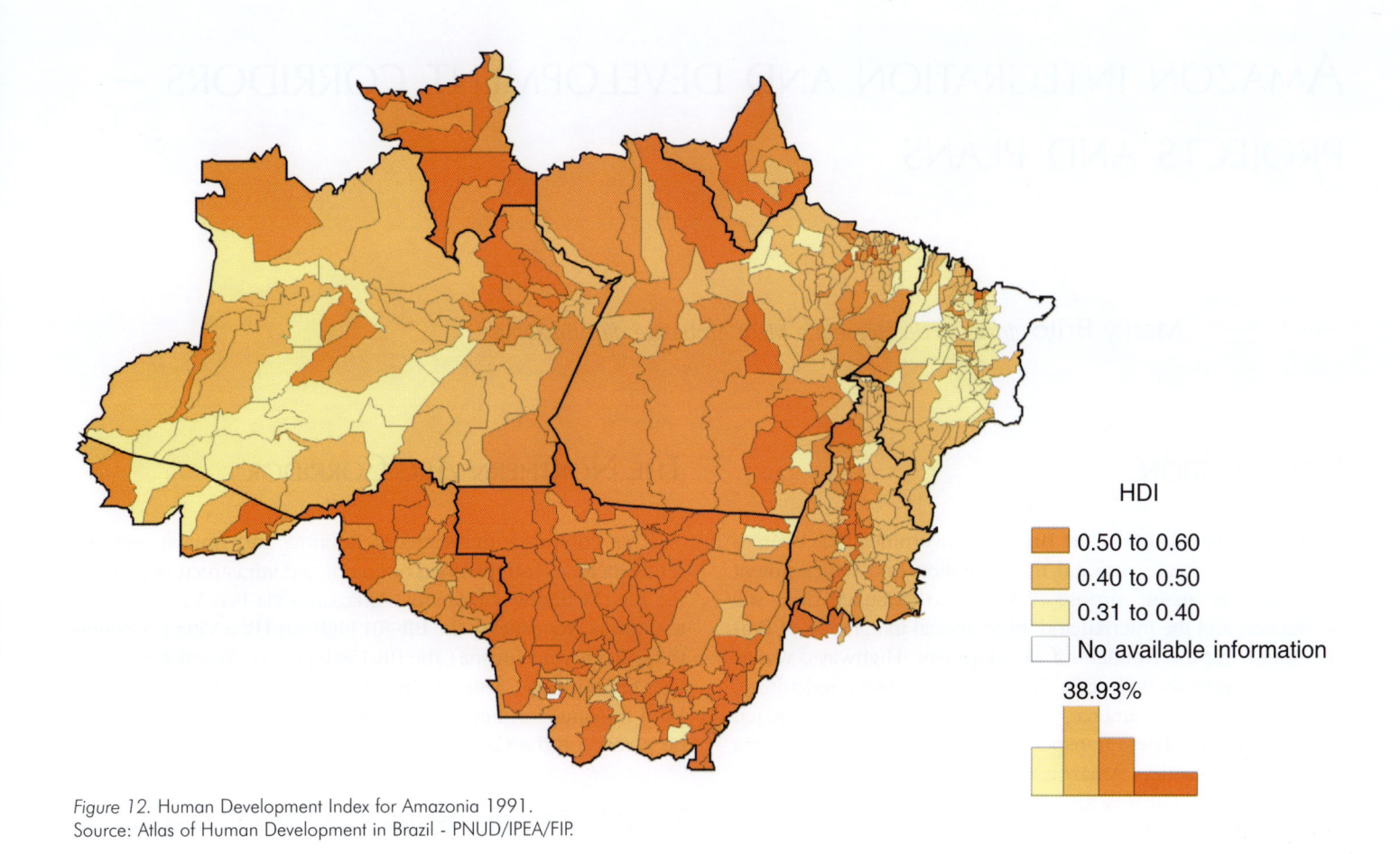

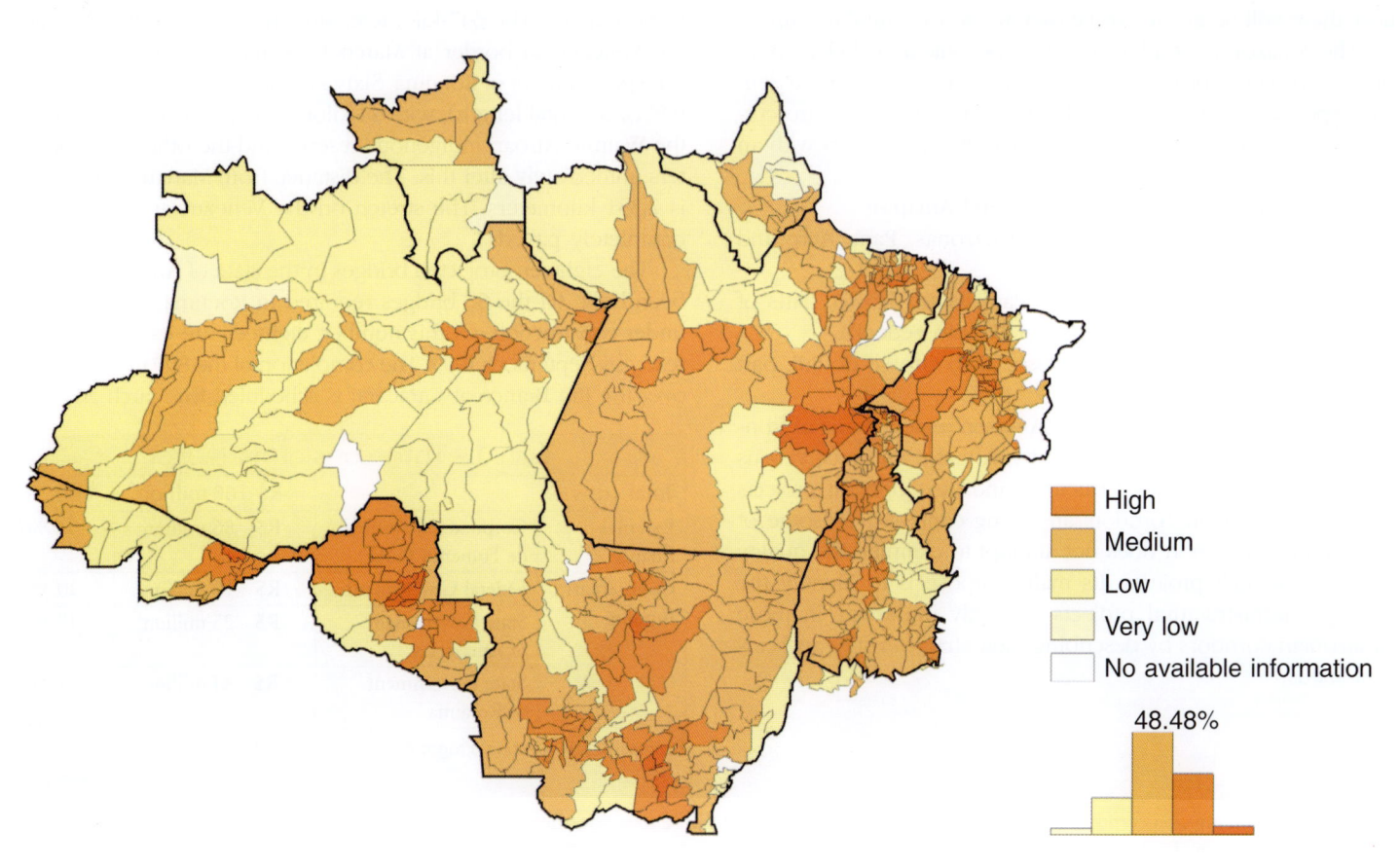

Figure 13. Anthropogenic Pressure Index for Amazonia.
Source: ISPN 1998.

SOCIOECONOMIC AND ANTHROPOGENIC PRESSURES

Amazon integration and development corridors – projects and plans

Marky Brito *Instituto do Homem e Meio Ambiente da Amazônia*

Introduction

An established goal of the Brazilian government has been to restructure or create national transportation and development corridors. The main purpose of this is to stimulate domestic production and the internal and international integration of Brazil, expanding the frontiers of development. Highways, waterways and railroads will open the way for industry, agriculture, stock raising and commerce, which will now be able to reach remote locations. These transportation and production corridors will link the Brazilian Amazon region to markets in Peru, Bolivia, Venezuela, Guyana and French Guiana, thereby shortening the distance to American and European export markets, as well as enabling communication with the Pacific.

The corridors have also been created to stimulate centers of production. Large scale cultivation of soybean and maize, cattle raising, timber production and agriculture will be encouraged by a reduction in transportation and production costs. In addition, there will be greater and easier access to natural resources.

The Amazon region has therefore become a vital element in the government's projects, since its rivers and roads form essential export routes that offer reductions in costs. There are currently four main integration and development corridors with an impact on the Amazon region[1]:

– Northern arc corridor (Roraima and Amapá);
– Madeira-Amazonas corridor (Amazonas, Pará, Acre and part of Rondônia);
– Araguaia-Tocantins corridor (Pará, Mato Grosso, parts of Maranhão, Tocantins, Goiás and the Distrito Federal);
– Western corridor (Mato Grosso, Mato Grosso do Sul, part of Rondônia and one city in Pará).

The traditional scenario of the Amazon region is one of frontiers, with different actors guided by different interests, visions and proposals. Some infrastructural and development projects in these Amazonian corridors are being contested by some of the actors. This report does not attempt to examine the quality and role of such projects. Its main purpose is to identify the principal infrastructural projects currently underway in these Amazonian corridors by describing their characteristics and current status.

The Northern Arc Corridor

This comprises the states of Roraima and Amapá and currently includes four planned or completed infrastructure projects: the BR-174 highway (Manaus, Amazonas via Boa Vista, Roraima to Caracas, Venezuela), the BR-401 highway (Boa Vista via Bonfim to Georgetown, Guyana), the BR-156 highway (Tracajuba, Amapá via Oiapoque to Cayenne, French Guiana) and the Guri to Boa Vista transmission line. These will enable Brazilian products to be placed on the Caribbean and American markets at less cost.

The BR-174 highway (Manaus–Boa Vista–Caracas)

Considered to be one of the most important construction projects within the northern corridor, the BR-174 will link the Brazilian market to markets in the Caribbean, Central America and the east coast of the Nafta member states. The highway crosses fourteen indigenous areas and five environmental protection areas.[2] The 347-kilometer stretch between Caracaraí and the Venezuelan border at Marco BV-8 has been paved by the state government of Roraima. Sixty kilometers remain to be paved (6% of the total length), with 44 kilometers of this located within the Waimiri-Atroari indigenous reserve and the other 16 kilometers immediately after this. The distance from Manaus to Caracas is 2,331 kilometers. The stretch on the Venezuelan side is also completely paved.

The eighteen projected bridges in the state of Amazonas have been built. Of the 56 bridges required in Roraima, nineteen are under construction. Of this number, eighteen are expected to be ready by September 1999. The completion of the 800 meter bridge over the Rio Branco at Caracaraí is scheduled for March 2000.

TABLE 1 - TOTAL COSTS OF THE PROJECT			
Total costs		R$ 168 million	100 %
External finance	Corporación Andina de Fomento (CAF)	R$ 86 million	51 %
Counterpart funding	Federal Government	R$ 16 million	10 %
	State Government of Amazonas	R$ 25 million	15 %
	State Government of Roraima	R$ 41 million	24 %

Source: 'Brazil in Action' Program.

---

1. Information on Amazon corridors and their respective projects is derived from various government documents (for instance: the 1996-1999 Multi-year Plan, the 'Brazil in Action' Programme and others). Further information was obtained from different government websites. Please refer to the bibliography below.
2. Amazon Watch. *Artérias para o comércio mundial, conseqüências para a Amazônia* [Arteries of global commerce, consequences for Amazonia]. Impact assessment report outlining planned transportation and energy infrastructure projects in the Amazon basin, 1997.

The government hopes to stimulate the agricultural sector by means of these projects, given that the Amazon region offers a wide variety of soils and climates. One example of such investment is the introduction of large scale cultivation of crops such as soybean and rice to the savannas of Roraima. In the eastern part of Roraima alone, according to the Federal Government, there are four million hectares of soil suitable for grain production. In addition, since the Caribbean represents a market of around R$ 6 billion a year in sales of products similar to those produced in the Zona Franca de Manaus (ZFM - the Manaus Free Zone), increased sales of ZFM products are hoped for.

The construction permit under the project's environmental and socio-economic sustainability plan was approved by Ibama on 11 April, 1997. At the end of the stipulated 730-day period, the operating licence was approved. The conditions imposed under the construction permit were submitted to the DNER (the national highways agency) by the Seinf (the department of infrastructure of Amazonas) and the DER/RR (the highways department of Roraima) after 30, 60 and 90 days.

The Guri (Venezuela) to Boa Vista (Brasil) transmission line

The Guri to Boa Vista transmission line will be 780 kilometers long (560 kilometers in Venezuela and 220 kilometers in Brazil) and will complement the BR-174 highway project. It will stretch from the Guri power station in the Macágua region, through Tumeremo, Las Cristinas and Santa Elena (all in Venezuela), to Boa Vista in Brazil. It will follow the highway and will carry fiber optic cables as well as the power line.

Given the inadequate and expensive energy generation options in Boa Vista and Manaus, the project has become a matter of priority for the Brazilian government. According to the agreement signed with Venezuela, the power line will improve the prospects for expanding industrial activity. The project is financed by the Corporación Andina de Fomento (CAF – the Andean Development Corporation) in the form of a R$ 94.6 million loan, R$ 60.5 million of which is to the Centrais Elétricas Brasileiras (Eletrobrás – the National Electricity Board of Brazil) and R$ 34.1 million to the Companhia Energética de Roraima (the State of Roraima Energy Authority). The agreed commitment period for energy supply is twenty years, to meet a demand of up to 200,000 kilowatts. The total value of the project is US$ 150 million, with US$ 100 million financed by Venezuela and the remainder by Brazil.

The Venezuelan company Electrificación del Caroni C. A. (Edelca) will be responsible for the construction work on the Venezuelan side and Eletronorte, a subsidiary of Eletrobrás, will be in charge of the 206 kilometer, 230 kilovolt stretch starting at the frontier.

Construction on the Venezuelan side is currently affected by the opposition of environmental and indigenous groups. The power line crosses several indigenous reserves and national parks. It thus fails to respect Venezuelan laws, which prohibit these types of projects in such areas. Given that the largest gold deposits in Venezuela are found along the route of line, there is the possibility of encouraging gold prospecting.

Despite these issues, the Brazilian government has indicated that 'in the future the line may be extended as far as Manaus and even, in the long term, be connected to the Tucuruí transmission line, enabling the interlinking of Latin American electricity grids'. The project is expected to be finished by October 1999.

The BR-401 highway (Boa Vista–Bonfim–Georgetown)

The paving of a 90 kilometer stretch between Boa Vista and Bonfim marks the start of the restoration of the highway to Georgetown, Guyana. The aim of this project is the integration of the Brazilian and Guyanese economies, thereby enabling Brazilian products to reach Latin American markets more rapidly. The 'Georgetown free port is an important attraction for the development of mineral transport on this highway, despite the precarious state of the road in Guyana'.

The highway forms part of the new plans that make up the federal government's 'Brazil in Action' program. It will cost R$ 35 million and is currently in its implementation phase.

The BR-156 highway (Tracajuba–Oiapoque–Caiena)

This is also a federal government project and the aim of this highway is the integration of the economy of Amapá, as well as linking Brazil to French Guiana by paving 460 kilometers of highway between Tracauba and Oiapoque. This will have an overall cost of R$ 140 million and work is expected to start in 1999.

The BR-156 will thus form a new corridor together with the Marajó waterway (should the latter be implemented). This production and export corridor would start with the Araguaia-Tocantins waterway and end in Cayenne, French Guiana. The proposal would establish a 'large multimodal corridor linking the central Brazilian savannas to the Caribbean seaboard'.

THE MADEIRA–AMAZONAS CORRIDOR

This is the Amazon corridor with the largest number of planned or completed projects. There are seven projects designed to integrate the Amazon region into the rest of the country. In addition to providing one more gateway to the Pacific, the corridor can also shorten the transport of Brazilian products to American, European and Caribbean markets.

The Madeira waterway

There are at least five indigenous reserves close to this waterway, which has been in operation since April 1997. It will permit intermodal transportation between the soybean producing areas of northern Mato Grosso and the Atlantic Ocean, through the grain terminals in Porto Velho, Rondônia and Itacoatiara, Amazonas. Total costs will be R$ 24 million, and it is expected to be completed by June 1999.

The objective of the project is to improve the navigability of 1,056 kilometers of the Madeira river, in order to reduce the cost of exporting grain from Acre, Amazonas, Rondônia and Mato Grosso. The cost of transport by road, now R$ 110 per ton from Sapezal, Mato Grosso to Paranaguá, Paraná, can be reduced to R$ 70 per ton by shipping from Itacoatiara. In addition, journey times to Itacoatiara, currently 60 hours, can also be reduced thanks to the possibility of safe operating at night.

The transport time of soybean to Rotterdam can thus be reduced by about ten days. The travel time via Paranaguá to European ports is around 27 days; via Itacoatiara, using the waterway, it is 17 days. According to federal government figures, around 3.2 million tons of cargo were transported via the waterway in 1998, compared with 2.5 million in 1997.

The Madeira waterway links the BR-364/070 and BR-163 highways with the Amazonas river. In addition to improving the movement of produce, the waterway-highway linkage can encourage the expansion of agricultural activities (grains, tropical fruits, and cattle, poultry and pig production). Thus 'new agricultural frontiers for grain production along the lines of the project under examination for the Humaitá, Amazonas region' can be opened up.

The Maggi Group, a large soybean, cotton, seeds and cattle producer, is a major participant in activities linked to the waterway. According to the government, there are 'potentially at least 20 million hectares of cultivable land (without the need for deforestation), which is equivalent to 60 million tons of soybean, or 2.4 times total Brazilian production. The area currently planted in the Chapada dos Parecis amounts to 1.5 million hectares of grains, leading to a production of 3.8 million tons'.

The Tapajós–Teles Pires waterway

This 1,043 kilometer waterway links 21 municipalities in Mato Grosso and 8 in Pará. Its purpose is to provide a viable outlet for the agricultural production of the northern and northeastern regions of Mato Grosso and of a large part of Pará. The main function of the waterway will initially be the export of grain. Total costs of the project amount to US$ 150 million.

Table 2 shows grain production over recent years for each these municipalities, together with estimates for the period 1995 to 2005.

According to the Administração das Hidrovias da Amazônia Oriental (Ahimor – Eastern Amazonia Waterways Management Agency), the Tapajós-Teles Pires waterway has high economic and social importance because:

– the average cost of transport from the Rasteira falls region to Santarém is R$ 10.20 per ton, leading to estimated overall savings on transport costs of R$ 158,755,000 over the first six years of the operations of this waterway;

– comparison of the transport costs using the corridor to be created by the waterway with the costs of alternative options for exporting the grain production of its area of influence showed that the saving varies from R$ 2.5 per ton to R$ 36.4 per ton, according to the municipality;

– the start of the construction alone will immediately provide around 5,000 jobs, while overall the project will create some 30,000 jobs, corresponding to a population of 150,000 counting employees and their families;

– a road-water grain transshipment terminal will be built in the Rasteira falls region, and the port of Santarém will be upgraded to allow transhipment of cargo from river to ocean-going vessels.

The environmental question is the great stumbling block for the implementation of the waterway. Its course includes waterfalls and rapids, which entails the study of alternatives and of potential environmental impacts within the Tapajós basin. Following a court decision, these studies and projects have been suspended because of the impacts caused by the construction work. However, the Companhia das Docas do Pará (Port Authority of Pará) and Ahimor have appealed and a judicial ruling is awaited.

The Marajó waterway

The objective of the project is the interlinkage of the Atuá (67 kilometers) and Anajás (207 kilometers) river basins on the island of Marajó, thereby forming a corridor which will shorten the sailing distance between the cities of Belém, Pará and Macapá, Amapá by more than 140 kilometers. Linking the rivers will be achieved by excavating a 32 kilometer long fluvial canal, resulting in a waterway with a total length of 306 kilometers.

Linking the BR-156 highway to the waterway will enable communication between the state of Amapá and the Brazil's central-northern corridor comprising the Araguaia-Tocantins waterway, the Belém-Brasília highway and the North-South railroad. In this way produce can be exported via this corridor to both internal and international markets (reaching Cayenne in French Guiana).

The environmental impact study has already been carried out and the waterway's executive project was finalized in April 1998, linking the Atuá and Anajás rivers. However the start of construction is dependent on the issue of the prior approval license by Sectam and Ibama.

The BR-163 highway (Santarém–Mato Grosso state border)

The government considers the paving of the BR-163 highway between Santarém, Pará and the state border with Mato Grosso to be essential. The road represents another option for exporting produce from northeastern Mato Grosso and western Pará through the port of Santarém. The highway runs for 983 kilometers through the state of Pará.[3]

It is currently expected that the federal government will commit R$ 7 million for the paving of the highway. There is strong pressure from politicians in Pará to start construction, which is seen as a big step forward in the occupation of the area between the Tapajós and Xingu rivers.

The BR-317 highway (Rio Branco–Assis Brasil)

This is one of the new projects under the federal government's 'Brazil in Action' program. It aims to improve the integration of Brazil (Acre), Bolivia and Peru by paving 200 kilometers of the BR-317 highway between the Fazenda Vaca Branca and Assis Brasil, Acre, and by repairing the 140 kilometer stretch between Rio Branco and the Fazenda Vaca Branca. Estimated costs are R$ 80 million and, when finished, the road will provide an outlet to the Pacific by means of its continuation on the Peruvian side.

The Tucuruí transmission line

This is one of the most important projects in the Madeira-Amazonas corridor. Its main objective is to 'supply the western region of Pará with reliable low-cost electricity through the

TABLE 2 - PRODUCTION OF GRAIN AND FERTILIZERS IN MUNICIPALITIES IN THE ZONE OF INFLUENCE OF THE TAPAJÓS – TELES PIRES			
Year	Grains	Fertilizers	Total
1995	1,252,972	313,243	1,566,215
2000	1,875,832	468,958	2,344,790
2005	2,455,910	613,978	3,069,888

Source: Ahimor.

---

3. Sant'Anna J. A. *Rede básica de transporte da Amazônia* [Amazonia's basic transport network]. IPEA. Discussion document 562. Brasília, June 1998.

construction of a 1,007 kilometer power line connecting Tucuruí, Altamira, Rurópolis, Santarém and Itaituba'. Construction has recently been completed.

Initially Tucuruí and Manaus were to be connected. However, because of the difficulties of running a major power line along the Amazon river and the existence of alternative energy sources for this region, it was decided to run the line towards the west of Pará (Altamira). The line also carries fiber optic cables to upgrade communications. Thus, 'if in the future the line is extended to Manaus, the city will be linked by a fiber optic network to the rest of the country. Similarly, if the power line from Guri in Venezuela reaches Manaus in the future, the entire electricity and communications network of South America will be interlinked'.

The current situation of the power line is as follows:
– The Tucuruí to Altamira stretch was completed in June 1998;
– The Altamira to Rurópolis stretch was completed in December 1998;
– The Rurópolis to Santarém was completed and began transmission on February 26, 1999;
– The Rurópolis to Itaituba stretch was completed and began transmission on June 17, 1999.

The Urucu–Juruá (Amazonas) natural gas pipeline

The construction of the gas pipeline linking Urucu to Coari, which was completed in December 1998, allows the exploitation of the Pólo Arara gas fields in Amazonas. The aim is to produce 4 million cubic meters of natural gas a day, thereby lowering manufacturing costs in the Amazon region. It is also planned to replace the oil-powered power plants that currently supply the region with electricity by gas-powered plants.

The sequence is as follows: the gas will be liquefied in Coari and transported in methane tankers down the Solimões River to Manaus, Porto Velho and Macapá, where gas-powered electricity generation plants will be built.

Petrobrás is also studying the possibility of replacing river transportation from Coari by a new gas pipeline approximately 420 kilometers long linking Coari and Manaus. There is also the possibility of building a further 500 kilometer pipeline linking Urucu and Porto Velho, at an estimated cost of around R$ 190 million.

According to Petrobrás, the potential regional demand for gas is 8 million cubic meters a day. Gas reserves in the Urucu field (including the as yet unexploited Juruá field) are estimated at around 80 billion cubic meters, meaning that reserves are sufficient for 19 years' supply.

As well as other benefits, the gas pipeline could stimulate the construction of slaughterhouses and chilling plants, taking advantage of the cold produced by the liquefied gas, as well as timber processing, one of the most important economic activities in the Amazon region. In Tartarugalzinho, Amapá an investment in the production of wooden roof tiles for export has already led to the creation of 250 jobs.

According to the government, 'from 1999 onwards, oil production will be increased to 45 million barrels a day, 950 cubic meters of LPG and 6 million cubic meters of natural gas daily. A 275 kilometer multi-purpose pipeline is under construction, linking the Urucu basin to the Solimões, where a port will be built to ship the oil and gas to Manaus, where they will be used for industrial production and, above all, for electricity generation by the private sector'.

The Araguaia–Tocantins Corridor

This comprises the states of Goiás and Tocantins, parts of Maranhão, Pará and Mato Grosso, and the Federal District and will permit important economic links between Brazilian regions. Its area of influence includes some of the most important grain producing and livestock areas, thereby allowing transport and distribution to internal and external markets at reduced distances and costs.

The Araguaia–Tocantins waterway

This is the most important construction project within this corridor and its purpose is to 'develop and implement, by means of public resources in partnership with private initiative, a multimodal transportation corridor between northern and southern Brazil offering a cheaper alternative to current long distance transport flows. It will be a more competitive option for exports via the North Atlantic'.

The waterway is made up of the Araguaia, Tocantins and das Mortes rivers. It contains a number of environmental barriers such as rapids and waterfalls. Furthermore it faces opposition

Stages	Stretch	Dist. (km)	Construction works	Costs (R$ millions)
1	Araguaia waterway, first stretch: Aruanã to Xambioá	1,230	Delimiting the shipping lane and signage, dredging of 675,000 m³ and removal of 164,060 m³ of rock	45.00
	Rio das Mortes waterway: Nova Xavantina to São Félix do Araguaia	580	Delimiting the shipping lane and signage	
	Tocantins waterway, first stretch: Miracema do Norte to Estreito	420	Delimiting the shipping lane and signage, dredging of 660,000 m³ and removal of 67,000 m³ of rock	
2	Araguaia waterway, second stretch: Xambioá to Foz do Araguaia	286	Delimiting the shipping lane and signage, removal of 303.500 m³ of rock, rock embankment, dyke and canals.	278.86
3	Tocantins waterway, second stretch: Estreito to Marabá	350	Delimiting the shipping lane and signage, dredging of 200,000 m³, removal of 57,000 m³ of rock, access canals and lock.	95.07
4	Tocantins waterway, third stretch: Marabá to rio Pará	458	Delimiting the shipping lane and signage, dredging of 334,000 m³, removal of 68,000 m³, and Tucuruí lock.	346.00
TOTAL				764.93

Table 3 – Implementation stages of the Araguaia–Tocantins waterway

Source: Adapted from the *Programa de Desenvolvimento Integrado do Corredor Centro-Norte -PDCN* (Program for the Integrated Development of the Centre-North Corridor). MPO (Ministry of Planning and Budgets), Brasilia, Jan. 1997.

by indigenous groups who fear the impact on the rivers and the fishing resulting from the movement of shipping. Total project costs are R$ 114.4 million and the construction is divided in three phases:

– Work on dredging, clearance and signage of the waterway (1,516 kilometers);

– Paving the section of the BR-153 highway from São Geraldo to Marabá in Pará;

– Completing a further 120 kilometer section of the railroad between Imperatriz and Estreito in Maranhão.

The Araguaia-Tocantins waterway, in conjunction with section of the North-South railroad between Imperatriz and Estreito and stretches of the BR-153 and state highways, will form a corridor that provides easy and cheap access to the Caribbean, North America and Asia. The multimodal design (highway-railroad-waterway) can allow regional agricultural produce to compete with foreign production. Completion of this waterway is expected in December 1999.

Products will initially be shipped from the Ponta da Madeira terminal in Maranhão; after completion of the waterway, products will be shipped from the port of Belém.

The Araguaia-Tocantins waterway is considered by the government to be essential for the consolidation of national integration. It is economically important to large grain producers who see it as a way of reducing their costs and placing their products on the international market at more competitive prices. As a consequence, there is an important lobby working for its implementation.

The clearing and dredging planning documents have been completed, as has the environmental impact assessment report. The next step is the issue by Ibama of the environmental licenses, following which public hearings will take place. Following these, the call for bids for the dredging and clearing works will be published.

The North–South railroad

This is intended to upgrade the transport infrastructure needed for the export of agricultural, livestock and agro-industrial production from Brazil's northern cerrado (savanna) region. It is made up of two sections:

– The northern section from Colinas do Tocantins to the Carajás railroad at Açailândia, Maranhão; 461 kilometers at a cost of R$ 336 million;

– The southern section from Porangatu, Goiás to meet the existing railroad system at Senador Canedo, Goiás; 502 kilometers at a cost of R$ 508 million.

The 95 kilometer stretch between Açailândia and Imperatriz has been completed and operates freight and passenger services under an agreement with the Carajás railroad. As far as the 120 kilometer stretch between Imperatriz and Estreito is concerned, 89% of the earthworks has been completed, together with 99.9% of the bridges and 56% of the permanent way. However, this stretch was not completed in 1998 because of insufficient resources.

The BR-153 highway (Marabá–São Geraldo, Pará)

Work is in progress on the 156 kilometer BR-153 highway from Marabá to São Geraldo in Pará; 86% of the earthworks, 73% of the sub-base, 65% of the base and 59% of the road surface have been completed.

The BR-230 highway (Marabá–Altamira, Pará)

The objective in paving the BR-230 highway is to extend the infrastructure of the northern region, linking it to the cerrado region and to the São Marcos Bay ports in Maranhão, by paving 132 kilometers of the Transamazônica highway between Marabá and Altamira in Pará. Work is expected to start in 2000.

The Rio Capim waterway

The project is still in its planning stage. At the moment the waterway only serves to transport a few products and minerals to the port of Belém. Studies on its technical and economic viability are being carried out under the responsibility of Ahimor.

Interlinking electricity grids

The objective of the project is to link the northern-northeastern electricity grid with the southern-southeastern-midwestern grid by building a 1,276 kilometer, 500 kilovolt transmission line. The route of the line will follow the Belém-Brasília (BR-010) highway, thus enabling improvements in the quality and reliability of the energy supply to Palmas, Gurupi and Colinas in Tocantins. The line was completed in December 1998 and was activated on January 25, 1999. Commercial operations began on 3 February, 1999.

THE WESTERN CORRIDOR

Mato Grosso, Mato Grosso do Sul, part of Rondônia and one city in Pará make up what is regarded as the new frontier of the country's economic and agricultural development. According to the federal government, 'the creation of this corridor will ensure that the southwest of the western Amazon region and northwestern Mato Grosso are linked to Brazil's southern and southeastern regions, creating a corridor between these regions and the municipality of Itacoatiara in the center of the state of Amazonas, where a grain terminal is located'.

The BR-364/070 and BR-163 highways

Together with the construction of the Ferronorte railroad (see below), the restoration and paving of the BR-364/070 and BR-163 highways will constitute one of the major transportation projects in Brazil. For this, 520 kilometers of the BR 364 and BR 163 highways have been chosen for repair.

In the case of the BR-364, this involves the following stretches: from Frutal, Mato Grosso to São Simão, Goiás; along the Paranaíba river, at Alto Araguaia and Cuiabá in Mato Grosso; at Porto Velho, along the Madeira river; and the central area of Acre. In the case of the BR-163, the stretches marked for restoration are located between Rondonópolis and Santa Helena in Mato Grosso, where the highway connects with the state MT-320 road to Alta Floresta. The estimated total costs are R$ 55 million.

In Acre, eight kilometers have already been restored, in Rondônia 193 kilometers, and in Mato Grosso 174 kilometers, giving a total of 395 kilometers and corresponding to 80% of the target. Completion is expected by December 1999.

The project is directly related to the development of the Madeira waterway and the construction of the Ferronorte railroad.

The aim is a better and cheaper export route for the grain production of the centre-west region.

The Ferronorte railroad

The aim is to create a rail transportation system connecting the cities of Cuiabá, Uberlândia, Uberaba, Aparecida do Taboado, Porto Velho and Santarém. Overall 'the Ferronorte (northern railroad) represents the largest transportation project in Brazil today and will constitute an important impetus towards the economic development of Brazil's northern and western regions. Given its dimensions, it can be compared to the transcontinental railroads in the United States and Europe'.

The enterprise is divided into two stages:

1. Construction of a 1,728 kilometer railroad comprising two main lines: Santa Fé do Sul, São Paulo via Alto Taquari, Mato Grosso to Cuiabá, Mato Grosso; and Uberlândia, Minas Gerais to Alto Araguaia, Mato Grosso.

2. Construction of two long sections toward the north: Cuiabá to Porto Velho, a distance of approximately 1,500 kilometers; and Cuiabá to Santarém, a distance of of around 2,000 kilometers.

According to the Government 'the intermodal transportation network that will result from the full implementation of the Ferronorte project will create competitive alternative outlets for the production of an area of 2.1 million square kilometers, 90% of which is located in the Legal Amazon region, and which accounts for 45% of the growth in Brazilian production of soybean, maize and rice during the last 15 years'.

The investment in the first stretch amounts to R$ 1.33 billion.

The construction of approximately 400 kilometers from Aparecida do Taboado, started in 1992, is expected to reach Alto Taquari by 1999. From Cuiabá, the Ferronorte will travel 1,500 kilometers northwest to Porto Velho to connect with the Madeira river and the inland navigation system of the Amazon basin. To the north it will reach Santárem, a distance of approximately of 2,000 kilometers, and will be able to to connect to the Amazon river at a point where long distance marine navigation is already in operation.

BIBLIOGRAPHY

AHIMOR. Administração das Hidrovias da Amazônia Oriental. Available at www.ahimor.gov.br.

AHITAR. Administração da Hidrovia Araguaia-Tocantins. Available at www.ahitar.com.br.

AMAZON WATCH. *Artérias para o comércio mundial, conseqüências para a Amazônia. Relatório de avaliação de impactos expondo projetos de infraestrutura para transporte e energia planejados para a bacia Amazônica*, April 1997.

BRASIL. Ministério do Planejamento e Orçamento. *Amazônia atlântica: bases para um programa de desenvolvimento sustentável*. Brasília, April 1998.

_____. *Bases para um programa de desenvolvimento integrado da região Centro-Oeste*. Brasília, May 1997.

_____. *Desenvolvimento sustentável da faixa de fronteira*. Brasília, May 1998.

_____. *Programa de desenvolvimento integrado do corredor Centro-Norte – PDCN*. Brasília, January 1997.

_____. *Programa de desenvolvimento integrado da região Norte*. Brasília, March 1997.

Programa Brasil em Ação. Available at www.mpo.gov.br.

SANT'ANNA, J. A. *Rede básica de transporte da Amazônia*. IPEA. Discussion document, no. 562. Brasília, June 1998.

SUDAM. *Plano Plurianual – 1996/1999: Amazônia Legal*. Belém, 1997.

Overview of land use in Amazonia:
timber, agriculture and livestock

Adalberto Veríssimo, Eugênio Arima and Eirivelthon Lima *Instituto do Homem e Meio Ambiente da Amazônia*

Introduction

The aim of this study is to support the preparation of a national biodiversity strategy by compiling a database on the most important economic activities carried out in the Amazon forest biome. When spatially analyzed, such data give a picture of those regions in Amazonia that are under economic pressure and thus prone to biodiversity loss.

The report is organized in three sections. First, we present the data on timber-related activities in the main regional centers of production. These data refer to: the number of companies in operation in 1997-1998, their production capacity (micro, small, medium, and large), volumes of unprocessed timber (sawlogs), volumes of processed timber (sawn, laminated and plywood), average ranges of activity (i.e. the distance between the extraction and processing sites), the intensity of logging (i.e. cubic meters per hectare), and the area affected. We then provide data on agriculture (temporary and perennial crops), livestock (cattle and buffalo), and land use within agricultural enterprises. The data is drawn from the IBGE agricultural and livestock censuses.

Aims

To prepare and organize a geo-referenced database on the principal land use activities in Amazonia: timber extraction, agriculture (temporary and perennial crops) and livestock.

Methodology

In order to carry out the survey and to develop an integrated analysis of available data on the main land use activities in Amazonia – timber extraction, agriculture and livestock – the following procedure was adopted:

Logging

Data on logging are drawn from field surveys carried out by Imazon during 1997-1998 in 74 timber processing centers (defined as municipalities where annual timber production is 100,000 cubic meters or more) within the Amazon region. These centers account for more than 90% of regional timber production.

A rapid assessment was carried out in each center to discover the number of companies operating, the type of industry (sawmill, laminate or plywood factory) and the size (micro, small, medium, or large). To gather this information, visits were made to areas with a high concentration of timber companies and these field findings were checked against information obtained from industry representatives and local offices of Ibama. Around half the companies identified by the survey were selected for interview. These lasted on average thirty minutes each and those interviewed were generally the owner or the manager of the company.

From this more in-depth survey, the main data elements giving an overview of the timber industry in Amazonia were extracted. These related to: the number of timber companies, their size (micro, small, medium, or large), the volume of production of sawlogs and processed wood, logging intensity (low, moderate or high) and distances between logging and processing sites (short, long or medium).

The area affected by logging (in square kilometers) was calculated on the basis of the information obtained from each of the 1,393 interviews. From this the average volume of timber extracted per hectare (cubic meters of sawlogs per hectare of forest) could be calculated. This in turn allowed calculation of the area of forest required to supply each center of timber production. The accuracy of the information obtained by means of the interviews was compared with that gained through field research on logging in sixteen study areas, nine studied by Imazon (Uhl et al. 1991, Veríssimo et al. 1992, Veríssimo et al. 1995) and seven by the Fundação Floresta Tropical (FFT – Tropical Forest Foundation, unpublished data). In each case the figures obtained directly from the field surveys proved to be within a 95% reliability range vis-à-vis the figures for average volumes obtained from interviews in the local wood processing centers.

To draw up a map of logging activity, all the centers of wood processing were located and digitized onto the 1995 IBGE map of the Legal Amazon region using ArcInfo 3.4d Plus software. The map showing the centers of wood processing was then linked to the database.

The economic radius of logging was calculated on the basis of the average distance between the logging area (forest) and the sawmills (city) for each of the 74 wood processing centers in the region.

Agriculture, livestock and land use

Data on agriculture, livestock and land use were compiled from the 1995-1996 agricultural census carried out by the IBGE and published in 1997-1998. The selected data can be divided into five groups:

Land use and type of economic activity

Size and number of enterprises devoted to temporary and perennial crops, grassland, woodland, secondary growth, and

Table 1 - Breakdown of logging actitivies in the Legal Amazon region by state, 1997-1998										
State	Total no. of wood processing centers	Total no. of companies	Companies interviewed (%)	Timber production (millions of m³/year)	Affected area (km²/year) 1997-98	Production of processed timber (millions of m³/year)				Overall total
						Plywood	Sawn	Laminated	Further improved	
Acre	1	15	55	0.3	80	-	0.12	-	-	0.12
Amapá	1	68	80	0.2	55	-	0.08	-	0.02	0.10
Amazonas	3	29	60	0.7	386	0.08	0.11	0.07	0.02	0.28
Maranhão	2	67	49	0.7	158	0.03	0.24	-	0.01	0.28
Mato Grosso	22	708	48	9.8	4,907	0.18	2.26	0.41	0.44	3.29
Pará	24	1,255	43	11.9	3,648	0.23	3.53	0.15	0.14	4.05
Rondônia	19	364	55	3.9	1,724	0.08	0.86	0.27	0.20	1.41
Roraima	1	15	52	0.2	175	0.01	0.08	0.01	0.01	0.10
Tocantins	1	12	53	0.1	65	-	0.03	-	0.00	0.04
Total	74	2,533	55	27.8	11,198	0.61	7.31	0.91	0.84	9.67

fallow lands; numbers of cattle, buffalo and the amount of sawlogs extracted, by municipality.

'Indicator' crops

Rice, manioc, maize, and soybean were selected as a means of identifying whether subsistence crops or agricultural commodities were of greater importance in each municipality. Subsistence crops, together with pastures, can be correlated with the occurrence of slash and burn agriculture and the use of family labor, whereas commodity crops can be correlated to the advancing frontier of large-scale, capital intensive agriculture (monocultures).

Technological level

Indicators were selected to show the level of agricultural technology, such as the number of warehouses, depots, and silos, and farming equipment such as trucks, tractors, ploughs, seed drills, harvesters and boats. The number of boats can also be used to show municipalities where river transport is important.

Employed people

(Persons in charge, unpaid family members, temporary and permanent employees etc.) These data can identify municipalities where family farms predominate and those where a labor market already exists, a characteristic of more intensive agriculture. From these data it is possible to estimate the gross return from agricultural production per unit of labor, in other words the productivity of agricultural workers by municipality.

Investment, financing, gross values of plant and animal production, levels of gross income

These data can also help identify municipalities where agriculture is directed more towards subsistence or municipalities with significant agricultural and livestock production.

A list of all the variables and their definitions can be found in Appendix 1.

Results

Timber-related activities

Location of the logging companies

The Imazon census identified the existence of 2,533 timber companies in operation in the period 1997-1998 in the 74 regional centers. Of these, 1,393 or 55% were interviewed (Table 1). Of the companies studied, 17% were classified as micro enterprises (annual consumption of sawlogs of less than 4,000 cubic meters), 35% as small enterprises (annual consumption of sawlogs of between 4,000 and 10,000 cubic meters), 35% were classified as medium-sized enterprises (annual consumption of sawlogs of between 10,000 and 20,000 cubic meters) and, finally, 13% were classified as large-scale enterprises (annual consumption of sawlogs of over 20,000 cubic meters) (Table 2).

Production

The annual consumption of sawlogs of the 2,533 timber enterprises in the 74 centers during 1997-1998 was approximately 27.8 million cubic meters. The majority of logging is concentrated in the states of Pará (42%), Mato Grosso (36%) and Rondônia (15%). For processed wood the figures are 63% sawn wood, 18% laminates, 10% plywood, and 9% further improved timber (Table 2).

Intensity of logging

There is a logging intensity curve in the Amazon region, which varies according to the type of forest (dense forests on terra firme are richer in commercial woods than open forests) and to accessibility (in frontier areas access is difficult and logging tends to be more selective). Virtually all the forests located in eastern Pará and southern Maranhão are subject to intensive exploitation (~40 cubic meters/hectare), while exploitation of the forests in central-southern Pará and in Rondônia is semi-intensive (~30 cubic meters/hectare). Selective logging (~20 cubic meters/hectare) occurs principally in Mato Grosso (open forests) and in dense forests in the more remote areas of the states of Acre and Amazonas.

Radius of logging

The forest areas affected by logging were defined as those lying within a radius that could extend from 10 to 650 kilometers around the centers of wood processing. The average distance from the center to the logging site, as given in the interviews, was used to calculate the radius. The areas most accessible for logging are found in eastern Pará (the BR-010 highway), northern Mato Grosso (the BR-163) and central Rondônia (the BR-364). The currently inaccessible areas are concentrated in Amazonas (terra firme forests), Roraima, Amapá and northern Pará. However, it is likely that this scenario will change in the next few years, should more roads be opened up and paved (Figure 1).

no.	Center	State	no. of companies	Size of companies (%)				Intensity volume / ha	Sawlogs m³/year (1997)	Radius			Affected area km² / year (1997)
				Micro	Small	Medium	Large			Medium	Small	Large	
1	Rio Branco	Acre	15	7	52	31	10	low	310,000	74	15	200	80
2	Macapá	Amapá	68	95	5	-	-	low	112,000	80	40	190	55
3	Itacoatiara	Amazonas	8	-	-	-	100	low	445,000	190	10	550	238
4	Manaus	Amazonas	9	-	-	70	30	low	147,000	250	45	650	90
5	Humaitá	Amazonas	12	30	70	-	-	low	125,000	50	20	80	58
6	Açailândia	Maranhão	39	24	12	35	29	high	455,000	250	90	300	96
7	Imperatriz	Maranhão	28	22	30	22	26	high	247,000	150	80	200	62
8	Alta Floresta	Mato Grosso	18	10	29	36	25	low	558,000	53	30	80	275
9	Aripuanã	Mato Grosso	20	16	41	43	-	low	375,000	73	12	150	190
10	Brasnorte	Mato Grosso	17	-	57	43	-	low	251,000	65	30	90	125
11	Claúdia	Mato Grosso	38	10	40	15	35	low	456,000	46	10	120	225
12	Comodoro	Mato Grosso	18	25	67	-	8	low	235,000	50	20	110	60
13	Cotriguaçu	Mato Grosso	16	10	33	38	19	low	282,000	37	15	100	140
14	Feliz Natal	Mato Grosso	46	-	23	69	8	low	570,000	50	10	110	325
15	Guarantã	Mato Grosso	42	12	35	38	15	low	589,000	50	15	80	313
16	Juara	Mato Grosso	26	14	32	41	14	low	345,000	87	20	150	190
17	Juina	Mato Grosso	33	8	38	46	8	low	392,000	76	30	300	200
18	Juruena	Mato Grosso	13	12	-	50	38	low	350,000	30	10	100	95
19	Marcelândia	Mato Grosso	52	-	43	50	7	low	657,000	39	15	80	345
20	Matupá	Mato Grosso	35	14	40	45	-	low	353,000	57	20	150	175
21	Porto dos Gauchos	Mato Grosso	21	17	33	50	-	low	245,000	52	20	90	128
22	Nova Bandeirantes	Mato Grosso	42	12	50	38	-	low	285,000	120	80	180	175
23	Santa Carmem	Mato Grosso	17	15	40	45	-	low	225,000	100	60	150	110
24	Sinop	Mato Grosso	105	4	37	42	17	low	1,935,000	120	80	180	950
25	Sorriso	Mato Grosso	36	17	50	22	11	low	286,000	120	90	200	143
26	Tabaporã	Mato Grosso	22	-	53	32	16	low	165,000	32	15	50	83
27	União do Sul	Mato Grosso	24	7	43	36	14	low	378,000	27	10	55	210
28	São José do Rio Claro	Mato Grosso	25	-	58	42	-	low	277,000	73	20	180	140
29	Vera	Mato Grosso	42	20	-	40	40	low	598,500	73	20	180	310
30	Altamira	Pará	19	22	50	22	6	moderate	248,500	70	30	100	77
31	Breves	Pará	166	81	6	8	5	moderate	598,000	83	12	200	177
32	Cametá	Pará	25	55	45	-	-	low	125,000	60	30	60	70
33	Dom Eliseu	Pará	35	31	26	29	14	moderate	459,000	80	20	120	150
34	Itaituba	Pará	20	25	50	25	-	high	195,000	54	20	100	55
35	Itupiranga	Pará	5	-	-	80	20	moderate	110,000	125	100	150	80
36	Afuá	Pará	350	100	-	-	-	low	476,000	120	30	300	325
37	Goianésia	Pará	14	-	45	30	25	moderate	298,000	80	60	250	117
38	Marabá	Pará	22	-	-	67	33	moderate	485,000	100	80	160	158
39	Uruará	Pará	10	8	30	42	20	moderate	255,000	35	20	55	60
40	Novo Progresso	Pará	10	-	-	70	30	low	285,000	98	60	150	195
41	Oeiras	Pará	88	86	14	-	-	moderate	259,000	120	100	150	61
42	Paragominas	Pará	215	-	46	35	18	high	3,550,000	160	90	350	155
43	Portel	Pará	6	-	-	75	25	moderate	325,000	250	100	400	613
44	Porto de Moz	Pará	12	10	50	30	10	moderate	155,000	100	80	200	93
45	Rondon	Pará	23	-	9	65	26	moderate	495,000	120	100	150	280
46	Redenção	Pará	35	10	31	44	16	moderate	725,000	250	100	500	243
47	Santarém	Pará	33	27	47	17	9	moderate	387,000	100	30	200	157
48	Novo Repartimento	Pará	15	25	42	33	-	moderate	285,000	85	40	140	51
49	Tucurui	Pará	26	24	30	30	17	moderate	295,000	58	15	120	65
50	Concórdia	Pará	12	30	58	12	-	moderate	168,000	70	20	110	195
51	Tome-Açu	Pará	42	9	23	57	11	moderate	468,000	120	80	250	88
52	Jacundá	Pará	28	-	30	50	20	moderate	429,000	90	40	100	70
53	Tailândia	Pará	44	-	35	55	10	moderate	875,000	80	30	140	113
54	Alta Floresta Oeste	Rondônia	14	18	62	20	-	moderate	130,000	85	50	130	367
55	Alto Paraiso	Rondônia	12	-	83	17	-	moderate	155,000	53	10	120	50
56	Ariquemes	Rondônia	55	23	38	23	15	moderate	525,000	40	10	80	78
57	Buritis	Rondônia	14	-	29	71	-	moderate	250,000	80	40	190	130
58	Campo Novo	Rondônia	14	30	50	20	-	moderate	135,000	28	5	40	67
59	Cacoal	Rondônia	10	20	60	20	-	low	110,000	80	30	150	80
60	Cujubim/RC	Rondônia	11	-	67	33	-	low	145,000	50	25	150	55
61	Espigão D'Oeste	Rondônia	14	-	86	14	-	moderate	165,000	40	25	100	73
62	Jaru	Rondônia	25	-	46	15	38	moderate	253,000	50	10	80	48
63	Ji-Paraná	Rondônia	45	18	32	29	21	moderate	325,000	95	25	200	83
64	Machadinho D'Oeste	Rondônia	15	18	27	45	9	moderate	235,000	90	25	120	117
65	Monte Negro	Rondônia	12	22	44	33	-	moderate	155,000	50	10	120	77
66	Ouro Preto D'Oeste	Rondônia	13	14	29	43	14	low	140,000	70	20	90	88
67	Nova Mamóre	Rondônia	12	-	55	23	22	moderate	135,000	50	30	120	47
68	Pimenta Bueno	Rondônia	13	14	29	43	14	low	155,000	60	25	98	125

continues

no.	Center	State	no. of companies	Size of companies (%)				Intensity volume / ha	Sawlogs m³/year (1997)	Radius			Affected area km² / year (1997)
				Micro	Small	Medium	Large			Medium	Small	Large	
69	Rolim de Moura	Rondônia	11	-	20	80	-	moderate	118,000	100	20	150	45
70	Seringueiras	Rondônia	14	-	45	40	15	moderate	150,000	105	80	190	36
71	Porto Velho	Rondônia	25	31	46	23	-	low	265,000	65	15	120	75
72	Vilhena	Rondônia	35	-	24	47	29	moderate	357,000	150	45	250	83
73	Boa Vista	Roraima	15	20	30	50	-	low	211,000	100	30	250	175
74	Araguaína	Tocantins	12	75	15	-	10	low	115,000	85	20	180	65
	TOTAL		2,533	16.9	35,1	34,9	13,1		27,828,000				11,198

Area of logging

It is estimated that 11,198 square kilometers a year of virgin forest were used for logging in 1997-1998 by the 2,533 timber companies operating in the Legal Amazon region (Table 1). This figure is based on a 95% degree of reliability for levels of logging obtained from the interviews with these enterprises. In comparative terms, this area affected by logging is equivalent to 50% to 80% of the deforested area of the Legal Amazon region in 1996.

Logging causes significant environmental impacts on the forest: severe losses of forest canopy, an increasing tendency for forest fires, and spreading of vines. In addition it acts as a catalyst for the disorderly settlement of the region and indirectly contributes to regional deforestation. Currently it is loggers who are generally responsible for the opening and maintenance of forest access roads which usually result in land occupation by farmers and ranchers (Uhl et al. 1997, Veríssimo et al. 1995).

The species logged

The impact of logging on economically important species has been studied by Martini et al. (1994). A summary of this article together with information on the main species logged by the processing centers can be found in the next chapter.

Agriculture and livestock

Agriculture and livestock

Agriculture and livestock activities are concentrated in the so-called 'arc of deforestation', a rainbow shaped region extending from northeastern Amazonia (Maranhão and northeastern Pará), through southern Pará, Tocantins and Mato Grosso, as far as southeastern Amazonia (Rondônia) (Figure 2). According to data from the agriculture and livestock census, within this arc the average proportion of the area of rural enterprises still covered by natural forests and woodlands is generally less than half.

The advance of large scale crops, such as maize and soybean, into Amazonia has concerned environmentalists because of the negative effects this type of farming can have on soils (erosion), watercourses (silting and release of chemical products), and on agrarian and social systems (land concentration, reduction in the need for labor). The IBGE data show that cultivation of maize and soybean is more intensive within the arc of deforestation, particularly in the municipalities of Balsas, Maranhão and in central Mato Grosso (Figure 4). However, the existence of centers of soybean cultivation can also be observed in other locations, such as the Santarém and Marabá regions of Pará. This pattern reflects the effects of state policies of providing incentives to large commercial cultivation in these locations. In Pará, for instance, the southern part of the state, the region along the Belém-Brasília highway, and the Santarém region were selected to be 'agricultural development centers'.

Growing subsistence crops, manioc and rice, is more important in municipalities in the state of Amazonas, in the Lower Amazon region of Pará, in northeastern Pará, and in Maranhão (Figure 3). In these places, a high percentage of the total area of farms recorded by the census (up to 80%) is planted with subsistence crops. Areas of 'capoeira' (secondary growth on previously cleared land) are also more common in these regions. The correlation between the area planted with rice and manioc and the area of 'capoeira' is relatively high at 0.40.

Cattle are also concentrated within the so-called arc of deforestation, particularly in southern Pará and in Mato Grosso (Figure 5). The correlation between the number of cattle and the area of planted pasture in municipalities in the Legal Amazon region is very high (0.90), which shows the important role this activity plays in deforestation. Buffalo herds, on the other hand, are concentrated in municipalities along the lower and middle reaches of the Amazon and in coastal areas of Pará and Maranhão (Figure 6). These animals adapt themselves well to the floodplain conditions that predominate in these locations. The productivity of buffalos on floodplains is much higher than that of cattle (Arima & Uhl 1998).

Timber activities

According to the agricultural and livestock census there is a higher concentration of timber activities along Amazonian rivers, above all on the Lower Amazon and the Upper Solimões (Figure 7). There are only two terra firme regions which stand out: along the Belém-Brasília highway in Pará and northern Mato Grosso. The correlation between timber production data from the census and the Imazon data is very low at only 0.09. Previous

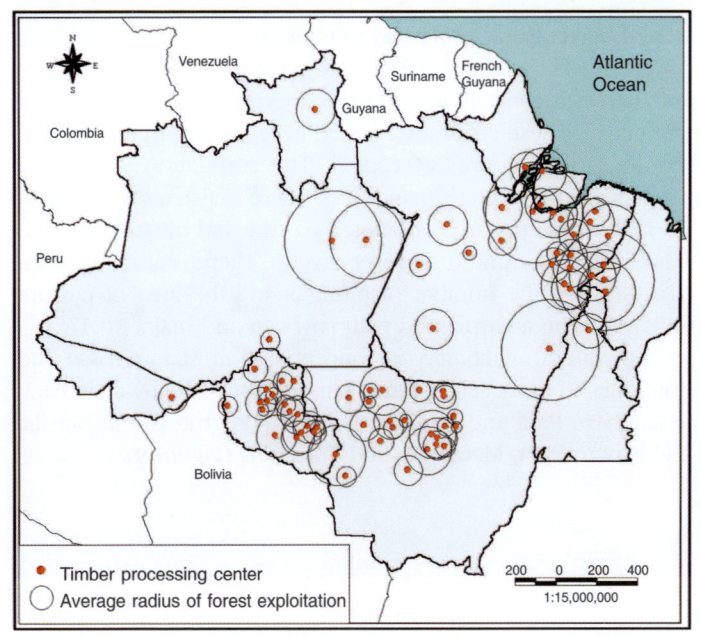

Figure 1. Average radius of logging activities by timber processing center, 1997-1998. Source: Imazon.

studies show terra firme regions are currently the major source of sawlogs. For instance, in Pará nearly 70% of timber is logged from terra firme regions (Barros & Uhl 1995). For this reason the Imazon data on timber production has been used as they are more reliable.

Agricultural and livestock incomes

Incomes received by farmers from the sale of agricultural and livestock products are more important in municipalities along the Belém-Brasília highway, southern Pará and in Mato Grosso and Rondônia (Figure 8). There is a strong correlation between income levels and gross plant production levels (0.94) and a weaker correlation with gross animal production levels (0.49) and areas of planted pasture (0.44). Taking plant production, the correlation between the incomes is stronger in areas planted with commodities such as soybean and maize (0.86) than in areas planted with subsistence crops such as rice and manioc (0.52), as would be expected. The correlation between incomes and areas planted with perennial cultivations is even lower (0.17), which shows that perennial crops are still of little significance in the Amazon Region.

Financing

The total value of financial support behaves in a way similar to that of agricultural and livestock incomes. There is a strong correlation between the volume of financial support and the area of temporary crops as a whole (0.85), in particular with the commodity crops of soybean and maize (0.82), while there is a weak correlation with subsistence crops (0.48).

There is a weak correlation between financial support and cattle and buffalo raising (0.29 and 0.05, respectively), as well as with the area of planted and natural pastures (0.33 and 0.11, respectively). These data reveal a significant change in the allocation of credit in Amazonia compared to the 1970s and 1980s, a period when livestock production was the activity that benefited most from credit (Schneider 1994).

It appears that financing is directed more towards the costs of planting than towards investments. The correlation between financial support and expenditures is 0.90, while the correlation between financial support and levels of investment is 0.49.

Use of agricultural tools and machinery

There is a correlation between the number of tractors, trucks and harvesting machines and the area planted with soybean and maize. These crops are planted in relatively large areas and require large amounts of capital. The correlation with these machines is between 0.79 and 0.98. There is also a strong correlation between the area of planted pasture and tractors and utility vehicles (0.62 and 0.74, respectively). There is also a correlation between the number of ploughs and the area of pasture (0.51) and the area planted with soybean and maize (0.47).

Agricultural machinery is concentrated in Mato Grosso and Rondônia, in the section of the Transamazônica highway in Pará, in southern Pará and in municipalities along the Belém-Brasília highway in Pará, Maranhão and Tocantins (Figure 9).

Conclusion

Agriculture and livestock activities are concentrated in the south of the Amazon Basin within an arc which that extends from northeastern and southern Pará through northern Mato Grosso to Rondônia. Logging occurs mainly in terra firme forests found in the north of the 'arc of deforestation'. This 'logging belt' can extend further into northern Mato Grosso and western Pará because of the presence of mahogany, a species of high commercial value. Logging also occurs along the main rivers of the Amazon Basin. The areas where intensive logging is taking place are those which are most likely to be deforested in the near future.

The geography of agricultural usage and of logging may change if the new infrastructure projects planned by the federal government are implemented (see the previous chapter). For instance, paving highways will reduce timber transportation costs and will increase the economic reach of logging (Souza Jr. et al. 1999). In the same way, incentives for large scale agriculture such as soybean will lead to changes in the geography of land use. It will be possible to plant soybean in forest areas or in areas that are currently used for grazing, thereby moving cattle-raising to even more marginal forest areas (Arima & Uhl 1997).

General observations

The data obtained from the IBGE agricultural and livestock censuses do not include the total number of municipalities in the Legal Amazon region, as new municipalities were created after the 1996-1996 agricultural and livestock census was carried out. The list containing all the municipalities of the Legal Amazon region and those municipalities without census data can be obtained by contacting the authors.

Efforts were made, albeit unsuccessfully, to obtain data on the use of fertilizers and improvers, the number of enterprises with electricity, and the number of enterprises receiving assistance from extension agents, agronomists, veterinarians and forestry engineers. An attempt was also made to obtain data on the number of farmers affiliated to co-operatives and associations. Various sources were consulted without success: electricity companies, banks, state agricultural extension services, etc.

Such information would be very useful for assessing the technological status of properties in each municipality and levels of social organization among farmers. These were included in previous agricultural censuses, but were not published in the hard copy and CD versions of the most recent census. An example of the questionnaire administered in the census was obtained and it can be seen that these data do exist. Gaining access to them however will depend on a process of consultation with the IBGE headquarters in Rio de Janeiro, which has not been possible. We suggest that others involved in the project and who have access to IBGE may be able to obtain these data.

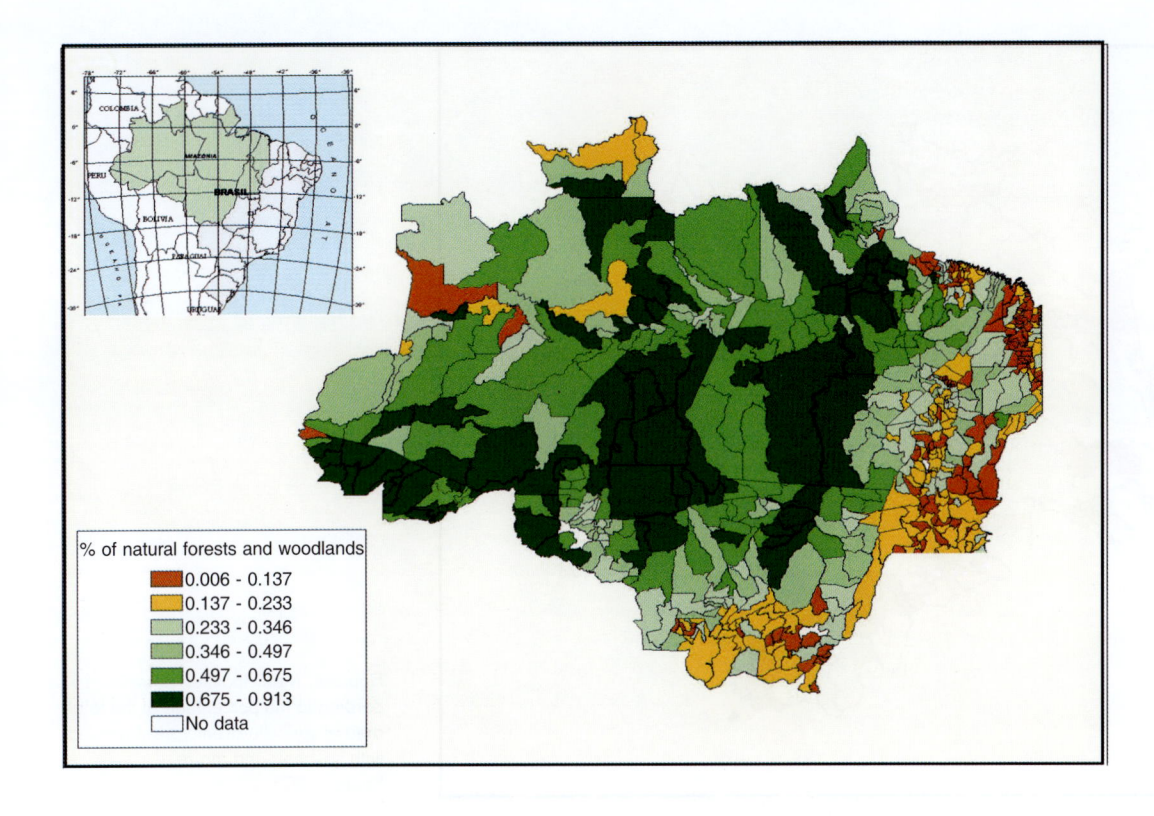

Figure 2. Municipalities classified according to the percentage of the total area of agricultural enterprises covered by natural forests and woodlands. Source: IBGE 1998.

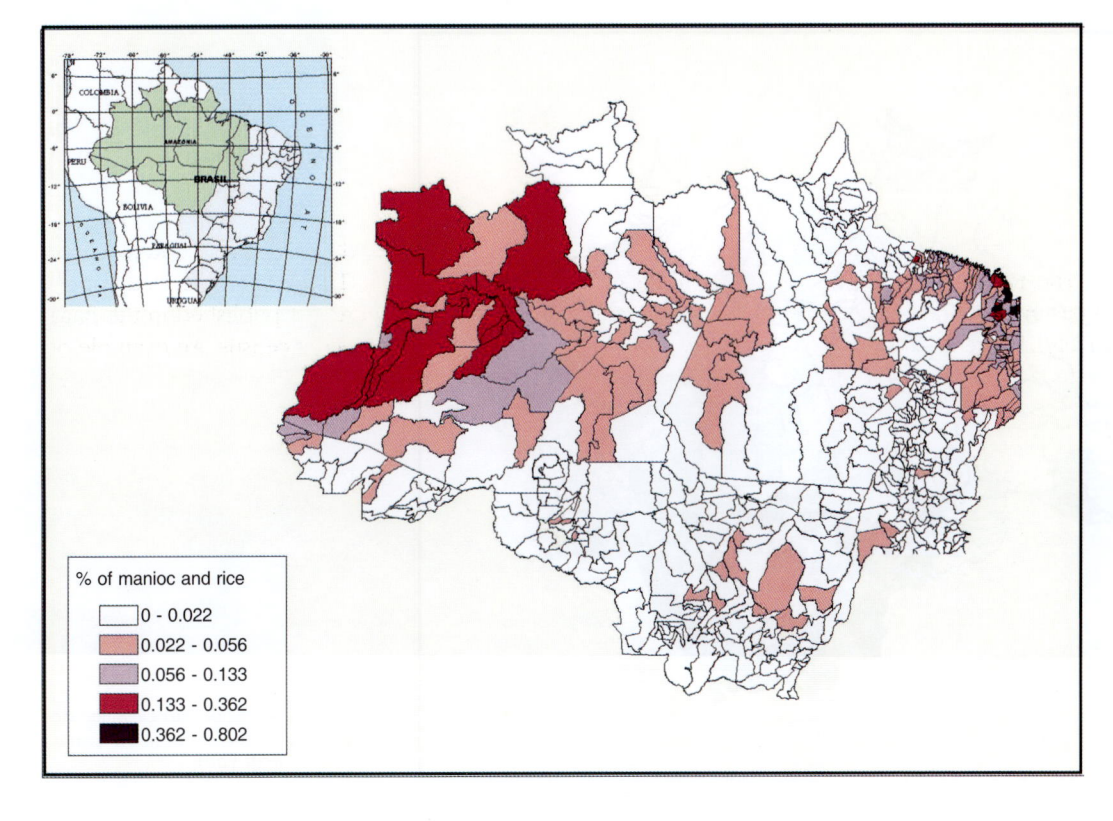

Figure 3. Municipalities classified according to the percentage of the total area of agricultural enterprises planted with manioc and rice. Source: IBGE 1998.

SOCIOECONOMIC AND ANTHROPOGENIC PRESSURES

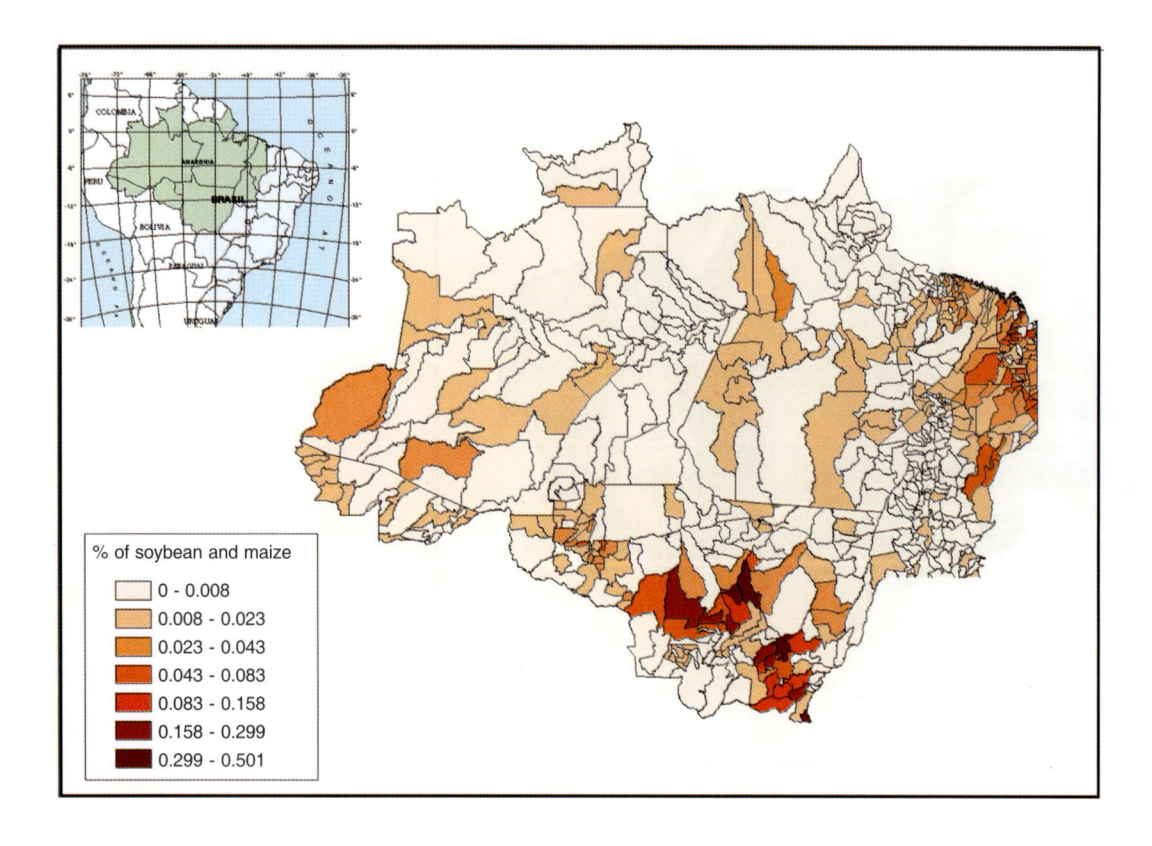

Figure 4. Municipalities classified according to the percentage of the total area of agricultural enterprises planted with soybean and maize.
Source: IBGE 1998.

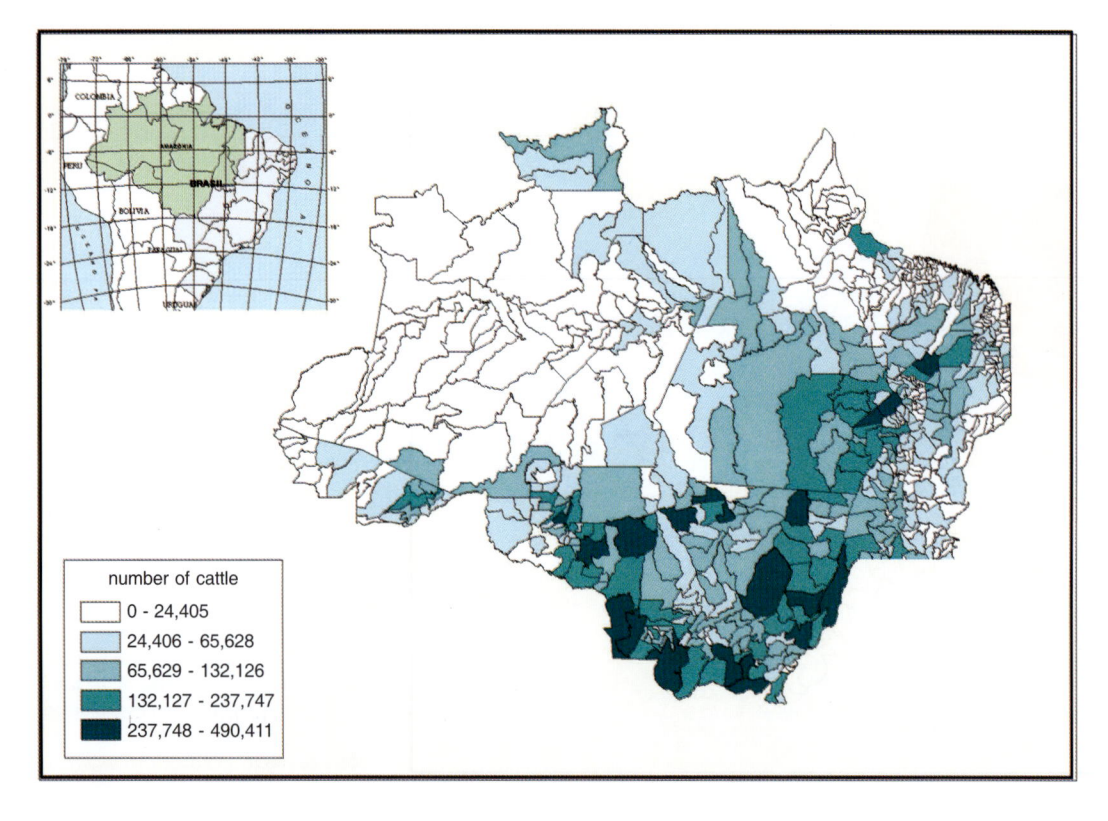

Figure 5. Municipalities classified according to the number of cattle.
Source: IBGE 1998.

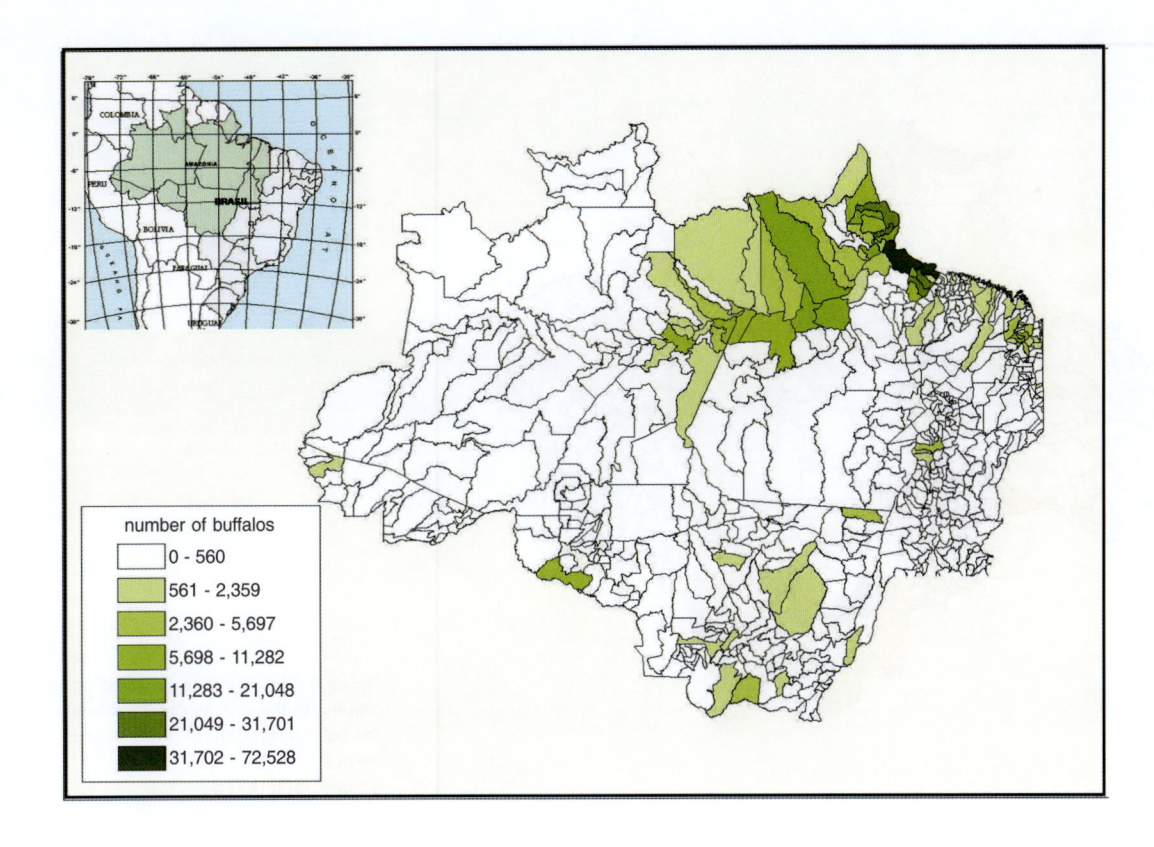

Figure 6. Municipalities classified according to the number of buffalo.
Source: IBGE 1998.

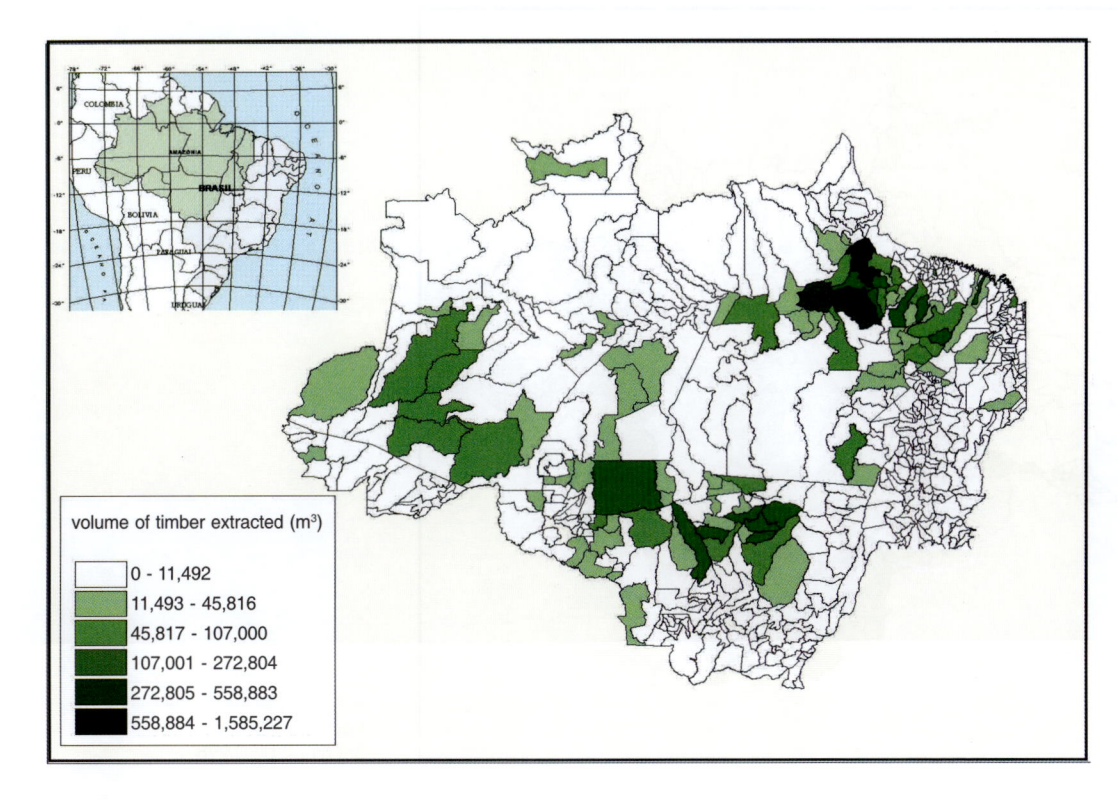

Figure 7. Municipalities classified according to the volume of sawlogs extracted.
Source: IBGE 1998.

SOCIOECONOMIC AND ANTHROPOGENIC PRESSURES

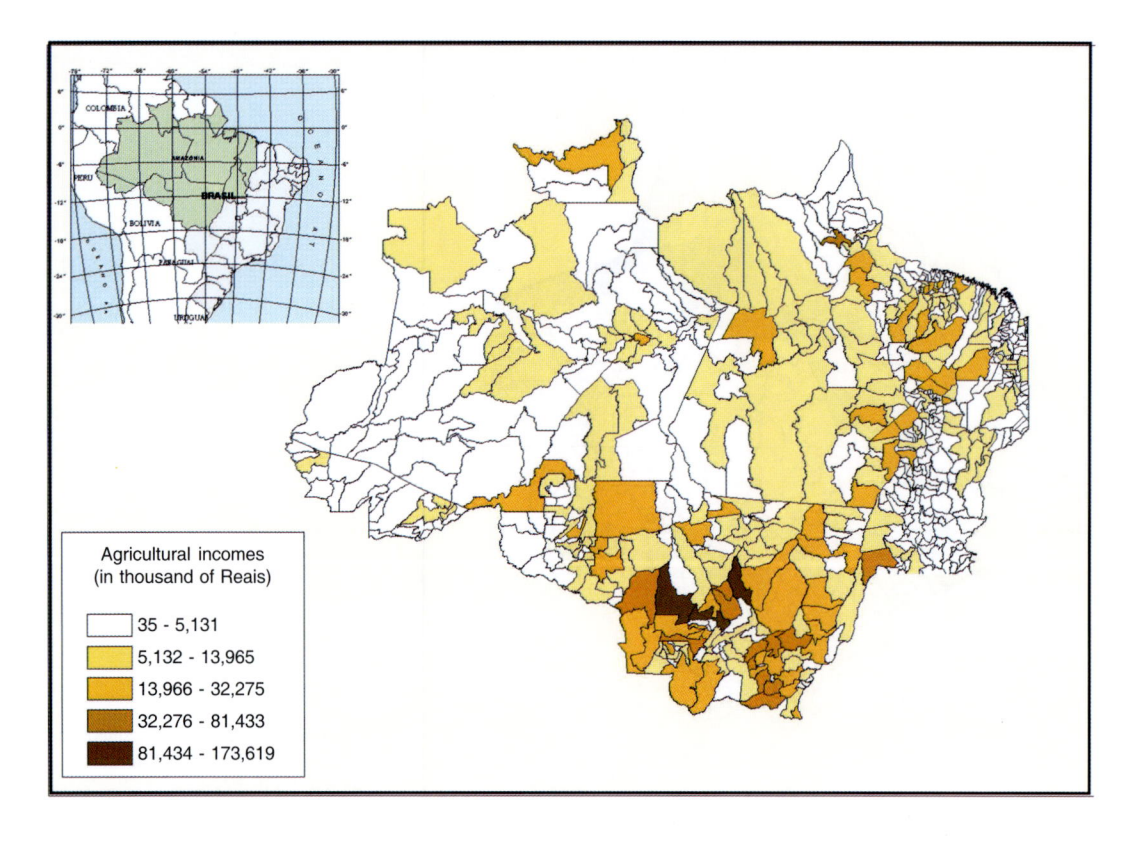

Figure 8. Municipalities classified according to the income obtained from the sale of agricultural products and services.
Source: IBGE 1998.

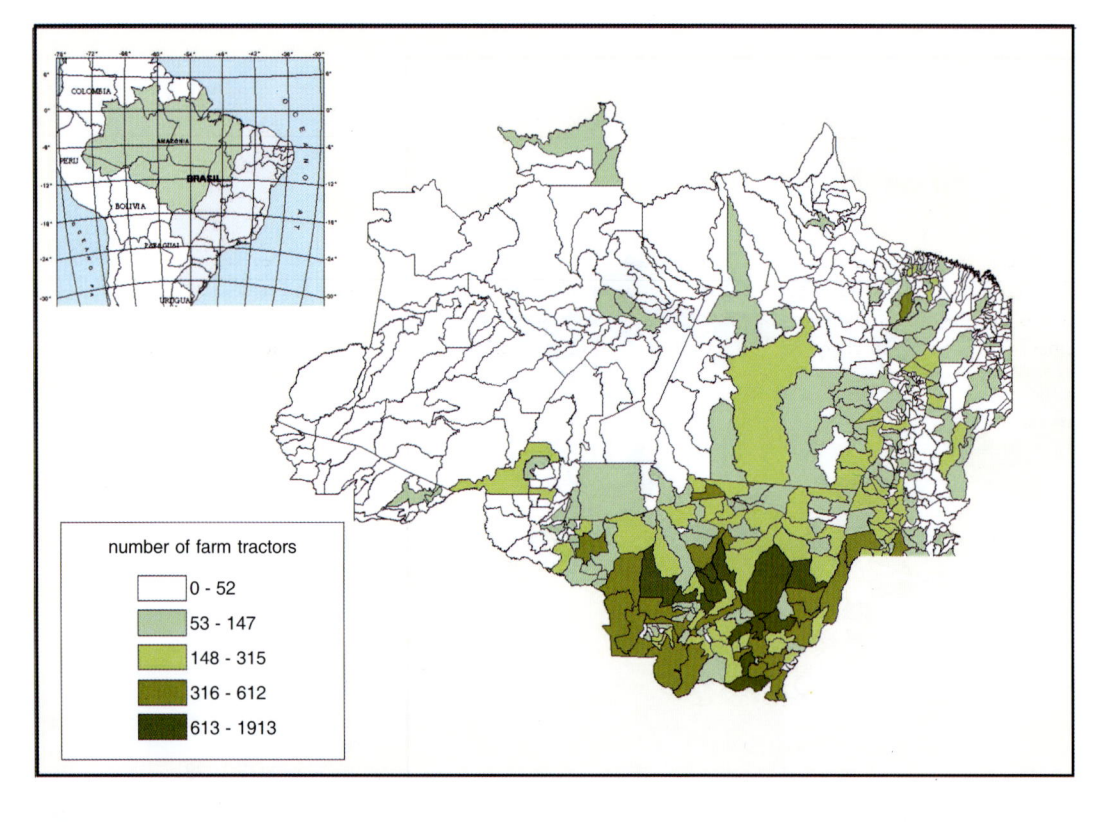

Figure 9. Municipalities classified according to the number of farm tractors.
Source: IBGE 1998.

	Appendix 1 - List of variables and their definitions
Br94_id	Municipality identification code used by the IBGE
Muni_nome	Name of municipality
Bov_num	Number of cattle
Buf_num	Number of buffalo
Area_tot	The total area of land making up the farms in the municipality (in hectares)
Lav_per	Area planted or being prepared for the planting of long-term crops (in hectares)
Lav_temp	Area planted or being prepared for the planting of short-term crops (in hectares)
Desc_temp	Lands normally used for the planting of temporary crops and which have been left fallow for a period of not more than four years since the most recent year of use (in hectares)
Pasto_nat	Area used for cattle pasture without having been sown as pasture (in hectares)
Pasto_plan	Area used for cattle pasture which have been sown as pasture (in hectares)
Flor_nat	Areas of natural forests and woodlands used for the extraction of products or conserved as forest reserves (in hectares)
Mad_nat	Quantity of timber extracted as sawlogs (in cubic meters)
Flor_plan	Area planted or being prepared for the planting of forest essences
Nao_util	Areas apt for the cultivation of crops, pastures or woodlands and which have not been used for such purposes for a period of more than 4 years (in hectares)
AR_qtd	Rice production (in tons)
AR_area	Area planted with rice (in hectares)
Mand_qtd	Manioc production (in tons)
Mand_area	Area planted with manioc (in hectares)
Mil_qtd	Maize production (in tons)
Mil_area	Area planted with maize (in hectares)
Soy_qtd	Soybean production (in tons)
Soy_area	Area planted with soybean (in hectares)
Granel_num	Number of depots for loose grain (units)
Granel_cap	Capacity of depots for loose grain (in tons)
Dep_num	Number of depots with packing facilities (units)
Dep_cap	Capacity of depots with packing facilities (in tons)
DepOT_num	Number of depots for other products (units)
DepOT_cap	Capacity of depots for other products (in tons)
GAE_temp	Number of enterprises whose economic activity is temporary crops
GAE_hort	Number of enterprises whose economic activity is horticulture
GAE_per	Number of enterprises whose economic activity is permanent crops
GAE_pec	Number of enterprises whose economic activity is raising livestock
GAE_PM	Number of enterprises whose economic activity is mixed production
GAE_SIL	Number of enterprises whose economic activity is forestry and timber production
GAE_PESC	Number of enterprises whose economic activity is fishing and aquiculture
GAE_CARV	Number of enterprises whose economic activity is charcoal production
MAQ_PLAN	Number of agricultural planting machines
MAQ_COL	Number of agricultural harvesting machines
ARADO_AN	Number of animal ploughs
ARADO_TRC	Number of mechanical ploughs
PO_TOTAL	Total number of persons, remunerated or otherwise, found carrying out services connected with the activities of the enterprise, except those performing tasks on behalf of sub-contractors
PO_RESP	Farmer or administrator responsible for the management of the enterprise being paid a fixed amount or a share of the production, and members of his family helping with carrying out such tasks without receiving remuneration of any kind for their services
PO_EPER	Persons hired to carry out permanent or long term tasks and remunerated in the form of money or a fixed amount of produce, including family members of the permanent employee who effectively helped in carrying out the respective tasks
PO_ETEM	Persons hired to carry out occasional or short term tasks and remunerated in the form of money or its equivalent in produce, including family members of such employees who assisted in carrying out the respective tasks
PO_PAR	Persons directly subordinate to the person in charge and who carry out tasks in return for a share of the production resulting from their work (a half, a quarter, etc.) and family members who assisted them in carrying out such tasks
PO_OUTRA	All other persons whose working conditions differed from those of people falling into the previous categories, such as servants, tenants etc.
PO_RSD	Total resident working personnel of the agriculture and livestock enterprise
EST_SEM	Enterprises without hired labor
SFAER	Upright fodder silos (units)
SFA_CAP	Capacity of upright fodder silos (in tons)
SFENC	Sloping or trench fodder silos (units)
SFE_CAP	Capacity of sloping or trench fodder silos (in tons)
CAMIN	Number of trucks used for purposes relating to the activities of the enterprise, including those leased, owned or borrowed
UTIL	Number of utility vehicles used for purposes relating to the activities of the enterprise
REBOQ	Number of trailers used for purposes relating to the activities of the enterprise
TRC_ANI	Number of vehicles powered by animal traction used for purposes relating to the activities of the enterprise

continues

EMBARQ	Number of boats used for purposes relating to the activities of the enterprise
TRATOR	Total number of tractors used for purposes relating to the activities of the enterprise
INVEST	Total value of investments made during the most recent agricultural period (1995-96) (in thousands of Reais)
FINANC	Value of financial support obtained and applied towards activities connected with agriculture and livestock (in thousands of Reais)
DESPES	Expenditures incurred during the most recent agricultural period on the maintenance and financing of the activities of the enterprise, as well as on salaries, payment of production shares to third parties, leasing and sharing of land, fertilizers and improvers, and other expenses (in thousands of Reais)
VBP_ANI	Value of animal production (in thousands of Reais)
VBP_VEG	Value of plant production (in thousands of Reais)
VREC	Revenues attributable to income from the sale of produce and the activities undertaken by the enterprise, including services (in thousands of Reais)

Bibliography

ARIMA, E.; UHL, C. Ranching in the Brazilian Amazon in a National Context: Economics, Policy and Practices. *Society and Natural Resources*, no. 10, p. 433-51, 1997.

BARROS, A. C.; UHL, C. Logging Along the Amazon River and Estuary: Patterns, Problems and Potential. *Forest Ecology and Management*, no. 77, p. 87-105, 1995.

IBGE. *Censo agropecuário*, vols. 2, 3, 4, 5, 6 e 7. Rio de Janeiro: IBGE, 1998.

NEPSTAD, D. et al. Large-Scale Impoverishment of Amazonian Forest by Logging and Fire. *Nature*, no. 398, p. 505-8, 1999.

SCHNEIDER, R. Government and the Economy on the Amazon Frontier. The World Bank, LATEN. *Report,* no. 34. Washington D.C.: World Bank, 1994.

SOUZA Jr., C.; VERÍSSIMO, A.; AMARAL, P. *Identificação de áreas com potencial para a criação de florestas nacionais no Estado do Pará*. Ministério do Meio Ambiente (MMA) and United Nations' Food and Agriculture Organization (FAO), 1999, 33 p.

UHL, C. et al. Social Economic and Ecological Consequences of Logging in the Amazon Frontier: the Case of Thayland. *Forest Ecology and Management*, n. 46, p. 243-73, 1991.

_____. An Integrated Research Approach to Address Natural Resource Problems in the Brazilian Amazon. *Bioscience*, n. 46, v. 3, p. 160-8, 1997.

VERÍSSIMO, A. et al. Logging Impacts and Prospects for Sustainable Forest Management in an Old Amazonia Frontier: the Case of Paragominas. *Forest Ecology and Management*, n. 55, p. 169-99, 1992.

_____. Extraction of a High Value Natural Resource from Amazonia: the Case of Mahogany. *Forest Ecology and Management*, n. 72, p. 39-60, 1995.

Tree species potentially threatened by logging activities in Amazonia

Adriana Martini, Nelson de Araújo Rosa and Christopher Uhl *Instituto do Homem e Meio Ambiente da Amazônia*

Logging activities are an important anthropogenic factor affecting the composition and distribution of species in Amazon forests. Certain ecological or economic characteristics can determine the increase or decline of populations of forest species. For example, those species of high commercial value whose geographical distribution is limited, and which have low capacity for dispersion, slow rates of growth, and a small number of young specimens will probably suffer population decline when exposed to severe logging (Martini et al. 1994). On the other hand, timber species of little commercial value, exposed to low logging pressure, but with a wide geographical range, fast growth and vigorous regeneration may experience a population increase in areas exploited for timber (Martini et al. 1994).

Martini et al. (1994) classified 305 tree species exploited for timber employing a linear score scale which took into account seven ecological variables: 1) ease of seed dispersion; 2) abundance of seedlings in regenerating forests; 3) growth rate; 4) capacity to re-sprout after cutting or breaking; 5) resistance to fire; 6) breadth of geographical distribution; and 7) abundance of adult individuals. The lower the total score, the higher the possibility of the species suffering population decline as a result of logging activities.[1]

In addition to ecological characteristics, the authors classified the species according to 'logging pressure'. In other words, those that are always logged when found (because of their high market value) received a lower score. Species frequently ignored by loggers, even when found in abundance, received a higher score.

The results of this study can be found in Table 1, along with the common Brazilian names of the species. Martini et al. (1994) classified the species into three groups:

Group I (10-15 points): species potentially susceptible to population reduction as a result of intensive logging. This group consists of 41 species, including *Euxylophora paraensis* (pau-amarelo), *Vouacapoua americana* (acapu), *Brosinum amplicoma* (amapá-amargoso), *Pithecellobium racemosum* (angelim-rajado-verdadeiro), *Copaifera reticulata* (copaíba), *Ocotea rubra* (louro-vermelho, louro-gamela), *Dipteryx magnífica* (cumaru-rosa), and *Swietenia macrophyla* (mogno).

Group II (16-21 points): comprising 217 tree species capable of reasonable resistance to logging pressure. These include some economically important species such as ipê (*Tabebuia serratifolia*), cedro (*Cedrela odo-rata*), jatobá (*Hymenaea courbaril*), virola (*Virola surinamensis*), andiroba (*Carapa guianensis*), freijó (*Cordia goeldiana*), maçaranduba (*Manilkara huberi*), pau-roxo (*Peltogyne paradoxa*), and macacaúba (*Platymiscium trinitatis*).

Group III (22-26 points): formed by a group of 47 species, including *Ocotea guianensis* (louro-branco), *Guatteria olivacea* (envira-preta-folha-grande) and *Guatteria procera* (envira preta), which may benefit from changes caused by logging. A good example of a species from this group is *Ormosia coutinhoi* (buiuçu), which can be found throughout Amazonia. Its seeds are dispersed over long distances and re-sprout quickly after felling or damage; it possesses a population structure with many seedlings and young individuals; and, finally, it benefits from the clearings created by logging, as it is a fast growing species which thrives in full sunlight.

According to Martini et al. (1994), the majority (89%) of the 305 studied species can be found throughout Amazonia; 4% are found mainly in eastern Amazonia, 1% in central Amazonia, and 6% in western Amazonia. In terms of ecosystem, the majority (64%) of the species occur in terra firme forests, 10% in floodplain (várzea) forests, and 24% in both environments.

In an unpublished study, Veríssimo and Lima recorded the most logged and traded species in 75 timber centers in Amazonia (Table 2). Although this list is incomplete, it includes the main traded species. By combining Tables 1 and 2 it is possible to determine which species are most susceptible to population reduction in each timber center.[2]

Bibliography

MARTINI, A.; ROSA, N.; UHL, C. An Attempt to Predict which Tree Species May Be Threatened by Logging Activities. *Environmental Conservation*, v. 21, n. 2, p. 152-62, 1994.

VERÍSSIMO, A.; LIMA, E. *Caracterização dos pólos madeireiros na Amazônia brasileira*. Imazon, internal non-published document.

---

1. See Martini et al. (1994) for more details of the methodology and for further explanation.
2. There is a difficulty in accurately linking the common and scientific names of each species. It is not unusual to find trees having the same common name despite belonging to different species.

TABLE 1 - LIST OF TIMBER SPECIES, COMMON NAME AND DEGREE OF THREAT OF POPULATION DECLINE AS A RESULT OF LOGGING (SOURCE: MARTINI ET AL. 1994)					
Scientific name	Common name	Family	Ecological characteristics	Logging pressure	Sum of ecological and commercial characteristics
Euxylophora paraensis Huber	Pau-amarelo	Rutaceae	9	1	10
Qualea coerulea Ducke	Mandioqueira-azul	Vochysiaceae	10	1	11
Brosimum amplicoma Ducke	Amapá-amargoso	Moraceae	11	1	12
Cassia scleroxylon Ducke	Muirapixuna	Caesalpiniaceae	11	1	12
Euplassa pinnata (Lam) Johnston	Louro-faia	Proteaceae	11	1	12
Batesia floribunda Spr. Et Benth	Acapurana- T. F./tento	Caesalpiniaceae	12	1	13
Buchenavia capitata Eichl.	Tanimbuca	Combretaceae	12	1	13
Minquartia guianensis Aubl	Acariquara/quariquara	Olacaeae	12	1	13
Peltogyne maranhensis Hub et Ducke	Roxinho	Caesalpiniaceae	12	1	13
Pithecellobium racemosum Ducke	Angelim-rajado-verdadeiro	Mimosaceae	12	1	13
Sacoglotis amazonica Benth	Uxirana	Humiriaceae	12	1	13
Tapura singularis Ducke	Pau-de-bicho	Didiapetalaceae	12	1	13
Vouacapoua americana Aubl	Acapu	Caesalpiniaceae	12	1	13
Aspidosperma album Jacq	Araracanga	Apocynaceae	13	1	14
Aspidosperma sandwithianum Mgf.	Araracanga-branca	Apocynaceae	13	1	14
Brosimum rubescens Taub.	Pau-aranha/muirapiranga	Moraceae	13	1	14
Buchenavia parvifolia Ducke	Tanimbuca-amarela/carará	Combretaceae	13	1	14
Centrolobium paraense Tul	Araribá-rajado/pau-rainha	Fabaceae	13	1	14
Diplotropis martiussii Bth	Sucupira-da-várzea	Fabaceae	13	1	14
Iryanthera grandis Ducke	Ucuubarana	Myristicaceae	13	1	14
Parkia veluntinia R. Benoist	Parkia veluntinia/esponjeira	Mimosaceae	13	1	14
Pouteria pariry (Ducke) Baehni	Frutão/pariri	Sapotaceae	13	1	14
Swietenia macrophylla King	Mogno/aguano/araputanga	Caesalpiniaceae	13	1	14
Torresia acreana Ducke	Cerejeira/imburana	Fabaceae	13	1	14
Aspidosperma desmathum Benth.	Araracanga	Apocynaceae	14	1	15
Brosimum parinarioides Ducke	Amapá-doce/amaparana	Moraceae	14	1	15
Calophylium brasiliense Camb.	Jacareúba/cedro-do pântano	Guttiferae	14	1	15
Chamaecrista adiantifolia (Bth) var. Pteridofita	Acapu-Ipixuna/coração-de-negro	Caesalpiniaceae	14	1	15
Clinostemon mahuba (A. Samp.) Kihlmann	Maúba	Lauraceae	14	1	15
Copaifera reticulata Ducke	Copaíba	Caesalpiniacea	14	1	15
Dipterix magnifica Ducke	Cumaru-rosa	Fabaceae	14	1	15
Humiriastrum excelsum Ducke	Achuá-pequeno/umiri	Humiriaceae	14	1	15
Licaria aritu Ducke	Louro-aritu	Lauraceae	14	1	15
Licana cannelli (Meissn) Kosterm	Louro-preto	Lauraceae	14	1	15
Martiodendron elatum (Ducke) Gleason	Jutaí-cica/muirapixuna	Caesalpiniaceae	14	1	15
Ocotea rubra Mez	Louro-vermelho/louro/gamela	Lauraceae	14	1	15
Parkia pendula Benth	Fava-bolota/visgueiro	Mimosaceae	14	1	15
Peltogyne paradoxa Ducke	Almirante/pau-roxo/guarabu	Caesalpiniaceae	14	1	15
Pithecellobium pedicellare (DC) Bth	Apuchiqui/mapuchiqui	Mimosaceae	14	1	15
Richardella macrocarpa (Hub) Aubl	Curitibá-grande	Sapotaceae	14	1	15
Swartzia grandifolia Benth	Gombeira/coração-de-negro	Caesalpiniaceae	14	1	15
Alchorneopsis floribunda Muell. Arg.	Canelarana	Euphorbiaceae	15	1	16
Anacardium spruceanum Benth ex Engl.	Cajuaçu/cajuí	Anacardiaceae	15	1	16
Aniba canelilla (H. B. K.) Mez	Preciosa	Lauraceae	15	1	16
Astronium lecointer Ducke	Muiracatiara/aroeira	Anacardiaceae	15	1	16
Bowdichia nitida Spruce ex Benth	Sucupira-amarela	Fabaceae	15	1	16
Brosimum acutifolium Huber	Muirapiranga/mururé	Moraceae	15	1	16
Brosimum potabile Ducke	Amapá-doce/garrote	Moraceae	15	1	16
Buchenavia grandis Ducke	Marindiba	Combretaceae	15	1	16
Caraipa richardiana Camb.	Tamaquaré/louro-tamaquaré	Guttiferae	15	1	16
Cariniana micrantha Ducke	Castanha-vermelha	Lecythidaceae	15	1	16
Chaunochiton Kappleri (Sag ex Engl) Ducke	Pau-vermelho	Olacaceae	15	1	16
Copaifera duckei Dwyer	Copaíba	Caesalpiniacea	15	1	16

continues

Scientific name	Common name	Family	Ecological characteristics	Logging pressure	Sum of ecological and commercial characteristics
Cordia bicolor D.C.	Freijó-branco	Boraginacea	15	1	16
Dalbergia spruceana Benth	Jacarandá-do-pará	Fabaceae	15	1	16
Dinizia excelsa Ducke	Angelim-pedra-verdadeiro	Mimosaceae	15	1	16
Diplotropis purpurea (Rich) Amsh	Sucupira-preta	Fabaceae	15	1	16
Dipterix ferrea Ducke	Cumaru	Fabaceae	15	1	16
Dipteryx polyphilla Huber	Cumaru	Fabaceae	15	1	16
Eperua falcata Aubl	Apazeiro	Caesalpiniaceae	15	1	16
Eschweilera coriacea (Ap Decand) Mart ex Berg	Matamatá-branco	Lecythidaceae	15	1	16
Goupia glabra Aubl	Cupiúba	Celastraceae	15	1	16
Hymenolobium excelsum Ducke	Angelim/angelim-pedra	Fabaceae	15	1	16
Hymenolobium flavum Ducke	Angelim	Fabaceae	15	1	16
Hymenolobium heterocarpum Ducke	Angelim-branco	Fabaceae	15	1	16
Hymenolobium modestum Ducke	Angelim-da-mata	Fabaceae	15	1	16
Hymenolobium nitidum Benth	Angelim	Fabaceae	15	1	16
Hymenolobium sericeum Ducke	Angelim	Fabaceae	15	1	16
Manilkara Inundata Ducke	Maçaranduba-da-folhagrande	Sapotaceae	15	1	16
Mezilaurus itauba (Meissn) Taubert ex Mez	Itaúba-amarela/itaúba	Lauraceae	15	1	16
Mezilaurus lindaviana Schw. & Mez.	Itaúba/itaúba-abacate	Lauraceae	15	1	16
Micropholis egensis (A.-DC.) Pier	Mangabarana	Sapotaceae	15	1	16
Moronobea coccinea Aubl	Anani-da-T.F./bacuri-falso	Guttiferae	15	1	16
Ocotea cymbarum H.B.K	Louro-inamui	Lauraceae	15	1	16
Panopsis sessilifolia (Rich) Sandw.	Faeira/louro-faia	Proteaceae	15	1	16
Parinari excelsa Sabine	Parinari	Chrysobalanaceae	15	1	16
Peltogyne paniculata (Bth) M.F. Silva	Pau-roxo/roxinho	Caesalpiniaceae	15	1	16
Roupalla montana Aubl	Faeira/louro-faia	Proteaceae	15	1	16
Sacoglottis ceratocarpa Ducke	Uxirana	Humiriaceae	15	1	16
Sclerolobium melanocarpum Ducke	Tachi-vermelho	Caesalpiniaceae	15	1	16
Scleronema praecox Ducke	Cardeiro/castanha-de-paca	Bombacaceae	15	1	16
Sterculia speciosa K. Schum	Axixá/tacacazeiro/capoteiro	Sterculiaceae	15	1	16
Vatairea sericea Ducke	Faveira-bolacha	Fabaceae	15	1	16
Virola duckei A.C. Sm	Ucuuba/virola	Mirysticaceae	15	1	16
Alexa grandiflora Ducke	Melancieira	Fabaceae	16	1	17
Andira parviflora Ducke	Angelim	Fabaceae	16	1	17
Apeiba echinata Gaertn	Pente-de-macaco	Tiliaceae	16	1	17
Apuleia leiocarpa (Vog) MacBr.	Muirajuba	Caesalpiniaceae	16	1	17
Apuleia molaris Spruce et Benth	Muirajuba/muirataua	Caesalpiniaceae	16	1	17
Astronium gracile Engl.	Muiracatiara/guarita	Anacardiaceae	16	1	17
Astronium urundeuva (Fr All.) Engl	Aroeira	Anacardiaceae	16	1	17
Bombax longipedicellatum Ducke	Munguba-grande da T. F.	Bombacaceae	16	1	17
Caryocar glabrum (Aubl.) Pers	Piquiarana	Caryocaraceae	16	1	17
Clarisia racemosa Ruiz e Pav.	Guariúba/oiticica-amarela	Moraceae	16	1	17
Crudia bracteata Benth	Pracuúba-mirim	Caesalpiniacea	16	1	17
Crudia oblonga Benth	Rim-de-paca	Caesalpiniacea	16	1	17
Crysophillum anomalum Pires	Abiu-rosadinho	Sapotaceae	16	1	17
Endopleura uchi (Huber) Cuatr	Uchi-louro/uchi	Humiriaceae	16	1	17
Eperua bijuga Mart ex Bth	Eperua/apazeiro/copaibarana	Caesalpiniaceae	16	1	17
Ficus insipida Wildenow var insipida	Caxinguba	Moraceae	16	1	17
Guarea kunthiana A. Juss.	Jatoá/andirobarana-preta	Meliaceae	16	1	17
Humiria floribunda Mart.	Umiri	Humiriaceae	16	1	17
Hymenolobium petraeum Ducke	Angelim/angelim-da-mata	Fabaceae	16	1	17
Lecythis idatimon Aubl	Jatereu	Lecythidaceae	16	1	17
Lecythis pisonis Cambess	Sapucaia	Lecythidaceae	16	1	17
Lecythis zabucaja Aubl.	Sapucaia	Lecythidaceae	16	1	17
Manilkara bidentata (D.C.) Chev	Maçaranduba/balateira	Sapotaceae	16	1	17
Manilkara huberi Standley	Maçaranduba/maparajuba	Sapotaceae	16	1	17
Myroxylon balsamum (L) Harms	Cabreúva-vermelha	Fabaceae	16	1	17

continues

Scientific name	Common name	Family	Ecological characteristics	Logging pressure	Sum of ecological and commercial characteristics
Newtonia psilostachya (DC) Brenan	Timborana-foliolo-graúdo	Mimosaceae	16	1	17
Newtonia suaveolens (Miq) Brenan	Timborana/fava-folha-fina	Mimosaceae	16	1	17
Ocotea baturitensis Vattimo	Louro-preto	Lauraceae	16	1	17
Ocotea canaliculata Mez	Louro-pimenta	Lauraceae	16	1	17
Ocotea caudata Mez	Louro-preto	Lauraceae	16	1	17
Ormosia paraensis Ducke	Tento	Fabaceae	16	1	17
Parkia multijuga Benth	Paricá-grande-T.F./fava-atanã	Mimosaceae	16	1	17
Platonia insignis Mart	Bacuri-pari/bacuri/bacuxiuba	Guttiferae	16	1	17
Platymiscium trinitatis Bth	Macacaúba	Fabaceae	16	1	17
Platymiscium ulei Harms	Macacaúba	Fabaceae	16	1	17
Pouteria guianensis Aubl	Guajará/abiurana-branca	Sapotaceae	16	1	17
Protium tenuifolium Engl.	Breu-preto/breu	Burseraceae	16	1	17
Qualea pararensis Ducke	Mandioqueira-escamosa	Vochysiaceae	16	1	17
Sandwithiodoxa egregia (Sandw) Aubr. et Pelleg	Abiu pitomba	Sapotaceae	16	1	17
Schilozobium amazonicum (Hub) Ducke	Paricá-grande/pinho-cuiabano	Caesalpinaceae	16	1	17
Sclerolobium chrysophyllum Poepp. et Endl	Tachi-pitomba	Caesalpiniaceae	16	1	17
Sclerolobium paraense Huber	Tachi-branco	Caesalpiniaceae	16	1	17
Stryphnodendron paniculatum P. et Endl	Cedro-tamaquaré/tachirana	Mimosaceae	16	1	17
Swartzia racemosa Benth	Gombeira/mututi-duro	Caesalpiniaceae	16	1	17
Tachigalia mimecophylla Ducke	Tachi-preto-folha-grande	Caesalpiniaceae	16	1	17
Taralea oppositifolia Aubl	Cumarurana	Fabaceae	16	1	17
Terminalia amazonica (Gmell.) Exell	Cuiarana	Combretaceae	16	1	17
Vantanea parviflora Lam	Uchirana	Humiriaceae	16	1	17
Vatairea guianensis Aubl	Fava-bolacha/impingeira	Fabaceae	16	1	17
Vatairea paraensis Ducke	Fava-amargosa	Fabaceae	16	1	17
Vataireopsis speciosa Ducke	Fava-amargosa	Fabaceae	16	1	17
Vochysia maxima Ducke	Quaruba	Vochysiaceae	16	1	17
Aniba parviflora Mez.	Louro-rosa	Lauraceae	17	1	18
Carapa guanensis Aubl.	Andiroba	Meliaceae	17	1	18
Cordia goeldiana Huber	Freijó/freijó-Jorge	Boraginacea	17	1	18
Cynometra hostmaniana Tul	Jutairana	Caesalpiniaceae	17	1	18
Cynometra Spruceana Benth	Rim-de-paca	Caesalpiniaceae	17	1	18
Dipteryx odorata Willd	Cumarú	Fabaceae	17	1	18
Enterolobium maximum Ducke	Faveira-tamboril/fava-bolacha	Mimosaceae	17	1	18
Erisma uncinatum Warm	Quarubarana/cambará	Vochisiaceae	17	1	18
Ficus maxima P. Miller	Caxinguba	Moraceae	17	1	18
Hieronyna alchorneoides Fr. All.	Urucurana/mangonçalo	Euphorbiaceae	17	1	18
Hymenaea parvifolia Huber	Jatobá/jutaí-vermelho	Caesalpiniaceae	17	1	18
Hymenolobium pucherrimum Ducke	Angelim-pedra	Fabaceae	17	1	18
Jacaranda copaia (Aubl) D. Don	Pará-pará/caroba	Bignoniaceae	17	1	18
Lecithis lurida (Miers) Mori	Jarana	Lecythidaceae	17	1	18
Luehea speciosa Willd	Açoita-cavalo	Tiliaceae	17	1	18
Macoubea guianensis Aubl	Amapá-amargoso	Apocynaceae	17	1	18
Manilkara amazonica (Huber) Standley	Maçaranduba/maparajuba	Sapotaceae	17	1	18
Maquira coriacea C.C. Berg	Muiratinga-da-várzea	Moraceae	17	1	18
Micropholis melinoniana Pierre	Corrupixá/bacuri d'anta	Sapotaceae	17	1	18
Ocotea costulata (Nees) Mez	Louro-abacaterana	Lauraceae	17	1	18
Sacoglottis guianensis Bth	Uchirana/achuá/paruru	Humiriaceae	17	1	18
Schefflera paraensis Hub Arg	Morototó-branco	Araliaceae	17	1	18
Sterculia pilosa Ducke	Tacacazeiro/achichá/axixá	Sterculiaceae	17	1	18
Tetragastris panamensis (Engl.) O. Kuntze	Breu-preto/sali/ barrotinho	Burseraceae	17	1	18
Virola michelii Hechel	Ucuúba-da-terra-firme	Mirysticaceae	17	1	18
Vochysia inundata Ducke	Quaruba-cedro-da-terra-firme	Vochysiaceae	17	1	18
Alchorneopsis trimera Lanj.	Canelarana	Euphorbiaceae	12	6	18
Labatia macrocarpa Mart.	Cabeça-de-macaco	Sapotaceae	12	6	18

continues

Scientific name	Common name	Family	Ecological characteristics	Logging pressure	Sum of ecological and commercial characteristics
Platymiscium filipes Benth	Macacaúba-da-várzea	Fabaceae	12	6	18
Pouteria macrocarpa (Huber) Ducke	Abiu-cabeça-de-macaco	Sapotaceae	12	6	18
Sclerolobium goeldianum Hub.	Tachi	Caesalpiniaceae	12	6	18
Zizyphus itacaiunensis Fróes	Maria-preta	Rhamnaceae	12	6	18
Apeiba burchelli Sprague	Pente-de-macaco	Tiliaceae	18	1	19
Bagassa guianensis Aubl.	Tatajuba/bagaceira	Moraceae	18	1	19
Byrsonima aerugo Sagot	Murucí	Malpighiaceae	18	1	19
Caraipa grandifolia Mart.	Tamaquaré/louro-tamaquaré	Guttiferae	18	1	19
Ceiba petrandra Gaertn.	Sumaúma	Bombacaceae	18	1	19
Cordia scabrifolia A. DC.	Freijó/freijó-branco	Boraginacea	18	1	19
Couratari multiflora (Smith) Eyma	Tauary-folha-miúda	Lecythidaceae	18	1	19
Couratari stellata A.C. Smith	Tauary	Lecythidaceae	18	1	19
Ecllinusa guianensis Eyma	Abiurana-balatinha	Sapotaceae	18	1	19
Enterolobium schombugkii Benth	Fava-rosca/orelha-de-negro	Mimosaceae	18	1	19
Hevea brasiliensis (Wild ex Juss) Muell. Arg.	Seringueira/seringa-da-mata	Euphorbiaceae	18	1	19
Hieronyma laxiflora (Tull) Marg.	Urucurana/muirá-gonçalo	Euphorbiaceae	18	1	19
Hymenea courbaril L.	Jatobá/jutaí-açu	Caesalpiniaceae	18	1	19
Inga paraensis Ducke	Ingá	Mimmosaceae	18	1	19
Laetia procera (P et E) Eichl	Pau-jacaré/periquiteira	Flacourtiaceae	18	1	19
Osteophloeum platyspermum (A.D.C.) Warb.	Ucuubão	Myristicaceae	18	1	19
Parahancornia amapa Hub	Amapá-amargoso-verdadeiro	Apocynaceae	18	1	19
Pouteria macrophylla Eyma	Abiurana-cutiti	Sapotaceae	18	1	19
Symphonia globulifera L.F	Anani/manil/canadi	Guttiferae	18	1	19
Terminalia dichotoma G Meyer	Cinzeiro	Combretaceae	18	1	19
Terminalia guianensis Eichl.	Cuiarana/tanimbuca	Combretaceae	18	1	19
Tetragastris altissima (Aubl.)Swartz	Breu-manga/sali	Burseraceae	18	1	19
Vochysia guianensis Aubl	Quaruba-rosa/quaruba-tinga	Vochysiaceae	18	1	19
Amanoa guianensis Aubl.	Amamoa	Euphorbiaceae	13	6	19
Ampelocera edentula Kuhlm.	Trapiara	Ulmaceae	13	6	19
Aspidosperma oblongum A. DC.	Carapanaúba	Apocynaceae	13	6	19
Diospyrus praetermissas Sandwith	Caqui	Ebenaceae	13	6	19
Hevea guianensis Aubl.	Seringa-itaúba	Euphorbiaceae	13	6	19
Ilex inundata Poepp	Ilex	Aquifoliaceae	13	6	19
Licania guianensis Benth	Macucu-folha-dourada	Chrysobalanaceae	13	6	19
Licania licaniaeflora Blake	Caripé	Chrysobalanaceae	13	6	19
Qualea albiflora Warm	Mandioqueira-lisa	Vochysiaceae	13	6	19
Swartzia corrugata Benth	Coração	Caesalpiniaceae	13	6	19
Zollernia paraensis Hub.	Pau-ferro/pau-santo	Caesalpiniaceae	13	6	19
Bertholletia excelsa Humb et Bonpl	Castanheira-do-pará	Lecythidaceae	19	1	20
Caryocar villosum (Aubl.) Pers	Piquiá	Caryocaraceae	19	1	20
Cedrela odorata L.	Cedro	Meliaceae	19	1	20
Couma guianensis Aubl	Sorva	Apocynaceae	19	1	20
Couma macrocarpa Barb Rodr	Sorva	Apocynaceae	19	1	20
Couratari guianesis Aubl	Tauari-folha-grande	Lecythidaceae	19	1	20
Couratari oblongifolia Ducke et Knuth	Tauari	Lecythidaceae	19	1	20
Didymopanax morototoni (Aubl) Decne et Planch	Morototó	Araliaceae	19	1	20
Guarea guidonia (L.) Sleum.	Jataúba-branca	Meliaceae	19	1	20
Hura creptans L.	Assacu/açacu	Euphorbiaceae	19	1	20
Ocotea glomerata (Nees) Mez	Louro	Lauraceae	19	1	20
Parkia gigantocarpa Ducke	Fava-atanã/coré-grande	Mimosaceae	19	1	20
Simaruba amara Aubl	Marupá/tamanqueira/paraíba	Simarubaceae	19	1	20
Tabebuia impetiginosa (Mart.)Standl	Ipê-roxo	Bignoniaceae	19	1	20
Tabebuia insignis (Miq) Sandw	Ipê/pau-d'arco	Bignoniaceae	19	1	20
Tabebuia serratifolia (Vahl) Nicholes	Ipê-amarelo/pau d'arco	Bignoniaceae	19	1	20
Trattinickia burserifolia (Mart) Wild	Amescla/breu-sucuruba-branco	Burseraceae	19	1	20
Trattinickia rhoifolia Willd	Breu-sucuruba	Burseraceae	19	1	20

continues

Scientific name	Common name	Family	Ecological characteristics	Logging pressure	Sum of ecological and commercial characteristics
Vochysia vismiaefolia Spruce ex Warm	Quaruba	Vochysiaceae	19	1	20
Xylopia nitida Dun	Envira-branca/envira-cana	Annonaceae	19	1	20
Anacardium giganteum Hanc. Ex Engl.	Cajuaçu/cajuí	Anacardiaceae	14	6	20
Brosimum Guianensis Aubl.	Janitá-branco	Moraceae	14	6	20
Erisma lanceolatum Stafl	Quarubarana/japurá	Vochisiaceae	14	6	20
Eschweilera grandiflora (Aubl) Sandw	Matamatá	Lecythidaceae	14	6	20
Licaria rigida Kosterm	Louro-amarelo/louro	Lauraceae	14	6	20
Micrandra elata Benth	Seringarana	Euphorbiaceae	14	6	20
Ormosia flava Ducke	Tento-preto/breu sucupira	Fabaceae	14	6	20
Scleronema micranthum Ducke	Cardeiro/cedro-cravo	Bombacaceae	14	6	20
Syzygiopsis oppositifolia Ducke	Abiu-branco/abiu-ucuubarana	Sapotaceae	14	6	20
Cedrelinga catenaeformis Ducke	Cedrorana/tornillo	Mimosaceae	20	1	21
Guarea trichiloides L.	Marinheiro	Meliaceae	20	1	21
Inga alba (SW) Willd	Ingá-vermelho/ingá-xixica	Mimmosaceae	20	1	21
Pseudobombax munguba Mart. et Zucc	Mungubeira	Bombacaceae	20	1	21
Virola surinamensis (Rol) Werb	Ucuuba-branca	Mirysticaceae	20	1	21
Allantoma lineata (Mart.ex Berg) Miers	Churu/cheru/ceru	Lecythidaceae	15	6	21
Anadenanthera peregrina (L.) Splg.	Angico	Mimosaceae	15	6	21
Bombax globosum Aubl	Mamorana	Bombacaceae	15	6	21
Caryocar microcarpum Ducke	Piquiarana	Caryocaraceae	15	6	21
Couroupita guianensis Aubl.	Castanha-de-macaco	Caesalpiniaceae	15	6	21
Crudia pubescens Bth	Jutairana	Caesalpiniacea	15	6	21
Dialium guianensis (Aubl) Sandw	Jutaí-pororoca	Caesalpiniacea	15	6	21
Dicorynia guianensis Amsh	Angelica-do-pará/tapaiúna	Caesalpiniacea	15	6	21
Elisabetha paraensis Ducke	Arapari/araparirana	Caesalpiniacea	15	6	21
Erisma calcaratum (Link) Warm	Verga-de-jaboti/caferana	Vochisiaceae	15	6	21
Franchetella sagotiana (Baill) Eyma	Abiu-brabo/guajará-mole	Sapotaceae	15	6	21
Glycydendron amazonicum Ducke	Glicia/pau-doce	Euphorbiaceae	15	6	21
Iryanthera sagotiana (Bth) Warb	Ucuubarana	Myristicaceae	15	6	21
Licania micrantra Miq	Cariperana	Chrysobalanaceae	15	6	21
Onichopetalum amazonicum R. E. Fries	Envira-preta	Anonaceae	15	6	21
Parinari rodolphii Huber	Parinari	Chrysobalanaceae	15	6	21
Pouteria hispida Eyma	Abiurana-jarani	Sapotaceae	15	6	21
Prieurella prieurii (A. DC) Aubr	Abiu-mocambo	Sapotaceae	15	6	21
Protium sagotianum March.	Breu-branco	Burseraceae	15	6	21
Pterodon pubescens Benth	Faveiro	Fabaceae	15	6	21
Trichillia lecointei Ducke	Pracuuba-da-T. F./cachuá	Anacardiaceae	15	6	21
Bombax paraensis Ducke	Mamorana da T. F.	Bombacaceae	16	6	22
Chumarrhis turbinata DC	Pau-de-remo	Rubiaceae	16	6	22
Chlorophora tinctoria (L) Gaudich	Limorana/amoreira	Moraceae	16	6	22
Crudia amazônica Spruce	Rim-de-paca-vermelha	Caesalpiniacea	16	6	22
Dendrobangia boliviana Rusbi	Caferana	Icacinaceae	16	6	22
Franchetella gongrijpii (Eyma) Aubrev.	Abiurana-branca/a. vermelha	Sapotaceae	16	6	22
Hymenaea palustris Ducke	Jutaí-mirim/jutaí-peluda	Caesalpiniaceae	16	6	22
Licania heteromorfa Bth	Macucu	Chrysobalanaceae	16	6	22
Licania longistyla Hook	Caiperana	Chrysobalanaceae	16	6	22
Licania macrophylla Bth	Anoerá	Chrysobalanaceae	16	6	22
Licania octandra O Kuntze	Caraipé	Chrysobalanaceae	16	6	22
Licania longistyla Hook	Caiperana	Chrysobalanaceae	16	6	22
Licania macrophylla Bth	Anoerá	Chrysobalanaceae	16	6	22
Licania octandra O Kuntze	Caraipé	Chrysobalanaceae	16	6	22
Mora paraensis Ducke	Pracuuba	Caesalpiniaceae	16	6	22
Perebea guianensis Aubl	Cachingubarana/cauchorana	Moraceae	16	6	22
Ragala sanguinolenta Pierre	Ucuquirana	Sapotaceae	16	6	22
Syzygiopsis pachycarpa Pires	Abiurana-amarela	Sapotaceae	16	6	22
Tachigalia alba Ducke	Tachi-preto-sem-formiga	Caesalpiniaceae	16	6	22
Bowdichia virgilioides H. B. K.	Sucupira-preta	Fabaceae	17	6	23

continues

Scientific name	Common name	Family	Ecological characteristics	Logging pressure	Sum of ecological and commercial characteristics
Campsiandra laurifolia Bth.	Acapurana-da-várzea	Caesalpiniaceae	17	6	23
Cordia exaltata Lam	Chapéu-de-sol/freijó-branco	Boraginacea	17	6	23
Erythrina glauca Willd	Mulungu/açacurana	Fabaceae	17	6	23
Ficus pulchella Schott	Caxinguba/gameleiro	Moraceae	17	6	23
Hirtella racemosa Lam.	Cariperana-branca	Chrysobalanaceae	17	6	23
Hymenaea oblongfolia Hub	Jutaí-da-várzea	Caesalpiniaceae	17	6	23
Lueheopsis duckeana Burret	Açoita-cavalo-folha-grande	Tiliaceae	17	6	23
Micropholis guianensis (D.C)Pierre	Rosadinha/mangabarana	Sapotaceae	17	6	23
Neoxythece elegans (A . DC) Aubr	Guajará-pedra	Sapotaceae	17	6	23
Rauwolfia pentaphylla Ducke	Pau-vitamina/coco de guariba	Apocynaceae	17	6	23
Sapium marmieri Hub	Murupita/burra leiteira	Euphorbiaceae	17	6	23
Virola cuspidata Warb	Ucuuba/virola	Mirysticaceae	17	6	23
Vitex triflora Vam	Tarumã	Verbenaceae	17	6	23
Vochysia obscura Warm	Quaruba-da-flor-pequena	Vochysiaceae	17	6	23
Andira Inermis H. B. K.	Uchirana/morcegueira	Fabaceae	18	6	24
Castilloa ulei Warb.	Gaucho	Moraceae	18	6	24
Guatteria olivacea R. E. Fries	Envira-preta-folha-grande	Annonaceae	18	6	24
Ocotea guinensis Aubl	Louro-branco/louro-prata	Lauraceae	18	6	24
Ormosia nobilis Tul	Tento-grande	Fabaceae	18	6	24
Pithecellobium jupunba Urb	Saboeiro	Mimosaceae	18	6	24
Sterculia pruriens (Aubl) Schum	Castanha-de-piriquito	Sterculiaceae	18	6	24
Tapirira guianensis Aubl	Tapiririca	Anacardiaceae	18	6	24
Andira refusa (Lam.) H. B. K.	Morcegueira/uchirana	Fabaceae	19	6	25
Guatteria poeppigiana Mart.	Envira-preta	Annonaceae	19	6	25
Guatteria procera R.E. Fries	Envira-preta	Annonaceae	19	6	25
Macrolobium acaciaefolium Bth.	Arapari	Caesalpiniaceae	19	6	25
Ormosia coutinhoi Ducke	Buiuçu/buiussu	Fabaceae	19	6	25
Spondias lutea Linn	Taperebá/cajá/cajarana	Anacardiaceae	19	6	25
Esterculia chicha St Hil	Xixá/axixá	Sterculiaceae	19	6	25
Pithecellobium samam (Jacq) Bth	Burdão-de-velho	Mimosaceae	20	6	26

TABLE 2 - LIST OF MAIN SPECIES LOGGED BY COMMON NAME FOR EACH TIMBER PROCESSING CENTER (SOURCE: VERÍSSIMO AND LIMA, UNPUBLISHED DATA)

no.	Centers	State	Species logged
1	Rio Branco	Acre	Sucupira, amarelão, sumaúma, pereira, pau-amarelo, mogno, jatobá, pau-ferro, copaíba, cerejeira, cedro, angelim-pedra, ipê-vermelho, tauari
2	Humaitá	Amazonas	Tatajuba, ipê-vermelho, itaúba, jatobá, louro, maçaranduba, mandiocão, sucupira, goiabão, muiracatiara, angico, angelim-pedra, copaíba, amarelão
3	Itacoatiara	Amazonas	Abiu, acuaricara, amapá, angelim-pedra, angelim-fava, angelim-rajado, ucuubarana, breu, cedrinho, cumaru, copaíba, fava, jacareúba, jarana, jatobá, louro, marupá, maçaranduba, muiracatiara, piquiá, sucupira, tachi, tanimbuca, ucuuba, freijó, goiabão, caucho, açacu
4	Manaus	Amazonas	Angelim-pedra, angelim-saia, angelim-vermelho, açacu, cajueiro, caucho, copaíba, faveira, jacareúba, louro, muiratinga, sumaúma, virola
5	Região Amapá	Amapá	Virola, macacaúba, maçaranduba, mandioqueira, pau-mulato, pracuuba, tamaquaré, uchirana, louro, piquiá, tauari, andiroba, roxinho, jatobá, anani, angelim-pedra, angelim-vermelho, faveira, acapú, jacareúba, cumaru, sumaúma, virola
6	Açailândia	Maranhão	Estopeiro, ipê-vermelho, itaúba, jatobá, louro, axixá, garrote, tatajuba, cumaru, caju-de-janeiro, amescla, amarelão, goiabão
7	Imperatriz	Maranhão	Morcegueiro, muiracatiara, muiratinga, paineira, paricá, marupá, rosinha, amazonense, jatobá, inahui, garapeira, cedrinho, angelim-pedra
8	Alta Floresta	Mato Grosso	Ipê-vermelho, ipê amarelo, jatobá, paricá, peroba, ipê, roxo, cedro, angelim-pedra, cerejeira, cumaru, cambará, caixeta, freijó
9	Brasnorte	Mato Grosso	Angelim-pedra, peroba, itaúba, cedro, cambará, pau-rosa, cedrinho
10	Cláudia	Mato Grosso	Cerejeira, peroba, cedro, cedrinho, cambará, pau-rosa
11	Colider	Mato Grosso	Angelim-pedra, cambará, cedrinho, pau-rosa, angelim-vermelho, itaúba, louro, faveira
12	Comodoro	Mato Grosso	Ipê-roxo, tatajuba, peroba, mogno, louro, jatobá, ipê-amarelo, cedrinho, angelim-pedra, itaúba, caixeta, freijó, cedro, cedrorana, cerejeira, champagne, caraobinha

continues

no.	Centers	State	Species logged
13	Cotriguaçu	Mato Grosso	Cedrinho, mandiocão, itaúba, farinha-seca, peroba, cedro, cambará, angelim-pedra, amescla, acapu, champagne, carobinha
14	Feliz Natal	Mato Grosso	Leiteiro, peroba, paraicá, morototó, maminha, freijó, faveira, cambará, amescla, marupá, copaíba, cajueiro, canelão, cedrinho, champagne, angelim-pedra
15	Guarantã do Norte	Mato Grosso	Jatobá, peroba, morcegueiro, itaúba, mandiocão, mogno, paineira, sucupira, paricá, pau-rosa, ipê amarelo, baião, pau-óleo, angelim-pedra, cambará, amescla, farinha-seca, angelim-saia, canelão, cedrinho, cedro, cerejeira, champagne, copaíba
16	Juara	Mato Grosso	Ipê-roxo, peroba, mogno, paricá, marupá, ipê-amarelo, cambará, cumaru, cerejeira, angelim-pedra, cedrinho, freijó, caixeta, cedro
17	Juína	Mato Grosso	Cedrorana, peroba, paricá, mogno, marupá, ipê-roxo, faveira, angelim-vermelho, champagne, angelim-pedra, cerejeira, cambará, cedrinho, cedro, amescla
18	Juruena	Mato Grosso	Cerdrino, champagne, peroba, mogno, itaúba, ipê-amarelo, amarelão, cerejeira, cambará, angelim- vermelho, angelim-saia, angelim-pedra, amescla, cedro
19	Marcelândia	Mato Grosso	Amescla, champagne, cedro-marinheiro, cedrinho, angelim-pedra, peroba, cambará
20	Matupá	Mato Grosso	Itaúba, jatobá, pau-rosa, champagne, cedrinho, angelim-pedra, peroba, cambará
21	Nova Bandeirantes	Mato Grosso	Amazonense, amescla, angelim-pedra, cambará, cedrinho, garapeira, inhaui, jatobá, mandiocão, marupá, morcegueira, muiracatiara, muiratinga, paineira, paricá, itaúba, pau-rosa, rosinha, cedro
22	Porto dos Gaúchos	Mato Grosso	Angelim-pedra, cambará, cedrinho, champagne, pau-rosa, peroba, itaúba
23	Santa Carmem	Mato Grosso	Cumaru, peroba, pau-óleo, morcegueira, mandiocão, itaúba, farinha-seca, cedro, cedrinho, carobinha, cambará, caixeta, angelim-saia, angelim-pedra, amescla, champagne
24	São José do Rio Claro	Mato Grosso	Cedro, farinha-seca, itaúba, sucupira, cambará, angelim-pedra, amescla, peroba
25	Sinop	Mato Grosso	Cedro, sucupira, peroba, champagne, cedrinho, cambará, angelim-pedra, amescla, itaúba
26	Sorriso	Mato Grosso	Cambará, ipê-Roxo, peroba, paricá, morcegueira, timburi, mandiocão, itaúba, cerejeira, cedrorana, cedrinho, caixeta, angelim-pedra, amescla, cedro
27	Tabaporã	Mato Grosso	Amescla, peroba, itaúba, cedro, cedrinho, angelim-pedra, cambará
28	União do Sul	Mato Grosso	Amescla, Cambará, Cedrinho, cedro, Itaúba, Peroba, Angelim pedra
29	Vera	Mato Grosso	Sumaúma, maçaranduba, melancieira, muiracatiara, pau-amarelo, piquiá, louro, quarubarana, sucupira, tauari, quaraúba, andiroba, tatajuba, jatobá, amarelão, amapá, angelim-pedra, angelim-vermelho, cedro, cedrorana, cumaru, freijó, ipê-roxo, ipê-amarelo
30	Afuá	Pará	Breu, piquiá, paricá, muiracatiara, roxinho, maçaranduba, cedro, angelim-vermelho, angelim-pedra, amescla, cedrorana, faveira
31	Altamira	Pará	Cumaru, mandioqueira, tatajuba, sucupira, quarubarana, pará-pará, mutitirona, marupá, virola, maçaranduba, louro, jatobá, esponja, cedrorana, cumaru, cedro, angelim-pedra, andiroba, faveira, ipê
32	Breves	Pará	Ipê-amarelo, tatajuba, quaruba, piquiá, maçaranduba, cumaru, cedrorana, bacurirana, angelim-vermelho, angelim-pedra, cutiúba, andiroba
33	Cametá	Pará	Angelim-pedra, angelim-vermelho, bacurirana, cedrorana, cumaru, cutiuba, ipê-amarelo, ipê-vermelho, maçaranduba, pequiá, quaruba, tatajuba
34	Concórdia	Pará	Amapá, mandioqueira, marupá, morototó, pará-pará, pau-óleo, piquiarana, quarubarana, tachi, timborana, maçaranduba, tanimbuca, cedrorana, cumaru, ipê-amarelo, jatobá, louro-tamaquaré, copaíba, angelim-pedra
35	Dom Eliseu	Pará	Ipê-amarelo, angeli-pedra, tatajuba, muiracatiara, jatobá, cedrorana, cajarana, maçaranduba
36	Goianésia	Pará	Estopeiro, tauari, tatajuba, sucupira-preta, muiracatiara, jatobá, faveira, curupixá, cumaru, cedrorana, cedro, angelim-pedra, amarelão, axixá, ipê-vermelho
37	Itaituba	Pará	Jatobá, andiroba, tatajuba, muiracatiara, melancieira, maçaranduba, ipê, faveira, curupixá, cedrorana, angelim-pedra, cedro
38	Itupiranga	Pará	Andiroba, angelim-pedra, cedro, cedrorana, curupixa, faveira, ipê, ipê-amarelo, jatobá, maçaranduba, melancieira, muiracatiara, tatajuba, tauari
39	Jacundá	Pará	Roxinho, louro-tamaquaré, sucupira, tauari, piquiá, pau-amarelo, paricá, muiracatiara, melancieira, maçaranduba, tatajuba, breu, louro, angelim-pedra, tanimbuca, bacurirana, caixeta, axixá, cajueiro, cedrorana, faveira, freijó, ipê-vermelho, angelim-vermelho
40	Marabá	Pará	Jatobá, andiroba, angelim pedra, cedro, cedrorana, cumaru, ipê-amarelo, frijó, muiracatiara, pau-amarelo, piquiá, tatajub
41	Novo Progresso	Pará	Mogno, cedro, freijó, ipê-amarelo, ipê-roxo
42	Novo Repartimento e Breu Branco	Pará	Tanimbuca, louro, maçaranduba, morototó, muiracatiara, pau-amarelo, piquiá, piquiarana, t imborana, sucupira, tatajuba, tauari, jarana, jatobá, roxinho, copaíba, louro-tamaquaré, ipê-amarelo, amescla, angelim-pedra, angelim-vermelho, cedrorana, cumaru, curupixá, faveira, freijó, goiabão, guajará, ipê-roxo, cedro
43	Oeiras	Pará	Andiroba, louro, sucupira, quarubarana, quaruba, pará-pará, marupá, jatobá, ipê-vermelho, goiabão, freijó, faveira, angelim-pedra, cumaru
44	Oeiras	Pará	Angelim-pedra, caixeta, maçaranduba, pará-pará, tauari, andiroba, arari, cajuarana, cinzeiro, mandioqueiro, pracuuba, sucupira, virola

continues

no.	Centers	State	Species logged
45	Paragominas	Pará	Amarelão, amescla, angelim-pedra, angelim-vermelho, cedro, cedrorana, copaíba, cumaru, curupixa, faveira, freijó, goiabão, guajará, ipê-roxo, ipê-amarelo, jarana, jatobá, louro, louro-tamaquaré, maçaranduba, morototo, muiracatiara, pequiá, piquiarana, roxinho, tanimbuca, tatajuba, tauari, timborana
46	Portel	Pará	Andiroba, angelim-pedra, angelim-vermelho, cumaru, faveira, goiabão, ipê, jatobá, louro, maçaranduba, marupá, pará-pará, quaruba, sucupira, tatajuba
47	Redenção	Pará	Ipê-vermelho, tauari, tatajuba, quaruba, piquiá, jatobá, ipê-vermelho, faveira, cedrorana, cedro, angelim-vermelho, angelim-pedra, andiroba
48	Rondon	Pará	Jatobá, axixá, pau-amarelo, mogno, cedrororana, cedro, angelim-pedra, faveira
49	Santarém	Pará	Quarubarana, ipê-vermelho, tauari, muiracatiara, mandioqueira, jatobá, caixeta, angelim-vermelho, angelim-pedra, andiroba, curupixá
50	Tailândia	Pará	Louro, maçaranduba, mandioqueira, pau-amarelo, quaruba, roxinho, tanimbuca, tatajuba, jatobá, timborana, muiracatiara, tauari, caixeta, piquiá, amescla, jarana, angelim-vermelho, copaíva, cumaru, curupixa, faveira, freijó, ipê-vermelho, ipê-amarelo, angelim-pedra
51	Tomé-Açu	Pará	Timborana, pau-amarelo, piquiá, piquiarana, roxinho, tanimbuca, tauari, maçaranduba, ipê-amarelo, tatajuba, angelim-pedra, louro, amescla, jatobá, angelim-vermelho, caixeta, copaíba, cumaru, freijó, guajará, ipê-vermelho
52	Tucuruí	Pará	Marupá, tauari, tatajuba, quaraubarana, piquiá, angelim-pedra, melancieira, maçaranduba, jatobá, ipê-amarelo, ipê-vermelho, faveira, cumaru, copaíba, angelim-vermelho, louro, muiracatiara
53	Uruara	Pará	Ipê, jatobá, tatajuba, cedro, cumaru, ipê, muiracatiara, pau-amarelo
54	Alta Floresta do Oeste	Rondônia	Cabriúva, caixeta, cerejeira, ipê-roxo, ipê-amarelo, jatobá, paraju, pariri, peroba, sumaúma, virola, angelim-pedra, angelim-fava
55	Alto Paraíso	Rondônia	Sumaúma, jatobá, maçaranduba, muiracatiara, paricá, pau-rosa, piquiá, sucupira, tamarindo, tauari, landil, roxinho, caucho, louro, bandarra, cedro, cedrorana
56	Alto Paraíso	Rondônia	Sumaúma, jatobá, maçaranduba, muiracatiara, paricá, pau-rosa, piquiá, sucupira, tamarindo, tauari, landil, roxinho, caucho, louro, bandarra, cedro, cedrorana, cumaru, faveira, freijó, ipê-roxo, ipê-vermelho, ipê-amarelo, angelim-pedra
57	Ariquemes	Rondônia	Tauari, muiracatiara, ipê-roxo, ipê-amarelo, jatobá, landil, maçaranduba, mogno, paricá, pau-rosa, piquiá, roxinho, sucupira, imbireira, tamarindo, cedrorana, sumaúma, canelão, amapá, angelim-pedra, angelim-vermelho, aquariquara, bandarra, cumaru, garapá, caucho, cedrinho, cedro, cerejeira, faveira, freijó, breu
58	Buritis	Rondônia	Pau Rosa, jatobá, sumaúma, paricá, caucho, canelão, angelim-pedra, bandarra, tauari, ipê-amarelo
59	Cacoal	Rondônia	Caixeta, ipê-amarelo
60	Campo Novo	Rondônia	Freijó, sucupira, muiracatiara, jito, jatobá, garapá, cumaru, cerejeira, cedro, angelim-pedra, abiu, ipê-amarelo
61	Cujubim	Rondônia	Ipê-amarelo, sucupira, roxinho, pau-rosa, tauari, muiracatiara, caucho, caixeta, bandarra, angelim-pedra, amescla, amapá, paricá, cedro
62	Espigão D'Oeste	Rondônia	Imbireira, tauari, ipê-amarelo, garapá, cedro, cedrinho, angelim-pedra, cerejeira, pau-rosa
63	Jaru	Rondônia	Sumaúma, jatobá, jito, maçaranduba, muiracatiara, parica, piquia, sucupira, surubim, tamarindo, ipê- amarelo, roxinho, canelão, ipê-vermelho, amescla, caixeta, caucho, cedro, cerejeira, ipê-roxo, peroba, faveira, freijó, garapá, garapeira, cumaru, angelim-pedra
64	Ji-Paraná	Rondônia	Angelim-pedra, amapá, angelim-vermelho, bandarra, caucho, cedrinho, cedro, cedrorana, cerejeira, cumaru, faveira, freijó, garapá, ipê-roxo, ipê, pau-amarelo, jatobá, landil, louro, muiracatiara, paricá, roxinho, sucupira, sumaúma, tamarindo, tauari
65	Machadinho D'Oeste	Rondônia	Muiracatiara, paricá, pau-rosa, roxinho, sucupira, sumaúma, tauari, ipê-amarelo, ipê-roxo, tamarindo, cedro, jatobá, garapá, azedinho, caixeta, cerejeira, cumaru, fava, faveira, freijó, angelim-pedra, bandarra
66	Monte Negro	Rondônia	Angelim-pedra, muiracatiara, garapeira, amescla, ipê, tamarindo, caixeta, jitó, abiu, sucupira, goiabão, roxinho, cumaru
67	Nova Mamoré	Rondônia	Angelim-pedra, cabriúva, cedro-rosa, cerejeira, freijó, garapeira, ipê, jatobá, muiracatiara, sucupira
68	Ouro Preto D'Oeste	Rondônia	Cumaru, jatobá, tauari, roxinho, muiracatiara, ipê-amarelo, ipê-roxo, freijó, angelim-pedra, abiu, garapá
69	Pimenta Bueno	Rondônia	Marupá, piquiá, peroba, pau-rosa, parica, mogno, ipê-roxo, cerejeira, cedro, caucho, caixeta, amescla, sumaúma, jatobá
70	Porto Velho	Rondônia	Cerejeira, garrote, tauari, sucupira, roxinho, muiracatiara, mandiocão, jatobá, ipê-amarelo, cedrinho, faveira, angelim-pedra, freijó, cedro, cedrorana, cumaru, faveira-ferro

continues

no.	Centers	State	Species logged
71	Rolim de Moura	Rondônia	Paineira, sumaúma, paricá, cerejeira, caucho, angelim-pedra, peroba
72	Seringueiras	Rondônia	Breu, caucho, caixeta, cedro-rosa, ipê, jatobá, muiracatiara, sumaúma, paineira, sucupira
73	Vilhena	Rondônia	Amescla, ipê-roxo, sumaúma, pariri, paricá, mogno, jatobá, sucupira, farinha-seca, cumaru, cerejeira, cedro, cedrinho, cambará, angelim-pedra, garrote, cabriúva
74	Boa Vista	Roraima	Cedro, rabo-de-arraia, mirarema, maçaranduba, louro, jatobá, ipê-vermelho, coxa-grossa, caixeta, caferana, angelim-pedra, faveira-ferro
75	Araguaína	Tocantins	Tauari, caixeta, cedrorana, jatobá, louro

BUSINESS OPPORTUNITIES IN AMAZONIA: SUSTAINABLE ALTERNATIVES

André Guimarães *World Bank*

BACKGROUND

When Brazilian business people think about environmental business opportunities, the first things that come to mind are pollution control, sanitation programs or steps to make industrial operations cleaner and more efficient. The most advanced thinking about products goes no further than the recycling of materials. This is fair enough since, from both the entrepreneur's and the consumer's point of view, the most visible environmental issues are pollution, waste, or the damage to urban environments caused by industrial operations. In the same way, both pollution and inefficiency, to take only two examples, are processes which generate additional costs for companies. In such a competitive world it is clear those who waste raw materials or energy will in the long term be less likely to survive.

However, the view of entrepreneurs that pollution, recycling and the efficient use of raw materials are the only environmentally related business opportunities available may represent a limited view of the true potential which the environment offers in many business areas. Few business people consider the opportunities for creating food brands based on Amazonian fruits, or a home furnishing range produced from fibers found in the region. However, the açaí fruit[1], currently widely traded on domestic markets, or other relatively unknown fruit, such as cupuaçu[2], taperabá[3] or graviola[4], are beginning to show that there is a potential market for products associated with the environment that goes beyond the simple installation of filters to reduce emissions of polluting gases.

The consumer, if properly informed, will find at least two good reasons for buying taperabá juice instead of orange juice. First, there is the fact that taperabá is an exotic fruit native to Amazonia which, in certain settings, will demonstrate the sophistication and knowledge of those offering such a product. In addition, taperabá may appeal more than orange because of how it is produced, either by traditional forest extractors or by small agricultural producers, as opposed to the industrial production of citrus fruit. These are the so-called market niches. This doesn't mean to say that one day taperabá will replace orange on the dining tables of middle class families, but that this Amazonian fruit, together with other forest products, may eventually gain a space of its own.

This appeal should, in theory, stimulate the production of more and better fruit, handicrafts or even sustainably managed and certified timber in Amazonia. In practice, however, what we see is the predatory exploitation of the forest, deforestation and burning; in short, the destruction of that which consumers in many regions in Brazil and abroad are willing to pay good money for. Amazonian producers and their suppliers are therefore out of step with consumers and their demands. This paper will attempt to explore some of the difficulties encountered by Amazonians in supplying the market with their products. The analysis will focus on economic and marketing problems, whilst recognizing that there are still technological, political, cultural, and infrastructural obstacles to forest products reaching the market.

THE DEVELOPMENT MODEL

Before addressing the economic and market limitations that impede the access of the sustainable production of Amazonia to the most demanding markets, we will briefly analyze the process of regional development in an attempt to illustrate the origin of the problem to be resolved.

Since the 1960s, development policy for the Brazilian Amazon region has been based on subsidies, tax incentives and other benefits for entrepreneurs willing to operate in the region. The explanation for such concessions is quite simple and even justifiable. The basic premise of the strategy carried out by the military governments and continued by the civilian governments that followed was to occupy the region at all costs. According to this model, those who bore the risks of raising cattle, setting up businesses or logging timber in the region would be entitled to subsidized credit, tax reductions, some infrastructure and the blessing of the federal government.

However, this development model for the Brazilian Amazon region generated all kinds of distortions, economic as well as social and political. In economic terms, it encouraged large-scale agricultural, livestock, mining and infrastructure enterprises, and even industrial projects such as the Manaus free trade zone. However, such initiatives were and continue to be incompatible with the characteristics of the region. The reduction of 464 tons

---

1. *Euterpe oleracea*, the assai.
2. *Theobroma grandiflorum*.
3. *Spondias sp.* (also known as the cajá in northeastern Brazil), the hog-plum or mombin.
4. *Annona muricata*, the custard apple or soursop (better known in external markets as the guanábana, its common name in Spanish).

of biomass and hundreds of plant and animal species present in a hectare of native forest to 11 tons of biomass and two species (cattle and pasture) (Fernside 1997) does not make much economic sense, if the possibilities for generating income from a sustainably managed forest are correctly analyzed. The return on investment in extensive production systems, such as extensive ranching, is also far lower compared to intensive production systems, such as diversified agriculture (Almeida and Uhl 1998). From an environmental point of view, the loss in biodiversity speaks for itself. This is true for any type of large-scale monoculture installed in the region, such as those which have been and continue to be promoted.

In social terms, employment creation by large enterprises, whether ranching or other types, create far fewer job opportunities than smaller farms which use intensive production methods (Almeida and Uhl 1998). From a political point of view this model, in the eyes of the rest of Brazil, has created a certain prejudice against people and projects in Amazonia. 'Southerners', as those from other parts of Brazil are called, frequently show their dissatisfaction at seeing their taxes being spent on areas such as Amazonia and the northeast. This perception, often erroneous, creates political differences that further increase the difficulties of attracting investments and entrepreneurs to the region.

In short, the distortions caused by the excess of incentives and their misuse have ended up encouraging a productive base in Amazonia which is hardly sustainable, as well as being socially, environmentally and economically unjust. However there still is an enormous potential to be exploited in a sustainable way, and which clearly has a greater capacity to generate income, employment, new products and a higher regard on the part of all Brazilians with respect to the region.

The potential of the region

There has never been so much local, national and international pressure to promote the sustainable use of the natural resources in Amazonia as there is today. On the one hand, that of discouraging traditional forms of utilization, Ibama has set up a series of initiatives for the inspection and environmental monitoring of economic activities in the region. Fines, or the threat of fines, increase the risk for those entrepreneurs failing to comply with environmental protection laws. This encourages those who respect the current rules of the game and discourages illegal practices, up to a point. There is still plenty to do, especially with respect to the consistency of action by Ibama; however, acting illegally in Amazonia is starting to become expensive.

On the other hand, that of incentives for sustainable use, many financial institutions and investors have started positioning themselves by offering resources for ventures in the Amazon region, provided that these are sustainable or entail environmental conservation. These include the Banco Axial and the Fundo Terra Capital, a risk capital fund, international and domestic donors such as the PPG7, foundations and large NGOs, as well as federal institutions such as the BNDES and BASA, which are nowadays far more rigorous than they used to be regarding environmental and social issues.

Another angle through which the potential of the forest products of the region can be analyzed is its own consumer market.

In a survey conducted by the United Nations in dozens of countries a few years ago, the word 'Amazon' was among the ten terms most cited by the general public. Others included trademarks such as Marlboro, Coca-Cola or Microsoft. So, out of the ten best-known terms worldwide, the only one that does not generate enormous volumes of resources is the Amazon. The others are trademarks of corporations with annual turnovers of billions of dollars. In other words, having the name of a product associated with Amazonia, especially if it is produced in an environmentally and socially sustainable way, should in theory offer a substantial advantage over those that do not possess such an appeal.

In light of this we can see that the basic conditions, such as laws, policies, financial resources and especially the consumer market are slowly turning towards the promotion of sustainable forest use and against harmful practices.

However, given this favorable scenario, or one becoming so, what is the missing link that will allow the trademark 'Amazonia' to realize its full potential?

Some ways to transform the potential into profitability

When asking consumers why they do not buy cupuaçu or açaí pulp, or any other product from the rain forest, the most common response will be another question: 'Where can I find it?' Those who already have a piece of handicraft or a table made of certified timber at home give answers such as: 'The quality is poor!', 'Sometimes I find the product on the market, sometimes I don't!' etc. This is the main reason why the orange still beats the taperabá. Given this, two obstacles can be seen as crucial to the opening or retention of the market for sustainable products from Amazonia: i) low quality and ii) unreliable supply.

Nonetheless, in order to improve the quality of the products as well the reliability of their supply, other aspects of the mode of production need to be analyzed.

'Money is not the problem, it is the solution'

There has never been so much money available for investment in the Amazon Region as there is at the present. To take just one example: the FNO[5], operated by BASA, has 600 million reais available annually for ventures in the region. About 70 to 80 percent of this is not used. The reason for this is quite simple, although not always well understood: BASA has increased the environmental and financial rigor of the process of selecting projects to receive financial support. In addition to the FNO, there is grant funding available from foundations, the PPG7, national and international NGOs and even from federal institutions such as the Ministry of the Environment and the BNDES (Funbio 1998).

The major difficulty for entrepreneurs in the region is gaining access to these financial resources; in other words, how to prepare a good project proposal, draw up a long-term business plan, carry out market research etc. They thus lack the capacity to show that their idea may be able to generate profits and benefits for the financial institution and society as a whole.

Points for discussion

How can access to financial resources by productive initiatives in Amazonia – the capacity to prepare projects and carry

---

5. Fundo Constitucional de Financiamento do Norte (Constitutional Financial Fund for the North)

out market research, financial and accounting analysis etc. – be improved?

Better business management skills

The difficulty for Amazonian ventures, especially those undertaken by small producers, to access capital is linked to another difficulty: the lack of business management skills.

There are, for example, few people better able to cultivate Brazil nuts than the extractive populations of Amazonia. Yet cultivating is one thing, selling is another. Co-operatives, small individual producers and Brazil nut gatherers urgently need capacity building in business management skills. This includes bookkeeping, paying taxes, programming reinvestments, efficiently distributing dividends, improving product quality, sourcing reliable suppliers and distributors, and so on.

Points for discussion

How can the management of Amazonian enterprises (accountancy skills, selection of good administrators, computerization, etc) be improved?

Better infrastructure for producing and getting to market

Energy, transport and telecommunications are the bottlenecks. Without energy, processing and adding value to forest products becomes almost impossible. Similarly, highways where traffic is precarious for large parts of the year impede regular distribution. Communication with the market depends fundamentally on contact with trading partners, and on knowledge of prices and the market in general.

The idea that within a short period of time all the communities, villages and towns in Amazonia will be equipped with telephones, paved roads and energy is, to say the least, naïve. In Brazil, infrastructure is the responsibility of the State, and it is common knowledge that the capacity for investment of the federal government is currently very limited. How can this dilemma therefore be resolved? The keyword here is prioritization. Instead of exerting general political pressure to obtain more highways and energy, the leaders and representatives of producers should organize themselves and indicate to the federal government those investments that will yield higher social and economic returns and less environmental damage.

Points for discussion

How can local leaders be helped to prepare good arguments that will enable official investments to be prioritized (economic and social cost-benefit analysis of infrastructure investments)? How can alternative forms of access to infrastructure (renewable energy, alternative means of transportation and communication, for example) be identified?

The impracticability of taking on the production chain alone

Many production initiatives in Amazonia, especially those that depend on middlemen to get their products to market, believe that the solution to their problems is to sell directly to the consumer. This could be a big strategic error. A producer who is successful at growing, processing and packaging cupuaçu, will not necessarily be successful at selling it to the consumer. In most cases, a commercial collaboration between complementary partners – producers and middlemen – can be highly profitable for both.

This is a two-way street, meaning that at the same time that the middleman guarantees markets and income (in general more profitable markets, since he is closer to consumers and can identify their demands), he can also provide the producer, isolated on his property and with little access to these variables, with information on improved packaging, product diversification, and so on. If the relationship is balanced, both the producer and the middleman have much to gain.

Points for discussion

How can commercial partnerships between rural producers and companies that distribute and/or consume their products be encouraged (through investment funds for joint ventures between producers and distributors, or market orientation programs for producer groups, for example)?

The need to adapt lines of credit

Obtaining a loan from BASA for cultivating agro-forestry systems is truly a headache. There are various reasons for this, including the fact that BASA appraisers are badly informed about agro-forestry systems, and the lack of knowledge on the part of the producers of how to prepare projects. In the same way, trying to obtain official credit for reforestation or forest management, when the prospect is of a return on investment in twenty or thirty years, is virtually impossible, given that the current lines of credit operate with a loan repayment period of at most ten or fifteen years. There are, therefore, incompatibilities between the credit currently available and the requirements to obtain it.

In this context, adapting both the procedures for appraising credit requests, and the credit lines themselves still needs to be thought through. A common action strategy to adapt the lines of credit currently available in Brazil and involving the representative bodies of small, medium, and large entrepreneurs in Amazonia is essential.

Points for discussion

How can banks and financial institutions be persuaded to adapt their credit lines to take account of the business realities of Amazonia (submitting proposals, political pressure, demonstrating the technical and financial feasibility of long-term credit etc.)?

Final considerations

The numerous other existing bottlenecks to improving the production model in Amazonia and the wise use of the enormous business potential that the region offers should not be forgotten when we consider the questions raised above. There are many other limiting factors such as cultural differences, illiteracy, lack of social organization, lack of political will etc., which impede the sustainable development of the region. The purpose of this paper is to initiate a discussion and to establish some parameters to be debated during the workshop.

In order to ensure that the process of sustainable development in the region becomes a reality, it is fundamentally important to keep in mind in discussions such as the ones which will occur in September in Macapá that some paradigms need to be changed. This being the case, there are other issues that need to be discussed and considered in Macapá:

1. Small producers must start behaving as small companies which use capital, create employment and tax revenues, and contribute to the country's growth.

2. Building capacity for business skills is totally incompatible with certain political ideologies, whether on the left or the right. Doing business with the objective of maximizing profits must be kept separate from political demands, and not get mixed up with them;

3. Good entrepreneurs are rare. We need to recognize that many production initiatives in Amazonia will not be successful. This recognition is of fundamental importance when talking about the prioritization of investments, irrespective of whether they are private or public.

4. Good entrepreneurs exist, but need to be introduced to commercial investors and partners. A great idea will not be of any use unless it is turned into production and income. In order to transform a good project into a profitable venture it is of the utmost importance to know how to 'sell' the project or idea. The marketing of good initiatives is key.

5. Subsidies and grants are fine, but they all end some day without exception. What are always there are the resources of investors seeking a return on capital (credit, risk capital, commercial partnerships). Although obvious, such an understanding is not always present and this creates a dependency on so-called 'cheap money', impeding and limiting the very growth of the business.

BIBLIOGRAPHY

ALMEIDA, O. T. & UHL, C. F. Planejamento do uso do solo do município de paragominas utilizando dados econômicos e ecológicos. *Série Amazônia*. Belém: Imazon, no. 9, 1998.

ESTUDOS FUNBIO 1. *Financiando o uso sustentável da biodiversidade*. Rio de Janeiro: 1998.

FERNSIDE, P. M. Greenhouse Gases from Deforestation in Brazilian Amazonia: Net Commited Emmissions. *Climatic Change*, no. 35, p. 321-60, 1997.

Brazilian Legal Amazonia

Thematic maps

VENEZUELA
GUYANA
COLOMBIA
RORAIMA
Boa Vista
AMAZONAS
Manaus
RIO NEGRO
ACRE
Rio Branco
Porto Velho
RONDÔNIA
PERU
BOLIVIA
TRANSAMAZÔNICA
MANAUS-PORTO VELHO
PERIMETRAL NORTE
4º
0º
-4º
-8º
-12º
-16º
72º
66º
60º

BRAZILIAN LEGAL AMAZON
BASE MAP

Transportation Network
- —— Paved highway
- —— Unpaved highway
- – – Planned highway
- ⊢⊢⊢ Railway
- ⊢⊢⊢ Planned railway

Transportation Network
- 100
- to
- 2900m

- ——— International boundary
- - - - - - State boundary
- ☐ Brazilian Legal Amazon
- ● State capital
- Main rivers
- Wetlands; lakes

Scale 1:9,000,000
100 0 100 200 km
Sinusoidal Projection
Central Meridian 54º WGr.

Base map:
Maps of Brazil to the scale 1:1,000,000

Map created by the
Geoprocessing Laboratory of the Instituto Socioambiental

Assessment and Identification of Priority Actions for the Conservation, Sustainable Use and Benefit Sharing of the Biodiversity of the Brazilian Amazon

PRONABIO
Programa Nacional da Diversidade Biológica (National Program for Biological Diversity)
Ministério do Meio Ambiente (Ministry of the Environment)

Coordinating consortium:
Instituto Socioambiental (Overall coordination)
Imazon - Instituto do Homem e Meio Ambiente da Amazônia
Ipam - Instituto de Pesquisa Ambiental da Amazônia
GTA - Grupo de Trabalho Amazônico
Conservation International
ISPN - Instituto Sociedade, População e Natureza

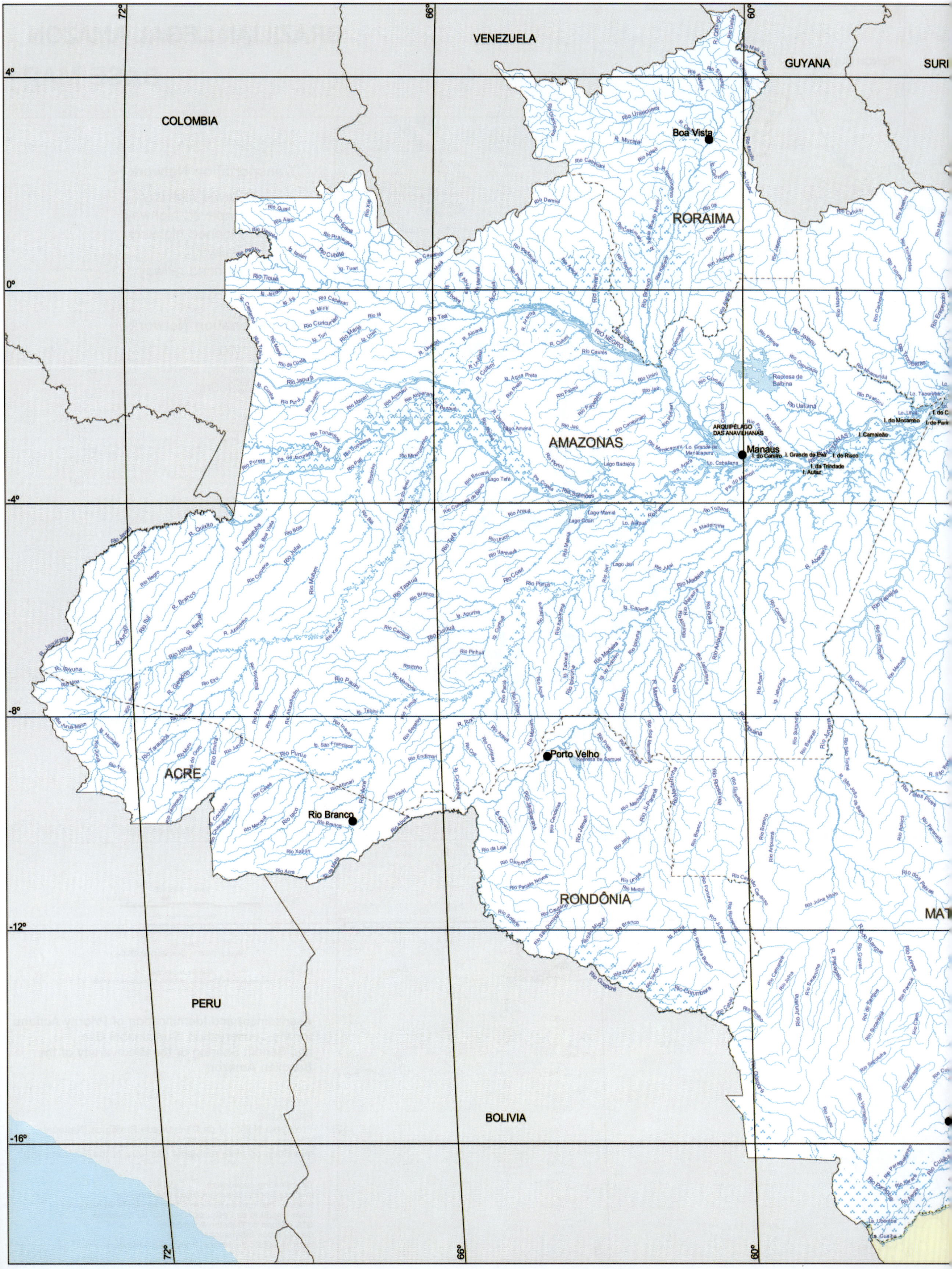
VENEZUELA
GUYANA
SURI
COLOMBIA
PERU
BOLIVIA
RORAIMA
AMAZONAS
ACRE
RONDÔNIA
MAT
Boa Vista
Manaus
Porto Velho
Rio Branco
ARQUIPÉLAGO DAS ANAVILHANAS
Represa de Balbina
Represa de Samuel
RIO NEGRO
Rio Solimões
72º
66º
60º
4º
0º
-4º
-8º
-12º
-16º

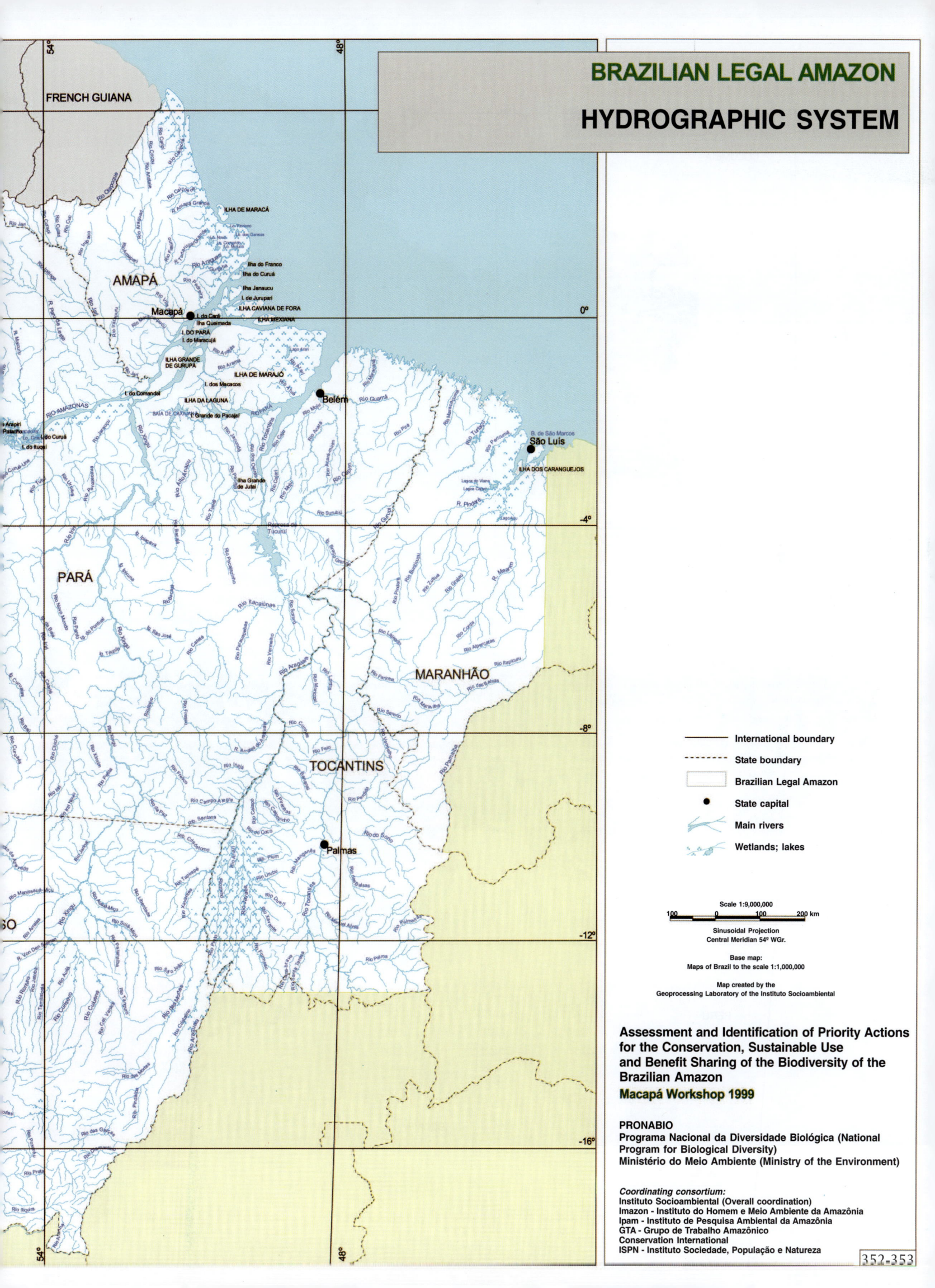

BRAZILIAN LEGAL AMAZON
HYDROGRAPHIC SYSTEM

Legend:
- International boundary
- State boundary
- Brazilian Legal Amazon
- State capital
- Main rivers
- Wetlands; lakes

Scale 1:9,000,000
Sinusoidal Projection
Central Meridian 54º WGr.

Base map:
Maps of Brazil to the scale 1:1,000,000

Map created by the
Geoprocessing Laboratory of the Instituto Socioambiental

Assessment and Identification of Priority Actions for the Conservation, Sustainable Use and Benefit Sharing of the Biodiversity of the Brazilian Amazon
Macapá Workshop 1999

PRONABIO
Programa Nacional da Diversidade Biológica (National Program for Biological Diversity)
Ministério do Meio Ambiente (Ministry of the Environment)

Coordinating consortium:
Instituto Socioambiental (Overall coordination)
Imazon - Instituto do Homem e Meio Ambiente da Amazônia
Ipam - Instituto de Pesquisa Ambiental da Amazônia
GTA - Grupo de Trabalho Amazônico
Conservation International
ISPN - Instituto Sociedade, População e Natureza

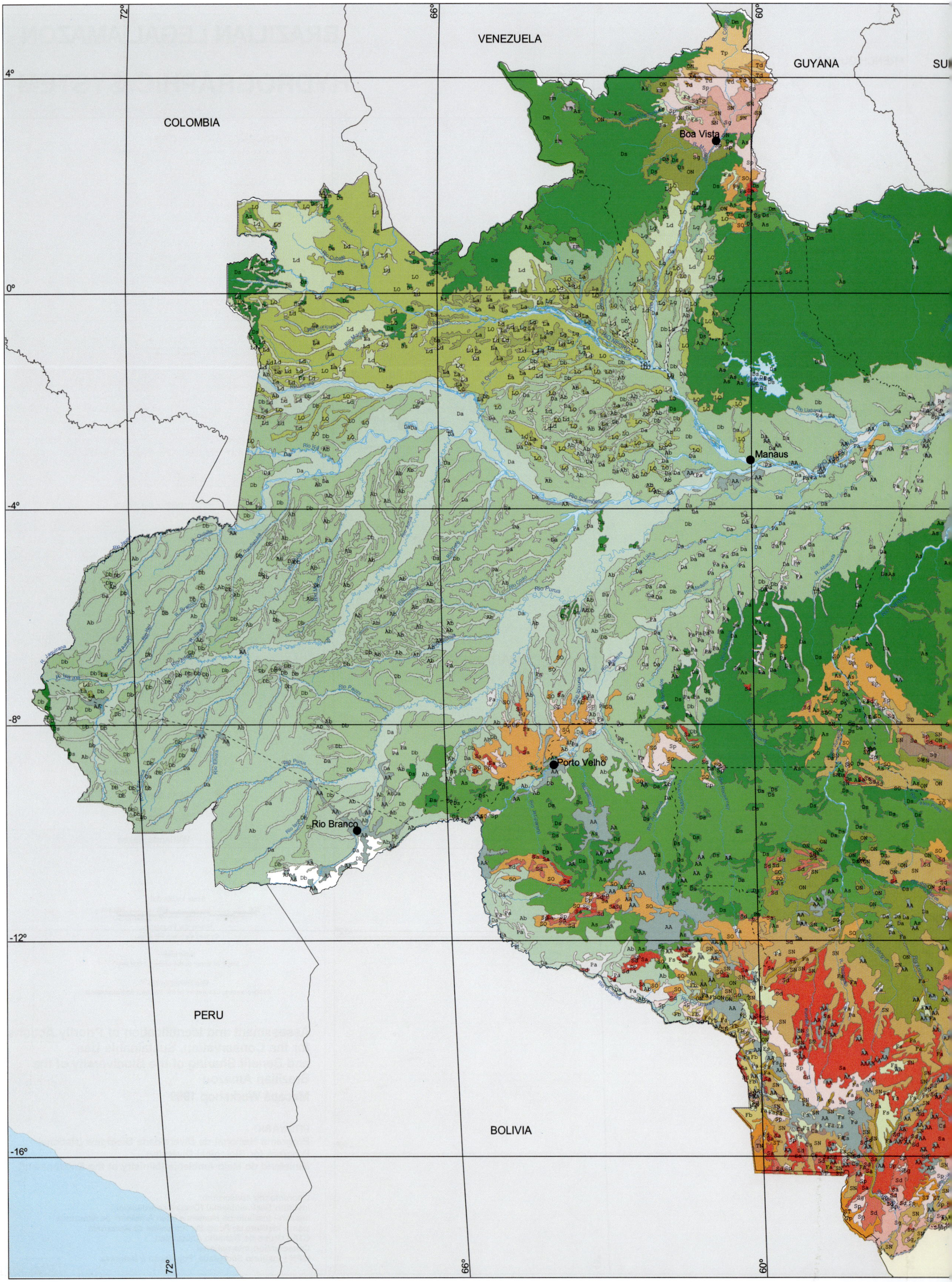
VENEZUELA
GUYANA
COLOMBIA
PERU
BOLIVIA
Boa Vista
Manaus
Porto Velho
Rio Branco
72°
66°
60°
4°
0°
-4°
-8°
-12°
-16°

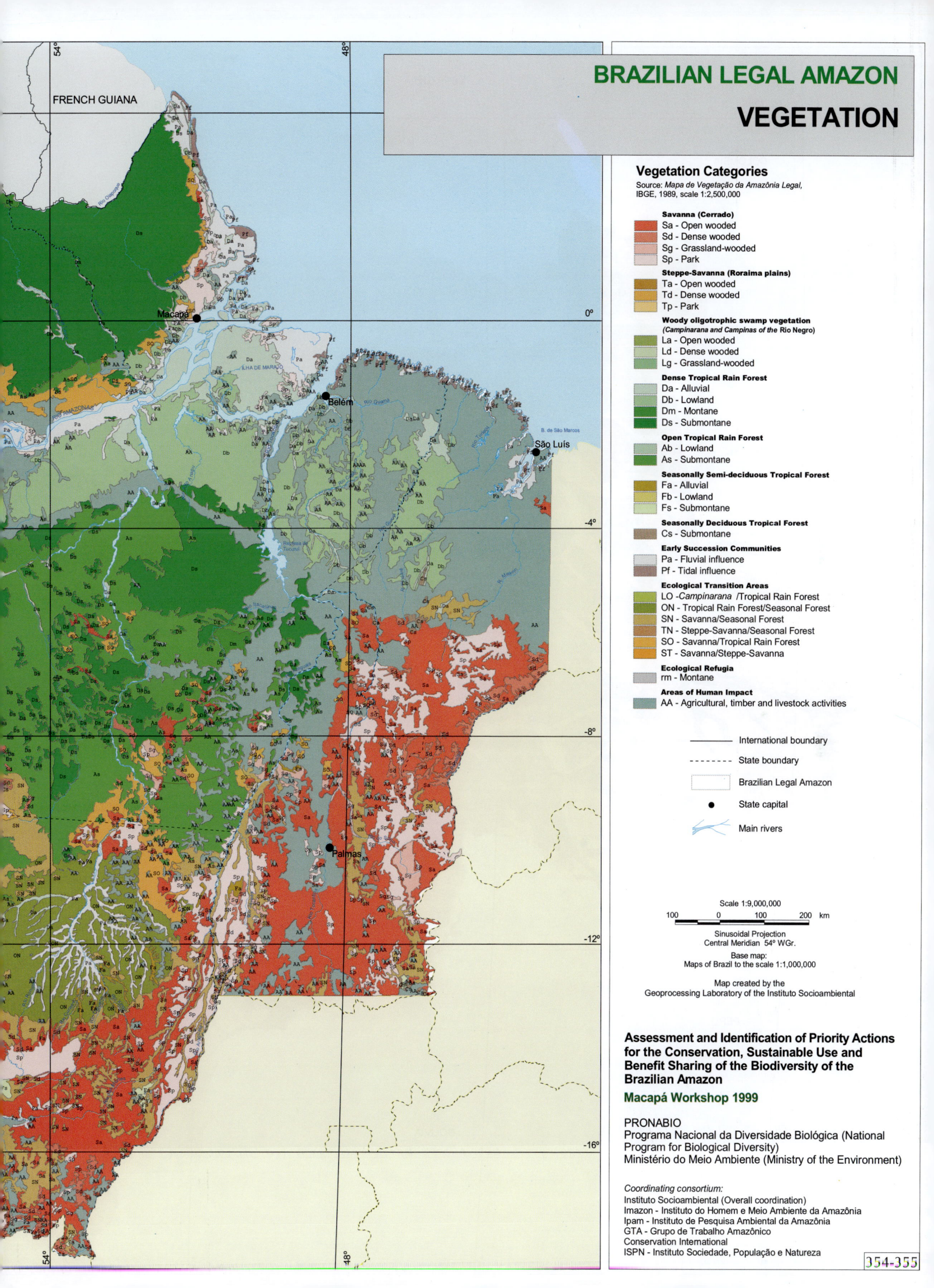

BRAZILIAN LEGAL AMAZON
VEGETATION

Vegetation Categories
Source: *Mapa de Vegetação da Amazônia Legal,* IBGE, 1989, scale 1:2,500,000

Savanna (Cerrado)
- Sa - Open wooded
- Sd - Dense wooded
- Sg - Grassland-wooded
- Sp - Park

Steppe-Savanna (Roraima plains)
- Ta - Open wooded
- Td - Dense wooded
- Tp - Park

Woody oligotrophic swamp vegetation
(*Campinarana* and *Campinas* of the Rio Negro)
- La - Open wooded
- Ld - Dense wooded
- Lg - Grassland-wooded

Dense Tropical Rain Forest
- Da - Alluvial
- Db - Lowland
- Dm - Montane
- Ds - Submontane

Open Tropical Rain Forest
- Ab - Lowland
- As - Submontane

Seasonally Semi-deciduous Tropical Forest
- Fa - Alluvial
- Fb - Lowland
- Fs - Submontane

Seasonally Deciduous Tropical Forest
- Cs - Submontane

Early Succession Communities
- Pa - Fluvial influence
- Pf - Tidal influence

Ecological Transition Areas
- LO - *Campinarana* /Tropical Rain Forest
- ON - Tropical Rain Forest/Seasonal Forest
- SN - Savanna/Seasonal Forest
- TN - Steppe-Savanna/Seasonal Forest
- SO - Savanna/Tropical Rain Forest
- ST - Savanna/Steppe-Savanna

Ecological Refugia
- rm - Montane

Areas of Human Impact
- AA - Agricultural, timber and livestock activities

- ―― International boundary
- ------ State boundary
- ☐ Brazilian Legal Amazon
- ● State capital
- Main rivers

Scale 1:9,000,000
100 0 100 200 km
Sinusoidal Projection
Central Meridian 54° WGr.
Base map:
Maps of Brazil to the scale 1:1,000,000

Map created by the
Geoprocessing Laboratory of the Instituto Socioambiental

Assessment and Identification of Priority Actions for the Conservation, Sustainable Use and Benefit Sharing of the Biodiversity of the Brazilian Amazon
Macapá Workshop 1999

PRONABIO
Programa Nacional da Diversidade Biológica (National Program for Biological Diversity)
Ministério do Meio Ambiente (Ministry of the Environment)

Coordinating consortium:
Instituto Socioambiental (Overall coordination)
Imazon - Instituto do Homem e Meio Ambiente da Amazônia
Ipam - Instituto de Pesquisa Ambiental da Amazônia
GTA - Grupo de Trabalho Amazônico
Conservation International
ISPN - Instituto Sociedade, População e Natureza

VENEZUELA
GUYANA
SURI
COLOMBIA
RORAIMA
Boa Vista
AMAZONAS
Manaus
Rio Solimões
ACRE
Rio Branco
Porto Velho
RONDÔNIA
MAT
PERU
BOLIVIA
72°
66°
60°
4°
0°
-4°
-8°
-12°
-16°

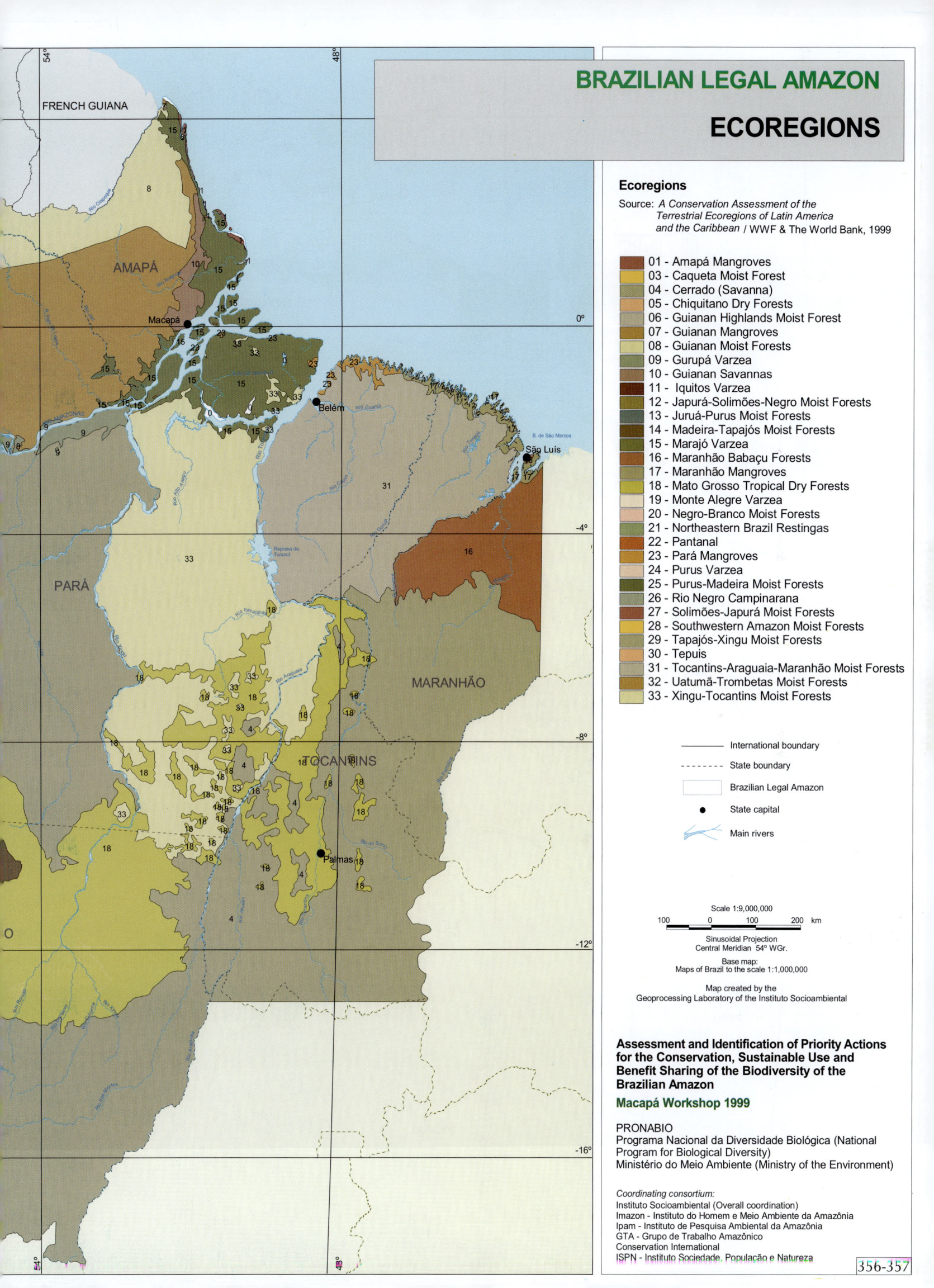

BRAZILIAN LEGAL AMAZON
ECOREGIONS

Ecoregions

Source: *A Conservation Assessment of the Terrestrial Ecoregions of Latin America and the Caribbean* / WWF & The World Bank, 1999

- 01 - Amapá Mangroves
- 03 - Caqueta Moist Forest
- 04 - Cerrado (Savanna)
- 05 - Chiquitano Dry Forests
- 06 - Guianan Highlands Moist Forest
- 07 - Guianan Mangroves
- 08 - Guianan Moist Forests
- 09 - Gurupá Varzea
- 10 - Guianan Savannas
- 11 - Iquitos Varzea
- 12 - Japurá-Solimões-Negro Moist Forests
- 13 - Juruá-Purus Moist Forests
- 14 - Madeira-Tapajós Moist Forests
- 15 - Marajó Varzea
- 16 - Maranhão Babaçu Forests
- 17 - Maranhão Mangroves
- 18 - Mato Grosso Tropical Dry Forests
- 19 - Monte Alegre Varzea
- 20 - Negro-Branco Moist Forests
- 21 - Northeastern Brazil Restingas
- 22 - Pantanal
- 23 - Pará Mangroves
- 24 - Purus Varzea
- 25 - Purus-Madeira Moist Forests
- 26 - Rio Negro Campinarana
- 27 - Solimões-Japurá Moist Forests
- 28 - Southwestern Amazon Moist Forests
- 29 - Tapajós-Xingu Moist Forests
- 30 - Tepuis
- 31 - Tocantins-Araguaia-Maranhão Moist Forests
- 32 - Uatumã-Trombetas Moist Forests
- 33 - Xingu-Tocantins Moist Forests

Legend:
- International boundary
- State boundary
- Brazilian Legal Amazon
- State capital
- Main rivers

Scale 1:9,000,000
Sinusoidal Projection
Central Meridian 54° WGr.

Base map:
Maps of Brazil to the scale 1:1,000,000

Map created by the Geoprocessing Laboratory of the Instituto Socioambiental

Assessment and Identification of Priority Actions for the Conservation, Sustainable Use and Benefit Sharing of the Biodiversity of the Brazilian Amazon

Macapá Workshop 1999

PRONABIO
Programa Nacional da Diversidade Biológica (National Program for Biological Diversity)
Ministério do Meio Ambiente (Ministry of the Environment)

Coordinating consortium:
Instituto Socioambiental (Overall coordination)
Imazon - Instituto do Homem e Meio Ambiente da Amazônia
Ipam - Instituto de Pesquisa Ambiental da Amazônia
GTA - Grupo de Trabalho Amazônico
Conservation International
ISPN - Instituto Sociedade, População e Natureza

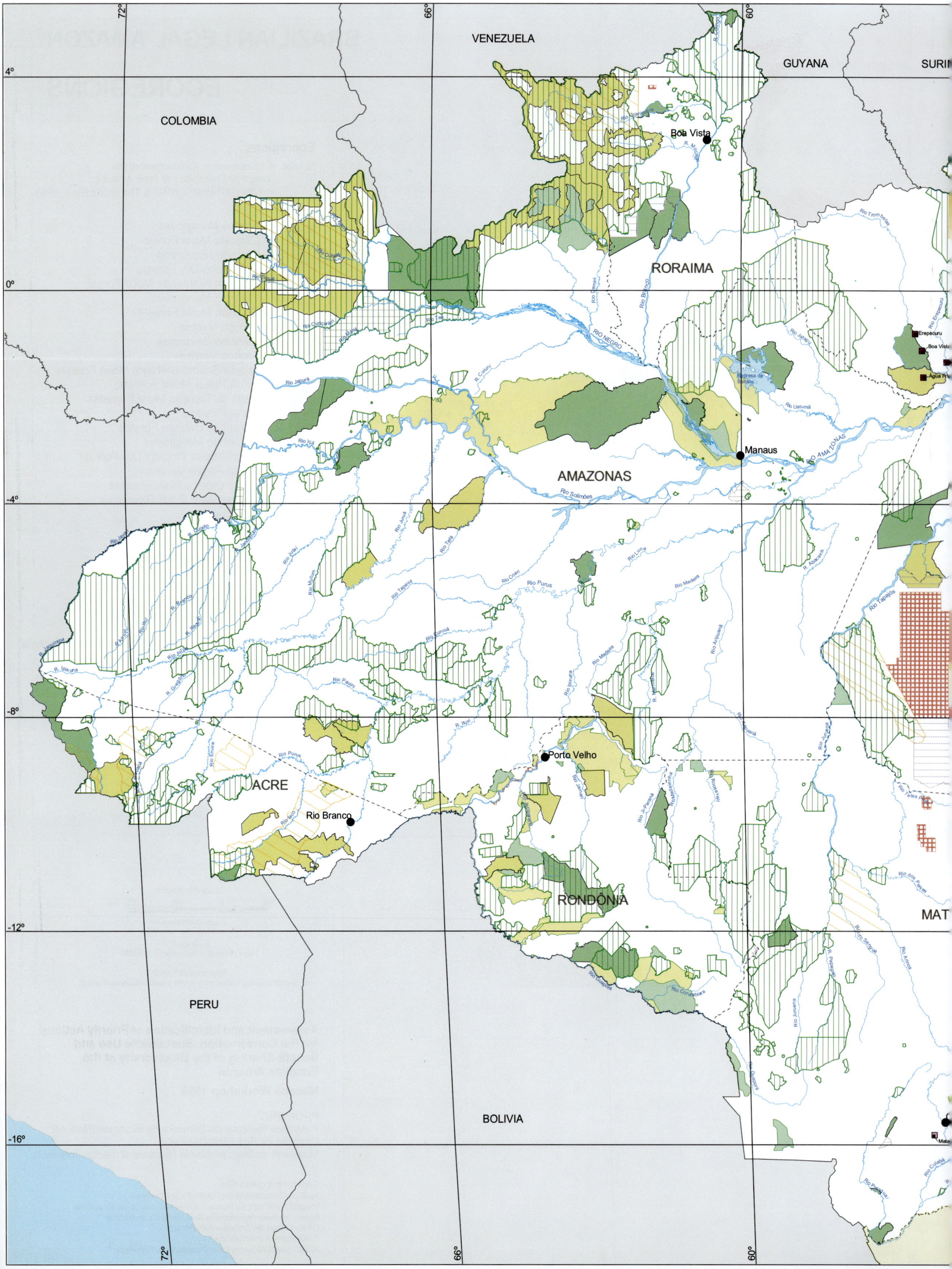

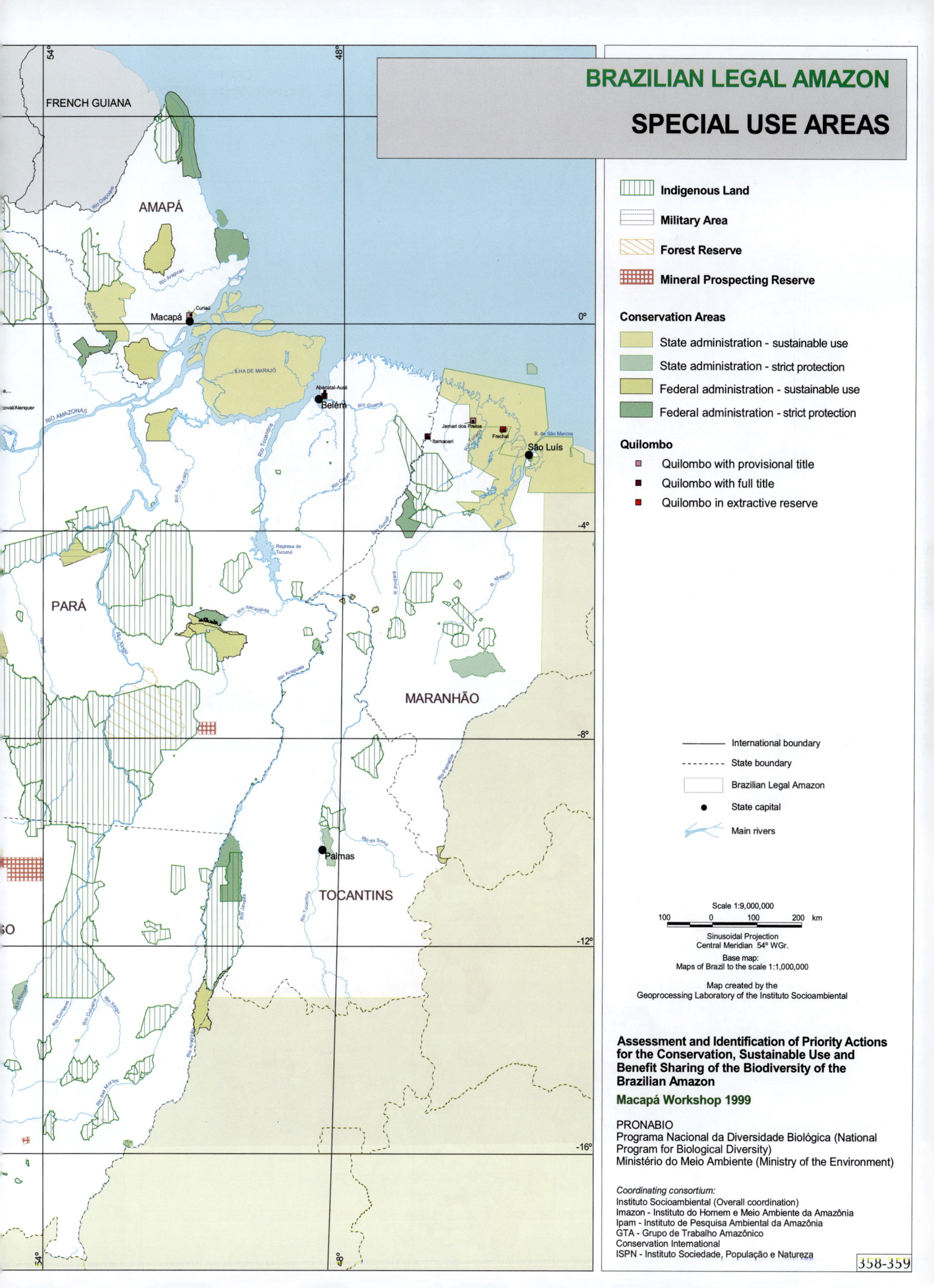

BRAZILIAN LEGAL AMAZON
SPECIAL USE AREAS

Legend:

- Indigenous Land
- Military Area
- Forest Reserve
- Mineral Prospecting Reserve

Conservation Areas
- State administration - sustainable use
- State administration - strict protection
- Federal administration - sustainable use
- Federal administration - strict protection

Quilombo
- Quilombo with provisional title
- Quilombo with full title
- Quilombo in extractive reserve

- International boundary
- State boundary
- Brazilian Legal Amazon
- State capital
- Main rivers

Scale 1:9,000,000
100 0 100 200 km

Sinusoidal Projection
Central Meridian 54° WGr.
Base map:
Maps of Brazil to the scale 1:1,000,000

Map created by the
Geoprocessing Laboratory of the Instituto Socioambiental

Assessment and Identification of Priority Actions for the Conservation, Sustainable Use and Benefit Sharing of the Biodiversity of the Brazilian Amazon

Macapá Workshop 1999

PRONABIO
Programa Nacional da Diversidade Biológica (National Program for Biological Diversity)
Ministério do Meio Ambiente (Ministry of the Environment)

Coordinating consortium:
Instituto Socioambiental (Overall coordination)
Imazon - Instituto do Homem e Meio Ambiente da Amazônia
Ipam - Instituto de Pesquisa Ambiental da Amazônia
GTA - Grupo de Trabalho Amazônico
Conservation International
ISPN - Instituto Sociedade, População e Natureza

CROPS
Soybean, Maize and Rice

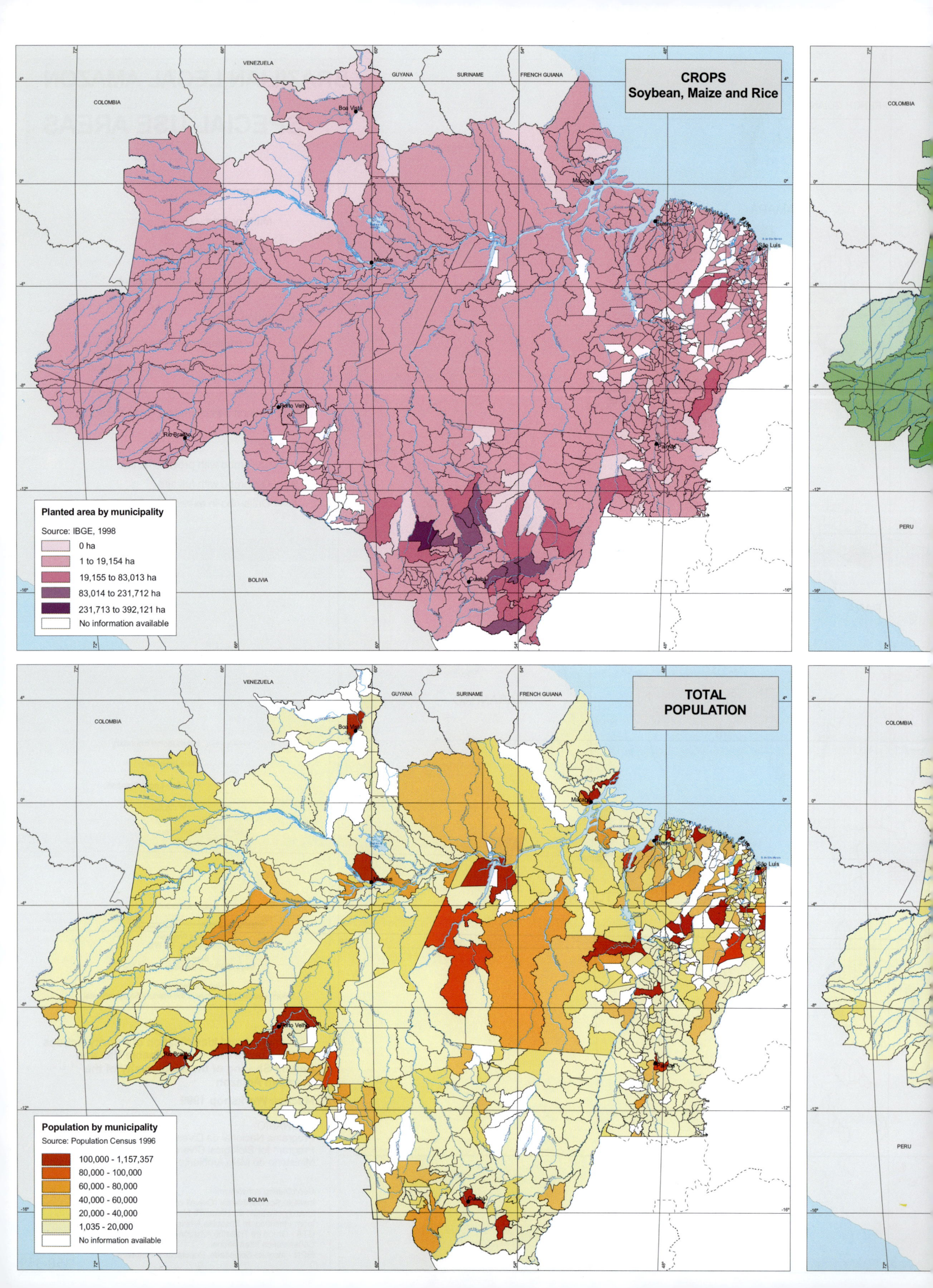

Planted area by municipality
Source: IBGE, 1998

- 0 ha
- 1 to 19,154 ha
- 19,155 to 83,013 ha
- 83,014 to 231,712 ha
- 231,713 to 392,121 ha
- No information available

TOTAL POPULATION

Population by municipality
Source: Population Census 1996

- 100,000 - 1,157,357
- 80,000 - 100,000
- 60,000 - 80,000
- 40,000 - 60,000
- 20,000 - 40,000
- 1,035 - 20,000
- No information available

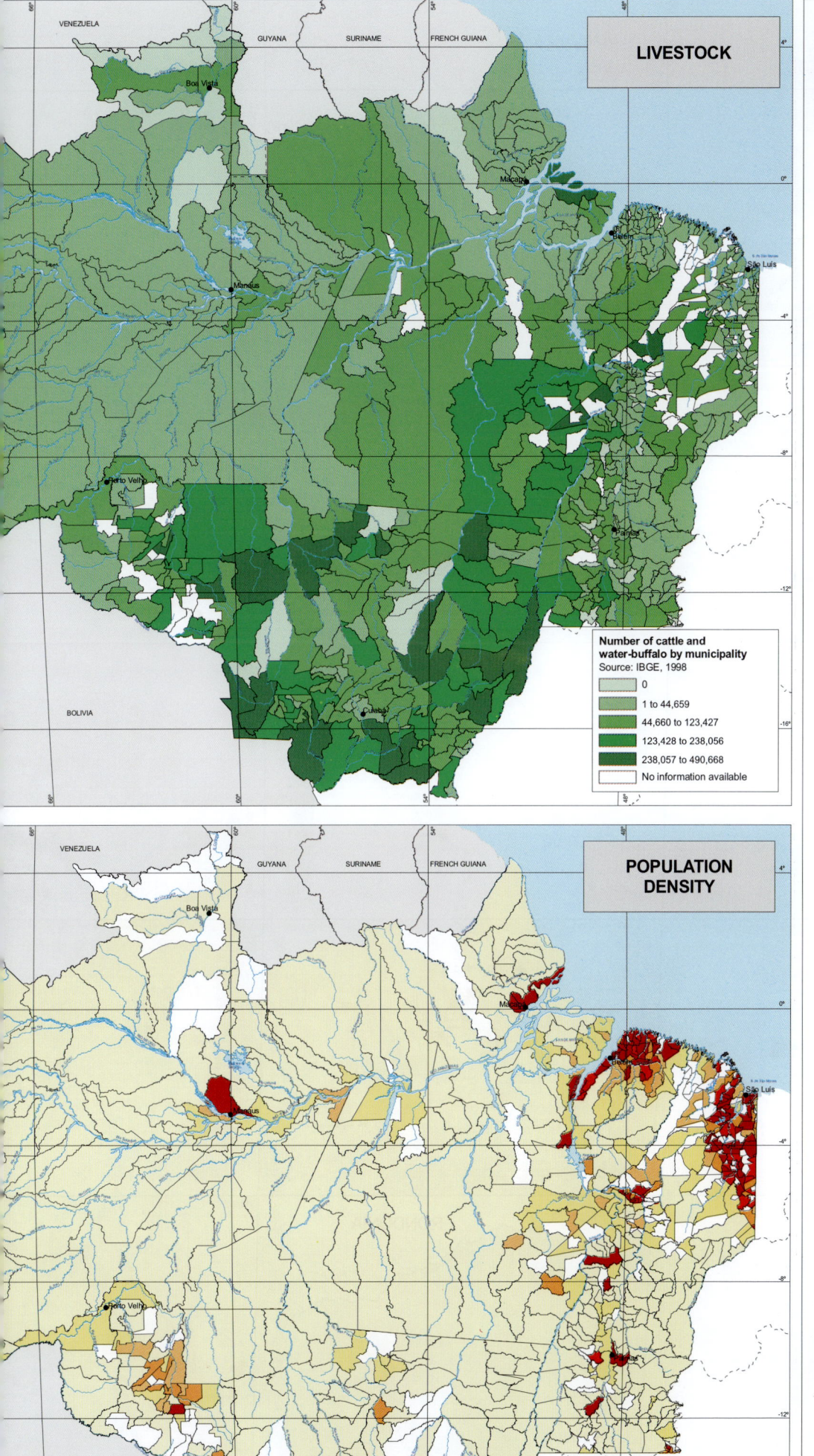

LIVESTOCK

Number of cattle and water-buffalo by municipality
Source: IBGE, 1998

- 0
- 1 to 44,659
- 44,660 to 123,427
- 123,428 to 238,056
- 238,057 to 490,668
- No information available

POPULATION DENSITY

Population density by municipality
Source: Population Census 1996

- 25 – 1,984.05
- 20 – 25
- 15 – 20
- 10 – 15
- 5 – 10
- 0.1 – 5
- No information available

BRAZILIAN LEGAL AMAZON

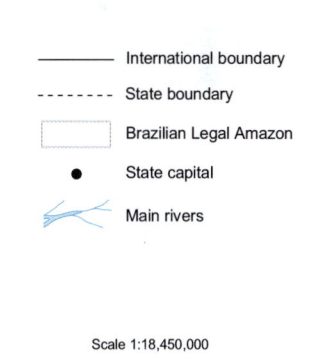

- International boundary
- State boundary
- Brazilian Legal Amazon
- State capital
- Main rivers

Scale 1:18,450,000
Sinusoidal Projection
Central Meridian 54° WGr.
Base map:
Maps of Brazil to the scale 1:1,000,000

Map created by the
Geoprocessing Laboratory of the Instituto Socioambiental

Assessment and Identification of Priority Actions for the Conservation, Sustainable Use and Benefit Sharing of the Biodiversity of the Brazilian Amazon

Macapá Workshop 1999

PRONABIO
Programa Nacional da Diversidade Biológica (National Program for Biological Diversity)
Ministério do Meio Ambiente (Ministry of the Environment)

Coordinating consortium:
Instituto Socioambiental (Overall coordination)
Imazon - Instituto do Homem e Meio Ambiente da Amazônia
Ipam - Instituto de Pesquisa Ambiental da Amazônia
GTA - Grupo de Trabalho Amazônico
Conservation International
ISPN - Instituto Sociedade, População e Natureza

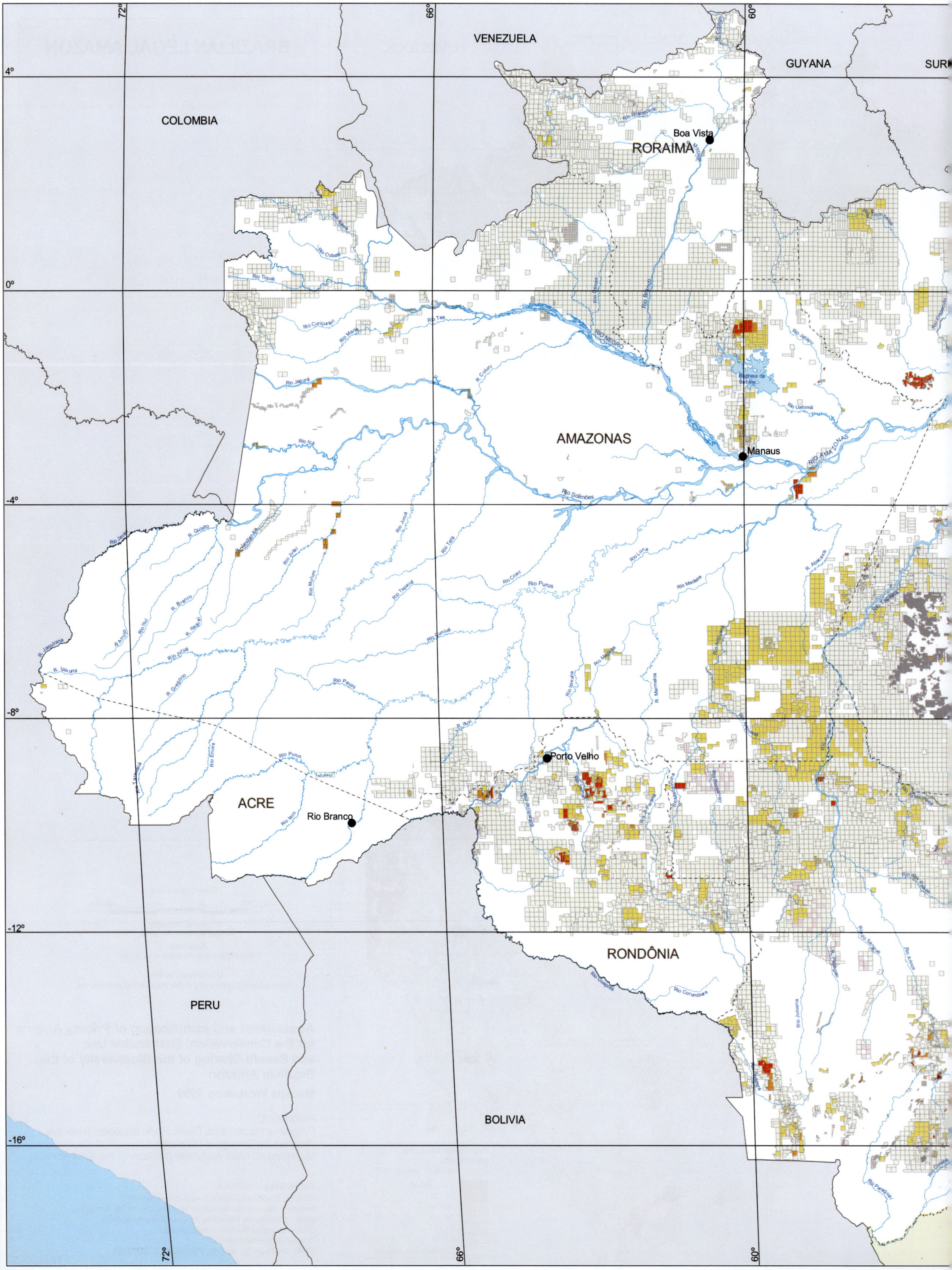

VENEZUELA
GUYANA
COLOMBIA
RORAIMA
Boa Vista
AMAZONAS
Manaus
ACRE
Rio Branco
Porto Velho
RONDÔNIA
PERU
BOLIVIA
Rio Negro
Rio Solimões
Rio Amazonas
Rio Branco
Rio Purus
Rio Juruá
Rio Madeira
72°
66°
60°
4°
0°
-4°
-8°
-12°
-16°

BRAZILIAN LEGAL AMAZON
MINING LICENSES

Mining licenses classified by procedural stage

Source: DNPM
(SICOM + ÁREAS database), 1998

- Final license approved
- Concession to work approved
- Concession to work requested
- Sampling approved
- Sampling requested
- Available
- Other

- International boundary
- State boundary
- Brazilian Legal Amazon
- State capital
- Main rivers

Scale 1:9,000,000
100 0 100 200 km

Sinusoidal Projection
Central Meridian 54° WGr.

Base map:
Maps of Brazil to the scale 1:1,000,000

Map created by the
Geoprocessing Laboratory of the Instituto Socioambiental

Assessment and Identification of Priority Actions for the Conservation, Sustainable Use and Benefit Sharing of the Biodiversity of the Brazilian Amazon

Macapá Workshop 1999

PRONABIO
Programa Nacional da Diversidade Biológica (National Program for Biological Diversity)
Ministério do Meio Ambiente (Ministry of the Environment)

Coordinating consortium:
Instituto Socioambiental (Overall coordination)
Imazon - Instituto do Homem e Meio Ambiente da Amazônia
Ipam - Instituto de Pesquisa Ambiental da Amazônia
GTA - Grupo de Trabalho Amazônico
Conservation International
ISPN - Instituto Sociedade, População e Natureza

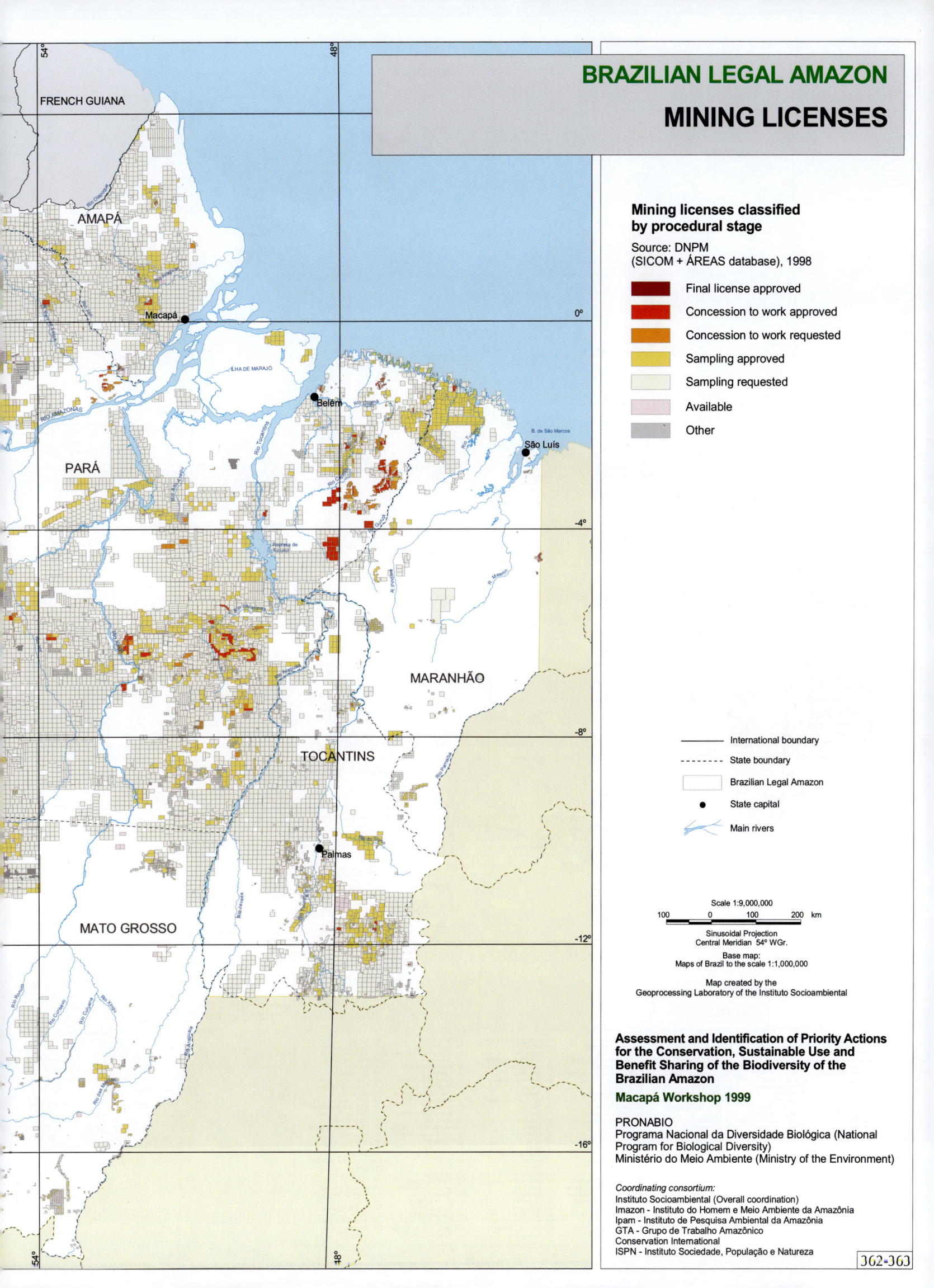

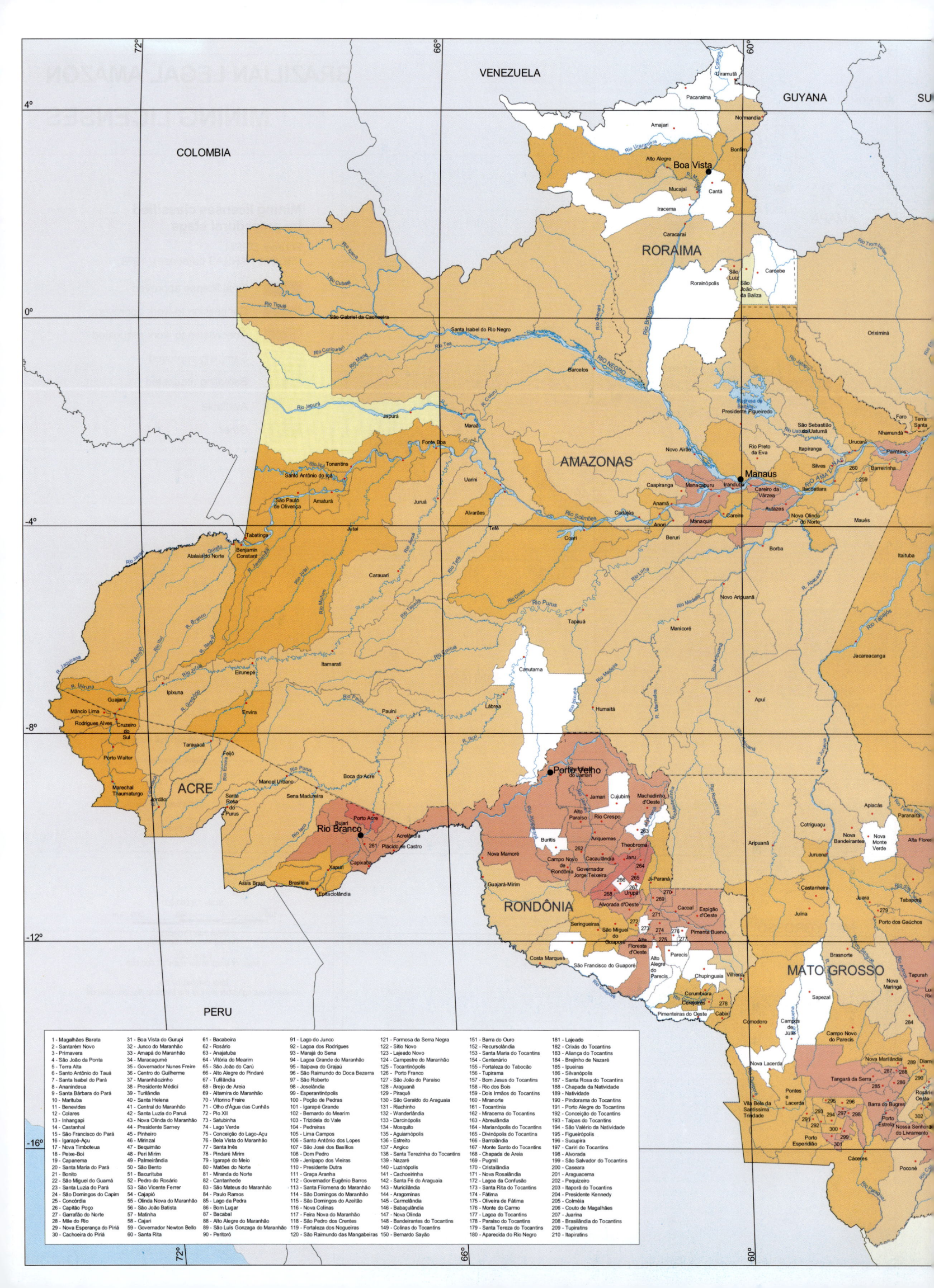

BRAZILIAN LEGAL AMAZON
MINING LICENSES

#	Name	#	Name	#	Name	#	Name	#	Name	#	Name
1	Magalhães Barata	31	Boa Vista do Gurupi	61	Bacabeira	91	Lago do Junco	121	Formosa da Serra Negra	151	Barra do Ouro	181	Lajeado
2	Santarém Novo	32	Junco do Maranhão	62	Rosário	92	Lagoa dos Rodrigues	122	Sítio Novo	152	Recursolândia	182	Crixás do Tocantins
3	Primavera	33	Amapá do Maranhão	63	Anajatuba	93	Maraiá do Sena	123	Lajeado Novo	153	Santa Maria do Tocantins	183	Aliança do Tocantins
4	São João da Ponta	34	Maracaçumé	64	Vitória do Mearim	94	Lagoa Grande do Maranhão	124	Campestre do Maranhão	154	Centenário	184	Brejinho de Nazaré
5	Terra Alta	35	Governador Nunes Freire	65	São João do Carú	95	Itaipava do Grajaú	125	Tocantinópolis	155	Fortaleza do Tabocão	185	Ipueiras
6	Santo Antônio do Tauá	36	Centro do Guilherme	66	Alto Alegre do Pindaré	96	São Raimundo da Doca Bezerra	126	Porto Franco	156	Tupirama	186	Silvanópolis
7	Santa Isabel do Pará	37	Maranhãozinho	67	Tufilândia	97	São Roberto	127	São João do Paraíso	157	Bom Jesus do Tocantins	187	Santa Rosa do Tocantins
8	Ananindeua	38	Presidente Médici	68	Brejo de Areia	98	Joselândia	128	Araguanã	158	Rio dos Bois	188	Chapada da Natividade
9	Santa Bárbara do Pará	39	Turilândia	69	Altamira do Maranhão	99	Esperantinópolis	129	Piraquê	159	Dois Irmãos do Tocantins	189	Natividade
10	Marituba	40	Santa Helena	70	Vitorino Freire	100	Poção de Pedras	130	São Geraldo do Araguaia	160	Miranorte	190	Pindorama do Tocantins
11	Benevides	41	Central do Maranhão	71	Olho d'Água das Cunhãs	101	Igarapé Grande	131	Riachinho	161	Tocantínia	191	Porto Alegre do Tocantins
12	Colares	42	Santa Luzia do Paruá	72	Pio XII	102	Bernardo do Mearim	132	Wanderlândia	162	Miracema do Tocantins	192	Conceição do Tocantins
13	Inhangapi	43	Presidente Sarney	73	Satubinha	103	Trizidela do Vale	133	Darcinópolis	163	Abreulândia	193	Taipas do Tocantins
14	Castanhal	44	Pinheiro	74	Lago Verde	104	Pedreiras	134	Mosquito	164	Marianópolis do Tocantins	194	São Valério da Natividade
15	São Francisco do Pará	45	Miranzal	75	Conceição do Lago-Açu	105	Lima Campos	135	Aguiarnópolis	165	Divinópolis do Tocantins	195	Figueirópolis
16	Igarapé-Açu	46	Bequimão	76	Bela Vista do Maranhão	106	Santo Antônio dos Lopes	136	Estreito	166	Barrolândia	196	Sucupira
17	Nova Timboteua	47	Peri Mirim	77	Santa Inês	107	São José dos Basílios	137	Angico	167	Monte Santo do Tocantins	197	Cariri do Tocantins
18	Peixe-Boi	48	Palmeirândia	78	Pindaré Mirim	108	Dom Pedro	138	Luzinópolis	168	Chapada de Areia	198	Alvorada
19	Capanema	49	Matinha	79	Igarapé do Meio	109	Jenipapo dos Vieiras	139	Nazaré	169	Pugmil	199	São Salvador do Tocantins
20	Santa Maria do Pará	50	São Bento	80	Matões do Norte	110	Presidente Dutra	140	Luzinópolis	170	Cristalândia	200	Caseara
21	Bonito	51	Bacurituba	81	Miranda do Norte	111	Graça Aranha	141	Cachoeirinha	171	Nova Rosalândia	201	Araguacema
22	São Miguel do Guamá	52	Pedro do Rosário	82	Cantanhede	112	Governador Eugênio Barros	142	Santa Fé de Araguaia	172	Lagoa da Confusão	202	Pequizeiro
23	Santa Luzia do Pará	53	São Vicente Ferrer	83	São Mateus do Maranhão	113	Santa Filomena do Maranhão	143	Murcilândia	173	Santa Rita do Tocantins	203	Itaporé do Tocantins
24	São Domingos do Capim	54	Cajapió	84	Paulo Ramos	114	São Domingos do Azeitão	144	Aragominas	174	Fátima	204	Presidente Kennedy
25	Concórdia	55	Olinda Nova do Maranhão	85	Lago da Pedra	115	São Domingos do Azeitão	145	Carmolândia	175	Oliveira de Fátima	205	Colméia
26	Capitão Poço	56	São João Batista	86	Bom Lugar	116	Nova Colinas	146	Babaçulândia	176	Monte do Carmo	206	Couto de Magalhães
27	Garrafão do Norte	57	Matinha	87	Bacabal	117	Feira Nova dos Crentes	147	Nova Olinda	177	Lagoa do Tocantins	207	Juarina
28	Mãe do Rio	58	Cajari	88	Alto Alegre do Maranhão	118	São Pedro dos Crentes	148	Bandeirantes do Tocantins	178	Paraíso do Tocantins	208	Brasilândia do Tocantins
29	Nova Esperança do Piriá	59	Governador Newton Bello	89	São Luís Gonzaga do Maranhão	119	Fortaleza dos Nogueiras	149	Colinas do Tocantins	179	Santa Tereza do Tocantins	209	Tupirantins
30	Cachoeira do Piriá	60	Santa Rita	90	Pindoré	120	São Raimundo das Mangabeiras	150	Bernardo Sayão	180	Aparecida do Rio Negro	210	Itapiratins

BRAZILIAN LEGAL AMAZON
ANTHROPOGENIC PRESSURE INDEX

Anthropogenic Pressure Index by Municipality
Source: ISPN, 1999

- 2 to 3.6 - very low
- 3.6 to 5.2 - low
- 5.2 to 6.8 - medium
- 6.8 to 8.4 - high
- 8.4 to 10 - very high
- No information available

— International boundary
--- State boundary
▢ Brazilian Legal Amazon
● State capital
Main rivers

Scale 1:9,000,000
100 0 100 200 km
Sinusoidal Projection
Central Meridian 54° WGr.
Base map:
Maps of Brazil to the scale 1:1,000,000

Map created by the
Geoprocessing Laboratory of the Instituto Socioambiental

Assessment and Identification of Priority Actions for the Conservation, Sustainable Use and Benefit Sharing of the Biodiversity of the Brazilian Amazon

Macapá Workshop 1999

PRONABIO
Programa Nacional da Diversidade Biológica (National Program for Biological Diversity)
Ministério do Meio Ambiente (Ministry of the Environment)

Coordinating consortium:
Instituto Socioambiental (Overall coordination)
Imazon - Instituto do Homem e Meio Ambiente da Amazônia
Ipam - Instituto de Pesquisa Ambiental da Amazônia
GTA - Grupo de Trabalho Amazônico
Conservation International
ISPN - Instituto Sociedade, População e Natureza

Municipality Index

#	Name	#	Name	#	Name	#	Name
211	São Domingos do Araguaia	241	Governador Edison Lobão	271	Castanheiras	301	Glória d'Oeste
212	São João do Araguaia	242	Montes Altos	272	Nova Brasilândia d'Oeste	302	Jangada
213	Esperantina	243	Itinga do Maranhão	273	Novo Horizonte do Oeste	303	Acorizal
214	Bom Jesus do Tocantins	244	Bom Jesus das Selvas	274	Rolim de Moura	304	Várzea Grande
215	Abel Figueiredo	245	Buriticupu	275	Santa Luzia d'Oeste	305	Nova Brasilândia
216	São Pedro da Água Branca	246	Nova Ipixuna	276	São Felipe d'Oeste	306	Planalto da Serra
217	São Sebastião do Tocantins	247	Ipixuna do Pará	277	Primavera de Rondônia	307	Jaciara
218	Vila Nova dos Martírios	248	Mocajuba	278	Colorado do Oeste	308	São Pedro da Cipa
219	Cidelândia	249	Igarapé-Miri	279	Novo Horizonte do Norte	309	Juscimeira
220	Brejo Grande do Araguaia	250	Limoeiro do Ajuru	280	Nova Guarita	310	Rondonópolis
221	Palestina do Pará	251	Abaetetuba	281	Terra Nova do Norte	311	São José do Povo
222	Buriti do Tocantins	252	Barcarena	282	Guarantã do Norte		
223	Carrasco Bonito	253	Ponta de Pedras	283	Porto Alegre do Norte		
224	Augustinópolis	254	Cachoeira do Arari	284	São José do Rio Claro		
225	Sampaio	255	Salvaterra	285	Nova Olímpia		
226	Praia Norte	256	Santa Cruz do Arari	286	Denise		
227	Imperatriz	257	São Sebastião da Boa Vista	287	Santo Afonso		
228	João Lisboa	258	Senador José Porfírio	288	Arenápolis		
229	Senador La Rocque	259	Boa Vista do Ramos	289	Nortelândia		
230	Buritirama	260	Urucurituba	290	Alto Paraguai		
231	Davinópolis	261	Senador Guiomard	291	Jauru		
232	São Francisco do Brejão	262	Monte Negro	292	Figueirópolis d'Oeste		
233	São Miguel do Tocantins	263	Vale do Anari	293	Indiavaí		
234	Sítio Novo do Tocantins	264	Vale do Paraíso	294	Araputanga		
235	Axixá do Tocantins	265	Ouro Preto do Oeste	295	Reserva do Cabaçal		
236	Araguatins	266	Nova União	296	Salto do Céu		
237	São Bento do Tocantins	267	Teixeirópolis	297	Rio Branco		
238	Itaguatins	268	Mirante da Serra	298	Lambari d'Oeste		
239	Maurilândia do Tocantins	269	Presidente Médici	299	Mirassol d'Oeste		
240	Ribamar Fiquene	270	Ministro Andreazza	300	São José dos Quatro Marcos		

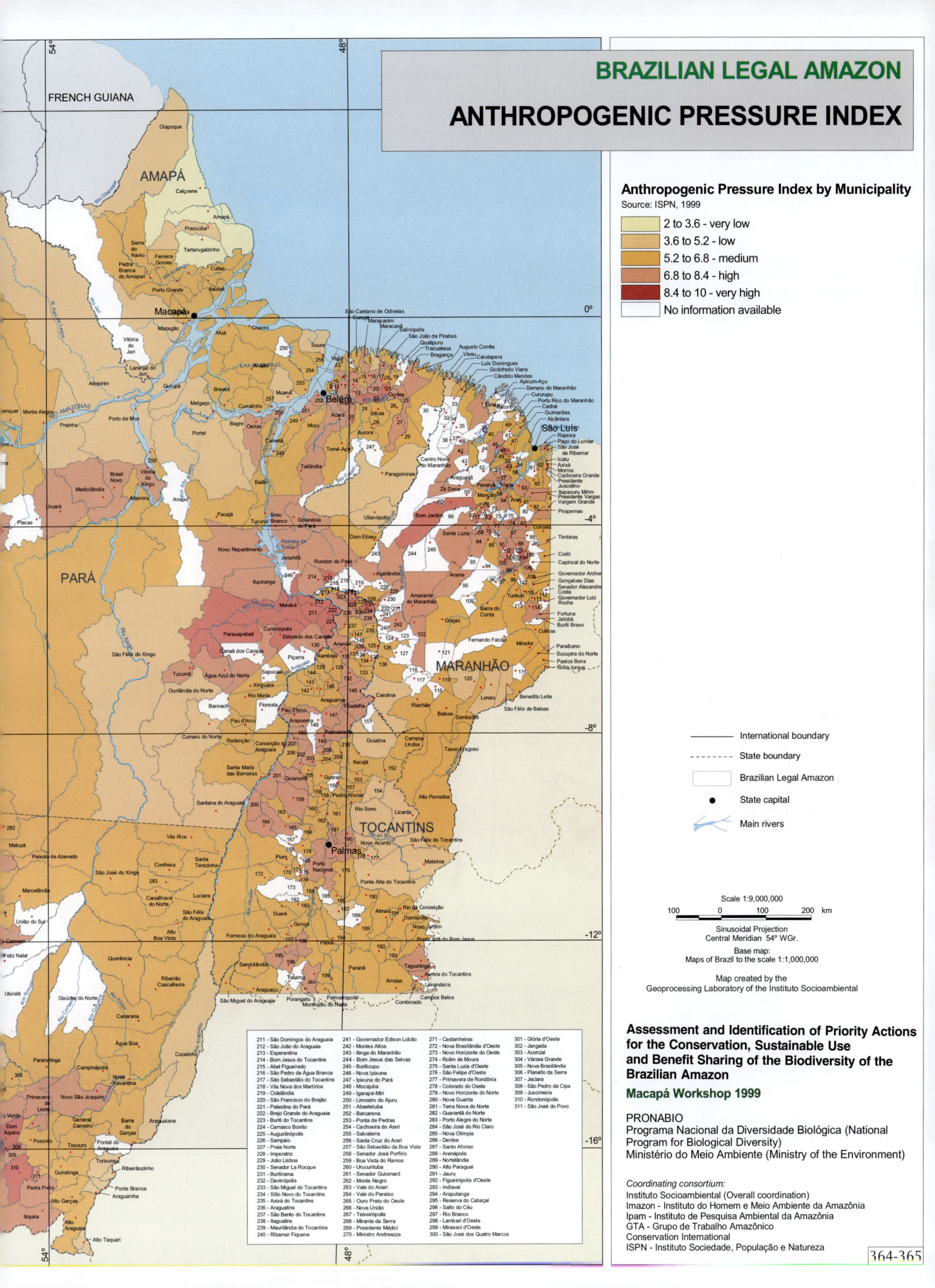

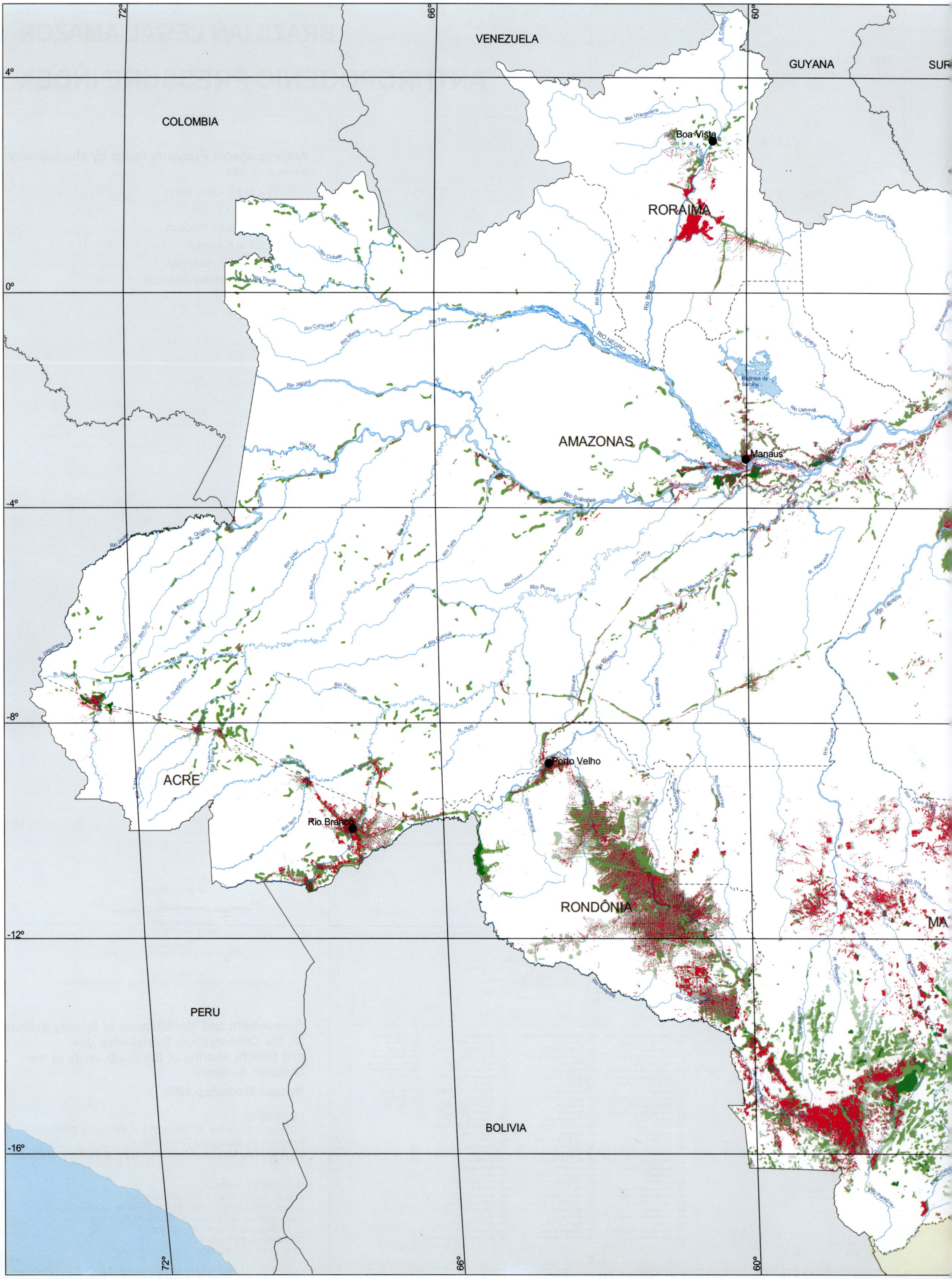

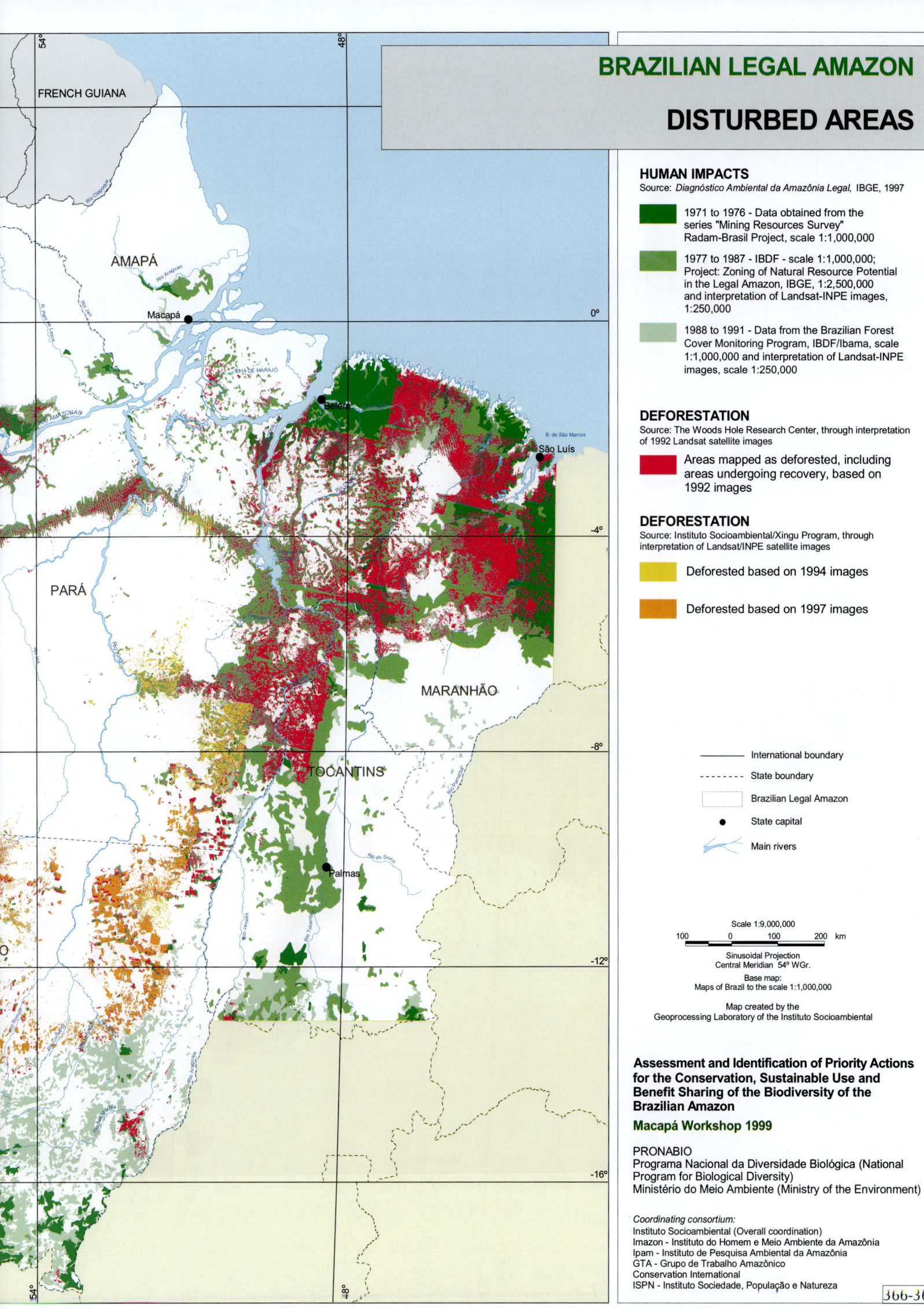

BRAZILIAN LEGAL AMAZON

DISTURBED AREAS

HUMAN IMPACTS
Source: *Diagnóstico Ambiental da Amazônia Legal*, IBGE, 1997

- 1971 to 1976 - Data obtained from the series "Mining Resources Survey" Radam-Brasil Project, scale 1:1,000,000
- 1977 to 1987 - IBDF - scale 1:1,000,000; Project: Zoning of Natural Resource Potential in the Legal Amazon, IBGE, 1:2,500,000 and interpretation of Landsat-INPE images, 1:250,000
- 1988 to 1991 - Data from the Brazilian Forest Cover Monitoring Program, IBDF/Ibama, scale 1:1,000,000 and interpretation of Landsat-INPE images, scale 1:250,000

DEFORESTATION
Source: The Woods Hole Research Center, through interpretation of 1992 Landsat satellite images

- Areas mapped as deforested, including areas undergoing recovery, based on 1992 images

DEFORESTATION
Source: Instituto Socioambiental/Xingu Program, through interpretation of Landsat/INPE satellite images

- Deforested based on 1994 images
- Deforested based on 1997 images

- International boundary
- State boundary
- Brazilian Legal Amazon
- State capital
- Main rivers

Scale 1:9,000,000
Sinusoidal Projection
Central Meridian 54° WGr.
Base map:
Maps of Brazil to the scale 1:1,000,000

Map created by the Geoprocessing Laboratory of the Instituto Socioambiental

Assessment and Identification of Priority Actions for the Conservation, Sustainable Use and Benefit Sharing of the Biodiversity of the Brazilian Amazon

Macapá Workshop 1999

PRONABIO
Programa Nacional da Diversidade Biológica (National Program for Biological Diversity)
Ministério do Meio Ambiente (Ministry of the Environment)

Coordinating consortium:
Instituto Socioambiental (Overall coordination)
Imazon - Instituto do Homem e Meio Ambiente da Amazônia
Ipam - Instituto de Pesquisa Ambiental da Amazônia
GTA - Grupo de Trabalho Amazônico
Conservation International
ISPN - Instituto Sociedade, População e Natureza

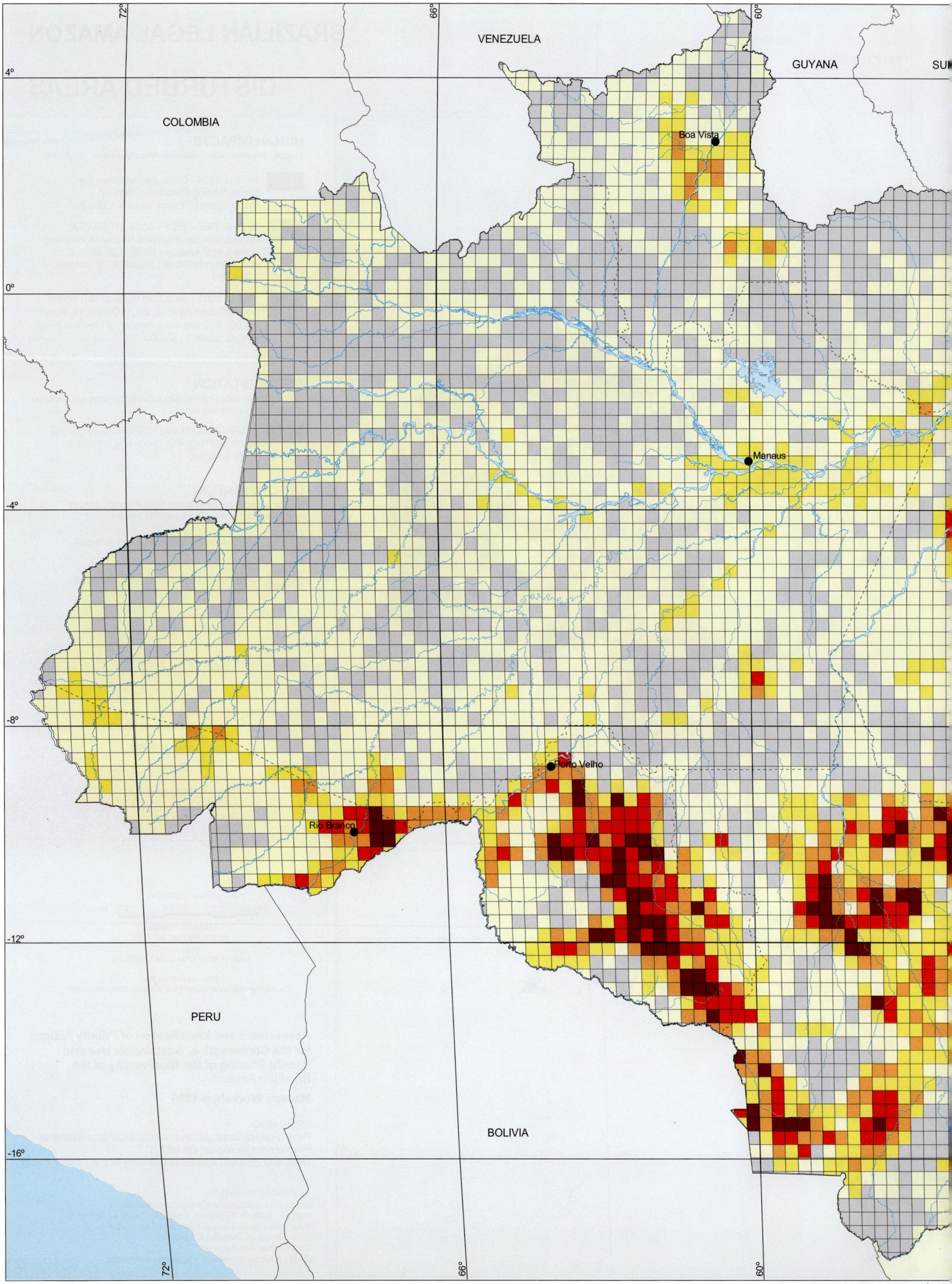

VENEZUELA
GUYANA
COLOMBIA
PERU
BOLIVIA
Boa Vista
Manaus
Porto Velho
Rio Branco
72°
66°
60°
4°
0°
-4°
-8°
-12°
-16°

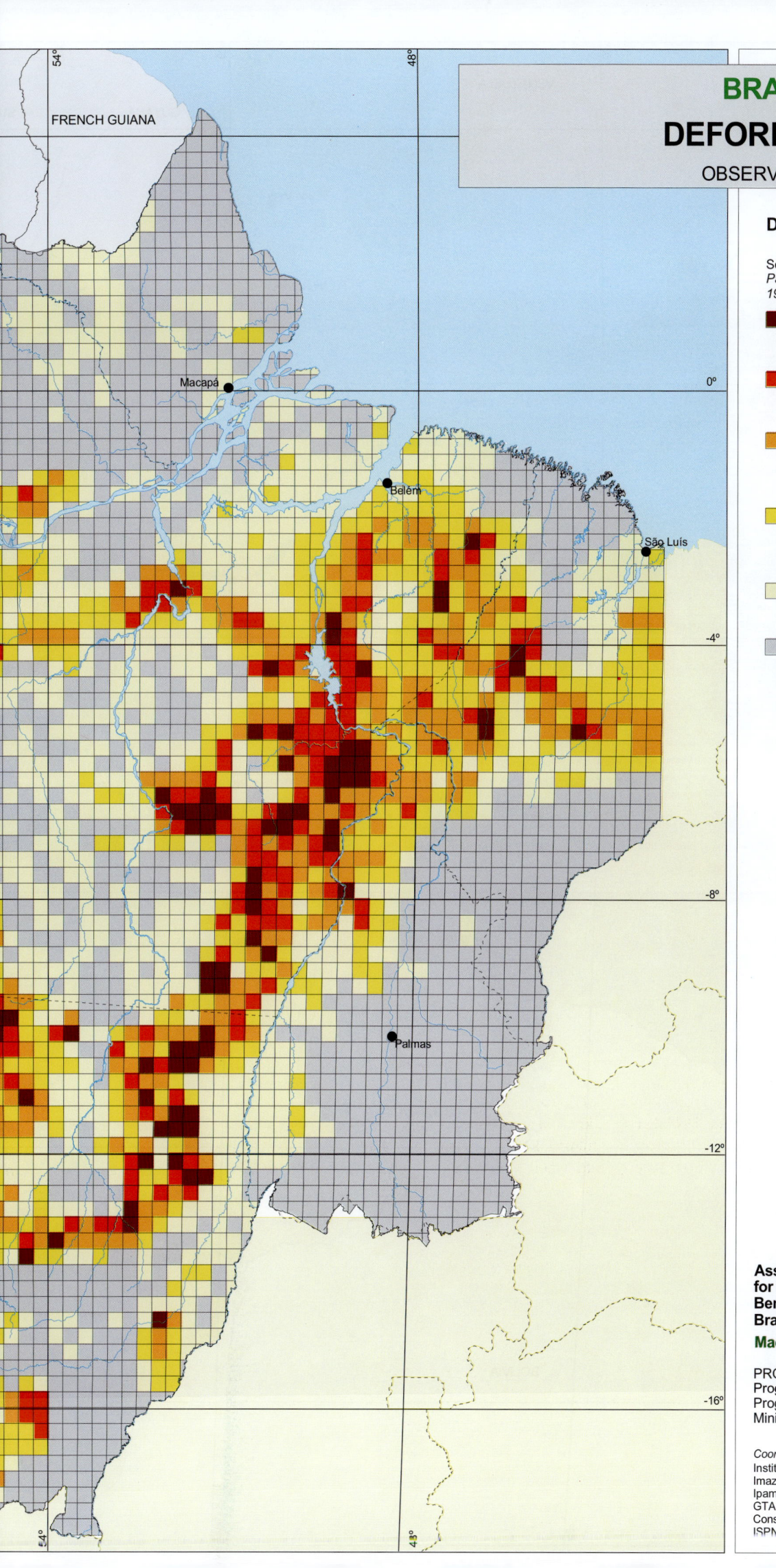

BRAZILIAN LEGAL AMAZON
DEFORESTATION PATTERNS
OBSERVED FOR THE PERIOD 1991 TO 1996

Deforestation Patterns

Source: ALVES, Diógenes S. *An Analysis of the Geographical Pattern of Deforestation in Brazilian Amazônia in the 1991 - 1996 period.* INPE. São Paulo/Brazil, 1999.

- Cells with high deforestation accounting for 25% of total observed deforestation
- Cells with high deforestation which, together with category A, account for 50% of total observed deforestation
- Cells with high deforestation which, together with category A and B, account for 75% of total observed deforestation
- Cells with high deforestation which, together with category A, B and C, account for 95% of total observed deforestation
- Cells with low deforestation accounting for 5 percent of the total observed deforestation
- Cells in which no deforestation was observed due to clouds, absence of human activity, or to *cerrado* vegetation

---

- International boundary
- State boundary
- Brazilian Legal Amazon
- State capital
- Main rivers

Scale 1:9,000,000
100 0 100 200 km
Sinusoidal Projection
Central Meridian 54° WGr.
Base map:
Maps of Brazil to the scale 1:1,000,000

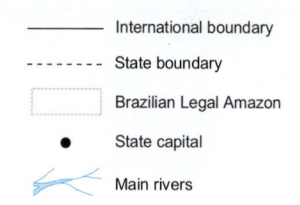

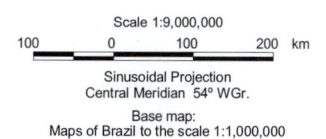

Map created by the
Geoprocessing Laboratory of the Instituto Socioambiental

Assessment and Identification of Priority Actions for the Conservation, Sustainable Use and Benefit Sharing of the Biodiversity of the Brazilian Amazon

Macapá Workshop 1999

PRONABIO
Programa Nacional da Diversidade Biológica (National Program for Biological Diversity)
Ministério do Meio Ambiente (Ministry of the Environment)

Coordinating consortium:
Instituto Socioambiental (Overall coordination)
Imazon - Instituto do Homem e Meio Ambiente da Amazônia
Ipam - Instituto de Pesquisa Ambiental da Amazônia
GTA - Grupo de Trabalho Amazônico
Conservation International
ISPN - Instituto Sociedade, População e Natureza

VENEZUELA

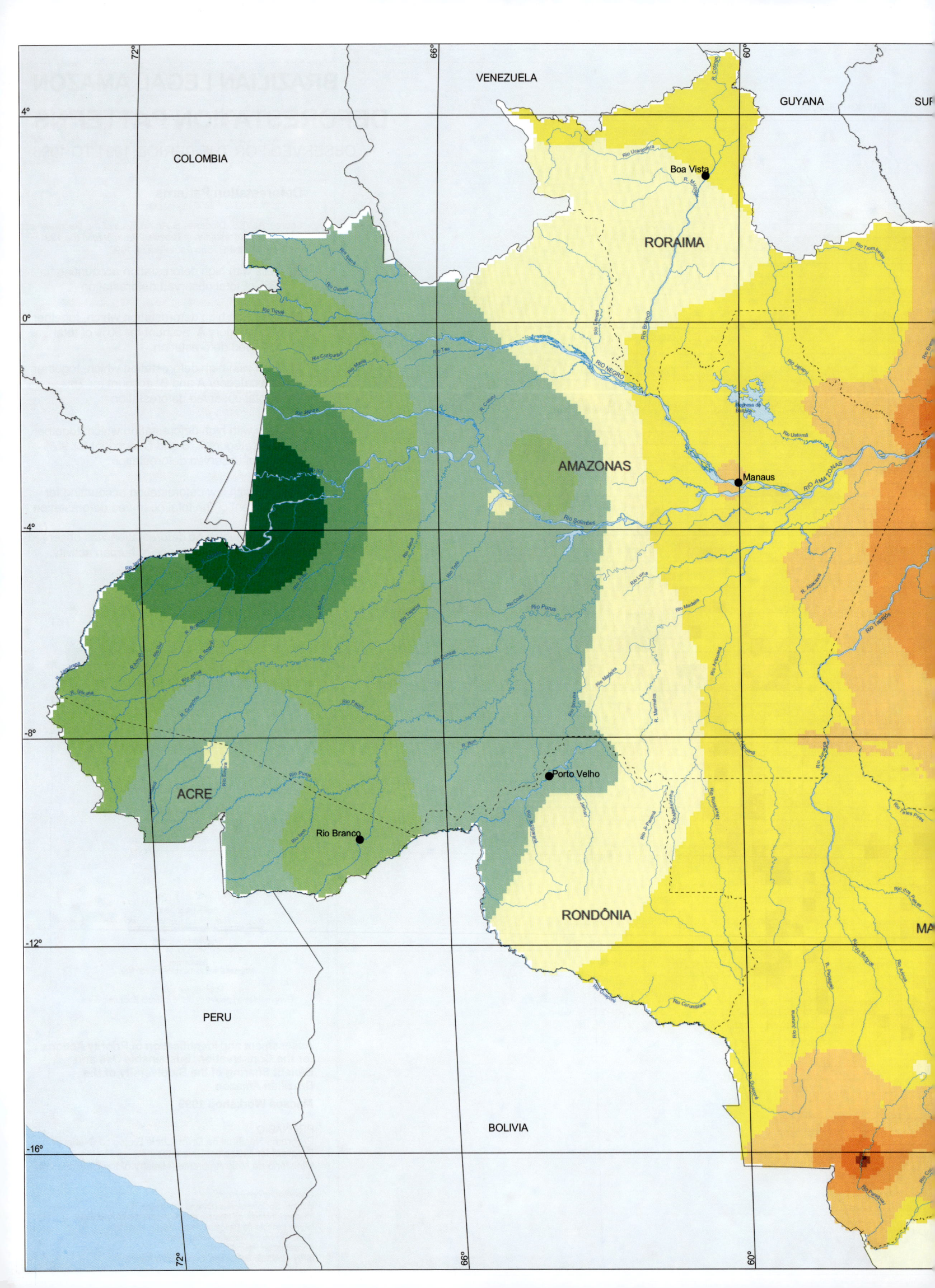

COLOMBIA

GUYANA

RORAIMA

Boa Vista

AMAZONAS

Manaus

ACRE

Porto Velho

Rio Branco

RONDÔNIA

PERU

BOLIVIA

BRAZILIAN LEGAL AMAZON
WATER BALANCE
for the period May 1997 to September 1997

WATER BALANCE
for the period May 1997 to September 1997
(total precipitation minus total evapotranspiration)

Source: Woods Hole Research Center, 1999

- -2,000 to -1,750 mm
- -1,750 to -1,500 mm
- -1,500 to -1,250 mm
- -1,250 to -1,000 mm
- -1,000 to -750 mm
- -750 to -500 mm
- -500 to -250 mm
- -250 to 0 mm
- 0 to 250 mm
- 250 to 500 mm
- 500 to 750 mm
- 750 to 1,000 mm
- no information available

--- International boundary
----- State boundary
Brazilian Legal Amazon
● State capital
Main rivers

Scale 1:9,000,000
100 0 100 200 km
Sinusoidal Projection
Central Meridian 54° WGr.
Base map:
Maps of Brazil to the scale 1:1,000,000

Map created by the
Geoprocessing Laboratory of the Instituto Socioambiental

Assessment and Identification of Priority Actions for the Conservation, Sustainable Use and Benefit Sharing of the Biodiversity of the Brazilian Amazon
Macapá Workshop 1999

PRONABIO
Programa Nacional da Diversidade Biológica (National Program for Biological Diversity)
Ministério do Meio Ambiente (Ministry of the Environment)

Coordinating consortium:
Instituto Socioambiental (Overall coordination)
Imazon - Instituto do Homem e Meio Ambiente da Amazônia
Ipam - Instituto de Pesquisa Ambiental da Amazônia
GTA - Grupo de Trabalho Amazônico
Conservation International
ISPN - Instituto Sociedade, População e Natureza

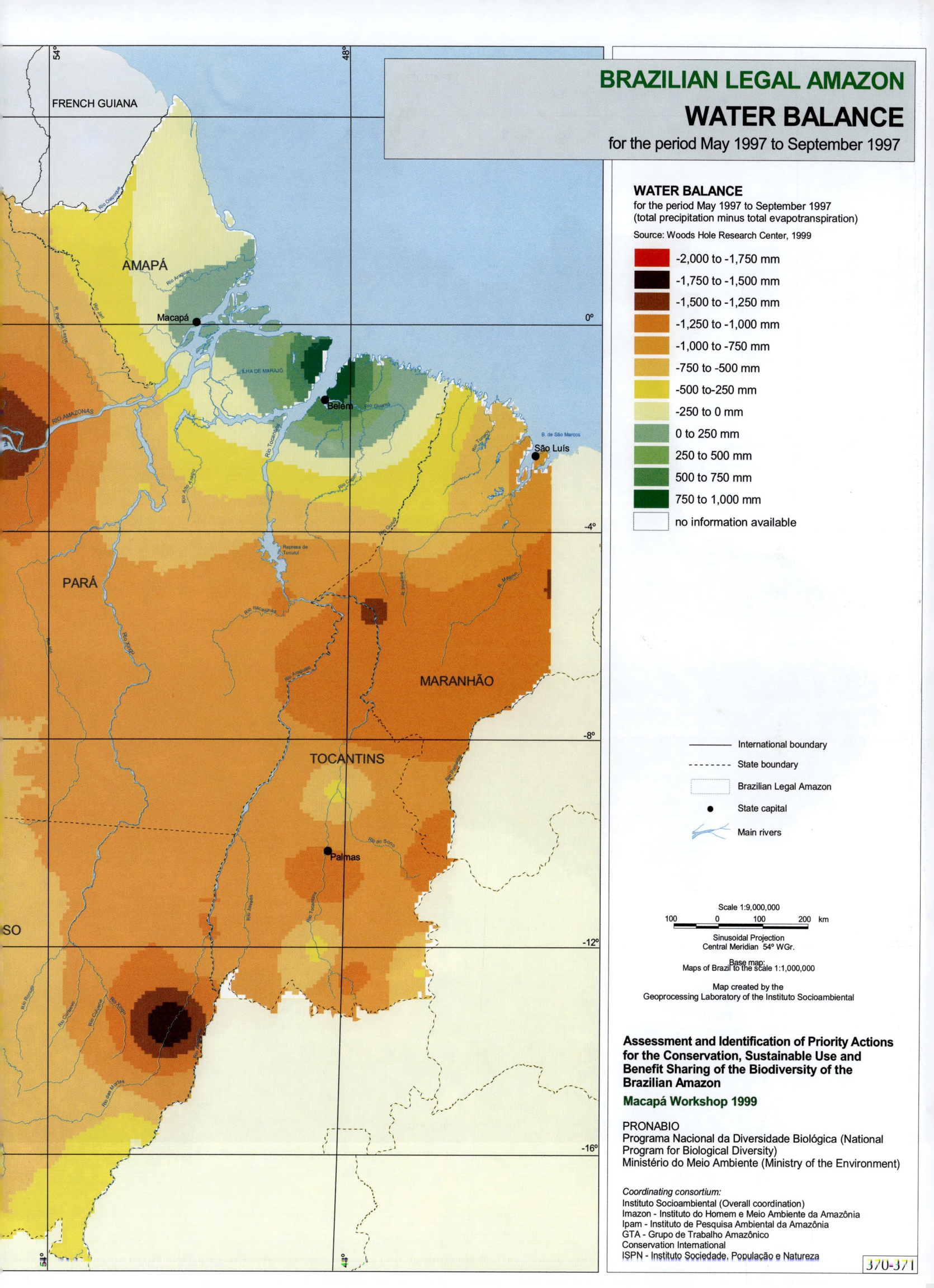

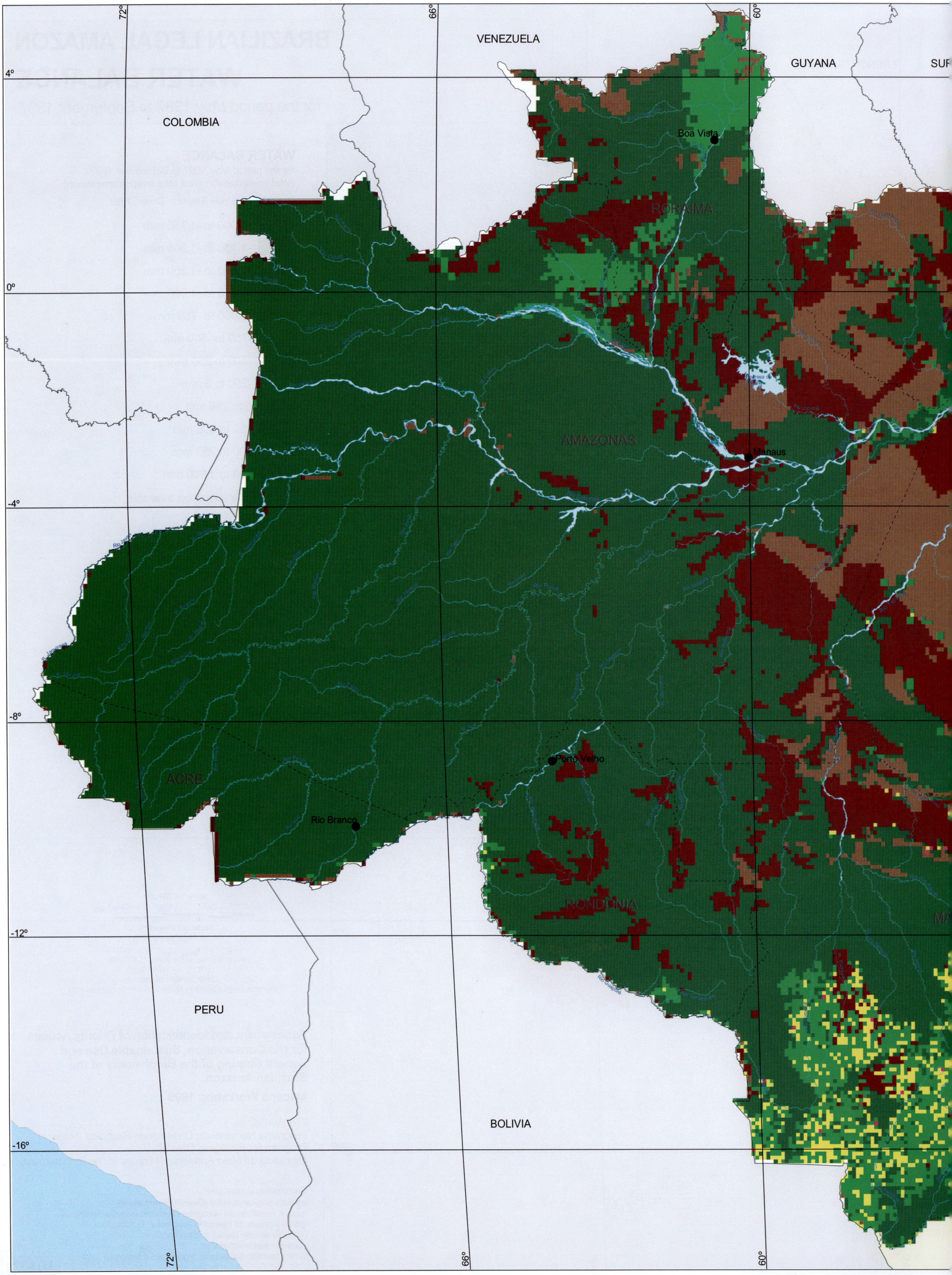
VENEZUELA
GUYANA
COLOMBIA
Boa Vista
RORAIMA
AMAZONAS
Manaus
Porto Velho
ACRE
Rio Branco
RONDÔNIA
PERU
BOLIVIA
72°
66°
60°
4°
0°
-4°
-8°
-12°
-16°

BRAZILIAN LEGAL AMAZON
FIRE RISK

Fire Risk Categories
IPAM / WHRC, 1999

Non-forest areas
- Low combustion probability
- Moderate combustion probability
- High combustion probability

Forest areas
- Low flammability
- Moderate flammability
- High flammability

- International boundary
- State boundary
- Brazilian Legal Amazon
- State capital
- Main rivers

Scale 1:9,000,000
100 0 100 200 km

Sinusoidal Projection
Central Meridian 54° WGr.
Base map:
Maps of Brazil to the scale 1:1,000,000

Map created by the
Geoprocessing Laboratory of the Instituto Socioambiental

Assessment and Identification of Priority Actions for the Conservation, Sustainable Use and Benefit Sharing of the Biodiversity of the Brazilian Amazon
Macapá Workshop 1999

PRONABIO
Programa Nacional da Diversidade Biológica (National Program for Biological Diversity)
Ministério do Meio Ambiente (Ministry of the Environment)

Coordinating consortium:
Instituto Socioambiental (Overall coordination)
Imazon - Instituto do Homem e Meio Ambiente da Amazônia
Ipam - Instituto de Pesquisa Ambiental da Amazônia
GTA - Grupo de Trabalho Amazônico
Conservation International
ISPN - Instituto Sociedade, População e Natureza

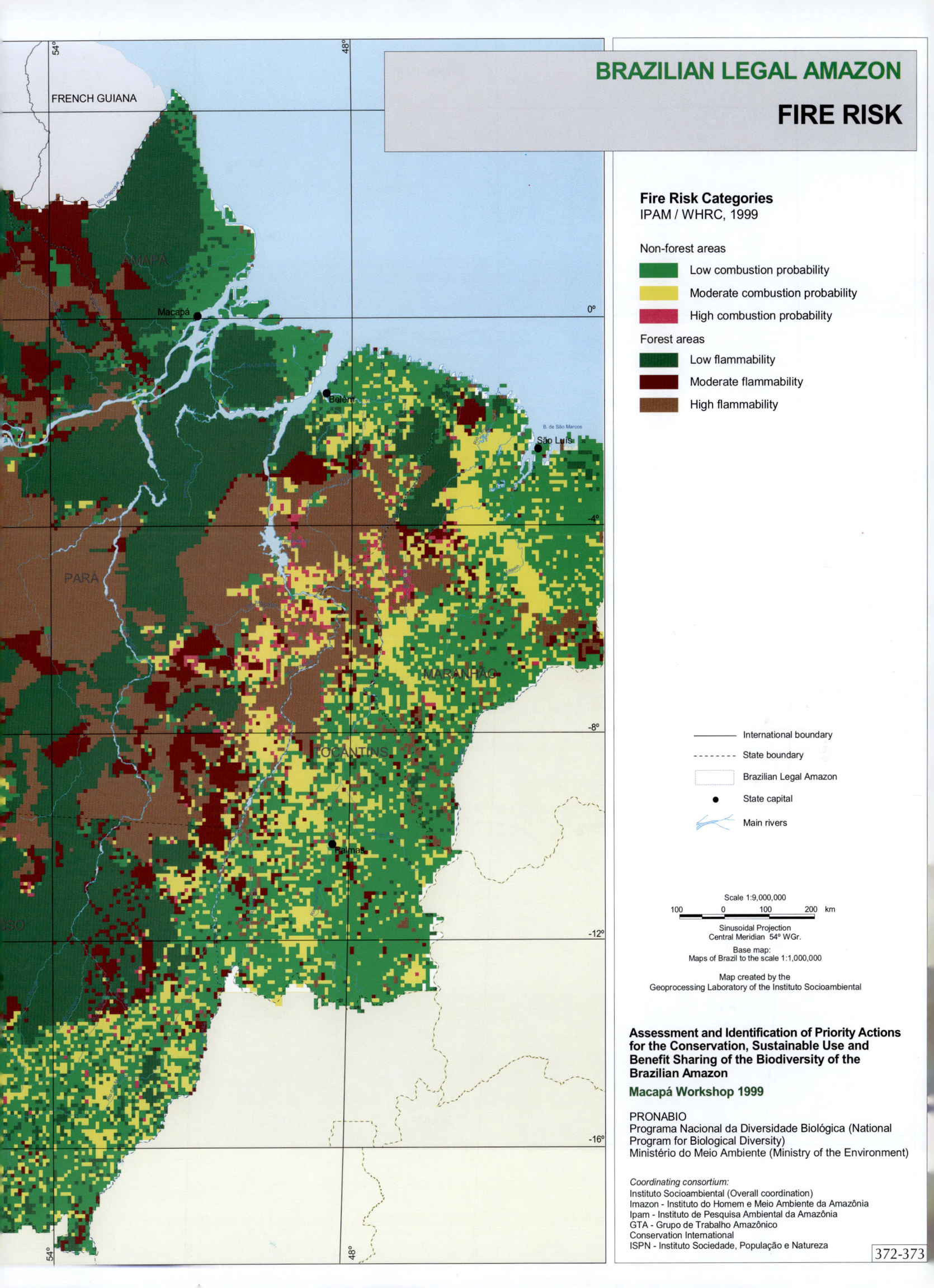

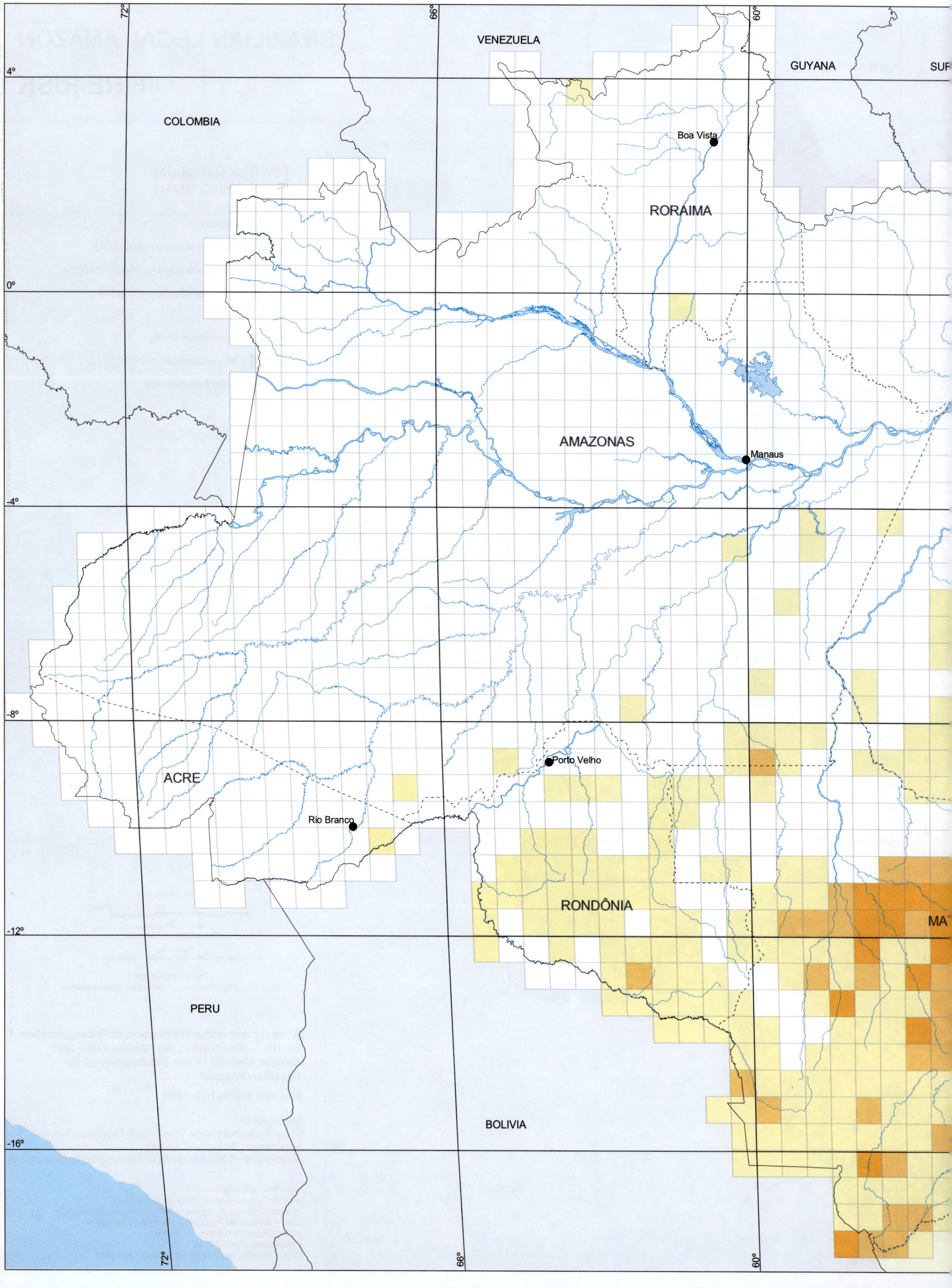

72°
66°
60°
4°
0°
-4°
-8°
-12°
-16°
VENEZUELA
GUYANA
SUR
COLOMBIA
Boa Vista
RORAIMA
AMAZONAS
Manaus
Porto Velho
ACRE
Rio Branco
RONDÔNIA
MA
PERU
BOLIVIA

BRAZILIAN LEGAL AMAZON
SATELLITE MONITORING OF FOREST FIRES

Observed fires

Data from the *Monitoramento Orbital de Queimadas* program, processed from the NOAA12 satellite, August 1999.
Source: INPE / EMBRAPA, 1999

- 0
- 1 to 55
- 56 to 110
- 111 to 319
- 320 to 565

— International boundary
--- State boundary
▢ Brazilian Legal Amazon
● State capital
～ Main rivers

Scale 1:9,000,000

Sinusoidal Projection
Central Meridian 54° WGr.

Base map:
Maps of Brazil to the scale 1:1,000,000

Map created by the
Geoprocessing Laboratory of the Instituto Socioambiental

Assessment and Identification of Priority Actions for the Conservation, Sustainable Use and Benefit Sharing of the Biodiversity of the Brazilian Amazon

Macapá Workshop 1999

PRONABIO
Programa Nacional da Diversidade Biológica (National Program for Biological Diversity)
Ministério do Meio Ambiente (Ministry of the Environment)

Coordinating consortium:
Instituto Socioambiental (Overall coordination)
Imazon - Instituto do Homem e Meio Ambiente da Amazônia
Ipam - Instituto de Pesquisa Ambiental da Amazônia
GTA - Grupo de Trabalho Amazônico
Conservation International
ISPN - Instituto Sociedade, População e Natureza

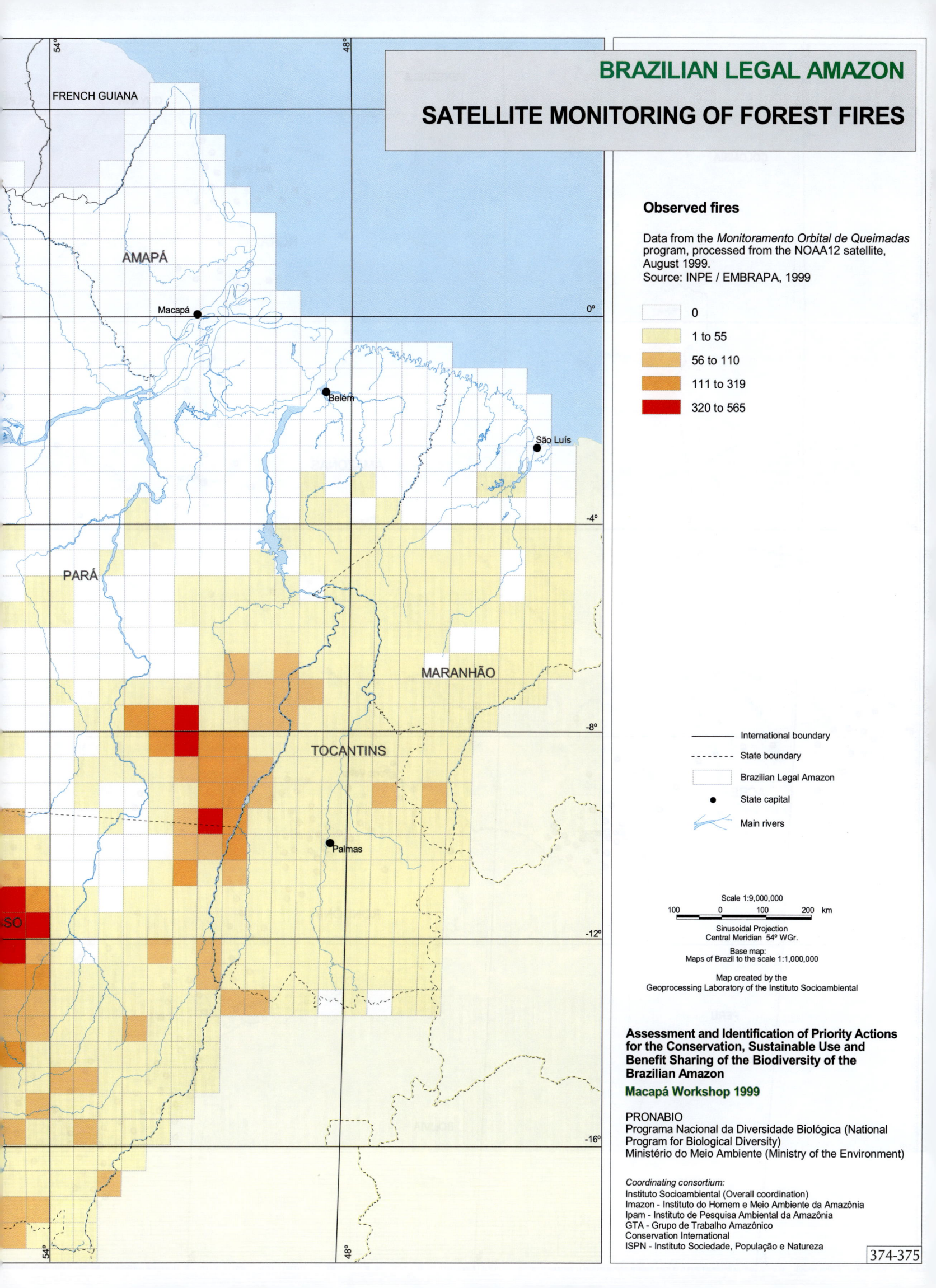

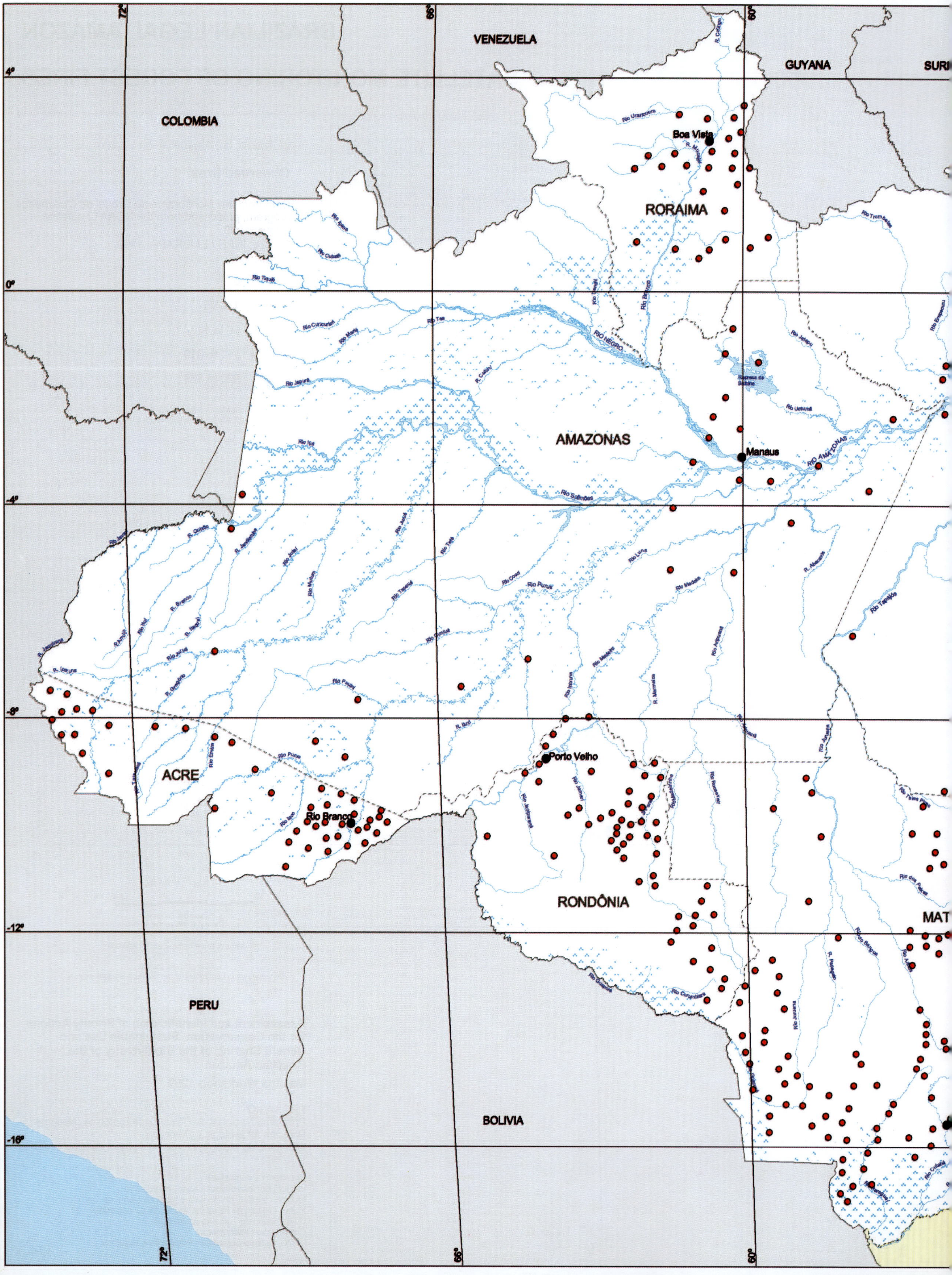

VENEZUELA
GUYANA
COLOMBIA
RORAIMA
Boa Vista
AMAZONAS
Manaus
RIO NEGRO
RIO AMAZONAS
Rio Solimões
Rio Purus
Rio Juruá
Rio Madeira
Rio Branco
Porto Velho
ACRE
RONDÔNIA
PERU
BOLIVIA
4º
0º
-4º
-8º
-12º
-16º
72º
66º
60º

BRAZILIAN LEGAL AMAZON
LAND SETTLEMENT PROJECTS

● Land Settlement Projects
Source: INCRA, 1998

— International boundary
--- State boundary
☐ Brazilian Legal Amazon
● State capital
〜 Main rivers
〜 Wetlands; lakes

Scale 1:9,000,000
Sinusoidal Projection
Central Meridian 54º WGr.

Base map:
Maps of Brazil to the scale 1:1,000,000

Map created by the
Geoprocessing Laboratory of the Instituto Socioambiental

Assessment and Identification of Priority Actions for the Conservation, Sustainable Use and Benefit Sharing of the Biodiversity of the Brazilian Amazon

Macapá Workshop 1999

PRONABIO
Programa Nacional da Diversidade Biológica (National Program for Biological Diversity)
Ministério do Meio Ambiente (Ministry of the Environment)

Coordinating consortium:
Instituto Socioambiental (Overall coordination)
Imazon - Instituto do Homem e Meio Ambiente da Amazônia
Ipam - Instituto de Pesquisa Ambiental da Amazônia
GTA - Grupo de Trabalho Amazônico
Conservation International
ISPN - Instituto Sociedade, População e Natureza

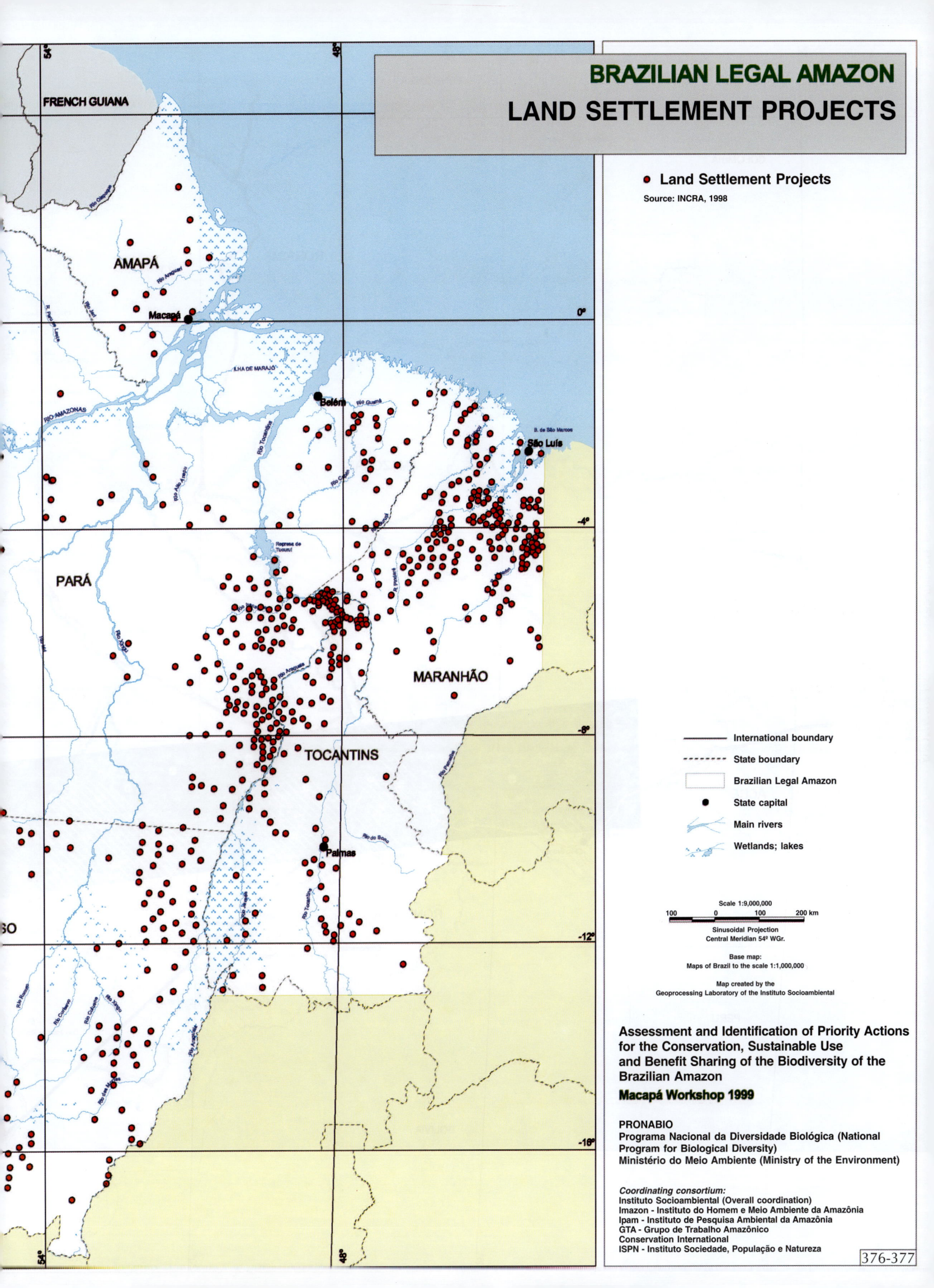

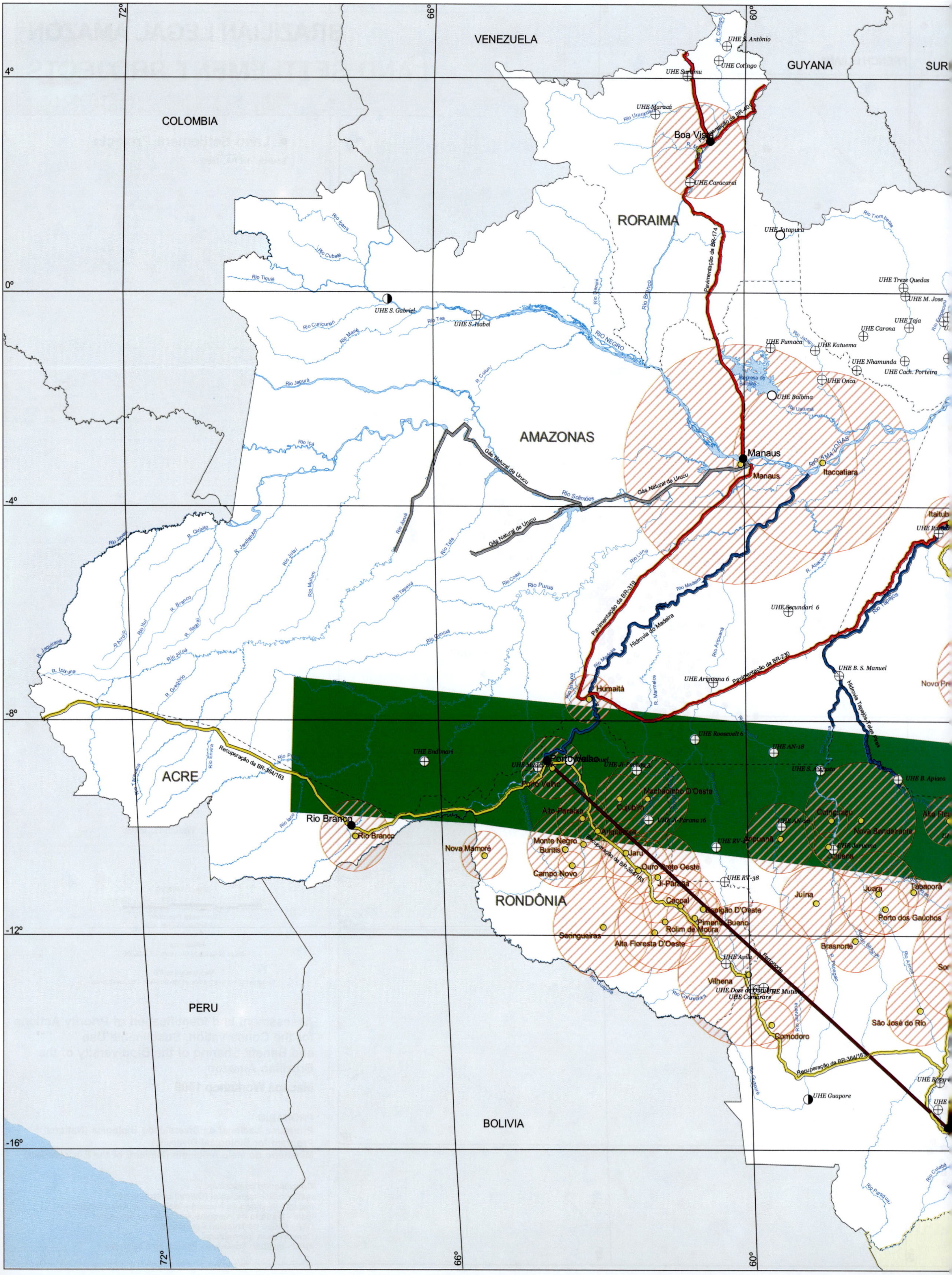
VENEZUELA
COLOMBIA
GUYANA
RORAIMA
AMAZONAS
ACRE
RONDÔNIA
PERU
BOLIVIA
72°
66°
60°
4°
0°
-4°
-8°
-12°
-16°
Boa Vista
Manaus
Itacoatiara
Humaitá
Porto Velho
Rio Branco
Pavimentação da BR-174
Pavimentação da BR-319
Pavimentação da BR-230
Recuperação da BR-364/163
Hidrovia do Madeira
Gás Natural de Urucu
RIO NEGRO
Rio Solimões
UHE S. Gabriel
UHE S. Isabel
UHE Balbina
UHE Caracaraí
UHE Jatapuru
UHE Secundari 6
UHE Aripuana 6
UHE Roosevelt 6
UHE B. S. Manuel
UHE Guapore
Nova Mamoré
Monte Negro
Buritis
Campo Novo
Ariquemes
Jaru
Ouro Preto Oeste
Ji-Paraná
Cacoal
Espigão D'Oeste
Pimenta Bueno
Rolim de Moura
Alta Floresta D'Oeste
Seringueiras
Vilhena
Comodoro
Machadinho D'Oeste
Cujubim
Alto Paraíso
Juína
Juara
Tabaporã
Porto dos Gaúchos
Brasnorte
Cotriguaçu
Nova Bandeirante
São José do Rio
Aripuanã

BRAZILIAN LEGAL AMAZON
LOGGING ACTIVITY AND DEVELOPMENT CORRIDORS

LOGGING ACTIVITY
source: Imazon, 1999

- Radius of logging activity
- Logging center

ARC OF DEFORESTATION
source: Proarco, 1999

HYDROELECTRIC PLANTS
source: compiled by ISA, 1999

- ○ Operating
- ◐ Under construction
- ⊕ Planned

"BRASIL EM AÇÃO" PROJECTS
source: compiled by ISA and Imazon, 1999

- Ferronorte railway
- Gas pipeline
- Power transmission line
- Electrical grid link
- Highway paving
- BR-364/163 highway improvement
- waterway

- International boundary
- State boundary
- Brazilian Legal Amazon
- ● State capital
- Main rivers

Scale 1:9,000,000
100 0 100 200 km

Sinusoidal Projection
Central Meridian 54° WGr.
Base map:
Maps of Brazil to the scale 1:1,000,000

Map created by the
Geoprocessing Laboratory of the Instituto Socioambiental

Assessment and Identification of Priority Actions for the Conservation, Sustainable Use and Benefit Sharing of the Biodiversity of the Brazilian Amazon

Macapá Workshop 1999

PRONABIO
Programa Nacional da Diversidade Biológica (National Program for Biological Diversity)
Ministério do Meio Ambiente (Ministry of the Environment)

Coordinating consortium:
Instituto Socioambiental (Overall coordination)
Imazon - Instituto do Homem e Meio Ambiente da Amazônia
Ipam - Instituto de Pesquisa Ambiental da Amazônia
GTA - Grupo de Trabalho Amazônico
Conservation International
ISPN - Instituto Sociedade, População e Natureza

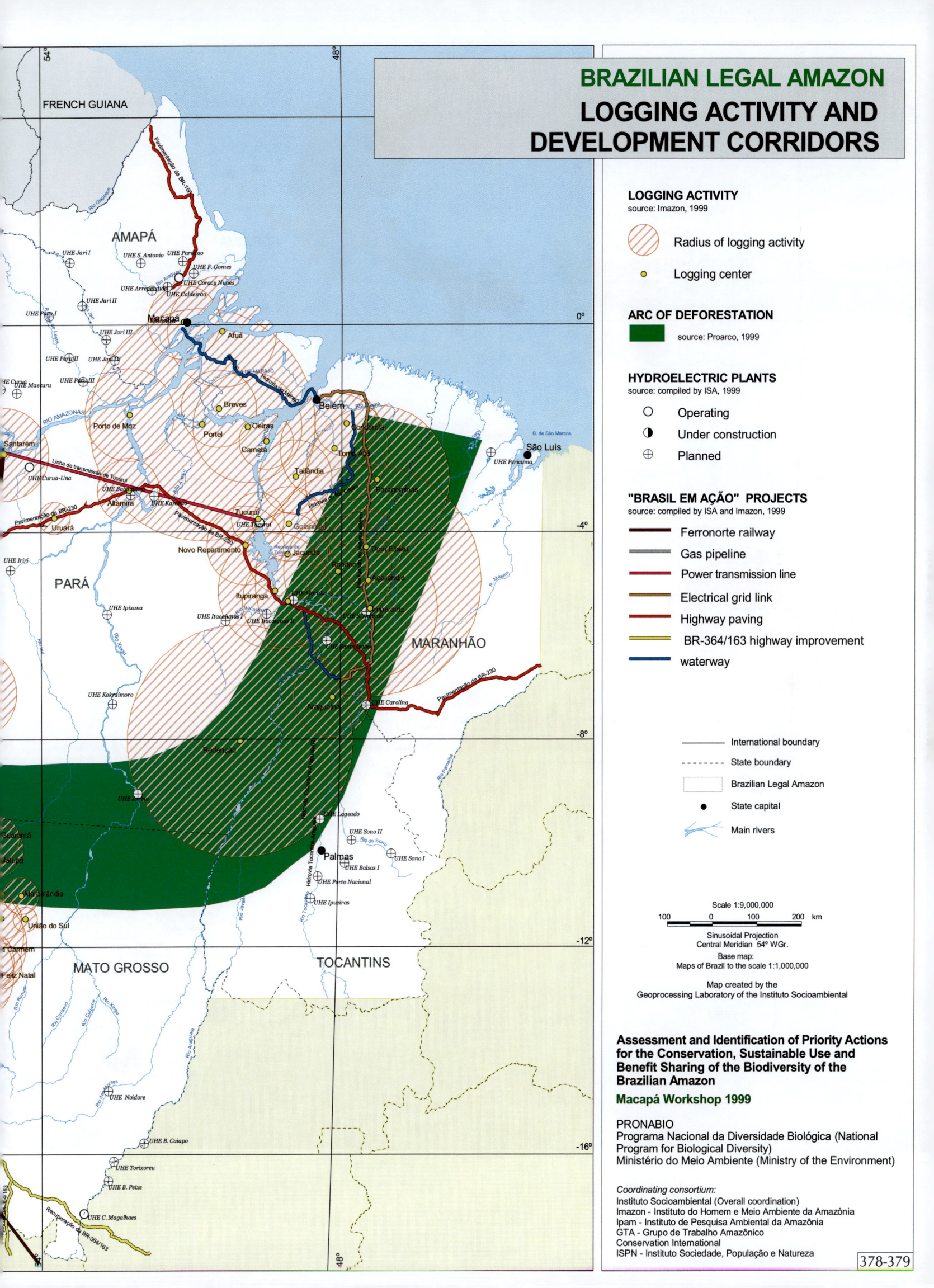

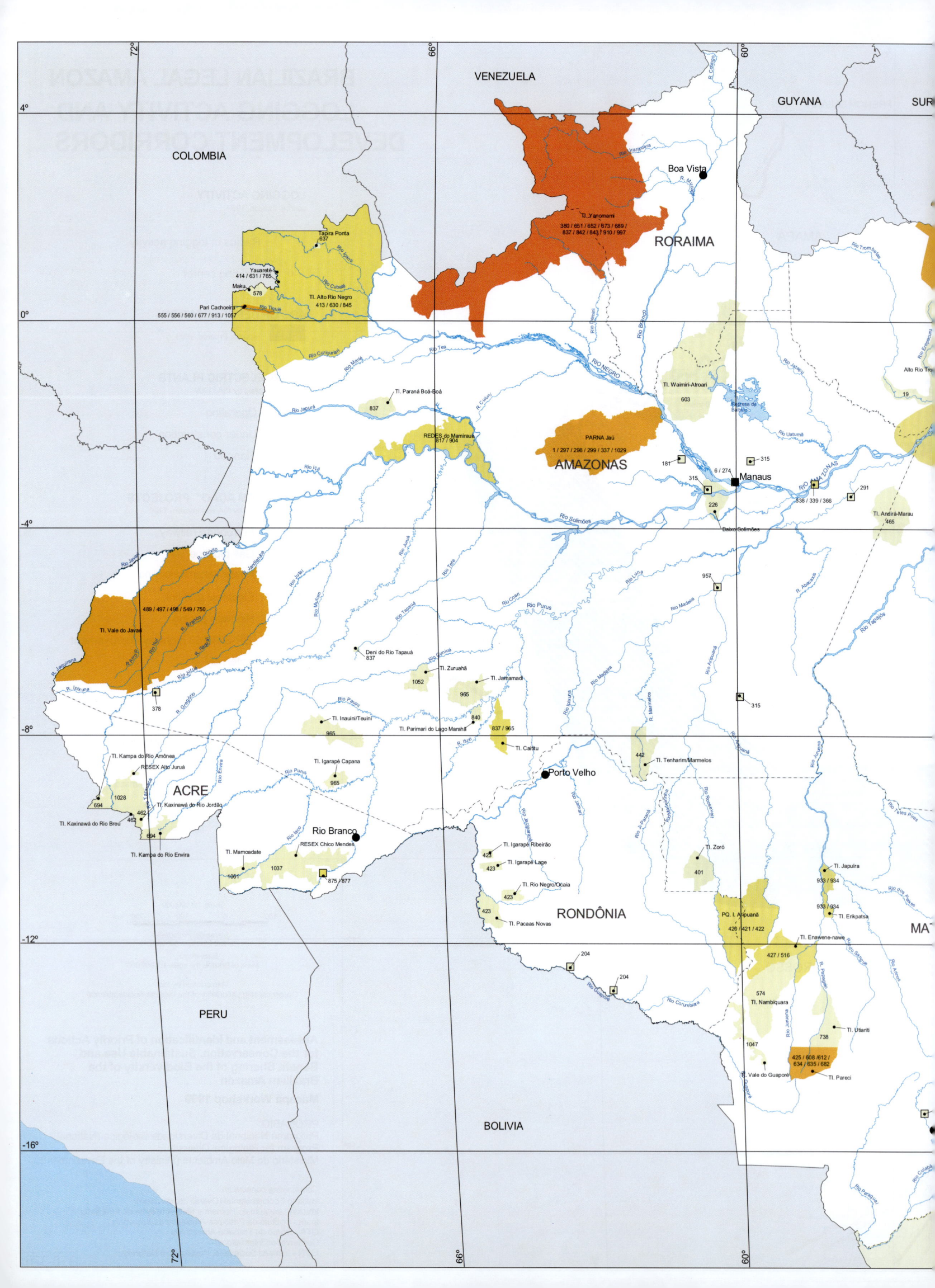

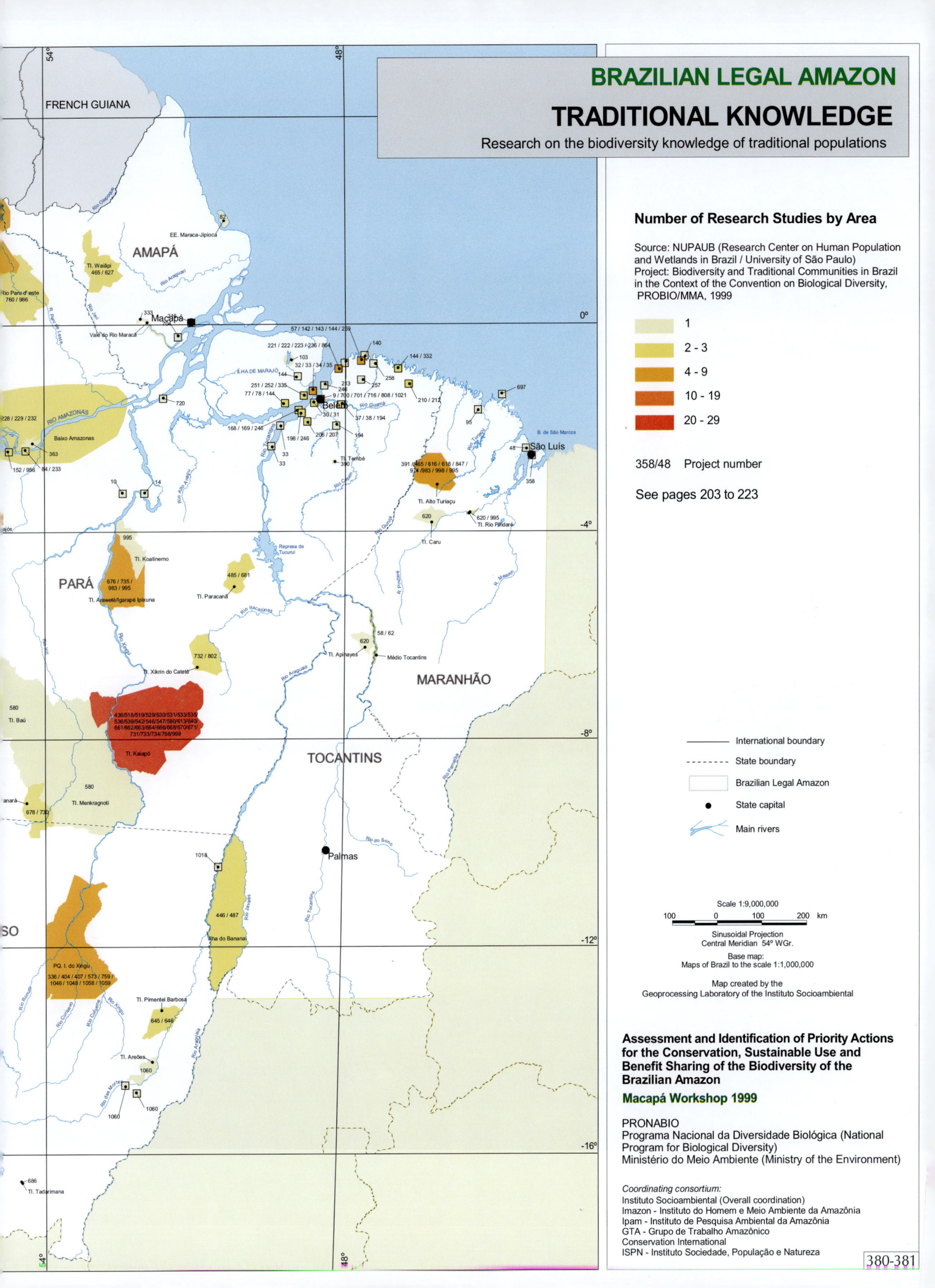

BRAZILIAN LEGAL AMAZON
TRADITIONAL KNOWLEDGE
Research on the biodiversity knowledge of traditional populations

Number of Research Studies by Area

Source: NUPAUB (Research Center on Human Population and Wetlands in Brazil / University of São Paulo)
Project: Biodiversity and Traditional Communities in Brazil in the Context of the Convention on Biological Diversity, PROBIO/MMA, 1999

- 1
- 2 - 3
- 4 - 9
- 10 - 19
- 20 - 29

358/48   Project number

See pages 203 to 223

Legend:
- International boundary
- State boundary
- Brazilian Legal Amazon
- State capital
- Main rivers

Scale 1:9,000,000
Sinusoidal Projection
Central Meridian 54° WGr.
Base map: Maps of Brazil to the scale 1:1,000,000
Map created by the Geoprocessing Laboratory of the Instituto Socioambiental

Assessment and Identification of Priority Actions for the Conservation, Sustainable Use and Benefit Sharing of the Biodiversity of the Brazilian Amazon
Macapá Workshop 1999

PRONABIO
Programa Nacional da Diversidade Biológica (National Program for Biological Diversity)
Ministério do Meio Ambiente (Ministry of the Environment)

Coordinating consortium:
Instituto Socioambiental (Overall coordination)
Imazon - Instituto do Homem e Meio Ambiente da Amazônia
Ipam - Instituto de Pesquisa Ambiental da Amazônia
GTA - Grupo de Trabalho Amazônico
Conservation International
ISPN - Instituto Sociedade, População e Natureza

Macapá Workshop

Priority areas for the biodiversity of the Brazilian Amazon

Methodology

The methodology adopted for the project 'Assessment and Identification of Priority Actions for the Conservation, Sustainable Use and Benefit Sharing of the Biodiversity of the Brazilian Amazon' was designed to start a cumulative process under which the scientific and academic community, governmental and non-governmental organizations, the business community, and social movements whose activities are directly connected to the purposes of the project would increasingly become involved in the project.

The work was planned to be carried out in four stages, with each stage leading to converging and complementary methodological steps as follows:
1. Preparatory stage;
2. Preparatory meeting for the Macapá Workshop;
3. The Macapá Workshop;
4. Consolidation and synthesis of results;
5. Dissemination of results and follow-up of their implementation.

Preparatory stage

The preparatory stage consisted of a detailed survey followed by the systemizing, statistical analysis, and integration of the available information on Brazilian Amazonia. The survey included both current data and data from the recent past obtained from institutions such as the Ministry of the Environment (MMA), the Brazilian Geographical and Statistical Institute (IBGE), the National Space Research Institute (INPE), the National Institute for Colonization and Agrarian Reform (INCRA), the Brazilian Institute for the Environment and Renewable Natural Resources (IBAMA), the Federal Indian Affairs Agency (Funai), the National Mineral Production Agency (DNPM), the National Water and Electricity Agency (DNAEE), and the Brazilian Agricultural Research Company (Embrapa), as well as from state ministries and municipal departments, research institutions, non-governmental organizations, and social movements.

On the basis of the information collected, a geographic information system (GIS) was specially devised for the project to enable both the geo-referencing of the data on a digitized base map and the preparation of regional thematic maps.

At the same time that this data base was being set up, the coordinating consortium hired specialists to prepare diagnostic reports and draft recommendations in the project's twelve areas of concern. The thematic areas and the respective specialists were:
- Birds: David Oren (MPEG)
- Aquatic Biota: Ronaldo Barthem (MPEG)
- Plants: Bruce Nelson (INPA) e Alexandre Oliveira (UNIP)
- Invertebrates: William Overal (MPEG)
- Mammals: Maria Nazareth Silva (INPA)
- Reptiles and amphibians: Cláudia Azevedo-Ramos (UFPA), amphibians, and Richard Vogt (INPA), reptiles
- Development corridors and hubs: Adalberto Veríssimo (IMAZON)
- Ecosystem goods and services: Daniel Nepstad (WHRC/IPAM)
- Economic opportunities: André Guimarães (PPG7/World Bank)
- Indigenous peoples and traditional populations: Beto Ricardo (ISA) e Mauro Almeida (UNICAMP)
- Anthropogenic pressures: Donald Sawyer (ISPN)
- Conservation areas: Rosa Lemos de Sá (WWF/Brazil)

The outputs from this stage, which took approximately 18 months, were: a digitized base map of Legal Amazonia with state and municipal boundaries, the highway network, relief contours, and the detailed hydrographic system; a set of 19 thematic maps (see pages 350-381); and 27 thematic documents (pages 51-348).

Preparatory meeting for the Macapá Workshop

As a way of assessing and improving the materials and documents developed during the preparatory stage, the organizations making up the coordinating consortium decided to include an expanded technical consultation stage prior to the Macapá Workshop.

Once the thematic and diagnostic maps were ready, the team began running preliminary cross checks and analyses of the data collected, and these were then submitted to a group of specialists at a preparatory meeting held in Belém, Pará on June 8-9, 1999.

The meeting was attended by specialists from the different organizations belonging to the coordinating consortium, all the thematic consultants, members of the Monitoring Committee, and other invited researchers. The contributions arising from this meeting were processed and incorporated into improved thematic maps, diagnoses, and analyses.

The Macapá Workshop

The Macapá Workshop was held from September 20-25, 1999 in Macapá, Amapá and was attended by 226 representatives of federal, state, and municipal government bodies, non-governmental organizations, social movements, public and private research institutions, the private sector, Brazilian and foreign researchers, and the press.

The Workshop was organized into four sessions over the five days, as follows: one day for meetings of the thematic working groups, including the preparation of reports of priority actions and maps of priority areas by theme; two days for meetings of the regional working groups, including preparation of reports and maps of priority areas by region; one day for meetings of the priority actions working groups to consolidate regional recommendations for priority actions; and a plenary session for final discussions and conclusions.

First session: defining priority areas by theme

For this phase, participants were divided into twelve thematic groups, covering six biology-related areas and six socio-economic themes. The participants drew on the documents and thematic maps from the preparatory stage.

Drawing on the thematic documents, which had been posted on the Internet prior to the workshop, and on the expertise of the specialist participants, the researchers in the six biology groups (birds, aquatic biota, plants, invertebrates, mammals, reptiles and amphibians) began tracing geographic distribution patterns on the maps provided and defining the most important areas for each group in accordance with the following criteria:

- species richness;
- phylogenetic diversity;
- species and higher taxa endemism;
- richness of rare or endangered species;
- hotspots (areas of high biological diversity and under high anthropogenic pressure);
- unusual biological phenomena (migrations, special communities);
- economically important species, including wild relatives of cultivated species;
- biological value (an assessment of the above elements combined);
- intrinsic system fragility;
- conservation level.

At the same time that these groups were preparing maps of the geographic distribution of biodiversity, the other six specialist groups were analyzing the main socio-economic aspects of Amazonia. They considered the following themes: anthropogenic pressures arising from social development, economic and demographic issues; conservation areas; development corridors and hubs, including the main federal and state government programs and infrastructure projects; ecosystem goods and services; indigenous peoples and traditional populations; and new economic opportunities including ecotourism, management of forest resources, fisheries, handicrafts, small-scale production, reforestation, and extractive activities.

By the end of this analysis, which took place during the first day of the workshop, twelve thematic maps had been prepared identifying 560 areas classified into the following four categories according to their importance for the theme being assessed:

- Category A – areas of extreme importance;
- Category B – areas of very high importance;
- Category C – areas of high importance;
- Category D – areas insufficiently known, but probably important.

Information on each of these 560 areas was recorded on a data sheet and entered into a database during the Workshop. In addition to the diagnostic elements, the database also contained the following information: vegetation type(s) covered; most important habitats; municipality(ies) and state(s) covered; recommended actions (protection, restoration, sustainable use of natural resources, need for further studies, and the creation of conservation areas); justification for inclusion of a particular area; main gaps in knowledge; and relevant bibliography and sources of unpublished data.

The maps prepared by the thematic working groups were digitized and printed overnight in order to be made available to the regional working groups the following morning.

Second session: integrating biological and socio-economic data

One of the major achievements of the Macapá meeting was the use of a methodology that allowed the integration of the biological data with data on the economy, development programs, population, economic activities, evolution of deforestation, and fire risk, amongst other themes.

In order to do this, participants were divided according to seven regions of Legal Amazonia, defined according to the following criteria: eco-regions, main hydrographic basins, development corridors, and current level of anthropogenic pressure (deforestation, demography, current transportation infrastructure, concentrations of burnings, susceptibility to forest fires, and economic activities, such as logging, soybean or maize farming, and ranching). Based on these criteria, the regions shown in the table and the map below were identified:

SUBDIVISIONS OF THE LEGAL AMAZON			
	Region	hectares	% of Legal Amazonia
AX	Upper Xingu/Tapajós/Rondônia/Mato Grosso	58,350,171	11.65
BX	Lower Xingu/Tapajós/Madeira	130,825,746	26.12
EG	Guiana Shields	46,054,851	9.20
JU	Juruá/Purus/Acre	72,158,391	14.41
RN	Rio Negro/Rio Branco	58,315,602	11.64
TO	Araguaia/Tocantins/Maranhão	81,159,631	16.21
VZ	Solimões/Amazonas floodplains	53,924,863	10.77

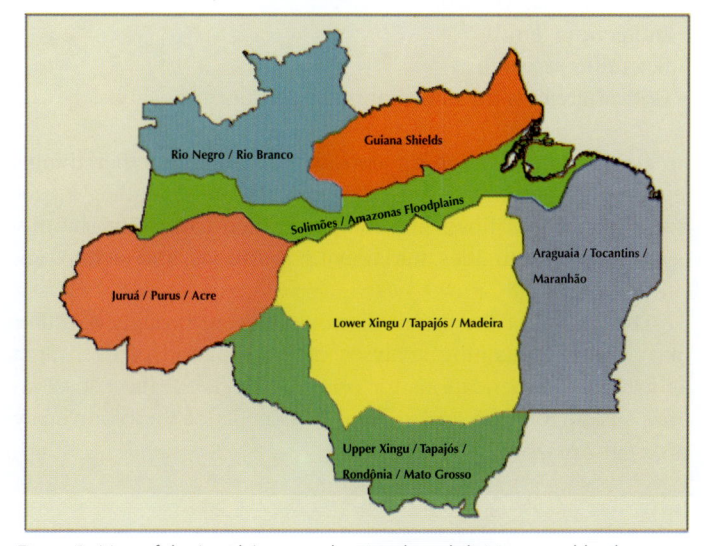

Figure 1. Map of the Legal Amazon showing the subdivisions used by the Macapá Workshop.

Using the maps of the areas identified by the thematic working groups and their respective data sheets, the regional working groups were able to identify those places in Legal Amazonia where at least two biologically important areas were present. All these overlapping areas were then considered as priority areas for these regions and were assessed from the point of view of their importance in terms of biodiversity and environmental services, as well as the risks and opportunities arising from the socio-economic context.

As a result of this two-day task, seven regional maps were drawn up and a set of 385 priority areas was identified. A data sheet was prepared for each area containing detailed information on the following: location; main characteristics; level of biological importance by thematic group and in general; level of importance in terms of environmental services; level of stability (in relation to its inclusion within conservation areas or indigenous lands); level of instability (in relation to anthropogenic pressure and development corridors or hubs); recommended actions (protection, restoration, sustainable use of natural resources, need for future studies, and establishment of conservation areas); justification for inclusion of a particular area; main gaps in knowledge identified; and relevant bibliography or sources of unpublished data. The information on each of the 385 areas, contained on the data sheets, was entered into a database during the Workshop.

The maps produced by the regional working groups were digitized and printed overnight to be made available for the following morning's work and to be used to for the presentation of results at the plenary meeting held on the afternoon of the third day.

Finally, the maps prepared by the seven regional working groups were combined into a single map: Priority Areas for the Conservation, Sustainable Use and Sharing of Benefits of the Biodiversity of the Brazilian Amazonia (Synthesis Map on pages 394-395 of this book).

Third session: defining prioritary actions

With the results of the previous three days, participants were re-divided into six groups to identify priority actions in respect of:

- Strict conservation areas;
- Sustainable use conservation areas and traditional populations;
- Economic use of degraded areas;
- Indigenous lands;
- Scientific research;
- Critical areas within development corridors and hubs.

To do this, each group considered, amongst other things, legal and institutional issues, the fiscal regime (including incentives), credit and financing, matters related to benefit sharing, economic opportunities, traditional populations, and technological development.

The results of the group discussions were brought together into reports containing analyses of the situation of each area and the recommendations for priority actions for the conservation, sustainable use and sharing of benefits of the biodiversity of Legal Amazonia.

Fourth session: plenary session

On the morning of the fifth and final day of the Workshop, the reports of the priority actions groups and the Map of Priority Areas for Conservation and Sustainable Use of the Biodiversity of the Legal Amazonia were submitted for the approval of all the participants.

Copies of the map were presented to the representatives of the Ministry of the Environment, the World Bank, the government of the State of Amapá, and to the press, all of whom attended the closing ceremony.

CONSOLIDATION AND SYNTHESIS OF RESULTS

This phase of the process involved revising all the maps produced during the Workshop and checking the accuracy of the database with regard to the references, diagnoses, and recommended actions for each of the priority areas identified.

Using the analysis of the results, a technical report was prepared for each thematic area, to include a summary of the information contained in the thematic documents and an analysis of the diagnoses and actions recommended by the Workshop.

All the revised material was prepared in such a way as to permit dissemination electronically and in hard copy.

DISSEMINATION OF RESULTS AND FOLLOW-UP OF THEIR IMPLEMENTATION

The following media were used to disseminate the results of the project:
- A website (www.socioambiental.org/website/bio/index.htm) containing information on the project; the thematic documents in full; simplified maps with priority areas for conservation, sustainable use and sharing of benefits of the biodiversity of Brazilian Amazonia; and the list of priority areas for each region covered during the Macapá Workshop;
- A synthesis map of priority areas for conservation, sustainable use and sharing of benefits from the biodiversity of Brazilian Amazonia;
- A CD-ROM containing the complete digital base and the thematic maps from the preparatory stage; the results from thematic and regional groups; the database with references, diagnoses and recommended actions for each priority area identified;
- A printed executive summary of the information contained in the thematic documents; the list of priority areas with detailed information; and an analysis of the diagnoses and recommended actions from the Macapá Workshop;
- The full publication of the results of the project including all the thematic documents, preparatory maps, thematic maps, regional maps, and the complete detailed list of priority areas (the present publication).

Overall assessment of the results

A general overview of the results

The Macapá Workshop ended with the identification of 385 priority areas for the conservation and sustainable use of the biodiversity of Legal Amazonia. Of these areas, 247 (64%) were classified as being of extremely high biological importance, 107 (28%) of very high importance, 8 (2%) of high importance, and 2 (1%) as insufficiently known but of probable high biological importance. As was described in the chapter on methodology, in addition to these areas that resulted from the work of the biological thematic working groups, the regional working groups also proposed 21 (5%) new areas that should be studied in greater depth in order to allow future classification of their biological importance.

This section provides a complete list of these priority areas, organized by sub-region and containing the following information: name, location, vegetation types, biological importance in general and by biological group, importance in terms of environmental goods and services, level of stability, level of instability, level of priority for action, main action recommended, other recommended actions, and notes.

There then follows a consolidated set of analyses of the priority areas for the biodiversity of Legal Amazonia, including their regional distribution, the main threats and recommended actions.

The distribution of priority areas among the seven regions of Legal Amazonia as adopted by the Macapá Workshop is shown in Table 1.

As can be seen, the Araguaia / Tocantins / Maranhão region contains the highest proportion of areas classified as category A (88%). This is followed by the upper Xingu region with 80%. The Guiana shield is the region with the fewest category A areas (44%).

Level of stability of priority areas

A spatial overlay of the areas identified as priority areas for biodiversity onto those areas of the region already under some form of legal protection allows some important conclusions to be drawn. Currently 122 (31.7%) of the areas identified are located within conservation areas of different types and 148 (38.4%) are located within indigenous lands. The remaining 115 (29.8%) areas are presently unprotected. It is however important to remember that the inclusion of an area in a conservation area is no guarantee of its effective protection, since very few conservation areas have been properly implemented or are able to be adequately supervised.

As can be seen in Table 2, only 15% of the areas classified as being of extremely high biological importance, 16.8% of areas of very high importance, and 12.5% of areas of high importance are found within strict protection conservation areas. This situation changes substantially when we include indigenous lands. The figures reveal both the present and future importance of including these human communities in biodiversity conservation and use processes. During the Macapá Workshop, several

Table 1 - Distribution of priority areas for the biodiversity of Legal Amazonia by sub-region as adopted by the Macapá Workshop

Region	Area totals		Level of biological importance									
			A		B		C		D		N	
	no.	%[1]	no.	%[2]	no.	%[2]	no.	%[2]	no.	%[2]	no.	%[2]
AX	61	16	49	80	8	13	-	-	-	-	4	7
BX	73	19	47	64	19	26	1	1	1	1	5	7
EG	36	9	16	44	16	44	3	8	1	3	-	-
JU	68	18	33	49	24	35	4	6	-	-	7	10
RN	49	13	27	55	17	35	-	-	-	-	5	10
TO	51	13	45	88	6	12	-	-	-	-	-	-
VZ	47	12	30	64	17	36	-	-	-	-	-	-
Totals	385	100	247	64	107	28	8	2	2	1	21	5

A – areas of extreme biological importance; B – areas of very high biological importance; C – areas of high biological importance; D – insufficiently known areas that are likely to be of biological importance; N – new areas proposed by the regional groups.
1. Of the overall total of priority areas.
2. Of the priority areas in the category.
AX - Upper Xingu/Tapajós/Roraima/Mato Grosso; BX - Lower Xingu/Tapajós/Madeira; EG - Guiana Shield; JU - Juruá/Purus/Acre; RN - Rio Negro/Rio Branco; TO - Araguaia/Tocantins/Maranhão; and VZ - Solimões/Amazonas floodplains.

Table 2 - Status of priority areas for biodiversity in Legal Amazonia located within conservation areas and indigenous lands																
	Full protection conservation area						Sustainable use conservation area						Total		Indigenous land		Total	
	Federal		State		Total		Federal		State		Total							
	no.	%	no.	%	no.	%	no.	%	no.	%	no.	%	no.	%	no.	%	no.	%
A	22	8.9	15	6.1	37	15.0	20	8.1	29	11.7	49	19.8	86	34.8	101	40.9	187	75.7
B	9	8.4	9	8.4	18	16.8	10	9.3	4	3.7	14	13.1	32	29.9	38	35.5	70	65.4
C	1	12.5	-	-	1	12.5	-	-	1	12.5	1	12.5	2	25.0	2	25.0	4	50.0
D	-	-	-	-	-	-	-	-	-	-	-	-	-	-	1	-	1	-
N	-	-	-	-	-	-	-	-	2	9.5	2	9.5	2	9.5	6	28.6	8	38.1
	32	8.3	24	6.2	56	14.5	30	7,8	36	9.4	66	17.1	122	31.7	148	38.4	270	70.1

A – areas of extreme biological importance; B – areas of very high biological importance; C – areas of high biological importance; D – insufficiently known areas that are likely to be of biological importance; N – new areas proposed by the regional groups.

actions were recommended in this respect, one of which was the creation of a new category of conservation area to be called an Indigenous Natural Resources Reserve.

Bearing in mind that the mere location of priority areas within legally protected spaces does not in itself signify stability, the Workshop participants assessed the status of conservation areas and indigenous lands using the following aspects and scores:

For areas included within strict protection conservation areas: 3 = conservation area not fully implemented and in areas subject to significant anthropogenic pressure; 6 = conservation area not fully implemented but not subject to significant anthropogenic pressure; 9 = fully implemented conservation area subject to significant anthropogenic pressure; and 12 = fully implemented conservation area not subject to significant anthropogenic pressure.

For areas included within indigenous lands: 1 = indigenous land not fully registered and under significant anthropogenic pressure; 3 = fully registered indigenous land but subject to significant anthropogenic pressure; 5 = fully registered indigenous land not subject to significant anthropogenic pressure.

As can be seen from this scoring system, the intention was to assess as accurately as possible the real protection status of the area in order to arrive at a mathematical value capable of rating the areas according to their effective stability.

By this method it was possible to classify each priority area for biodiversity in Legal Amazonia according to its degree of stability. This information can be found in the complete listing of the priority areas contained in this book and a compilation of the results is given in Table 3.

As can be seen, only six (2.4%) of the areas of extremely high biological importance and seven (6.5%) of those of very high biological importance received the maximum score in terms of degree of stability for their location within either a conservation area or an indigenous land. The great majority of the areas were classified as having low stability, mainly due to the fact that protected areas in Amazonia are not fully implemented and supervised.

Level of instability

Another aspect worth noting is the assessment of the level of instability in priority areas for biodiversity in Amazonia in respect of anthropogenic pressures, development programs, and the undertaking of infrastructure works planned by both federal and state governments. According to the analyses of the specialists who took part in the Macapá Workshop, 56% of these areas are already feeling such impacts, or will feel them in the near future if current trends in the growth of unplanned occupation

Table 3 - Level of stability of the priority areas for biodiversity in Legal Amazonia located within conservation areas and indigenous lands							
Biological importance	Total	High[1]		Medium[2]		Low[3]	
		no.	%	no.	%	no.	%
A	247	6	2.4	45	18.2	196	79.4
B	107	7	6.5	15	14.0	85	79.4
C	8	-	-	1	12.5	7	87.5
D	2	-	-	-	-	2	100.0
N	21	-	-	2	9.5	19	90.5
	385	13	3.4	63	16.4	309	80.3

A – Extremely important; B – Very highly important; C – Highly important; D – Insufficiently known, but probably highly important; N – New areas proposed by the regional groups for study in greater depth.
1. Score of 10 or higher
2. Score of between 6 and 9
3. Score of 5 or lower

Table 4 – Level of instability of the priority areas for biodiversity in Legal Amazonia in respect of anthropogenic pressures, development programs and the carrying out of planned infrastructure works									
Biological importance	Total	maximum[1]		high[2]		medium[3]		low[4]	
		n.	%	n.	%	n.	%	n.	%
A	247	42	17	56	23	52	21	97	39
B	107	15	14	20	19	18	17	54	50
C	8	-	-	3	38	2	25	3	38
D	2	-	-	-	-	-	-	2	100
N	21	2	10	1	5	6	29	12	57
	385	59	15	80	21	78	20	168	44

A – Extremely important; B – Very highly important; C – Highly important; D – Insufficiently known, but probably highly important; N – New areas proposed by the regional groups for study in greater depth.
1. Score of 10 or higher
2. Score of between 8 and 9
3. Score of between 5 and 7
4. Score of 4 or lower

of the region persist. From the information summarized in Table 4, it can be seen that the areas most threatened are precisely those classified as being of extremely high or very high biological importance.

In terms of geographical distribution, the sub-regions in which the areas of extremely high biological importance (A) are most threatened are the Araguaia / Tocantins / Maranhão region with 84.4% under high or maximum pressure, the Upper Xingu region with 63.2% and the southern part of the Lower Xingu with

40.4%. For areas classified as being of very high biological importance (B), figures are even more striking: 100% are under maximum pressure in the Tocantins sub-region and 88% in the Lower Xingu. These two sub-regions correspond to the zone known as the Arc of Deforestation where urgent measures need to be taken in order to prevent areas of highly important biological richness from completely disappearing.

The areas in category A currently least threatened are in the Rio Negro / Rio Branco region, with 63% experiencing low impacts, followed by the Solimões / Amazonas floodplain with 60% and the Guiana shield with 56%.

Summary of recommendations

On the basis of the detailed assessment of the priority areas for biodiversity identified in the Macapá Workshop, recommendations were made on the most appropriate actions for the specific situation of each area.

The options for recommendations were: protection on the basis of instruments other than the creation of a conservation area; restoration; sustainable use of natural resources; need for further studies; need to create a conservation area; and other options.

As regards the main recommendations, that is, actions which obtained the highest score on a scale from zero ('not recommended') to five ('priority action'), the results were as follows: for 39.2% of the priority areas for biodiversity, the sustainable use of resources was recommended; for 24.9%, protective measures were suggested; the creation of conservation areas was recommended for 20.8% of the areas; 14% of the areas were considered as requiring further studies, and restoration was recommended for only 1% of the areas.

Table 5 shows the consolidated results by sub-region.

The large number of areas for which sustainable use of natural resources was proposed, with high scores for five sub-regions, notably the Solimões / Amazonas floodplains (70.2% of the priority areas in this sub-region), shows that the majority of the participants in the Macapá Workshop recognize the importance of finding alternatives that combine conservation and the improvement of living standards of traditional Amazonian populations. This view is bolstered by the fact that such priority was given even to areas classified as being of extremely high biological importance.

Other suggestions deserve mention. In the Araguaia / Tocantins / Maranhão sub-region, one of the regions under most anthropogenic pressure, the main recommendation, in terms of number of areas, was environmental protection (52%). For the Juruá / Purus / Acre sub-region, one the least studied regions in Amazonia, the most important recommendation was the need for further studies (41.2%). The main recommendation for the Lower Xingu region, one of the least protected regions, was the creation of conservation areas.

Area proposed for the creation of conservation areas

Participants suggested that 80 conservation areas be created as follows: 24 strict protection areas; 22 sustainable use areas; 6 mixed category (mosaic) areas; and 15 areas requiring further studies to define the appropriate group and category.

In the case of the strict protection areas, 12 were proposed for the Lower Xingu sub-region, 4 for the Araguaia / Tocantins / Maranhão region; 3 for the Guiana shield; 3 for the Rio Negro / Rio Branco region; 1 in the Upper Xingu region; and 1 in the Solimões / Amazonian floodplains region.

Of the sustainable use areas, 8 were proposed for the Juruá / Purús / Acre sub-region; 5 for the Lower Xingu; 3 for the Araguaia / Tocantins / Maranhão region, 3 for the Solimões / Amazonas floodplains region, 2 for the Guiana shield; and 1 for the Rio Negro / Rio Branco region.

Of the fifteen areas requiring further studies to define the most appropriate category, 6 are in the Lower Xingu; 3 each in the Upper Xingu and Guiana shield sub-regions; and 1 in each of the Juruá / Purús / Acre, Rio Negro / Rio Branco and Araguaia / Tocantins / Maranhão regions.

Finally, two mosaics were proposed for the Upper Xingu sub-region and four for the Lower Xingu.

The creation of these conservation areas would result in an increase of 69,760,925 ha or 117.1% in relation to the area currently under environmental protection in Legal Amazonia and would represent the minimum necessary cover for the vegetation types and ecoregions of Legal Amazonia. Table 6 shows a comparison between the current and future status, should the proposed conservation areas be created.

The areas for incorporation into existing conservation areas are as follows:

TABLE 5 - MAIN ACTION RECOMMENDED FOR THE PRIORITY AREAS FOR BIODIVERSITY IN LEGAL AMAZONIA																
	AX		BX		EG		JU		RN		TO		VZ		Total	
	no.	%	no.	%	no.	%	no.	%	no.	%	no.	%	no.	%	no.	%
Protection	12	19.7	10	13.7	10	27.8	19	27.9	11	22.4	27	52.9	7	14.9	96	24.9
Restoration	-	-	-	-	-	-	-	-	-	-	4	7.8	-	-	4	1.0
Sustainable use of natural resources	24	39.3	34	46.6	16	44.4	10	14.7	25	51.0	9	17.6	33	70.2	151	39.2
Need for studies	14	23.0	-	-	2	5.6	28	41.2	5	10.2	2	3.9	3	6.4	54	14.0
Creation of conservation areas	11	18.0	29	39.7	8	22.2	11	16.2	8	16.3	9	17.6	4	8.5	80	20.8
	61		73		36		68		49		51		47		385	

AX - Upper Xingu/Tapajós/Roraima/Mato Grosso; BX - Lower Xingu/Tapajós/Madeira; EG - Guiana Shield; JU - Juruá/Purus/Acre; RN - Rio Negro/Rio Branco; TO - Araguaia/Tocantins/Maranhão; and VZ - Solimões/Amazonas floodplains.

TABLE 6 - PRIORITY AREAS FOR THE CREATION OF CONSERVATION AREAS IN LEGAL AMAZONIA – COMPARISON BETWEEN THE CURRENT AND FUTURE SITUATIONS BY AREA (HECTARES)*, SEE MAP ON PAGES 396-397										
Conservation area group / category	Current situation			New conservation areas proposed			New situation			
	no.	area (ha.)	%[1]	no.	area (ha.)	%[1]	no.	area (ha.)	%[1]	%[2]
Strict protection conservation area	64	19,544,943	3.9	24	15,812,262	3.2	88	35,357,205	44.72	80.9
Sustainable use conservation area	93	40,023,749	8.0	22	15,936,006	3.2	115	55,959,755	28.48	39.8
Mixed category				6	7,721,724	1.5	6	7,721,724		
Undefined category				15	25,518,048	5.1	15	25,518,048		
Incorporation into existing strict protection conservation area				12	3,956,321	0.8	12	3,956,321		
Incorporation into existing sustainable use conservation area				1	51,736	0.0	1	51,736		
Change of category				2	764,828	0.2	2	764,828		
Totals	157	59,568,692	11.9	82	69,760,925	13.9	239	129,329,617	25.8	117.1

* Calculated using the ISA GIS for the Legal Amazon region. Figures for existing conservation areas have been updated to September 2001.
1. % of total area of Legal Amazonia.
2. % increase over the current situation
Mixed category: mosaic of strict protection conservation area and sustainable use conservation area
Undefined category: group or category to be defined by means of specific studies

- AX 028 - The incorporation of the Fazenda Pau d'Óleo into the Guaporé Biological Reserve;
- AX 042 - The incorporation of the Ji-Paraná river into the Jaru Biological Reserve by extending the reserve boundaries up to the river;
- AX 061 - The expansion of the Jaru Biological Reserve eastward as far as the Madeirinha river;
- BX 032 - The expansion of the western part of the Apiacás Ecological Reserve;
- BX 040 - The incorporation of part of the Aripuanã river into the Guariba-Roosevelt Extractive Reserve;
- JU 007 - The expansion of the Serra do Divisor National Park northwards;
- JU 008 - The expansion of the Serra do Divisor National Park in a northeasterly direction;
- RN 002- The incorporation of the area between the Pico da Neblina National Park and the Alto do Rio Negro Indigenous Land into the National Park;
- RN 014 - The incorporation of the area between the Serra da Mocidade National Park and the Yanomani Indigenous Land into the National Park;
- RN 015 - The incorporation of the area between the Niquá Ecological Station, the Serra da Mocidade National Park and the Yanomami Indigenous Land into the Ecological Station;
- RN 018 - The incorporation into the Maracá Ecological Station of the area to the north;
- RN 041 - The incorporation of the area between the Jaú National Park and the right bank of the Rio Negro Environmental Protection Area into the National Park;
- TO031 - The incorporation of the area surrounding the Serra das Andorinhas into the São Geraldo do Araguaia Environmental Protection Area to include Serra dos Martírios/Andorinhas State Park.

Other recommendations

· In addition to the main recommendations for each area described above, the participants made other suggestions and proposals for the various areas studied. Table 7 contains a

TABLE 7 - ADDITIONAL RECOMMENDATIONS FOR THE PRIORITY AREAS FOR BIODIVERSITY IN THE LEGAL AMAZON		
Recommendations	no.	%*
Environmental education	30	8.5
Development of sustainable use of natural resources plans	37	10.5
Anthropological studies	29	8.3
Ethnobotanical studies	16	4.6
Studies of the physical environment	5	1.4
Monitoring	90	25.6
Biological inventories	126	35.9
Preparation/implementation of management plans	18	5.1
Total	351	100.0

* In relation to the total of priority areas with additional recommendations.

consolidated list of these additional suggestions and proposals, detailed information on which can be found in the lists of priority areas in this book.

As can be seen, the most common recommendation was for biological inventories. These were proposed for 126 areas, or 32.7% of the total number of areas. This was followed by monitoring, which was recommended for 90 of the proposed areas (23.3%). These results reinforce the general view that we still know very little about the biodiversity of Amazonia and that many areas that are practically unknown run the risk of degradation before the necessary research and inventories can be carried out.

Levels of priority

The *level of priority for intervention* could be calculated on the basis of an integrated analysis of the levels of stability, instability, biological importance, and importance for environmental goods and services in the ecosystems in question.

The aim of this indicator was to separate the 385 priority areas identified by the Macapá Workshop into three groups according to the urgency of the need for the intervention. In this way, those areas of greatest environmental and social importance which are under most threat and which, therefore, require immediate action to avoid losing the very attributes giving rise to their priority status can be distinguished from areas whose situation is relatively more stable and which can be dealt with on a medium or long term basis.

Given the large number of areas identified as important and the limited capacity to deal with all these demands, the creation of a plan of action is fundamentally important to enable the efforts made by all the parties involved in this project to be as effective as possible.

However, it is important to point out that this indicator of level of priority is only a tool to assist decision-making and should not be used in isolation, as the situation in Amazonia is extremely dynamic and subject to change within short time frames. In addition, attention needs to be paid to political opportunities that may favor interventions in areas which are less vulnerable but nevertheless important from a socio-environmental point of view.

The following tables 8, 9 and 10 show the results of applying the level of priority indicator to the main recommendations of the Macapá Workshop. The scoring refers to: short-term action (8 to 10), medium-term action (6 to 7), and long-term action (5 or less).

TABLE 8 - LEVEL OF PRIORITY FOR THE CREATION OF CONSERVATION AREAS
SEE MAP ON PAGES 398-399

CREATION OF STRICT PROTECTION CONSERVATION AREAS

Area	Biological importance (average)	Priority level
TO 051	A	10
BX 021	A	10
EG 007	A	10
TO 041	A	10
TO 040	B	10
BX 002	N	10
BX 025	N	10
BX 064	A	9
AX 008	A	9
TO 042	A	9
BX 065	A	8
RN 034	A	8
BX 059	N	8
RN 015	A	5
BX 054	A	5
BX 073	A	5
VZ 027	A	5
BX 056	B	5
EG 030	A	4
EG 031	B	4
BX 055	A	3
BX 013	B	3
RN 014	N	3
BX 004	N	3

CREATION OF SUSTAINABLE USE CONSERVATION AREAS

Area	Biological importance (average)	Priority level
TO 027	A	10
BX 014	B	9
EG 005	B	9
JU 067	B	9
JU 068	B	9
JU 066	N	9
VZ 033	A	8
BX 001	A	8
TO 008	A	8
JU 063	A	8
VZ 014	B	8
JU 064	N	8
JU 065	N	8
BX 052	B	7
JU 059	N	7
EG 011	A	6
TO 005	A	6
BX 008	B	6
VZ 041	B	6
BX 028	A	5
JU 062	N	5
RN 045	A	4

CREATION OF STRICT PROTECTION AND SUSTAINABLE USE (MOSAIC) CONSERVATION AREAS

Area	Biological importance (average)	Priority level
AX 001	A	9
BX 016	B	9
BX 049	A	7
AX 058	N	5
BX 023	C	3
BX 022	D	3

CREATION OF CONSERVATION AREAS OF UNDEFINED CATEGORY (SUBJECT TO STUDIES)

Area	Biological importance (average)	Priority level
AX 010	A	10
EG 025	A	10
AX 027	A	9
AX 025	A	9
BX 027	A	7
BX 038	A	7
BX 048	A	5
BX 072	A	5
EG 012	A	5
BX 044	A	6
BX 061	N	5
JU 022	A	4
EG 019	A	4
RN 038	B	4
TO 001	A	3

Table 9 - Priority level for undertaking biological inventories (see map on pages 402-403)

Area	Priority level	Area	Priority level
AX 042	10	JU 001	5
AX 061	10	JU 006	5
BX 027	10	AX 019	5
BX 021	10	VZ 017	5
EG 010	10	VZ 011	5
AX 032	10	AX 030	5
BX 002	10	BX 040	5
BX 025	10	BX 056	5
BX 064	9	RN 049	5
RN 038	9	BX 072	5
VZ 023	9	AX 058	5
BX 014	9	BX 030	4
AX 020	9	BX 037	4
BX 062	8	EG 030	4
BX 065	8	BX 003	4
VZ 021	8	RN 045	4
RN 034	8	VZ 025	4
VZ 033	8	BX 036	4
BX 007	8	BX 042	4
BX 035	8	VZ 018	4
VZ 022	8	AX 051	4
EG 014	8	BX 006	4
VZ 034	8	VZ 024	4
BX 059	8	RN 018	4
JU 065	8	EG 020	4
BX 024	7	EG 018	4
BX 026	7	EG 031	4
EG 027	7	RN 009	4
BX 029	7	BX 020	4
AX 026	7	RN 012	4
BX 034	7	VZ 001	4
BX 049	7	EG 035	4
BX 033	7	AX 057	4
JU 002	7	AX 037	3
JU 009	7	BX 068	3
VZ 016	7	BX 041	3
VZ 020	7	AX 052	3
BX 051	7	AX 025	3
VZ 044	7	RN 020	3
BX 058	6	RN 044	3
VZ 035	6	VZ 013	3
BX 050	6	VZ 005	3
BX 067	6	VZ 010	3
AX 048	6	VZ 007	3
AX 049	6	BX 013	3
EG 011	6	EG 013	3
RN 013	6	RN 047	3
VZ 030	6	RN 004	3
BX 069	6	BX 022	3
JU 032	6	BX 004	3
EG 034	6	JU 060	3
BX 028	5	EG 028	2
BX 032	5	AX 033	2
BX 061	5	RN 042	2
AX 043	5	BX 039	2
BX 038	5	AX 024	2
BX 057	5	VZ 006	2
VZ 015	5	AX 018	2
BX 053	5	RN 001	2
BX 054	5	BX 066	2
BX 073	5	JU 029	2
AX 041	5	AX 038	2
BX 044	5	RN 048	2

Table 10 - Priority level for undertaking monitoring (see map on pages 400-401).

Area	Priority level	Area	Priority level
EG 010	10	JU 001	5
EG 006	10	AX 040	5
BX 002	10	AX 019	5
BX 025	10	TO 004	5
RN 038	9	VZ 011	5
VZ 023	9	EG 016	5
AX 028	9	BX 017	5
VZ 031	9	BX 045	4
VZ 032	9	AX 035	4
AX 020	9	BX 015	4
AX 029	9	BX 019	4
BX 012	8	RN 045	4
TO 018	8	AX 034	4
RN 037	8	AX 051	4
BX 007	8	BX 006	4
EG 014	8	VZ 024	4
VZ 014	8	EG 009	4
AX 022	8	VZ 004	4
AX 031	7	EG 020	4
BX 011	7	RN 009	4
RN 016	7	BX 020	4
AX 055	7	EG 001	4
AX 015	7	BX 009	4
EG 004	7	VZ 001	4
EG 015	7	EG 035	4
BX 051	7	EG 021	4
VZ 044	7	AX 057	4
BX 058	6	RN 011	3
BX 060	6	AX 036	3
RN 039	6	RN 020	3
BX 067	6	VZ 003	3
AX 048	6	VZ 013	3
AX 049	6	EG 024	3
AX 005	6	BX 013	3
EG 003	6	BX 010	3
EG 011	6	EG 017	3
EG 032	6	EG 028	2
RN 013	6	EG 026	2
EG 002	6	EG 008	2
BX 008	6	RN 017	2
EG 036	6	EG 033	2
BX 061	5	RN 010	2
RN 015	5	BX 018	2
BX 038	5	VZ 002	2
BX 057	5	AX 038	2

TABLE 11 - PRIORITY LEVEL FOR ENVIRONMENTAL EDUCATION ACTIVITIES (SEE MAP ON PAGES 400-401)		
Area	Biological importance (average)	Priority Level
BX 027	A	10
BX 021	A	10
EG 010	A	10
EG 006	B	10
BX 002	N	10
BX 025	N	10
BX 064	A	9
BX 014	B	9
BX 001	A	8
BX 007	A	8
BX 035	A	8
BX 029	A	7
BX 034	A	7
BX 049	A	7
BX 033	A	7
EG 004	A	7
BX 051	B	7
EG 003	A	6
EG 011	A	6
EG 002	B	6
EG 036	C	6
EG 016	B	5
BX 072	N	5
BX 003	A	4
EG 009	A	4
EG 001	B	4
EG 017	B	3
BX 004	N	3
EG 008	A	2
BX 066	B	2

TABLE 12 - PRIORITY LEVEL FOR UNDERTAKING ANTHROPOLOGICAL STUDIES (SEE MAP ON PAGES 402-403)		
Area	Biological importance (average)	Priority level
BX 027	A	10
VZ 023	A	9
VZ 021	A	8
VZ 022	A	8
BX 024	A	7
BX 026	A	7
BX 029	A	7
BX 034	A	7
BX 033	A	7
VZ 020	A	7
BX 028	A	5
BX 053	A	5
AX 041	A	5
VZ 017	A	5
VZ 011	A	5
BX 072	N	5
BX 030	A	4
BX 037	A	4
RN 045	A	4
BX 036	A	4
VZ 018	A	4
BX 068	A	3
VZ 026	A	3
VZ 010	A	3
VZ 012	A	3
VZ 007	A	3
VZ 006	A	2
VZ 009	A	2
RN 048	N	2

TABLE 13 - PRIORITY LEVEL FOR PREPARATION OF MANAGEMENT PLANS (SEE MAP ON PAGES 400-401)		
Area	Biological importance (average)	Priority level
RN 037	A	8
RN 040	A	8
VZ 029	B	8
AX 023	B	8
VZ 047	B	8
RN 016	A	7
AX 055	A	7
AX 048	A	6
AX 049	A	6
AX 040	A	5
AX 037	A	3
RN 011	A	3
RN 043	A	3
AX 046	A	3
VZ 040	B	3
AX 038	B	2
RN 035	N	2
RN 036	A	1

TABLE 14 - PRIORITY LEVEL FOR THE PREPARATION OF SUSTAINABLE USE PLANS (SEE MAP ON PAGES 400-401)		
Area	Biological importance (average)	Priority level
RN 038	A	9
BX 014	B	9
VZ 031	B	9
AX 020	B	9
BX 012	A	8
RN 034	A	8
VZ 033	A	8
VZ 029	B	8
VZ 014	B	8
AX 022	B	8
AX 026	A	7
BX 049	A	7
JU 002	A	7
RN 019	A	7
VZ 016	A	7
VZ 044	B	7
VZ 035	A	6
VZ 030	B	6
VZ 015	A	5
RN 049	B	5
AX 035	A	4
RN 045	A	4
AX 039	A	4
RN 021	A	4
RN 022	A	4
RN 002	B	4
AX 056	N	4
RN 005	A	3
VZ 008	A	3
RN 043	A	3
AX 052	A	3
RN 047	B	3
AX 033	A	2
RN 042	A	2
AX 024	A	2
AX 018	A	2
RN 001	A	2

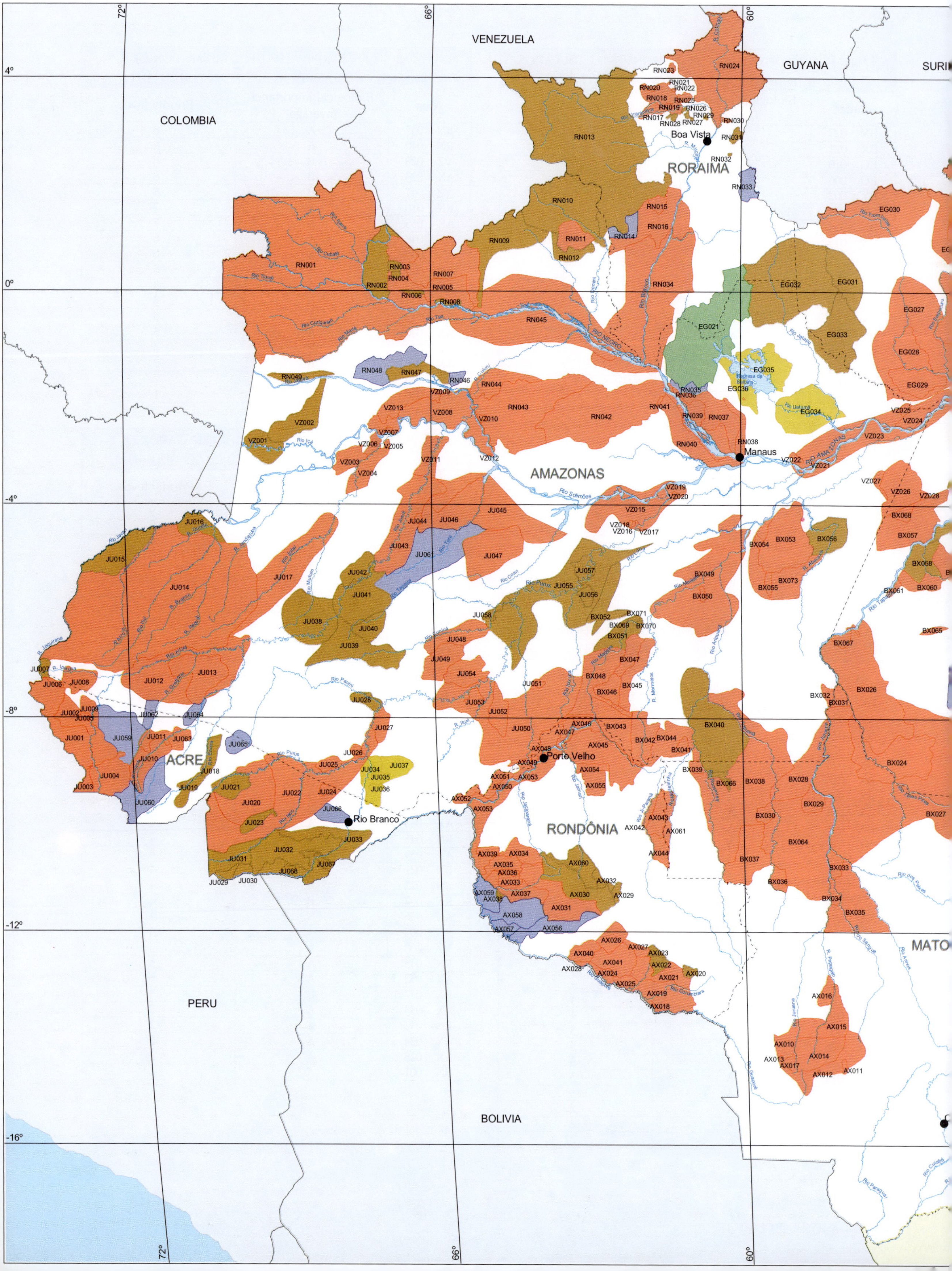

72°
66°
60°
4°
0°
-4°
-8°
-12°
-16°
VENEZUELA
GUYANA
SURI
COLOMBIA
PERU
BOLIVIA
MATO
RORAIMA
AMAZONAS
ACRE
RONDÔNIA
Boa Vista
Manaus
Porto Velho
Rio Branco
RIO NEGRO
RIO AMAZONAS
Rio Solimões
Rio Purus
Rio Madeira
Rio Juruá
Rio Tapajós
Rio Trombetas
Rio Jatapu
Rio Uatumã
Represa de Balbina
Rio Içá
Rio Japurá
Rio Tiquié
Rio Tea
Rio Curicuriari
Rio Uaupés
Rio Cuiuni
Rio Coari
Rio Tefé
Rio Mutum
Rio Tarauacá
Rio Envira
Rio Iaco
Rio Pauini
Rio Ituxi
Rio Abacaxis
Rio Aripuanã
Rio Roosevelt
Rio Jiparaná
Rio Jamari
Rio Jaciparaná
Rio Guaporé
Rio Corumbiara
Rio Juruena
Rio Papagaio
Rio Arinos
Rio dos Peixes
Rio Teles Pires
Rio Sangue
Rio Cuiabá
Rio Paraguai
Rio Guaporé
R. Jaquirana
R. Ipixuna
R. Marmelos
R. Mucajaí
R. Cotingo
RN001
RN002
RN003
RN004
RN005
RN006
RN007
RN008
RN009
RN010
RN011
RN012
RN013
RN014
RN015
RN016
RN017
RN018
RN019
RN020
RN021
RN022
RN023
RN024
RN025
RN026
RN027
RN028
RN029
RN030
RN031
RN032
RN033
RN034
RN035
RN036
RN037
RN038
RN039
RN040
RN041
RN042
RN043
RN044
RN045
RN046
RN047
RN048
RN049
EG021
EG027
EG028
EG029
EG030
EG031
EG032
EG033
EG034
EG035
EG036
VZ001
VZ002
VZ003
VZ004
VZ005
VZ006
VZ007
VZ008
VZ009
VZ010
VZ011
VZ012
VZ013
VZ015
VZ016
VZ017
VZ018
VZ019
VZ020
VZ021
VZ022
VZ023
VZ024
VZ025
VZ026
VZ027
VZ028
JU001
JU002
JU003
JU004
JU006
JU007
JU008
JU009
JU010
JU011
JU012
JU013
JU014
JU015
JU016
JU017
JU018
JU019
JU020
JU021
JU022
JU023
JU024
JU025
JU026
JU027
JU028
JU029
JU030
JU031
JU032
JU033
JU034
JU035
JU036
JU037
JU038
JU039
JU040
JU041
JU042
JU043
JU044
JU045
JU046
JU047
JU048
JU049
JU050
JU051
JU052
JU053
JU054
JU055
JU056
JU057
JU058
JU059
JU060
JU061
JU062
JU063
JU064
JU065
JU066
JU067
JU068
BX024
BX026
BX027
BX028
BX029
BX030
BX031
BX032
BX033
BX034
BX035
BX036
BX037
BX038
BX039
BX040
BX041
BX042
BX043
BX044
BX045
BX046
BX047
BX048
BX049
BX050
BX051
BX052
BX053
BX054
BX055
BX056
BX057
BX058
BX060
BX061
BX064
BX065
BX066
BX067
BX068
BX069
BX070
BX071
BX073
AX010
AX011
AX012
AX013
AX014
AX015
AX016
AX017
AX018
AX019
AX020
AX021
AX022
AX023
AX024
AX025
AX026
AX027
AX028
AX029
AX030
AX031
AX032
AX033
AX034
AX035
AX036
AX037
AX038
AX039
AX040
AX041
AX042
AX043
AX044
AX045
AX046
AX047
AX048
AX049
AX050
AX051
AX052
AX053
AX054
AX055
AX056
AX057
AX058
AX059
AX060
AX061

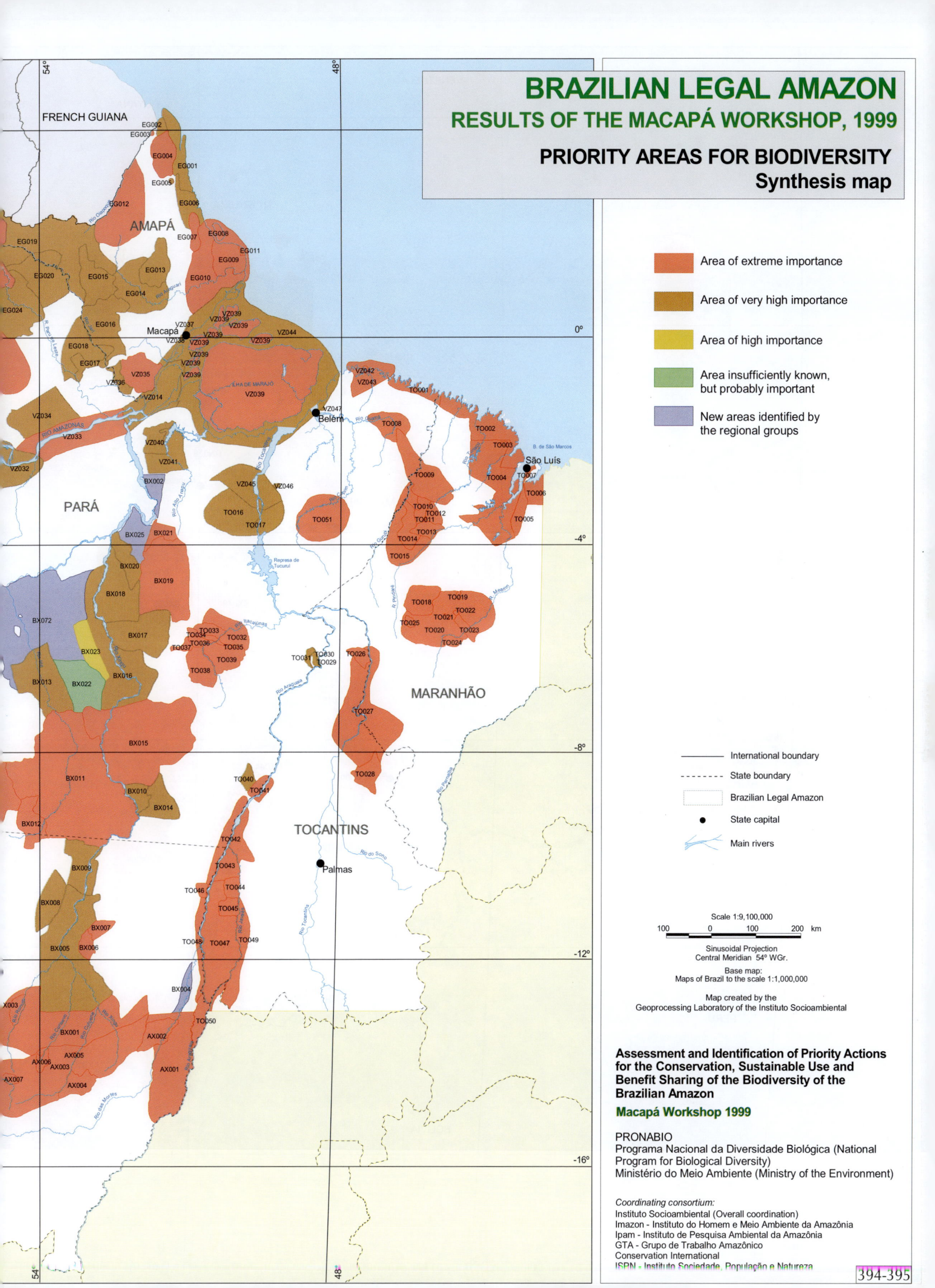

BRAZILIAN LEGAL AMAZON
RESULTS OF THE MACAPÁ WORKSHOP, 1999
PRIORITY AREAS FOR BIODIVERSITY
Synthesis map

Legend:
- Area of extreme importance
- Area of very high importance
- Area of high importance
- Area insufficiently known, but probably important
- New areas identified by the regional groups

- International boundary
- State boundary
- Brazilian Legal Amazon
- State capital
- Main rivers

Scale 1:9,100,000

Sinusoidal Projection
Central Meridian 54° WGr.

Base map:
Maps of Brazil to the scale 1:1,000,000

Map created by the
Geoprocessing Laboratory of the Instituto Socioambiental

Assessment and Identification of Priority Actions for the Conservation, Sustainable Use and Benefit Sharing of the Biodiversity of the Brazilian Amazon

Macapá Workshop 1999

PRONABIO
Programa Nacional da Diversidade Biológica (National Program for Biological Diversity)
Ministério do Meio Ambiente (Ministry of the Environment)

Coordinating consortium:
Instituto Socioambiental (Overall coordination)
Imazon - Instituto do Homem e Meio Ambiente da Amazônia
Ipam - Instituto de Pesquisa Ambiental da Amazônia
GTA - Grupo de Trabalho Amazônico
Conservation International
ISPN - Instituto Sociedade, População e Natureza

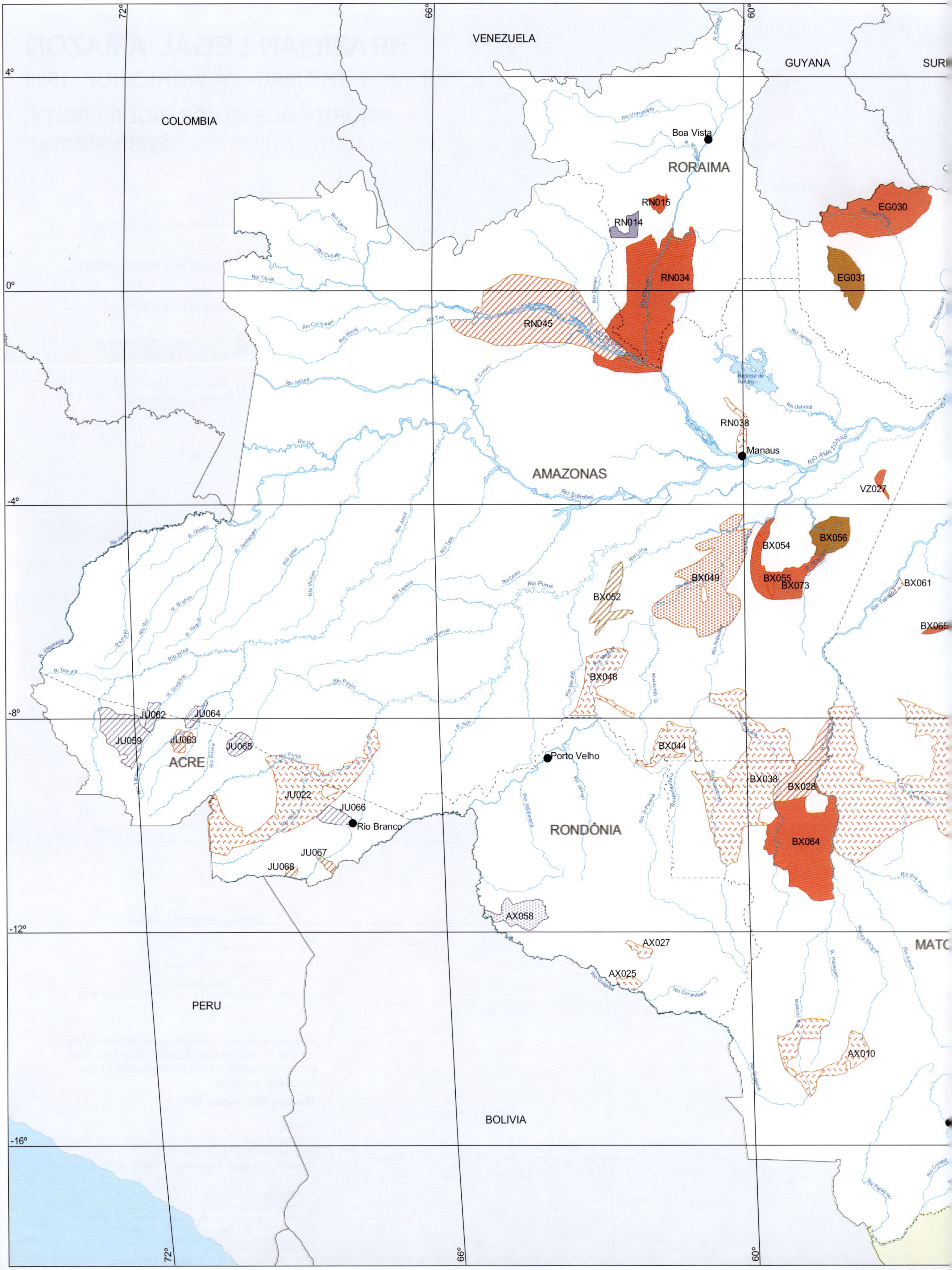
VENEZUELA
GUYANA
COLOMBIA
RORAIMA
Boa Vista
RN015
RN014
RN034
EG030
EG031
RN045
RN038
Manaus
AMAZONAS
VZ027
BX054
BX056
BX049
BX055
BX073
BX061
BX052
BX065
BX048
JU062
JU064
JU059
JU063
JU065
ACRE
Porto Velho
BX044
BX038
BX028
JU022
JU066
Rio Branco
RONDÔNIA
BX064
JU067
JU068
AX058
AX027
AX025
PERU
AX010
BOLIVIA

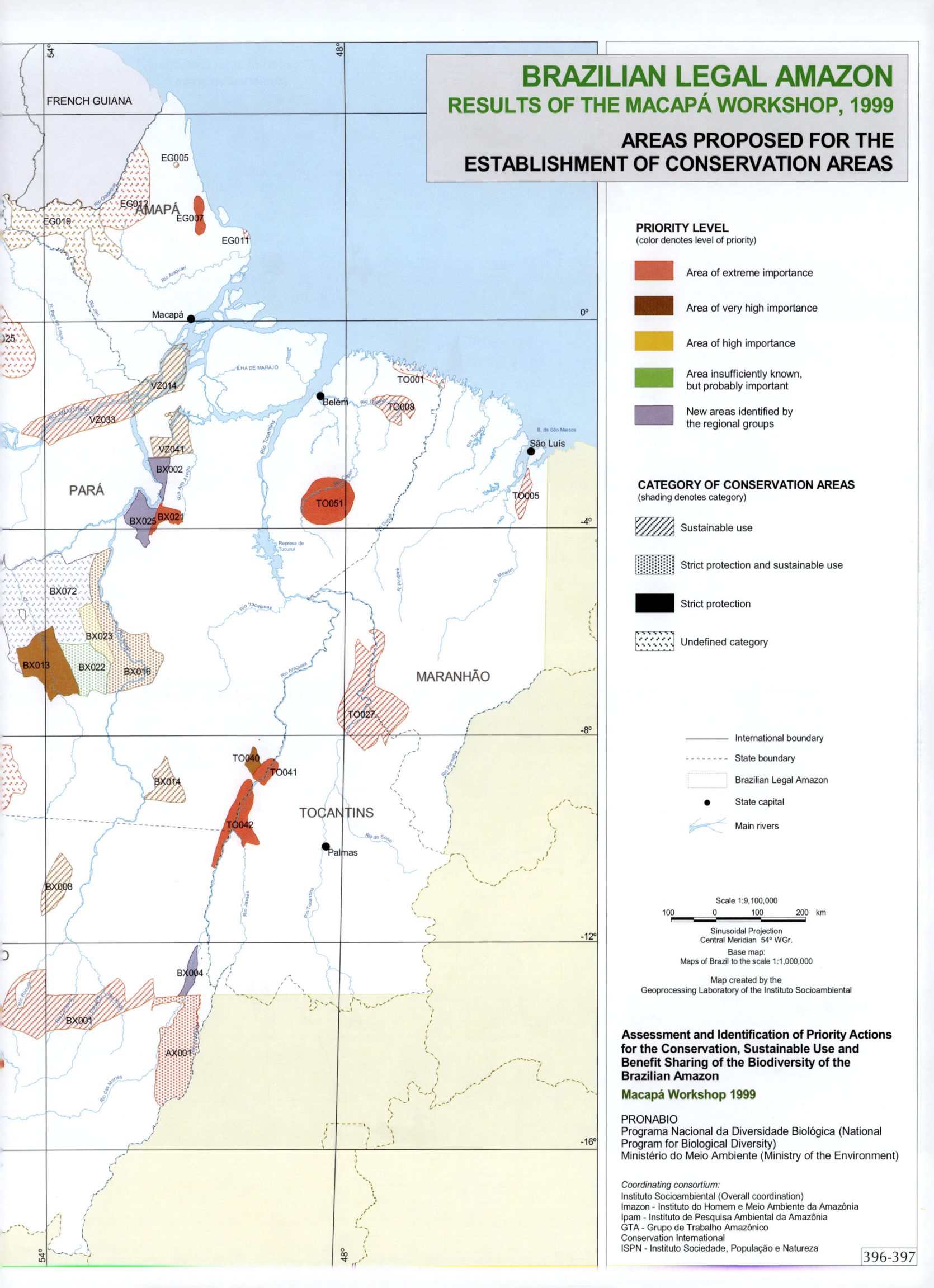

BRAZILIAN LEGAL AMAZON
RESULTS OF THE MACAPÁ WORKSHOP, 1999

AREAS PROPOSED FOR THE ESTABLISHMENT OF CONSERVATION AREAS

PRIORITY LEVEL
(color denotes level of priority)

- Area of extreme importance
- Area of very high importance
- Area of high importance
- Area insufficiently known, but probably important
- New areas identified by the regional groups

CATEGORY OF CONSERVATION AREAS
(shading denotes category)

- Sustainable use
- Strict protection and sustainable use
- Strict protection
- Undefined category

- International boundary
- State boundary
- Brazilian Legal Amazon
- State capital
- Main rivers

Scale 1:9,100,000
Sinusoidal Projection
Central Meridian 54° WGr.
Base map:
Maps of Brazil to the scale 1:1,000,000

Map created by the
Geoprocessing Laboratory of the Instituto Socioambiental

Assessment and Identification of Priority Actions for the Conservation, Sustainable Use and Benefit Sharing of the Biodiversity of the Brazilian Amazon

Macapá Workshop 1999

PRONABIO
Programa Nacional da Diversidade Biológica (National Program for Biological Diversity)
Ministério do Meio Ambiente (Ministry of the Environment)

Coordinating consortium:
Instituto Socioambiental (Overall coordination)
Imazon - Instituto do Homem e Meio Ambiente da Amazônia
Ipam - Instituto de Pesquisa Ambiental da Amazônia
GTA - Grupo de Trabalho Amazônico
Conservation International
ISPN - Instituto Sociedade, População e Natureza

396-397

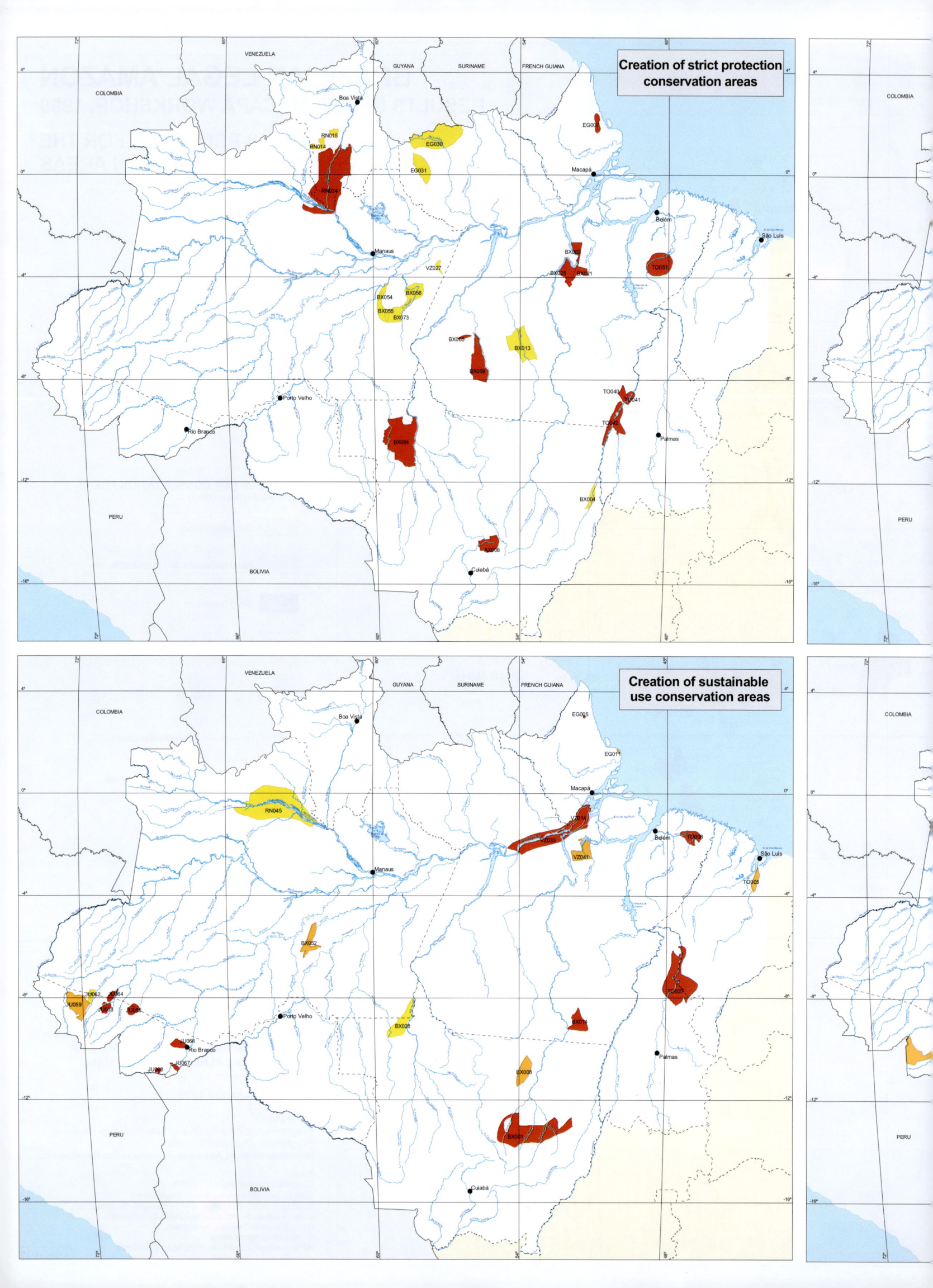

Creation of strict protection conservation areas

Creation of sustainable use conservation areas

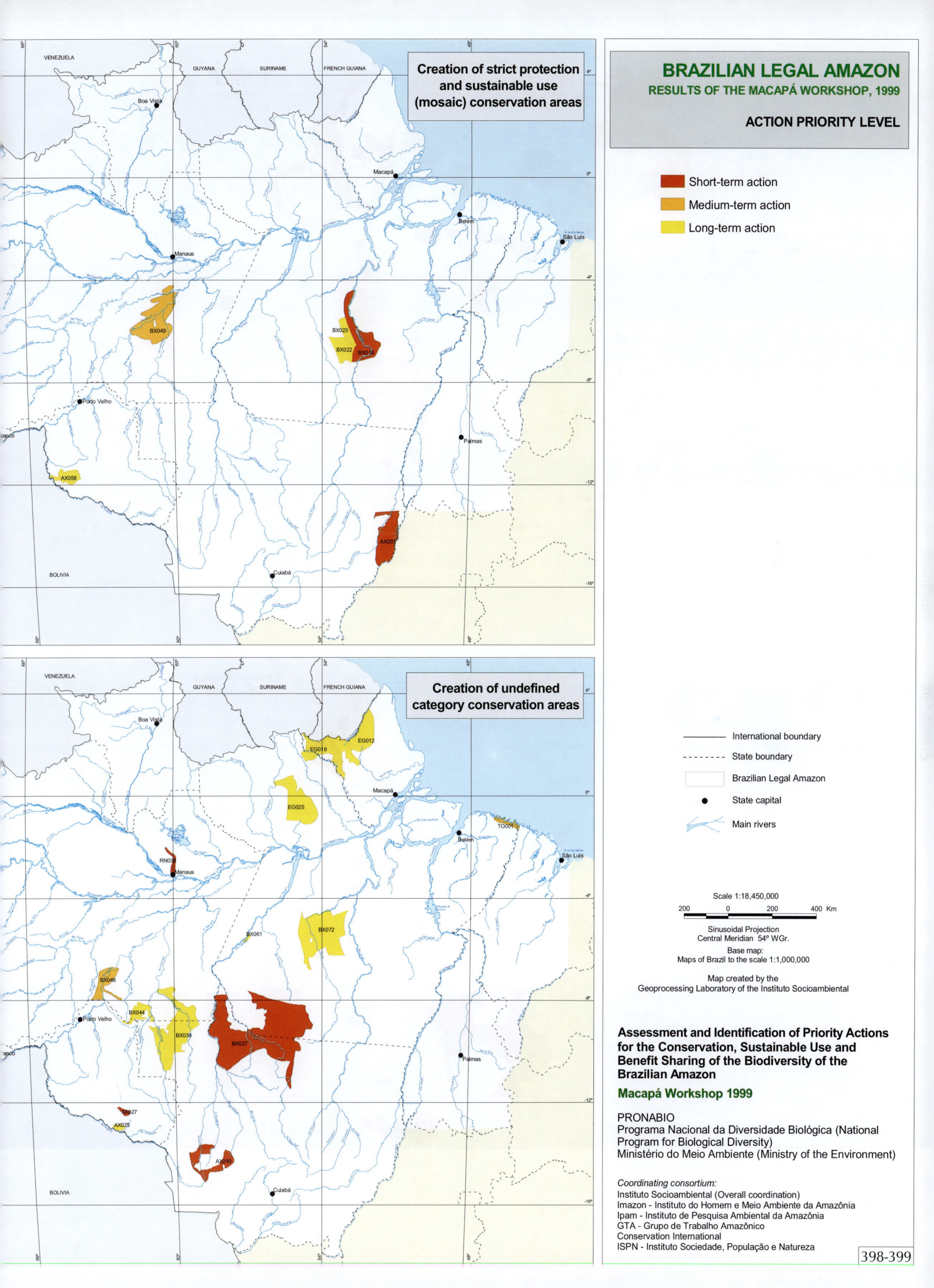

Creation of strict protection and sustainable use (mosaic) conservation areas

Creation of undefined category conservation areas

BRAZILIAN LEGAL AMAZON
RESULTS OF THE MACAPÁ WORKSHOP, 1999

ACTION PRIORITY LEVEL

- Short-term action
- Medium-term action
- Long-term action

- International boundary
- State boundary
- Brazilian Legal Amazon
- State capital
- Main rivers

Scale 1:18,450,000
200 0 200 400 Km

Sinusoidal Projection
Central Meridian 54° WGr.
Base map:
Maps of Brazil to the scale 1:1,000,000

Map created by the
Geoprocessing Laboratory of the Instituto Socioambiental

Assessment and Identification of Priority Actions for the Conservation, Sustainable Use and Benefit Sharing of the Biodiversity of the Brazilian Amazon

Macapá Workshop 1999

PRONABIO
Programa Nacional da Diversidade Biológica (National Program for Biological Diversity)
Ministério do Meio Ambiente (Ministry of the Environment)

Coordinating consortium:
Instituto Socioambiental (Overall coordination)
Imazon - Instituto do Homem e Meio Ambiente da Amazônia
Ipam - Instituto de Pesquisa Ambiental da Amazônia
GTA - Grupo de Trabalho Amazônico
Conservation International
ISPN - Instituto Sociedade, População e Natureza

Monitoring

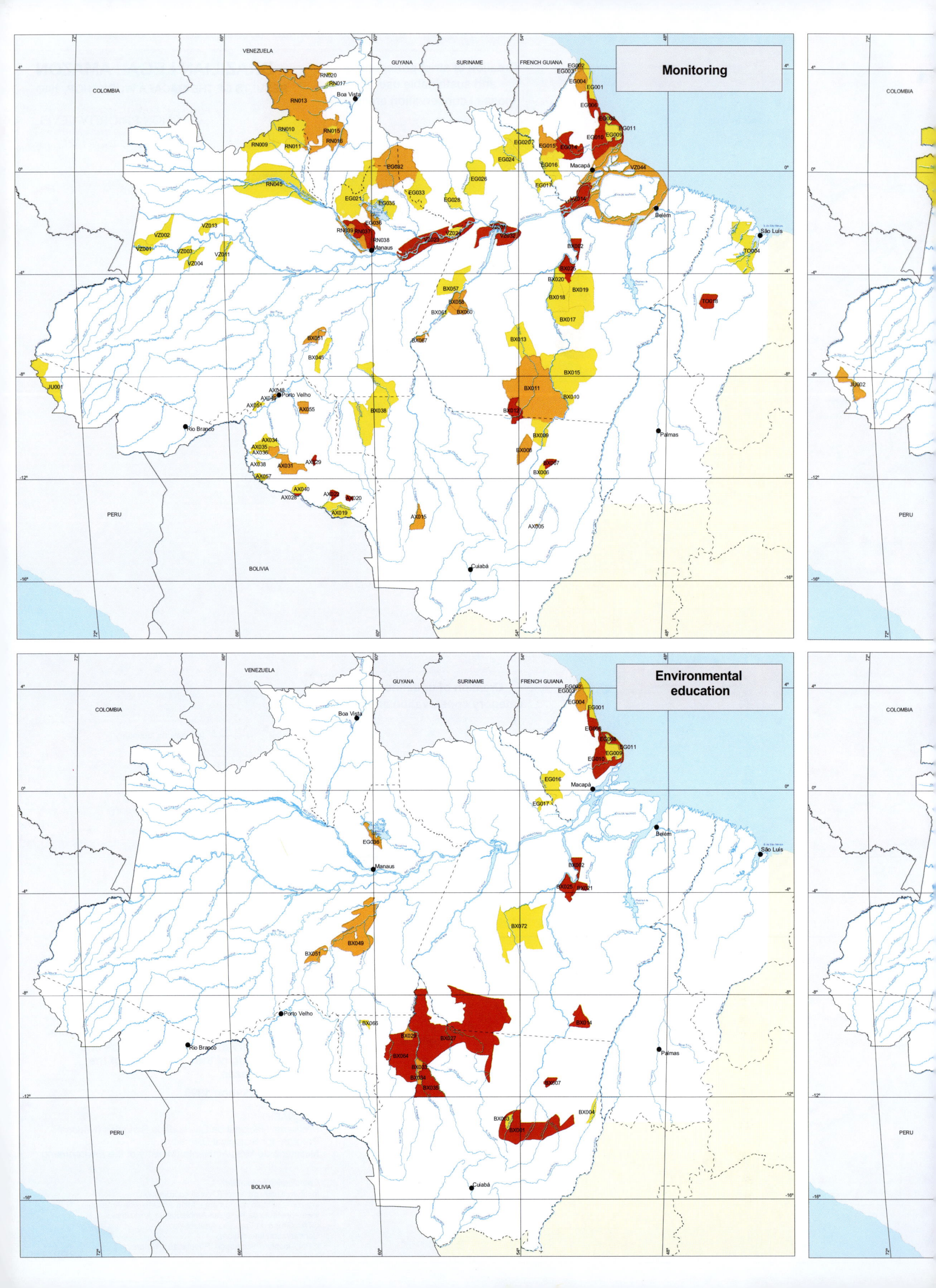

Environmental education

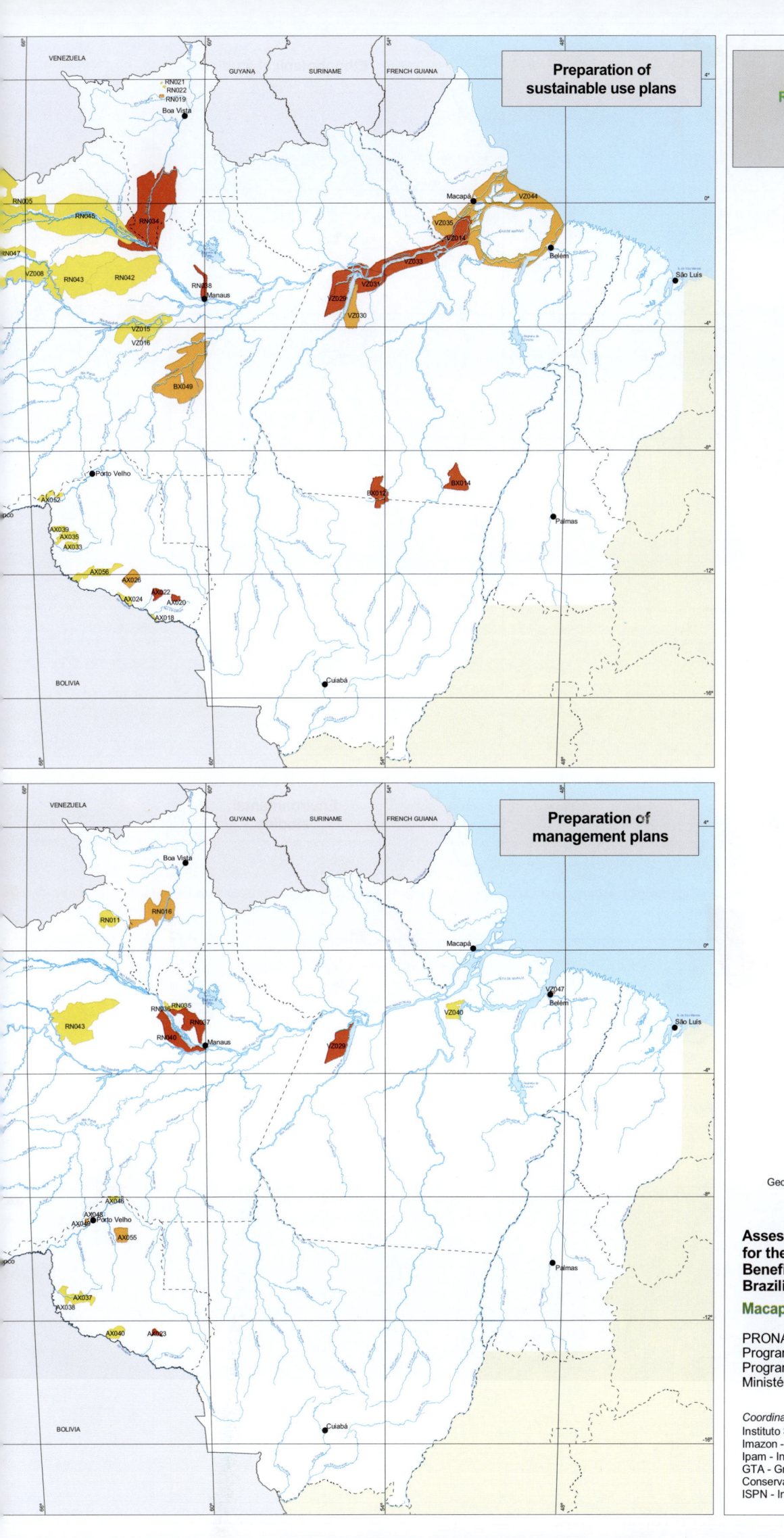

BRAZILIAN LEGAL AMAZON
RESULTS OF THE MACAPÁ WORKSHOP, 1999

ACTION PRIORITY LEVEL

- Short-term action
- Medium-term action
- Long-term action

Preparation of sustainable use plans

Preparation of management plans

- International boundary
- State boundary
- Brazilian Legal Amazon
- State capital
- Main rivers

Scale 1:18,450,000
200 0 200 400 Km

Sinusoidal Projection
Central Meridian 54° WGr.
Base map:
Maps of Brazil to the scale 1:1,000,000

Map created by the
Geoprocessing Laboratory of the Instituto Socioambiental

Assessment and Identification of Priority Actions for the Conservation, Sustainable Use and Benefit Sharing of the Biodiversity of the Brazilian Amazon

Macapá Workshop 1999

PRONABIO
Programa Nacional da Diversidade Biológica (National Program for Biological Diversity)
Ministério do Meio Ambiente (Ministry of the Environment)

Coordinating consortium:
Instituto Socioambiental (Overall coordination)
Imazon - Instituto do Homem e Meio Ambiente da Amazônia
Ipam - Instituto de Pesquisa Ambiental da Amazônia
GTA - Grupo de Trabalho Amazônico
Conservation International
ISPN - Instituto Sociedade, População e Natureza

400-401

Ethnobotanical studies

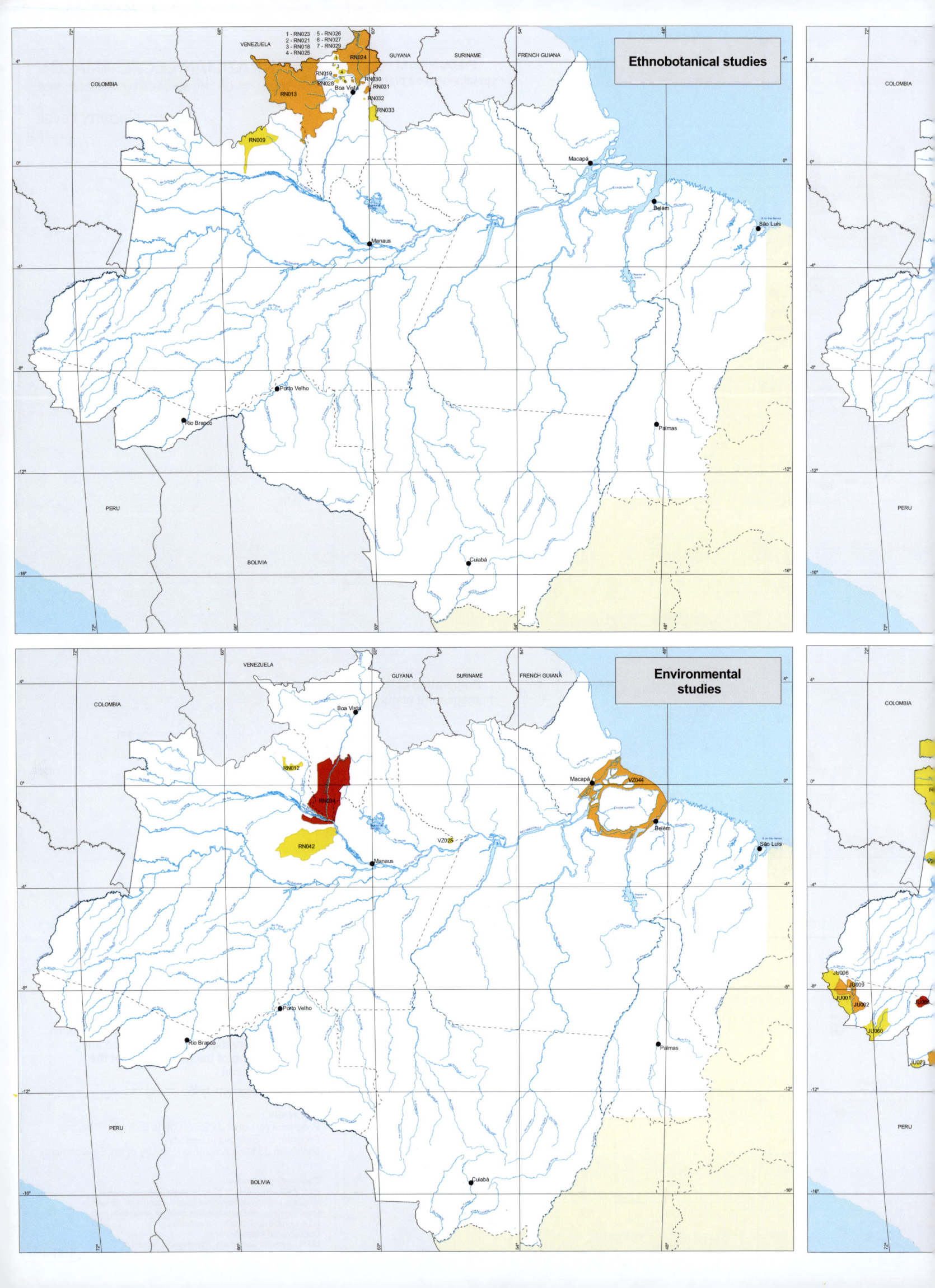

1 - RN023 5 - RN026
2 - RN021 6 - RN027
3 - RN018 7 - RN029
4 - RN025

Environmental studies

BRAZILIAN LEGAL AMAZON
RESULTS OF THE MACAPÁ WORKSHOP, 1999

ACTION PRIORITY LEVEL

- Short-term action
- Medium-term action
- Long-term action

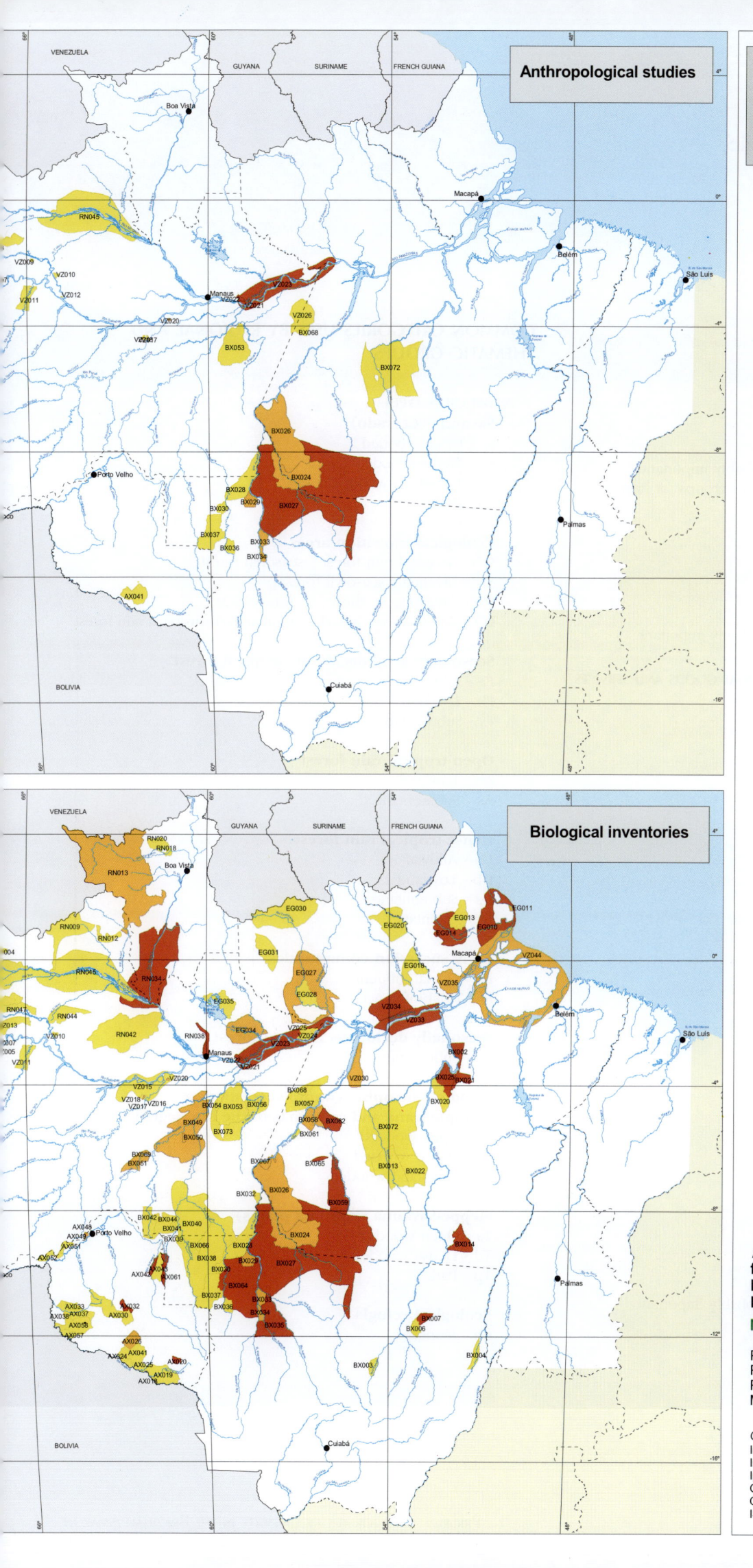

Anthropological studies

Biological inventories

- International boundary
- ––– State boundary
- Brazilian Legal Amazon
- ● State capital
- Main rivers

Scale 1:18,450,000
200 0 200 400 Km

Sinusoidal Projection
Central Meridian 54° WGr.
Base map:
Maps of Brazil to the scale 1:1,000,000

Map created by the
Geoprocessing Laboratory of the Instituto Socioambiental

Assessment and Identification of Priority Actions for the Conservation, Sustainable Use and Benefit Sharing of the Biodiversity of the Brazilian Amazon

Macapá Workshop 1999

PRONABIO
Programa Nacional da Diversidade Biológica (National Program for Biological Diversity)
Ministério do Meio Ambiente (Ministry of the Environment)

Coordinating consortium:
Instituto Socioambiental (Overall coordination)
Imazon - Instituto do Homem e Meio Ambiente da Amazônia
Ipam - Instituto de Pesquisa Ambiental da Amazônia
GTA - Grupo de Trabalho Amazônico
Conservation International
ISPN - Instituto Sociedade, População e Natureza

Keys to Priority Area Levels

REGIONAL GROUPS

PRIORITY LEVEL
A - Area of extreme importance
B - Area of very high importance
C - Area of high importance
D - Area insufficiently known, but probably important
N - New areas identified by the regional groups for further study

BIOLOGICAL IMPORTANCE
A - Area of extreme importance
B - Area of very high importance
C - Area of high importance
D - Area insufficiently known, but probably important

LEVEL OF IMPORTANCE FOR ENVIRONMENTAL GOODS AND SERVICES
A - Area of extreme importance
B - Area of very high importance
C - Area of high importance

STABILITY LEVEL
High: 10 and above
Medium: between 6 and 9
Low: 5 and below

INSTABILITY LEVEL
Maximum: 10
High: between 8 and 9
Medium: between 5 and 7
Low: 4 and below

ACTION PRIORITY LEVEL
Short term: 8 to 10
Medium term: 6 to 7
Long term: 5 and below

THEMATIC GROUPS

PRIORITY LEVEL
A - Area of extreme importance
B - Area of very high importance
C - Area of high importance
D - Area insufficiently known, but probably important

DIAGNOSTIC WEIGHTING
1 (lowest) to 5 (highest)

ACTION RECOMMENDED
1 (low importance) to 5 (high importance)

COMMON CATEGORIES USES BY REGIONAL AND THEMATIC GROUPS

VEGETATION TYPES

Savanna (Cerrado)
Sa - Open wooded
Sd - Dense wooded
Sg - Grassland-wooded
Sp - Park

Ecological transition areas
ON - Tropical rain forest / seasonal forest
SN - Savanna / seasonal forest
SO - Savanna / tropical rain forest (SO)
LO - Forest on sandy soil (campinarana) / tropical rain forest

Seasonally semi-deciduous tropical forest
Fa - Alluvial
Fb - Lowland
Fs - Submontane

Open tropical rain forest
Ab - Lowland
As - Submontane

Dense tropical rain forest
Da - Alluvial
Db - Lowland
Ds - Submontane
Dm - Montane

Early sucession communities
Pa - Fluvial influence
Pf - Tidal influence

Seasonally deciduous tropical forest
Cs - Submontane

Wood oligotrophic swamp vegetation (campinarana and campinas of the Rio Negro)
La - Open wooded
Ld - Dense wooded
Lg - Grassland-wooded

Steppe-Savanna (Roraima plains)
Ta - Open wooded
Td - Dense wooded
Tp - Park

Ecological refugia
rm - Montane

Priority areas for conservation, sustainable use and benefit sharing by region of the Brazilian Amazon

Araguaia / Tocantins / Maranhão
Upper Xingu / Tapajós / Rondônia / Mato Grosso
Solimões / Amazonas Floodplains

Maps on pages 406-407

Guiana Shield
Lower Xingu / Tapajós / Madeira
Rio Negro / Rio Branco
Juruá / Purus / Acre

Maps on pages 408-409

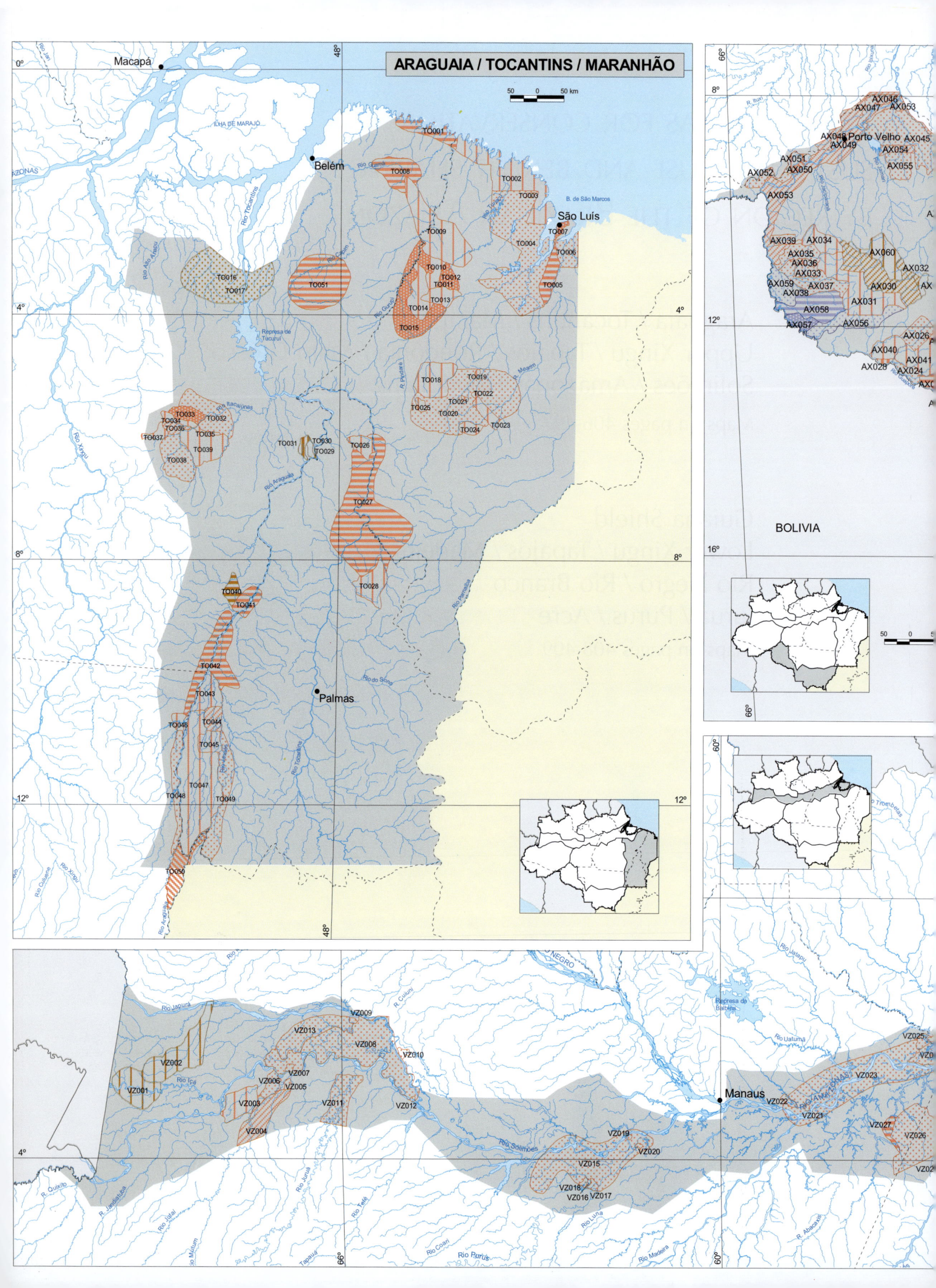

ARAGUAIA / TOCANTINS / MARANHÃO

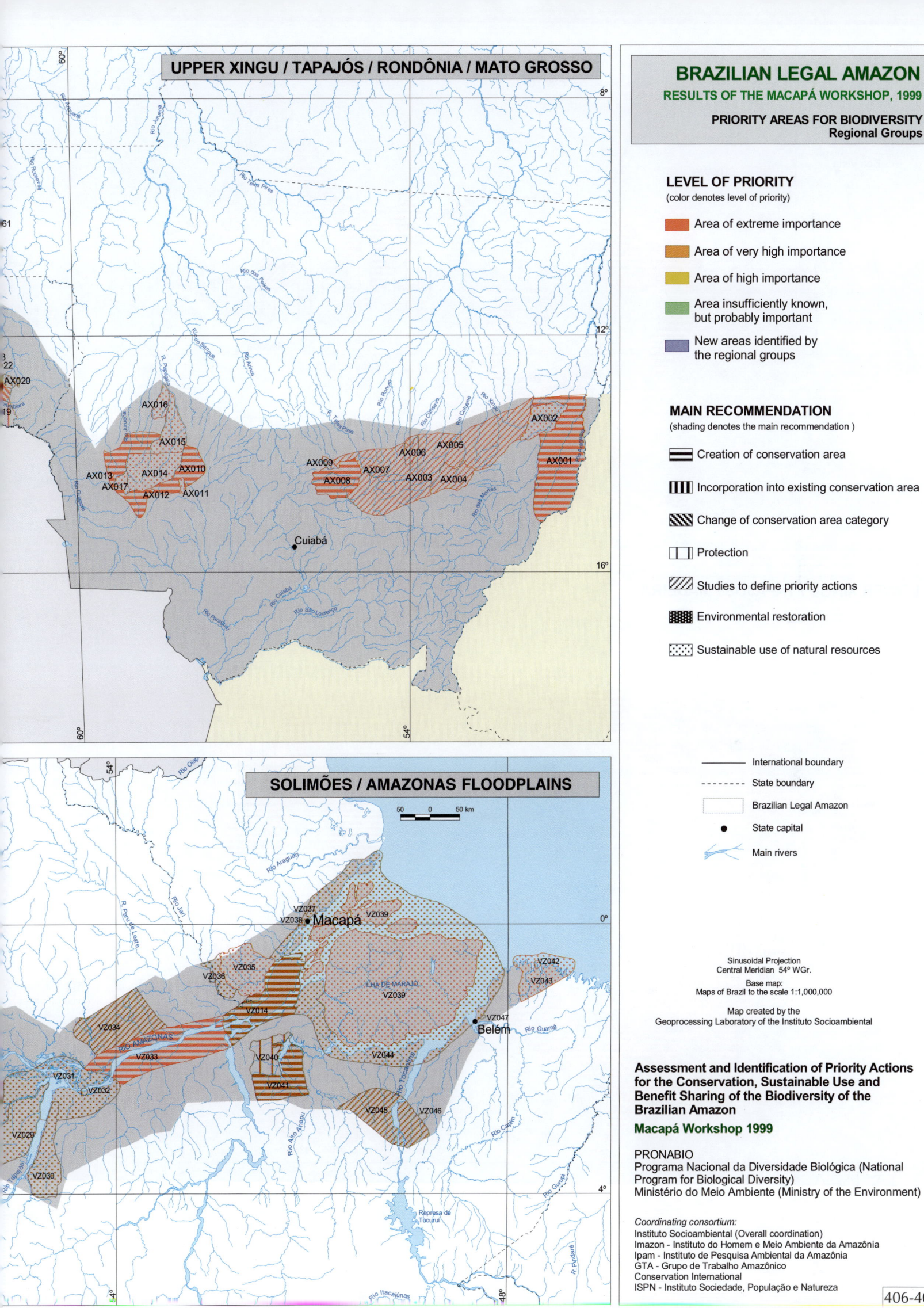

UPPER XINGU / TAPAJÓS / RONDÔNIA / MATO GROSSO

SOLIMÕES / AMAZONAS FLOODPLAINS

BRAZILIAN LEGAL AMAZON
RESULTS OF THE MACAPÁ WORKSHOP, 1999
PRIORITY AREAS FOR BIODIVERSITY
Regional Groups

LEVEL OF PRIORITY
(color denotes level of priority)

- Area of extreme importance
- Area of very high importance
- Area of high importance
- Area insufficiently known, but probably important
- New areas identified by the regional groups

MAIN RECOMMENDATION
(shading denotes the main recommendation)

- Creation of conservation area
- Incorporation into existing conservation area
- Change of conservation area category
- Protection
- Studies to define priority actions
- Environmental restoration
- Sustainable use of natural resources

- International boundary
- State boundary
- Brazilian Legal Amazon
- State capital
- Main rivers

Sinusoidal Projection
Central Meridian 54° WGr.
Base map:
Maps of Brazil to the scale 1:1,000,000

Map created by the
Geoprocessing Laboratory of the Instituto Socioambiental

Assessment and Identification of Priority Actions for the Conservation, Sustainable Use and Benefit Sharing of the Biodiversity of the Brazilian Amazon

Macapá Workshop 1999

PRONABIO
Programa Nacional da Diversidade Biológica (National Program for Biological Diversity)
Ministério do Meio Ambiente (Ministry of the Environment)

Coordinating consortium:
Instituto Socioambiental (Overall coordination)
Imazon - Instituto do Homem e Meio Ambiente da Amazônia
Ipam - Instituto de Pesquisa Ambiental da Amazônia
GTA - Grupo de Trabalho Amazônico
Conservation International
ISPN - Instituto Sociedade, População e Natureza

GUIANA SHIELD

LOWER XINGU / TAPAJÓS / MADEIRA

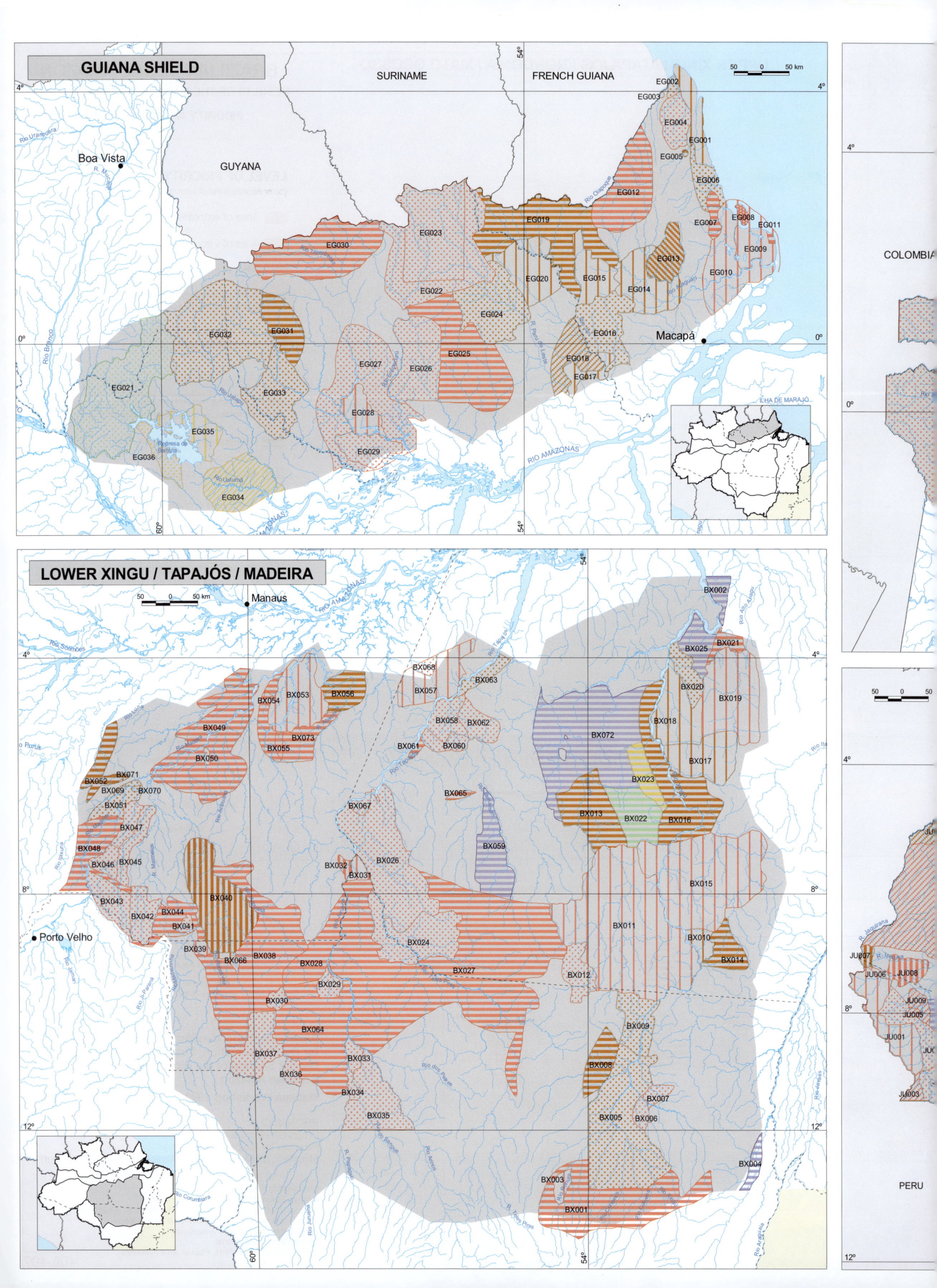

BRAZILIAN LEGAL AMAZON
RESULTS OF THE MACAPÁ WORKSHOP, 1999
PRIORITY AREAS FOR BIODIVERSITY
Regional Groups

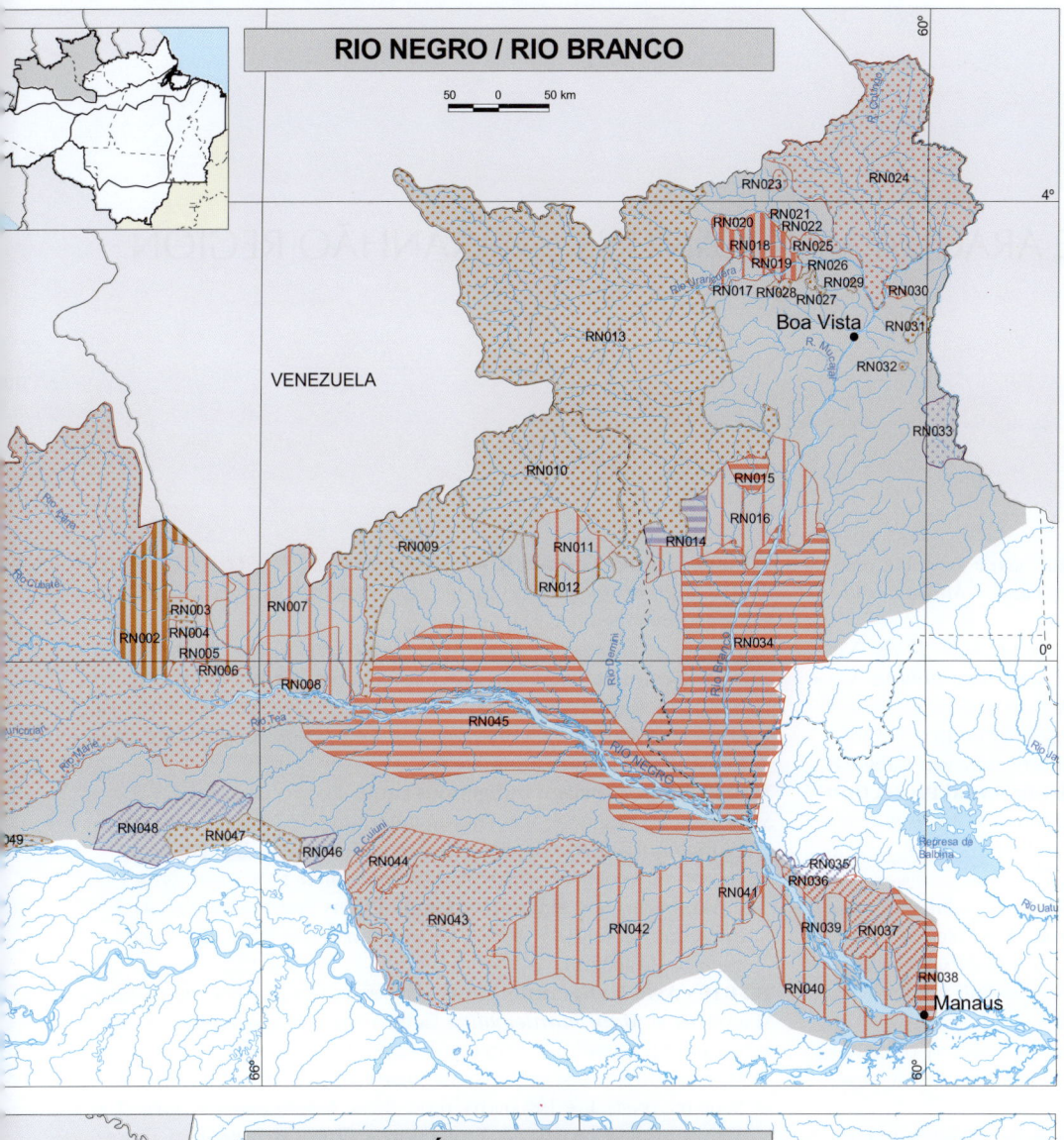

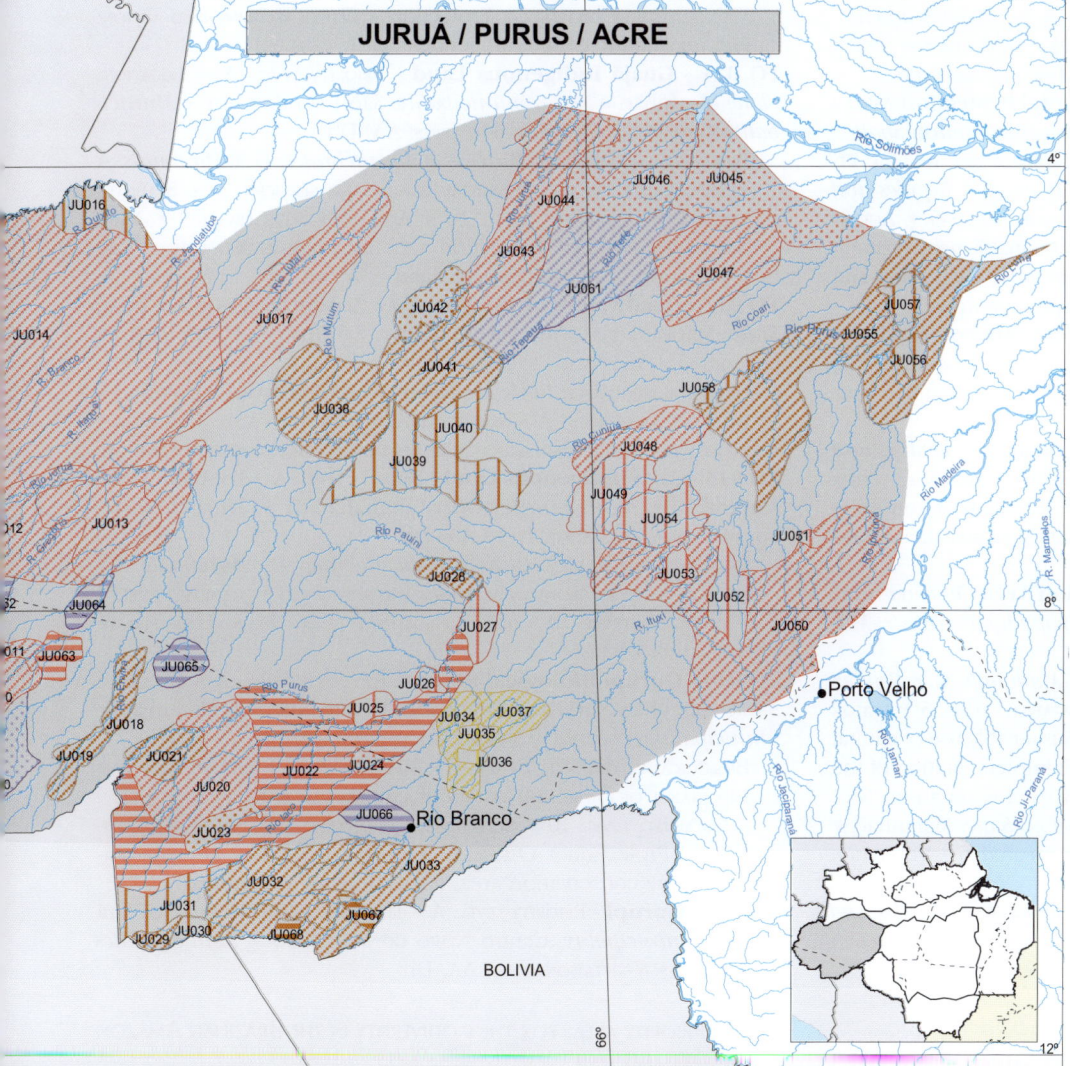

RIO NEGRO / RIO BRANCO

JURUÁ / PURUS / ACRE

LEVEL OF PRIORITY
(color denotes level of priority)

- Area of extreme importance
- Area of very high importance
- Area of high importance
- Area insufficiently known, but probably important
- New areas identified by the regional groups

MAIN RECOMMENDATION
(shading denotes the main recommendation)

- Creation of conservation area
- Incorporation into existing conservation area
- Change of conservation area category
- Protection
- Studies to define priority actions
- Environmental restoration
- Sustainable use of natural resources

- International boundary
- State boundary
- Brazilian Legal Amazon
- State capital
- Main rivers

Sinusoidal Projection
Central Meridian 54° WGr.
Base map:
Maps of Brazil to the scale 1:1,000,000

Map created by the
Geoprocessing Laboratory of the Instituto Socioambiental

Assessment and Identification of Priority Actions for the Conservation, Sustainable Use and Benefit Sharing of the Biodiversity of the Brazilian Amazon

Macapá Workshop 1999

PRONABIO
Programa Nacional da Diversidade Biológica (National Program for Biological Diversity)
Ministério do Meio Ambiente (Ministry of the Environment)

Coordinating consortium:
Instituto Socioambiental (Overall coordination)
Imazon - Instituto do Homem e Meio Ambiente da Amazônia
Ipam - Instituto de Pesquisa Ambiental da Amazônia
GTA - Grupo de Trabalho Amazônico
Conservation International
ISPN - Instituto Sociedade, População e Natureza

1
PRIORITY AREAS IN THE ARAGUAIA / TOCANTINS / MARANHÃO REGION

TO 001 - Reentrâncias Paraenses - PRIORITY LEVEL: A • LOCATION: *State:* Pará/Maranhão • *Main municipality:* Vieu • *Municipalities covered:* 9 • VEGETATION TYPES: AA, Pa, Pf.
  BIOLOGICAL IMPORTANCE: *Birds:* A • *Aquatic Biota:* A • *Plants:* A • *Invertebrates:* D • *Mammals:* A • *Reptiles and amphibians:* A • STABILITY LEVEL: 0 • INSTABILITY LEVEL: 5 • ACTION PRIORITY LEVEL: 6 • MAIN ACTION RECOMMENDED: Creation of conservation area • OTHER RECOMMENDED ACTION: Studies to define the conservation area category.

TO 002 - Reentrâncias Maranhenses Environmental Protection Area - PRIORITY LEVEL: A • LOCATION: *State:* Maranhão • *Main municipality:* Serrano do Maranhão • *Municipalities covered:* 38 • VEGETATION TYPES: AA, Pa, Pf.
  BIOLOGICAL IMPORTANCE: *Birds:* A • *Aquatic Biota:* A • *Invertebrates:* D • *Mammals:* A • *Reptiles and amphibians:* A • STABILITY LEVEL: 2 • INSTABILITY LEVEL: 5 • ACTION PRIORITY LEVEL: 5 • MAIN ACTION RECOMMENDED: Protection • OTHER RECOMMENDED ACTION: Full implementation of the environmental protection area.

TO 003 - Quilombo Flexal Extractive Reserve - PRIORITY LEVEL: A • LOCATION: *State:* Maranhão • *Main municipality:* Mirinzal • *Municipalities covered:* 2 • VEGETATION TYPES: AA.
  BIOLOGICAL IMPORTANCE: *Birds:* B • *Aquatic Biota:* A • *Reptiles and amphibians:* A • STABILITY LEVEL: 6 • INSTABILITY LEVEL: 5 • ACTION PRIORITY LEVEL: 4 • MAIN ACTION RECOMMENDED: Sustainable use of natural resources.

TO 004 - Baixada Maranhense Environmental Protection Area - PRIORITY LEVEL: A • LOCATION: *State:* Maranhão • *Main municipality:* Pinheiro • *Municipalities covered:* 48 • VEGETATION TYPES: AA, Pa, Pf.
  BIOLOGICAL IMPORTANCE: *Birds:* B • *Aquatic Biota:* A • *Reptiles and amphibians:* A • STABILITY LEVEL: 2 • INSTABILITY LEVEL: 5 • ACTION PRIORITY LEVEL: 5 • MAIN ACTION RECOMMENDED: Sustainable use of natural resources • OTHER RECOMMENDED ACTION: Monitoring, inspection and full implementation of the environmental protection area.

TO 005 - Polygon next to the Baixada Maranhense Environmental Protection Area - PRIORITY LEVEL: A • LOCATION: *State:* Maranhão • *Main municipality:* Anajatuba • *Municipalities covered:* 8 • VEGETATION TYPES: AA, Pa.
  BIOLOGICAL IMPORTANCE: *Birds:* B • *Aquatic Biota:* A • *Reptiles and amphibians:* A • STABILITY LEVEL: 0 • INSTABILITY LEVEL: 5 • ACTION PRIORITY LEVEL: 6 • MAIN ACTION RECOMMENDED: Creation of conservation area • OTHER RECOMMENDED ACTION: Creation of sustainable use conservation area.

TO 006 - Miritiba Environmental Protection Area - PRIORITY LEVEL: A • LOCATION: *State:* Maranhão • *Main municipality:* Rosário • *Municipalities covered:* 9 • VEGETATION TYPES: AA, Pa, Pf.
  BIOLOGICAL IMPORTANCE: *Aquatic Biota:* A • *Mammals:* C • *Reptiles and amphibians:* A • STABILITY LEVEL: 2 • INSTABILITY LEVEL: 5 • ACTION PRIORITY LEVEL: 5 • MAIN ACTION RECOMMENDED: Sustainable use of natural resources • OTHER RECOMMENDED ACTION: Full implementation of the environmental protection area. Area of sources of water abstraction.

TO 007 - São Luiz - PRIORITY LEVEL: A • LOCATION: *State:* Maranhão • *Main municipality:* São Luís • *Municipalities covered:* 5 • VEGETATION TYPES: AA, Pa.
  BIOLOGICAL IMPORTANCE: *Birds:* A • *Aquatic Biota:* A • *Reptiles and amphibians:* A • STABILITY LEVEL: 5 • INSTABILITY LEVEL: 5 • ACTION PRIORITY LEVEL: 4 • MAIN ACTION RECOMMENDED: Environmental restoration.

TO 008 - Upper Guamá River - PRIORITY LEVEL: A • LOCATION: *State:* Pará • *Main municipality:* Capitão Poço • *Municipalities covered:* 10 • VEGETATION TYPES: AA, Da.
  BIOLOGICAL IMPORTANCE: *Birds:* B • *Aquatic Biota:* D • *Mammals:* A • *Reptiles and amphibians:* A • STABILITY LEVEL: 3 • INSTABILITY LEVEL: 10 • ACTION PRIORITY LEVEL: 8 • MAIN ACTION RECOMMENDED: Creation of conservation area • OTHER RECOMMENDED ACTION: Creation of sustainable use conservation area.

TO 009 - Upper Turiaçu Indigenous Land - PRIORITY LEVEL: A • LOCATION: *State:* Pará/Maranhão • *Main municipality:* Centro Novo do Maranhão • *Municipalities covered:* 13 • VEGETATION TYPES: AA, Da, Db.
  BIOLOGICAL IMPORTANCE: *Birds:* A • *Aquatic Biota:* D • *Invertebrates:* D • *Mammals:* A • *Reptiles and amphibians:* A • STABILITY LEVEL: 3 • INSTABILITY LEVEL: 10 • ACTION PRIORITY LEVEL: 8 • MAIN ACTION RECOMMENDED: Protection.

TO 010 - Awá Indigenous Land - PRIORITY LEVEL: A • LOCATION: *State:* Maranhão • *Main municipality:* Centro Novo do Maranhão • *Municipalities covered:* 6 • VEGETATION TYPES: AA, Db.
  BIOLOGICAL IMPORTANCE: *Birds:* A • *Invertebrates:* D • *Mammals:* A • STABILITY LEVEL: 1 • INSTABILITY LEVEL: 10 • ACTION PRIORITY LEVEL: 9 • MAIN ACTION RECOMMENDED: Protection • OTHER RECOMMENDED ACTION: Full registration of the indigenous land.

TO 011 - Guajá Indigenous Land - PRIORITY LEVEL: A • LOCATION: *State:* Maranhão • *Main municipality:* São João do Caru • *Municipalities covered:* 3 • VEGETATION TYPES: AA, Db.
  BIOLOGICAL IMPORTANCE: *Birds:* A • *Invertebrates:* D • *Mammals:* A • IMPORTANCE OF ENVIRONMENTAL GOODS AND SERVICES: A • STABILITY LEVEL: 1 • INSTABILITY LEVEL: 10 • ACTION PRIORITY LEVEL: 9 • MAIN ACTION RECOMMENDED: Protection • OTHER RECOMMENDED ACTION: Full registration of the indigenous land.

TO 012 - Headwaters of the Turiaçu - PRIORITY LEVEL: A • LOCATION: *State:* Maranhão • *Main municipality:* Zé Doca • *Municipalities covered:* 5 • VEGETATION TYPES: AA, Db.
  BIOLOGICAL IMPORTANCE: *Birds:* A • *Mammals:* A • IMPORTANCE OF ENVIRONMENTAL GOODS AND SERVICES: A • STABILITY LEVEL: 0 • INSTABILITY LEVEL: 10 • ACTION PRIORITY LEVEL: 10 • MAIN ACTION RECOMMENDED: Environmental restoration.

TO 013 - Caru Indigenous Land - PRIORITY LEVEL: A • LOCATION: *State:* Maranhão • *Main municipality:* Bom Jardim • *Municipalities covered:* 3 • VEGETATION TYPES: AA, Db.
  BIOLOGICAL IMPORTANCE: *Birds:* A • *Invertebrates:* D • *Mammals:* A • IMPORTANCE OF ENVIRONMENTAL GOODS AND SERVICES: B • STABILITY LEVEL: 3 • INSTABILITY LEVEL: 10 • ACTION PRIORITY LEVEL: 8 • MAIN ACTION RECOMMENDED: Protection.

TO 014 - Gurupi Biological Reserve - PRIORITY LEVEL: A • LOCATION: *State:* Maranhão • *Main municipality:* Centro Novo do Maranhão • *Municipalities covered:* 4 • VEGETATION TYPES: AA, Db.
  BIOLOGICAL IMPORTANCE: *Birds:* A • *Invertebrates:* D • *Mammals:* A • IMPORTANCE OF ENVIRONMENTAL GOODS AND SERVICES: A • STABILITY LEVEL: 9 • INSTABILITY LEVEL: 10 • ACTION PRIORITY LEVEL: 6 • MAIN ACTION RECOMMENDED: Protection • OTHER RECOMMENDED ACTION: Full implementation of the conservation area, inspection and monitoring.

TO 015 - Gurupi - PRIORITY LEVEL: A • LOCATION: *State:* Maranhão/Pará • *Main municipality:* Centro Novo do Maranhão • *Municipalities covered:* 9 • VEGETATION TYPES: AA, Db.

BIOLOGICAL IMPORTANCE: *Birds:* A • *Aquatic Biota:* D • *Invertebrates:* D • *Mammals:* A • *Importance of environmental goods and services:* A • STABILITY LEVEL: 0 • INSTABILITY LEVEL: 10 • ACTION PRIORITY LEVEL: 10 • MAIN ACTION RECOMMENDED: Environmental restoration.

TO 016 - Lower Tocantins - PRIORITY LEVEL: B • LOCATION: *State:* Pará • *Main municipality:* Pacajá • *Municipalities covered:* 8 • VEGETATION TYPES: AA, As, Da, Db, Ds.

BIOLOGICAL IMPORTANCE: *Birds:* B • *Aquatic Biota:* D • *Mammals:* C • *Reptiles and amphibians:* A • IMPORTANCE OF ENVIRONMENTAL GOODS AND SERVICES: B • STABILITY LEVEL: 0 • INSTABILITY LEVEL: 10 • ACTION PRIORITY LEVEL: 10 • MAIN ACTION RECOMMENDED: Sustainable use of natural resources.

TO 017 - Trocará Indigenous Land - PRIORITY LEVEL: B • LOCATION: *State:* Pará • *Main municipality:* Tucuruí • *Municipalities covered:* 3 • VEGETATION TYPES: AA, As, Da, Db.

BIOLOGICAL IMPORTANCE: *Birds:* B • *Mammals:* C • *Reptiles and amphibians:* A • IMPORTANCE OF ENVIRONMENTAL GOODS AND SERVICES: B • STABILITY LEVEL: 3 • INSTABILITY LEVEL: 10 • ACTION PRIORITY LEVEL: 8 • MAIN ACTION RECOMMENDED: Protection • OTHER RECOMMENDED ACTION: Creation of sustainable use conservation area around the indigenous land.

TO 018 - Araribóia Indigenous Land - PRIORITY LEVEL: A • LOCATION: *State:* Maranhão • *Main municipality:* Amarante do Maranhão • *Municipalities covered:* 4 • VEGETATION TYPES: AA, Cs, Da, Db, SN.

BIOLOGICAL IMPORTANCE: *Birds:* A • *Aquatic Biota:* D • *Mammals:* B • IMPORTANCE OF ENVIRONMENTAL GOODS AND SERVICES: B • STABILITY LEVEL: 3 • INSTABILITY LEVEL: 10 • ACTION PRIORITY LEVEL: 8 • MAIN ACTION RECOMMENDED: Protection • OTHER RECOMMENDED ACTION: Inspection and protection. Area at high risk from pressure caused by the development corridor.

TO 019 - Geralda/Toco Preto Indigenous Land - PRIORITY LEVEL: A • LOCATION: *State:* Maranhão • *Main municipality:* Arame • *Municipalities covered:* 2 • VEGETATION TYPES: AA.

BIOLOGICAL IMPORTANCE: *Birds:* A • *Aquatic Biota:* D • *Mammals:* B • IMPORTANCE OF ENVIRONMENTAL GOODS AND SERVICES: B • STABILITY LEVEL: 3 • INSTABILITY LEVEL: 10 • ACTION PRIORITY LEVEL: 8 • MAIN ACTION RECOMMENDED: Protection.

TO 020 - Barra do Corda - PRIORITY LEVEL: A • LOCATION: *State:* Maranhão • *Main municipality:* Grajaú • *Municipalities covered:* 10 • VEGETATION TYPES: AA, Cs, Da, Sa, SN.

BIOLOGICAL IMPORTANCE: *Birds:* A • *Aquatic Biota:* D • *Mammals:* B • IMPORTANCE OF ENVIRONMENTAL GOODS AND SERVICES: B • STABILITY LEVEL: 0 • INSTABILITY LEVEL: 10 • ACTION PRIORITY LEVEL: 10 • MAIN ACTION RECOMMENDED: Sustainable use of natural resources.

TO 021 - Urucu-Juruá Indigenous Land - PRIORITY LEVEL: A • LOCATION: *State:* Maranhão • *Main municipality:* Itaipava do Grajaú • *Municipalities covered:* 1 • VEGETATION TYPES: AA, Da, SN.

BIOLOGICAL IMPORTANCE: *Birds:* A • *Aquatic Biota:* D • *Mammals:* B • IMPORTANCE OF ENVIRONMENTAL GOODS AND SERVICES: B • STABILITY LEVEL: 3 • INSTABILITY LEVEL: 10 • ACTION PRIORITY LEVEL: 8 • MAIN ACTION RECOMMENDED: Protection.

TO 022 - Lagoa Comprida Indigenous Land - PRIORITY LEVEL: A • LOCATION: *State:* Maranhão • *Main municipality:* Itaipava do Grajaú • *Municipalities covered:* 2 • VEGETATION TYPES: AA, SN.

BIOLOGICAL IMPORTANCE: *Birds:* A • *Aquatic Biota:* D • *Mammals:* B • IMPORTANCE OF ENVIRONMENTAL GOODS AND SERVICES: B • STABILITY LEVEL: 3 • INSTABILITY LEVEL: 10 • ACTION PRIORITY LEVEL: 8 • MAIN ACTION RECOMMENDED: Protection.

TO 023 - Cana Brava Indigenous Land - PRIORITY LEVEL: A • LOCATION: *State:* Maranhão • *Main municipality:* Jenipapo dos Vieiras • *Municipalities covered:* 3 • VEGETATION TYPES: AA, SN.

BIOLOGICAL IMPORTANCE: *Birds:* A • *Aquatic Biota:* D • *Mammals:* B • IMPORTANCE OF ENVIRONMENTAL GOODS AND SERVICES: B • STABILITY LEVEL: 3 • INSTABILITY LEVEL: 10 • ACTION PRIORITY LEVEL: 8 • MAIN ACTION RECOMMENDED: Protection.

TO 024 - Bacurizinho Indigenous Land - PRIORITY LEVEL: A • LOCATION: *State:* Maranhão • *Main municipality:* Grajaú • *Municipalities covered:* 2 • VEGETATION TYPES: AA, SN.

BIOLOGICAL IMPORTANCE: *Birds:* A • *Aquatic Biota:* D • *Mammals:* B • IMPORTANCE OF ENVIRONMENTAL GOODS AND SERVICES: B • STABILITY LEVEL: 3 • INSTABILITY LEVEL: 10 • ACTION PRIORITY LEVEL: 8 • MAIN ACTION RECOMMENDED: Protection.

TO 025 - Governador Indigenous Land - PRIORITY LEVEL: A • LOCATION: *State:* Maranhão • *Main municipality:* Amarante do Maranhão • *Municipalities covered:* 1 • VEGETATION TYPES: AA, SN.

BIOLOGICAL IMPORTANCE: *Birds:* A • *Aquatic Biota:* D • *Mammals:* B • IMPORTANCE OF ENVIRONMENTAL GOODS AND SERVICES: B • STABILITY LEVEL: 3 • INSTABILITY LEVEL: 10 • ACTION PRIORITY LEVEL: 8 • MAIN ACTION RECOMMENDED: Protection.

TO 026 - Apinayés Indigenous Land - PRIORITY LEVEL: A • LOCATION: *State:* Tocantins • *Main municipality:* Tocantinópolis • *Municipalities covered:* 6 • VEGETATION TYPES: AA, Sa.

BIOLOGICAL IMPORTANCE: *Aquatic Biota:* A • *Mammals:* D • *Reptiles and amphibians:* A • IMPORTANCE OF ENVIRONMENTAL GOODS AND SERVICES: B • STABILITY LEVEL: 3 • INSTABILITY LEVEL: 10 • ACTION PRIORITY LEVEL: 8 • MAIN ACTION RECOMMENDED: Protection • OTHER RECOMMENDED ACTION: Environmental impact assessment of the Carolina hydroelectric project.

TO 027 - Carolina - Porto Franco (Maranhão) to Itacajá (Tocantins) - PRIORITY LEVEL: A • LOCATION: *State:* Maranhão/Tocantins • *Main municipality:* Carolina • *Municipalities covered:* 24 • VEGETATION TYPES: AA, As, Sa, Sd, SO, Sp.

BIOLOGICAL IMPORTANCE: *Birds:* A • *Aquatic Biota:* A • *Plants:* A • *Mammals:* D • *Reptiles and amphibians:* A • IMPORTANCE OF ENVIRONMENTAL GOODS AND SERVICES: B • STABILITY LEVEL: 0 • INSTABILITY LEVEL: 10 • ACTION PRIORITY LEVEL: 10 • MAIN ACTION RECOMMENDED: Creation of conservation area • OTHER RECOMMENDED ACTION: Creation of sustainable use conservation area connecting the Apinayés and Kraolândia indigenous lands.

TO 028 - Kraolândia Indigenous Land - PRIORITY LEVEL: A • LOCATION: *State:* Tocantins • *Main municipality:* Goiatins • *Municipalities covered:* 4 • VEGETATION TYPES: AA, Sa, Sd, Sp.

BIOLOGICAL IMPORTANCE: *Birds:* A • *Aquatic Biota:* A • *Mammals:* D • IMPORTANCE OF ENVIRONMENTAL GOODS AND SERVICES: C • STABILITY LEVEL: 3 • INSTABILITY LEVEL: 9 • ACTION PRIORITY LEVEL: 7 • MAIN ACTION RECOMMENDED: Protection • OTHER RECOMMENDED ACTION: Environmental impact assessment of the Carolina hydroelectric project.

TO 029 - São Geraldo do Araguaia Environmental Protection Area and Serra dos Martírios/Andorinhas State Park - PRIORITY LEVEL: B • LOCATION: *State:* Pará/Tocantins • *Main municipality:* São Geraldo do Araguaia • *Municipalities covered:* 2 • VEGETATION TYPES: AA, Ds.

BIOLOGICAL IMPORTANCE: *Birds:* B • *Plants:* B • *Mammals:* D • IMPORTANCE OF ENVIRONMENTAL GOODS AND SERVICES: A • STABILITY LEVEL: 15 • INSTABILITY LEVEL: 10 • ACTION PRIORITY LEVEL: 4 • MAIN ACTION RECOMMENDED: Protection • OTHER RECOMMENDED ACTION: Full implementation of the environmental protection area.

TO 030 - Serra dos Martírios/Andorinhas State Park - PRIORITY LEVEL: B • LOCATION: *State:* Pará • *Main municipality:* São Geraldo do Araguaia • *Municipalities covered:* 3 • VEGETATION TYPES: AA, As, Ds.

BIOLOGICAL IMPORTANCE: *Birds:* B • *Plants:* B • *Mammals:* D • IMPORTANCE OF ENVIRONMENTAL GOODS AND SERVICES: A • STABILITY LEVEL: 15 • INSTABILITY LEVEL: 10 • ACTION PRIORITY LEVEL: 4 • MAIN ACTION RECOMMENDED: Protection.

TO 031 - Area surrounding the Serra das Andorinhas - PRIORITY LEVEL: B • LOCATION: *State:* Pará • *Main municipality:* São Geraldo do Araguaia • *Municipalities covered:* 3 • VEGETATION TYPES: AA, Ds.

BIOLOGICAL IMPORTANCE: *Birds:* B • *Plants:* B • *Mammals:* D • IMPORTANCE OF ENVIRONMENTAL GOODS AND SERVICES: A • STABILITY LEVEL: 0 • INSTABILITY LEVEL: 10 • ACTION PRIORITY LEVEL: 10 • MAIN ACTION RECOMMENDED: Incorporation of the existing conservation area • OTHER RECOMMENDED ACTION: Incorporation of the area into the São Geraldo do Araguaia Environmental Protection Area, which includes the Serra dos Martírios/Andorinhas State Park.

TO 032 - Carajás - PRIORITY LEVEL: A • LOCATION: *State:* Pará • *Main municipality:* Marabá • *Municipalities covered:* 3 • VEGETATION TYPES: AA, As, Ds.

BIOLOGICAL IMPORTANCE: *Birds:* A • *Aquatic Biota:* D • *Plants:* A • *Invertebrates:* A • *Mammals:* D • *Reptiles and amphibians:* A • IMPORTANCE OF ENVIRONMENTAL GOODS AND SERVICES: A • STABILITY LEVEL: 0

• Instability level: 10 • Action priority level: 10 • Main action recommended: Sustainable use of natural resources.

TO 033 - Tapirapé Biological Reserve - Priority level: A • Location: *State:* Pará • *Main municipality:* Marabá • *Municipalities covered:* 2 • Vegetation types: As, Ds.

Biological importance: *Birds:* A • *Aquatic Biota:* D • *Plants:* A • *Invertebrates:* A • *Mammals:* D • *Reptiles and amphibians:* A • Importance of environmental goods and services: A • Stability level: 9 • Instability level: 10 • Action priority level: 6 • Main action recommended: Environmental restoration • Other recommended action: Full implementation of the biological reserve.

TO 034 - Tapirapé-Aquiri National Forest - Priority level: A • Location: *State:* Pará • *Main municipality:* Marabá • *Municipalities covered:* 2 • Vegetation types: As, Ds.

Biological importance: *Birds:* A • *Aquatic Biota:* D • *Plants:* A • *Invertebrates:* A • *Mammals:* D • *Reptiles and amphibians:* A • Importance of environmental goods and services: A • Stability level: 6 • Instability level: 10 • Action priority level: 7 • Main action recommended: Protection • Other recommended action: Transformation of the edges of the national forest into a direct use conservation area and studies on the reclassification of the conservation area, from National Forest to Biological Reserve.

TO 035 - Igarapé Gelado Environmental Protection Area - Priority level: A • Location: *State:* Pará • *Main municipality:* Parauapebas • *Municipalities covered:* 2 • Vegetation types: AA, As, Dm, Ds.

Biological importance: *Birds:* A • *Aquatic Biota:* D • *Plants:* A • *Invertebrates:* A • *Mammals:* D • Importance of environmental goods and services: A • Stability level: 6 • Instability level: 10 • Action priority level: 7 • Main action recommended: Protection.

TO 036 - Carajás 1 - Overlap between the Itacaiúnas and Tapirapé-Aquiri National Forests - Priority level: A • Location: *State:* Pará • *Main municipality:* Marabá • *Municipalities covered:* 3 • Vegetation types: As, Ds.

Biological importance: *Aquatic Biota:* D • *Plants:* A • *Invertebrates:* A • *Mammals:* D • *Reptiles and amphibians:* A • Importance of environmental goods and services: A • Stability level: 6 • Instability level: 10 • Action priority level: 7 • Main action recommended: Studies to identify priority actions • Other recommended action: Studies to find a legal solution for the overlap.

TO 037 - Itacaiúnas National Forest - Priority level: A • Location: *State:* Pará • *Main municipality:* Marabá • *Municipalities covered:* 3 • Vegetation types: As, Ds.

Biological importance: *Aquatic Biota:* D • *Plants:* A • *Invertebrates:* A • Importance of environmental goods and services: A • Stability level: 6 • Instability level: 10 • Action priority level: 7 • Main action recommended: Protection.

TO 038 - Xikrin do Cateté Indigenous Land - Priority level: A • Location: *State:* Pará • *Main municipality:* Parauapebas • *Municipalities covered:* 4 • Vegetation types: AA, As, Dm, Ds.

Biological importance: *Aquatic Biota:* D • *Plants:* A • *Invertebrates:* A • *Mammals:* D • *Reptiles and amphibians:* D • Importance of environmental goods and services: A • Stability level: 3 • Instability level: 10 • Action priority level: 8 • Main action recommended: Sustainable use of natural resources.

TO 039 - Carajás National Forest - Priority level: A • Location: *State:* Pará • *Main municipality:* Parauapebas • *Municipalities covered:* 4 • Vegetation types: AA, As, Dm, Ds.

Biological importance: *Birds:* A • *Aquatic Biota:* D • *Plants:* A • *Invertebrates:* A • *Mammals:* D • Importance of environmental goods and services: A • Stability level: 6 • Instability level: 10 • Action priority level: 7 • Main action recommended: Protection.

TO 040 - Arraias River - Priority level: B • Location: *State:* Pará • *Main municipality:* Santa Maria das Barreiras • *Municipalities covered:* 3 • Vegetation types: AA, Sa, Sg, SN, SO.

Biological importance: *Birds:* B • *Invertebrates:* D • *Reptiles and amphibians:* D • Stability level: 0 • Instability level: 10 • Action priority level: 10 • Main action recommended: Creation of conservation area • Other recommended action: Creation of full protection conservation area.

TO 041 - Conceição do Araguaia - Priority level: A • Location: *State:* Pará/Tocantins • *Main municipality:* Conceição do Araguaia • *Municipalities covered:* 4 • Vegetation types: AA, As, Fa, Sa, Sg, SN.

Biological importance: *Birds:* B • *Aquatic Biota:* A • *Invertebrates:* D • Stability level: 0 • Instability level: 10 • Action priority level: 10 • Main action recommended: Creation of conservation area • Other recommended action: Creation of full protection conservation area in that part of the area on the left bank of the Araguaia river, avoiding overlap with the Maracandyba indigenous land.

TO 042 - Area to the north of the Ilha do Bananal - Priority level: A • Location: *State:* Pará/Mato Grosso/Tocantins • *Main municipality:* Pium • *Municipalities covered:* 8 • Vegetation types: AA, As, Sa, SN, SO, Sp.

Biological importance: *Birds:* A • *Aquatic Biota:* A • *Plants:* A • *Mammals:* C • Stability level: 0 • Instability level: 9 • Action priority level: 9 • Main action recommended: Creation of conservation area • Other recommended action: Creation of full protection conservation area in the remaining areas of open rainforest, cerrados and transition zones.

TO 043 - Ilha do Bananal 1 - Araguaia National Park • Priority level: A • Location: *State:* Tocantins • *Main municipality:* Pium • *Municipalities covered:* 3 • Vegetation types: AA, SN, Sp.

Biological importance: *Birds:* A • *Aquatic Biota:* A • *Mammals:* C • Stability level: 9 • Instability level: 8 • Action priority level: 5 • Main action recommended: Protection • Other recommended action: Full implementation of the conservation area.

TO 044 - Ilha do Bananal 2 - Araguaia National Park and Boto Velho Indigenous Land - Priority level: A • Location: *State:* Tocantins • *Main municipality:* Lagoa da Confusão • *Municipalities covered:* 2 • Vegetation types: Fa, Sd, SN, Sp.

Biological importance: *Birds:* A • *Aquatic Biota:* A • *Mammals:* C • Stability level: 10 • Instability level: 9 • Action priority level: 5 • Main action recommended: Studies to identify priority actions • Other recommended action: Actions to resolve the conflict of the overlap between the indigenous land and the national park, in a way that it doesn't compromise the conservation area.

TO 045 - Ilha do Bananal 3 - South of the Araguaia National Park - Priority level: A • Location: *State:* Tocantins • *Main municipality:* Lagoa da Confusão • *Municipalities covered:* 1 • Vegetation types: Fa, Sd, Sg, Sp.

Biological importance: *Birds:* A • *Aquatic Biota:* A • *Mammals:* C • Stability level: 9 • Instability level: 9 • Action priority level: 5 • Main action recommended: Protection • Other recommended action: Full implementation of the conservation area.

TO 046 - Tapirapé/Karajá Indigenous Land - Priority level: A • Location: *State:* Mato Grosso • *Main municipality:* Santa Terezinha • *Municipalities covered:* 2 • Vegetation types: AA, Sd, SN, Sp.

Biological importance: *Birds:* A • *Aquatic Biota:* A • *Mammals:* C • Stability level: 3 • Instability level: 8 • Action priority level: 7 • Main action recommended: Protection.

TO 047 - Ilha do Bananal 4 - Araguaia Indigenous Park • Priority level: A • Location: *State:* Tocantins/Goiás • *Main municipality:* Formoso do Araguaia • *Municipalities covered:* 9 • Vegetation types: AA, Fa, Sa, Sd, Sg, SN, Sp.

Biological importance: *Birds:* A • *Aquatic Biota:* A • *Mammals:* C • Stability level: 3 • Instability level: 9 • Action priority level: 7 • Main action recommended: Protection.

TO 048 - Araguaia River and estuary of the Rio das Mortes - Priority level: A • Location: *State:* Mato Grosso • *Main municipality:* Cocalinho • *Municipalities covered:* 5 • Vegetation types: Sa, Sg, SN, Sp.

Biological importance: *Birds:* A • *Aquatic Biota:* A • *Mammals:* C • Stability level: 0 • Instability level: 9 • Action priority level: 9 • Main action recommended: Sustainable use of natural resources.

TO 049 - Right Floodplains of the Javaés - Priority level: A • Location: *State:* Tocantins • *Main municipality:* Formoso do Araguaia • *Municipalities covered:* 5 • Vegetation types: AA, Sa, Sd, SN, Sp.

Biological importance: *Birds:* A • *Aquatic Biota:* A • *Mammals:* C • Stability level: 0 • Instability level: 9 • Action priority level: 9 • Main action recommended: Sustainable use of natural resources.

TO 050 - Araguaia Environmental Protection Area - Priority level: A • Location: *State:* Mato Grosso/Goiás • *Main municipality:* Cocalinho • *Municipalities covered:* 5 • Vegetation types: Sa, Sg, SN, Sp.
  Biological importance: *Birds:* A • *Aquatic Biota:* A • *Mammals:* C • *Reptiles and amphibians:* B • Stability level: 6 • Instability level: 9 • Action priority level: 6 • Main action recommended: Change the conservation area category • Other recommended action: Reclassification of the conservation area from Environmental Protection Area to full protection conservation area.

TO 051 - Capim River - Priority level: A • Location: *State:* Pará • *Main municipality:* Paragominas • *Municipalities covered:* 6 • Vegetation types: AA, Da, Db.
  Biological importance: *Birds:* A • *Aquatic Biota:* D • *Plants:* A Importance of environmental goods and services: A • Stability level: 0 • Instability level: 10 • Action priority level: 10 • Main action recommended: Creation of conservation area • Other recommended action: Creation of full protection conservation area.

2
PRIORITY AREAS IN THE SOLIMÕES / AMAZONAS FLOODPLAINS REGION

VZ 001 - Içá - Upper Solimões - PRIORITY LEVEL: B • LOCATION: *State:* Amazonas • *Main municipality:* Santo Antônio do Içá • *Municipalities covered:* 2 • VEGETATION TYPES: Da, Db, LO • COMMENTS: Catfish migration route; biological importance. Deforestation in Brazil: frontier area. Drug trafficking; illegal fishing by Colombian and entry point for Colombian ornamental fish collectors.
BIOLOGICAL IMPORTANCE: *Birds:* D • *Aquatic biota:* A • *Mammals:* D • *Reptiles and amphibians:* C • STABILITY LEVEL: 0 • INSTABILITY LEVEL: 2 • ACTION PRIORITY LEVEL: 4 • MAIN ACTION RECOMMENDED: Protection • OTHER RECOMMENDED ACTION: Inspection and biological inventories.

VZ 002 - Juami-Japurá Ecological Station - PRIORITY LEVEL: B • LOCATION: *State:* Amazonas • *Main municipality:* Japurá • *Municipalities covered:* 3 • VEGETATION TYPES: Da, Db, Ld, LO • COMMENTS: Biological importance; full implementation of conservation area; conservation area.
BIOLOGICAL IMPORTANCE: *Birds:* D • *Aquatic biota:* A • *Mammals:* D • *Reptiles and amphibians:* C • STABILITY LEVEL: 6 • INSTABILITY LEVEL: 1 • ACTION PRIORITY LEVEL: 2 • MAIN ACTION RECOMMENDED: Protection • OTHER RECOMMENDED ACTION: Inspection and full implementation of conservation area.

VZ 003 - Jutaí/Solimões Ecological Reserve - PRIORITY LEVEL: A • LOCATION: *State:* Amazonas • *Main municipality:* Jutaí • *Municipalities covered:* 3 • VEGETATION TYPES: Da, Db • COMMENTS: Biological importance; unique conservation area/habitat; need for full implementation of conservation area; anthropogenic pressure.
BIOLOGICAL IMPORTANCE: *Birds:* A • *Aquatic biota:* A • *Mammals:* D • STABILITY LEVEL: 6 • INSTABILITY LEVEL: 3 • ACTION PRIORITY LEVEL: 3 • MAIN ACTION RECOMMENDED: Protection • OTHER RECOMMENDED ACTION: Inspection to ensure appropriate management of fishing occurring in the area; studies to evaluate the possible need for reclassification to sustainable use conservation area.

VZ 004 - Middle Jutaí - PRIORITY LEVEL: A • LOCATION: *State:* Amazonas • *Main municipality:* Jutaí • *Municipalities covered:* 1 • VEGETATION TYPES: Ab, Da, Db • COMMENTS: Biological importance. Located between conservation area and indigenous lands.
BIOLOGICAL IMPORTANCE: *Birds:* A • *Aquatic biota:* B • STABILITY LEVEL: 0 • INSTABILITY LEVEL: 1 • ACTION PRIORITY LEVEL: 4 • MAIN ACTION RECOMMENDED: Identify priority actions • OTHER RECOMMENDED ACTION: Inspection.

VZ 005 - Estrela da Paz Indigenous Land - PRIORITY LEVEL: A • LOCATION: *State:* Amazonas • *Main municipality:* Jutaí • *Municipalities covered:* 1 • VEGETATION TYPES: Da, Db • COMMENTS: Adjacent to indigenous land and area of biological importance (conservation thematic working group). Indigenous population with prior demands for support in undertaking sustainable area management.
BIOLOGICAL IMPORTANCE: *Birds:* A • *Aquatic biota:* A • STABILITY LEVEL: 3 • INSTABILITY LEVEL: 1 • ACTION PRIORITY LEVEL: 3 • MAIN ACTION RECOMMENDED: Sustainable use of natural resources • OTHER RECOMMENDED ACTION: Biological inventories.

VZ 006 - Macarrão and Espírito Santo Indigenous Lands - PRIORITY LEVEL: A • LOCATION: *State:* Amazonas • *Main municipality:* Jutaí • *Municipalities covered:* 1 • VEGETATION TYPES: Da, Db • COMMENTS: Indigenous land in an area of extreme/high biological importance. Population interested in sustainable use and resource management.
BIOLOGICAL IMPORTANCE: *Birds:* A • *Aquatic biota:* A • *Mammals:* A • STABILITY LEVEL: 3 • INSTABILITY LEVEL: 0 • ACTION PRIORITY LEVEL: 2 • MAIN ACTION RECOMMENDED: Sustainable use of natural resources • OTHER RECOMMENDED ACTION: Biological inventories and anthropological studies.

VZ 007 - Acapuri de Cima Indigenous Land - PRIORITY LEVEL: A • LOCATION: *State:* Amazonas • *Main municipality:* Fonte Boa • *Municipalities covered:* 2 • VEGETATION TYPES: Da • COMMENTS: Indigenous land, not fully demarcated, located in state conservation area. Populations interested in resource management.
BIOLOGICAL IMPORTANCE: *Birds:* A • *Aquatic biota:* A • *Mammals:* A • STABILITY LEVEL: 7 • INSTABILITY LEVEL: 2 • ACTION PRIORITY LEVEL: 3 • MAIN ACTION RECOMMENDED: Sustainable use of natural resources • OTHER RECOMMENDED ACTION: Biological inventories and anthropological studies.

VZ 008 - Mamirauá Sustainable Development Reserve - PRIORITY LEVEL: A • LOCATION: *State:* Amazonas • *Main municipality:* Fonte Boa • *Municipalities covered:* 8 • VEGETATION TYPES: Da, Db, LO • COMMENTS: Conservation area located in a region of biological importance. Central Amazon ecological corridor. The only conservation area located entirely on floodplains.
BIOLOGICAL IMPORTANCE: *Birds:* B • *Aquatic biota:* A • *Invertebrates:* A • *Mammals:* A • IMPORTANCE FOR ECOLOGICAL GOODS AND SERVICES: B • STABILITY LEVEL: 6 • INSTABILITY LEVEL: 3 • ACTION PRIORITY LEVEL: 3 • MAIN ACTION RECOMMENDED: Sustainable use of natural resources • OTHER RECOMMENDED ACTION: Promotion of fishery management in the major river valleys (Solimões and Japurá).

VZ 009 - Paraná do Lago Paricá Indigenous Land - PRIORITY LEVEL: A • LOCATION: *State:* Amazonas • *Main municipality:* Maraã • *Municipalities covered:* 1 • VEGETATION TYPES: Da • COMMENTS: Indigenous land located in an area classified by the biota thematic working group as maximum priority. Area fully registered. Populations interested in the sustainable use and resource management.
BIOLOGICAL IMPORTANCE: *Birds:* B • *Aquatic biota:* A • *Mammals:* A • STABILITY LEVEL: 5 • INSTABILITY LEVEL: 0 • ACTION PRIORITY LEVEL: 2 • MAIN ACTION RECOMMENDED: Sustainable use of natural resources • OTHER RECOMMENDED ACTION: Anthropological studies.

VZ 010 - Cuiú-Cuiú Indigenous Land - PRIORITY LEVEL: A • LOCATION: *State:* Amazonas • *Main municipality:* Maraã • *Municipalities covered:* 1 • VEGETATION TYPES: Da, Db • COMMENTS: Delimited indigenous land; biological importance classified as A by the biota thematic working group. Threats of illegal occupation. Populations interested in the sustainable use and resource management, in conjunction with the Mamirauá Project.
BIOLOGICAL IMPORTANCE: *Birds:* B • *Invertebrates:* A • *Mammals:* A • STABILITY LEVEL: 3 • INSTABILITY LEVEL: 1 • ACTION PRIORITY LEVEL: 3 • MAIN ACTION RECOMMENDED: Sustainable use of natural resources • OTHER RECOMMENDED ACTION: Biological inventories and anthropological studies.

VZ 011 - Lower Juruá - PRIORITY LEVEL: A • LOCATION: *State:* Amazonas • *Main municipality:* Juruá • *Municipalities covered:* 3 • VEGETATION TYPES: Da, Db • COMMENTS: Important for birds and fishes (biota working group). Presence of traditional populations, involved with sustainable development program (presence of MEB/GPD), practicing management of lakes. Anthropogenic pressure to the north, in the area influenced by the Amazon central corridor.

BIOLOGICAL IMPORTANCE: *Birds:* A • *Aquatic biota:* B • STABILITY LEVEL: 0 • INSTABILITY LEVEL: 3 • ACTION PRIORITY LEVEL: 5 • MAIN ACTION RECOMMENDED: Sustainable use of natural resources • OTHER RECOMMENDED ACTION: Inspection of turtles and fishery; biological inventories; anthropological and social studies.

VZ 012 - Jaquiri Indigenous Land - PRIORITY LEVEL: A • LOCATION: *State:* Amazonas • *Main municipality:* Alvarães • *Municipalities covered:* 2 • VEGETATION TYPES: Da • COMMENTS: Indigenous land located in area identified as biologically important by of the thematic working group. Anthropogenic pressure caused by outside fishermen using the Lago Branco area. Populations interested in sustainable use and management, in conjunction with the Mamirauá Project.

BIOLOGICAL IMPORTANCE: *Birds:* A • *Aquatic biota:* A • *Invertebrates:* A • *Mammals:* A • STABILITY LEVEL: 9 • INSTABILITY LEVEL: 3 • ACTION PRIORITY LEVEL: 3 • MAIN ACTION RECOMMENDED: Sustainable use of natural resources • OTHER RECOMMENDED ACTION: Anthropological studies.

VZ 013 - Japurá - PRIORITY LEVEL: A • LOCATION: *State:* Amazonas • *Main municipality:* Japurá • *Municipalities covered:* 3 • VEGETATION TYPES: Da, Db, Pa • COMMENTS: Area proposed by the bird and aquatic biota thematic working groups. Taking of young fish. Agrarian threats (sales of inappropriate lands). Located in the zone of influence of the Amazon central corridor and adjacent to the Mamirauá and Amanã Sustainable Development Reserves.

BIOLOGICAL IMPORTANCE: *Birds:* B • *Aquatic biota:* A • *Mammals:* A • STABILITY LEVEL: 0 • INSTABILITY LEVEL: 0 • ACTION PRIORITY LEVEL: 3 • MAIN ACTION RECOMMENDED: Sustainable use of natural resources • OTHER RECOMMENDED ACTION: Inspection and biological inventories.

VZ 014 - Estuário (Gurupá Islands) - PRIORITY LEVEL: B • LOCATION: *State:* Pará/Amapá • *Main municipality:* Gurupá • *Municipalities covered:* 8 • VEGETATION TYPES: AA, Da, Db, Pa • COMMENTS: Area of high population density; pressured from fishing and logging. Proposed for genetic conservation of threatened species, such as *virola* and *açaí*. Creation of conservation area (environmental protection area) proposed by the *Associação Comunitária* and *Fase*. Area recommended by the conservation areas thematic working group – landscape blocks.

BIOLOGICAL IMPORTANCE: *Birds:* B • *Aquatic biota:* A • *Mammals:* C • *Reptiles and amphibians:* B • IMPORTANCE FOR ECOLOGICAL GOODS AND SERVICES: B • STABILITY LEVEL: 0 • INSTABILITY LEVEL: 7 • ACTION PRIORITY LEVEL: 8 • MAIN ACTION RECOMMENDED: Creation of conservation area • OTHER RECOMMENDED ACTION: Creation of environmental protection area already proposed by the local community; inspection; socio-economic assessment.

VZ 015 - Lower Solimões - PRIORITY LEVEL: A • LOCATION: *State:* Amazonas • *Main municipality:* Anori • *Municipalities covered:* 6 • VEGETATION TYPES: AA, Da, Db, Ds • COMMENTS: Biological importance for mammals, aquatic biota and birds. Threatened by anthropogenic pressure (logging activities), mainly near development corridors.

BIOLOGICAL IMPORTANCE: *Birds:* B • *Aquatic biota:* A • *Plants:* A • *Mammals:* A • IMPORTANCE FOR ECOLOGICAL GOODS AND SERVICES: B • STABILITY LEVEL: 0 • INSTABILITY LEVEL: 4 • ACTION PRIORITY LEVEL: 5 • MAIN ACTION RECOMMENDED: Sustainable use of natural resources • OTHER RECOMMENDED ACTION: Biological inventories and socio-economic assessment.

VZ 016 - Lower Solimões - PRIORITY LEVEL: A • LOCATION: *State:* Amazonas • *Main municipality:* Anori • *Municipalities covered:* 2 • VEGETATION TYPES: Da • COMMENTS: Biological priority area with indigenous lands and one direct use environmental protection area. Impact caused by Urucu oil and gas pipelines.

BIOLOGICAL IMPORTANCE: *Birds:* C • *Aquatic biota:* A • *Plants:* A • *Mammals:* A • STABILITY LEVEL: 3 • INSTABILITY LEVEL: 8 • ACTION PRIORITY LEVEL: 7 • MAIN ACTION RECOMMENDED: Sustainable use of natural resources • OTHER RECOMMENDED ACTION: Biological inventories and anthropological and socio-economic assessments.

VZ 017 - Lower Solimões/Medium Purus Environmental Protection Area - PRIORITY LEVEL: A • LOCATION: *State:* Amazonas • *Main municipality:* Beruri • *Municipalities covered:* 2 • VEGETATION TYPES: Da, Db • COMMENTS: Impact caused by the Urucu oil pipeline. Biological importance. Area of direct use environmental protection area.

BIOLOGICAL IMPORTANCE: *Birds:* C • *Aquatic biota:* A • *Plants:* A • *Mammals:* A • STABILITY LEVEL: 2 • INSTABILITY LEVEL: 5 • ACTION PRIORITY LEVEL: 5 • MAIN ACTION RECOMMENDED: Sustainable use of natural resources • OTHER RECOMMENDED ACTION: Biological inventories and anthropological studies.

VZ 018 - Lower Solimões/Lago Aiapoá Indigenous Land - PRIORITY LEVEL: A • LOCATION: *State:* Amazonas • *Main municipality:* Anori • *Municipalities covered:* 2 • VEGETATION TYPES: Da • COMMENTS: Overlap between an indigenous land and a state direct use environmental protection area in the zone of influenc of the Urucu oilfields.

BIOLOGICAL IMPORTANCE: *Birds:* C • *Aquatic biota:* A • *Plants:* A • *Mammals:* A • STABILITY LEVEL: 3 • INSTABILITY LEVEL: 5 • ACTION PRIORITY LEVEL: 4 • MAIN ACTION RECOMMENDED: Sustainable use of natural resources • OTHER RECOMMENDED ACTION: Biological inventories and anthropological studies.

VZ 019 - Lower Solimões/Ilha do Camaleão Indigenous Land - PRIORITY LEVEL: A • LOCATION: *State:* Amazonas • *Main municipality:* Beruri • *Municipalities covered:* 3 • VEGETATION TYPES: Da • COMMENTS: Indigenous land near the zone of influence of Manaus. Oilfields.

BIOLOGICAL IMPORTANCE: *Birds:* C • *Aquatic biota:* A • STABILITY LEVEL: 0 • INSTABILITY LEVEL: 8 • ACTION PRIORITY LEVEL: 8 • MAIN ACTION RECOMMENDED: Sustainable use of natural resources.

VZ 020 - Lower Solimões/Lago Beruri Indigenous Land - PRIORITY LEVEL: A • LOCATION: *State:* Amazonas • *Main municipality:* Beruri • *Municipalities covered:* 1 • VEGETATION TYPES: Da, Db • COMMENTS: Indigenous land near the zone of influence of Manaus and the Uraí oilfields.

BIOLOGICAL IMPORTANCE: *Birds:* C • *Aquatic biota:* A • *Mammals:* A • STABILITY LEVEL: 3 • INSTABILITY LEVEL: 8 • ACTION PRIORITY LEVEL: 7 • MAIN ACTION RECOMMENDED: Sustainable use of natural resources • OTHER RECOMMENDED ACTION: Biological inventories and anthropological studies.

VZ 021 - Paraná do Arauató Indigenous Land/Medium Amazonas - PRIORITY LEVEL: A • LOCATION: *State:* Amazonas • *Main municipality:* Itacoatiara • *Municipalities covered:* 1 • VEGETATION TYPES: AA, Da • COMMENTS: Indigenous land adjacent to a biological priority polygon. Area of anthropogenic pressure and a development corridor.

BIOLOGICAL IMPORTANCE: *Birds:* A • *Aquatic biota:* A • *Mammals:* B • IMPORTANCE FOR ECOLOGICAL GOODS AND SERVICES: B • STABILITY LEVEL: 1 • INSTABILITY LEVEL: 9 • ACTION PRIORITY LEVEL: 8 • MAIN ACTION RECOMMENDED: Sustainable use of natural resources • OTHER RECOMMENDED ACTION: Demarcation of the indigenous land; biological inventories and anthropological studies.

VZ 022 - Rio Urubu Indigenous Land - PRIORITY LEVEL: A • LOCATION: *State:* Amazonas • *Main municipality:* Itacoatiara • *Municipalities covered:* 1 • VEGETATION TYPES: Db • COMMENTS: Area not yet demarcated, adjacent to a biological priority polygon. Area influenced by Manaus. Logging pressure.

BIOLOGICAL IMPORTANCE: *Birds:* A • *Aquatic biota:* A • *Mammals:* B • STABILITY LEVEL: 1 • INSTABILITY LEVEL: 9 • ACTION PRIORITY LEVEL: 8 • MAIN ACTION RECOMMENDED: Sustainable use of natural resources • OTHER RECOMMENDED ACTION: Demarcation of the indigenous land; biological inventories and anthropological studies.

VZ 023 - Medium Amazonas - PRIORITY LEVEL: A • LOCATION: *State:* Amazonas/Pará • *Main municipality:* Itacoatiara • *Municipalities covered:* 16 • VEGETATION TYPES: AA, Da, Db, Pa, SO, Sp • COMMENTS: Area of biological and anthropological importance with the presence of community capable of fishery resource management and with ecotourism potential.

BIOLOGICAL IMPORTANCE: *Birds:* A • *Aquatic biota:* A • *Mammals:* B • IMPORTANCE FOR ECOLOGICAL GOODS AND SERVICES: B • STABILITY LEVEL: 0 • INSTABILITY LEVEL: 9 • ACTION PRIORITY LEVEL: 9 • MAIN ACTION RECOMMENDED: Sustainable use of natural resources • OTHER RECOMMENDED ACTION: Full registration of the indigenous land located in the area; management of lakes; biological inventories and anthropological studies.

VZ 024 - Nhamundá Environmental Protection Area - PRIORITY LEVEL: A • LOCATION: *State:* Amazonas • *Main municipality:* Parintins •

Municipalities covered: 5 • Vegetation types: AA, Da, Pa, Sp • Comments: Area affected by fishery and logging. Lack of biological studies, especially related to fauna.

    Biological importance: *Birds:* A • *Aquatic biota:* A • *Mammals:* C • Stability level: 2 • Instability level: 3 • Action priority level: 4 • Main action recommended: Sustainable use of natural resources • Other recommended action: Inspection and biological inventories.

VZ 025 - Nhamundá Park - Priority level: A • Location: *State:* Amazonas/Pará • *Main municipality:* Nhamundá • *Municipalities covered:* 2 • Vegetation types: AA, Da, Db, Pa, Sp • Comments: Located in area classified as A by the bird and aquatic biota thematic working groups. State conservation area – the only floodplain area.

    Biological importance: *Birds:* A • *Aquatic biota:* A • *Mammals:* C • Importance for ecological goods and services: B • Stability level: 3 • Instability level: 3 • Action priority level: 4 • Main action recommended: Sustainable use of natural resources • Other recommended action: Biological inventories and environment studies.

VZ 026 - Andirá-Marau Indigenous Land - Priority level: A • Location: *State:* Amazonas/Pará • *Main municipality:* Aveiro • *Municipalities covered:* 6 • Vegetation types: Da, Db, Pa.

    Biological importance: *Birds:* A • *Plants:* A • *Mammals:* B • Importance for ecological goods and services: B • Stability level: 5 • Instability level: 3 • Action priority level: 3 • Main action recommended: Sustainable use of natural resources • Other recommended action: Anthropological studies.

VZ 027 - Paraná dos Ramos - Priority level: A • Location: *State:* Amazonas • *Main municipality:* Maués • *Municipalities covered:* 3 • Vegetation types: Da, Db, Pa • Comments: Area of biological importance with the presence of various groups of primates requiring conservation. Area should be increased precisely in order to protect these primates and other biological groups.

    Biological importance: *Plants:* A • *Mammals:* B • Importance for ecological goods and services: B • Stability level: 0 • Instability level: 3 • Action priority level: 5 • Main action recommended: Creation of conservation area • Other recommended action: Creation of full protection conservation area. Area with over fifteen species of primates.

VZ 028 - Area between the Andirá-Marau and Parna of Amazônia Indigenous Lands - Priority level: A • Location: *State:* Pará • *Main municipality:* Aveiro • *Municipalities covered:* 1 • Vegetation types: Da, Db • Comments: Area adjacent to the Maraú Indigenous Land and the Amazonia National Park conservation area.

    Biological importance: *Birds:* A • *Mammals:* B • Importance for ecological goods and services: B • Stability level: 0 • Instability level: 3 • Action priority level: 5 • Main action recommended: Sustainable use of natural resources.

VZ 029 - Tapajós-Arapiuns Extractive Reserve - Priority level: B • Location: *State:* Pará • *Main municipality:* Santarém • *Municipalities covered:* 2 • Vegetation types: Db, SO • Comments: High potential for extractive products and with strong institutional support of NGOs (GDA, Ceapac, Pastoral da Terra, Ipam) and government bodies (CNPT/Ibama, Ceplac, Embrapa).

    Biological importance: *Birds:* C • *Aquatic biota:* A • *Plants:* D • *Mammals:* B • *Reptiles and amphibians:* B • Importance for ecological goods and services: B • Stability level: 2 • Instability level: 9 • Action priority level: 8 • Main action recommended: Sustainable use of natural resources • Other recommended action: Management plans; socio-economic and extraction assessments.

VZ 030 - Tapajós National Forest - Priority level: B • Location: *State:* Pará • *Main municipality:* Santarém • *Municipalities covered:* 5 • Vegetation types: AA, Db, Ds • Comments: High biodiversity and with strong institutional support of NGOs (Projeto Saúde e Alegria, GDA, etc.) and government bodies (Ibama, CNPT, Embrapa, Ipam, STR).

    Biological importance: *Birds:* A • *Mammals:* B • *Reptiles and amphibians:* B • Importance for ecological goods and services: B • Stability level: 6 • Instability level: 9 • Action priority level: 6 • Main action recommended: Sustainable use of natural resources • Other recommended action: Biological inventories and socio-economic assessments.

VZ 031 - Lower Amazonas - Santarém - Priority level: B • Location: *State:* Pará • *Main municipality:* Santarém • *Municipalities covered:* 7 • Vegetation types: AA, Db, Pa, SO, Sp • Comments: Area of high importance for fishery, an important migration route for catfishes. Turtle breeding grounds within the area. There are various community, non-governmental and governmental organizations engaged in the management of natural resources of the floodplain, including fishery, agro-forestry and family agricultural systems.

    Biological importance: *Birds:* B • *Aquatic biota:* A • *Plants:* D • *Invertebrates:* B • *Mammals:* B • *Reptiles and amphibians:* B • Importance for ecological goods and services: B • Stability level: 0 • Instability level: 9 • Action priority level: 9 • Main action recommended: Sustainable use of natural resources • Other recommended action: Inspection; support to sustainable management of natural resources; land use (agriculture, livestock), management and socio-economics studies.

VZ 032 - Quilombo Pacoval - Priority level: B • Location: *State:* Pará • *Main municipality:* Santarém • *Municipalities covered:* 2 • Vegetation types: Pa, Sp • Comments: Institutional capacity. Pressure from seasonal visitors second homes.

    Biological importance: *Aquatic biota:* A • *Invertebrates:* B • *Mammals:* B • *Reptiles and amphibians:* B • Importance for ecological goods and services: B • Stability level: 0 • Instability level: 9 • Action priority level: 9 • Main action recommended: Protection • Other recommended action: Inspection to control influx of holiday makers.

VZ 033 - Lower Amazonas - Priority level: A • Location: *State:* Pará • *Main municipality:* Prainha • *Municipalities covered:* 4 • Vegetation types: AA, Da, Db, Ds, Pa, SO, Sp • Comments: Migration routes of big catfishes, high levels of shrimp fishing. Large scale commercial fishing. Identified by the conservation areas thematic working group as an important landscape area. Area of ecological transition.

    Biological importance: *Birds:* B • *Aquatic biota:* A • *Plants:* A • *Mammals:* B • *Reptiles and amphibians:* D • Importance for ecological goods and services: B • Stability level: 0 • Instability level: 8 • Action priority level: 8 • Main action recommended: Creation of conservation area • Other recommended action: Creation of sustainable use conservation areas; biological inventories and fishery management plans.

VZ 034 - Medium Amazonas - Priority level: B • Location: *State:* Pará • *Main municipality:* Monte Alegre • *Municipalities covered:* 4 • Vegetation types: AA, As, Ds, SO • Comments: Area identified by the reptiles thematic working group. All large floodplain areas suffer anthropogenic pressure. Suggested area crossed by development corridors.

    Biological importance: *Birds:* B • *Mammals:* C • *Reptiles and amphibians:* D • Importance for ecological goods and services: B • Stability level: 0 • Instability level: 8 • Action priority level: 8 • Main action recommended: Identify priority actions • Other recommended action: Biological inventories, mainly of reptiles.

VZ 035 - Cajari Extractive Reserve - Priority level: A • Location: *State:* Amapá • *Main municipality:* Mazagão • *Municipalities covered:* 3 • Vegetation types: Da, Db, Ds, Pa, SO • Comments: Threats: proposed old-style INCRA settlement project in the buffer zone; high pressure by loggers and squatters, with subsistance crops inside the reserve boundaries. High variety of ecosystems (grasslands, floodplains), but influenced by the tidal floodplain. Area already ecologically zoned. Extension of the extractive reserve to the north.

    Biological importance: *Birds:* D • *Aquatic biota:* A • *Plants:* A • *Mammals:* C • Importance for ecological goods and services: A • Stability level: 6 • Instability level: 8 • Action priority level: 6 • Main action recommended: Sustainable use of natural resources • Other recommended action: Solution of agrarian problems, ecological inventories and studies of economic sustainability.

VZ 036 - Jari River - Priority level: B • Location: *State:* Amapá/Pará • *Main municipality:* Laranjal do Jari • *Municipalities covered:* 3 • Vegetation types: AA, Db, Ds, Pa • Comments: Threats: Mining (the CADAM company). Mammal and plants diversity.

    Biological importance: *Birds:* D • *Aquatic biota:* B • *Plants:* A • *Mammals:* C • Importance for ecological goods and services: A •

Stability level: 0 • Instability level: 7 • Action priority level: 8 • Main action recommended: Sustainable use of natural resources.

VZ 037 - Curiaú Environmental Protection Area - Priority level: B • Location: *State:* Amapá • *Main municipality:* Macapá • *Municipalities covered:* 1 • Vegetation types: Da, Sp • Comments: Classified by the biology thematic working group as important. Can be managed, as a tourism plan for the area is being drawn up. Near the capital of Amapá.

Biological importance: *Aquatic biota:* A • *Invertebrates:* D • *Reptiles and amphibians:* B • Stability level: 0 • Instability level: 6 • Action priority level: 7 • Main action recommended: Sustainable use of natural resources.

VZ 038 - Fazendinha Biological Reserve - Priority level: B • Location: *State:* Amapá • *Main municipality:* Macapá • *Municipalities covered:* 2 • Vegetation types: SO, Sp • Comments: Estuary area with high anthropogenic pressure. Agrarian problems, Amapá environment department has already registered the resident populations. Reclassification from Biological Reserve to Environmental Protection Area. Legal issues at state level. Pollution caused by clandestine slaughterhouses.

Biological importance: *Birds:* B • *Aquatic biota:* A • *Mammals:* C • *Reptiles and amphibians:* B • Stability level: 9 • Instability level: 8 • Action priority level: 5 • Main action recommended: Sustainable use of natural resources.

VZ 039 - Arquipélago do Marajó Environmental Protection Area - Priority level: A • Location: *State:* Pará • *Main municipality:* Anajás • *Municipalities covered:* 28 • Vegetation types: AA, Da, Db, Pa, Pf, Sp • Comments: Rich fauna and endemic species. Area subject to anthropogenic pressure from expansion of agricultural and ranching. Construction of waterway is another threat which may cause serious environmental damages.

Biological importance: *Birds:* B • *Aquatic biota:* A • *Plants:* A • *Invertebrates:* D • *Mammals:* C • *Reptiles and amphibians:* B • Stability level: 2 • Instability level: 3 • Action priority level: 4 • Main action recommended: Sustainable use of natural resources • Other recommended action: Assess the impact of buffalo raising.

VZ 040 - Caxiuana National Forest - Priority level: B • Location: *State:* Pará • *Main municipality:* Portel • *Municipalities covered:* 4 • Vegetation types: Da, Db, Pa.

Biological importance: *Birds:* B • *Aquatic biota:* D • *Invertebrates:* A • *Mammals:* C • Stability level: 6 • Instability level: 3 • Action priority level: 3 • Main action recommended: Protection • Other recommended action: Preparation of a management plan.

VZ 041 - Expanded area of the Caxiuana National Forest - Priority level: B • Location: *State:* Pará • *Main municipality:* Portel • *Municipalities covered:* 3 • Vegetation types: AA, Da, Db • Comments: Area of high biodiversity, under threat from logging activities. The creation of an extractive reserve is recommended, in collaboration with local residents.

Biological importance: *Birds:* B • *Aquatic biota:* D • *Invertebrates:* A • *Mammals:* C • Stability level: 0 • Instability level: 5 • Action priority level: 6 • Main action recommended: Creation of conservation area • Other recommended action: Creation of sustainable use conservation area (extractive reserve).

VZ 042 - Ilha de Algodoal - Priority level: A • Location: *State:* Pará • *Main municipality:* Maracanã • *Municipalities covered:* 2 • Vegetation types: AA, Pf • Comments: Area of mangroves and old dune ecosystems with their own biological diversity potential. Institutional capacity. Overlap with the landscape blocks proposed by the conservation areas thematic working group. Area of international importance for species for migratory bird species reproducing in the Canadian Arctic. Reproduction of species in danger of extinction.

Biological importance: *Birds:* C • *Aquatic biota:* A • *Plants:* A • *Reptiles and amphibians:* A • Stability level: 2 • Instability level: 5 • Action priority level: 5 • Main action recommended: Sustainable use of natural resources.

VZ 043 - Salgado - Priority level: A • Location: *State:* Pará • *Main municipality:* Marapanim • *Municipalities covered:* 22 • Vegetation types: AA, Pf • Comments: Mangrove areas. Areas with projects being carried out by the Federal University of Pará/Museu Paraense Emílio Goeldi/Federal University of Maranhão. Area of international importance for migratory bird species reproducing in the Canadian Arctic. Reproduction of species in danger of extinction, such as the *guará*.

Biological importance: *Birds:* C • *Aquatic biota:* A • *Plants:* A • *Invertebrates:* D • *Reptiles and amphibians:* A • Stability level: 0 • Instability level: 5 • Action priority level: 6 • Main action recommended: Sustainable use of natural resources.

VZ 044 - Coastal Zone - Golfo do Marajoara • Priority level: B • Location: *State:* Amapá/Pará • *Main municipality:* Chaves • *Municipalities covered:* 34 • Vegetation types: AA, Da, Db, Pa, Pf, SO, Sp • Comments: Area at the mouth of the Amazon. Biological importance. Affected by the Atlantic Ocean. In the shipping area, impact on the ecosystem by sea transportation. Use of the area by the riverbank populations, resource management. Vulnerability to natural erosion and silting.

Biological importance: *Birds:* B • *Aquatic biota:* A • *Invertebrates:* D • *Mammals:* C • *Reptiles and amphibians:* B • Stability level: 0 • Instability level: 6 • Action priority level: 7 • Main action recommended: Sustainable use of natural resources • Other recommended action: Monitoring of the coastal area of Pará. Biological, socio-economic and physical environment assessments.

VZ 045 - Lower Tocantins - Priority level: B • Location: *State:* Pará • *Main municipality:* Moju • *Municipalities covered:* 7 • Vegetation types: AA, Da, Db, Pa • Comments: Biological importance.

Biological importance: *Birds:* B • *Mammals:* C • *Reptiles and amphibians:* A • Importance for ecological goods and services: B • Stability level: 0 • Instability level: 9 • Action priority level: 9 • Main action recommended: Identify priority actions.

VZ 046 - Anambé Indigenous Land - Priority level: B • Location: *State:* Pará • *Main municipality:* Moju • *Municipalities covered:* 1 • Vegetation types: Db • Comments: Adjacent to an area of biological importance.

Biological importance: *Birds:* B • *Mammals:* C • *Reptiles and amphibians:* A • Importance for ecological goods and services: B • Stability level: 3 • Instability level: 9 • Action priority level: 7 • Main action recommended: Protection.

VZ 047 - Belém State Park - Priority level: B • Location: *State:* Pará • *Main municipality:* Ananindeua • *Municipalities covered:* 3 • Vegetation types: AA • Comments: This area has been a study site for the UN International Year of Biology (1966-1967) and for Embrapa-CPATU and Museu Paraense Emílio Goeldi.

Biological importance: *Aquatic biota:* D • *Invertebrates:* B • *Reptiles and amphibians:* B • Stability level: 3 • Instability level: 10 • Action priority level: 8 • Main action recommended: Protection • Other recommended action: Management plan.

3
PRIORITY AREAS IN THE UPPER XINGU / TAPAJÓS / RONDÔNIA / MATO GROSSO REGION

AX 001 - Araguaia/Mortes Interfluve - PRIORITY LEVEL: A • LOCATION: *State:* Mato Grosso • *Main municipality:* Cocalinho • *Municipalities covered:* 6 • VEGETATION TYPES: Sa, Sd, SN, Sp • COMMENTS: Area of high biological importance (birds, mammals, aquatic biota) not represented in conservation areas, and under anthropogenic pressure.
> BIOLOGICAL IMPORTANCE: *Birds:* A • *Aquatic biota:* A • *Reptiles and amphibians:* B • STABILITY LEVEL: 0 • INSTABILITY LEVEL: 5 • ACTION PRIORITY LEVEL: 9 • MAIN ACTION RECOMMENDED: Creation of conservation area • OTHER RECOMMENDED ACTION: Transformation of the area into Park and Environmental Protection Area.

AX 002 - Pimentel Barbosa Indigenous Land - PRIORITY LEVEL: A • LOCATION: *State:* Mato Grosso • *Main municipality:* Ribeirão Cascalheira • *Municipalities covered:* 4 • VEGETATION TYPES: Sa, SN, Sp • COMMENTS: This reserve contains an area of high biological importance, as well as the Xingu/Mortes interfluve, where there are likely to be differentiated species.
> BIOLOGICAL IMPORTANCE: *Birds:* D • *Aquatic biota:* A • STABILITY LEVEL: 3 • INSTABILITY LEVEL: 8 • ACTION PRIORITY LEVEL: 7 • MAIN ACTION RECOMMENDED: Sustainable use of natural resources.

AX 003 - Headwaters of the Xingu and the Teles Pires rivers - PRIORITY LEVEL: A • LOCATION: *State:* Mato Grosso • *Main municipality:* Paranatinga • *Municipalities covered:* 14 • VEGETATION TYPES: AA, Fa, Fs, ON, Pa, Sa, Sd, SN, Sp • COMMENTS: Area of biological importance, coupled with being a transition between cerrado and Amazon and includes the headwaters of the Xingu and Teles Pires.
> BIOLOGICAL IMPORTANCE: *Birds:* A • *Aquatic biota:* A • *Reptiles and amphibians:* B • IMPORTANCE FOR ECOLOGICAL GOODS AND SERVICES: B • STABILITY LEVEL: 0 • INSTABILITY LEVEL: 9 • ACTION PRIORITY LEVEL: 9 • MAIN ACTION RECOMMENDED: Identify priority actions.

AX 004 - Parabubure Indigenous Land - PRIORITY LEVEL: A • LOCATION: *State:* Mato Grosso • *Main municipality:* Campinápolis • *Municipalities covered:* 5 • VEGETATION TYPES: Sa, SN, Sp • COMMENTS: Reserve containing an area considered to be of high biological importance. Headwaters of the Culuene, one of the main tributaries of the Xingu.
> BIOLOGICAL IMPORTANCE: *Birds:* A • *Aquatic biota:* A • IMPORTANCE FOR ECOLOGICAL GOODS AND SERVICES: C • STABILITY LEVEL: 3 • INSTABILITY LEVEL: 4 • ACTION PRIORITY LEVEL: 4 • MAIN ACTION RECOMMENDED: Identify priority actions.

AX 005 - Culuene Ecological Reserve - PRIORITY LEVEL: A • LOCATION: *State:* Mato Grosso • *Main municipality:* Paranatinga • *Municipalities covered:* 2 • VEGETATION TYPES: Sa, SN • COMMENTS: Located in an area of high biological importance.
> BIOLOGICAL IMPORTANCE: *Birds:* A • *Aquatic biota:* A • *Reptiles and amphibians:* B • STABILITY LEVEL: 3 • INSTABILITY LEVEL: 7 • ACTION PRIORITY LEVEL: 6 • MAIN ACTION RECOMMENDED: Identify priority actions. • OTHER RECOMMENDED ACTION: Monitoring and inspection.

AX 006 - Marechal Rondon Indigenous Land - PRIORITY LEVEL: A • LOCATION: *State:* Mato Grosso • *Main municipality:* Paranatinga • *Municipalities covered:* 2 • VEGETATION TYPES: Sa, Sd, SN, Sp • COMMENTS: Located in an area of high biological importance. Headwaters of the Curisevo, an important tributary of the Xingu.
> BIOLOGICAL IMPORTANCE: *Birds:* D • *Aquatic biota:* A • *Reptiles and amphibians:* B • IMPORTANCE FOR ECOLOGICAL GOODS AND SERVICES: B • STABILITY LEVEL: 3 • INSTABILITY LEVEL: 7 • ACTION PRIORITY LEVEL: 6 • MAIN ACTION RECOMMENDED: Identify priority actions.

AX 007 - Bakairi Indigenous Land - PRIORITY LEVEL: A • LOCATION: *State:* Mato Grosso • *Main municipality:* Paranatinga • *Municipalities covered:* 2 • VEGETATION TYPES: Sp • COMMENTS: Located in an area of high biological importance. Headwaters of the Ronuro, an important tributary of the Xingu.
> BIOLOGICAL IMPORTANCE: *Birds:* D • *Aquatic biota:* A • IMPORTANCE FOR ECOLOGICAL GOODS AND SERVICES: C • STABILITY LEVEL: 3 • INSTABILITY LEVEL: 8 • ACTION PRIORITY LEVEL: 7 • MAIN ACTION RECOMMENDED: Identify priority actions.

AX 008 - Cabeceiras do Rio Cuiabá Environmental Protection Area - PRIORITY LEVEL: A • LOCATION: *State:* Mato Grosso • *Main municipality:* Rosário Oeste • *Municipalities covered:* 5 • VEGETATION TYPES: AA, Fs, Sa, Sd, SN, Sp • COMMENTS: Located in an area of high biological importance. Protects the headwaters of Cuiabá river, closely linked to the conservation of another biome: the Pantanal. Headwaters of Arinos, an important tributary of the Tapajós.
> BIOLOGICAL IMPORTANCE: *Birds:* D • *Aquatic biota:* A • IMPORTANCE FOR ECOLOGICAL GOODS AND SERVICES: C • STABILITY LEVEL: 2 • INSTABILITY LEVEL: 10 • ACTION PRIORITY LEVEL: 9 • MAIN ACTION RECOMMENDED: Change of conservation area category • OTHER RECOMMENDED ACTION: Transformation of part of the area, the present Cabeceiras do Rio Cuiabá Environmental Protection Area, into a strict conservation area, increasing the protection of the headwaters of the Cuiabá river; development of a management plan for the existing environmental protection area; and full implementation of monitoring actions.

AX 009 - Santana Indigenous Land - PRIORITY LEVEL: A • LOCATION: *State:* Mato Grosso • *Main municipality:* Nobres • *Municipalities covered:* 1 • VEGETATION TYPES: Sa, SN • COMMENTS: Located in an area of high biological importance. Headwaters of the Arinos, an important tributary of the Juruena/Tapajós.
> BIOLOGICAL IMPORTANCE: *Birds:* D • *Aquatic biota:* A • STABILITY LEVEL: 3 • INSTABILITY LEVEL: 10 • ACTION PRIORITY LEVEL: 8 • MAIN ACTION RECOMMENDED: Sustainable use of natural resources.

AX 010 - Headwaters of the Juruena, Papagaio, Sangue and Guaporé - PRIORITY LEVEL: A • LOCATION: *State:* Mato Grosso • *Main municipality:* Tangará da Serra • *Municipalities covered:* 12 • VEGETATION TYPES: AA, Fa, Sa, Sd, SN, Sp • COMMENTS: Located in an area of high biological importance. Acts as a buffer area for other conservation areas. Headwaters of the Juruena, an important tributary of the Tapajós river.
> BIOLOGICAL IMPORTANCE: *Birds:* B • *Aquatic biota:* A • *Plants:* D • IMPORTANCE FOR ECOLOGICAL GOODS AND SERVICES: C • STABILITY LEVEL: 0 • INSTABILITY LEVEL: 9 • ACTION PRIORITY LEVEL: 9 • MAIN ACTION RECOMMENDED: Creation of conservation area • OTHER RECOMMENDED ACTION: Creation of environmental protection area in the headwaters of the Juruena.

AX 011 - Rio Formoso Indigenous Land - PRIORITY LEVEL: A • LOCATION: *State:* Mato Grosso • *Main municipality:* Tangará da Serra • *Municipalities covered:* 1 • VEGETATION TYPES: Fa, Sa, Sp • COMMENTS: Located in an area of high biological importance.
> BIOLOGICAL IMPORTANCE: *Birds:* B • *Aquatic biota:* A • IMPORTANCE FOR ECOLOGICAL GOODS AND SERVICES: C • STABILITY LEVEL: 3 • INSTABILITY LEVEL: 9

• ACTION PRIORITY LEVEL: 7 • MAIN ACTION RECOMMENDED: Sustainable use of natural resources.

AX 012 - Estivadinho Indigenous Land - PRIORITY LEVEL: A • LOCATION: *State:* Mato Grosso • *Main municipality:* Tangará da Serra • *Municipalities covered:* 1 • VEGETATION TYPES: AA, Sa, Sp • COMMENTS: Located in an area of high biological importance.

BIOLOGICAL IMPORTANCE: *Birds:* B • *Aquatic biota:* A • IMPORTANCE FOR ECOLOGICAL GOODS AND SERVICES: C • STABILITY LEVEL: 3 • INSTABILITY LEVEL: 9 • ACTION PRIORITY LEVEL: 7 • MAIN ACTION RECOMMENDED: Sustainable use of natural resources.

AX 013 - Capitão Marcos/Uirapuru Indigenous Land - PRIORITY LEVEL: A • LOCATION: *State:* Mato Grosso • *Main municipality:* Nova Lacerda • *Municipalities covered:* 2 • VEGETATION TYPES: Sp • COMMENTS: Located in an area of high biological importance.

BIOLOGICAL IMPORTANCE: *Birds:* B • *Aquatic biota:* A • IMPORTANCE FOR ECOLOGICAL GOODS AND SERVICES: C • STABILITY LEVEL: 1 • INSTABILITY LEVEL: 9 • ACTION PRIORITY LEVEL: 8 • MAIN ACTION RECOMMENDED: Sustainable use of natural resources.

AX 014 - Pareci Indigenous Land - PRIORITY LEVEL: A • LOCATION: *State:* Mato Grosso • *Main municipality:* Tangará da Serra • *Municipalities covered:* 6 • VEGETATION TYPES: AA, Sa, SN, Sp • COMMENTS: Headwaters of the Papagaio, an important tributary of the Tapajós river. Located in an area of biological importance.

BIOLOGICAL IMPORTANCE: *Birds:* B • *Aquatic biota:* A • IMPORTANCE FOR ECOLOGICAL GOODS AND SERVICES: C • STABILITY LEVEL: 3 • INSTABILITY LEVEL: 9 • ACTION PRIORITY LEVEL: 7 • MAIN ACTION RECOMMENDED: Sustainable use of natural resources.

AX 015 - Utiariti Indigenous Land - PRIORITY LEVEL: A • LOCATION: *State:* Mato Grosso • *Main municipality:* Campo Novo do Parecis • *Municipalities covered:* 3 • VEGETATION TYPES: AA, Pa, Sa, SN • COMMENTS: Located in a polygon of high biological importance.

BIOLOGICAL IMPORTANCE: *Birds:* B • *Aquatic biota:* A • *Plants:* D • IMPORTANCE FOR ECOLOGICAL GOODS AND SERVICES: C • STABILITY LEVEL: 3 • INSTABILITY LEVEL: 9 • ACTION PRIORITY LEVEL: 7 • MAIN ACTION RECOMMENDED: Sustainable use of natural resources • OTHER RECOMMENDED ACTION: Monitoring and creation of an Indigenous Natural Resources Reserve.

AX 016 - Tirecatinga Indigenous Land - PRIORITY LEVEL: A • LOCATION: *State:* Mato Grosso • *Main municipality:* Sapezal • *Municipalities covered:* 3 • VEGETATION TYPES: Pa, Sa, SN • COMMENTS: Located in an area of high biological importance.

BIOLOGICAL IMPORTANCE: *Aquatic biota:* A • *Plants:* D • IMPORTANCE FOR ECOLOGICAL GOODS AND SERVICES: C • STABILITY LEVEL: 3 • INSTABILITY LEVEL: 4 • ACTION PRIORITY LEVEL: 4 • MAIN ACTION RECOMMENDED: Sustainable use of natural resources.

AX 017 - Juininha Indigenous Land - PRIORITY LEVEL: A • LOCATION: *State:* Mato Grosso • *Main municipality:* Pontes e Lacerda • *Municipalities covered:* 4 • VEGETATION TYPES: Sd, Sp • COMMENTS: Headwaters of the Juruena, an important tributary of the Tapajós river. Located in an area of biological importance.

BIOLOGICAL IMPORTANCE: *Birds:* B • *Aquatic biota:* A • IMPORTANCE FOR ECOLOGICAL GOODS AND SERVICES: C • STABILITY LEVEL: 3 • INSTABILITY LEVEL: 9 • ACTION PRIORITY LEVEL: 7 • MAIN ACTION RECOMMENDED: Sustainable use of natural resources.

AX 018 - Laranjeiras Extractive Forest - PRIORITY LEVEL: A • LOCATION: *State:* Rondônia • *Main municipality:* Pimenteiras do Oeste • *Municipalities covered:* 2 • VEGETATION TYPES: Ab, Da • COMMENTS: Area of high biological importance (birds, reptiles), located in the Pantanal do Guaporé and part of the western Amazon ecological corridor, border area. Located in the Guaporé ecotourism district (Proecotur).

BIOLOGICAL IMPORTANCE: *Birds:* A • *Aquatic biota:* B • *Mammals:* B • *Reptiles and amphibians:* A • STABILITY LEVEL: 4 • INSTABILITY LEVEL: 0 • ACTION PRIORITY LEVEL: 2 • MAIN ACTION RECOMMENDED: Sustainable use of natural resources • OTHER RECOMMENDED ACTION: Preparation of plan for sustainable use of natural resources plan and of biological inventories.

AX 019 - Corumbiara State Park - PRIORITY LEVEL: A • LOCATION: *State:* Rondônia • *Main municipality:* Pimenteiras do Oeste • *Municipalities covered:* 6 • VEGETATION TYPES: Ab, Da, Fa, Fb, Pa, Sd, Sg, SO, Sp • COMMENTS: Area of high biological importance containing threatened species, in the transition region between savanna, wetlands and forest. Part of the western Amazon ecological corridor; borders the Noel Kempff Mercado National Park (Bolivia). Located in the Guaporé ecotourism district (Proecotur).

BIOLOGICAL IMPORTANCE: *Birds:* A • *Aquatic biota:* B • *Mammals:* B • *Reptiles and amphibians:* A • STABILITY LEVEL: 2 • INSTABILITY LEVEL: 5 • ACTION PRIORITY LEVEL: 5 • MAIN ACTION RECOMMENDED: Protection • OTHER RECOMMENDED ACTION: Monitoring and protection of the headwaters and biological inventories.

AX 020 - Igarapé Omerê Indigenous Land - PRIORITY LEVEL: B • LOCATION: *State:* Rondônia • *Main municipality:* Corumbiara • *Municipalities covered:* 2 • VEGETATION TYPES: AA, Fa, Fb, ON • COMMENTS: Area located in the western Amazon ecological corridor and in the Guaporé ecotourism district (Proecotur); high biodiversity, strong anthropogenic pressure.

BIOLOGICAL IMPORTANCE: *Aquatic biota:* B • *Mammals:* B • IMPORTANCE FOR ECOLOGICAL GOODS AND SERVICES: C • STABILITY LEVEL: 1 • INSTABILITY LEVEL: 10 • ACTION PRIORITY LEVEL: 9 • MAIN ACTION RECOMMENDED: Sustainable use of natural resources • OTHER RECOMMENDED ACTION: Development of economic and socioenvironmental sustainability program; monitoring and biological inventories.

AX 021 - Rio Mequéns Sustainable Use Forest - PRIORITY LEVEL: A • LOCATION: *State:* Rondônia • *Main municipality:* Pimenteiras do Oeste • *Municipalities covered:* 6 • VEGETATION TYPES: AA, Ab, As, Fa, Fb, Fs, ON, Pa, Sa, Sd, SO • COMMENTS: Area of high semi-deciduous forest of southern Amazonia. Links indigenous lands and other areas in the western Amazon ecological corridor. It is a buffer zone for the Corumbiara National Park. Under high pressure from logging activities and settlements; partially destroyed.

BIOLOGICAL IMPORTANCE: *Birds:* A • *Aquatic biota:* B • *Mammals:* B • *Reptiles and amphibians:* A • IMPORTANCE FOR ECOLOGICAL GOODS AND SERVICES: C • STABILITY LEVEL: 2 • INSTABILITY LEVEL: 10 • ACTION PRIORITY LEVEL: 9 • MAIN ACTION RECOMMENDED: Change conservation area category • OTHER RECOMMENDED ACTION: Incorporation of the area into the Corumbiara National Park.

AX 022 - Rio Mequéns Indigenous Land - PRIORITY LEVEL: B • LOCATION: *State:* Rondônia • *Main municipality:* Alto Alegre do Parecis • *Municipalities covered:* 2 • VEGETATION TYPES: Ab, As, Fs, Pa, SO • COMMENTS: Located in the transition area between the central highlands of Rondônia and the Vale do Guaporé. Reveals high habitat diversity in a region considered biologically rich. Part of the western Amazon ecological corridor.

BIOLOGICAL IMPORTANCE: *Birds:* A • *Aquatic biota:* B • *Mammals:* B • IMPORTANCE FOR ECOLOGICAL GOODS AND SERVICES: C • STABILITY LEVEL: 3 • INSTABILITY LEVEL: 10 • ACTION PRIORITY LEVEL: 8 • MAIN ACTION RECOMMENDED: Sustainable use of natural resources • OTHER RECOMMENDED ACTION: Development of an economical and socio-environmental viability program for the area and monitoring.

AX 023 - Serra dos Parecis State Park - PRIORITY LEVEL: B • LOCATION: *State:* Rondônia • *Main municipality:* Alto Alegre do Parecis • *Municipalities covered:* 3 • VEGETATION TYPES: As, Fs, Sa, SO • COMMENTS: Located in the western Amazon ecological corridor, in the Guaporé ecotourism district, has high biodiversity levels and high levels of linkage to floodplains, conservation areas and adjacent indigenous lands. Conservation area totally altered by settlement projects, which have destroyed watersheds of some Guaporé tributaries.

BIOLOGICAL IMPORTANCE: *Aquatic biota:* B • *Mammals:* B • IMPORTANCE FOR ECOLOGICAL GOODS AND SERVICES: C • STABILITY LEVEL: 3 • INSTABILITY LEVEL: 10 • ACTION PRIORITY LEVEL: 8 • MAIN ACTION RECOMMENDED: Protection • OTHER RECOMMENDED ACTION: Preparation and full implementation of management plan.

AX 024 - Pedras Negras Extractive Reserve - PRIORITY LEVEL: A • LOCATION: *State:* Rondônia • *Main municipality:* São Francisco do Guaporé • *Municipalities covered:* 3 • VEGETATION TYPES: Ab, Da, Pa, Sa • COMMENTS: Mosaic of forest and flooded areas with high habitat diversity. High biological richness including threatened species. Located on the border, guarantees the linkage with the western Amazon ecological corridor. Focal point for Proecotur in

Rondônia. Problems with the excessive hunting and fires in the flooded grasslands.

BIOLOGICAL IMPORTANCE: *Birds:* A • *Aquatic biota:* B • *Mammals:* B • *Reptiles and amphibians:* A • IMPORTANCE FOR ECOLOGICAL GOODS AND SERVICES: C • STABILITY LEVEL: 8 • INSTABILITY LEVEL: 0 • ACTION PRIORITY LEVEL: 2 • MAIN ACTION RECOMMENDED: Sustainable use of natural resources • OTHER RECOMMENDED ACTION: Development of economic and socio-environmental sustainability program; and biological inventories.

AX 025 - Colorado River - PRIORITY LEVEL: A • LOCATION: *State:* Rondônia • *Main municipality:* Alta Floresta D'Oeste • *Municipalities covered:* 4 • VEGETATION TYPES: Ab, Da, Pa, Sa, SO • COMMENTS: Area located in the western Amazon ecological corridor and in the Guaporé ecotourism district, with high levels of diversity and of linkage.

BIOLOGICAL IMPORTANCE: *Birds:* A • *Aquatic biota:* B • *Mammals:* B • *Reptiles and amphibians:* A • STABILITY LEVEL: 0 • INSTABILITY LEVEL: 0 • ACTION PRIORITY LEVEL: 3 • MAIN ACTION RECOMMENDED: Creation of conservation area • OTHER RECOMMENDED ACTION: Biological inventories.

AX 026 - Rio Branco Indigenous Land - PRIORITY LEVEL: A • LOCATION: *State:* Rondônia • *Main municipality:* São Miguel do Guaporé • *Municipalities covered:* 3 • VEGETATION TYPES: Ab, As, Da, Ds, Pa • COMMENTS: Area adjacent to the Guaporé Biological Reserve, protects terra firme forests, bordering the Guaporé wetlands. Part of the western Amazon ecological corridor, acting as a buffer for biological reserve. The headwaters of the Rio Branco have been degraded by the construction of a hydroelectric plant and by deforestation.

BIOLOGICAL IMPORTANCE: *Birds:* A • *Aquatic biota:* B • *Mammals:* B • *Reptiles and amphibians:* A • IMPORTANCE FOR ECOLOGICAL GOODS AND SERVICES: C • STABILITY LEVEL: 3 • INSTABILITY LEVEL: 9 • ACTION PRIORITY LEVEL: 7 • MAIN ACTION RECOMMENDED: Sustainable use of natural resources • OTHER RECOMMENDED ACTION: Development of economic and socio-environmental sustainability program and preparation of biological inventories.

AX 027 - Area between the Rio Branco Indigenous Land and the Serra dos Parecis State Park - PRIORITY LEVEL: A • LOCATION: *State:* Rondônia • *Main municipality:* Alta Floresta D'Oeste • *Municipalities covered:* 3 • VEGETATION TYPES: Ab, As, Sa, SO, Sp • COMMENTS: Area located in the western Amazon ecological corridor in a region of high biodiversity and strong linkage with existing indigenous lands and conservation areas. Part of the Guaporé ecotourism district. Its creation will help consolidate the corridor.

BIOLOGICAL IMPORTANCE: *Birds:* A • *Aquatic biota:* B • *Mammals:* B • *Reptiles and amphibians:* A • IMPORTANCE FOR ECOLOGICAL GOODS AND SERVICES: C • STABILITY LEVEL: 0 • INSTABILITY LEVEL: 10 • ACTION PRIORITY LEVEL: 10 • MAIN ACTION RECOMMENDED: Creation of conservation area.

AX 028 - Pau d'Óleo Farm - PRIORITY LEVEL: A • LOCATION: *State:* Rondônia • *Main municipality:* São Francisco do Guaporé • *Municipalities covered:* 2 • VEGETATION TYPES: Da, Pa, Sd • COMMENTS: Area in the Guaporé wetlands with numerous rare and threatened species, adjacent to the Guaporé Biological Reserve. Located on the border, within the western Amazon ecological corridor. Belongs to the Rondônia state government; there are human occupation pressures and buffalo ranching has destroyed floodplain areas.

BIOLOGICAL IMPORTANCE: *Birds:* A • *Aquatic biota:* B • *Mammals:* B • *Reptiles and amphibians:* A • STABILITY LEVEL: 0 • INSTABILITY LEVEL: 9 • ACTION PRIORITY LEVEL: 9 • MAIN ACTION RECOMMENDED: Incorporation of existing conservation area • OTHER RECOMMENDED ACTION: Incorporation of the area into the Guaporé Biological Reserve and action against illegal hunting.

AX 029 - Rio Muqui Indigenous Land - PRIORITY LEVEL: B • LOCATION: *State:* Rondônia • *Main municipality:* Alvorada D' Oeste • *Municipalities covered:* 3 • VEGETATION TYPES: AA, As, SO • COMMENTS: Extension of the Uru-Eu-Wau-Wau Indigenous Land and the Serra dos Pacaás Novos National Park, to which it is connected. Part of the western Amazon ecological corridor. Area considered to be of high biodiversity on the basis of inventories of the adjacent areas.

BIOLOGICAL IMPORTANCE: *Birds:* C • *Aquatic biota:* B • *Invertebrates:* D • *Mammals:* B • *Reptiles and amphibians:* A • IMPORTANCE FOR ECOLOGICAL GOODS AND SERVICES: C • STABILITY LEVEL: 1 • INSTABILITY LEVEL: 10 • ACTION PRIORITY LEVEL: 9 • MAIN ACTION RECOMMENDED: Protection • OTHER RECOMMENDED ACTION: Action to prevent logging activities and illegal occupation.

AX 030 - Pacaás Novos National Park, Uru-Eu-Wau-Wau Indigenous Land - PRIORITY LEVEL: B • LOCATION: *State:* Rondônia • *Main municipality:* São Miguel do Guaporé • *Municipalities covered:* 7 • VEGETATION TYPES: AA, Ab, As, Ds, Sa, Sd, SO, Sp • COMMENTS: Area with some physical and personnel infrastructure; high diversity levels; under strong pressure from the most important expanding settlement frontiers in the state: cattle raising, logging activities and settlement.

BIOLOGICAL IMPORTANCE: *Birds:* A • *Aquatic biota:* B • *Invertebrates:* D • *Mammals:* B • *Reptiles and amphibians:* A • IMPORTANCE FOR ECOLOGICAL GOODS AND SERVICES: A • STABILITY LEVEL: 12 • INSTABILITY LEVEL: 10 • ACTION PRIORITY LEVEL: 5 • MAIN ACTION RECOMMENDED: Identify priority actions • OTHER RECOMMENDED ACTION: Effective establishment of the national park; preparation of sustainable management plan for the conservation area and of biological inventories.

AX 031 - Uru-Eu-Wau-Wau Indigenous Land - PRIORITY LEVEL: A • LOCATION: *State:* Rondônia • *Main municipality:* Guajará-Mirim • *Municipalities covered:* 5 • VEGETATION TYPES: AA, Ab, As, Sa, Sd, SO, Sp • COMMENTS: Area of high relief and diversity of vegetation type, including Andean elements. High species diversity, including endemisms and threatened species. Under high pressure from logging activities and squatters.

BIOLOGICAL IMPORTANCE: *Birds:* A • *Aquatic biota:* B • *Invertebrates:* D • *Mammals:* B • *Reptiles and amphibians:* A • IMPORTANCE FOR ECOLOGICAL GOODS AND SERVICES: A • STABILITY LEVEL: 3 • INSTABILITY LEVEL: 9 • ACTION PRIORITY LEVEL: 7 • MAIN ACTION RECOMMENDED: Protection • OTHER RECOMMENDED ACTION: Action to control logging activities, squatters and gold prospecting.

AX 032 - Urupá River - PRIORITY LEVEL: B • LOCATION: *State:* Rondônia • *Main municipality:* Mirante da Serra • *Municipalities covered:* 5 • VEGETATION TYPES: AA, As, Sd, SO, Sp • COMMENTS: Area of endemism, adjacent to one of the cone-areas of the western Amazon ecological corridor, protects headwaters of important rivers. Under high anthropogenic pressure from human occupation arriving via the BR-364 highway.

BIOLOGICAL IMPORTANCE: *Birds:* C • *Aquatic biota:* D • *Invertebrates:* D • *Mammals:* B • *Reptiles and amphibians:* A • IMPORTANCE FOR ECOLOGICAL GOODS AND SERVICES: A • STABILITY LEVEL: 0 • INSTABILITY LEVEL: 10 • ACTION PRIORITY LEVEL: 10 • MAIN ACTION RECOMMENDED: Identify priority actions • OTHER RECOMMENDED ACTION: Biological inventories.

AX 033 - Rio Negro/Ocaia Indigenous Land - PRIORITY LEVEL: A • LOCATION: *State:* Rondônia • *Main municipality:* Guajará-Mirim • *Municipalities covered:* 1 • VEGETATION TYPES: Ab, As, Da • COMMENTS: Area of high biodiversity, wedged in between conservation areas, part of the western Amazon ecological corridor.

BIOLOGICAL IMPORTANCE: *Birds:* A • *Aquatic biota:* B • *Invertebrates:* D • *Mammals:* A • *Reptiles and amphibians:* A • IMPORTANCE FOR ECOLOGICAL GOODS AND SERVICES: A • STABILITY LEVEL: 5 • INSTABILITY LEVEL: 0 • ACTION PRIORITY LEVEL: 2 • MAIN ACTION RECOMMENDED: Sustainable use of natural resources • OTHER RECOMMENDED ACTION: Development of economic and socio-environmental sustainability program and biological inventories.

AX 034 - Guajará-Mirim State Park - PRIORITY LEVEL: A • LOCATION: *State:* Rondônia • *Main municipality:* Nova Mamoré • *Municipalities covered:* 3 • VEGETATION TYPES: Ab, As, Sa, Sd, SO • COMMENTS: Area with completed biological surveys, high biodiversity, endemism in central Rondônia. Under pressure from the opening of the BR-421 highway and INCRA settlement projects. High logging pressure in the region.

BIOLOGICAL IMPORTANCE: *Birds:* A • *Aquatic biota:* D • *Invertebrates:* D • *Mammals:* A • *Reptiles and amphibians:* A • STABILITY LEVEL: 3 • INSTABILITY LEVEL: 4 • ACTION PRIORITY LEVEL: 4 • MAIN ACTION RECOMMENDED: Protection • OTHER RECOMMENDED ACTION: Action to control pressures resulting from the proximity to roads.

AX 035 - Rio Ouro Preto Extractive Reserve - PRIORITY LEVEL: A • LOCATION: *State:* Rondônia • *Main municipality:* Guajará-Mirim • *Municipalities covered:* 2 • VEGETATION TYPES: Ab, As, Da, Sd, SO •

Comments: Area of high biological importance; part of the western Amazon ecological corridor. Ensures the connectivons between the corridor's conservation areas. Deforestation and fire problems, caused in some cases by the resident population.

Biological importance: *Birds:* A • *Aquatic biota:* B • *Invertebrates:* D • *Mammals:* A • *Reptiles and amphibians:* A • Importance for ecological goods and services: A • Stability level: 3 • Instability level: 4 • Action priority level: 4 • Main action recommended: Sustainable use of natural resources • Other recommended action: Economic and socio-environmental sustainability program and action to prevent logging invasions.

AX 036 - Rio Ouro Preto Biological Reserve - Priority level: A • Location: *State:* Rondônia • *Main municipality:* Guajará-Mirim • *Municipalities covered:* 1 • Vegetation types: Ab, As, SO • Comments: Area of high biological diversity with populations of species endemic to central Rondônia. Part of the western Amazon ecological corridor. Mountain enclaves within the terra firme forest.

Biological importance: *Birds:* A • *Aquatic biota:* B • *Invertebrates:* D • *Mammals:* A • *Reptiles and amphibians:* A • Importance for ecological goods and services: A • Stability level: 9 • Instability level: 4 • Action priority level: 3 • Main action recommended: Protection • Other recommended action: Monitoring.

AX 037 - Pacaás Novos Extractive Forest - Priority level: A • Location: *State:* Rondônia • *Main municipality:* Guajará-Mirim • *Municipalities covered:* 1 • Vegetation types: Ab, As, Da • Comments: High biodiversity, part of the western Amazon ecological corridor, strong linkages.

Biological importance: *Birds:* A • *Aquatic biota:* B • *Invertebrates:* D • *Mammals:* A • *Reptiles and amphibians:* A • Importance for ecological goods and services: A • Stability level: 6 • Instability level: 4 • Action priority level: 3 • Main action recommended: Sustainable use of natural resources • Other recommended action: Full implementation of management plan and preparation of biological inventory.

AX 038 - Traçadal Biological Reserve - Priority level: B • Location: *State:* Rondônia • *Main municipality:* Guajará-Mirim • *Municipalities covered:* 1 • Vegetation types: Ab, Da, Pa • Comments: Area of high biological diversity; part of a mosaic of areas making up the western Amazon ecological corridor. Campinarana enclave in the Guaporé basin.

Biological importance: *Birds:* B • *Aquatic biota:* B • *Invertebrates:* D • *Mammals:* A • Stability level: 12 • Instability level: 0 • Action priority level: 2 • Main action recommended: Protection • Other recommended action: Monitoring, preparation of a management plan and of biological inventories.

AX 039 - Igarapé Lage Indigenous Land - Priority level: A • Location: *State:* Rondônia • *Main municipality:* Nova Mamoré • *Municipalities covered:* 2 • Vegetation types: AA, As, Sd, SO • Comments: Adjacent to area of high biological richness (Guajará-Mirim State Park); acts as a buffer for areas of growing pressure (Nova Mamoré/Guajará-Mirim). Part of the western Amazon ecological corridor.

Biological importance: *Birds:* A • *Aquatic biota:* A • *Mammals:* A • *Reptiles and amphibians:* A • Stability level: 3 • Instability level: 4 • Action priority level: 4 • Main action recommended: Sustainable use of natural resources • Other recommended action: Preparation of economic and socio-environmental sustainability program.

AX 040 - Guaporé Biological Reserve (part) - Priority level: A • Location: *State:* Rondônia • *Main municipality:* São Francisco do Guaporé • *Municipalities covered:* 4 • Vegetation types: Ab, Da, Pa, Sd • Comments: Area of high biological diversity, covers the transition between the terra firme forest and the Guaporé wetlands. Occurrence of various rare and threatened species. Core area of the western Amazon ecological corridor. Overlap between the Massaco Indigenous Land and uncontacted indians.

Biological importance: *Birds:* A • *Aquatic biota:* B • *Mammals:* B • *Reptiles and amphibians:* A • Stability level: 9 • Instability level: 9 • Action priority level: 5 • Main action recommended: Protection • Other recommended action: Monitoring of the northern borders of the biological reserve and revision of the management plan.

AX 041 - Massaco Indigenous Land and Guaporé Biological Reserve - Priority level: A • Location: *State:* Rondônia • *Main municipality:* São Francisco do Guaporé • *Municipalities covered:* 2 • Vegetation types: Ab, As, Da, Pa, Sa, Sd, Sp • Comments: Located within an area of high biological importance. Biodiversity linked to soil-decernity.

Biological importance: *Birds:* A • *Aquatic biota:* B • *Mammals:* B • *Reptiles and amphibians:* A • Importance for ecological goods and services: C • Stability level: 12 • Instability level: 10 • Action priority level: 5 • Main action recommended: Protection • Other recommended action: Protection for uncontacted indians; biological inventories; anthropological studies; and studies on the viability of creating an Indigenous Natural Resources Reserve.

AX 042 - Ji-Paraná River - Priority level: A • Location: *State:* Rondônia • *Main municipality:* Vale do Anari • *Municipalities covered:* 5 • Vegetation types: As, Da • Comments: Inclusion of areas would complement and protect the Jaru Biological Reserve, with the Ji-Paraná river as the western boundary, including the river-related ecosystems. Need to strenghten the infrastructure of the Jaru biological reserve, which could incorporate this area. There are recent invasions of the area, encouraged by local politicians. Area of high biological diversity and endemism.

Biological importance: *Birds:* A • *Aquatic biota:* A • Importance for ecological goods and services: A • Stability level: 0 • Instability level: 10 • Action priority level: 10 • Main action recommended: Incorporation into existing conservation area • Other recommended action: Incorporation of the area into the Jaru biological reserve, through its expansion as far as the Ji-Paraná river and preparation of biological inventories.

AX 043 - Jaru Biological Reserve - Priority level: A • Location: *State:* Rondônia • *Main municipality:* Ji-Paraná • *Municipalities covered:* 6 • Vegetation types: As, Ds • Comments: High biodiversity; important levels of activity; reasonable levels of implementation of the biological reserve. It is the fourth most important area for the occurrence of birds in the Amazon. Under high pressure from illegal occupation.

Biological importance: *Birds:* A • *Aquatic biota:* A • Importance for ecological goods and services: A • Stability level: 9 • Instability level: 8 • Action priority level: 5 • Main action recommended: Protection • Other recommended action: Effective establishment and sustainable maintenance of the biological reserve; preparation biological inventories.

AX 044 - Igarapé Lourdes Indigenous Land - Priority level: A • Location: *State:* Rondônia • *Main municipality:* Ji-Paraná • *Municipalities covered:* 3 • Vegetation types: AA, As, Ds • Comments: Within an area of biological importance. Need for institutional strengthening and improvement of inter-agency relations between Ibama and Funai.

Biological importance: *Birds:* A • *Aquatic biota:* A • Importance for ecological goods and services: A • Stability level: 3 • Instability level: 10 • Action priority level: 8 • Main action recommended: Sustainable use of natural resources.

AX 045 - Rio Preto/Jacundá Extractive Forest - Priority level: A • Location: *State:* Rondônia • *Main municipality:* Porto Velho • *Municipalities covered:* 5 • Vegetation types: AA, Ab, As, Da, Db, Ds, SO • Comments: Area within a region of high biodiversity and subject to impacts; anthropogenic pressure from settlement projects.

Biological importance: *Birds:* B • *Aquatic biota:* A • *Plants:* A • *Mammals:* A • *Reptiles and amphibians:* A • Importance for ecological goods and services: B • Stability level: 6 • Instability level: 9 • Action priority level: 6 • Main action recommended: Sustainable use of natural resources.

AX 046 - Rio Madeira Sustainable Use Forest (a) - Priority level: A • Location: *State:* Rondônia • *Main municipality:* Porto Velho • *Municipalities covered:* 1 • Vegetation types: Da, SO, Sp • Comments: Area of high biological importance – high diversity.

Biological importance: *Birds:* C • *Aquatic biota:* A • *Mammals:* A • *Reptiles and amphibians:* A • Stability level: 6 • Instability level: 3 • Action priority level: 3 • Main action recommended: Identify priority actions • Other recommended action: Unimplemented area, needs a management plan and monitoring.

AX 047 - Lago Cuniá Environmental Protection Area - PRIORITY LEVEL: A • LOCATION: *State:* Rondônia • *Main municipality:* Porto Velho • *Municipalities covered:* 1 • VEGETATION TYPES: Ab, Da, Pa, SO • COMMENTS: Within an area of high biological importance. Great potential for ecological tourism. Presence of a large population of *Caiman Niger* (listed under CITES Appendix 1) and *Caiman crocodilus* (listed under Appendix 2). Occurrence of manatee.

BIOLOGICAL IMPORTANCE: *Birds:* C • *Aquatic biota:* A • *Mammals:* A • *Reptiles and amphibians:* A • STABILITY LEVEL: 6 • INSTABILITY LEVEL: 8 • ACTION PRIORITY LEVEL: 6 • MAIN ACTION RECOMMENDED: Sustainable use of natural resources • OTHER RECOMMENDED ACTION: Needs legal review and revision of management category.

AX 048 - Rio Madeira Environmental Protection Area - PRIORITY LEVEL: A • LOCATION: *State:* Rondônia • *Main municipality:* Porto Velho • *Municipalities covered:* 1 • VEGETATION TYPES: AA, As • COMMENTS: Area of high biodiversity, located in northern channel of the Rio Madeira, in an environment different from most of the environments studied in Rondônia.

BIOLOGICAL IMPORTANCE: *Aquatic biota:* A • *Mammals:* A • *Reptiles and amphibians:* A • STABILITY LEVEL: 6 • INSTABILITY LEVEL: 9 • ACTION PRIORITY LEVEL: 6 • MAIN ACTION RECOMMENDED: Protection • OTHER RECOMMENDED ACTION: Preparation of management plan, biological inventories and monitoring.

AX 049 - Rio Vermelho Sustainable Use Forest (c) - PRIORITY LEVEL: A • LOCATION: *State:* Rondônia • *Main municipality:* Porto Velho • *Municipalities covered:* 2 • VEGETATION TYPES: AA, Ab, As, SO • COMMENTS: High biodiversity, signifying increased level of pressure. Area located in the northern channel of the Madeira (environmental density).

BIOLOGICAL IMPORTANCE: *Birds:* A • *Aquatic biota:* A • *Mammals:* A • *Reptiles and amphibians:* A • STABILITY LEVEL: 6 • INSTABILITY LEVEL: 9 • ACTION PRIORITY LEVEL: 6 • MAIN ACTION RECOMMENDED: Protection • OTHER RECOMMENDED ACTION: Preparation of management plan, biological inventories and monitoring.

AX 050 - Rio Vermelho Sustainable Use Forest (a) - PRIORITY LEVEL: A • LOCATION: *State:* Rondônia • *Main municipality:* Porto Velho • *Municipalities covered:* 1 • VEGETATION TYPES: Ab, As • COMMENTS: Adjacent to the ecological station and with high species diversity, including endemism on the left bank of the Madeira and threatened species. It acts as a buffer for the ecological station, covering the floodplain areas not included in this; should be incorporated into the ecological station, or transformed into strict conservation area.

BIOLOGICAL IMPORTANCE: *Birds:* A • *Aquatic biota:* A • *Mammals:* A • STABILITY LEVEL: 6 • INSTABILITY LEVEL: 4 • ACTION PRIORITY LEVEL: 3 • MAIN ACTION RECOMMENDED: Change of the type of conservation area • OTHER RECOMMENDED ACTION: Inclusion of the area in the Serra dos Três Irmãos Ecological Station.

AX 051 - Serra dos Três Irmãos Ecological Station - PRIORITY LEVEL: A • LOCATION: *State:* Rondônia • *Main municipality:* Porto Velho • *Municipalities covered:* 2 • VEGETATION TYPES: Ab, As, Ds, SO • COMMENTS: Area under anthropogenic pressure, with fauna and flora representative of floodplain and dense terra firme rainforest environments. It is already a conservation area.

BIOLOGICAL IMPORTANCE: *Birds:* A • *Aquatic biota:* A • *Plants:* A • *Mammals:* A • *Reptiles and amphibians:* A • STABILITY LEVEL: 3 • INSTABILITY LEVEL: 4 • ACTION PRIORITY LEVEL: 4 • MAIN ACTION RECOMMENDED: Protection • OTHER RECOMMENDED ACTION: Monitoring and biological inventories.

AX 052 - Rio Vermelho Sustainable Use Forest (b) - PRIORITY LEVEL: A • LOCATION: *State:* Rondônia • *Main municipality:* Porto Velho • *Municipalities covered:* 3 • VEGETATION TYPES: AA, As, Ds, SO • COMMENTS: Area of high biodiversity and with a use plan in preparation, under strong anthropogenic pressure (mining activities) to the north of the Madeira river. Like most of the areas proposed for Rondônia it is an environment at risk, with the occurrence of plant species, some of which threatened by economic activities.

BIOLOGICAL IMPORTANCE: *Birds:* D • *Aquatic biota:* A • *Mammals:* A • STABILITY LEVEL: 6 • INSTABILITY LEVEL: 4 • ACTION PRIORITY LEVEL: 3 • MAIN ACTION RECOMMENDED: Sustainable use of natural resources • OTHER RECOMMENDED ACTION: Implementation of use plan; preparation of biological inventories and of the natural resources base.

AX 053 - Rio Madeira basin - PRIORITY LEVEL: A • LOCATION: *State:* Rondônia • *Main municipality:* Porto Velho • *Municipalities covered:* 8 • VEGETATION TYPES: AA, Ab, As, Da, Db, Pa, SO, Sp • COMMENTS: Area of high biological importance (biodiversity) subject to growing anthropogenic pressure. Increasing pressure of fishing on the Rio Madeira on fish populations.

BIOLOGICAL IMPORTANCE: *Birds:* A • *Aquatic biota:* A • *Plants:* A • *Invertebrates:* D • *Mammals:* A • *Reptiles and amphibians:* A • IMPORTANCE FOR ECOLOGICAL GOODS AND SERVICES: B • STABILITY LEVEL: 0 • INSTABILITY LEVEL: 9 • ACTION PRIORITY LEVEL: 9 • MAIN ACTION RECOMMENDED: Identify priority actions.

AX 054 - Samuel Ecological Station - PRIORITY LEVEL: A • LOCATION: *State:* Rondônia • *Main municipality:* Candeias do Jamari • *Municipalities covered:* 3 • VEGETATION TYPES: Ab, As • COMMENTS: Area of known biological importance, especially mammals, and less important for birds and flora. Anthropogenic pressure is of little importance.

BIOLOGICAL IMPORTANCE: *Birds:* B • *Mammals:* A • IMPORTANCE FOR ECOLOGICAL GOODS AND SERVICES: B • STABILITY LEVEL: 9 • INSTABILITY LEVEL: 10 • ACTION PRIORITY LEVEL: 6 • MAIN ACTION RECOMMENDED: Identify priority actions.

AX 055 - Jamari National Forest - PRIORITY LEVEL: A • LOCATION: *State:* Rondônia • *Main municipality:* Jamari • *Municipalities covered:* 3 • VEGETATION TYPES: Ab, As • COMMENTS: High biodiversity with strong anthropogenic pressure; area degraded by mining.

BIOLOGICAL IMPORTANCE: *Birds:* B • *Mammals:* A • IMPORTANCE FOR ECOLOGICAL GOODS AND SERVICES: B • STABILITY LEVEL: 6 • INSTABILITY LEVEL: 10 • ACTION PRIORITY LEVEL: 7 • MAIN ACTION RECOMMENDED: Sustainable use of natural resources • OTHER RECOMMENDED ACTION: Preparation of management plan and monitoring.

AX 056 - Rio Cautário Extractive Reserve - PRIORITY LEVEL: N • LOCATION: *State:* Rondônia • *Main municipality:* São Francisco do Guaporé • *Municipalities covered:* 6 • VEGETATION TYPES: AA, Ab, As, Da, Pa, SO • COMMENTS: Part of the western Amazon ecological corridor, and is the buffer for the future Serra da Cotia National Park.

BIOLOGICAL IMPORTANCE: *Aquatic biota:* 1 • STABILITY LEVEL: 8 • INSTABILITY LEVEL: 6 • ACTION PRIORITY LEVEL: 4 • MAIN ACTION RECOMMENDED: Sustainable use of natural resources • OTHER RECOMMENDED ACTION: Full implementation of the natural resource use plan and strengthening of the residents association.

AX 057 - Rio Guaporé Indigenous Land - PRIORITY LEVEL: N • LOCATION: *State:* Rondônia • *Main municipality:* Guajará-Mirim • *Municipalities covered:* 2 • VEGETATION TYPES: Ab, Da, Pa • COMMENTS: Part of the western Amazon ecological corridor. Border area. Adjacent to areas of high biodiversity.

BIOLOGICAL IMPORTANCE: *Aquatic biota:* B • STABILITY LEVEL: 5 • INSTABILITY LEVEL: 4 • ACTION PRIORITY LEVEL: 4 • MAIN ACTION RECOMMENDED: Protection and environmental recovery • OTHER RECOMMENDED ACTION: Monitoring, restoration of some degraded areas, and biological inventories.

AX 058 - Serra do Cotia - PRIORITY LEVEL: N • LOCATION: *State:* Rondônia • *Main municipality:* Guajará-Mirim • *Municipalities covered:* 3 • VEGETATION TYPES: Ab, As, Da, Pa, Sa, Sd, SO, Sp • COMMENTS: Key area for the consolidation of the western Amazon ecological corridor, under pressure from uncontrolled settlement. High biological diversity in adjacent areas. Area belongs to INCRA.

BIOLOGICAL IMPORTANCE: *Birds:* B • *Aquatic biota:* B • *Plants:* A • *Mammals:* B • STABILITY LEVEL: 0 • INSTABILITY LEVEL: 4 • ACTION PRIORITY LEVEL: 5 • MAIN ACTION RECOMMENDED: Creation of conservation area • OTHER RECOMMENDED ACTION: Transformation of the area into National Park and Extractive Reserve; and biological inventories.

AX 059 - Pacaás Novas Indigenous Land - PRIORITY LEVEL: N • LOCATION: *State:* Rondônia • *Main municipality:* Guajará-Mirim • *Municipalities covered:* 2 • VEGETATION TYPES: Ab, Da, Pa • COMMENTS: Located in region adjacent to area of high biological diversity, border area, and part of the western Amazon ecological corridor.

BIOLOGICAL IMPORTANCE: *Aquatic biota:* B • *Invertebrates:* D •

Mammals: A • Stability level: 3 • Instability level: 4 • Action priority level: 4 • Main action recommended: Sustainable use of natural resources • Other recommended action: Full implementation of actions to consolidate the western Amazon ecological corridor.

AX 060 - Uru-Eu-Wau-Wau Indigenous Land (eastern boundary) - Priority level: B • Location: *State:* Rondônia • *Main municipality:* Governador Jorge Teixeira • *Municipalities covered:* 8 • Vegetation types: AA, As, Ds, Sd, SO, Sp • Comments: Area of high diversity of relief and vegetation types, including Andean elements. High species diversity, including endemism and threatened species. Under strong pressure from loggers and squatters.

Biological importance: *Birds:* C • *Aquatic biota:* D • *Invertebrates:* D • *Mammals:* B • *Reptiles and amphibians:* A • Importance for ecological goods and services: A • Stability level: 3 • Instability level: 10 • Action priority level: 8 • Main action recommended: Protection.

AX 061 - Madeirinha River - Priority level: A • Location: *State:* Rondônia • *Main municipality:* Aripuanã • *Municipalities covered:* 3 • Vegetation types: As, Ds • Comments: The incorporation of the area would complement and protect the Jaru Biological Reserve, with the Madeirinha River as the eastern boundary, including river-related ecosystems. Need to strengthen the infrastructure of the Jaru Biological Reserve, which could include this area. There are recent invasions in the area, encouraged by local politicians. Area of high biodiversity and endemisms.

Biological importance: *Birds:* A • *Aquatic biota:* A • Importance for ecological goods and services: A • Stability level: 0 • Instability level: 10 • Action priority level: 10 • Main action recommended: Incorporation into existing conservation area • Other recommended action: Incorporation of the area into the Jaru Biological Reserve, through the expansion of its eastern boundary to the Madeirinha River; and biological inventories.

4
PRIORITY AREAS IN THE GUIANA SHIELD REGION

EG 001 - Cabo Orange National Park - PRIORITY LEVEL: B • LOCATION: *State:* Amapá • *Main municipality:* Oiapoque • *Municipalities covered:* 3 • VEGETATION TYPES: Da, Db, Ds, Pa, Pf, SO • COMMENTS: One of the last untouched swamp areas in the Brazilian coast. Ecological breeding ground (shrimp, crustaceans, fish, birds, and others). The only breeding area of *Phoenicopterus ruber* (scarlet ibis). Border area with the state of Alagoas. International boundary.
  BIOLOGICAL IMPORTANCE: *Birds:* B • *Aquatic biota:* A • *Mammals:* B • STABILITY LEVEL: 9 • INSTABILITY LEVEL: 7 • ACTION PRIORITY LEVEL: 4 • MAIN ACTION RECOMMENDED: Protection • OTHER RECOMMENDED ACTION: Monitoring and full implementation of an environmental education program.

EG 002 - Juminá Indigenous Land - PRIORITY LEVEL: B • LOCATION: *State:* Amapá • *Main municipality:* Oiapoque • *Municipalities covered:* 2 • VEGETATION TYPES: Da, Pa, Pf • COMMENTS: Continuous area of high floristic and faunistic diversity. Border area. Cultural influence of French Guiana. Area of strategic importance (French Guiana).
  BIOLOGICAL IMPORTANCE: *Birds:* C • *Aquatic biota:* A • *Mammals:* B • STABILITY LEVEL: 3 • INSTABILITY LEVEL: 7 • ACTION PRIORITY LEVEL: 6 • MAIN ACTION RECOMMENDED: Sustainable use of natural resources • OTHER RECOMMENDED ACTION: Monitoring and protection of the area surrounding the indigenous land to prevent illegal occupation and to secure the area as a refuge for hunted species; implementation of an environmental education program for local populations.

EG 003 - Galibi Indigenous Land - PRIORITY LEVEL: A • LOCATION: *State:* Amapá • *Main municipality:* Oiapoque • *Municipalities covered:* 2 • VEGETATION TYPES: Ds • COMMENTS: Part of an extensive and rich network of areas with indigenous populations and abundant flora and fauna. Threat to the integrity of the environments managed by the indigenous population. Border area. Cultural influence of French Guiana. Area of strategic importance (French Guiana).
  BIOLOGICAL IMPORTANCE: *Aquatic biota:* A • *Mammals:* B • STABILITY LEVEL: 3 • INSTABILITY LEVEL: 7 • ACTION PRIORITY LEVEL: 6 • MAIN ACTION RECOMMENDED: Sustainable use of natural resources • OTHER RECOMMENDED ACTION: Monitoring and protection of the indigenous land to prevent illegal occupation and to secure area as a refuge for hunted species; implementation of an environmental education program for local populations.

EG 004 - Uaçá Indigenous Land - PRIORITY LEVEL: A • LOCATION: *State:* Amapá • *Main municipality:* Oiapoque • *Municipalities covered:* 1 • VEGETATION TYPES: Da, Ds, Pa, SO • COMMENTS: Threat to the society and to the environments managed by the indigenous population. Border area. Lack of knowledge of its biological diversity.
  BIOLOGICAL IMPORTANCE: *Birds:* C • *Aquatic biota:* A • *Mammals:* B • STABILITY LEVEL: 3 • INSTABILITY LEVEL: 8 • ACTION PRIORITY LEVEL: 7 • MAIN ACTION RECOMMENDED: Sustainable use of natural resources • OTHER RECOMMENDED ACTION: Monitoring and protection of the indigenous land to prevent illegal occupation and to secure area as a refuge for hunted species; implementation of an environmental education program for local populations.

EG 005 - Cacaual do Caciporé - PRIORITY LEVEL: B • LOCATION: *State:* Amapá • *Main municipality:* Calçoene • *Municipalities covered:* 2 • VEGETATION TYPES: Ds • COMMENTS: Improvement of local economy. Conservation of germplasm. Endemism.
  BIOLOGICAL IMPORTANCE: *Plants:* B • *Mammals:* B • STABILITY LEVEL: 0 • INSTABILITY LEVEL: 9 • ACTION PRIORITY LEVEL: 9 • MAIN ACTION RECOMMENDED: Creation of conservation area • OTHER RECOMMENDED ACTION: Creation of sustainable use conservation area, with expectation of silvicultural activities, management and germplasm conservation.

EG 006 - Calçoene - PRIORITY LEVEL: B • LOCATION: *State:* Amapá • *Main municipality:* Calçoene • *Municipalities covered:* 4 • VEGETATION TYPES: Da, Db, Ds, Pa, Pf, Sa, SO, Sp • COMMENTS: Almost untouched mangrove area. Direct road access to the coast. Suffering high anthropogenic impacts from ranching, agriculture and tourism. Area of great natural beauty. Fishing. Historical and cultural importance.
  BIOLOGICAL IMPORTANCE: *Birds:* B • *Aquatic biota:* A • *Mammals:* B • STABILITY LEVEL: 0 • INSTABILITY LEVEL: 10 • ACTION PRIORITY LEVEL: 10 • MAIN ACTION RECOMMENDED: Sustainable use of natural resources • OTHER RECOMMENDED ACTION: Monitoring and implementation of an environmental education program.

EG 007 - Amapá e Tartarugalzinho Cerrados - PRIORITY LEVEL: A • LOCATION: *State:* Amapá • *Main municipality:* Amapá • *Municipalities covered:* 3 • VEGETATION TYPES: Da, Ds, Pa, Sa, SO, Sp • COMMENTS: Cerrado area; the only region to the north of the equator with an example of the savannas of central Brazil, and entirely unprotected. The only ecosystem in the state not protected by conservation area. A cerrado enclave in the forest and the coastal mangroves.
  BIOLOGICAL IMPORTANCE: *Birds:* A • *Aquatic biota:* A • *Plants:* A • *Mammals:* B • STABILITY LEVEL: 0 • INSTABILITY LEVEL: 10 • ACTION PRIORITY LEVEL: 10 • MAIN ACTION RECOMMENDED: Creation of conservation area • OTHER RECOMMENDED ACTION: Creation of full protection conservation area.

EG 008 - Maracá-Jipioca Ecological Station - PRIORITY LEVEL: A • LOCATION: *State:* Amapá • *Main municipality:* Amapá • *Municipalities covered:* 2 • VEGETATION TYPES: Pa, Pf • COMMENTS: The conservation area covers the whole island of Macapá and other nearby islands with predominantly mangrove vegetation. Includes breeding populations of the scarlet ibis (*Eudocimus ruber*), a bird species on the official IBAMA list of threatened species. Largest marine island in Amapá.
  BIOLOGICAL IMPORTANCE: *Birds:* A • *Aquatic biota:* A • STABILITY LEVEL: 12 • INSTABILITY LEVEL: 3 • ACTION PRIORITY LEVEL: 2 • MAIN ACTION RECOMMENDED: Protection and restoration • OTHER RECOMMENDED ACTION: Inspection; monitoring and environment restoration; implementation of an environmental education program.

EG 009 - Lago Piratuba Biological Reserve - PRIORITY LEVEL: A • LOCATION: *State:* Amapá • *Main municipality:* Amapá • *Municipalities covered:* 5 • VEGETATION TYPES: Da, Pa, Pf • COMMENTS: Example of an important ecosystem in Amapá. Lake environment.
  BIOLOGICAL IMPORTANCE: *Birds:* A • *Aquatic biota:* A • *Mammals:* B • STABILITY LEVEL: 9 • INSTABILITY LEVEL: 6 • ACTION PRIORITY LEVEL: 4 • MAIN ACTION RECOMMENDED: Protection • OTHER RECOMMENDED ACTION: Monitoring and environmental education.

EG 010 - Lower Araguari - PRIORITY LEVEL: A • LOCATION: *State:* Amapá • *Main municipality:* Tartarugalzinho • *Municipalities covered:* 9 • VEGETATION TYPES: AA, Da, Ds, Pa, Pf, Sd, SO, Sp • COMMENTS: Area rich in aquatic and terrestrial systems. Ecological refuge. Occurrence of tidal bore (*pororoca*). Important area for ecotourism projects.
  BIOLOGICAL IMPORTANCE: *Birds:* A • *Aquatic biota:* A • *Plants:* A •

Mammals: B • IMPORTANCE FOR ECOLOGICAL GOODS AND SERVICES: C • STABILITY LEVEL: 0 • INSTABILITY LEVEL: 10 • ACTION PRIORITY LEVEL: 10 • MAIN ACTION RECOMMENDED: Protection • OTHER RECOMMENDED ACTION: Monitoring; preparation of biological inventories; implementation of an environmental education program.

EG 011 - Sucuriju - PRIORITY LEVEL: A • LOCATION: *State:* Amapá • *Main municipality:* Amapá • *Municipalities covered:* 2 • VEGETATION TYPES: Pa, Pf • COMMENTS: Identify forms of sustainable use of the aquatic resources, ensuring the survival of fishing communities.

BIOLOGICAL IMPORTANCE: *Birds:* A • *Aquatic biota:* A • *Mammals:* B • STABILITY LEVEL: 0 • INSTABILITY LEVEL: 5 • ACTION PRIORITY LEVEL: 6 • MAIN ACTION RECOMMENDED: Creation of conservation area • OTHER RECOMMENDED ACTION: Creation of marine extractive reserve; preparation of biological inventories; monitoring; implementation of an environmental education program.

EG 012 - Middle Oiapoque - PRIORITY LEVEL: A • LOCATION: *State:* Amapá • *Main municipality:* Oiapoque • *Municipalities covered:* 5 • VEGETATION TYPES: Ds • COMMENTS: Area of low anthropogenic pressure, adjacent to forests in similar situation in French Guiana, ideal for a conservation area to protect a large part of the Oiapoque river basin. Area of strategic national security importance.

BIOLOGICAL IMPORTANCE: *Birds:* A • *Aquatic biota:* B • *Plants:* B • *Mammals:* D • *Reptiles and amphibians:* A • IMPORTANCE FOR ECOLOGICAL GOODS AND SERVICES: C • STABILITY LEVEL: 0 • INSTABILITY LEVEL: 2 • ACTION PRIORITY LEVEL: 4 • MAIN ACTION RECOMMENDED: Creation of conservation area.

EG 013 - Amapá National Forest - PRIORITY LEVEL: B • LOCATION: *State:* Amapá • *Main municipality:* Pracuúba • *Municipalities covered:* 8 • VEGETATION TYPES: Ds • COMMENTS: High level of richness of forest flora and fauna components, representative of the Guiana shield. Special characteristics relating to sub-montane environment.

BIOLOGICAL IMPORTANCE: *Birds:* C • *Aquatic biota:* B • *Mammals:* B • *Reptiles and amphibians:* B • IMPORTANCE FOR ECOLOGICAL GOODS AND SERVICES: C • STABILITY LEVEL: 6 • INSTABILITY LEVEL: 2 • ACTION PRIORITY LEVEL: 3 • MAIN ACTION RECOMMENDED: Reclassification of the conservation area • OTHER RECOMMENDED ACTION: Reclassification to full protection conservation area and preparation of biological inventories.

EG 014 - Middle Araguari - PRIORITY LEVEL: B • LOCATION: *State:* Amapá • *Main municipality:* Pedra Branca do Amapari • *Municipalities covered:* 7 • VEGETATION TYPES: AA, Db, Ds, SO • COMMENTS: Area of endemism and rare and threatened species in the Serra do Navio. Important mineral area of the state.

BIOLOGICAL IMPORTANCE: *Birds:* C • *Aquatic biota:* B • *Invertebrates:* D • *Reptiles and amphibians:* B • IMPORTANCE FOR ECOLOGICAL GOODS AND SERVICES: A • STABILITY LEVEL: 0 • INSTABILITY LEVEL: 8 • ACTION PRIORITY LEVEL: 8 • MAIN ACTION RECOMMENDED: Protection • OTHER RECOMMENDED ACTION: Monitoring and preparation of biological inventories.

EG 015 - Waiãpi Indigenous Land - PRIORITY LEVEL: B • LOCATION: *State:* Amapá • *Main municipality:* Vitória do Jari • *Municipalities covered:* 4 • VEGETATION TYPES: Da, Ds • COMMENTS: Area with very high proportion of natural ecosystems conserved; richness and abundance of fauna and flora.

BIOLOGICAL IMPORTANCE: *Birds:* C • *Aquatic biota:* B • *Plants:* B • *Invertebrates:* D • *Mammals:* D • IMPORTANCE FOR ECOLOGICAL GOODS AND SERVICES: A • STABILITY LEVEL: 3 • INSTABILITY LEVEL: 9 • ACTION PRIORITY LEVEL: 7 • MAIN ACTION RECOMMENDED: Protection • OTHER RECOMMENDED ACTION: Monitoring and protection of the area surrounding the indigenous land.

EG 016 - Rio Iratapuru Sustainable Development Reserve - PRIORITY LEVEL: B • LOCATION: *State:* Amapá • *Main municipality:* Vitória do Jari • *Municipalities covered:* 5 • VEGETATION TYPES: Da, Ds • COMMENTS: Biological importance. Area under anthropogenic pressure. High potential for sustainable use: forest products, ecotourism.

BIOLOGICAL IMPORTANCE: *Birds:* C • *Aquatic biota:* B • *Plants:* A • *Invertebrates:* D • *Mammals:* C • IMPORTANCE FOR ECOLOGICAL GOODS AND SERVICES: A • STABILITY LEVEL: 6 • INSTABILITY LEVEL: 7 • ACTION PRIORITY LEVEL: 5 • MAIN ACTION RECOMMENDED: Sustainable use of natural resources • OTHER RECOMMENDED ACTION: Monitoring and implementation of an environmental education program.

EG 017 - Jari Ecological Station - PRIORITY LEVEL: B • LOCATION: *State:* Amapá/Pará • *Main municipality:* Almeirim • *Municipalities covered:* 2 • VEGETATION TYPES: As, Da, Ds • COMMENTS: Area of inter-state reserve. Anthropogenic pressure.

BIOLOGICAL IMPORTANCE: *Birds:* C • *Aquatic biota:* B • *Plants:* A • *Mammals:* C • IMPORTANCE FOR ECOLOGICAL GOODS AND SERVICES: A • STABILITY LEVEL: 6 • INSTABILITY LEVEL: 2 • ACTION PRIORITY LEVEL: 3 • MAIN ACTION RECOMMENDED: Protection • OTHER RECOMMENDED ACTION: Monitoring and full implementation of an environmental education program.

EG 018 - Mid Jari - PRIORITY LEVEL: B • LOCATION: *State:* Pará • *Main municipality:* Almeirim • *Municipalities covered:* 2 • VEGETATION TYPES: As, Da, Ds • COMMENTS: Protection of the first rapids of the Jari river and of the remaining dense rainforests near the Monte Dourado Company.

BIOLOGICAL IMPORTANCE: *Birds:* C • *Aquatic biota:* B • *Plants:* A • *Mammals:* C • IMPORTANCE FOR ECOLOGICAL GOODS AND SERVICES: A • STABILITY LEVEL: 0 • INSTABILITY LEVEL: 2 • ACTION PRIORITY LEVEL: 4 • MAIN ACTION RECOMMENDED: Identify priority actions • OTHER RECOMMENDED ACTION: Studies and preparation of biological inventories for the expansion of the Jari Ecological Station.

EG 019 - Upper Jari River - Tumucumaque • PRIORITY LEVEL: B • LOCATION: *State:* Amapá/Pará • *Main municipality:* Vitória do Jari • *Municipalities covered:* 6 • VEGETATION TYPES: Dm, Ds • COMMENTS: Important region of submontane dense rainforest.

BIOLOGICAL IMPORTANCE: *Birds:* D • *Aquatic biota:* B • *Plants:* B • *Mammals:* D • *Reptiles and amphibians:* A • IMPORTANCE FOR ECOLOGICAL GOODS AND SERVICES: A • STABILITY LEVEL: 0 • INSTABILITY LEVEL: 1 • ACTION PRIORITY LEVEL: 4 • MAIN ACTION RECOMMENDED: Creation of conservation area.

EG 020 - Jari Rapids - PRIORITY LEVEL: B • LOCATION: *State:* Amapá/Pará • *Main municipality:* Almeirim • *Municipalities covered:* 2 • VEGETATION TYPES: Da, Ds • COMMENTS: Important aquatic ecosystems. Untouched dense rainforest.

BIOLOGICAL IMPORTANCE: *Aquatic biota:* B • *Plants:* D • *Mammals:* D • *Reptiles and amphibians:* A • IMPORTANCE FOR ECOLOGICAL GOODS AND SERVICES: A • STABILITY LEVEL: 0 • INSTABILITY LEVEL: 2 • ACTION PRIORITY LEVEL: 4 • MAIN ACTION RECOMMENDED: Protection • OTHER RECOMMENDED ACTION: Hunting inspection; protection of the aquatic ecosystems; and preparation of biological inventories.

EG 021 - Waimiri-Atroari Indigenous Land - PRIORITY LEVEL: D • LOCATION: *State:* Amazonas/Roraima • *Main municipality:* Novo Airão • *Municipalities covered:* 5 • VEGETATION TYPES: Ab, As, Da, Db, Ds, Ld, LO • COMMENTS: No information available.

BIOLOGICAL IMPORTANCE: *Birds:* A • *Aquatic biota:* ? • IMPORTANCE FOR ECOLOGICAL GOODS AND SERVICES: A • STABILITY LEVEL: 5 • INSTABILITY LEVEL: 4 • ACTION PRIORITY LEVEL: 4 • MAIN ACTION RECOMMENDED: Sustainable use of natural resources • OTHER RECOMMENDED ACTION: Monitoring.

EG 022 - Tumucumaque Indigenous Land - PRIORITY LEVEL: A • LOCATION: *State:* Amapá/Pará • *Main municipality:* Almeirim • *Municipalities covered:* 6 • VEGETATION TYPES: Da, Dm, Ds, Sd, SO, Sp • COMMENTS: Indigenous area with indications of high diversity.

BIOLOGICAL IMPORTANCE: *Birds:* B • *Aquatic biota:* A • *Plants:* D • *Invertebrates:* D • *Mammals:* D • *Reptiles and amphibians:* A • IMPORTANCE FOR ECOLOGICAL GOODS AND SERVICES: A • STABILITY LEVEL: 5 • INSTABILITY LEVEL: 1 • ACTION PRIORITY LEVEL: 2 • MAIN ACTION RECOMMENDED: Sustainable use of natural resources.

EG 023 - Tumucumaque Forest Reserve and Tumucumaque Indigenous Land - PRIORITY LEVEL: A • LOCATION: *State:* Pará • *Main municipality:* Almeirim • *Municipalities covered:* 5 • VEGETATION TYPES: Dm, Ds, SO, Sp • COMMENTS: Headwater region of high richness and endemism. Overlap between conservation area and indigenous land.

BIOLOGICAL IMPORTANCE: *Birds:* B • *Aquatic biota:* A • *Plants:* D • *Invertebrates:* D • *Mammals:* D • *Reptiles and amphibians:* A • IMPORTANCE FOR ECOLOGICAL GOODS AND SERVICES: A • STABILITY LEVEL: 7 • INSTABILITY LEVEL: 1 • ACTION PRIORITY LEVEL: 2 • MAIN ACTION RECOMMENDED: Sustainable use of natural resources

EG 024 - Paru de Leste Indigenous Land - PRIORITY LEVEL: B • LOCATION: *State:* Pará • *Main municipality:* Almeirim • *Municipalities covered:* 3 • VEGETATION TYPES: Da, Ds, SO • COMMENTS: Probable high diversity with pressure or impacts from mining.

Biological importance: *Birds:* B • *Aquatic biota:* B • *Plants:* D • *Mammals:* D • Importance for ecological goods and services: A • Stability level: 5 • Instability level: 3 • Action priority level: 3 • Main action recommended: Sustainable use of natural resources • Other recommended action: Monitoring and control of mining activities in the area surrounding the indigenous land.

EG 025 - Cuminapanema - Alto Maicuru • Priority level: A • Location: *State:* Pará • *Main municipality:* Alenquer • *Municipalities covered:* 5 • Vegetation types: Da, Ds, Sd, SO • Comments: Integrity of the natural environments. Risks of predatory anthropogenic activity.

Biological importance: *Birds:* B • *Aquatic biota:* A • *Plants:* A • *Invertebrates:* D • *Mammals:* C • *Reptiles and amphibians:* A • Importance for ecological goods and services: A • Stability level: 0 • Instability level: 1 • Action priority level: 4 • Main action recommended: Creation of conservation area • Other recommended action: Creation of conservation area in a cerrado enclave in the headwaters of the Maicuru. Totally conserved environments with no human populations, but with the risk of development of mining activities and/or predatory settlement in an area located between three large indigenous areas with low population density.

EG 026 - Zoé Indigenous Land - Priority level: A • Location: *State:* Pará • *Main municipality:* Óbidos • *Municipalities covered:* 3 • Vegetation types: Da, Ds, Pa, Sd, SO • Comments: Indigenous land in an area of potential interest for its biodiversity.

Biological importance: *Birds:* A • *Aquatic biota:* A • *Plants:* A • *Invertebrates:* D • *Mammals:* C • Importance for ecological goods and services: A • Stability level: 5 • Instability level: 0 • Action priority level: 2 • Main action recommended: Sustainable use of natural resources • Other recommended action: Monitoring and protection of the indigenous land.

EG 027 - Middle Trombetas - Priority level: A • Location: *State:* Pará • *Main municipality:* Oriximiná • *Municipalities covered:* 5 • Vegetation types: AA, Db, Ds, Pa, SO, Sp • Comments: Area of important mineral deposits.

Biological importance: *Birds:* A • *Aquatic biota:* A • *Plants:* D • *Mammals:* C • *Reptiles and amphibians:* B • Importance for ecological goods and services: A • Stability level: 0 • Instability level: 6 • Action priority level: 7 • Main action recommended: Sustainable use of natural resources • Other recommended action: Preparation of biological inventories.

EG 028 - Rio Trombetas Biological Reserve - Priority level: A • Location: *State:* Pará • *Main municipality:* Oriximiná • *Municipalities covered:* 1 • Vegetation types: Db, Ds • Comments: High diversity; spawning grounds for turtles.

Biological importance: *Birds:* A • *Aquatic biota:* A • *Mammals:* C • *Reptiles and amphibians:* B • Importance for ecological goods and services: A • Stability level: 6 • Instability level: 1 • Action priority level: 2 • Main action recommended: Protection • Other recommended action: Monitoring and preparation of biological inventories.

EG 029 - Saracataqüera National Forest - Priority level: A • Location: *State:* Pará • *Main municipality:* Oriximiná • *Municipalities covered:* 3 • Vegetation types: AA, Db, Ds, Pa • Comments: National forest near the Trombetas Biological Reserve needing to be sustainably managed.

Biological importance: *Birds:* A • *Aquatic biota:* A • *Mammals:* C • *Reptiles and amphibians:* B • Importance for ecological goods and services: B • Stability level: 6 • Instability level: 2 • Action priority level: 3 • Main action recommended: Sustainable use of natural resources.

EG 030 - Upper Trombetas - Priority level: A • Location: *State:* Pará • *Main municipality:* Oriximiná • *Municipalities covered:* 2 • Vegetation types: Da, Dm, Ds • Comments: Little known area, but (on the evidence of the neighboring countries) probably rich in biodiversity and endemism (montane forests), not represented in any conservation area.

Biological importance: *Birds:* D • *Aquatic biota:* A • *Plants:* D • *Mammals:* D • *Reptiles and amphibians:* A • Importance for ecological goods and services: A • Stability level: 0 • Instability level: 1 • Action priority level: 4 • Main action recommended: Creation of conservation area • Other recommended action: Creation of full protection conservation area and preparation of biological inventories.

EG 031 - Upper Mapuera - Priority level: B • Location: *State:* Pará • *Main municipality:* Oriximiná • *Municipalities covered:* 1 • Vegetation types: As, Ds • Comments: Protection of the Mapuera headwaters and of the basin, important for the aquatic biota (high levels of endemism).

Biological importance: *Birds:* B • *Aquatic biota:* A • *Plants:* D • *Mammals:* D • Importance for ecological goods and services: A • Stability level: 0 • Instability level: 1 • Action priority level: 4 • Main action recommended: Creation of conservation area • Other recommended action: Creation of full protection conservation area and preparation of biological inventories.

EG 032 - Trombetas/Mapuera Indigenous Land - Priority level: B • Location: *State:* Pará/Roraima/Amazonas • *Main municipality:* Urucará • *Municipalities covered:* 7 • Vegetation types: As, Dm, Ds, SO • Comments: Extremely important area for the protection of turtle spawning.

Biological importance: *Birds:* B • *Aquatic biota:* A • *Plants:* D • *Mammals:* C • Importance for ecological goods and services: A • Stability level: 1 • Instability level: 6 • Action priority level: 6 • Main action recommended: Sustainable use of natural resources • Other recommended action: Monitoring.

EG 033 - Nhamundá-Mapuera Indigenous Land - Priority level: B • Location: *State:* Pará/Amazonas • *Main municipality:* Oriximiná • *Municipalities covered:* 4 • Vegetation types: Db, Ds • Comments: Protection of the Mapuera headwaters and of the basin, important for the aquatic biota (high levels of endemism).

Biological importance: *Birds:* B • *Aquatic biota:* A • *Plants:* D • *Mammals:* C • Importance for ecological goods and services: A • Stability level: 5 • Instability level: 1 • Action priority level: 2 • Main action recommended: Sustainable use of natural resources • Other recommended action: Monitoring and protection of the indigenous land.

EG 034 - Lower Uatumã - Priority level: C • Location: *State:* Amazonas • *Main municipality:* São Sebastião do Uatumã • *Municipalities covered:* 7 • Vegetation types: Da, Db, Ds, Pa • Comments: Dense rainforest, similar to the area located in the mangrove region, able to be transformed into strict conservation area.

Biological importance: *Birds:* C • *Aquatic biota:* D • *Mammals:* C • Importance for ecological goods and services: B • Stability level: 0 • Instability level: 5 • Action priority level: 6 • Main action recommended: Identify priority actions • Other recommended action: Preparation of biological inventories.

EG 035 - Uatumã Biological Reserve - Priority level: C • Location: *State:* Amazonas • *Main municipality:* Presidente Figueiredo • *Municipalities covered:* 3 • Vegetation types: Ds • Comments: Area witness to lost biota, resulting from the filling of the Balbina hydro plant reservoir.

Biological importance: *Mammals:* C • Importance for ecological goods and services: A • Stability level: 3 • Instability level: 3 • Action priority level: 4 • Main action recommended: Protection • Other recommended action: Monitoring and preparation of biological inventories.

EG 036 - Caverna do Moroaga Environmental Protection Area - Priority level: C • Location: *State:* Amazonas • *Main municipality:* Presidente Figueiredo • *Municipalities covered:* 2 • Vegetation types: As, Db, Ds, LO • Comments: Area of importance for bordering and being under direct influence of the Balbina reservoir.

Biological importance: *Plants:* B • *Mammals:* C • Importance for ecological goods and services: A • Stability level: 6 • Instability level: 8 • Action priority level: 6 • Main action recommended: Sustainable use of natural resources • Other recommended action: Inspection; monitoring of the impact of the reservoir: and implementation of an environmental education program.

5
PRIORITY AREAS IN THE LOWER XINGU / TAPAJÓS / MADEIRA REGION

BX 001 - Headwaters of the Xingu - PRIORITY LEVEL: A • LOCATION: *State:* Mato Grosso • *Main municipality:* Gaúcha do Norte • *Municipalities covered:* 8 • VEGETATION TYPES: AA, Fa, ON, Pa, Sa, Sd, SN, Sp • COMMENTS: The headwaters of the Xingu are under strong pressure from monocultures. Pressure on indigenous lands. Reforestation and permanent agriculture. Fire prevention. Restoration of gallery forests. Basic sanitation for the municipalities.
> BIOLOGICAL IMPORTANCE: *Birds:* A • *Aquatic biota:* A • *Plants:* D • *Reptiles and amphibians:* B • IMPORTANCE FOR ECOLOGICAL GOODS AND SERVICES: B • STABILITY LEVEL: 0 • INSTABILITY LEVEL: 7 • ACTION PRIORITY LEVEL: 8 • MAIN ACTION RECOMMENDED: Creation of conservation area • OTHER RECOMMENDED ACTION: Creation of an environmental protection area protecting the headwaters of the Xingu; encouragement and support to the basin committees; development of an environmental education program for the region.

BX 002 - Tabuleiro das Tartarugas - PRIORITY LEVEL: N • LOCATION: *State:* Pará • *Main municipality:* Anapu • *Municipalities covered:* 4 • VEGETATION TYPES: AA, As, Da, Db, Ds • COMMENTS: Very high biological importance.
> BIOLOGICAL IMPORTANCE: *Mammals:* C • *Reptiles and amphibians:* A • IMPORTANCE FOR ECOLOGICAL GOODS AND SERVICES: C • STABILITY LEVEL: 0 • INSTABILITY LEVEL: 10 • ACTION PRIORITY LEVEL: 10 • MAIN ACTION RECOMMENDED: Creation of conservation area • OTHER RECOMMENDED ACTION: Reclassification of the area to full protection conservation area; monitoring; biological inventories; development of an environmental education program.

BX 003 - Ronuro Ecological Station - PRIORITY LEVEL: A • LOCATION: *State:* Mato Grosso • *Main municipality:* Nova Ubiratã • *Municipalities covered:* 2 • VEGETATION TYPES: AA, ON, Pa.
> BIOLOGICAL IMPORTANCE: *Birds:* D • *Aquatic biota:* A • *Plants:* D • *Reptiles and amphibians:* B • IMPORTANCE FOR ECOLOGICAL GOODS AND SERVICES: B • STABILITY LEVEL: 3 • INSTABILITY LEVEL: 4 • ACTION PRIORITY LEVEL: 4 • MAIN ACTION RECOMMENDED: Protection • OTHER RECOMMENDED ACTION: Expropriation of private properties; biological inventories;

BX 004 - Rio das Mortes - PRIORITY LEVEL: N • LOCATION: *State:* Mato Grosso • *Main municipality:* Ribeirão Cascalheira • *Municipalities covered:* 3 • VEGETATION TYPES: Sa, SN, Sp.
> BIOLOGICAL IMPORTANCE: *Birds:* D • *Aquatic biota:* A • IMPORTANCE FOR ECOLOGICAL GOODS AND SERVICES: S • STABILITY LEVEL: 0 • INSTABILITY LEVEL: 0 • ACTION PRIORITY LEVEL: 3 • MAIN ACTION RECOMMENDED: Creation of conservation area • OTHER RECOMMENDED ACTION: Reclassification of the area to full protection conservation area; biological inventories; development of an environmental education program.

BX 005 - Xingu Indigenous Park, including Batovi Indigenous Land - PRIORITY LEVEL: B • LOCATION: *State:* Mato Grosso • *Main municipality:* Gaúcha do Norte • *Municipalities covered:* 11 • VEGETATION TYPES: AA, Da, Fa, ON, Pa, SN • COMMENTS: Support better understanding of traditional production systems, including natural resources (specially the archeological black soil lands, where there is a marked contrast with the diversity of adjacent areas), and study the economic relations between the indians and Brazilian society.
> BIOLOGICAL IMPORTANCE: *Birds:* B • *Aquatic biota:* A • *Plants:* D • *Reptiles and amphibians:* B • IMPORTANCE FOR ECOLOGICAL GOODS AND SERVICES: B • STABILITY LEVEL: 3 • INSTABILITY LEVEL: 4 • ACTION PRIORITY LEVEL: 4 • MAIN ACTION RECOMMENDED: Sustainable use of natural resources • OTHER RECOMMENDED ACTION: Full implementation of a buffer zone around the Xingu Indigenous Park; support and encouragement to the protection, sustainable use and monitoring actions being carried out.

BX 006 - Wawi Indigenous Land - PRIORITY LEVEL: A • LOCATION: *State:* Mato Grosso • *Main municipality:* Querência • *Municipalities covered:* 2 • VEGETATION TYPES: ON, Pa.
> BIOLOGICAL IMPORTANCE: *Birds:* B • *Aquatic biota:* A • STABILITY LEVEL: 3 • INSTABILITY LEVEL: 4 • ACTION PRIORITY LEVEL: 4 • MAIN ACTION RECOMMENDED: Sustainable use of natural resources • OTHER RECOMMENDED ACTION: Monitoring and preparation of biological inventories.

BX 007 - Xingu 1 - PRIORITY LEVEL: A • LOCATION: *State:* Mato Grosso • *Main municipality:* São Félix do Araguaia • *Municipalities covered:* 2 • VEGETATION TYPES: AA, ON, Pa • COMMENTS: Area adjacent to the Xingu National Park, with substantial recent deforestation, of extreme biological importance for aquatic biota.
> BIOLOGICAL IMPORTANCE: *Birds:* B • *Aquatic biota:* A • IMPORTANCE FOR ECOLOGICAL GOODS AND SERVICES: B • STABILITY LEVEL: 0 • INSTABILITY LEVEL: 7 • ACTION PRIORITY LEVEL: 8 • MAIN ACTION RECOMMENDED: Sustainable use of natural resources • OTHER RECOMMENDED ACTION: Monitoring; biological inventories; ecological-economic zoning; and implementation of an environmental education program.

BX 008 - Xingu 2 - PRIORITY LEVEL: B • LOCATION: *State:* Mato Grosso • *Main municipality:* Marcelândia • *Municipalities covered:* 4 • VEGETATION TYPES: AA, As, Da, Ds, ON, SN • COMMENTS: Creation of an Indigenous Natural Resources Reserve, harmonizing the conservation of natural resources and the sustainable use of those resources important to indigenous populations.
> BIOLOGICAL IMPORTANCE: *Birds:* B • *Plants:* D • *Reptiles and amphibians:* B • STABILITY LEVEL: 0 • INSTABILITY LEVEL: 5 • ACTION PRIORITY LEVEL: 6 • MAIN ACTION RECOMMENDED: Creation of conservation area • OTHER RECOMMENDED ACTION: Reclassification of the area to a sustainable use area (Indigenous Natural Resources Reserve), and review of forest management plans that include logging in gallery forests.

BX 009 - Capoto/Jarina Indigenous Land - PRIORITY LEVEL: B • LOCATION: *State:* Mato Grosso • *Main municipality:* Peixoto de Azevedo • *Municipalities covered:* 2 • VEGETATION TYPES: As, ON, Pa, Sa, Sd, SO, Sp.
> BIOLOGICAL IMPORTANCE: *Birds:* B • *Aquatic biota:* B • *Plants:* B • *Mammals:* A • STABILITY LEVEL: 3 • INSTABILITY LEVEL: 4 • ACTION PRIORITY LEVEL: 4 • MAIN ACTION RECOMMENDED: Sustainable use of natural resources • OTHER RECOMMENDED ACTION: Protection and monitoring of boundaries and of the adjacent buffer zone.

BX 010 - Badjônkôre Indigenous Land - PRIORITY LEVEL: B • LOCATION: *State:* Pará • *Main municipality:* São Félix do Xingu • *Municipalities covered:* 2 • VEGETATION TYPES: As, Sa, Sd, Sg, SO, Sp.
> BIOLOGICAL IMPORTANCE: *Aquatic biota:* B • *Plants:* B • *Reptiles and amphibians:* D • IMPORTANCE FOR ECOLOGICAL GOODS AND SERVICES: A • STABILITY LEVEL: 1 • INSTABILITY LEVEL: 0 • ACTION PRIORITY LEVEL: 3 • MAIN ACTION RECOMMENDED: Protection • OTHER RECOMMENDED ACTION: Protection and monitoring.

BX 011 - Menkragnoti Indigenous Land - PRIORITY LEVEL: A • LOCATION: *State:* Pará/Mato Grosso • *Main municipality:* Altamira • *Municipalities covered:* 4 • VEGETATION TYPES: As, Ds, Sa, Sd, SO, Sp.

BIOLOGICAL IMPORTANCE: *Birds:* A • *Aquatic biota:* B • *Plants:* B • *Invertebrates:* D • *Mammals:* A • *Reptiles and amphibians:* D • IMPORTANCE FOR ECOLOGICAL GOODS AND SERVICES: A • STABILITY LEVEL: 3 • INSTABILITY LEVEL: 8 • ACTION PRIORITY LEVEL: 7 • MAIN ACTION RECOMMENDED: Protection • OTHER RECOMMENDED ACTION: Protection and monitoring of boundaries.

BX 012 - Panará Indigenous Land - PRIORITY LEVEL: A • LOCATION: *State:* Pará/Mato Grosso • *Main municipality:* Altamira • *Municipalities covered:* 3 • VEGETATION TYPES: As, Ds, Sa, Sd, Sg, SN.

BIOLOGICAL IMPORTANCE: *Birds:* A • *Plants:* D • *Mammals:* A • *Reptiles and amphibians:* D • IMPORTANCE FOR ECOLOGICAL GOODS AND SERVICES: A • STABILITY LEVEL: 1 • INSTABILITY LEVEL: 9 • ACTION PRIORITY LEVEL: 8 • MAIN ACTION RECOMMENDED: Sustainable use of natural resources • OTHER RECOMMENDED ACTION: Protection and monitoring of boundaries and full implementation of an economic and socio-environmental sustainability program in the area.

BX 013 - Iriri River - PRIORITY LEVEL: B • LOCATION: *State:* Pará • *Main municipality:* Altamira • *Municipalities covered:* 1 • VEGETATION TYPES: As, Ds, Sa, SO • COMMENTS: Site of high biological importance (mammals).

BIOLOGICAL IMPORTANCE: *Birds:* D • *Plants:* D • *Mammals:* B • *Reptiles and amphibians:* D • IMPORTANCE FOR ECOLOGICAL GOODS AND SERVICES: A • STABILITY LEVEL: 0 • INSTABILITY LEVEL: 0 • ACTION PRIORITY LEVEL: 3 • MAIN ACTION RECOMMENDED: Creation of conservation area • OTHER RECOMMENDED ACTION: Reclassification of the area to full protection conservation area; monitoring; and biological inventories.

BX 014 - Area to the east of the Badjônkôre Indigenous Land - PRIORITY LEVEL: B • LOCATION: *State:* Pará • *Main municipality:* Cumaru do Norte • *Municipalities covered:* 2 • VEGETATION TYPES: AA, As, Sa, Sd, Sg, SO, Sp • COMMENTS: This area constitutes an important buffer zone for the indigenous lands of the Xingu (Gorotine, Badjônkôre and Menkragnoti). It is showing increasing anthropogenic pressure on the protected areas.

BIOLOGICAL IMPORTANCE: *Aquatic biota:* B • *Plants:* A • *Reptiles and amphibians:* D • IMPORTANCE FOR ECOLOGICAL GOODS AND SERVICES: A • STABILITY LEVEL: 0 • INSTABILITY LEVEL: 9 • ACTION PRIORITY LEVEL: 9 • MAIN ACTION RECOMMENDED: Creation of conservation area • OTHER RECOMMENDED ACTION: Conversion of the area into conservation area as a buffer zone for the Badjônkôre Indigenous Land; biological inventories; development of socio-economic and environmental assessments; implementation of an environmental education program.

BX 015 - Kayapó Indigenous Land - PRIORITY LEVEL: A • LOCATION: *State:* Pará • *Main municipality:* São Félix do Xingu • *Municipalities covered:* 6 • VEGETATION TYPES: AA, As, Ds, Sa, Sd, Sg, SO, Sp.

BIOLOGICAL IMPORTANCE: *Birds:* A • *Aquatic biota:* B • *Plants:* B • *Invertebrates:* D • *Mammals:* A • *Reptiles and amphibians:* B • IMPORTANCE FOR ECOLOGICAL GOODS AND SERVICES: A • STABILITY LEVEL: 3 • INSTABILITY LEVEL: 4 • ACTION PRIORITY LEVEL: 4 • MAIN ACTION RECOMMENDED: Protection • OTHER RECOMMENDED ACTION: Protection and monitoring of logging activities.

BX 016 - Middle Xingu - PRIORITY LEVEL: B • LOCATION: *State:* Pará • *Main municipality:* São Félix do Xingu • *Municipalities covered:* 2 • VEGETATION TYPES: AA, As, Da, Ds, Sa, SO • COMMENTS: Area of high biological diversity, located in a region of high fire risk; part of a larger region, between the Xingu and the Iriri rivers, under anthropogenic pressure from logging activities. Part of a complex formed by areas 16, 23, 13 and 72.

BIOLOGICAL IMPORTANCE: *Birds:* D • *Aquatic biota:* B • *Plants:* A • *Mammals:* C • *Reptiles and amphibians:* B • IMPORTANCE FOR ECOLOGICAL GOODS AND SERVICES: A • STABILITY LEVEL: 0 • INSTABILITY LEVEL: 9 • ACTION PRIORITY LEVEL: 9 • MAIN ACTION RECOMMENDED: Creation of conservation area • OTHER RECOMMENDED ACTION: Conversion of the polygon formed by the Iriri and Xingu rivers into full protection and sustainable use conservation areas, creating a buffer zone for the Xingu indigenous lands.

BX 017 - Apyterewa Indigenous Land - PRIORITY LEVEL: B • LOCATION: *State:* Pará • *Main municipality:* São Félix do Xingu • *Municipalities covered:* 2 • VEGETATION TYPES: As, Da, Ds, SO.

BIOLOGICAL IMPORTANCE: *Birds:* D • *Aquatic biota:* B • *Plants:* D • *Mammals:* C • IMPORTANCE FOR ECOLOGICAL GOODS AND SERVICES: A • STABILITY LEVEL: 1 • INSTABILITY LEVEL: 4 • ACTION PRIORITY LEVEL: 5 • MAIN ACTION RECOMMENDED: Protection • OTHER RECOMMENDED ACTION: Protection and monitoring of boundaries.

BX 018 - Araweté/Igararé Ipixuna Indigenous Land - PRIORITY LEVEL: B • LOCATION: *State:* Pará • *Main municipality:* Altamira • *Municipalities covered:* 3 • VEGETATION TYPES: AA, As, Da, Ds.

BIOLOGICAL IMPORTANCE: *Birds:* D • *Aquatic biota:* B • *Plants:* D • *Mammals:* C • *Reptiles and amphibians:* A • IMPORTANCE FOR ECOLOGICAL GOODS AND SERVICES: A • STABILITY LEVEL: 5 • INSTABILITY LEVEL: 0 • ACTION PRIORITY LEVEL: 2 • MAIN ACTION RECOMMENDED: Protection • OTHER RECOMMENDED ACTION: Protection and monitoring of boundaries.

BX 019 - Trincheira/Bacajá Indigenous Land - PRIORITY LEVEL: A • LOCATION: *State:* Pará • *Main municipality:* Senador José Porfírio • *Municipalities covered:* 5 • VEGETATION TYPES: As, Ds.

BIOLOGICAL IMPORTANCE: *Aquatic biota:* D • *Mammals:* C • *Reptiles and amphibians:* A • IMPORTANCE FOR ECOLOGICAL GOODS AND SERVICES: A • STABILITY LEVEL: 3 • INSTABILITY LEVEL: 3 • ACTION PRIORITY LEVEL: 4 • MAIN ACTION RECOMMENDED: Protection • OTHER RECOMMENDED ACTION: Protection and monitoring of logging activities.

BX 020 - Koatinemo Indigenous Land - PRIORITY LEVEL: B • LOCATION: *State:* Pará • *Main municipality:* Altamira • *Municipalities covered:* 2 • VEGETATION TYPES: As, Da, Ds.

BIOLOGICAL IMPORTANCE: *Birds:* D • *Aquatic biota:* B • *Plants:* D • *Mammals:* C • *Reptiles and amphibians:* A • IMPORTANCE FOR ECOLOGICAL GOODS AND SERVICES: B • STABILITY LEVEL: 3 • INSTABILITY LEVEL: 3 • ACTION PRIORITY LEVEL: 4 • MAIN ACTION RECOMMENDED: Sustainable use of natural resources • OTHER RECOMMENDED ACTION: Protection and monitoring of logging activities; preparation of biological inventories.

BX 021 - Anapu River - PRIORITY LEVEL: A • LOCATION: *State:* Pará • *Main municipality:* Senador José Porfírio • *Municipalities covered:* 3 • VEGETATION TYPES: As, Ds.

BIOLOGICAL IMPORTANCE: *Aquatic biota:* D • *Plants:* A • *Mammals:* C • *Reptiles and amphibians:* A • IMPORTANCE FOR ECOLOGICAL GOODS AND SERVICES: C • STABILITY LEVEL: 0 • INSTABILITY LEVEL: 10 • ACTION PRIORITY LEVEL: 10 • MAIN ACTION RECOMMENDED: Creation of conservation area • OTHER RECOMMENDED ACTION: Conversion of the area into full protection conservation area; preparation of biological inventories; implementation of an environmental education program.

BX 022 - Xingu-Iriri 1 Interfluve - PRIORITY LEVEL: D • LOCATION: *State:* Pará • *Main municipality:* São Félix do Xingu • *Municipalities covered:* 2 • VEGETATION TYPES: As, Ds, Sa, SO • COMMENTS: Located in a region of high importance biologically and for ecological service.

BIOLOGICAL IMPORTANCE: *Birds:* D • *Aquatic biota:* D • *Plants:* A • *Reptiles and amphibians:* D • IMPORTANCE FOR ECOLOGICAL GOODS AND SERVICES: A • STABILITY LEVEL: 0 • INSTABILITY LEVEL: 0 • ACTION PRIORITY LEVEL: 3 • MAIN ACTION RECOMMENDED: Creation of conservation area • OTHER RECOMMENDED ACTION: Conversion of the area into full protection and sustainable use conservation areas; preparation of biological inventories.

BX 023 - Xingu-Iriri 2 Interfluve - PRIORITY LEVEL: C • LOCATION: *State:* Pará • *Main municipality:* São Félix do Xingu • *Municipalities covered:* 2 • VEGETATION TYPES: As, Ds, Sa, SO • COMMENTS: Area at high risk of forest fires, near the banks of the Xingu river. Biologically little known. Intact forest cover.

BIOLOGICAL IMPORTANCE: *Birds:* D • *Plants:* A • *Mammals:* C • *Reptiles and amphibians:* D • IMPORTANCE FOR ECOLOGICAL GOODS AND SERVICES: A • STABILITY LEVEL: 0 • INSTABILITY LEVEL: 0 • ACTION PRIORITY LEVEL: 3 • MAIN ACTION RECOMMENDED: Creation of conservation area • OTHER RECOMMENDED ACTION: Conversion of the area into full protection conservation area and extractive reserve.

BX 024 - Kayabi Indigenous Land - PRIORITY LEVEL: A • LOCATION: *State:* Pará/Mato Grosso • *Main municipality:* Jacareacanga • *Municipalities covered:* 4 • VEGETATION TYPES: As, Cs, Da, Ds, ON, Sa, Sd, Sg, SN, SO, Sp • COMMENTS: Area of very high biological importance within unregistered indigenous land.

BIOLOGICAL IMPORTANCE: *Birds:* A • *Aquatic biota:* A • *Plants:* D • *Mammals:* A • *Reptiles and amphibians:* B • IMPORTANCE FOR ECOLOGICAL GOODS AND SERVICES: A • STABILITY LEVEL: 1 • INSTABILITY LEVEL: 7 • ACTION PRIORITY LEVEL: 7 • MAIN ACTION RECOMMENDED: Sustainable use of natural resources • OTHER RECOMMENDED ACTION: Full registration of indigenous land and preparation of biological and anthropological inventories.

BX 025 - Transiriri - PRIORITY LEVEL: N • LOCATION: *State:* Pará • *Main municipality:* Altamira • *Municipalities covered:* 2 • VEGETATION TYPES: AA, As.

BIOLOGICAL IMPORTANCE: *Aquatic biota:* B • *Plants:* A • *Mammals:* C • *Reptiles and amphibians:* A • IMPORTANCE FOR ECOLOGICAL GOODS AND SERVICES: C • STABILITY LEVEL: 0 • INSTABILITY LEVEL: 10 • ACTION PRIORITY LEVEL: 10 • MAIN ACTION RECOMMENDED: Creation of conservation area • OTHER RECOMMENDED ACTION: Conversion of the area into full protection conservation area; monitoring; preparation of biological inventories; development of an environmental education program.

BX 026 - Mundurucu Indigenous Land - PRIORITY LEVEL: A • LOCATION: *State:* Pará • *Main municipality:* Jacareacanga • *Municipalities covered:* 4 • VEGETATION TYPES: As, Cs, Da, Ds, Fs, ON, Sa, Sd, Sg, SN, SO, Sp • COMMENTS: Area of very high biological importance within an indigenous land.

BIOLOGICAL IMPORTANCE: *Birds:* A • *Aquatic biota:* A • *Plants:* D • *Mammals:* A • *Reptiles and amphibians:* D • IMPORTANCE FOR ECOLOGICAL GOODS AND SERVICES: A • STABILITY LEVEL: 1 • INSTABILITY LEVEL: 7 • ACTION PRIORITY LEVEL: 7 • MAIN ACTION RECOMMENDED: Sustainable use of natural resources • OTHER RECOMMENDED ACTION: Preparation of biological inventories and anthropological assessments.

BX 027 - Teles Pires River - PRIORITY LEVEL: A • LOCATION: *State:* Mato Grosso/Pará • *Main municipality:* Novo Progresso • *Municipalities covered:* 23 • VEGETATION TYPES: AA, As, Cs, Da, Ds, ON, Sa, Sd, SN, SO, Sp • COMMENTS: Area of extreme biological and ecological importance under strong anthropogenic pressures, needs the urgent creation and full implementation of conservation areas of different types (direct use and strict). Strategies for the creation of buffer areas for the indigenous lands and conservation areas. There are indigenous lands of isolated groups of indians in the area, needing full registration.

BIOLOGICAL IMPORTANCE: *Birds:* A • *Aquatic biota:* A • *Plants:* A • *Mammals:* A • *Reptiles and amphibians:* A • IMPORTANCE FOR ECOLOGICAL GOODS AND SERVICES: A • STABILITY LEVEL: 0 • INSTABILITY LEVEL: 10 • ACTION PRIORITY LEVEL: 10 • MAIN ACTION RECOMMENDED: Creation of conservation area • OTHER RECOMMENDED ACTION: Preparation of biological inventories and anthropological assessments; development of an environmental education program.

BX 028 - Juruena River - PRIORITY LEVEL: A • LOCATION: *State:* Amazonas/Mato Grosso • *Main municipality:* Cotriguaçu • *Municipalities covered:* 4 • VEGETATION TYPES: As, Ds, SN • COMMENTS: Area of very high biological importance, practically untouched, with indications of the presence of isolated indigenous populations.

BIOLOGICAL IMPORTANCE: *Birds:* B • *Aquatic biota:* A • *Invertebrates:* D • *Mammals:* A • *Reptiles and amphibians:* A • IMPORTANCE FOR ECOLOGICAL GOODS AND SERVICES: A • STABILITY LEVEL: 0 • INSTABILITY LEVEL: 4 • ACTION PRIORITY LEVEL: 5 • MAIN ACTION RECOMMENDED: Creation of conservation area • OTHER RECOMMENDED ACTION: Conversion of the area into sustainable development conservation area; preparation of biological and anthropological inventories.

BX 029 - Escondido Indigenous Land - PRIORITY LEVEL: A • LOCATION: *State:* Mato Grosso • *Main municipality:* Cotriguaçu • *Municipalities covered:* 1 • VEGETATION TYPES: As, Ds • COMMENTS: Area of high biological importance.

BIOLOGICAL IMPORTANCE: *Aquatic biota:* A • *Mammals:* A • *Reptiles and amphibians:* A • IMPORTANCE FOR ECOLOGICAL GOODS AND SERVICES: A • STABILITY LEVEL: 3 • INSTABILITY LEVEL: 8 • ACTION PRIORITY LEVEL: 7 • MAIN ACTION RECOMMENDED: Sustainable use of natural resources • OTHER RECOMMENDED ACTION: Preparation of biological inventories and anthropological studies; development of an environmental education program.

BX 030 - Arara do Rio Branco Indigenous Land - PRIORITY LEVEL: A • LOCATION: *State:* Mato Grosso • *Main municipality:* Aripuanã • *Municipalities covered:* 1 • VEGETATION TYPES: As.

BIOLOGICAL IMPORTANCE: *Aquatic biota:* A • *Invertebrates:* D • *Mammals:* B • *Reptiles and amphibians:* A • IMPORTANCE FOR ECOLOGICAL GOODS AND SERVICES: A • STABILITY LEVEL: 3 • INSTABILITY LEVEL: 4 • ACTION PRIORITY LEVEL: 4 • MAIN ACTION RECOMMENDED: Sustainable use of natural resources • OTHER RECOMMENDED ACTION: Preparation of biological inventories and anthropological studies.

BX 031 - Apiacás Ecological Reserve - PRIORITY LEVEL: A • LOCATION: *State:* Mato Grosso • *Main municipality:* Apiacás • *Municipalities covered:* 3 • VEGETATION TYPES: As, Da, Ds, SO.

BIOLOGICAL IMPORTANCE: *Birds:* B • *Aquatic biota:* A • *Mammals:* A • IMPORTANCE FOR ECOLOGICAL GOODS AND SERVICES: A • STABILITY LEVEL: 6 • INSTABILITY LEVEL: 4 • ACTION PRIORITY LEVEL: 3 • MAIN ACTION RECOMMENDED: Protection.

BX 032 - Area to the west of the Apiacás Ecological Reserve - PRIORITY LEVEL: A • LOCATION: *State:* Amazonas • *Main municipality:* Apuí • *Municipalities covered:* 3 • VEGETATION TYPES: As, Ds, SO • COMMENTS: Area of high biological importance and suffering severe threats.

BIOLOGICAL IMPORTANCE: *Birds:* D • *Aquatic biota:* A • IMPORTANCE FOR ECOLOGICAL GOODS AND SERVICES: A • STABILITY LEVEL: 0 • INSTABILITY LEVEL: 4 • ACTION PRIORITY LEVEL: 5 • MAIN ACTION RECOMMENDED: Incorporation into existing conservation area • OTHER RECOMMENDED ACTION: Incoporation of the area into the Apiacás Ecological Reserve; preparation of biological inventories.

BX 033 - Japuíra Indigenous Land - PRIORITY LEVEL: A • LOCATION: *State:* Mato Grosso • *Main municipality:* Juara • *Municipalities covered:* 2 • VEGETATION TYPES: As, Ds, ON • COMMENTS: Indigenous area of high biological importance and subject to strong anthropogenic pressure in the surrounding area.

BIOLOGICAL IMPORTANCE: *Birds:* D • *Aquatic biota:* A • *Plants:* D • *Mammals:* A • STABILITY LEVEL: 3 • INSTABILITY LEVEL: 9 • ACTION PRIORITY LEVEL: 7 • MAIN ACTION RECOMMENDED: Sustainable use of natural resources • OTHER RECOMMENDED ACTION: Preparation of biological inventories and anthropological studies; development of an environmental education program.

BX 034 - Erikpatsa Indigenous Land - PRIORITY LEVEL: A • LOCATION: *State:* Mato Grosso • *Main municipality:* Brasnorte • *Municipalities covered:* 4 • VEGETATION TYPES: As, Ds, ON, Sp • COMMENTS: Area surrounding the indigenous land under high pressure.

BIOLOGICAL IMPORTANCE: *Birds:* A • *Aquatic biota:* A • *Plants:* D • IMPORTANCE FOR ECOLOGICAL GOODS AND SERVICES: C • STABILITY LEVEL: 3 • INSTABILITY LEVEL: 9 • ACTION PRIORITY LEVEL: 7 • MAIN ACTION RECOMMENDED: Sustainable use of natural resources • OTHER RECOMMENDED ACTION: Preparation of biological inventories and anthropological studies; development of an environmental education program in the surrounding region.

BX 035 - Juruena Forest Reserve - PRIORITY LEVEL: A • LOCATION: *State:* Mato Grosso • *Main municipality:* Juara • *Municipalities covered:* 7 • VEGETATION TYPES: AA, As, Da, Ds, Fa, ON, SN, SO, Sp • COMMENTS: Need to prevent fire in the area surrounding the indigenous lands.

BIOLOGICAL IMPORTANCE: *Birds:* D • *Aquatic biota:* A • *Plants:* D • *Mammals:* A • IMPORTANCE FOR ECOLOGICAL GOODS AND SERVICES: C • STABILITY LEVEL: 2 • INSTABILITY LEVEL: 9 • ACTION PRIORITY LEVEL: 8 • MAIN ACTION RECOMMENDED: Sustainable use of natural resources • OTHER RECOMMENDED ACTION: Preparation of biological inventories and development of an environmental protection and outreach program.

BX 036 - Serra Morena Indigenous Land - PRIORITY LEVEL: A • LOCATION: *State:* Mato Grosso • *Main municipality:* Juína • *Municipalities covered:* 2 • VEGETATION TYPES: As, ON • COMMENTS: Indigenous land within an area of high biological importance.

BIOLOGICAL IMPORTANCE: *Birds:* A • *Aquatic biota:* A • *Plants:* D • IMPORTANCE FOR ECOLOGICAL GOODS AND SERVICES: C • STABILITY LEVEL: 3 • INSTABILITY LEVEL: 4 • ACTION PRIORITY LEVEL: 4 • MAIN ACTION RECOMMENDED: Sustainable use of natural resources • OTHER RECOMMENDED ACTION: Preparation of biological inventories and anthropological studies; creation of a buffer zone.

BX 037 - Aripuanã Indigenous Land - PRIORITY LEVEL: A • LOCATION: *State:* Mato Grosso • *Main municipality:* Aripuanã • *Municipalities* *covered:* 3 • Vegetation types: As, Ds, ON, Sd, SO • Comments: Indigenous land within an area of high biological importance.

Biological importance: *Birds:* A • *Aquatic biota:* A • *Mammals:* B • Importance for ecological goods and services: A • Stability level: 3 • Instability level: 4 • Action priority level: 4 • Main action recommended: Sustainable use of natural resources • Other recommended action: Preparation of biological inventories and anthropological studies; creation of a buffer zone.

BX 038 - Rio Roosevelt - Priority level: A • Location: *State:* Mato Grosso/Amazonas • *Main municipality:* Aripuanã • *Municipalities covered:* 4 • Vegetation types: AA, As, Db, Ds, SO, Sp • Comments: Protect the headwaters of the Aripuanã, areas of high endemism, which implies the creation of strict conservation area.

Biological importance: *Birds:* B • *Aquatic biota:* A • *Invertebrates:* D • *Mammals:* B • *Reptiles and amphibians:* A • Importance for ecological goods and services: A • Stability level: 0 • Instability level: 3 • Action priority level: 5 • Main action recommended: Creation of conservation area • Other recommended action: Protection of the headwaters of the Aripuanã river and preparation of biological inventories.

BX 039 - Rio Roosevelt Ecological Station - Priority level: A • Location: *State:* Mato Grosso • *Main municipality:* Aripuanã • *Municipalities covered:* 2 • Vegetation types: As, Da, Ds, SO, Sp.

Biological importance: *Birds:* B • *Aquatic biota:* A • *Mammals:* B • Importance for ecological goods and services: C • Stability level: 6 • Instability level: 0 • Action priority level: 2 • Main action recommended: Protection • Other recommended action: Preparation of biological inventories.

BX 040 - Aripuanã River - Priority level: B • Location: *State:* Mato Grosso/Amazonas • *Main municipality:* Novo Aripuanã • *Municipalities covered:* 3 • Vegetation types: As, Da, Db, Ds, Pa, Sg, SO, Sp • Comments: Site of high biological importance.

Biological importance: *Birds:* B • *Aquatic biota:* A • *Mammals:* B • *Reptiles and amphibians:* D • Importance for ecological goods and services: A • Stability level: 0 • Instability level: 3 • Action priority level: 5 • Main action recommended: Incorporation into existing conservation area • Other recommended action: Incorporation of part of the area into the Guariba-Roosevelt Extractive Reserve and preparation of biological inventories.

BX 041 - Tenharim do Igarapé Preto Indigenous Land - Priority level: A • Location: *State:* Amazonas • *Main municipality:* Novo Aripuanã • *Municipalities covered:* 1 • Vegetation types: As, SO, Sp • Comments: Indigenous land of high biological importance, with special reference to aquatic biota (presence of endemic species) and reptiles and amphibians.

Biological importance: *Birds:* D • *Aquatic biota:* A • *Plants:* A • *Reptiles and amphibians:* A • Importance for ecological goods and services: C • Stability level: 1 • Instability level: 0 • Action priority level: 3 • Main action recommended: Sustainable use of natural resources • Other recommended action: Full registration of indigenous land, with the completion of the demarcation procedure; monitoring; and preparation of biological inventory.

BX 042 - Tenharim/Marmelos Indigenous Land - Priority level: A • Location: *State:* Amazonas • *Main municipality:* Humaitá • *Municipalities covered:* 3 • Vegetation types: As, Db, Pa, SO, Sp • Comments: Part of the last cerrado enclave in the region.

Biological importance: *Birds:* D • *Plants:* A • *Mammals:* A • *Reptiles and amphibians:* A • Importance for ecological goods and services: C • Stability level: 3 • Instability level: 3 • Action priority level: 4 • Main action recommended: Sustainable use of natural resources • Other recommended action: Preparation of biological inventory.

BX 043 - Humaitá National Forest and Rio Machado Sustainable Use Forest - Priority level: A • Location: *State:* Amazonas/Rondônia • *Main municipality:* Humaitá • *Municipalities covered:* 3 • Vegetation types: As, Da, Db, Pa, SO, Sp.

Biological importance: *Birds:* D • *Aquatic biota:* A • *Plants:* A • *Mammals:* A • *Reptiles and amphibians:* A • Importance for ecological goods and services: 0 • Stability level: 2 • Instability level: 6 • Action priority level: 6 • Main action recommended: Sustainable use of natural resources • Other recommended action: Full implementation of the National Forest.

BX 044 - Area between the Tenharim do Igarapé Preto and the Tenharim/Marmelos Indigenous Lands - Priority level: A • Location: *State:* Amazonas/Rondônia • *Main municipality:* Novo Aripuanã • *Municipalities covered:* 5 • Vegetation types: As, Da, Db, Ds, Sa, Sd, SO, Sp • Comments: Connect the corridor between two indigenous areas. Serves as an ecological buffer and preserves the last cerrado enclave in the region.

Biological importance: *Birds:* D • *Aquatic biota:* A • *Plants:* A • *Reptiles and amphibians:* A • Importance for ecological goods and services: C • Stability level: 0 • Instability level: 3 • Action priority level: 5 • Main action recommended: Creation of conservation area • Other recommended action: Preparation of biological inventories.

BX 045 - Pirahã Indigenous Land - Priority level: A • Location: *State:* Amazonas • *Main municipality:* Humaitá • *Municipalities covered:* 2 • Vegetation types: As, Da, Db.

Biological importance: *Mammals:* A • *Reptiles and amphibians:* A • Importance for ecological goods and services: 0 • Stability level: 3 • Instability level: 3 • Action priority level: 4 • Main action recommended: Sustainable use of natural resources • Other recommended action: Monitoring.

BX 046 - Nove de Janeiro Indigenous Land - Priority level: A • Location: *State:* Amazonas • *Main municipality:* Humaitá • *Municipalities covered:* 1 • Vegetation types: Da, Db, SO.

Biological importance: *Birds:* D • *Aquatic biota:* A • *Mammals:* A • *Reptiles and amphibians:* A • Stability level: 3 • Instability level: 6 • Action priority level: 5 • Main action recommended: Sustainable use of natural resources.

BX 047 - Ipixuna Indigenous Land - Priority level: A • Location: *State:* Amazonas • *Main municipality:* Humaitá • *Municipalities covered:* 1 • Vegetation types: Da, Db.

Biological importance: *Birds:* D • *Aquatic biota:* A • *Mammals:* A • *Reptiles and amphibians:* A • Stability level: 3 • Instability level: 6 • Action priority level: 5 • Main action recommended: Sustainable use of natural resources.

BX 048 - Upper Madeira - Priority level: A • Location: *State:* Amazonas • *Main municipality:* Humaitá • *Municipalities covered:* 2 • Vegetation types: Ab, As, Da, Db, Pa, SO, Sp • Comments: The suggested area includes a portion of the upper Madeira, suffering strong impacts along its length. Also serves as a buffer between the indigenous lands to the east of the suggested area and the front line of impacts along the Madeira.

Biological importance: *Birds:* D • *Aquatic biota:* A • *Mammals:* A • *Reptiles and amphibians:* A • Stability level: 0 • Instability level: 6 • Action priority level: 7 • Main action recommended: Creation of conservation area • Other recommended action: Conversion into conservation area of the area between the right bank of the Madeira and the Nove de Julho e Ipixuna indigenous lands.

BX 049 - Middle Madeira - Priority level: A • Location: *State:* Amazonas • *Main municipality:* Manicoré • *Municipalities covered:* 5 • Vegetation types: Da, Db, Ds, Pa • Comments: Site of high biological importance with recording of new species of primates and other mammals. This area is under strong anthropogenic pressure along the Madeira corridor, with significant impacts on the floodplains.

Biological importance: *Birds:* A • *Aquatic biota:* A • *Plants:* A • *Mammals:* A • *Reptiles and amphibians:* D • Importance for ecological goods and services: C • Stability level: 0 • Instability level: 6 • Action priority level: 7 • Main action recommended: Creation of conservation area • Other recommended action: Creation of full protection and sustainable use conservation areas to form buffer zone around the Pinatuba Indigenous Land; preparation of biological inventories and socio-economic diagnosis; implementation of an environmental education program.

BX 050 - Pinatuba Indigenous Land - Priority level: A • Location: *State:* Amazonas • *Main municipality:* Manicoré • *Municipalities covered:* 1 • Vegetation types: Da, Db, Pa • Comments: Part of a region of extremely high biological diversity for aquatic, bird and mammal groups, encompassing an indigenous land.

BIOLOGICAL IMPORTANCE: *Birds:* A • *Aquatic biota:* A • *Mammals:* A • IMPORTANCE FOR ECOLOGICAL GOODS AND SERVICES: C • STABILITY LEVEL: 1 • INSTABILITY LEVEL: 6 • ACTION PRIORITY LEVEL: 6 • MAIN ACTION RECOMMENDED: Sustainable use of natural resources • OTHER RECOMMENDED ACTION: Conclusion of the process of demarcation of the area; monitoring; and preparation of biological inventories.

BX 051 - Mid Madeira - PRIORITY LEVEL: B • LOCATION: *State:* Amazonas • *Main municipality:* Humaitá • *Municipalities covered:* 2 • VEGETATION TYPES: Ab, Da, Db, Pa • COMMENTS: Area of high importance; region under strong anthropogenic pressure, although still only little deforested.

BIOLOGICAL IMPORTANCE: *Birds:* D • *Aquatic biota:* A • STABILITY LEVEL: 0 • INSTABILITY LEVEL: 6 • ACTION PRIORITY LEVEL: 7 • MAIN ACTION RECOMMENDED: Sustainable use of natural resources • OTHER RECOMMENDED ACTION: Effective protection of the banks of the Madeira; preparation of biological inventories; and full implementation of an environmental education program.

BX 052 - Headwaters of the Luna - PRIORITY LEVEL: B • LOCATION: *State:* Amazonas • *Main municipality:* Tapauá • *Municipalities covered:* 3 • VEGETATION TYPES: Ab, Da, Db • COMMENTS: Area whose biological groups are little known, with intact vegetation and under high anthropogenic pressure, near the paving of the BR-139 highway.

BIOLOGICAL IMPORTANCE: *Birds:* D • *Plants:* A • *Mammals:* B • *Reptiles and amphibians:* B • STABILITY LEVEL: 0 • INSTABILITY LEVEL: 6 • ACTION PRIORITY LEVEL: 7 • MAIN ACTION RECOMMENDED: Creation of conservation area • OTHER RECOMMENDED ACTION: Conversion of the area into sustainable use conservation area (extractive reserve).

BX 053 - Coatá-Laranjal Indigenous Land - PRIORITY LEVEL: A • LOCATION: *State:* Amazonas • *Main municipality:* Borba • *Municipalities covered:* 1 • VEGETATION TYPES: Da, Db, Pa • COMMENTS: Unregistered indigenous area within an area of high biological importance.

BIOLOGICAL IMPORTANCE: *Birds:* A • *Plants:* A • *Mammals:* A • *Reptiles and amphibians:* D • IMPORTANCE FOR ECOLOGICAL GOODS AND SERVICES: B • STABILITY LEVEL: 1 • INSTABILITY LEVEL: 4 • ACTION PRIORITY LEVEL: 5 • MAIN ACTION RECOMMENDED: Protection • OTHER RECOMMENDED ACTION: Full registration of the indigenous land; preparation of biological inventories and anthropological studies.

BX 054 - Area to the west of the Coatá-Laranjal Indigenous Land - PRIORITY LEVEL: A • LOCATION: *State:* Amazonas • *Main municipality:* Borba • *Municipalities covered:* 1 • VEGETATION TYPES: Db, Pa • COMMENTS: The area selected represents a pole of high biological diversity and should be included in a buffer zone around the Coatá-Laranjal Indigenous Land. The presence of undescribed (and apparently endemic) animal species, sensitive to environmental disturbance, argues for the creation of a strict conservation area.

BIOLOGICAL IMPORTANCE: *Birds:* A • *Plants:* A • *Mammals:* A • IMPORTANCE FOR ECOLOGICAL GOODS AND SERVICES: B • STABILITY LEVEL: 0 • INSTABILITY LEVEL: 3 • ACTION PRIORITY LEVEL: 5 • MAIN ACTION RECOMMENDED: Creation of conservation area • OTHER RECOMMENDED ACTION: Creation of full protection conservation area, forming a buffer zone around the Coatá-Laranjal Indigenous Land; preparation of biological inventories.

BX 055 - Area to the south of the Coatá-Laranjal Indigenous Land - PRIORITY LEVEL: A • LOCATION: *State:* Amazonas • *Main municipality:* Borba • *Municipalities covered:* 1 • VEGETATION TYPES: Da, Db, Ds, Pa • COMMENTS: Area of high biological importance; near others under anthropogenic pressure and in the middle of some considered biologically significant. A buffer-zone around the Coatá-Laranjal Indigenous Land (combining areas 54, 55, 56) would protect the indigenous land and guarantee no direct use of the area.

BIOLOGICAL IMPORTANCE: *Plants:* A • *Mammals:* A • *Reptiles and amphibians:* D • IMPORTANCE FOR ECOLOGICAL GOODS AND SERVICES: B • STABILITY LEVEL: 0 • INSTABILITY LEVEL: 0 • ACTION PRIORITY LEVEL: 3 • MAIN ACTION RECOMMENDED: Creation of conservation area • OTHER RECOMMENDED ACTION: Creation of full protection conservation area, forming a buffer zone around the Coatá-Laranjal Indigenous Land.

BX 056 - Abacaxi River - PRIORITY LEVEL: B • LOCATION: *State:* Amazonas • *Main municipality:* Borba • *Municipalities covered:* 3 • VEGETATION TYPES: Da, Db, Pa • COMMENTS: Area adjacent to the indigenous reserve, 40 kilometers from the Madeira waterway.

BIOLOGICAL IMPORTANCE: *Aquatic biota:* D • *Plants:* A • *Mammals:* B • *Reptiles and amphibians:* D • IMPORTANCE FOR ECOLOGICAL GOODS AND SERVICES: B • STABILITY LEVEL: 0 • INSTABILITY LEVEL: 4 • ACTION PRIORITY LEVEL: 5 • MAIN ACTION RECOMMENDED: Creation of conservation area • OTHER RECOMMENDED ACTION: Creation of full protection conservation area, forming a buffer zone around the Coatá-Laranjal Indigenous Land; preparation of biological inventories.

BX 057 - Amazônia National Park - PRIORITY LEVEL: A • LOCATION: *State:* Pará • *Main municipality:* Itaituba • *Municipalities covered:* 3 • VEGETATION TYPES: AA, As, Da, Db, Ds.

BIOLOGICAL IMPORTANCE: *Birds:* A • *Aquatic biota:* B • *Invertebrates:* D • *Mammals:* B • *Reptiles and amphibians:* B • IMPORTANCE FOR ECOLOGICAL GOODS AND SERVICES: B • STABILITY LEVEL: 6 • INSTABILITY LEVEL: 7 • ACTION PRIORITY LEVEL: 5 • MAIN ACTION RECOMMENDED: Protection • OTHER RECOMMENDED ACTION: Monitoring and preparation of biological inventories, with focus on reptiles and amphibians.

BX 058 - Itaituba II National Forest - PRIORITY LEVEL: A • LOCATION: *State:* Pará • *Main municipality:* Trairão • *Municipalities covered:* 2 • VEGETATION TYPES: As, Ds.

BIOLOGICAL IMPORTANCE: *Birds:* A • *Aquatic biota:* B • *Invertebrates:* D • *Mammals:* C • IMPORTANCE FOR ECOLOGICAL GOODS AND SERVICES: A • STABILITY LEVEL: 2 • INSTABILITY LEVEL: 7 • ACTION PRIORITY LEVEL: 6 • MAIN ACTION RECOMMENDED: Sustainable use of natural resources • OTHER RECOMMENDED ACTION: Monitoring and preparation of biological inventories.

BX 059 - Jamanxim River - PRIORITY LEVEL: N • LOCATION: *State:* Pará • *Main municipality:* Novo Progresso • *Municipalities covered:* 2 • VEGETATION TYPES: As, Ds.

BIOLOGICAL IMPORTANCE: *Plants:* D • *Reptiles and amphibians:* D • IMPORTANCE FOR ECOLOGICAL GOODS AND SERVICES: A • STABILITY LEVEL: 0 • INSTABILITY LEVEL: 7 • ACTION PRIORITY LEVEL: 8 • MAIN ACTION RECOMMENDED: Creation of conservation area • OTHER RECOMMENDED ACTION: Creation of full protection conservation area; and preparation of biological inventories; assessment of land ownership in the region.

BX 060 - Itaituba I National Forest - PRIORITY LEVEL: A • LOCATION: *State:* Pará • *Main municipality:* Trairão • *Municipalities covered:* 2 • VEGETATION TYPES: As, Ds.

BIOLOGICAL IMPORTANCE: *Birds:* A • *Aquatic biota:* B • *Invertebrates:* D • *Mammals:* C • IMPORTANCE FOR ECOLOGICAL GOODS AND SERVICES: A • STABILITY LEVEL: 2 • INSTABILITY LEVEL: 7 • ACTION PRIORITY LEVEL: 6 • MAIN ACTION RECOMMENDED: Sustainable use of natural resources • OTHER RECOMMENDED ACTION: Monitoring.

BX 061 - Itaituba - PRIORITY LEVEL: A • LOCATION: *State:* Pará • *Main municipality:* Itaituba • *Municipalities covered:* 1 • VEGETATION TYPES: Ds.

BIOLOGICAL IMPORTANCE: *Birds:* A • *Aquatic biota:* B • IMPORTANCE FOR ECOLOGICAL GOODS AND SERVICES: A • STABILITY LEVEL: 0 • INSTABILITY LEVEL: 4 • ACTION PRIORITY LEVEL: 5 • MAIN ACTION RECOMMENDED: Creation of conservation area • OTHER RECOMMENDED ACTION: Monitoring of the area around the Itaituba I National Forest and preparation of biological inventories.

BX 062 - Jamanxim River - PRIORITY LEVEL: A • LOCATION: *State:* Pará • *Main municipality:* Trairão • *Municipalities covered:* 3 • VEGETATION TYPES: AA, As, Ds • COMMENTS: Site of high biological importance.

BIOLOGICAL IMPORTANCE: *Birds:* A • *Aquatic biota:* D • *Invertebrates:* D • *Mammals:* C • IMPORTANCE FOR ECOLOGICAL GOODS AND SERVICES: A • STABILITY LEVEL: 0 • INSTABILITY LEVEL: 7 • ACTION PRIORITY LEVEL: 8 • MAIN ACTION RECOMMENDED: Sustainable use of natural resources • OTHER RECOMMENDED ACTION: Preparation of biological inventories.

BX 063 - Tapajós - PRIORITY LEVEL: B • LOCATION: *State:* Pará • *Main municipality:* Itaituba • *Municipalities covered:* 4 • VEGETATION TYPES: AA, Db, Ds.

BIOLOGICAL IMPORTANCE: *Aquatic biota:* B • *Invertebrates:* D • *Mammals:* C • *Reptiles and amphibians:* B • IMPORTANCE FOR ECOLOGICAL GOODS AND SERVICES: B • STABILITY LEVEL: 0 • INSTABILITY LEVEL: 7 • ACTION PRIORITY LEVEL: 8 • MAIN ACTION RECOMMENDED: Sustainable use of natural resources.

BX 064 - Headwaters of the Aripuanã - PRIORITY LEVEL: A • LOCATION: *State:* Mato Grosso • *Main municipality:* Aripuanã • *Municipalities covered:* 8 • VEGETATION TYPES: AA, As, Ds, ON, Sd, SN • COMMENTS:

Area of biological importance under high anthropogenic pressure (ranching and logging).

> BIOLOGICAL IMPORTANCE: *Birds:* A • *Aquatic biota:* A • *Plants:* D • *Mammals:* A • IMPORTANCE FOR ECOLOGICAL GOODS AND SERVICES: A • STABILITY LEVEL: 0 • INSTABILITY LEVEL: 9 • ACTION PRIORITY LEVEL: 9 • MAIN ACTION RECOMMENDED: Creation of conservation area • OTHER RECOMMENDED ACTION: Creation of full protection conservation area to the south of the Escondido Indigenous Land; preparation of biological inventories and implementation of an environmental education program.

BX 065 - Canoa - PRIORITY LEVEL: A • LOCATION: *State:* Pará • *Main municipality:* Itaituba • *Municipalities covered:* 1 • VEGETATION TYPES: As, Ds • COMMENTS: High biological importance.

> BIOLOGICAL IMPORTANCE: *Birds:* A • *Aquatic biota:* D • *Reptiles and amphibians:* D • IMPORTANCE FOR ECOLOGICAL GOODS AND SERVICES: A • STABILITY LEVEL: 0 • INSTABILITY LEVEL: 7 • ACTION PRIORITY LEVEL: 8 • MAIN ACTION RECOMMENDED: Creation of conservation area • OTHER RECOMMENDED ACTION: Creation of full protection conservation area and preparation of biological inventories.

BX 066 - Guariba-Roosevelt Extractive Reserve - PRIORITY LEVEL: B • LOCATION: *State:* Mato Grosso • *Main municipality:* Aripuanã • *Municipalities covered:* 1 • VEGETATION TYPES: As, Ds • COMMENTS: The importance of the extractive reserve, within present boundaries, is still insufficient for the protection and the sustainable management of resources.

> BIOLOGICAL IMPORTANCE: *Birds:* B • *Aquatic biota:* A • *Mammals:* B • IMPORTANCE FOR ECOLOGICAL GOODS AND SERVICES: C • STABILITY LEVEL: 8 • INSTABILITY LEVEL: 0 • ACTION PRIORITY LEVEL: 2 • MAIN ACTION RECOMMENDED: Protection • OTHER RECOMMENDED ACTION: Creation of buffer zone, extending the boundary of the extractive reserve to the north; preparation of biological inventories; implementation of an environmental education and outreach program.

BX 067 - Sai Cinza Indigenous Land - PRIORITY LEVEL: A • LOCATION: *State:* Pará • *Main municipality:* Jacareacanga • *Municipalities covered:* 1 • VEGETATION TYPES: As, Da, Ds, SO.

> BIOLOGICAL IMPORTANCE: *Birds:* B • *Aquatic biota:* B • *Mammals:* A • IMPORTANCE FOR ECOLOGICAL GOODS AND SERVICES: C • STABILITY LEVEL: 3 • INSTABILITY LEVEL: 7 • ACTION PRIORITY LEVEL: 6 • MAIN ACTION RECOMMENDED: Sustainable use of natural resources • OTHER RECOMMENDED ACTION: Protection and monitoring of the boundaries; control of the impact on indians caused by prospecting in the region; preparation of biological inventory.

BX 068 - Area of overlap between the Amazônia National Park and the Andirá-Marau Indigenous Land - PRIORITY LEVEL: A • LOCATION: *State:* Pará • *Main municipality:* Itaituba • *Municipalities covered:* 2 • VEGETATION TYPES: Da, Db • COMMENTS: Overlap between the indigenous land and the national park in a site of high biological importance.

> BIOLOGICAL IMPORTANCE: *Birds:* A • *Aquatic biota:* B • *Invertebrates:* D • *Mammals:* B • IMPORTANCE FOR ECOLOGICAL GOODS AND SERVICES: B • STABILITY LEVEL: 5 • INSTABILITY LEVEL: 3 • ACTION PRIORITY LEVEL: 3 • MAIN ACTION RECOMMENDED: Sustainable use of natural resources • OTHER RECOMMENDED ACTION: Preparation of biological inventory and anthropological assessment.

BX 069 - Ariramba Indigenous Land - PRIORITY LEVEL: B • LOCATION: *State:* Amazonas • *Main municipality:* Manicoré • *Municipalities covered:* 1 • VEGETATION TYPES: D.

> BIOLOGICAL IMPORTANCE: *Birds:* D • *Aquatic biota:* A • STABILITY LEVEL: 1 • INSTABILITY LEVEL: 6 • ACTION PRIORITY LEVEL: 6 • MAIN ACTION RECOMMENDED: Sustainable use of natural resources • OTHER RECOMMENDED ACTION: Full registration of the indigenous land and preparation of biological inventory.

BX 070 - Lago Jauari Indigenous Land - PRIORITY LEVEL: B • LOCATION: *State:* Amazonas • *Main municipality:* Manicoré • *Municipalities covered:* 2 • VEGETATION TYPES: D.

> BIOLOGICAL IMPORTANCE: *Birds:* D • *Aquatic biota:* A • STABILITY LEVEL: 1 • INSTABILITY LEVEL: 6 • ACTION PRIORITY LEVEL: 6 • MAIN ACTION RECOMMENDED: Sustainable use of natural resources • OTHER RECOMMENDED ACTION: Full registration of the indigenous land.

BX 071 - Lago Capana and Ariramba Indigenous Lands - PRIORITY LEVEL: B • LOCATION: *State:* Amazonas • *Main municipality:* Manicoré • *Municipalities covered:* 1 • VEGETATION TYPES: Da, Db.

> BIOLOGICAL IMPORTANCE: *Birds:* D • *Reptiles and amphibians:* B • STABILITY LEVEL: 1 • INSTABILITY LEVEL: 6 • ACTION PRIORITY LEVEL: 6 • MAIN ACTION RECOMMENDED: Sustainable use of natural resources • OTHER RECOMMENDED ACTION: Full registration of the indigenous lands.

BX 072 - Xingu-Iriri Interfluve - PRIORITY LEVEL: N • LOCATION: *State:* Pará • *Main municipality:* Altamira • *Municipalities covered:* 2 • VEGETATION TYPES: As, Da, Ds, Sa, SO • COMMENTS: Together with the surrounding indigenous areas, this area represents a large area of land suitable for biodiversity conservation, of great importance for the stability of regional hydrological cycles. Extreme risk of forest fires.

> BIOLOGICAL IMPORTANCE: *Birds:* D • *Plants:* A • *Mammals:* B • *Reptiles and amphibians:* D • IMPORTANCE FOR ECOLOGICAL GOODS AND SERVICES: A • STABILITY LEVEL: 0 • INSTABILITY LEVEL: 4 • ACTION PRIORITY LEVEL: 5 • MAIN ACTION RECOMMENDED: Creation of conservation area • OTHER RECOMMENDED ACTION: Preparation of biological inventories and anthropological studies in order to identify the resident indigenous populations and to define the types of conservation areas; implementation of environmental education programs in the nearby municipalities.

BX 073 - Area surrounding the Coatá-Laranjal Indigenous Land - PRIORITY LEVEL: A • LOCATION: *State:* Amazonas • *Main municipality:* Borba • *Municipalities covered:* 3 • VEGETATION TYPES: Da, Db, Ds, Pa • COMMENTS: Necessity of uniting proposed areas, which were used for the methodology; in order to protect the region around the indigenous land, the union of the areas 72 to 54 and 55 is needed.

> BIOLOGICAL IMPORTANCE: *Birds:* A • *Aquatic biota:* D • *Plants:* A • *Mammals:* A • *Reptiles and amphibians:* D • IMPORTANCE FOR ECOLOGICAL GOODS AND SERVICES: B • STABILITY LEVEL: 0 • INSTABILITY LEVEL: 3 • ACTION PRIORITY LEVEL: 5 • MAIN ACTION RECOMMENDED: Creation of conservation area • OTHER RECOMMENDED ACTION: Creation of full protection conservation area and preparation of biological inventories.

6
PRIORITY AREAS IN THE RIO NEGRO / RIO BRANCO REGION

RN 001 - Upper Rio Negro, Middle Rio Negro I, Middle Rio Negro II, Rio Téa and Rio Apaporis Indigenous Lands - PRIORITY LEVEL: A • LOCATION: *State:* Amazonas • *Main municipality:* São Gabriel da Cachoeira • *Municipalities covered:* 4 • VEGETATION TYPES: Ab, As, Ds, La, Ld, LO, rm • COMMENTS: Areas of traditional occupation by twenty-two indigenous populations and of high biological importance.

BIOLOGICAL IMPORTANCE: *Birds:* A • *Aquatic biota:* B • *Plants:* A • *Invertebrates:* D • *Mammals:* B • *Reptiles and amphibians:* D • STABILITY LEVEL: 9 • INSTABILITY LEVEL: 1 • ACTION PRIORITY LEVEL: 2 • MAIN ACTION RECOMMENDED: Sustainable use of natural resources • OTHER RECOMMENDED ACTION: Implementation of a protection and monitoring plan for the indigenous lands; preparation of biological inventories; development of applied research (ecology, fish culture and useful plants) and traditional knowledge; annulment of the National Forests superimposed on the Upper Rio Negro Indigenous Land; and study the viability of an indigenous nucleus of ecological and scientific tourism.

RN 002 - Area between the Pico da Neblina National Park and the Upper Rio Negro Indigenous Land - PRIORITY LEVEL: B • LOCATION: *State:* Amazonas • *Main municipality:* São Gabriel da Cachoeira • *Municipalities covered:* 2 • VEGETATION TYPES: Ld, LO • COMMENTS: Land occupied by indians and of high biological importance.

BIOLOGICAL IMPORTANCE: *Birds:* B • *Aquatic biota:* B • *Invertebrates:* D • *Mammals:* A • *Reptiles and amphibians:* D • STABILITY LEVEL: 0 • INSTABILITY LEVEL: 2 • ACTION PRIORITY LEVEL: 4 • MAIN ACTION RECOMMENDED: Incoporation into existing conservation area • OTHER RECOMMENDED ACTION: Study the expansion of the Pico da Neblina National Park; creation of a FUNAI working group to identify the Marabitanas Cué-Cué Indigenous Land; and development of sustainable agricultural activities in the area surrounding the urban center of São Gabriel.

RN 003 - Balaio Indigenous Land - PRIORITY LEVEL: B • LOCATION: *State:* Amazonas • *Main municipality:* São Gabriel da Cachoeira • *Municipalities covered:* 1 • VEGETATION TYPES: LO • COMMENTS: Traditional indigenous occupation and of high biological importance.

BIOLOGICAL IMPORTANCE: *Birds:* B • *Aquatic biota:* B • *Invertebrates:* D • *Mammals:* A • *Reptiles and amphibians:* D • STABILITY LEVEL: 7 • INSTABILITY LEVEL: 2 • ACTION PRIORITY LEVEL: 3 • MAIN ACTION RECOMMENDED: Sustainable use of natural resources • OTHER RECOMMENDED ACTION: Creation of a multidisciplinary working group with indigenous participation (*Associação Indígena do Balaio* - Ainbal) to resolve the conflict caused by the overlap between the conservation area and the indigenous land, redefining borders and management categories in part of or in the whole of the overlapping area.

RN 004 - Morro dos Seis Lagos Biological Reserve - PRIORITY LEVEL: B • LOCATION: *State:* Amazonas • *Main municipality:* São Gabriel da Cachoeira • *Municipalities covered:* 1 • VEGETATION TYPES: LO • COMMENTS: High biological importance. Latent use conflict.

BIOLOGICAL IMPORTANCE: *Birds:* B • *Aquatic biota:* B • *Invertebrates:* D • *Mammals:* A • *Reptiles and amphibians:* D • STABILITY LEVEL: 6 • INSTABILITY LEVEL: 2 • ACTION PRIORITY LEVEL: 3 • MAIN ACTION RECOMMENDED: Sustainable use of natural resources • OTHER RECOMMENDED ACTION: Creation of a multidisciplinary working group with indigenous participation (*Associação Indígena do Balaio* – Ainbal) to resolve the conflict caused by the overlap between the Pico da Neblina National Park, Morro dos Seis Lagos Biological Reserve and Balaio Indigenous Land; assessments of endemism.

RN 005 - Pico da Neblina National Park - PRIORITY LEVEL: A • LOCATION: *State:* Amazonas • *Main municipality:* São Gabriel da Cachoeira • *Municipalities covered:* 3 • VEGETATION TYPES: As, Ds, La, Ld, LO • COMMENTS: Threats from the presence of prospecting in the Cavaboris river and on the high plateau (2,800 meters). High levels of endemism and presence of high altitude fauna and flora (biota) unique in Amazonia.

BIOLOGICAL IMPORTANCE: *Birds:* B • *Aquatic biota:* B • *Plants:* A • *Invertebrates:* D • *Mammals:* A • *Reptiles and amphibians:* D • IMPORTANCE FOR ECOLOGICAL GOODS AND SERVICES: B • STABILITY LEVEL: 3 • INSTABILITY LEVEL: 2 • ACTION PRIORITY LEVEL: 3 • MAIN ACTION RECOMMENDED: Protection • OTHER RECOMMENDED ACTION: Preparation of a management plan, defining the use of natural resources by traditional populations; study of the potential for ecotourism and visitor control; and conversion of a stretch of the São Miguer/Cucuí road and the Maturacá branch road, within the National Park area, into Highway Park. Area with high levels of endemisms of mountain biota.

RN 006 - Area between the Pico da Neblina National Park and the Middle Rio Negro II Indigenous Land - PRIORITY LEVEL: B • LOCATION: *State:* Amazonas • *Main municipality:* São Gabriel da Cachoeira • *Municipalities covered:* 2 • VEGETATION TYPES: Ld, LO • COMMENTS: There is a mining company operating in the area. Occurrence of titica vine (*Heteropsis flexuosa*) for handicrafts.

BIOLOGICAL IMPORTANCE: *Birds:* B • *Aquatic biota:* B • *Invertebrates:* D • *Mammals:* A • *Reptiles and amphibians:* D • STABILITY LEVEL: 0 • INSTABILITY LEVEL: 2 • ACTION PRIORITY LEVEL: 4 • MAIN ACTION RECOMMENDED: Protection • OTHER RECOMMENDED ACTION: Annulment of mining licenses granted within the area, highly likely to lead to deforestation in the National Park and the Indigenous Land, through immediate application of the Conama resolution on the protection of areas surrounding conservation areas.

RN 007 - Overlap between the Pico da Neblina National Park and the Yanomami Indigenous Land - PRIORITY LEVEL: A • LOCATION: *State:* Amazonas • *Main municipality:* Santa Isabel do Rio Negro • *Municipalities covered:* 3 • VEGETATION TYPES: Dm, Ds, La, LO, rm • COMMENTS: Area of traditional indigenous occupation and of high biological importance.

BIOLOGICAL IMPORTANCE: *Birds:* A • *Aquatic biota:* B • *Plants:* A • *Mammals:* A • *Reptiles and amphibians:* D • IMPORTANCE FOR ECOLOGICAL GOODS AND SERVICES: B • STABILITY LEVEL: 6 • INSTABILITY LEVEL: 5 • ACTION PRIORITY LEVEL: 4 • MAIN ACTION RECOMMENDED: Protection • OTHER RECOMMENDED ACTION: Creation of a multidisciplinary working group with indigenous participation (Federação das Organizações Indígenas do Rio Negro – FOIRN and Associação Yanomami Rio Canaberis e Afluentes – Ayrca) to redefine borders and management categories in part of or in the whole of the overlapping area.

RN 008 - Overlap between the Pico da Neblina National Park and the Middle Rio Negro II Indigenous Land - PRIORITY LEVEL: B • LOCATION: *State:* Amazonas • *Main municipality:* Santa Isabel do Rio

Negro • *Municipalities covered:* 2 • VEGETATION TYPES: La, LO • COMMENTS: Area of traditional indigenous occupation and of biological and ecological importance.

> BIOLOGICAL IMPORTANCE: *Aquatic biota:* B • *Mammals:* A • *Reptiles and amphibians:* D • STABILITY LEVEL: 6 • INSTABILITY LEVEL: 2 • ACTION PRIORITY LEVEL: 3 • MAIN ACTION RECOMMENDED: Protection • OTHER RECOMMENDED ACTION: Creation of a multidisciplinary working group with indigenous participation (FOIRN and Associação das Comunidades Indígenas do Baixo Rio Negro – Acibrin) to redefine borders and management categories in part of or in the whole of the overlapping area.

RN 009 - Yanomami Indigenous Land in the state of Amazonas - PRIORITY LEVEL: B • LOCATION: *State:* Amazonas • *Main municipality:* Barcelos • *Municipalities covered:* 3 • VEGETATION TYPES: As, Dm, Ds, La, Ld, Lg, LO • COMMENTS: Area of traditional indigenous occupation and of high biological and ecological importance.

> BIOLOGICAL IMPORTANCE: *Birds:* C • *Aquatic biota:* B • *Invertebrates:* D • *Mammals:* A • IMPORTANCE FOR ECOLOGICAL GOODS AND SERVICES: B • STABILITY LEVEL: 5 • INSTABILITY LEVEL: 4 • ACTION PRIORITY LEVEL: 4 • MAIN ACTION RECOMMENDED: Sustainable use of natural resources • OTHER RECOMMENDED ACTION: Monitoring and protection against illegal occupation; preparation of ethnobiological, biological and ecological inventories; and annulment of national forests improperly included within the Yanomami Indigenous Land, created for geopolitical purposes connected to the Calha Norte project in the late 1980s and imcompatible with those of indigenous lands.

RN 010 - Overlap between the Yanomami Indigenous Land, the Serra do Araçá State Park and the Amazonas National Forest - PRIORITY LEVEL: B • LOCATION: *State:* Amazonas • *Main municipality:* Barcelos • *Municipalities covered:* 4 • VEGETATION TYPES: As, Dm, Ds, Lg • COMMENTS: Area of traditional indigenous occupation and of high biological and ecological importance.

> BIOLOGICAL IMPORTANCE: *Birds:* C • *Aquatic biota:* B • *Invertebrates:* D • *Mammals:* A • IMPORTANCE FOR ECOLOGICAL GOODS AND SERVICES: A • STABILITY LEVEL: 14 • INSTABILITY LEVEL: 4 • ACTION PRIORITY LEVEL: 2 • MAIN ACTION RECOMMENDED: Sustainable use of natural resources • OTHER RECOMMENDED ACTION: Monitoring to prevent invasions of gold prospectors in the Demini area.

RN 011 - Serra do Araçá State Park - PRIORITY LEVEL: A • LOCATION: *State:* Amazonas • *Main municipality:* Barcelos • *Municipalities covered:* 1 • VEGETATION TYPES: Dm, Ds, Lg, rm • COMMENTS: Occurrence of endemic species. Threats from the Perimetral Norte highway.

> BIOLOGICAL IMPORTANCE: *Birds:* C • *Aquatic biota:* B • *Plants:* A • *Mammals:* A • IMPORTANCE FOR ECOLOGICAL GOODS AND SERVICES: A • STABILITY LEVEL: 9 • INSTABILITY LEVEL: 4 • ACTION PRIORITY LEVEL: 3 • MAIN ACTION RECOMMENDED: Protection • OTHER RECOMMENDED ACTION: Monitoring to prevent invasions of gold prospectors in the Demini area and preparation of management plan.

RN 012 - Area to the south of the Serra do Araçá State Park - PRIORITY LEVEL: B • LOCATION: *State:* Amazonas • *Main municipality:* Barcelos • *Municipalities covered:* 1 • VEGETATION TYPES: Dm, Ds, Lg, rm • COMMENTS: Mosaic of vegetation types including those typical of ecological refugia. Possible occurrence of endemic species.

> BIOLOGICAL IMPORTANCE: *Birds:* C • *Aquatic biota:* B • *Plants:* A • IMPORTANCE FOR ECOLOGICAL GOODS AND SERVICES: B • STABILITY LEVEL: 0 • INSTABILITY LEVEL: 1 • ACTION PRIORITY LEVEL: 4 • MAIN ACTION RECOMMENDED: Protection • OTHER RECOMMENDED ACTION: Preparation of biological and environmental inventories.

RN 013 - Yanomami Indigenous Land in the state of Roraima - PRIORITY LEVEL: B • LOCATION: *State:* Roraima/Amazonas • *Main municipality:* Alto Alegre • *Municipalities covered:* 7 • VEGETATION TYPES: As, Dm, Ds, Ld, Lg, LO, ON, rm • COMMENTS: Area of traditional indigenous occupation and of biological and ecological importance.

> BIOLOGICAL IMPORTANCE: *Birds:* A • *Aquatic biota:* B • *Plants:* C • *Invertebrates:* D • *Mammals:* B • *Reptiles and amphibians:* D • IMPORTANCE FOR ECOLOGICAL GOODS AND SERVICES: A • STABILITY LEVEL: 5 • INSTABILITY LEVEL: 8 • ACTION PRIORITY LEVEL: 6 • MAIN ACTION RECOMMENDED: Sustainable use of natural resources • OTHER RECOMMENDED ACTION: Monitoring of illegal occupation and protection of the surrounding area; evaluation of the environmental degradation caused by prospecting and fires; preparation of bio-ecological and ethnobiological inventories; and annulment of national forests improperly included within the Yanomami Indigenous Land, created for geopolitical purposes connected to the Calha Norte project in the late 1980s and imcompatible with those of indigenous lands.

RN 014 - Area between the Serra da Mocidade National Park and the Yanomami Indigenous Land - PRIORITY LEVEL: N • LOCATION: *State:* Roraima/Amazonas • *Main municipality:* Caracaraí • *Municipalities covered:* 2 • VEGETATION TYPES: As, Ds, Lg, LO • COMMENTS: Area to be proposed for incorporation into the Serra da Mocidade National Park.

> BIOLOGICAL IMPORTANCE: *Aquatic biota:* B • IMPORTANCE FOR ECOLOGICAL GOODS AND SERVICES: A • STABILITY LEVEL: 0 • INSTABILITY LEVEL: 0 • ACTION PRIORITY LEVEL: 3 • MAIN ACTION RECOMMENDED: Creation of conservation area • OTHER RECOMMENDED ACTION: Creation of full protection conservation area or incorporation into the Serra da Mocidade National Park.

RN 015 - Area between the Niquiá Ecological Station, Serra da Mocidade National Park and Yanomami Indigenous Land - PRIORITY LEVEL: A • LOCATION: *State:* Roraima • *Main municipality:* Caracaraí • *Municipalities covered:* 1 • VEGETATION TYPES: As, Ds, Ld, LO • COMMENTS: Area to be proposed for incorporation into the Niquiá Ecological Station.

> BIOLOGICAL IMPORTANCE: *Birds:* A • *Aquatic biota:* B • IMPORTANCE FOR ECOLOGICAL GOODS AND SERVICES: A • STABILITY LEVEL: 0 • INSTABILITY LEVEL: 4 • ACTION PRIORITY LEVEL: 5 • MAIN ACTION RECOMMENDED: Creation of conservation area • OTHER RECOMMENDED ACTION: Creation of full protection conservation area or incorporation into the Niquiá Ecological Station; monitoring; prevention of illegal occupation.

RN 016 - Serra da Mocidade National Park, Caracaraí Ecological Station, Niquiá Ecological Station and Viruá National Park - PRIORITY LEVEL: A • LOCATION: *State:* Amazonas/Roraima • *Main municipality:* Caracaraí • *Municipalities covered:* 3 • VEGETATION TYPES: As, Da, Ds, Ld, Lg, LO, ON • COMMENTS: Set of two ecological stations and two adjacent national parks. High biological importance. Adjacent to two military lands to the north. Buffer zone for the Yanomami Indigenous Land.

> BIOLOGICAL IMPORTANCE: *Birds:* A • *Aquatic biota:* B • *Mammals:* A • IMPORTANCE FOR ECOLOGICAL GOODS AND SERVICES: A • STABILITY LEVEL: 3 • INSTABILITY LEVEL: 8 • ACTION PRIORITY LEVEL: 7 • MAIN ACTION RECOMMENDED: Protection • OTHER RECOMMENDED ACTION: Monitoring and protection in the area of influence of the BR-174 highway; and preparation of a management plan.

RN 017 - Maracá Ecological Station - PRIORITY LEVEL: A • LOCATION: *State:* Roraima • *Main municipality:* Amajari • *Municipalities covered:* 2 • VEGETATION TYPES: Ds, Fs, ON, Sp • COMMENTS: Biological importance: large fluvial island in Brazil, forest/savanna transition, research station established twenty years ago.

> BIOLOGICAL IMPORTANCE: *Birds:* A • *Aquatic biota:* B • *Plants:* A • *Mammals:* B • STABILITY LEVEL: 12 • INSTABILITY LEVEL: 0 • ACTION PRIORITY LEVEL: 2 • MAIN ACTION RECOMMENDED: Protection • OTHER RECOMMENDED ACTION: Intensified monitoring.

RN 018 - Area to the north of the Maracá Ecological Station - PRIORITY LEVEL: A • LOCATION: *State:* Roraima • *Main municipality:* Amajari • *Municipalities covered:* 2 • VEGETATION TYPES: As, Ds, Fs, ON, rm, Sg, SN, Sp • COMMENTS: Corridor around the north of the Maracá Island as far as the Tepequém mountains. Important ecological transition region between forest and savanna. Threats from mining and ranching.

> BIOLOGICAL IMPORTANCE: *Birds:* A • *Aquatic biota:* B • *Plants:* A • *Invertebrates:* D • *Mammals:* B • *Reptiles and amphibians:* A • STABILITY LEVEL: 0 • INSTABILITY LEVEL: 1 • ACTION PRIORITY LEVEL: 4 • MAIN ACTION RECOMMENDED: Incorporation into existing conservation area • OTHER RECOMMENDED ACTION: Incorporation into the Maracá Ecological Station; monitoring the growth of anthropogenic impacts; preparation of biological inventories.

RN 019 - Aningal Indigenous Land - PRIORITY LEVEL: A • LOCATION: *State:* Roraima • *Main municipality:* Amajari • *Municipalities covered:* 1 • VEGETATION TYPES: ON, Sp • COMMENTS: Indigenous land located in an area of high ecological importance.

BIOLOGICAL IMPORTANCE: *Birds:* A • *Aquatic biota:* B • *Plants:* A • *Mammals:* B • STABILITY LEVEL: 3 • INSTABILITY LEVEL: 8 • ACTION PRIORITY LEVEL: 7 • MAIN ACTION RECOMMENDED: Sustainable use of natural resources • OTHER RECOMMENDED ACTION: Removal of illegal occupants; restoration of altered areas; monitoring of the growth of anthropogenic impacts; preparation of assessments on the relationship between biodiversity, traditional knowledge and indigenous forms of management; and development of socio-economic sustainability alternatives for the indigenous population.

RN 020 - Boa Vista Prospecting Reserve - PRIORITY LEVEL: A • LOCATION: *State:* Roraima • *Main municipality:* Amajari • *Municipalities covered:* 1 • VEGETATION TYPES: ON, rm • COMMENTS: Isolated mountain top (tepui) considered to be of very high biological importance.

BIOLOGICAL IMPORTANCE: *Birds:* A • *Aquatic biota:* B • *Plants:* A • *Invertebrates:* D • *Mammals:* B • STABILITY LEVEL: 0 • INSTABILITY LEVEL: 0 • ACTION PRIORITY LEVEL: 3 • MAIN ACTION RECOMMENDED: Sustainable use of natural resources • OTHER RECOMMENDED ACTION: Preparation of assessments on the environmental impact of traditional mining activities and of biological inventories; and protection of headwaters.

RN 021 - Ananás Indigenous Land - PRIORITY LEVEL: A • LOCATION: *State:* Roraima • *Main municipality:* Amajari • *Municipalities covered:* 1 • VEGETATION TYPES: Fs, Sp • COMMENTS: Indigenous land located in an area of high biological importance.

BIOLOGICAL IMPORTANCE: *Birds:* A • *Aquatic biota:* B • *Invertebrates:* D • *Mammals:* B • *Reptiles and amphibians:* A • STABILITY LEVEL: 3 • INSTABILITY LEVEL: 4 • ACTION PRIORITY LEVEL: 4 • MAIN ACTION RECOMMENDED: Sustainable use of natural resources • OTHER RECOMMENDED ACTION: Removal of illegal occupants; monitoring of the growth of anthropogenic impacts; preparation of assessments on the relationship between biodiversity, traditional knowledge and indigenous forms of management; and development of socio-economic sustainability alternatives for the indigenous population.

RN 022 - Cajueiro Indigenous Land - PRIORITY LEVEL: A • LOCATION: *State:* Roraima • *Main municipality:* Amajari • *Municipalities covered:* 1 • VEGETATION TYPES: Fs, Sp • COMMENTS: Indigenous land located in an area of high biological importance.

BIOLOGICAL IMPORTANCE: *Birds:* A • *Aquatic biota:* B • *Invertebrates:* D • *Mammals:* B • *Reptiles and amphibians:* A • STABILITY LEVEL: 3 • INSTABILITY LEVEL: 4 • ACTION PRIORITY LEVEL: 4 • MAIN ACTION RECOMMENDED: Sustainable use of natural resources • OTHER RECOMMENDED ACTION: Removal of illegal occupation; monitoring of the growth of anthropogenic impacts; preparation of assessments on the relationship between biodiversity, traditional knowledge and indigenous forms of management; and development of socio-economic sustainability alternatives for the indigenous population.

RN 023 - Santa Inês Indigenous Land - PRIORITY LEVEL: A • LOCATION: *State:* Roraima • *Main municipality:* Amajari • *Municipalities covered:* 1 • VEGETATION TYPES: Ds, ON, Sp, Tp • COMMENTS: Indigenous land located in an area of high biological importance.

BIOLOGICAL IMPORTANCE: *Birds:* A • *Aquatic biota:* B • *Invertebrates:* D • *Mammals:* B • *Reptiles and amphibians:* A • IMPORTANCE FOR ECOLOGICAL GOODS AND SERVICES: A • STABILITY LEVEL: 3 • INSTABILITY LEVEL: 4 • ACTION PRIORITY LEVEL: 4 • MAIN ACTION RECOMMENDED: Sustainable use of natural resources • OTHER RECOMMENDED ACTION: Removal of illegal occupation; monitoring of the growth of anthropogenic impacts; preparation of assessments on the relationship between biodiversity, traditional knowledge and indigenous forms of management.

RN 024 - São Marcos and Raposa Serra do Sol Indigenous Lands - PRIORITY LEVEL: A • LOCATION: *State:* Roraima • *Main municipality:* Uiramutã • *Municipalities covered:* 7 • VEGETATION TYPES: Dm, Ds, ON, Sg, SN, Sp, Ta, Td, Tp • COMMENTS: Indigenous lands located in an area of high ecological importance. Priority area identified by the savanna and wetlands workshop.

BIOLOGICAL IMPORTANCE: *Birds:* A • *Aquatic biota:* A • *Invertebrates:* D • *Mammals:* B • *Reptiles and amphibians:* A • IMPORTANCE FOR ECOLOGICAL GOODS AND SERVICES: A • STABILITY LEVEL: 6 • INSTABILITY LEVEL: 8 • ACTION PRIORITY LEVEL: 6 • MAIN ACTION RECOMMENDED: Sustainable use of natural resources • OTHER RECOMMENDED ACTION: Demarcation; removal of illegal occupants; monitoring of the growth of anthropogenic impacts; and preparation of assessments on the relationship between biodiversity, traditional knowledge and indigenous forms of management.

RN 025 - Araçá Indigenous Land - PRIORITY LEVEL: A • LOCATION: *State:* Roraima • *Main municipality:* Amajari • *Municipalities covered:* 1 • VEGETATION TYPES: Fs, Sg, SN, Sp, Tp • COMMENTS: Indigenous land located in an area of high biological importance.

BIOLOGICAL IMPORTANCE: *Birds:* A • *Aquatic biota:* B • *Mammals:* B • *Reptiles and amphibians:* A • STABILITY LEVEL: 3 • INSTABILITY LEVEL: 4 • ACTION PRIORITY LEVEL: 4 • MAIN ACTION RECOMMENDED: Sustainable use of natural resources • OTHER RECOMMENDED ACTION: Removal of illegal occupants; monitoring of the growth of anthropogenic impacts; and preparation of assessments on the relationship between biodiversity, traditional knowledge and indigenous forms of management.

RN 026 - Anta and Pium Indigenous Lands - PRIORITY LEVEL: B • LOCATION: *State:* Roraima • *Main municipality:* Alto Alegre • *Municipalities covered:* 2 • VEGETATION TYPES: Fs, ON, Sg, Sp • COMMENTS: Indigenous lands located in an area of high biological importance.

BIOLOGICAL IMPORTANCE: *Aquatic biota:* B • *Mammals:* B • STABILITY LEVEL: 3 • INSTABILITY LEVEL: 4 • ACTION PRIORITY LEVEL: 4 • MAIN ACTION RECOMMENDED: Sustainable use of natural resources • OTHER RECOMMENDED ACTION: Removal of illegal occupants; monitoring of the growth of anthropogenic impacts; and preparation of assessments on the relationship between biodiversity, traditional knowledge and indigenous forms of management.

RN 027 - Barata/Livramento and Truaru Indigenous Lands - PRIORITY LEVEL: B • LOCATION: *State:* Roraima • *Main municipality:* Alto Alegre • *Municipalities covered:* 2 • VEGETATION TYPES: Fs, ON, Sg, Sp • COMMENTS: Indigenous lands located in an area of high biological importance.

BIOLOGICAL IMPORTANCE: *Aquatic biota:* B • *Mammals:* B • STABILITY LEVEL: 1 • INSTABILITY LEVEL: 4 • ACTION PRIORITY LEVEL: 5 • MAIN ACTION RECOMMENDED: Sustainable use of natural resources • OTHER RECOMMENDED ACTION: Removal of illegal occupants; monitoring of the growth of anthropogenic impacts; and preparation of assessments on the relation between biodiversity, traditional knowledge and indigenous forms of management.

RN 028 - Mangueira and Boqueirão Indigenous Lands - PRIORITY LEVEL: B • LOCATION: *State:* Roraima • *Main municipality:* Alto Alegre • *Municipalities covered:* 1 • VEGETATION TYPES: ON, Sp • COMMENTS: Indigenous lands located in an area of high biological importance.

BIOLOGICAL IMPORTANCE: *Aquatic biota:* B • *Plants:* A • *Mammals:* B • STABILITY LEVEL: 3 • INSTABILITY LEVEL: 4 • ACTION PRIORITY LEVEL: 4 • MAIN ACTION RECOMMENDED: Sustainable use of natural resources • OTHER RECOMMENDED ACTION: Removal of illegal occupants; monitoring of the growth of anthropogenic impacts; and preparation of assessments on the relationship between biodiversity, traditional knowledge and indigenous forms of management.

RN 029 - Serra da Moça Indigenous Land - PRIORITY LEVEL: B • LOCATION: *State:* Roraima • *Main municipality:* Boa Vista • *Municipalities covered:* 1 • VEGETATION TYPES: Sg, SN • COMMENTS: Indigenous land located in an area of high ecological importance.

BIOLOGICAL IMPORTANCE: *Aquatic biota:* B • *Mammals:* B • *Reptiles and amphibians:* A • STABILITY LEVEL: 3 • INSTABILITY LEVEL: 8 • ACTION PRIORITY LEVEL: 7 • MAIN ACTION RECOMMENDED: Sustainable use of natural resources • OTHER RECOMMENDED ACTION: Removal of illegal occupants; monitoring of the growth of anthropogenic impacts; and preparation of assessments on the relationship between biodiversity, traditional knowledge and indigenous forms of management.

RN 030 - Jaboti Indigenous Land - PRIORITY LEVEL: A • LOCATION: *State:* Roraima • *Main municipality:* Bonfim • *Municipalities covered:* 2 • VEGETATION TYPES: Sg, SN • COMMENTS: Indigenous land located in an area of high biological importance.

BIOLOGICAL IMPORTANCE: *Aquatic biota:* A • *Invertebrates:* D • *Mammals:* B • *Reptiles and amphibians:* A • STABILITY LEVEL: 3 • INSTABILITY LEVEL: 8 • ACTION PRIORITY LEVEL: 7 • MAIN ACTION RECOMMENDED:

Sustainable use of natural resources • OTHER RECOMMENDED ACTION: Removal of illegal occupants; monitoring of the growth of anthropogenic impacts; and preparation of assessments on the relationship between biodiversity, traditional knowledge and indigenous forms of management.

RN 031 - Manoá/Pium and Moskow Indigenous Lands - PRIORITY LEVEL: B • LOCATION: *State:* Roraima • *Main municipality:* Bonfim • *Municipalities covered:* 2 • VEGETATION TYPES: As, Sg, Sp • COMMENTS: Indigenous land located in an area of high biological importance.

BIOLOGICAL IMPORTANCE: *Invertebrates:* D • *Mammals:* B • *Reptiles and amphibians:* A • STABILITY LEVEL: 3 • INSTABILITY LEVEL: 8 • ACTION PRIORITY LEVEL: 7 • MAIN ACTION RECOMMENDED: Sustainable use of natural resources • OTHER RECOMMENDED ACTION: Removal of illegal occupants; monitoring of the growth of anthropogenic impacts; and preparation of assessments on the relationship between biodiversity, traditional knowledge and indigenous forms of management.

RN 032 - Muriru Indigenous Land - PRIORITY LEVEL: B • LOCATION: *State:* Roraima • *Main municipality:* Cantá • *Municipalities covered:* 2 • VEGETATION TYPES: Ds, Sp • COMMENTS: Indigenous land located in an area of high biological importance.

BIOLOGICAL IMPORTANCE: *Invertebrates:* D • *Mammals:* B • STABILITY LEVEL: 1 • INSTABILITY LEVEL: 4 • ACTION PRIORITY LEVEL: 5 • MAIN ACTION RECOMMENDED: Sustainable use of natural resources • OTHER RECOMMENDED ACTION: Removal of illegal occupants; monitoring of the growth of anthropogenic impacts; and preparation of assessments on the relationship between biodiversity, traditional knowledge and indigenous forms of management.

RN 033 - Jacamim Indigenous Land - PRIORITY LEVEL: N • LOCATION: *State:* Roraima • *Main municipality:* Caracaraí • *Municipalities covered:* 3 • VEGETATION TYPES: As, Ds, Sa, SO, Sp • COMMENTS: Indigenous land located in an area of high biological importance.

BIOLOGICAL IMPORTANCE: *Mammals:* B • STABILITY LEVEL: 1 • INSTABILITY LEVEL: 0 • ACTION PRIORITY LEVEL: 3 • MAIN ACTION RECOMMENDED: Sustainable use of natural resources • OTHER RECOMMENDED ACTION: Removal of illegal occupants; monitoring of the growth of anthropogenic impacts; and preparation of assessments on the relation between biodiversity, traditional knowledge and indigenous forms of management.

RN 034 - Middle and Lower Rio Branco - PRIORITY LEVEL: A • LOCATION: *State:* Roraima/Amazonas • *Main municipality:* Rorainópolis • *Municipalities covered:* 4 • VEGETATION TYPES: Ab, Da, Db, La, Ld, Lg, LO • COMMENTS: Area of high biological importance lacking conservation areas; area little known with local formations, especially the Rio Branco floodplains; potentially located in a area of high endemism; campinas and campinaranas potentially distinct from those of the Rio Negro; area of low population density; occurrence of species endemic to the Rio Branco basin; gaps in conservation areas for several vegetation types; ancient dunes.

BIOLOGICAL IMPORTANCE: *Birds:* A • *Aquatic biota:* B • *Plants:* D • *Mammals:* A • *Reptiles and amphibians:* A • IMPORTANCE FOR ECOLOGICAL GOODS AND SERVICES: B • STABILITY LEVEL: 0 • INSTABILITY LEVEL: 8 • ACTION PRIORITY LEVEL: 8 • MAIN ACTION RECOMMENDED: Creation of conservation area • OTHER RECOMMENDED ACTION: Creation of full protection conservation area (national park); preparation of studies to classify ecosystems and of biological, social and environmental inventories; monitoring and regulation of fishing activities.

RN 035 - Overlap between Waimiri-Atroari Indigenous Land and Left Bank of the Rio Negro Environmental Protection Area - PRIORITY LEVEL: N • LOCATION: *State:* Amazonas • *Main municipality:* Novo Airão • *Municipalities covered:* 1 • VEGETATION TYPES: Db, Ds, LO • COMMENTS: The Rio Negro State Park increases the conservation area for the biota occurring on the left bank of the Rio Negro and is part of the western Amazonia biogeographical province. Opportunity for a state environmental institute (Ipaam) to fully implement the Rio Negro State Park.

BIOLOGICAL IMPORTANCE: *Birds:* A • *Aquatic biota:* ? • IMPORTANCE FOR ECOLOGICAL GOODS AND SERVICES: B • STABILITY LEVEL: 9 • INSTABILITY LEVEL: 0 • ACTION PRIORITY LEVEL: 2 • MAIN ACTION RECOMMENDED: Identify priority actions • OTHER RECOMMENDED ACTION: Evaluation of the situation of populations in the Jacaré/Xipaca indigenous land; creation of a FUNAI working group to verify the presence of indians; and preparation of a management plan for the Left Bank of the Rio Negro Environmental Protection Area.

RN 036 - Overlap between the northern sector of the Rio Negro and the Ilha Jacaré Xipaca Indigenous Land - PRIORITY LEVEL: A • LOCATION: *State:* Amazonas • *Main municipality:* Novo Airão • *Municipalities covered:* 1 • VEGETATION TYPES: Db, LO • COMMENTS: State conservation area overlapping an indigenous land.

BIOLOGICAL IMPORTANCE: *Birds:* A • *Aquatic biota:* B • IMPORTANCE FOR ECOLOGICAL GOODS AND SERVICES: B • STABILITY LEVEL: 29 • INSTABILITY LEVEL: 0 • ACTION PRIORITY LEVEL: 1 • MAIN ACTION RECOMMENDED: Identify priority actions • OTHER RECOMMENDED ACTION: Evaluation of the situation of populations in the Jacará/Xipaca indigenous land; creation of a FUNAI working group to verify the presence of indians; and preparation of a management plan for the Rio Negro State Park.

RN 037 - Left Bank of the Rio Negro Environmental Protection Area - PRIORITY LEVEL: A • LOCATION: *State:* Amazonas • *Main municipality:* Manaus • *Municipalities covered:* 3 • VEGETATION TYPES: Da, Db, Ds, LO • COMMENTS: Area of high biological importance under the influence of the economic and demographic center of Manaus.

BIOLOGICAL IMPORTANCE: *Birds:* A • *Aquatic biota:* B • *Plants:* B • *Invertebrates:* A • *Mammals:* C • IMPORTANCE FOR ECOLOGICAL GOODS AND SERVICES: B • STABILITY LEVEL: 2 • INSTABILITY LEVEL: 9 • ACTION PRIORITY LEVEL: 8 • MAIN ACTION RECOMMENDED: Identify priority actions • OTHER RECOMMENDED ACTION: Monitoring, preparation of a management plan and coordinated zoning with the nearby conservation areas.

RN 038 - Cuieiras River - PRIORITY LEVEL: A • LOCATION: *State:* Amazonas • *Main municipality:* Manaus • *Municipalities covered:* 2 • VEGETATION TYPES: Db, Ds, LO • COMMENTS: Biological studies reserve (INPA and Universidade Federal do Amazonas/Manaus). High population and anthropogenic pressures. The region of Manaus needs special attention for the development of economically sustainable alternatives.

BIOLOGICAL IMPORTANCE: *Aquatic biota:* A • *Plants:* B • *Invertebrates:* A • *Mammals:* C • IMPORTANCE FOR ECOLOGICAL GOODS AND SERVICES: B • STABILITY LEVEL: 0 • INSTABILITY LEVEL: 9 • ACTION PRIORITY LEVEL: 9 • MAIN ACTION RECOMMENDED: Creation of conservation area • OTHER RECOMMENDED ACTION: Area near Manaus subject to anthropogenic pressure; monitoring; preparation of biological inventories and studies to create small conservation areas of campina/campinarana; and development of tourism and ecotourism activities, biotechnology and transformation of natural resources industries, furniture industry, musical instruments, fruit pulp and environmental education.

RN 039 - Anavilhanas Ecological Station and Rio Negro State Park - PRIORITY LEVEL: A • LOCATION: *State:* Amazonas • *Main municipality:* Novo Airão • *Municipalities covered:* 5 • VEGETATION TYPES: Da, Db, Ds, LO • COMMENTS: High levels of floristic and faunistic endemism.

BIOLOGICAL IMPORTANCE: *Birds:* A • *Aquatic biota:* B • *Plants:* A • *Invertebrates:* A • *Mammals:* C • *Reptiles and amphibians:* D • IMPORTANCE FOR ECOLOGICAL GOODS AND SERVICES: B • STABILITY LEVEL: 6 • INSTABILITY LEVEL: 9 • ACTION PRIORITY LEVEL: 6 • MAIN ACTION RECOMMENDED: Protection • OTHER RECOMMENDED ACTION: Upgrade monitoring of the Anavilhanas Ecological Station.

RN 040 - Right bank of the Rio Negro Environmental Protection Area - PRIORITY LEVEL: A • LOCATION: *State:* Amazonas • *Main municipality:* Novo Airão • *Municipalities covered:* 5 • VEGETATION TYPES: Ab, Da, Db, Ds, LO • COMMENTS: High anthropogenic pressure. High biological diversity.

BIOLOGICAL IMPORTANCE: *Birds:* A • *Aquatic biota:* A • *Invertebrates:* A • *Mammals:* B • *Reptiles and amphibians:* C • IMPORTANCE FOR ECOLOGICAL GOODS AND SERVICES: B • STABILITY LEVEL: 2 • INSTABILITY LEVEL: 9 • ACTION PRIORITY LEVEL: 8 • MAIN ACTION RECOMMENDED: Protection • OTHER RECOMMENDED ACTION: Preparation of a management plan for the two existing conservation areas in the region.

RN 041 - Area between the Jaú National Park and Right Bank of the Rio Negro Environmental Protection Area - PRIORITY LEVEL: A • LOCATION: *State:* Amazonas • *Main municipality:* Novo Airão •

Municipalities covered: 1 • VEGETATION TYPES: Ab, Da, Db, Ds, LO • COMMENTS: Correction of the cartographic error and complete conservation of the area.

> BIOLOGICAL IMPORTANCE: *Birds:* A • *Aquatic biota:* A • *Mammals:* B • IMPORTANCE FOR ECOLOGICAL GOODS AND SERVICES: B • STABILITY LEVEL: 0 • INSTABILITY LEVEL: 0 • ACTION PRIORITY LEVEL: 3 • MAIN ACTION RECOMMENDED: Incorporation into existing conservation area • OTHER RECOMMENDED ACTION: Incorporation into the Jaú National Park.

RN 042 - Jaú National Park - PRIORITY LEVEL: A • LOCATION: *State:* Amazonas • *Main municipality:* Novo Airão • *Municipalities covered:* 3 • VEGETATION TYPES: Ab, Da, Db, Ds, La, Ld, LO • COMMENTS: The area houses over 60% of the species in the Rio Negro basin. It is a pilot-experiment of institutional relations involving NGOs, IBAMA, researchers and local residents where, for the first time, residents of a national park participate in its management instead of being expelled from the area. The interruption of this experiment would mean the return to the previous practice of expelling residents of conservation areas. Well protected area, with tourist potential and infrastructure for organized research. This area protects the linkage between headwaters of black-water and white-water rivers.

> BIOLOGICAL IMPORTANCE: *Birds:* A • *Aquatic biota:* A • *Mammals:* B • *Reptiles and amphibians:* D • IMPORTANCE FOR ECOLOGICAL GOODS AND SERVICES: B • STABILITY LEVEL: 12 • INSTABILITY LEVEL: 0 • ACTION PRIORITY LEVEL: 2 • MAIN ACTION RECOMMENDED: Protection • OTHER RECOMMENDED ACTION: Development of programs to form volunteer environmental agents; capacity building for residents in activities for the implementation of the park; support to low impact alternatives for residents; continuation of biological inventories, environmental, social and non-biotic assessments; and extension of the experiment of involving local residents in the management of the Jaú National Park to other conservation areas.

RN 043 - Amanã Sustainable Development Reserve - PRIORITY LEVEL: A • LOCATION: *State:* Amazonas • *Main municipality:* Barcelos • *Municipalities covered:* 6 • VEGETATION TYPES: Ab, Da, Db, La, Ld, LO • COMMENTS: Part of the Central Amazon corridor. High biological diversity, linkage of headwaters of white-water and black-water rivers.

> BIOLOGICAL IMPORTANCE: *Birds:* C • *Aquatic biota:* A • *Invertebrates:* A • *Mammals:* B • *Reptiles and amphibians:* D • STABILITY LEVEL: 4 • INSTABILITY LEVEL: 3 • ACTION PRIORITY LEVEL: 3 • MAIN ACTION RECOMMENDED: Sustainable use of natural resources • OTHER RECOMMENDED ACTION: Preparation of a management plan; support to social organizations of local residents to participate in the management of the region; and training of residents in the monitoring and sustainable use of the conservation area.

RN 044 - Cuiuni - PRIORITY LEVEL: A • LOCATION: *State:* Amazonas • *Main municipality:* Barcelos • *Municipalities covered:* 2 • VEGETATION TYPES: Da, Db, La, Ld, LO • COMMENTS: Part of the Central Amazon corridor. High biological diversity, linkage of headwaters of white-water and black-water rivers.

> BIOLOGICAL IMPORTANCE: *Birds:* C • *Aquatic biota:* A • *Invertebrates:* A • *Mammals:* B • STABILITY LEVEL: 0 • INSTABILITY LEVEL: 0 • ACTION PRIORITY LEVEL: 3 • MAIN ACTION RECOMMENDED: Identify priority actions • OTHER RECOMMENDED ACTION: Area adjacent to the Amanã Sustainable Development Reserve. Preparation of biological inventories.

RN 045 - Middle Rio Negro - PRIORITY LEVEL: A • LOCATION: *State:* Amazonas • *Main municipality:* Barcelos • *Municipalities covered:* 2 • VEGETATION TYPES: Da, Db, Ds, La, Ld, Lg, LO • COMMENTS: Presence of archeological sites and ancient dunes. Area of *caboclo* population practicing subsistence agriculture with little deforestation and diversified extractive activities (piassava palm, titica vine, fish, Brazil nuts). Population probably originating from the Upper Rio Negro. The increase in fishing is threatening the fauna. Presence of an indigenous association in Santa Isabel, member of FOIRN. Urgent need to find new ecological alternatives.

> BIOLOGICAL IMPORTANCE: *Birds:* A • *Aquatic biota:* B • *Plants:* A • *Mammals:* A • *Reptiles and amphibians:* B • IMPORTANCE FOR ECOLOGICAL GOODS AND SERVICES: B • STABILITY LEVEL: 0 • INSTABILITY LEVEL: 2 • ACTION PRIORITY LEVEL: 4 • MAIN ACTION RECOMMENDED: Creation of conservation area • OTHER RECOMMENDED ACTION: Creation of sustainable use conservation area; monitoring the capture of turtles and ornamental fish; preparation of assessments on the ecology of ornamental fish, plants, anthropology and socio-economic aspects.

RN 046 - Maraã/Urubaxi Indigenous Land - PRIORITY LEVEL: N • LOCATION: *State:* Amazonas • *Main municipality:* Santa Isabel do Rio Negro • *Municipalities covered:* 3 • VEGETATION TYPES: Da, La, Ld, LO • COMMENTS: Area of biological interest (Japurá floodplains).

> BIOLOGICAL IMPORTANCE: *Birds:* C • *Aquatic biota:* B • STABILITY LEVEL: 5 • INSTABILITY LEVEL: 0 • ACTION PRIORITY LEVEL: 2 • MAIN ACTION RECOMMENDED: Identify priority actions.

RN 047 - Floodplains of the Middle Japurá - PRIORITY LEVEL: B • LOCATION: *State:* Amazonas • *Main municipality:* Santa Isabel do Rio Negro • *Municipalities covered:* 3 • VEGETATION TYPES: Da, La, LO • COMMENTS: Biological importance: breeding ground for aquatic animals. Fishing.

> BIOLOGICAL IMPORTANCE: *Birds:* C • *Aquatic biota:* B • STABILITY LEVEL: 0 • INSTABILITY LEVEL: 0 • ACTION PRIORITY LEVEL: 3 • MAIN ACTION RECOMMENDED: Sustainable use of natural resources • OTHER RECOMMENDED ACTION: Preparation of floristic and faunistic inventories and studies of fishery management.

RN 048 - Uneuixi and Paraná Boá-Boá Indigenous Lands - PRIORITY LEVEL: N • LOCATION: *State:* Amazonas • *Main municipality:* Santa Isabel do Rio Negro • *Municipalities covered:* 2 • VEGETATION TYPES: Da, Ds, La, Ld, LO • COMMENTS: Area of high ecological importance (Japurá floodplains). Application for mining in the Uneuixi Indigenous Land, covering 20% of the territory. Five mining applications in the Parana Boá-Boá, covering 5% of the territory.

> BIOLOGICAL IMPORTANCE: *Aquatic biota:* B • STABILITY LEVEL: 5 • INSTABILITY LEVEL: 0 • ACTION PRIORITY LEVEL: 2 • MAIN ACTION RECOMMENDED: Identify priority actions • OTHER RECOMMENDED ACTION: Preparation of biological inventories and anthropological studies.

RN 049 - Upper Japurá Floodplains - PRIORITY LEVEL: B • LOCATION: *State:* Amazonas • *Main municipality:* Japurá • *Municipalities covered:* 1 • VEGETATION TYPES: Ab, Da, Ds, La, Ld, LO • COMMENTS: Biological importance: breeding of aquatic animals. Fishing.

> BIOLOGICAL IMPORTANCE: *Aquatic biota:* B • *Plants:* A • *Reptiles and amphibians:* D • STABILITY LEVEL: 0 • INSTABILITY LEVEL: 4 • ACTION PRIORITY LEVEL: 5 • MAIN ACTION RECOMMENDED: Sustainable use of natural resources • OTHER RECOMMENDED ACTION: Preparation of floristic and faunistic inventories and studies of fishery management.

7
PRIORITY AREAS IN THE JURUÁ / PURUS / ACRE REGION

JU 001 - Serra do Divisor National Park - PRIORITY LEVEL: A • LOCATION: *State:* Acre • *Main municipality:* Mâncio Lima • *Municipalities covered:* 6 • VEGETATION TYPES: Ab, Da, Db, Ds • COMMENTS: Exceptional biological importance diagnosed by the rapid ecological appraisal already undertaken. Management plan being implemented. Large number of families within the area. Regularization of land titles urgently needed. Extremely high importance for plants, invertebrates, reptiles, amphibians and birds. Very high importance for mammals and aquatic biota.
　　BIOLOGICAL IMPORTANCE: *Birds:* A • *Aquatic biota:* B • *Plants:* A • *Invertebrates:* D • *Mammals:* B • *Reptiles and amphibians:* B • STABILITY LEVEL: 3 • INSTABILITY LEVEL: 6 • ACTION PRIORITY LEVEL: 5 • MAIN ACTION RECOMMENDED: Protection • OTHER RECOMMENDED ACTION: Monitoring and finalization of biological inventories.

JU 002 - Eastern extension of the Serra do Divisor National Park - PRIORITY LEVEL: A • LOCATION: *State:* Acre • *Main municipality:* Porto Walter • *Municipalities covered:* 5 • VEGETATION TYPES: Ab, Da, Db • COMMENTS: High biological importance, conservation area buffer zone (Serra do Divisor National Park). Very high importance for biota. Extremely high importance for plants, invertebrates, reptiles, amphibians, birds and mammals.
　　BIOLOGICAL IMPORTANCE: *Birds:* A • *Aquatic biota:* B • *Plants:* A • *Invertebrates:* D • *Mammals:* A • *Reptiles and amphibians:* B • STABILITY LEVEL: 0 • INSTABILITY LEVEL: 6 • ACTION PRIORITY LEVEL: 7 • MAIN ACTION RECOMMENDED: Sustainable use of natural resources • OTHER RECOMMENDED ACTION: Regulation of activities permitted in the buffer zone of the Serra do Divisor National Park; preparation of biological inventories; and assessments of natural resources use alternatives.

JU 003 - Kampa do Rio Amônea Indigenous Land - PRIORITY LEVEL: A • LOCATION: *State:* Acre • *Main municipality:* Marechal Thaumaturgo • *Municipalities covered:* 2 • VEGETATION TYPES: Ab, Da.
　　BIOLOGICAL IMPORTANCE: *Birds:* A • *Aquatic biota:* B • *Plants:* A • *Invertebrates:* D • *Mammals:* B • *Reptiles and amphibians:* B • STABILITY LEVEL: 5 • INSTABILITY LEVEL: 2 • ACTION PRIORITY LEVEL: 3 • MAIN ACTION RECOMMENDED: Identify priority actions.

JU 004 - Alto Juruá Extractive Reserve - PRIORITY LEVEL: A • LOCATION: *State:* Acre • *Main municipality:* Marechal Thaumaturgo • *Municipalities covered:* 5 • VEGETATION TYPES: Ab, Da, Db • COMMENTS: Extremely high importance for plants, invertebrates, birds and mammals. Very high importance for reptiles, amphibians and biota.
　　BIOLOGICAL IMPORTANCE: *Birds:* A • *Aquatic biota:* B • *Plants:* A • *Invertebrates:* D • *Mammals:* A • *Reptiles and amphibians:* B • STABILITY LEVEL: 8 • INSTABILITY LEVEL: 2 • ACTION PRIORITY LEVEL: 2 • MAIN ACTION RECOMMENDED: Sustainable use of natural resources.

JU 005 - Jaminawá do Igarapé Preto Indigenous Land - PRIORITY LEVEL: A • LOCATION: *State:* Acre • *Main municipality:* Cruzeiro do Sul • *Municipalities covered:* 1 • VEGETATION TYPES: Ab, Da, Db.
　　BIOLOGICAL IMPORTANCE: *Birds:* A • *Aquatic biota:* B • *Plants:* A • *Invertebrates:* D • *Mammals:* B • STABILITY LEVEL: 3 • INSTABILITY LEVEL: 6 • ACTION PRIORITY LEVEL: 5 • MAIN ACTION RECOMMENDED: Identify priority actions

JU 006 - Nukini Indigenous Land - PRIORITY LEVEL: A • LOCATION: *State:* Acre • *Main municipality:* Mâncio Lima • *Municipalities covered:* 2 • VEGETATION TYPES: Ab, Da, Ds • COMMENTS: Area of high biological importance, located in the buffer zone of the Serra do Divisor National Park and subject to high pressure from hunting. Extremely high importance for plants and birds. Very high importance for reptiles, amphibians, mammals and aquatic biota.
　　BIOLOGICAL IMPORTANCE: *Birds:* A • *Aquatic biota:* B • *Plants:* A • *Mammals:* B • *Reptiles and amphibians:* B • STABILITY LEVEL: 3 • INSTABILITY LEVEL: 6 • ACTION PRIORITY LEVEL: 5 • MAIN ACTION RECOMMENDED: Sustainable use of natural resources • OTHER RECOMMENDED ACTION: Preparation of biological inventories.

JU 007 - Northern extension of the Serra do Divisor National Park - PRIORITY LEVEL: B • LOCATION: *State:* Acre/Amazonas • *Main municipality:* Guajará • *Municipalities covered:* 4 • VEGETATION TYPES: Ab, Db, Ds • COMMENTS: Extremely high biological importance. Large vegetation types, poorly represented in the current system of conservation areas, serving as a corridor connecting the western and northern Amazon corridors; area of low population density with no anthropogenic pressure; area of very high biological diversity; the expansion of the National Park is recommended in its management plan.
　　BIOLOGICAL IMPORTANCE: *Birds:* D • *Aquatic biota:* B • *Plants:* A • *Reptiles and amphibians:* B • STABILITY LEVEL: 0 • INSTABILITY LEVEL: 2 • ACTION PRIORITY LEVEL: 4 • MAIN ACTION RECOMMENDED: Incorporation into existing conservation area • OTHER RECOMMENDED ACTION: Incorporation of the area into the Serra do Divisor National Park, through the northward expansion of the park, in order to serve as an ecological corridor.

JU 008 - Northeastern extension of the Serra do Divisor National Park - PRIORITY LEVEL: A • LOCATION: *State:* Acre/Amazonas • *Main municipality:* Guajará • *Municipalities covered:* 2 • VEGETATION TYPES: AA, Ab, Da, Db, La, Ld • COMMENTS: Large area of campinas and principally campinaranas, not connected to the other main areas on the Madeira and the Rio Negro. Very fragile environment, much regional level (i.e., unconnected) endemism. Very high importance for reptiles, amphibians and aquatic biota. Extremely high importance for plants.
　　BIOLOGICAL IMPORTANCE: *Birds:* A • *Aquatic biota:* B • *Plants:* A • *Mammals:* B • *Reptiles and amphibians:* B • STABILITY LEVEL: 0 • INSTABILITY LEVEL: 7 • ACTION PRIORITY LEVEL: 8 • MAIN ACTION RECOMMENDED: Incorporation into existing conservation area • OTHER RECOMMENDED ACTION: Incorporation of the area into the Serra do Divisor National Park, through the northeastwards expansion of the park, in order to encompass a unique ecosystem which, although, still protected, is under great threat.

JU 009 - Area to the northeast of the Serra do Divisor National Park - PRIORITY LEVEL: A • LOCATION: *State:* Acre • *Main municipality:* Cruzeiro do Sul • *Municipalities covered:* 4 • VEGETATION TYPES: AA, Ab, Da, Db • COMMENTS: Extremely high importance for mammals. Very high importance for aquatic biota.
　　BIOLOGICAL IMPORTANCE: *Birds:* A • *Aquatic biota:* B • *Mammals:* A • STABILITY LEVEL: 0 • INSTABILITY LEVEL: 6 • ACTION PRIORITY LEVEL: 7 • MAIN ACTION RECOMMENDED: Identify priority actions • OTHER RECOMMENDED ACTION: Preparation of biological inventories for mammals and aquatic biota.

JU 010 - Tarauacá River - PRIORITY LEVEL: A • LOCATION: *State:* Acre • *Main municipality:* Jordão • *Municipalities covered:* 3 • VEGETATION

TYPES: Ab, Da, Db • COMMENTS: Area of very high importance for plants and aquatic biota. Extremely high importance for mammals.

BIOLOGICAL IMPORTANCE: *Birds:* D • *Aquatic biota:* B • *Plants:* A • *Mammals:* A • STABILITY LEVEL: 0 • INSTABILITY LEVEL: 0 • ACTION PRIORITY LEVEL: 3 • MAIN ACTION RECOMMENDED: Identify priority actions.

JU 011 - Praia do Carapanã, Gregório River and Kampa do Igarapé Primavera Indigenous Lands - PRIORITY LEVEL: A • LOCATION: *State:* Acre • *Main municipality:* Tarauacá • *Municipalities covered:* 1 • VEGETATION TYPES: Ab, Da, Db • COMMENTS: Area of very high importance for plants and aquatic biota. Extremely high importance for mammals.

BIOLOGICAL IMPORTANCE: *Birds:* D • *Aquatic biota:* B • *Plants:* A • *Mammals:* A • STABILITY LEVEL: 5 • INSTABILITY LEVEL: 0 • ACTION PRIORITY LEVEL: 2 • MAIN ACTION RECOMMENDED: Identify priority actions.

JU 012 - Jutaí and Gregório rivers - PRIORITY LEVEL: A • LOCATION: *State:* Amazonas • *Main municipality:* Ipixuna • *Municipalities covered:* 7 • VEGETATION TYPES: AA, Ab, Da, Db • COMMENTS: Area of very high importance for plants and aquatic biota. Extremely high importance for reptiles, amphibians and mammals.

BIOLOGICAL IMPORTANCE: *Birds:* B • *Aquatic biota:* B • *Mammals:* A • *Reptiles and amphibians:* A • STABILITY LEVEL: 0 • INSTABILITY LEVEL: 3 • ACTION PRIORITY LEVEL: 5 • MAIN ACTION RECOMMENDED: Identify priority actions.

JU 013 - Middle Juruá - PRIORITY LEVEL: A • LOCATION: *State:* Amazonas • *Main municipality:* Eirunepé • *Municipalities covered:* 3 • VEGETATION TYPES: Ab, Da, Db • COMMENTS: Area of very high importance for plants and aquatic biota. Extremely high importance for reptiles, amphibians and mammals.

BIOLOGICAL IMPORTANCE: *Birds:* B • *Aquatic biota:* B • *Mammals:* A • *Reptiles and amphibians:* A • STABILITY LEVEL: 3 • INSTABILITY LEVEL: 6 • ACTION PRIORITY LEVEL: 5 • MAIN ACTION RECOMMENDED: Identify priority actions.

JU 014 - Vale do Javari Indigenous Land - PRIORITY LEVEL: A • LOCATION: *State:* Amazonas • *Main municipality:* Atalaia do Norte • *Municipalities covered:* 8 • VEGETATION TYPES: Ab, Da, Db, La • COMMENTS: Area of very high importance for plants and aquatic biota. Extremely high importance for reptiles, amphibians and mammals.

BIOLOGICAL IMPORTANCE: *Birds:* B • *Aquatic biota:* B • *Plants:* D • *Invertebrates:* D • *Mammals:* A • *Reptiles and amphibians:* A • STABILITY LEVEL: 1 • INSTABILITY LEVEL: 3 • ACTION PRIORITY LEVEL: 4 • MAIN ACTION RECOMMENDED: Identify priority actions.

JU 015 - Right bank of the Javari River - PRIORITY LEVEL: B • LOCATION: *State:* Amazonas • *Main municipality:* Atalaia do Norte • *Municipalities covered:* 2 • VEGETATION TYPES: Ab, Da, Db • COMMENTS: Area of very high importance for plants, aquatic biota and mammals.

BIOLOGICAL IMPORTANCE: *Aquatic biota:* B • *Plants:* D • *Mammals:* B • STABILITY LEVEL: 0 • INSTABILITY LEVEL: 0 • ACTION PRIORITY LEVEL: 3 • MAIN ACTION RECOMMENDED: Identify priority actions.

JU 016 - Quixito River - PRIORITY LEVEL: B • LOCATION: *State:* Amazonas • *Main municipality:* Atalaia do Norte • *Municipalities covered:* 3 • VEGETATION TYPES: Ab, Da, Db • COMMENTS: Area of very high importance for mammals and aquatic biota.

BIOLOGICAL IMPORTANCE: *Birds:* D • *Aquatic biota:* B • *Invertebrates:* D • *Mammals:* B • STABILITY LEVEL: 0 • INSTABILITY LEVEL: 2 • ACTION PRIORITY LEVEL: 4 • MAIN ACTION RECOMMENDED: Protection • OTHER RECOMMENDED ACTION: Regularization of the Lameirão Indigenous Land.

JU 017 - Jutaí River - PRIORITY LEVEL: A • LOCATION: *State:* Amazonas • *Main municipality:* Jutaí • *Municipalities covered:* 1 • VEGETATION TYPES: Ab, Da, Db, Pa • COMMENTS: Area of very high importance for aquatic biota. Extremely high importance for mammals.

BIOLOGICAL IMPORTANCE: *Birds:* B • *Aquatic biota:* B • *Plants:* D • *Mammals:* A • *Reptiles and amphibians:* A • STABILITY LEVEL: 0 • INSTABILITY LEVEL: 3 • ACTION PRIORITY LEVEL: 5 • MAIN ACTION RECOMMENDED: Studies to identify priority actions.

JU 018 - Envira River - PRIORITY LEVEL: B • LOCATION: *State:* Acre • *Main municipality:* Feijó • *Municipalities covered:* 1 • VEGETATION TYPES: AA, Ab, Da • COMMENTS: Area of very high importance for reptiles, amphibians and aquatic biota.

BIOLOGICAL IMPORTANCE: *Birds:* D • *Aquatic biota:* B • *Mammals:* A • *Reptiles and amphibians:* B • STABILITY LEVEL: 0 • INSTABILITY LEVEL: 6 • ACTION PRIORITY LEVEL: 7 • MAIN ACTION RECOMMENDED: Identify priority actions.

JU 019 - Kulina do Rio Envira/Kulina do Igarapé do Pau Indigenous Lands - PRIORITY LEVEL: B • LOCATION: *State:* Acre • *Main municipality:* Feijó • *Municipalities covered:* 2 • VEGETATION TYPES: Ab, Da • COMMENTS: Area of very high importance for aquatic biota. Extremely high importance for mammals.

BIOLOGICAL IMPORTANCE: *Birds:* D • *Aquatic biota:* B • *Mammals:* A • *Reptiles and amphibians:* B • STABILITY LEVEL: 3 • INSTABILITY LEVEL: 6 • ACTION PRIORITY LEVEL: 5 • MAIN ACTION RECOMMENDED: Identify priority actions.

JU 020 - Upper Purus - PRIORITY LEVEL: A • LOCATION: *State:* Acre • *Main municipality:* Sena Madureira • *Municipalities covered:* 4 • VEGETATION TYPES: Ab, Da • COMMENTS: Area of very high importance for reptiles and aquatic biota. Extremely high importance for mammals.

BIOLOGICAL IMPORTANCE: *Birds:* D • *Aquatic biota:* B • *Plants:* A • *Mammals:* A • *Reptiles and amphibians:* B • STABILITY LEVEL: 0 • INSTABILITY LEVEL: 6 • ACTION PRIORITY LEVEL: 7 • MAIN ACTION RECOMMENDED: Identify priority actions.

JU 021 - Alto Purus Indigenous Land - PRIORITY LEVEL: B • LOCATION: *State:* Acre • *Main municipality:* Santa Rosa do Purus • *Municipalities covered:* 3 • VEGETATION TYPES: Ab, Da • COMMENTS: Area of very high importance for reptiles and amphibians. Extremely high importance for mammals.

BIOLOGICAL IMPORTANCE: *Birds:* D • *Aquatic biota:* B • *Mammals:* A • *Reptiles and amphibians:* B • STABILITY LEVEL: 3 • INSTABILITY LEVEL: 3 • ACTION PRIORITY LEVEL: 4 • MAIN ACTION RECOMMENDED: Identify priority actions.

JU 022 - Purus River - PRIORITY LEVEL: A • LOCATION: *State:* Acre • *Main municipality:* Sena Madureira • *Municipalities covered:* 9 • VEGETATION TYPES: AA, Ab, Da, Db • COMMENTS: Area with gasps in information, but of probable high biological importance. The area can serve as a gene flow corridor in the western Amazon corridor and connects the indigenous land with the national forest and the extractive reserve. Extremely high importance for plants and mammals. Very high importance for aquatic biota. Lack of knowledge of birds; plant endemism on the Macanã River.

BIOLOGICAL IMPORTANCE: *Birds:* D • *Aquatic biota:* B • *Plants:* A • *Mammals:* A • *Reptiles and amphibians:* B • STABILITY LEVEL: 0 • INSTABILITY LEVEL: 6 • ACTION PRIORITY LEVEL: 7 • MAIN ACTION RECOMMENDED: Creation of conservation area.

JU 023 - Macauã National Forest - PRIORITY LEVEL: B • LOCATION: *State:* Acre • *Main municipality:* Sena Madureira • *Municipalities covered:* 1 • VEGETATION TYPES: Ab, Da • COMMENTS: Endemism of dense *tabocal* bamboo species, including various habitat specialists. Intact un-hunted fauna in need of protection in the medium term. High habitat diversity. Occurrence of the highest recorded density of *Callimico goeldi*. Extremely high importance for mammals.

BIOLOGICAL IMPORTANCE: *Birds:* D • *Aquatic biota:* B • *Mammals:* A • *Reptiles and amphibians:* B • STABILITY LEVEL: 8 • INSTABILITY LEVEL: 0 • ACTION PRIORITY LEVEL: 2 • MAIN ACTION RECOMMENDED: Sustainable use of natural resources.

JU 024 - Antimari State Forest - PRIORITY LEVEL: A • LOCATION: *State:* Acre • *Main municipality:* Bujari • *Municipalities covered:* 3 • VEGETATION TYPES: AA, Ab, Da, Db • COMMENTS: Protected forest of high biological importance, but low level of implementation. Extremely high importance for plants and mammals. High importance for aquatic biota.

BIOLOGICAL IMPORTANCE: *Birds:* D • *Aquatic biota:* B • *Plants:* A • *Mammals:* A • *Reptiles and amphibians:* B • STABILITY LEVEL: 6 • INSTABILITY LEVEL: 6 • ACTION PRIORITY LEVEL: 5 • MAIN ACTION RECOMMENDED: Sustainable use of natural resources.

JU 025 - Igarapé Capana Indigenous Land - PRIORITY LEVEL: A • LOCATION: *State:* Amazonas • *Main municipality:* Boca do Acre • *Municipalities covered:* 1 • VEGETATION TYPES: Ab, Da, Db • COMMENTS: Highly diversified primate fauna representative of terra firme and alluvial forests in the middle and upper Purus. Extremely high importance for mammals. High importance for plants.

BIOLOGICAL IMPORTANCE: *Birds:* D • *Aquatic biota:* B • *Plants:* A • *Mammals:* A • *Reptiles and amphibians:* B • STABILITY LEVEL: 3 • INSTABILITY LEVEL: 7 • ACTION PRIORITY LEVEL: 6 • MAIN ACTION RECOMMENDED: Protection.

JU 026 - Camicuã Indigenous Land - PRIORITY LEVEL: A • LOCATION: *State:* Amazonas • *Main municipality:* Boca do Acre • *Municipalities covered:* 2 • VEGETATION TYPES: Da, Db • COMMENTS: Extremely high importance for mammals. Lack of knowledge about birds.

BIOLOGICAL IMPORTANCE: *Birds:* D • *Aquatic biota:* B • *Plants:* A • *Mammals:* A • *Reptiles and amphibians:* B • STABILITY LEVEL: 3 • INSTABILITY LEVEL: 7 • ACTION PRIORITY LEVEL: 6 • MAIN ACTION RECOMMENDED: Protection.

JU 027 - Peneri/Tacaquiri Indigenous Land - PRIORITY LEVEL: A • LOCATION: *State:* Amazonas • *Main municipality:* Pauini • *Municipalities covered:* 1 • VEGETATION TYPES: Da, Db • COMMENTS: Extremely high importance for mammals. High importance for aquatic biota. Lack of knowledge about birds.

BIOLOGICAL IMPORTANCE: *Birds:* D • *Aquatic biota:* B • *Plants:* A • *Mammals:* A • *Reptiles and amphibians:* B • STABILITY LEVEL: 3 • INSTABILITY LEVEL: 4 • ACTION PRIORITY LEVEL: 4 • MAIN ACTION RECOMMENDED: Protection.

JU 028 - Pauini River - PRIORITY LEVEL: B • LOCATION: *State:* Amazonas • *Main municipality:* Pauini • *Municipalities covered:* 1 • VEGETATION TYPES: Da, Db • COMMENTS: Extremely high importance for mammals. Very high importance for aquatic biota, reptiles and amphibians.

BIOLOGICAL IMPORTANCE: *Birds:* D • *Aquatic biota:* B • *Plants:* D • *Mammals:* A • *Reptiles and amphibians:* B • STABILITY LEVEL: 0 • INSTABILITY LEVEL: 0 • ACTION PRIORITY LEVEL: 3 • MAIN ACTION RECOMMENDED: Identify priority actions.

JU 029 - Rio Acre Ecological Station - PRIORITY LEVEL: B • LOCATION: *State:* Acre • *Main municipality:* Assis Brasil • *Municipalities covered:* 3 • VEGETATION TYPES: Ab • COMMENTS: Extremely high importance for plants. Very high importance for mammals and aquatic biota.

BIOLOGICAL IMPORTANCE: *Aquatic biota:* B • *Plants:* A • *Mammals:* B • STABILITY LEVEL: 12 • INSTABILITY LEVEL: 1 • ACTION PRIORITY LEVEL: 2 • MAIN ACTION RECOMMENDED: Identify priority actions • OTHER RECOMMENDED ACTION: Preparation of biological inventories.

JU 030 - Cabeceira do Rio Acre Indigenous Land - PRIORITY LEVEL: B • LOCATION: *State:* AC • *Main municipality:* Assis Brasil • *Municipalities covered:* 3 • VEGETATION TYPES: Ab • COMMENTS: Extremely high importance for plants. Very high importance for mammals and aquatic biota.

BIOLOGICAL IMPORTANCE: *Birds:* D • *Aquatic biota:* B • *Plants:* A • *Mammals:* B • STABILITY LEVEL: 3 • INSTABILITY LEVEL: 4 • ACTION PRIORITY LEVEL: 4 • MAIN ACTION RECOMMENDED: Protection.

JU 031 - Mamoadate Indigenous Land - PRIORITY LEVEL: B • LOCATION: *State:* Acre • *Main municipality:* Sena Madureira • *Municipalities covered:* 3 • VEGETATION TYPES: Ab, Da • COMMENTS: Extremely high importance for mammals. Very high importance for aquatic biota. Lack of knowledge about birds.

BIOLOGICAL IMPORTANCE: *Birds:* D • *Aquatic biota:* B • *Mammals:* A • STABILITY LEVEL: 5 • INSTABILITY LEVEL: 0 • ACTION PRIORITY LEVEL: 2 • MAIN ACTION RECOMMENDED: Protection.

JU 032 - Chico Mendes Extractive Reserve - PRIORITY LEVEL: B • LOCATION: *State:* Acre • *Main municipality:* Xapuri • *Municipalities covered:* 7 • VEGETATION TYPES: AA, Ab, Da, Db • COMMENTS: Extremely high importance for plants. Very high importance for mammals and aquatic biota.

BIOLOGICAL IMPORTANCE: *Birds:* D • *Aquatic biota:* B • *Plants:* A • *Mammals:* B • STABILITY LEVEL: 6 • INSTABILITY LEVEL: 9 • ACTION PRIORITY LEVEL: 6 • MAIN ACTION RECOMMENDED: Identify priority actions • OTHER RECOMMENDED ACTION: Preparation of biological inventories.

JU 033 - Middle Acre River - PRIORITY LEVEL: B • LOCATION: *State:* Acre • *Main municipality:* Rio Branco • *Municipalities covered:* 10 • VEGETATION TYPES: AA, Ab, Da, Db • COMMENTS: Extremely high importance for plants. Very high importance for mammals and aquatic biota. Lack of knowledge about birds.

BIOLOGICAL IMPORTANCE: *Birds:* D • *Aquatic biota:* B • *Plants:* A • *Mammals:* B • STABILITY LEVEL: 0 • INSTABILITY LEVEL: 9 • ACTION PRIORITY LEVEL: 9 • MAIN ACTION RECOMMENDED: Identify priority actions.

JU 034 - Lower Acre River - PRIORITY LEVEL: C • LOCATION: *State:* Amazonas/Acre • *Main municipality:* Boca do Acre • *Municipalities covered:* 5 • VEGETATION TYPES: AA, Ab, Da, Db • COMMENTS: High importance for reptiles and amphibians. Very high importance for aquatic biota.

BIOLOGICAL IMPORTANCE: *Birds:* D • *Aquatic biota:* B • *Reptiles and amphibians:* C • IMPORTANCE FOR ECOLOGICAL GOODS AND SERVICES: C • STABILITY LEVEL: 0 • INSTABILITY LEVEL: 9 • ACTION PRIORITY LEVEL: 9 • MAIN ACTION RECOMMENDED: Identify priority actions.

JU 035 - Boca do Acre Indigenous Land - PRIORITY LEVEL: C • LOCATION: *State:* Amazonas • *Main municipality:* Lábrea • *Municipalities covered:* 2 • VEGETATION TYPES: AA, Ab, Da, Db • COMMENTS: Very high importance for aquatic biota, reptiles and amphibians. Lack of knowledge about birds.

BIOLOGICAL IMPORTANCE: *Birds:* D • *Aquatic biota:* B • *Reptiles and amphibians:* C • IMPORTANCE FOR ECOLOGICAL GOODS AND SERVICES: C • STABILITY LEVEL: 3 • INSTABILITY LEVEL: 4 • ACTION PRIORITY LEVEL: 4 • MAIN ACTION RECOMMENDED: Protection.

JU 036 - Apurinã Indigenous Land - PRIORITY LEVEL: C • LOCATION: *State:* Amazonas • *Main municipality:* Lábrea • *Municipalities covered:* 2 • VEGETATION TYPES: AA, Ab, Da, Db • COMMENTS: Very high importance for aquatic biota. High importance for reptiles and amphibians.

BIOLOGICAL IMPORTANCE: *Birds:* D • *Aquatic biota:* B • *Reptiles and amphibians:* C • IMPORTANCE FOR ECOLOGICAL GOODS AND SERVICES: C • STABILITY LEVEL: 3 • INSTABILITY LEVEL: 9 • ACTION PRIORITY LEVEL: 7 • MAIN ACTION RECOMMENDED: Protection.

JU 037 - Eastern bank of the Acre River - PRIORITY LEVEL: C • LOCATION: *State:* Amazonas • *Main municipality:* Lábrea • *Municipalities covered:* 2 • VEGETATION TYPES: AA, Ab, Da, Db, Ds • COMMENTS: Very high importance for reptiles and amphibians. Lack of knowledge about birds.

BIOLOGICAL IMPORTANCE: *Birds:* D • *Aquatic biota:* B • *Reptiles and amphibians:* C • IMPORTANCE FOR ECOLOGICAL GOODS AND SERVICES: C • STABILITY LEVEL: 0 • INSTABILITY LEVEL: 4 • ACTION PRIORITY LEVEL: 5 • MAIN ACTION RECOMMENDED: Identify priority actions.

JU 038 - Juruá/Mutum River - PRIORITY LEVEL: B • LOCATION: *State:* Amazonas • *Main municipality:* Itamarati • *Municipalities covered:* 3 • VEGETATION TYPES: Ab, Da, Db • COMMENTS: Very high importance for plants and aquatic biota. Lack of knowledge about birds.

BIOLOGICAL IMPORTANCE: *Birds:* D • *Aquatic biota:* B • *Plants:* B • STABILITY LEVEL: 0 • INSTABILITY LEVEL: 0 • ACTION PRIORITY LEVEL: 3 • MAIN ACTION RECOMMENDED: Identify priority actions.

JU 039 - Deni Indigenous Land - PRIORITY LEVEL: B • LOCATION: *State:* Amazonas • *Main municipality:* Itamarati • *Municipalities covered:* 4 • VEGETATION TYPES: Ab, Da, Db • COMMENTS: Extremely high importance for mammals. Very high importance for plants. Lack of knowledge about birds.

BIOLOGICAL IMPORTANCE: *Birds:* D • *Aquatic biota:* B • *Plants:* B • *Mammals:* A • STABILITY LEVEL: 1 • INSTABILITY LEVEL: 0 • ACTION PRIORITY LEVEL: 3 • MAIN ACTION RECOMMENDED: Protection.

JU 040 - Tapauá River - PRIORITY LEVEL: B • LOCATION: *State:* Amazonas • *Main municipality:* Tapauá • *Municipalities covered:* 2 • VEGETATION TYPES: Ab, Da, Db • COMMENTS: Very high importance for plants. Lack of knowledge about birds.

BIOLOGICAL IMPORTANCE: *Birds:* D • *Plants:* B • *Mammals:* B • STABILITY LEVEL: 0 • INSTABILITY LEVEL: 0 • ACTION PRIORITY LEVEL: 3 • MAIN ACTION RECOMMENDED: Protection.

JU 041 - Middle Juruá - PRIORITY LEVEL: B • LOCATION: *State:* Amazonas • *Main municipality:* Carauari • *Municipalities covered:* 3 • VEGETATION TYPES: Ab, Da, Db • COMMENTS: Very high importance for plants, mammals and aquatic biota. Lack of knowledge about birds and invertebrates.

BIOLOGICAL IMPORTANCE: *Birds:* D • *Aquatic biota:* B • *Plants:* B • *Invertebrates:* D • *Mammals:* B • *Reptiles and amphibians:* A • STABILITY LEVEL: 0 • INSTABILITY LEVEL: 0 • ACTION PRIORITY LEVEL: 3 • MAIN ACTION RECOMMENDED: Identify priority actions.

JU 042 - Médio Juruá Extractive Reserve - PRIORITY LEVEL: B • LOCATION: *State:* Amazonas • *Main municipality:* Carauari • *Municipalities covered:* 1 • VEGETATION TYPES: Ab, Da, Db • COMMENTS: Region with no knowledge about plants, invertebrates and birds; classified as of high importance for mammals and aquatic biota.

BIOLOGICAL IMPORTANCE: *Birds:* D • *Aquatic biota:* B • *Plants:* D • *Invertebrates:* D • *Mammals:* B • *Reptiles and amphibians:* A • STABILITY LEVEL: 6 • INSTABILITY LEVEL: 0 • ACTION PRIORITY LEVEL: 2 • MAIN ACTION RECOMMENDED: Sustainable use of natural resources.

JU 043 - Lower Juruá River - PRIORITY LEVEL: A • LOCATION: *State:* Amazonas • *Main municipality:* Carauari • *Municipalities covered:* 5 • VEGETATION TYPES: Ab, Da, Db • COMMENTS: Extremely high importance for reptiles and amphibians. Very high importance for mammals and aquatic biota. Lack of knowledge about plants and invertebrates.

BIOLOGICAL IMPORTANCE: *Birds:* A • *Aquatic biota:* B • *Plants:* D • *Invertebrates:* D • *Mammals:* B • *Reptiles and amphibians:* A • STABILITY LEVEL: 0 • INSTABILITY LEVEL: 3 • ACTION PRIORITY LEVEL: 5 • MAIN ACTION RECOMMENDED: Identify priority actions.

JU 044 - Juruá Indigenous Land - PRIORITY LEVEL: A • LOCATION: *State:* Amazonas • *Main municipality:* Juruá • *Municipalities covered:* 2 • VEGETATION TYPES: Da • COMMENTS: Very high importance for mammals and aquatic biota.

BIOLOGICAL IMPORTANCE: *Birds:* A • *Aquatic biota:* B • *Plants:* D • *Invertebrates:* D • *Mammals:* B • *Reptiles and amphibians:* A • STABILITY LEVEL: 1 • INSTABILITY LEVEL: 0 • ACTION PRIORITY LEVEL: 3 • MAIN ACTION RECOMMENDED: Protection.

JU 045 - Solimões (Tefé-Coari) - PRIORITY LEVEL: A • LOCATION: *State:* Amazonas • *Main municipality:* Coari • *Municipalities covered:* 5 • VEGETATION TYPES: Da, Db • COMMENTS: Very high importance for birds and mammals. Region classified as priority for the establishment of new conservation area.

BIOLOGICAL IMPORTANCE: *Birds:* A • *Plants:* A • *Invertebrates:* D • *Mammals:* B • *Reptiles and amphibians:* A • IMPORTANCE FOR ECOLOGICAL GOODS AND SERVICES: B • STABILITY LEVEL: 0 • INSTABILITY LEVEL: 6 • ACTION PRIORITY LEVEL: 7 • MAIN ACTION RECOMMENDED: Sustainable use of natural resources.

JU 046 - Tefé National Forest - PRIORITY LEVEL: A • LOCATION: *State:* Amazonas • *Main municipality:* Tefé • *Municipalities covered:* 4 • VEGETATION TYPES: Da, Db • COMMENTS: Extremely high importance for birds, high importance for mammals.

BIOLOGICAL IMPORTANCE: *Birds:* A • *Invertebrates:* D • *Mammals:* B • *Reptiles and amphibians:* A • IMPORTANCE FOR ECOLOGICAL GOODS AND SERVICES: B • STABILITY LEVEL: 6 • INSTABILITY LEVEL: 6 • ACTION PRIORITY LEVEL: 5 • MAIN ACTION RECOMMENDED: Sustainable use of natural resources.

JU 047 - Coari River - PRIORITY LEVEL: A • LOCATION: *State:* Amazonas • *Main municipality:* Coari • *Municipalities covered:* 1 • VEGETATION TYPES: Ab, Da, Db • COMMENTS: Extremely high importance for reptiles and amphibians. Very high importance for birds and mammals. Lack of knowledge about invertebrates; area included in a region recommended for conservation area.

BIOLOGICAL IMPORTANCE: *Birds:* B • *Plants:* A • *Invertebrates:* D • *Mammals:* B • *Reptiles and amphibians:* A • IMPORTANCE FOR ECOLOGICAL GOODS AND SERVICES: B • STABILITY LEVEL: 0 • INSTABILITY LEVEL: 6 • ACTION PRIORITY LEVEL: 7 • MAIN ACTION RECOMMENDED: Identify priority action.

JU 048 - Cuniuá River - PRIORITY LEVEL: A • LOCATION: *State:* Amazonas • *Main municipality:* Tapauá • *Municipalities covered:* 1 • VEGETATION TYPES: Ab, Da, Db • COMMENTS: Extremely high importance for reptiles and amphibians. Very high importance for plants and aquatic biota.

BIOLOGICAL IMPORTANCE: *Birds:* A • *Aquatic biota:* B • *Plants:* B • *Reptiles and amphibians:* A • STABILITY LEVEL: 0 • INSTABILITY LEVEL: 0 • ACTION PRIORITY LEVEL: 3 • MAIN ACTION RECOMMENDED: Identify priority actions.

JU 049 - Hi-Merimã Indigenous Land - PRIORITY LEVEL: A • LOCATION: *State:* Amazonas • *Main municipality:* Tapauá • *Municipalities covered:* 2 • VEGETATION TYPES: Da, Db, Pa • COMMENTS: Extremely high importance for reptiles and amphibians. Very high importance for plants.

BIOLOGICAL IMPORTANCE: *Birds:* A • *Aquatic biota:* B • *Plants:* B • *Reptiles and amphibians:* A • STABILITY LEVEL: 1 • INSTABILITY LEVEL: 0 • ACTION PRIORITY LEVEL: 3 • MAIN ACTION RECOMMENDED: Protection.

JU 050 - Boundary with Rondônia - PRIORITY LEVEL: A • LOCATION: *State:* Amazonas/Rondônia • *Main municipality:* Canutama • *Municipalities covered:* 4 • VEGETATION TYPES: AA, Ab, As, Da, Db, Pa, Sa, Sg, SO, Sp • COMMENTS: Extremely high importance for reptiles, amphibians and mammals. Lack of knowledge about birds. High levels of threat and anthropogenic pressure.

BIOLOGICAL IMPORTANCE: *Birds:* A • *Aquatic biota:* B • *Plants:* A • *Mammals:* A • *Reptiles and amphibians:* A • STABILITY LEVEL: 0 • INSTABILITY LEVEL: 7 • ACTION PRIORITY LEVEL: 8 • MAIN ACTION RECOMMENDED: Identify priority actions.

JU 051 - Juma Indigenous Land - PRIORITY LEVEL: A • LOCATION: *State:* Amazonas • *Main municipality:* Canutama • *Municipalities covered:* 1 • VEGETATION TYPES: Ab, Da, SO • COMMENTS: Extremely high importance for birds. Very high importance for mammals; anthropogenic impacts nearby.

BIOLOGICAL IMPORTANCE: *Birds:* A • *Mammals:* A • *Reptiles and amphibians:* A • STABILITY LEVEL: 1 • INSTABILITY LEVEL: 3 • ACTION PRIORITY LEVEL: 4 • MAIN ACTION RECOMMENDED: Protection.

JU 052 - Caetitu Indigenous Land - PRIORITY LEVEL: A • LOCATION: *State:* Amazonas • *Main municipality:* Lábrea • *Municipalities covered:* 1 • VEGETATION TYPES: Ab, Da, Sa, SO, Sp • COMMENTS: Extremely high importance for birds, reptiles and amphibians. Very high importance for aquatic flora.

BIOLOGICAL IMPORTANCE: *Birds:* A • *Aquatic biota:* B • *Plants:* A • *Mammals:* A • *Reptiles and amphibians:* A • STABILITY LEVEL: 5 • INSTABILITY LEVEL: 0 • ACTION PRIORITY LEVEL: 2 • MAIN ACTION RECOMMENDED: Protection.

JU 053 - Paumari do Lago Marahã Indigenous Land - PRIORITY LEVEL: A • LOCATION: *State:* Amazonas • *Main municipality:* Lábrea • *Municipalities covered:* 1 • VEGETATION TYPES: Da, Pa • COMMENTS: Extremely high importance for birds, amphibians and reptiles. Very high importance for aquatic flora. Large flooded area.

BIOLOGICAL IMPORTANCE: *Birds:* A • *Aquatic biota:* B • *Mammals:* A • *Reptiles and amphibians:* A • STABILITY LEVEL: 0 • INSTABILITY LEVEL: 0 • ACTION PRIORITY LEVEL: 3 • MAIN ACTION RECOMMENDED: Protection.

JU 054 - Jarawara/Jamamadi/Kanamanti Indigenous Land - PRIORITY LEVEL: A • LOCATION: *State:* Amazonas • *Main municipality:* Tapauá • *Municipalities covered:* 2 • VEGETATION TYPES: Da, Db • COMMENTS: Extremely high importance for reptiles, amphibians and birds. Very high importance for aquatic biota.

BIOLOGICAL IMPORTANCE: *Birds:* A • *Aquatic biota:* B • *Plants:* B • *Reptiles and amphibians:* A • STABILITY LEVEL: 5 • INSTABILITY LEVEL: 0 • ACTION PRIORITY LEVEL: 2 • MAIN ACTION RECOMMENDED: Protection.

JU 055 - Lower Purus - PRIORITY LEVEL: B • LOCATION: *State:* Amazonas • *Main municipality:* Tapauá • *Municipalities covered:* 4 • VEGETATION TYPES: Ab, Da, Db, Ds, SO • COMMENTS: Very high importance for plants, reptiles, mammals and aquatic biota. Region classified as priority for the establishment of new conservation area.

BIOLOGICAL IMPORTANCE: *Birds:* D • *Aquatic biota:* B • *Plants:* A • *Mammals:* B • *Reptiles and amphibians:* B • IMPORTANCE FOR ECOLOGICAL GOODS AND SERVICES: B • STABILITY LEVEL: 0 • INSTABILITY LEVEL: 3 • ACTION PRIORITY LEVEL: 5 • MAIN ACTION RECOMMENDED: Identify priority actions.

JU 056 - Apurinã do Igarapé Tauamirim Indigenous Land - PRIORITY LEVEL: B • LOCATION: *State:* Amazonas • *Main municipality:* Tapauá • *Municipalities covered:* 1 • VEGETATION TYPES: Ab, Da, Db • COMMENTS: Very high importance for amphibians, reptiles, mammals and aquatic biota. Lack of knowledge about birds.

BIOLOGICAL IMPORTANCE: *Birds:* D • *Aquatic biota:* B • *Mammals:* B • *Reptiles and amphibians:* B • IMPORTANCE FOR ECOLOGICAL GOODS AND SERVICES: B • STABILITY LEVEL: 5 • INSTABILITY LEVEL: 0 • ACTION PRIORITY LEVEL: 2 • MAIN ACTION RECOMMENDED: Protection.

JU 057 - Abufari Biological Reserve - PRIORITY LEVEL: B • LOCATION: *State:* Amazonas • *Main municipality:* Tapauá • *Municipalities covered:* 1 • VEGETATION TYPES: Ab, Da • COMMENTS: Very high importance for reptiles and amphibians, mammals and aquatic biota. Lack of knowledge about birds.

BIOLOGICAL IMPORTANCE: *Birds:* D • *Aquatic biota:* B • *Plants:* A • *Mammals:* B • *Reptiles and amphibians:* B • IMPORTANCE FOR ECOLOGICAL GOODS AND SERVICES: B • STABILITY LEVEL: 12 • INSTABILITY LEVEL: 0 • ACTION PRIORITY LEVEL: 2 • MAIN ACTION RECOMMENDED: Protection.

JU 058 - Cuniuá River - PRIORITY LEVEL: B • LOCATION: *State:* Amazonas • *Main municipality:* Tapauá • *Municipalities covered:* 1 • VEGETATION TYPES: Da, Db • COMMENTS: Very high importance for plants and mammals.
    BIOLOGICAL IMPORTANCE: *Birds:* D • *Aquatic biota:* B • *Plants:* B • *Mammals:* B • STABILITY LEVEL: 5 • INSTABILITY LEVEL: 3 • ACTION PRIORITY LEVEL: 3 • MAIN ACTION RECOMMENDED: Protection.

JU 059 - Riozinho do Humaitá - PRIORITY LEVEL: N • LOCATION: *State:* Acre • *Main municipality:* Tarauacá • *Municipalities covered:* 6 • VEGETATION TYPES: Ab, Da, Db • COMMENTS: Forest almost untouched, ensuring the contiguity of the conservation areas network at differing levels of protection. The area has high habitat diversity and a fauna typical of Acre. Buffer zone against anthropogenic activities in adjacent areas.
    BIOLOGICAL IMPORTANCE: *Mammals:* A • STABILITY LEVEL: 0 • INSTABILITY LEVEL: 6 • ACTION PRIORITY LEVEL: 7 • MAIN ACTION RECOMMENDED: Creation of conservation area • OTHER RECOMMENDED ACTION: Creation of sustainable use conservation area.

JU 060 - Upper Turauacá - PRIORITY LEVEL: N • LOCATION: *State:* Acre • *Main municipality:* Jordão • *Municipalities covered:* 5 • VEGETATION TYPES: Ab, Da, Db • COMMENTS: Consolidation of the east-west chain of conservation areas in Acre. Conservation of endemic especies (e.g. *Callimico goeldi*) and sub-Andean species occurring in the extreme west of Amazonia.
    BIOLOGICAL IMPORTANCE: *Mammals:* A • STABILITY LEVEL: 0 • INSTABILITY LEVEL: 0 • ACTION PRIORITY LEVEL: 3 • MAIN ACTION RECOMMENDED: Sustainable use of natural resources • OTHER RECOMMENDED ACTION: Preparation of biological inventories.

JU 061 - Rio Tefé Basin - PRIORITY LEVEL: N • LOCATION: *State:* Amazonas • *Main municipality:* Tefé • *Municipalities covered:* 4 • VEGETATION TYPES: Ab, Da, Db • COMMENTS: Conservation of the fauna in the Tefé headwaters. Strategic management of the catchment area feeding the Tefé river and the city of Tefé. Consolidation of the conservation area network of the Tefé/Juruá interfluve. Adjacent to the national security area created by Petrobrás.
    BIOLOGICAL IMPORTANCE: *Reptiles and amphibians:* A • STABILITY LEVEL: 0 • INSTABILITY LEVEL: 6 • ACTION PRIORITY LEVEL: 7 • MAIN ACTION RECOMMENDED: Identify priority actions.

JU 062 - Riozinho da Liberdade - PRIORITY LEVEL: N • LOCATION: *State:* Acre/Amazonas • *Main municipality:* Tarauacá • *Municipalities covered:* 2 • VEGETATION TYPES: Ab, Da • COMMENTS: Area of maximum biological importance, claimed by extractive populations, dampening the impacts of the BR-364 highway.
    BIOLOGICAL IMPORTANCE: *Mammals:* A • STABILITY LEVEL: 0 • INSTABILITY LEVEL: 4 • ACTION PRIORITY LEVEL: 5 • MAIN ACTION RECOMMENDED: Creation of conservation area • OTHER RECOMMENDED ACTION: Creation of sustainable use conservation area in a region suffering the impacts of the BR-364 highway.

JU 063 - Muru River (area added during the review phase) - PRIORITY LEVEL: A • LOCATION: *State:* Acre • *Main municipality:* Tarauacá • *Municipalities covered:* 1 • VEGETATION TYPES: Ab, Da, Db • COMMENTS: Sought by the communities of the extractive reserve. Extremely high biological importance.
    BIOLOGICAL IMPORTANCE: *Birds:* D • *Aquatic biota:* B • *Plants:* A • *Mammals:* A • STABILITY LEVEL: 0 • INSTABILITY LEVEL: 7 • ACTION PRIORITY LEVEL: 8 • MAIN ACTION RECOMMENDED: Creation of conservation area • OTHER RECOMMENDED ACTION: Creation of sustainable use conservation area.

JU 064 - Liberdade River - PRIORITY LEVEL: N • LOCATION: *State:* Acre/Amazonas • *Main municipality:* Envira • *Municipalities covered:* 2 • VEGETATION TYPES: AA, Ab, Da, Db • COMMENTS: Area sought by the communities of the extractive reserve and by the Grito da Terra group. Area of high biological importance.
    BIOLOGICAL IMPORTANCE: *Mammals:* A • STABILITY LEVEL: 0 • INSTABILITY LEVEL: 7 • ACTION PRIORITY LEVEL: 8 • MAIN ACTION RECOMMENDED: Creation of conservation area • OTHER RECOMMENDED ACTION: Creation of sustainable use conservation area.

JU 065 - Middle Envira - PRIORITY LEVEL: N • LOCATION: *State:* Acre/Amazonas • *Main municipality:* Feijó • *Municipalities covered:* 3 • VEGETATION TYPES: Ab, Da • COMMENTS: Sought by the communities of the extractive reserve and of high biological importance.
    BIOLOGICAL IMPORTANCE: *Birds:* D • *Mammals:* A • *Reptiles and amphibians:* B • STABILITY LEVEL: 0 • INSTABILITY LEVEL: 7 • ACTION PRIORITY LEVEL: 8 • MAIN ACTION RECOMMENDED: Creation of conservation area • OTHER RECOMMENDED ACTION: Creation of sustainable use conservation area and preparation of biological inventories.

JU 066 - Rio Branco/Antimari - PRIORITY LEVEL: N • LOCATION: *State:* Acre • *Main municipality:* Bujari • *Municipalities covered:* 2 • VEGETATION TYPES: AA, Ab, Da • COMMENTS: High biological importance; sought as an extractive reserve.
    BIOLOGICAL IMPORTANCE: *Aquatic biota:* B • STABILITY LEVEL: 0 • INSTABILITY LEVEL: 9 • ACTION PRIORITY LEVEL: 9 • MAIN ACTION RECOMMENDED: Creation of conservation area • OTHER RECOMMENDED ACTION: Creation of sustainable use conservation area.

JU 067 - Xapuri - PRIORITY LEVEL: B • LOCATION: *State:* Acre • *Main municipality:* Epitaciolândia • *Municipalities covered:* 3 • VEGETATION TYPES: AA, Ab, Da, Db • COMMENTS: Area sought by the extractive communities. Area of very high biological importance.
    BIOLOGICAL IMPORTANCE: *Birds:* D • *Aquatic biota:* B • *Plants:* A • *Mammals:* B • STABILITY LEVEL: 0 • INSTABILITY LEVEL: 9 • ACTION PRIORITY LEVEL: 9 • MAIN ACTION RECOMMENDED: Creation of conservation area • OTHER RECOMMENDED ACTION: Creation of sustainable use conservation area.

JU 068 - Rio Acre/Xapuri - PRIORITY LEVEL: B • LOCATION: *State:* Acre • *Main municipality:* Brasiléia • *Municipalities covered:* 2 • VEGETATION TYPES: AA, Db • COMMENTS: High biological importance.
    BIOLOGICAL IMPORTANCE: *Birds:* D • *Aquatic biota:* B • *Plants:* A • *Mammals:* B • STABILITY LEVEL: 0 • INSTABILITY LEVEL: 9 • ACTION PRIORITY LEVEL: 9 • MAIN ACTION RECOMMENDED: Creation of conservation area • OTHER RECOMMENDED ACTION: Creation of sustainable use conservation area.

Priority areas for conservation, sustainable use and benefit sharing by thematic working group

Birds
Aquatic biota
Mammals
Invertebrates
Maps on pages 444-445

Plants
Reptiles and amphibians
Conservation areas
Environmental goods and services
Maps on pages 446-447

Economic opportunities
Traditional populations and indigenous peoples
Anthropogenic pressures
Development corridors
Maps on pages 448-449

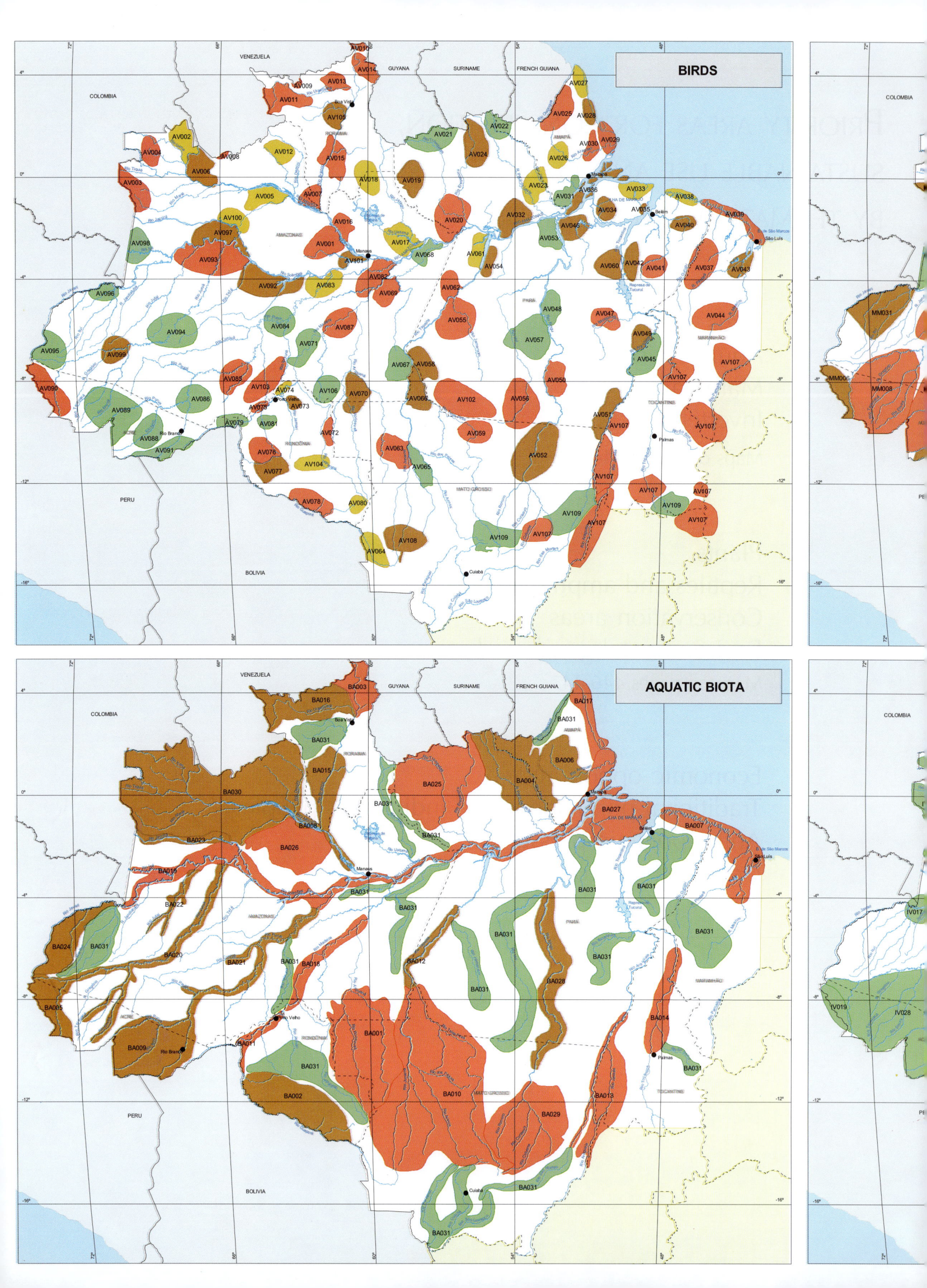

BIRDS

AQUATIC BIOTA

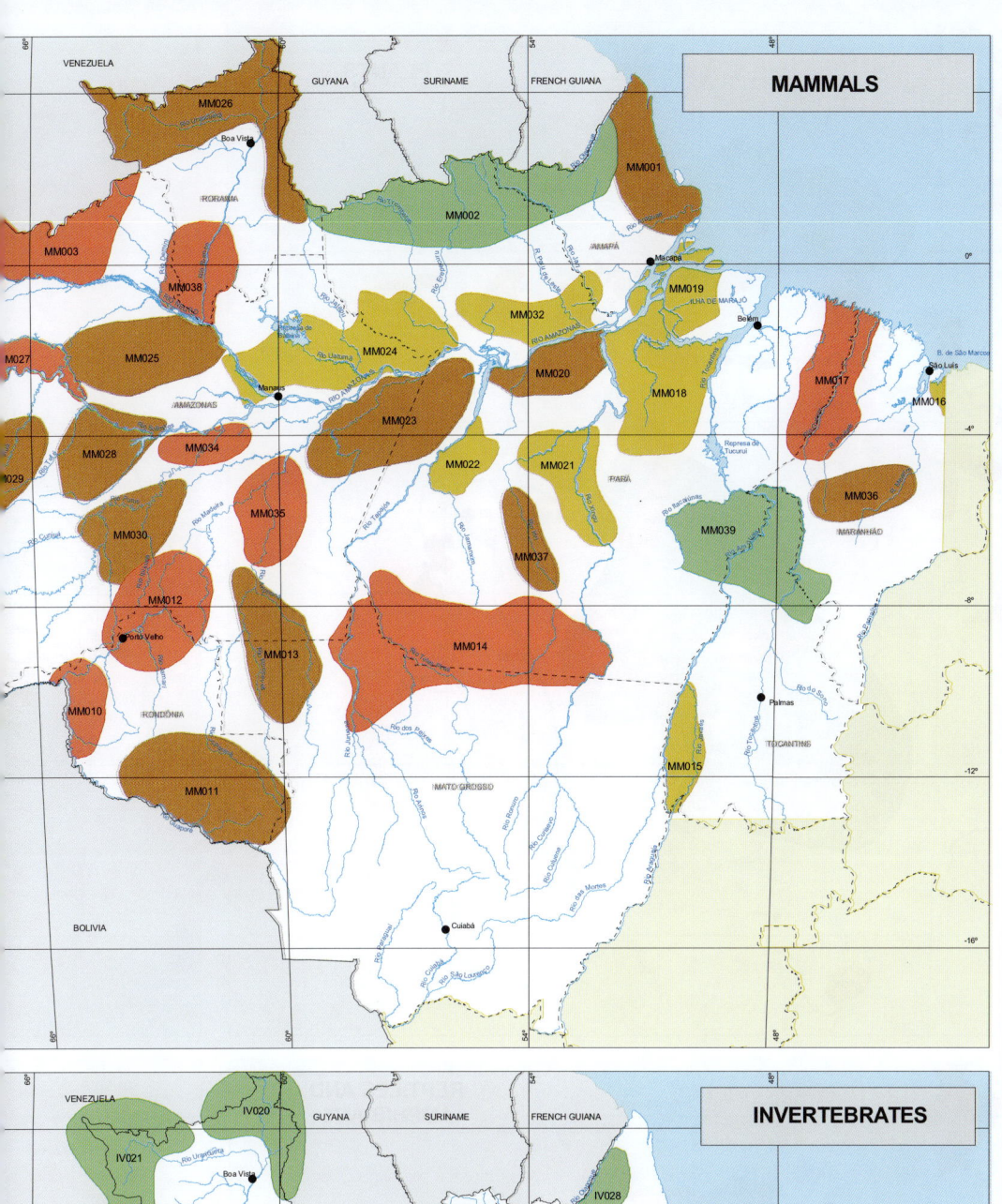

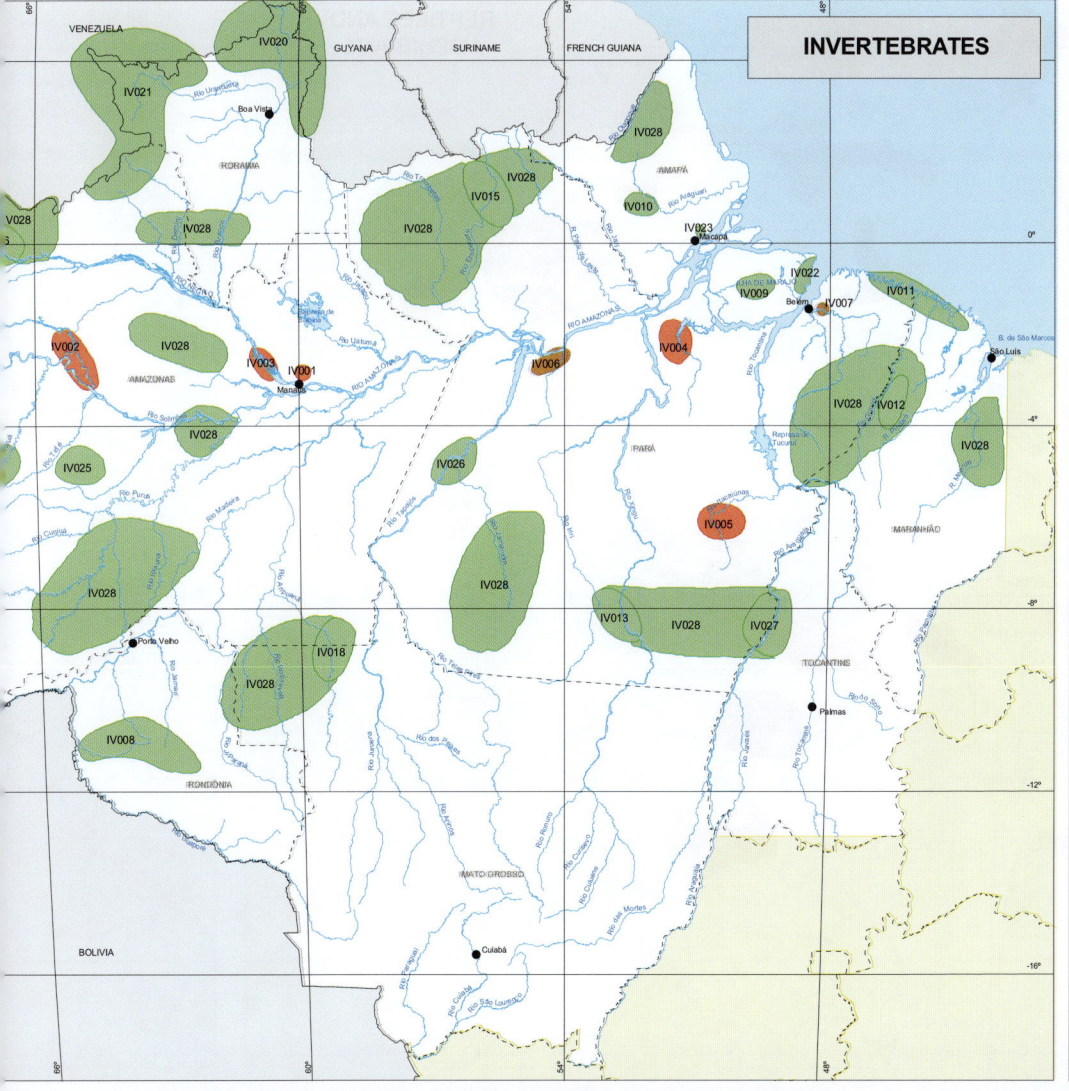

BRAZILIAN LEGAL AMAZON
RESULTS OF THE MACAPÁ WORKSHOP, 1999

PRIORITY AREAS FOR BIODIVERSITY
Thematic Groups

MAMMALS

INVERTEBRATES

Level of priority
- Area of extreme importance
- Area of very high importance
- Area of high importance
- Area insufficiently known, but probably important

- International boundary
- State boundary
- Brazilian Legal Amazon
- State capital
- Main rivers

Scale 1:18,450,000
200 0 200 400 Km

Sinusoidal Projection
Central Meridian 54° WGr.
Base map:
Maps of Brazil to the scale 1:1,000,000

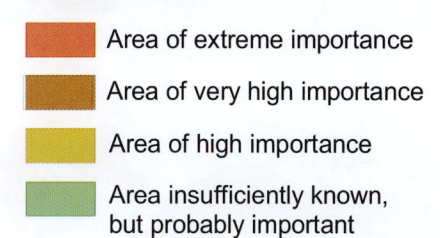

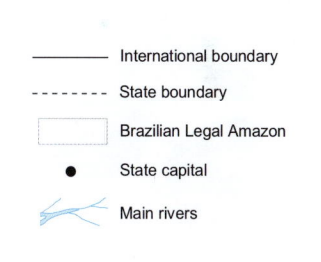

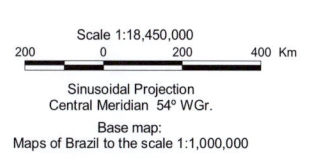

Map created by the
Geoprocessing Laboratory of the Instituto Socioambiental

Assessment and Identification of Priority Actions for the Conservation, Sustainable Use and Benefit Sharing of the Biodiversity of the Brazilian Amazon

Macapá Workshop 1999

PRONABIO
Programa Nacional da Diversidade Biológica (National Program for Biological Diversity)
Ministério do Meio Ambiente (Ministry of the Environment)

Coordinating consortium:
Instituto Socioambiental (Overall coordination)
Imazon - Instituto do Homem e Meio Ambiente da Amazônia
Ipam - Instituto de Pesquisa Ambiental da Amazônia
GTA - Grupo de Trabalho Amazônico
Conservation International
ISPN - Instituto Sociedade, População e Natureza

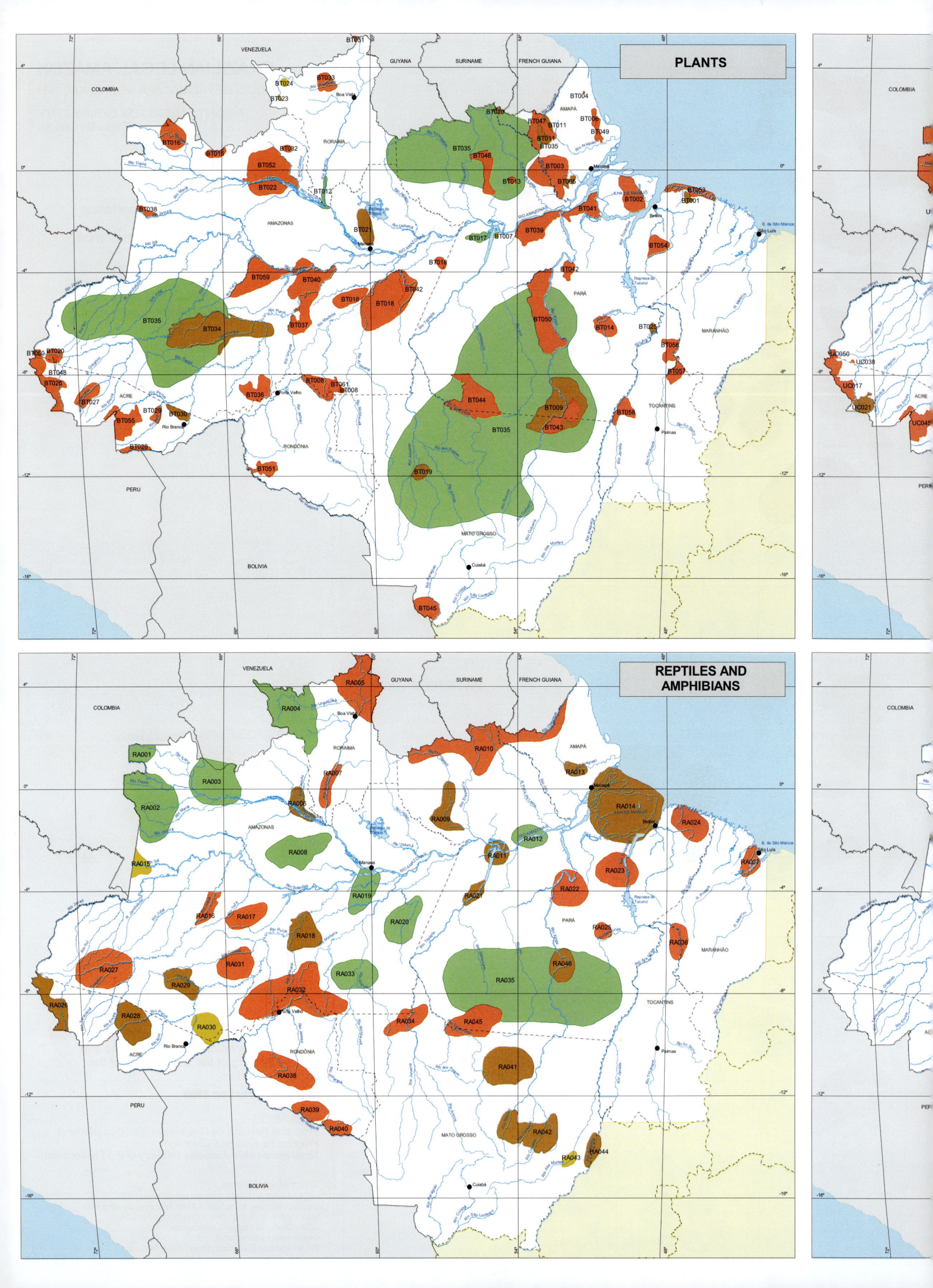

PLANTS

REPTILES AND AMPHIBIANS

BRAZILIAN LEGAL AMAZON
RESULTS OF THE MACAPÁ WORKSHOP, 1999
PRIORITY AREAS FOR BIODIVERSITY
Thematic Groups

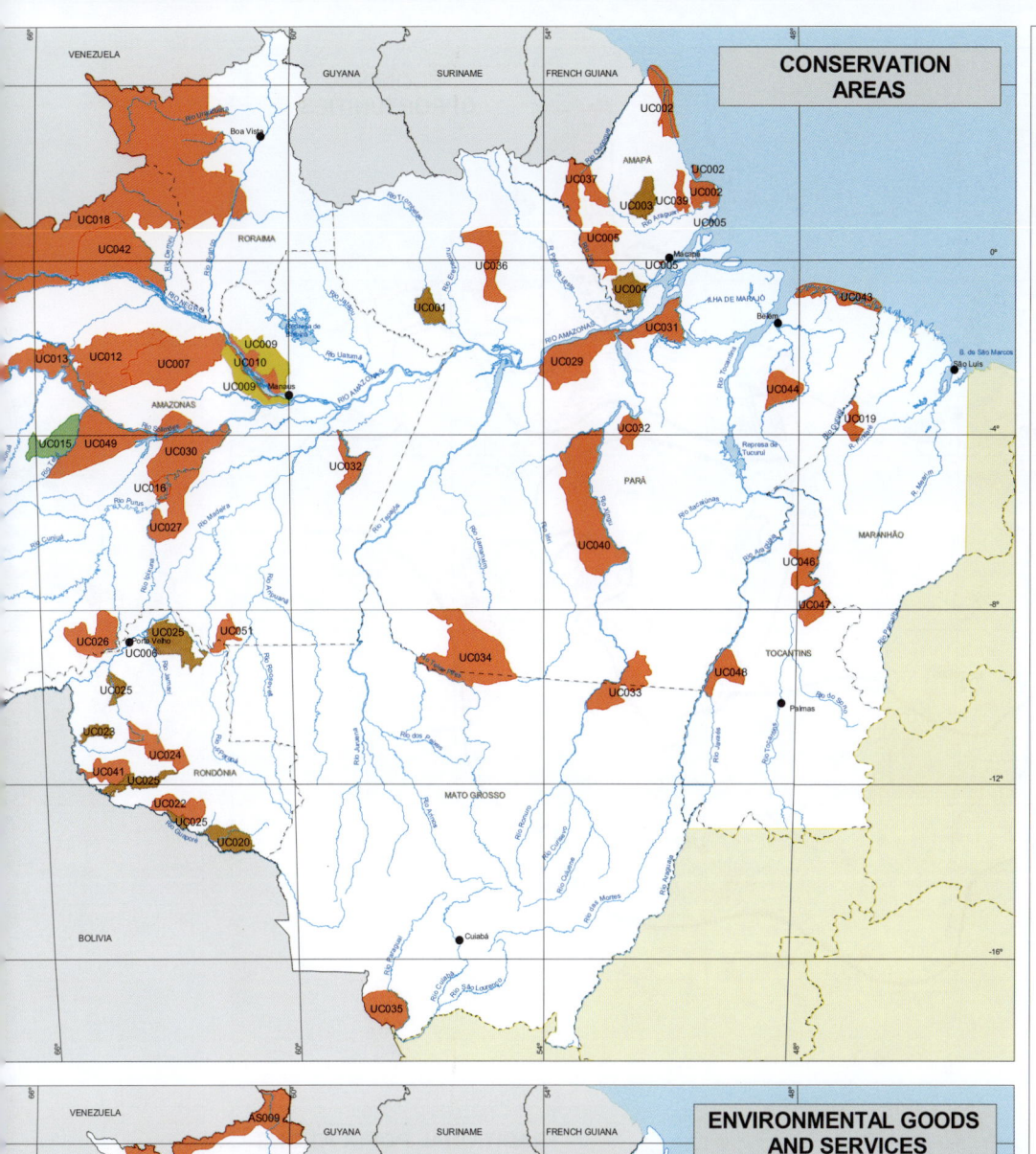

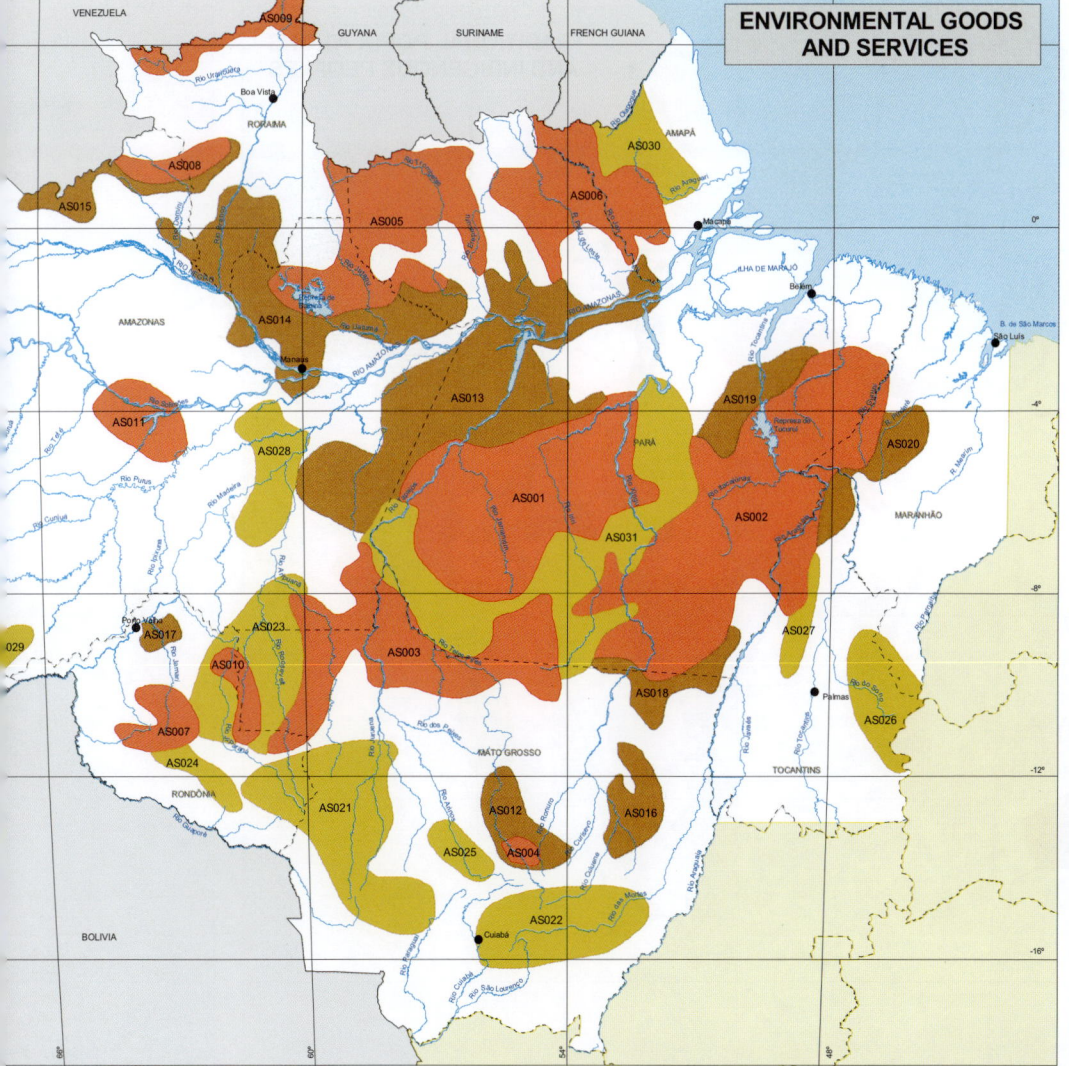

Level of priority
- Area of extreme importance
- Area of very high importance
- Area of high importance
- Area insufficiently known, but probably important

CONSERVATION AREAS

ENVIRONMENTAL GOODS AND SERVICES

- International boundary
- State boundary
- Brazilian Legal Amazon
- State capital
- Main rivers

Scale 1:18,450,000
200   0   200   400 Km
Sinusoidal Projection
Central Meridian 54° WGr.
Base map:
Maps of Brazil to the scale 1:1,000,000

Map created by the
Geoprocessing Laboratory of the Instituto Socioambiental

Assessment and Identification of Priority Actions for the Conservation, Sustainable Use and Benefit Sharing of the Biodiversity of the Brazilian Amazon

Macapá Workshop 1999

PRONABIO
Programa Nacional da Diversidade Biológica (National Program for Biological Diversity)
Ministério do Meio Ambiente (Ministry of the Environment)

Coordinating consortium:
Instituto Socioambiental (Overall coordination)
Imazon - Instituto do Homem e Meio Ambiente da Amazônia
Ipam - Instituto de Pesquisa Ambiental da Amazônia
GTA - Grupo de Trabalho Amazônico
Conservation International
ISPN - Instituto Sociedade, População e Natureza

ECONOMIC OPPORTUNITIES

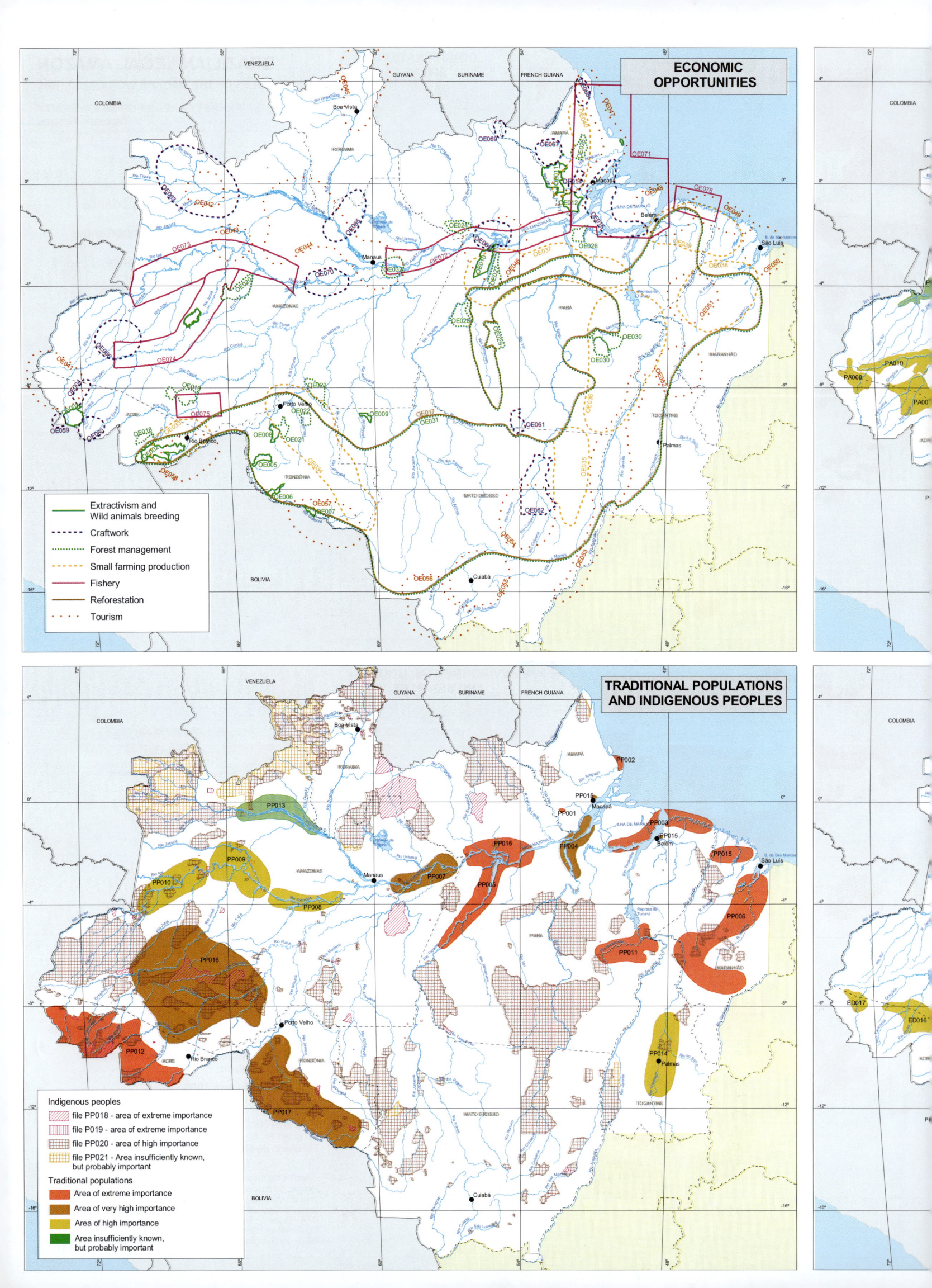

Legend:
- Extractivism and Wild animals breeding
- Craftwork
- Forest management
- Small farming production
- Fishery
- Reforestation
- Tourism

TRADITIONAL POPULATIONS AND INDIGENOUS PEOPLES

Indigenous peoples:
- file PP018 - area of extreme importance
- file P019 - area of extreme importance
- file PP020 - area of high importance
- file PP021 - Area insufficiently known, but probably important

Traditional populations:
- Area of extreme importance
- Area of very high importance
- Area of high importance
- Area insufficiently known, but probably important

ANTHROPOGENIC PRESSURES

Legend:
- Area of extreme importance
- Area of very high importance
- Area of high importance
- Area insufficiently known, but probably important

DEVELOPMENT CORRIDORS

Legend:
- Area of extreme importance
- Area of very high importance
- Area of high importance

BRAZILIAN LEGAL AMAZON
RESULTS OF THE MACAPÁ WORKSHOP, 1999
PRIORITY AREAS FOR BIODIVERSITY
Thematic Groups

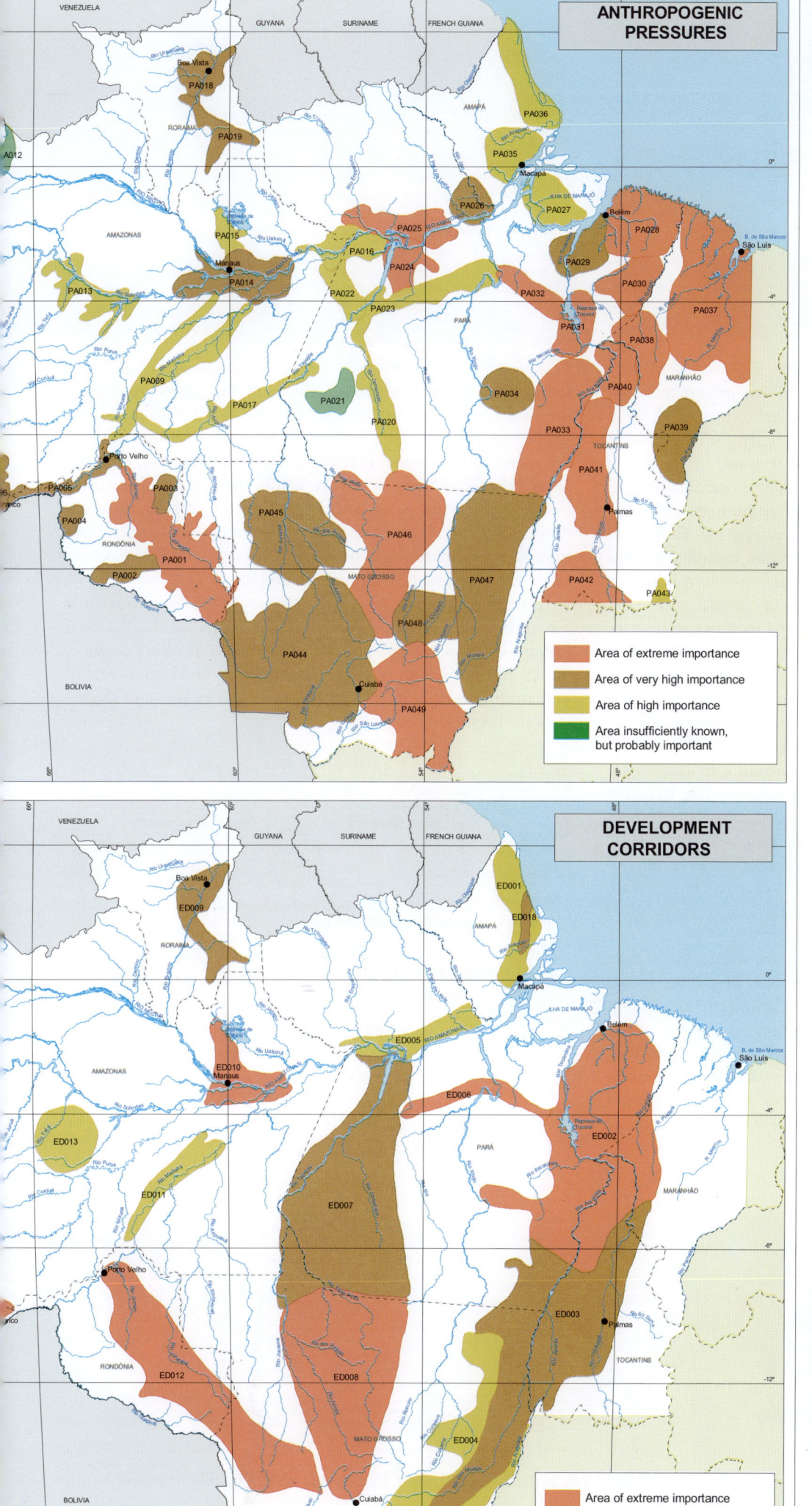

Legend:
- International boundary
- State boundary
- Brazilian Legal Amazon
- State capital
- Main rivers

Scale 1:18,450,000
200 0 200 400 Km

Sinusoidal Projection
Central Meridian 54° WGr.
Base map:
Maps of Brazil to the scale 1:1,000,000

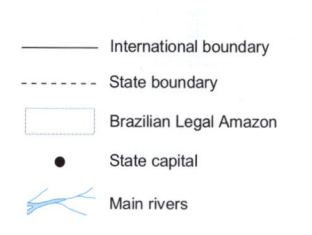

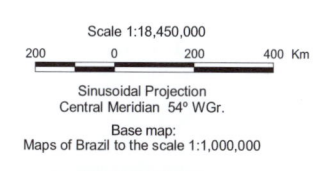

Map created by the
Geoprocessing Laboratory of the Instituto Socioambiental

Assessment and Identification of Priority Actions for the Conservation, Sustainable Use and Benefit Sharing of the Biodiversity of the Brazilian Amazon

Macapá Workshop 1999

PRONABIO
Programa Nacional da Diversidade Biológica (National Program for Biological Diversity)
Ministério do Meio Ambiente (Ministry of the Environment)

Coordinating consortium:
Instituto Socioambiental (Overall coordination)
Imazon - Instituto do Homem e Meio Ambiente da Amazônia
Ipam - Instituto de Pesquisa Ambiental da Amazônia
GTA - Grupo de Trabalho Amazônico
Conservation International
ISPN - Instituto Sociedade, População e Natureza

1
PRIORITY AREAS FOR BIRDS*

Birds constitute one of the better studied groups amongst vertebrates, with a total number of species estimated at 9,700 globally and with 1,677 represented in Brazil (Silva 1998). In Amazonia there are around a thousand species, 283 of which are of limited distribution or rare, including those occurring in just one of the three major divisions within the region (the Rio Negro to the Atlantic, the Rio Madeira or the Rio Tapajós to Maranhão, and the remaining western portion including the Rio Negro and the Madeira or Tapajós to Brazil's western borders).

Given that the region is shared between Brazil and seven other neighboring countries, only about 32 species can be considered endemic to the Brazilian Amazon. In terms of endangered species, on the basis of the official Ibama listing plus two other species that appear as 'vulnerable' on the IUCN Red List, there are 15 species threatened with extinction and 11 potentially vulnerable species in the region.

There are serious problems with attempting to assess species richness by comparing lists of localities in the Brazilian Amazon that have been inventoried, as is the case throughout the neotropical region (Remsen 1994). Research efforts vary from place to place, as do the methods used and the experiences of the teams. Coverage of areas surveyed is not standardized and distinctions need to be made between resident and migratory species.

In Amazonia there are several regions where birds have been little studied. In the state of Tocantins, only three localities have so far been inventoried, while Southern Maranhão is unknown in ornithological terms. Other regions which are totally unknown in terms of ornithological inventories include the middle and upper reaches of the rivers draining the Guiana shield, northwestern Roraima, the upper Japurá, the upper Javari, the Tarauacá, the upper Purus in Acre, tributaries on both banks of the Madeira, the Juruena, the upper reaches of the Teles Pires, the upper Iriri and the middle Xingu above Cachoeira Grande. It is important to note that the state of Tocantins and the upper reaches of the Purus, Madeira, Juruena, Teles Prires and Xingu rivers are within the Brazilian Amazon's 'Arc of Deforestation'. In addition to the lack of basic information about their fauna and flora, these areas are undergoing high rates of environmental change, and the need for efforts to carry out biological inventories is urgent.

During the Macapá Workshop, 109 priority areas in Amazonia for birds were identified (see the map on pages 444 and the listing). Of these, 39 (35.8%) are of high biological importance, 32 (29.4%) have high phylogenetic diversity and high levels of endemism, and 29 (26.6%) suffer high levels of threat of degradation (Table 1).

TABLE 1 - PRIORITY AREAS FOR BIRDS DIAGNOSTIC ELEMENTS THAT SCORE HIGHEST		
Diagnostic element	Number of areas	%[1]
Species richness	27	24.8
Phylogenetic diversity	32	29.4
Endemism	32	29.4
Richness of rare or threatened species	21	19.3
Hotspots	22	20.2
Special biological features	23	21.1
Economically important species	14	12.8
Biological importance	39	35.8
Intrinsic fragility	29	26.6
Conservation level	12	11.0
Level of threat	29	26.6

1. Of the total proposed areas (109).

---

* Text drawn in part from 'The biogeography and conservation of birds in the Amazon region' by David C. Oren, the full version of which can be found on page 97 of this book.

AV 001 - Novo Airão - PRIORITY LEVEL: A • LOCATION: *State:* Amazonas • *Main municipality:* Novo Airão • *Municipalities covered:* 4 • VEGETATION TYPES: Ab, Da, Db, Ds, La, LO • COMMENTS: Local occurrence of rare species (e.g. *Nonnula amaurocephala, Nyctibius leucopterus, Myrmeciza desjuncta*). Occurrence of species with distribution restricted to the Rio Negro basin. Occurrence of endangered species: *Harpia harpyja, Hemitriccus minimus, Nyctibius leucopterus.*

DIAGNOSTIC ELEMENTS: *Phylogenetic diversity:* 4 • *Endemism:* 5 • *Richness of rare/threatened species:* 1 • *Hotspots:* 1 • *Special biological features:* 1 • *Economically important species:* 1 • *Biological importance:* 4 • *Intrinsic fragility:* 5 • *Conservation level:* 1 • *Level of threat:* 3 • ACTION RECOMMENDED: *Biological inventory:* 2 • *Creation of conservation area:* 3 • *Management:* 5.

AV 002 - Içana - PRIORITY LEVEL: C • LOCATION: *State:* Amazonas • *Main municipality:* São Gabriel da Cachoeira • *Municipalities covered:* 1 • VEGETATION TYPES: As, Ds, Ld, LO • COMMENTS: Large areas covered by dystrophic vegetation with several strict species. Well conserved area. Problems of overlaps between types of conservation areas.

DIAGNOSTIC ELEMENTS: *Phylogenetic diversity:* 5 • *Endemism:* 4 • *Richness of rare/threatened species:* 1 • *Hotspots:* 1 • *Special biological features:* 1 • *Economically important species:* 1 • *Biological importance:* 4 • *Intrinsic fragility:* 5 • *Conservation level:* 1 • *Level of threat:* 1 • ACTION RECOMMENDED: *Biological inventory:* 3 • *Creation of conservation area:* 3 • *Management:* 5.

AV 003 - Caquetá - PRIORITY LEVEL: A • LOCATION: *State:* Amazonas • *Main municipality:* Japurá • *Municipalities covered:* 2 • VEGETATION TYPES: Ab, Ds, La, Ld, LO • COMMENTS: Area with no biological inventory. Only area encompassing the Caquetá ecological region (WWF *moist forest* category). Well conserved area. Problems of overlap with indigenous lands.

DIAGNOSTIC ELEMENTS: *Endemism:* 5 • *Richness of rare/threatened species:* 1 • *Hotspots:* 1 • *Special biological features:* 1 • *Economically important species:* 1 • *Biological importance:* 5 • *Intrinsic fragility:* 3 • *Conservation level:* 1 • *Level of threat:* 2 • ACTION RECOMMENDED: *Biological inventory:* 5.

AV 004 - Upper Rio Negro Campinarana - PRIORITY LEVEL: A • LOCATION: *State:* Amazonas • *Main municipality:* São Gabriel da Cachoeira • *Municipalities covered:* 1 • VEGETATION TYPES: Ds, Ld, LO • COMMENTS: Includes the largest campinarana area of the Upper Rio Negro, increasing its biological importance for supporting bird populations of restricted distribution. Problems of overlap with indigenous lands.

DIAGNOSTIC ELEMENTS: *Phylogenetic diversity:* 5 • *Endemism:* 4 • *Richness of rare/threatened species:* 1 • *Hotspots:* 1 • *Special biological features:* 1 • *Economically important species:* 1 • *Biological importance:* 4 • *Intrinsic fragility:* 5 • *Conservation level:* 1 • *Level of threat:* 1 • ACTION RECOMMENDED: *Biological inventory:* 3 • *Creation of conservation area:* 3 • *Management:* 5.

AV 005 - Middle Rio Negro Campinarana - PRIORITY LEVEL: C • LOCATION: *State:* Amazonas • *Main municipality:* Barcelos • *Municipalities covered:* 1 • VEGETATION TYPES: La, Ld, Lg, LO • COMMENTS: Area poorly inventoried. Includes an area of heterogenous vegetation, increasing its biological importance.

DIAGNOSTIC ELEMENTS: *Phylogenetic diversity:* 4 • *Endemism:* 5 • *Richness of rare/threatened species:* 1 • *Hotspots:* 1 • *Special biological features:* 1 • *Economically important species:* 1 • *Biological importance:* 4 • *Intrinsic fragility:* 5 • *Conservation level:* 1 • *Level of threat:* 1 • ACTION RECOMMENDED: *Biological inventory:* 4 • *Creation of conservation area:* 5 • *Management:* 4.

AV 006 - São Gabriel da Cachoeira - PRIORITY LEVEL: B • LOCATION: *State:* Amazonas • *Main municipality:* São Gabriel da Cachoeira • *Municipalities covered:* 2 • VEGETATION TYPES: Dm, Ds, La, Ld, LO • COMMENTS: Overlaps indigenous and military lands.

DIAGNOSTIC ELEMENTS: *Phylogenetic diversity:* 4 • *Endemism:* 5 • *Richness of rare/threatened species:* 1 • *Hotspots:* 2 • *Special biological features:* 1 • *Economically important species:* 1 • *Biological importance:* 5 • *Intrinsic fragility:* 5 • *Conservation level:* 2 • *Level of threat:* 2 • ACTION RECOMMENDED: *Biological inventory:* 2 • *Creation of conservation area:* 2 • *Management:* 5.

AV 007 - Negro/Branco - PRIORITY LEVEL: A • LOCATION: *State:* Amazonas/Roraima • *Main municipality:* Caracaraí • *Municipalities covered:* 3 • VEGETATION TYPES: Da, Db, La, Ld, Lg, LO • COMMENTS: Largest and most continuous of the Negro/Branco interfluve. The absence of human population in the proposed area will assist its conservation.

DIAGNOSTIC ELEMENTS: *Species richness:* 3 • *Conservation level:* 1 • *Level of threat:* 1 • ACTION RECOMMENDED: *Biological inventory:* 5 • *Management:* 4.

AV 008 - Neblina - PRIORITY LEVEL: A • LOCATION: *State:* Amazonas • *Main municipality:* Santa Isabel do Rio Negro • *Municipalities covered:* 1 • VEGETATION TYPES: Dm, Ds, rm • COMMENTS: One of the highest points in Brazil (Pico da Neblina) with a very specific bird fauna. Overlaps indigenous and military lands.

DIAGNOSTIC ELEMENTS: *Phylogenetic diversity:* 4 • *Endemism:* 5 • *Richness of rare/threatened species:* 1 • *Hotspots:* 2 • *Special biological features:* 1 • *Economically important species:* 1 • *Biological importance:* 5 • *Intrinsic fragility:* 5 • *Conservation level:* 2 • *Level of threat:* 2 • ACTION RECOMMENDED: *Biological inventory:* 2 • *Creation of conservation area:* 2 • *Management:* 5.

AV 009 - Urutani - PRIORITY LEVEL: A • LOCATION: *State:* Roraima • *Main municipality:* Amajari • *Municipalities covered:* 1 • VEGETATION TYPES: Dm, Ds • COMMENTS: The most important rim of the central *tepuis*, extending from southern Venezuela and with substantial bird endemism.

DIAGNOSTIC ELEMENTS: *Species richness:* 3 • *Phylogenetic diversity:* 5 • *Conservation level:* 1 • *Level of threat:* 1 • ACTION RECOMMENDED: *Management:* 5.

AV 010 - Mount Roraima - PRIORITY LEVEL: A • LOCATION: *State:* Roraima • *Main municipality:* Uiramutã • *Municipalities covered:* 1 • VEGETATION TYPES: Dm, Tp • COMMENTS: It is the Brazilian edge of the eastern tepuis, extending from southern Venezuela to the western part of the Guiana shield. Region with a high degree of bird endemism.

DIAGNOSTIC ELEMENTS: *Species richness:* 3 • *Endemism:* 5 • *Conservation level:* 2 • *Level of threat:* 2 • ACTION RECOMMENDED: *Management:* 5.

AV 011 - Uraricoera - PRIORITY LEVEL: A • LOCATION: *State:* Roraima • *Main municipality:* Alto Alegre • *Municipalities covered:* 2 • VEGETATION TYPES: As, Dm, Ds, ON, rm • COMMENTS: Mosaic of vegetation types. Overlaps indigenous lands.

DIAGNOSTIC ELEMENTS: *Phylogenetic diversity:* 5 • *Endemism:* 4 • *Richness of rare/threatened species:* 1 • *Hotspots:* 1 • *Special biological features:* 1 • *Economically important species:* 1 • *Biological importance:* 4 • *Intrinsic fragility:* 5 • *Conservation level:* 1 • *Level of threat:* 1 • ACTION RECOMMENDED: *Biological inventory:* 4 • *Creation of conservation area:* 2 • *Management:* 5.

AV 012 - Serra do Aracá - PRIORITY LEVEL: C • LOCATION: *State:* Amazonas • *Main municipality:* Barcelos • *Municipalities covered:* 1 • VEGETATION TYPES: As, Dm, Ds, Lg, rm • COMMENTS: Mosaic of vegetation types with potential for biological inventory. Area in good state of conservation.

DIAGNOSTIC ELEMENTS: *Phylogenetic diversity:* 3 • *Endemism:* 5 • *Richness of rare/threatened species:* 1 • *Hotspots:* 2 • *Special biological features:* 1 • *Economically important species:* 1 • *Biological importance:* 5 • *Intrinsic fragility:* 5 • *Conservation level:* 2 • *Level of threat:* 2 • ACTION RECOMMENDED: *Biological inventory:* 5 • *Creation of conservation area:* 1 • *Management:* 5.

AV 013 - Amapari - PRIORITY LEVEL: A • LOCATION: *State:* Roraima • *Main municipality:* Amajari • *Municipalities covered:* 4 • VEGETATION TYPES: Ds, Fs, ON, rm, Sg, SN, Sp, Ta, Td, Tp • COMMENTS: Eastern sector of the Roraima *lavrados*, a vegetation type with endemic birds species, such as *Poecilurus kollari*. Area recommend by Savanna and Wetlands Workshop.

DIAGNOSTIC ELEMENTS: *Species richness:* 3 • *Phylogenetic diversity:* 3 • *Endemism:* 3 • *Richness of rare/threatened species:* 3 • *Hotspots:* 3 • *Special biological features:* 3 • *Biological importance:* 5 • *Intrinsic fragility:* 5 • *Conservation level:* 3 • *Level of threat:* 4 • ACTION RECOMMENDED: *Restoration:* 2 • *Biological inventory:* 5 • *Creation of conservation area:* 2 • *Management:* 5.

AV 014 - Normandia - PRIORITY LEVEL: A • LOCATION: *State:* Roraima • *Main municipality:* Uiramutã • *Municipalities covered:* 2 • VEGETATION TYPES: Dm, Sg, Sp, Td, Tp • COMMENTS: Eastern part of the Roraima lavrados, a vegetation type home to endemic bird species such as *Poecilurus kollari*. Recommended by the Savanna and Wetlands Workshop.

DIAGNOSTIC ELEMENTS: *Species richness:* 3 • *Phylogenetic diversity:* 3 • *Endemism:* 3 • *Richness of rare/threatened species:* 3 • *Hotspots:* 3 • *Special biological features:* 3 • *Biological importance:* 3 • *Intrinsic fragility:* 3 • *Conservation level:* 2 • *Level of threat:* 4 • ACTION RECOMMENDED: *Restoration:* 2 • *Biological inventory:* 5 • *Creation of conservation area:* 2 • *Management:* 5.

AV 015 - Middle Rio Branco - PRIORITY LEVEL: A • LOCATION: *State:* Roraima • *Main municipality:* Rorainópolis • *Municipalities covered:* 2 • VEGETATION TYPES: As, Da, Ds, Ld, Lg, LO • COMMENTS: Large area of campina along the middle Rio Branco, encompassing both banks. Typical (endemic) campina species are expected in this region, such as *Xenopipo atronitens, Neopelma chysocephalum* and others.

DIAGNOSTIC ELEMENTS: *Species richness:* 4 • *Phylogenetic diversity:* 5 • *Endemism:* 5 • *Richness of rare/threatened species:* 4 • *Hotspots:* 4 • *Special biological features:* 5 • *Biological importance:* 4 • *Intrinsic fragility:* 5 • *Conservation level:* 2 • *Level of threat:* 4 • ACTION RECOMMENDED: *Restoration:* 4 • *Biological inventory:* 4 • *Creation of conservation area:* 5 • *Management:* 4.

AV 016 - Apiaú - PRIORITY LEVEL: A • LOCATION: *State:* Amazonas • *Main municipality:* Novo Airão • *Municipalities covered:* 4 • VEGETATION TYPES: Da, Db, Ds, LO • COMMENTS: Fauna representative of the left bank of the Rio Negro. Occurrence of rare species (*Hemitriccus inornatus*). Overlaps indigenous lands.

DIAGNOSTIC ELEMENTS: *Phylogenetic diversity:* 3 • *Endemism:* 5 • *Richness of rare/threatened species:* 1 • *Hotspots:* 2 • *Special biological features:* 1 • *Economically important species:* 1 • *Biological importance:* 5 • *Intrinsic fragility:* 5 • *Conservation level:* 2 • *Level of threat:* 2 • ACTION RECOMMENDED: *Biological inventory:* 1 • *Creation of conservation area:* 2 • *Management:* 5.

AV 017 - Uatumã - PRIORITY LEVEL: C • LOCATION: *State:* Amazonas • *Main municipality:* São Sebastião do Uatumã • *Municipalities covered:* 8 • VEGETATION TYPES: AA, Da, Db, Ds, Pa, SO, Sp.

DIAGNOSTIC ELEMENTS: *Species richness:* 4 • *Phylogenetic diversity:* 4 • *Endemism:* 3 • *Richness of rare/threatened species:* 3 • *Hotspots:* 4 • *Economically important species:* 2 • *Biological importance:* 3 • *Intrinsic fragility:* 4 • *Conservation level:* 4 • *Level of threat:* 5 • ACTION RECOMMENDED: *Management:* 5.

AV 018 - Pitinga - PRIORITY LEVEL: C • LOCATION: *State:* Amazonas/Roraima • *Main municipality:* Urucará • *Municipalities covered:* 6 • VEGETATION TYPES: Ds.

DIAGNOSTIC ELEMENTS: *Species richness:* 4 • *Phylogenetic diversity:* 4 • *Endemism:* 3 • *Richness of rare/threatened species:* 3 • *Hotspots:* 4 • *Economically important species:* 2 • *Biological importance:* 3 • *Intrinsic fragility:* 4 • *Conservation level:* 4 • *Level of threat:* 4 • ACTION RECOMMENDED: *Management:* 5.

AV 019 - Mapuera - PRIORITY LEVEL: D • LOCATION: *State:* Pará • *Main municipality:* Oriximiná • *Municipalities covered:* 2 • VEGETATION TYPES: As, Ds • COMMENTS: Continuous and uninhabited stretch of the upper Rio Mapuera. Entirely covered by dense rainforest.

DIAGNOSTIC ELEMENTS: *Conservation level:* 1 • *Level of threat:* 1 • ACTION RECOMMENDED: *Biological inventory:* 5 • *Creation of conservation area:* 3.

AV 020 - Trombetas - PRIORITY LEVEL: A • LOCATION: *State:* Amazonas/Pará • *Main municipality:* Oriximiná • *Municipalities covered:* 7 • VEGETATION TYPES: AA, Da, Db, Ds, Pa, SO, Sp.

DIAGNOSTIC ELEMENTS: *Species richness:* 4 • *Conservation level:* 3 • *Level of threat:* 3 • ACTION RECOMMENDED: Extend the area of the Trombetas Biological Reserve to the banks of the Amazon.

AV 021 - Upper Trombetas - PRIORITY LEVEL: D • LOCATION: *State:* Pará • *Main municipality:* Oriximiná • *Municipalities covered:* 1 • VEGETATION TYPES: Da, Dm, Ds • COMMENTS: Region of headwaters in an area of ornithologically unexplored uplands, especially on the Brazilian side.

DIAGNOSTIC ELEMENTS: *Conservation level:* 1 • *Level of threat:* 1 • ACTION RECOMMENDED: *Biological inventory:* 5.

AV 022 - Upper Paru - Jari - PRIORITY LEVEL: A • LOCATION: *State:* Amapá/Pará • *Main municipality:* Almeirim • *Municipalities covered:* 2 • VEGETATION TYPES: Dm, Ds, SO • COMMENTS: Ornithologically unknown region.

ACTION RECOMMENDED: *Biological inventory:* 5.

AV 023 - Lower Jari - Paru - PRIORITY LEVEL: C • LOCATION: *State:* Amapá/Pará • *Main municipality:* Almeirim • *Municipalities covered:* 2 • VEGETATION TYPES: As, Da, Ds, SO • COMMENTS: Interfluve region between the Paru do Leste and Jari rivers. Area in excellent state of conservation.

DIAGNOSTIC ELEMENTS: *Species richness:* 4 • *Phylogenetic diversity:* 4 • *Endemism:* 3 • *Richness of rare/threatened species:* 3 • *Hotspots:* 4 • *Economically important species:* 4 • *Biological importance:* 3 • *Intrinsic fragility:* 3 • *Conservation level:* 3 • *Level of threat:* 4 • ACTION RECOMMENDED: *Creation of conservation area:* 4 • *Management:* 5.

AV 024 - Upper Paru savannas - PRIORITY LEVEL: B • LOCATION: *State:* Pará • *Main municipality:* Óbidos • *Municipalities covered:* 4 • VEGETATION TYPES: Da, Ds, Sd, SO, Sp • COMMENTS: Studies in similar habitats on the other side of the border (Suriname) suggest the presence of at least one endemic form of Arapaçu (Dendrocolaptidae) of the genus *Lepidocolaptes*.

DIAGNOSTIC ELEMENTS: *Species richness:* 3 • *Phylogenetic diversity:* 3 • *Endemism:* 5 • *Richness of rare/threatened species:* 3 • *Hotspots:* 2 • *Biological importance:* 3 • *Intrinsic fragility:* 3 • *Conservation level:* 5 • ACTION RECOMMENDED: *Biological inventory:* 5.

AV 025 - Oiapoque - PRIORITY LEVEL: A • LOCATION: *State:* Amapá • *Main municipality:* Oiapoque • *Municipalities covered:* 4 • VEGETATION TYPES: Ds • COMMENTS: Represents the most important intact ecoregion in a national frontier area.

DIAGNOSTIC ELEMENTS: *Conservation level:* 1 • *Level of threat:* 1 • ACTION RECOMMENDED: *Biological inventory:* 4 • *Creation of conservation area:* 5.

AV 026 - Serra do Navio - PRIORITY LEVEL: C • LOCATION: *State:* Amapá • *Main municipality:* Pedra Branca do Amapari • *Municipalities covered:* 7 • VEGETATION TYPES: AA, Ds • COMMENTS: Adjacent to the Serra do Navio, sub-montane and to the east of Guianan forests.

DIAGNOSTIC ELEMENTS: *Species richness:* 4 • *Conservation level:* 3 • *Level of threat:* 3 • ACTION RECOMMENDED: *Restoration:* 4 • *Management:* 5.

AV 027 - Cabo Orange - PRIORITY LEVEL: B • LOCATION: *State:* Amapá • *Main municipality:* Oiapoque • *Municipalities covered:* 2 • VEGETATION TYPES: Da, Db, Ds, Pa, Pf, SO • COMMENTS: Area of occurrence of the flamingo *Phoenicopterus ruber*, threatened with extinction. Resting and feeding grounds for several Canadian Arctic species, such as Anatidae who use the area as a resting place during migration.

DIAGNOSTIC ELEMENTS: *Richness of rare/threatened species:* 5 • *Hotspots:* 1 • *Special biological features:* 5 • *Biological importance:* 5 • *Intrinsic fragility:* 5 • *Conservation level:* 5 • *Level of threat:* 1 • ACTION RECOMMENDED: *Management:* 5.

AV 028 - Northern Amapá savannas - PRIORITY LEVEL: C • LOCATION: *State:* Amapá • *Main municipality:* Calçoene • *Municipalities covered:* 2 • VEGETATION TYPES: Da, Ds, Pa, Pf, Sa, SO, Sp • COMMENTS: Northern part of the Amapá savannas, with structure and composition different of those of the southern savannas. Cerrado (*Formicivora rufa*) and northern South American savanna (*Burhinus bistriatus* and *Sturnella magna*) species are found in the region.

DIAGNOSTIC ELEMENTS: *Species richness:* 3 • *Phylogenetic diversity:* 2 • *Endemism:* 2 • *Richness of rare/threatened species:* 3 • *Special biological features:* 4 • *Biological importance:* 3 • *Intrinsic fragility:* 4 • *Conservation level:* 5 • *Level of threat:* 5 • ACTION RECOMMENDED: *Restoration:* 4 • *Biological inventory:* 3 • *Creation of conservation area:* 5 • *Management:* 4.

AV 029 - Maracá - Mouth of the Araguari - PRIORITY LEVEL: A • LOCATION: *State:* Amapá • *Main municipality:* Amapá • *Municipalities covered:* 5 • VEGETATION TYPES: Da, Pa, Pf • COMMENTS: Occurrence of species such as the scarlet ibis (*Eudocimus Ruber*). Migration corridor for limicolous bird species, reproducing in the Arctic.

DIAGNOSTIC ELEMENTS: *Species richness:* 1 • *Richness of rare/threatened species:* 5 • *Hotspots:* 2 • *Special biological features:* 5 •

Economically important species: 2 • *Biological importance:* 5 • *Intrinsic fragility:* 3 • *Conservation level:* 3 • *Level of threat:* 1 • ACTION RECOMMENDED: *Management:* 0.

AV 030 - Araguari savannas - PRIORITY LEVEL: A • LOCATION: *State:* Amapá • *Main municipality:* Tartarugalzinho • *Municipalities covered:* 7 • VEGETATION TYPES: AA, Da, Ds, Pa, Sd, SO, Sp • COMMENTS: Most diverse area in the Amazon savanna. Recommended by the Savanna and Wetlands Workshop. Contains isolated population of cerrado bird species (e.g. *Suriri affinis, Lepidocoeaptes angustirostris, Neothraupis fasciata, Cypsnagra hirundiracea*), some of which are threatened with extinction (e.g. *Euscarthmus rufomarginatus*).

DIAGNOSTIC ELEMENTS: *Species richness:* 4 • *Phylogenetic diversity:* 5 • *Endemism:* 3 • *Richness of rare/threatened species:* 4 • *Hotspots:* 5 • *Special biological features:* 5 • *Biological importance:* 4 • *Intrinsic fragility:* 5 • *Conservation level:* 4 • *Level of threat:* 5 • ACTION RECOMMENDED: *Restoration:* 4 • *Biological inventory:* 2 • *Creation of conservation area:* 5 • *Management:* 4.

AV 031 - Amapá floodplain forests - PRIORITY LEVEL: D • LOCATION: *State:* Amapá/Pará • *Main municipality:* Mazagão • *Municipalities covered:* 5 • VEGETATION TYPES: AA, Da, Db, Ds, Pa, SO, Sp • COMMENTS: Area basically unknown in terms of bird fauna and under strong anthropogenic pressure.

DIAGNOSTIC ELEMENTS: *Intrinsic fragility:* 4 • *Level of threat:* 5 • ACTION RECOMMENDED: *Creation of conservation area:* 5.

AV 032 - Monte Alegre - PRIORITY LEVEL: B • LOCATION: *State:* Pará • *Main municipality:* Monte Alegre • *Municipalities covered:* 5 • VEGETATION TYPES: AA, As, Ds, Pa, SO, Sp • COMMENTS: Important savanna area located to the north of the Amazon river. True evolutionary laboratory for the consequences of the isolation of savanna plant and animal populations in the center of the Amazon forest. Good bird populations typical of savanna and the semi-arid *caatinga*, such as *Lepidocolaptes angustirostris, Formicivora rura, Xenopipo atrenitens, Sicalis citrine* and others.

DIAGNOSTIC ELEMENTS: *Species richness:* 3 • *Phylogenetic diversity:* 4 • *Endemism:* 3 • *Richness of rare/threatened species:* 4 • *Hotspots:* 3 • *Special biological features:* 5 • *Biological importance:* 4 • *Intrinsic fragility:* 5 • *Conservation level:* 4 • *Level of threat:* 5 • ACTION RECOMMENDED: *Restoration:* 4 • *Biological inventory:* 3 • *Creation of conservation area:* 5.

AV 033 - Marajó grasslands - PRIORITY LEVEL: C • LOCATION: *State:* Pará • *Main municipality:* Chaves • *Municipalities covered:* 7 • VEGETATION TYPES: Da, Pa, Pf, Sp • COMMENTS: Breeding place for bird colonies such as herons, ibis, bitterns and others. The area receives migrants from the Canadian Arctic on their way to the south of the country. Area of occurrence of Anatidae during migration.

DIAGNOSTIC ELEMENTS: *Species richness:* 2 • *Phylogenetic diversity:* 1 • *Richness of rare/threatened species:* 5 • *Hotspots:* 2 • *Special biological features:* 5 • *Biological importance:* 5 • *Intrinsic fragility:* 2 • *Conservation level:* 2 • *Level of threat:* 2 • ACTION RECOMMENDED: *Biological inventory:* 4 • *Management:* 5.

AV 034 - Breves - Anajás forests - PRIORITY LEVEL: B • LOCATION: *State:* Pará • *Main municipality:* Breves • *Municipalities covered:* 4 • VEGETATION TYPES: AA, Da, Db • COMMENTS: Richest region on Marajó for forest birds; only example of large stretches of terra firme vegetation (dense forest) on the island; high anthropogenic pressure.

ACTION RECOMMENDED: *Management:* 5.

AV 035 - Arari Fluvial Forest - PRIORITY LEVEL: C • LOCATION: *State:* Pará • *Main municipality:* Ponta de Pedras • *Municipalities covered:* 2 • VEGETATION TYPES: AA, Da, Pa, Sp • COMMENTS: Area of known endemism of other groups of animals; forest species richness in eastern Marajó, highly threatened.

DIAGNOSTIC ELEMENTS: *Species richness:* 3 • *Phylogenetic diversity:* 3 • *Endemism:* 2 • *Richness of rare/threatened species:* 3 • *Hotspots:* 4 • *Special biological features:* 4 • *Economically important species:* 3 • *Biological importance:* 3 • *Intrinsic fragility:* 4 • *Conservation level:* 5 • *Level of threat:* 5 • ACTION RECOMMENDED: *Management:* 5.

AV 036 - Amazon estuary islands - PRIORITY LEVEL: B • LOCATION: *State:* Amapá/Pará • *Main municipality:* Chaves • *Municipalities covered:* 9 • VEGETATION TYPES: Da, Pa, Sp • COMMENTS: Area receiving coastal bird populations from Canadian Arctic, acting as part of the only corridor for some species. Occurrence of scarlet ibis (*Eudocimus ruber*), threatened with extinction.

DIAGNOSTIC ELEMENTS: *Species richness:* 2 • *Phylogenetic diversity:* 1 • *Richness of rare/threatened species:* 5 • *Special biological features:* 5 • *Economically important species:* 2 • *Biological importance:* 4 • *Intrinsic fragility:* 2 • *Conservation level:* 4 • *Level of threat:* 1 • ACTION RECOMMENDED: *Management:* 0.

AV 037 - Serra do Tiracambu - PRIORITY LEVEL: A • LOCATION: *State:* MA/Pará • *Main municipality:* Centro Novo do Maranhão • *Municipalities covered:* 16 • VEGETATION TYPES: AA, Da, Db • COMMENTS: Only conservation area to the east of the Tocantins river, with 17 globally threatened bird taxa.

DIAGNOSTIC ELEMENTS: *Species richness:* 5 • *Phylogenetic diversity:* 4 • *Endemism:* 4 • *Richness of rare/threatened species:* 5 • *Hotspots:* 5 • *Special biological features:* 3 • *Economically important species:* 3 • *Biological importance:* 4 • *Intrinsic fragility:* 5 • *Conservation level:* 4 • *Level of threat:* 5 • ACTION RECOMMENDED: *Biological inventory:* 4 • *Creation of conservation area:* 4 • *Management:* 5.

AV 038 - Pará mangroves - PRIORITY LEVEL: C • LOCATION: *State:* Pará • *Main municipality:* São João de Pirabas • *Municipalities covered:* 14 • VEGETATION TYPES: AA, Pa, Pf • COMMENTS: Area of occurrence of high numbers of intercontinental migratory limicolous bird species. Breeding area for threatened species, such as the scarlet ibis (*Eudocimus ruber*).

DIAGNOSTIC ELEMENTS: *Species richness:* 2 • *Phylogenetic diversity:* 1 • *Endemism:* 5 • *Richness of rare/threatened species:* 5 • *Hotspots:* 2 • *Special biological features:* 5 • *Economically important species:* 2 • *Biological importance:* 5 • *Intrinsic fragility:* 5 • *Conservation level:* 2 • *Level of threat:* 1 • ACTION RECOMMENDED: *Management:* 5.

AV 039 - Maranhão mangroves - PRIORITY LEVEL: A • LOCATION: *State:* MA/Pará • *Main municipality:* Alcântara • *Municipalities covered:* 21 • VEGETATION TYPES: AA, Pf • COMMENTS: Area of occurrence of large numbers of intercontinental migratory limicolous bird species. Breeding area for threatened species, such as the scarlet ibis (*Eudocimus ruber*).

DIAGNOSTIC ELEMENTS: *Species richness:* 2 • *Phylogenetic diversity:* 1 • *Endemism:* 2 • *Richness of rare/threatened species:* 5 • *Hotspots:* 2 • *Special biological features:* 5 • *Economically important species:* 2 • *Biological importance:* 5 • *Intrinsic fragility:* 5 • *Conservation level:* 2 • *Level of threat:* 1 • ACTION RECOMMENDED: *Creation of conservation area:* 5.

AV 040 - Upper Guamá - PRIORITY LEVEL: A • LOCATION: *State:* Pará • *Main municipality:* Capitão Poço • *Municipalities covered:* 13 • VEGETATION TYPES: AA, Da • COMMENTS: Former area of occurrence of *Crax fasciolata pinima, Guaruba guarouba* and other endangered species; important area for the hydrological equilibrium of the region.

DIAGNOSTIC ELEMENTS: *Intrinsic fragility:* 5 • *Conservation level:* 5 • *Level of threat:* 5 • ACTION RECOMMENDED: *Restoration:* 5 • *Creation of conservation area:* 4.

AV 041 - Upper Capim - PRIORITY LEVEL: B • LOCATION: *State:* Pará • *Main municipality:* Paragominas • *Municipalities covered:* 6 • VEGETATION TYPES: AA, Da, Db • COMMENTS: One of the last remaining areas of intact forest to the east of the Tocantins with 17 globally threatened bird taxa.

DIAGNOSTIC ELEMENTS: *Species richness:* 4 • *Phylogenetic diversity:* 4 • *Endemism:* 4 • *Richness of rare/threatened species:* 4 • *Hotspots:* 5 • *Special biological features:* 3 • *Economically important species:* 3 • *Biological importance:* 4 • *Intrinsic fragility:* 3 • *Conservation level:* 4 • *Level of threat:* 2 • ACTION RECOMMENDED: *Creation of conservation area:* 5.

AV 042 - Baião - PRIORITY LEVEL: B • LOCATION: *State:* Pará • *Main municipality:* Moju • *Municipalities covered:* 7 • VEGETATION TYPES: AA, As, Da, Db • COMMENTS: Last remaining forest areas to the east of the Tocantins, with 17 globally threatened bird taxa and one of the last areas where these can be found.

DIAGNOSTIC ELEMENTS: *Species richness:* 5 • *Phylogenetic diversity:* 5 • *Endemism:* 5 • *Richness of rare/threatened species:* 5 • *Hotspots:* 5 • *Special biological features:* 4 • *Economically important species:* 4

• *Biological importance:* 5 • *Intrinsic fragility:* 3 • *Conservation level:* 3 • *Level of threat:* 2 • ACTION RECOMMENDED: *Creation of conservation area:* 5.

AV 043 - Baixada Maranhense - PRIORITY LEVEL: B • LOCATION: *State:* MA • *Main municipality:* Anajatuba • *Municipalities covered:* 24 • VEGETATION TYPES: AA, Pa, Pf • COMMENTS: Resting and feeding site for several species of intercontinental migratory limicolous birds on their way to southern Brazil. Breeding ground for colonial bird species (herons, divers, bitterns and others).

DIAGNOSTIC ELEMENTS: *Species richness:* 3 • *Phylogenetic diversity:* 2 • *Endemism:* 5 • *Richness of rare/threatened species:* 5 • *Hotspots:* 5 • *Special biological features:* 5 • *Economically important species:* 5 • *Biological importance:* 5 • *Intrinsic fragility:* 5 • *Conservation level:* 5 • *Level of threat:* 3 • ACTION RECOMMENDED: *Creation of conservation area:* 5.

AV 044 - Barra do Corda - PRIORITY LEVEL: A • LOCATION: *State:* MA • *Main municipality:* Grajaú • *Municipalities covered:* 8 • VEGETATION TYPES: AA, Cs, Da, Db, Sa, SN • COMMENTS: Pressure of deforestation in a region housing rare and/or endangered species, such as *Xiphocolaptes falcirostris, Herpsilochmus pectoralis, Procnias a. averano, Megaxenops parnaguae* e *Amaurospiza moesta*. Area proposed by the Amazonia 1990 workshop, with unique vegetation for Maranhão.

DIAGNOSTIC ELEMENTS: *Species richness:* 4 • *Phylogenetic diversity:* 4 • *Endemism:* 4 • *Richness of rare/threatened species:* 5 • *Hotspots:* 5 • *Biological importance:* 4 • *Intrinsic fragility:* 5 • *Conservation level:* 3 • *Level of threat:* 5 • ACTION RECOMMENDED: *Biological inventory:* 4 • *Management:* 5.

AV 045 - Araguaína - PRIORITY LEVEL: D • LOCATION: *State:* Pará/Tocantins • *Main municipality:* Araguaína • *Municipalities covered:* 22 • VEGETATION TYPES: AA, As, Ds, Sa, SO • COMMENTS: Only area of dense forest in the state of Tocantins.

DIAGNOSTIC ELEMENTS: *Intrinsic fragility:* 5 • *Conservation level:* 4 • *Level of threat:* 5 • ACTION RECOMMENDED: *Restoration:* 3 • *Biological inventory:* 5.

AV 046 - Caxiuanã - PRIORITY LEVEL: B • LOCATION: *State:* Pará • *Main municipality:* Portel • *Municipalities covered:* 4 • VEGETATION TYPES: AA, Da, Db, Pa • COMMENTS: The Caixuanã National Forest and its surroundings form an extensive area of forest near the mouth of the Xingu. It includes important areas of terra firme forest, floodplain and igapó. Contains bird populations at risk of extinction (e.g. *Guaruba guarouba*) or endemic to the region between the Tocantins and the Xingu rivers (e.g. *Hylexetastes brigidai*).

DIAGNOSTIC ELEMENTS: *Species richness:* 4 • *Phylogenetic diversity:* 4 • *Endemism:* 3 • *Richness of rare/threatened species:* 4 • *Hotspots:* 4 • *Special biological features:* 4 • *Biological importance:* 4 • *Conservation level:* 1 • *Level of threat:* 2 • ACTION RECOMMENDED: *Biological inventory:* 4 • *Creation of conservation area:* 2 • *Management:* 5.

AV 047 - Carajás - PRIORITY LEVEL: A • LOCATION: *State:* Pará • *Main municipality:* Marabá • *Municipalities covered:* 6 • VEGETATION TYPES: AA, As, Dm, Ds • COMMENTS: Has vegetation covering the iron ore deposits on the top of the mountain ranges. This vegetation houses a residual bird fauna typical of more open areas, such as the semi-arid *caatinga*, with sub-especific endemic forms.

DIAGNOSTIC ELEMENTS: *Species richness:* 5 • *Phylogenetic diversity:* 5 • *Richness of rare/threatened species:* 2 • *Hotspots:* 2 • *Biological importance:* 4 • *Intrinsic fragility:* 4 • *Conservation level:* 2 • *Level of threat:* 3 • ACTION RECOMMENDED: *Management:* 5.

AV 048 - Ipixuna - PRIORITY LEVEL: A • LOCATION: *State:* Pará • *Main municipality:* Altamira • *Municipalities covered:* 2 • VEGETATION TYPES: AA, As, Da, Ds, SO • COMMENTS: There are no conservation areas in the middle Xingu River. Potential corridor in open rainforest.

DIAGNOSTIC ELEMENTS: *Conservation level:* 0 • ACTION RECOMMENDED: *Biological inventory:* 5 • *Management:* 5.

AV 049 - São Geraldo do Araguaia - PRIORITY LEVEL: B • LOCATION: *State:* Pará/Tocantins • *Main municipality:* São Geraldo do Araguaia • *Municipalities covered:* 11 • VEGETATION TYPES: AA, As, Ds • COMMENTS: Area with a mosaic rich in habitats, covering floodplains, chalk downs and dense rainforests. Bird fauna includes three species of macaw, *Anodorhynchus, Penelope pileata*. High anthropogenic pressure; includes the Serra das Andorinhas State Park.

DIAGNOSTIC ELEMENTS: *Species richness:* 4 • *Phylogenetic diversity:* 4 • *Endemism:* 3 • *Richness of rare/threatened species:* 4 • *Hotspots:* 4 • *Biological importance:* 4 • *Intrinsic fragility:* 4 • *Conservation level:* 5 • *Level of threat:* 5 • ACTION RECOMMENDED: *Restoration:* 4 • *Management:* 5.

AV 050 - Gradaús - PRIORITY LEVEL: A • LOCATION: *State:* Pará • *Main municipality:* São Félix do Xingu • *Municipalities covered:* 3 • VEGETATION TYPES: As, Ds, Sd, Sg, SO, Sp • COMMENTS: Ecotone and transition area of species typical of this environment. High presence of several species with distribution confined to eastern Amazonia, including species associated with bamboos. Area with an abundance of species endemic to the region between the Xingu and the Tocantins and high anthropogenic pressure (logging and prospecting).

DIAGNOSTIC ELEMENTS: *Species richness:* 4 • *Phylogenetic diversity:* 5 • *Endemism:* 5 • *Richness of rare/threatened species:* 4 • *Hotspots:* 5 • *Special biological features:* 3 • *Economically important species:* 3 • *Biological importance:* 5 • *Intrinsic fragility:* 3 • *Conservation level:* 2 • *Level of threat:* 5 • ACTION RECOMMENDED: *Management:* 5.

AV 051 - Santana do Araguaia - PRIORITY LEVEL: B • LOCATION: *State:* Mato Grosso/Pará/Tocantins • *Main municipality:* Santana do Araguaia • *Municipalities covered:* 9 • VEGETATION TYPES: AA, As, Sa, Sg, SN, SO, Sp • COMMENTS: Area in the arc of deforestation, with open rainforest and savannas. Forest species in contact with cerrado species. *Aramides ypecaha, Rhea americana* and *Cariama cristata* together with *Pipile pipile, Cephalopterus ornatus, Ara macao, Anodorhynchus hyacinthinus* etc. Important area for species migrating from the south. Area of contact between substitute species (e.g. *Thraupis episcopus* and *Thraupis sayaca*).

DIAGNOSTIC ELEMENTS: *Species richness:* 5 • *Phylogenetic diversity:* 2 • *Endemism:* 3 • *Richness of rare/threatened species:* 3 • *Hotspots:* 4 • *Special biological features:* 5 • *Economically important species:* 4 • *Biological importance:* 4 • *Intrinsic fragility:* 4 • *Conservation level:* 2 • *Level of threat:* 4 • ACTION RECOMMENDED: *Creation of conservation area:* 5.

AV 052 - Upper Xingu - PRIORITY LEVEL: A • LOCATION: *State:* Mato Grosso/Pará • *Main municipality:* São José do Xingu • *Municipalities covered:* 9 • VEGETATION TYPES: AA, As, Da, Ds, ON, Pa, Sa, Sd, SN, SO, Sp • COMMENTS: Indigenous Park surrounded by SUDAM farms. Contains unique vegetation types in a vegetation mosaic.

DIAGNOSTIC ELEMENTS: *Phylogenetic diversity:* 5 • *Level of threat:* 5 • ACTION RECOMMENDED: *Biological inventory:* 5.

AV 053 - Jaraucu River - PRIORITY LEVEL: D • LOCATION: *State:* Pará • *Main municipality:* Porto de Moz • *Municipalities covered:* 6 • VEGETATION TYPES: Da, Db, Ds, Pa • COMMENTS: Region on the left bank of the Xingu, where its width is at its greatest and an area where the river can be seen as a between allopatric forms. On the right bank, the Caxiuanã National Forest.

DIAGNOSTIC ELEMENTS: *Conservation level:* 0 • ACTION RECOMMENDED: *Biological inventory:* 5.

AV 054 - Aveiro - PRIORITY LEVEL: B • LOCATION: *State:* Pará • *Main municipality:* Belterra • *Municipalities covered:* 5 • VEGETATION TYPES: AA, Db, Ds • COMMENTS: Currently the Tajapós National Forest, an island. The southern part of the Cupari river is well conserved and warrants a restricted conservation area. The presence of *Guaruba guarouba* is recorded. It constitutes the northern limit of *Anodorhynchus hyacinthinus*.

DIAGNOSTIC ELEMENTS: *Species richness:* 5 • *Phylogenetic diversity:* 5 • *Endemism:* 4 • *Richness of rare/threatened species:* 3 • *Hotspots:* 5 • *Economically important species:* 5 • *Biological importance:* 4 • *Intrinsic fragility:* 4 • *Conservation level:* 2 • *Level of threat:* 5 • ACTION RECOMMENDED: *Biological inventory:* 5.

AV 055 - Jamanxim - PRIORITY LEVEL: A • LOCATION: *State:* Pará • *Main municipality:* Itaituba • *Municipalities covered:* 4 • VEGETATION TYPES: AA, As, Ds • COMMENTS: Reclassification from direct use to strict conservation area. Area of forest reserves with threatened endemic species.

DIAGNOSTIC ELEMENTS: *Species richness:* 5 • *Phylogenetic diversity:* 5 • *Endemism:* 3 • *Richness of rare/threatened species:* 4 • *Hotspots:* 2

• *Special biological features:* 3 • *Economically important species:* 5 • *Biological importance:* 5 • *Intrinsic fragility:* 2 • *Conservation level:* 2 • *Level of threat:* 2 • ACTION RECOMMENDED: *Management:* 0.

AV 056 - Upper Iriri - PRIORITY LEVEL: A • LOCATION: *State:* Mato Grosso/Pará • *Main municipality:* Altamira • *Municipalities covered:* 5 • VEGETATION TYPES: As, Ds, Sa, Sd, Sg, SN, SO • COMMENTS: Area of submontane and montane dense rainforest with enclaves of open areas.

DIAGNOSTIC ELEMENTS: *Conservation level:* 0 • ACTION RECOMMENDED: *Management:* 5.

AV 057 - Pardo River - PRIORITY LEVEL: D • LOCATION: *State:* Pará • *Main municipality:* Altamira • *Municipalities covered:* 2 • VEGETATION TYPES: As, Da, Ds, Sa, SO • COMMENTS: Extremely heterogenous transitional area of vegetation on the left bank of the middle Xingu. Ornithologically unexplored.

DIAGNOSTIC ELEMENTS: *Conservation level:* 2 • *Level of threat:* 3 • ACTION RECOMMENDED: *Biological inventory:* 5 • *Creation of conservation area:* 3.

AV 058 - Mundurucânia - PRIORITY LEVEL: B • LOCATION: *State:* Amazonas/Mato Grosso/Pará • *Main municipality:* Jacareacanga • *Municipalities covered:* 5 • VEGETATION TYPES: As, Da, Ds, Fs, Sd, Sg, SN, SO, Sp • COMMENTS: Only known region of occurrence of *Pipra vivasboasi* (Sick 1959).

DIAGNOSTIC ELEMENTS: *Species richness:* 3 • *Conservation level:* 2 • *Level of threat:* 4 • ACTION RECOMMENDED: *Restoration:* 2 • *Biological inventory:* 4 • *Creation of conservation area:* 2 • *Management:* 5.

AV 059 - Alta Floresta - PRIORITY LEVEL: A • LOCATION: *State:* Mato Grosso • *Main municipality:* Novo Mundo • *Municipalities covered:* 11 • VEGETATION TYPES: As, Da, Ds, ON, Sd, SN, SO • COMMENTS: Ecological transition area between savanna and forest with species of both environments. Headwaters of the Tapajós: mixture of populations from both banks of the river, and area of contact and biogeographical transition. Second richest area in Brazil for bird species, with abundance of endemic species in the region between the Madeira and the Tapajós. High anthropogenic pressure: logging and prospecting.

DIAGNOSTIC ELEMENTS: *Species richness:* 5 • *Phylogenetic diversity:* 5 • *Endemism:* 5 • *Richness of rare/threatened species:* 3 • *Hotspots:* 5 • *Special biological features:* 4 • *Economically important species:* 2 • *Biological importance:* 5 • *Intrinsic fragility:* 3 • *Conservation level:* 3 • *Level of threat:* 5 • ACTION RECOMMENDED: *Creation of conservation area:* 5.

AV 060 - Tucuruí - PRIORITY LEVEL: B • LOCATION: *State:* Pará • *Main municipality:* Pacajá • *Municipalities covered:* 8 • VEGETATION TYPES: AA, As, Da, Db, Ds • COMMENTS: Area of ecotone between dense and open rainforests. Several endemic species in the region between the Xingu and the Tocantins. High anthropogenic pressure.

DIAGNOSTIC ELEMENTS: *Species richness:* 4 • *Phylogenetic diversity:* 5 • *Endemism:* 5 • *Richness of rare/threatened species:* 3 • *Hotspots:* 5 • *Special biological features:* 3 • *Economically important species:* 3 • *Biological importance:* 5 • *Intrinsic fragility:* 3 • *Conservation level:* 3 • *Level of threat:* 5 • ACTION RECOMMENDED: *Creation of conservation area:* 5.

AV 061 - Boim - PRIORITY LEVEL: C • LOCATION: *State:* Pará • *Main municipality:* Santarém • *Municipalities covered:* 4 • VEGETATION TYPES: Db, Ds, Pa, SO, Sp • COMMENTS: Ecotone area: savanna – dense rainforest. Richness of endemic species in the region between the Madeira and the Tapajós. Area under anthropogenic impact. Conservation of populations of species from the lower Tapajós.

DIAGNOSTIC ELEMENTS: *Species richness:* 4 • *Phylogenetic diversity:* 5 • *Endemism:* 5 • *Richness of rare/threatened species:* 4 • *Hotspots:* 5 • *Economically important species:* 3 • *Biological importance:* 5 • *Intrinsic fragility:* 3 • *Conservation level:* 4 • *Level of threat:* 5 • ACTION RECOMMENDED: *Management:* 5.

AV 062 - Itaituba - PRIORITY LEVEL: A • LOCATION: *State:* Pará • *Main municipality:* Itaituba • *Municipalities covered:* 3 • VEGETATION TYPES: AA, As, Da, Db, Ds, Pa • COMMENTS: Diversity of environments (transition dense to open rainforest). Abundance and richness of endemic species in the region between the Madeira and the Tapajós. Conservation of populations of species in the lower part of the Tapajós river.

DIAGNOSTIC ELEMENTS: *Species richness:* 5 • *Phylogenetic diversity:* 5 • *Endemism:* 5 • *Richness of rare/threatened species:* 4 • *Hotspots:* 5 • *Special biological features:* 3 • *Biological importance:* 5 • *Intrinsic fragility:* 3 • *Conservation level:* 2 • *Level of threat:* 5 • ACTION RECOMMENDED: *Management:* 5.

AV 063 - Aripuanã - PRIORITY LEVEL: A • LOCATION: *State:* Mato Grosso • *Main municipality:* Aripuanã • *Municipalities covered:* 7 • VEGETATION TYPES: AA, As, Ds, ON, Sd, SN, SO • COMMENTS: Ecotone between savanna, dense rainforest, open rainforest and seasonal semi-deciduous forest with very high species richness. High richness and abundance of endemic species in the region between the Madeira and the Tapajós. Richness of species of residual distribution in central-southern Amazonia, such as species associated with bamboos. Conservation of residual populations of several species.

DIAGNOSTIC ELEMENTS: *Species richness:* 5 • *Phylogenetic diversity:* 5 • *Endemism:* 5 • *Richness of rare/threatened species:* 5 • *Hotspots:* 5 • *Special biological features:* 4 • *Biological importance:* 5 • *Intrinsic fragility:* 5 • *Conservation level:* 2 • *Level of threat:* 5 • ACTION RECOMMENDED: *Creation of conservation area:* 5.

AV 064 - Upper Guaporé - PRIORITY LEVEL: C • LOCATION: *State:* Mato Grosso • *Main municipality:* Vila Bela da Santíssima Trindade • *Municipalities covered:* 4 • VEGETATION TYPES: AA, Cs, Fa, Fb, Fs, Pa, Sa, Sd, Sg, SN, Sp • COMMENTS: Area of high heterogeneity of habitats and relief, located on the upper part of the Guaporé. Presence of semi-deciduous forests, of restricted occurrence in Amazonia and suffering drastic reduction due to the expansion of agricultural and ranching. Occurrence of endemic savanna species, some of them rare (*Sporophila nigrorufa*). Part of a unit with the Noel Kempf Mercado National Park, in Bolivia, and part of the Guaporé-Mamoré ecological corridor.

DIAGNOSTIC ELEMENTS: *Species richness:* 5 • *Endemism:* 3 • *Richness of rare/threatened species:* 4 • *Hotspots:* 3 • *Special biological features:* 4 • *Biological importance:* 3 • *Intrinsic fragility:* 5 • *Conservation level:* 3 • *Level of threat:* 4 • ACTION RECOMMENDED: *Management:* 5.

AV 065 - Arinos River - PRIORITY LEVEL: D • LOCATION: *State:* Mato Grosso • *Main municipality:* Juara • *Municipalities covered:* 8 • VEGETATION TYPES: AA, As, Da, Ds, ON, SO • COMMENTS: High diversity of environments, probably with abundance of species richness in areas experiencing high anthropogenic impact.

DIAGNOSTIC ELEMENTS: *Endemism:* 5 • *Richness of rare/threatened species:* 5 • *Hotspots:* 5 • *Biological importance:* 5 • *Level of threat:* 5 • ACTION RECOMMENDED: *Biological inventory:* 5.

AV 066 - Pontal do Mato Grosso - PRIORITY LEVEL: B • LOCATION: *State:* Amazonas/Mato Grosso/Pará • *Main municipality:* Apiacás • *Municipalities covered:* 3 • VEGETATION TYPES: As, Da, Ds, Sa, Sd, SN, SO, Sp • COMMENTS: High environmental heterogeneity. Area of biogeographical transition between both banks of the Tapajós. Richness of endemic species in the region between the Madeira and the Tapajós. Expansion of the Apiacás State Reserve to the south to cover a larger diversity of environments.

DIAGNOSTIC ELEMENTS: *Species richness:* 5 • *Phylogenetic diversity:* 5 • *Endemism:* 5 • *Richness of rare/threatened species:* 4 • *Hotspots:* 5 • *Special biological features:* 4 • *Biological importance:* 5 • *Intrinsic fragility:* 3 • *Conservation level:* 2 • *Level of threat:* 5 • ACTION RECOMMENDED: *Biological inventory:* 4.

AV 067 - Upper Sucunduri River - PRIORITY LEVEL: D • LOCATION: *State:* Amazonas/Mato Grosso/Pará • *Main municipality:* Apuí • *Municipalities covered:* 4 • VEGETATION TYPES: As, Da, Ds, Sd, SN, SO • COMMENTS: High environmental diversity. Probable richness of endemic species in the region between the Madeira and the middle Tapajós. Conservation of populations on the left bank of the middle Tapajós.

DIAGNOSTIC ELEMENTS: *Species richness:* 5 • *Phylogenetic diversity:* 5 • *Hotspots:* 5 • *Biological importance:* 5 • *Intrinsic fragility:* 3 • *Level of threat:* 5 • ACTION RECOMMENDED: *Biological inventory:* 5.

AV 068 - Maués - PRIORITY LEVEL: D • LOCATION: *State:* Amazonas • *Main municipality:* Urucurituba • *Municipalities covered:* 9 • VEGETATION TYPES: AA, Da, Db, Pa, SO, Sp • COMMENTS: Area of high environmental heterogeneity. Conservation of populations on the right bank of the lower Tapajós. Probable richness of endemic species in the region between the Xingu and the Tapajós.

DIAGNOSTIC ELEMENTS: *Hotspots:* 5 • *Biological importance:* 5 • *Level of threat:* 5 • ACTION RECOMMENDED: *Biological inventory:* 5.

AV 069 - Borba - PRIORITY LEVEL: A • LOCATION: *State:* Amazonas • *Main municipality:* Borba • *Municipalities covered:* 2 • VEGETATION TYPES: Da, Db, Pa • COMMENTS: High species richness due to environmental heterogeneity. Richness of endemic species in the region between the Madeira and the Tapajós. Conservation of populations on the right bank of the middle Madeira.

DIAGNOSTIC ELEMENTS: *Species richness:* 5 • *Phylogenetic diversity:* 5 • *Endemism:* 5 • *Richness of rare/threatened species:* 5 • *Hotspots:* 5 • *Special biological features:* 4 • *Biological importance:* 5 • *Intrinsic fragility:* 3 • *Conservation level:* 2 • *Level of threat:* 5 • ACTION RECOMMENDED: *Creation of conservation area:* 5.

AV 070 - Lower Roosevelt - PRIORITY LEVEL: B • LOCATION: *State:* Amazonas/Mato Grosso • *Main municipality:* Novo Aripuanã • *Municipalities covered:* 3 • VEGETATION TYPES: As, Da, Db, Ds, Sg, SO, Sp • COMMENTS: High richness of species by environment. Very heterogenous area. High density and richness of endemic species in the region between the Madeira and the Tapajós. Protection of populations in the middle Madeira-Tapajós.

DIAGNOSTIC ELEMENTS: *Species richness:* 5 • *Phylogenetic diversity:* 5 • *Endemism:* 5 • *Richness of rare/threatened species:* 5 • *Hotspots:* 5 • *Biological importance:* 5 • *Intrinsic fragility:* 4 • *Level of threat:* 5 • ACTION RECOMMENDED: *Creation of conservation area:* 5.

AV 071 - Middle Madeira - PRIORITY LEVEL: A • LOCATION: *State:* Amazonas • *Main municipality:* Humaitá • *Municipalities covered:* 4 • VEGETATION TYPES: Ab, Da, Db, Pa, SO • COMMENTS: Lack of information on the area

DIAGNOSTIC ELEMENTS: *Conservation level:* 0 • ACTION RECOMMENDED: *Biological inventory:* 5.

AV 072 - Jaru - PRIORITY LEVEL: A • LOCATION: *State:* Mato Grosso/Rondônia • *Main municipality:* Ji-Paraná • *Municipalities covered:* 4 • VEGETATION TYPES: As, Ds • COMMENTS: One of the most diverse areas in the Brazilian Amazon, with 450 bird species. Only region of collection of *Clytoctantes atrogularis* and recording of the majority of the endemic species in the region between the Madeira and the Tapajós (*Rhegmatorhina hoffmannsi, Hylexetastes uniformis, Psophia viridis* etc.), and some rare species, such as *Nothocrax urumutum*. This area is under pressure from illegal (landless) occupants supported by local politicians. Interesting species: *Pyrrhura perlata, Capito dayi, Pionopsitta barrabandi, Synallaxis cherriei,* among others.

DIAGNOSTIC ELEMENTS: *Species richness:* 5 • *Phylogenetic diversity:* 5 • *Endemism:* 5 • *Richness of rare/threatened species:* 4 • *Hotspots:* 5 • *Special biological features:* 5 • *Economically important species:* 5 • *Biological importance:* 5 • *Intrinsic fragility:* 2 • *Conservation level:* 4 • *Level of threat:* 4 • ACTION RECOMMENDED: *Management:* 5.

AV 073 - Jamari - PRIORITY LEVEL: B • LOCATION: *State:* Rondônia • *Main municipality:* Candeias do Jamari • *Municipalities covered:* 4 • VEGETATION TYPES: Ab, As, SO • COMMENTS: Surveys in the Samuel hydroelectric plant area found a very diverse fauna, including the majority of the endemic species of 'Rondonia Center' (*Psophia viridis, Pyrrhura perlata, Xiphorhynchus elegans, Pipra nattereri* etc.), and some rare species, such as *Nothocrax urumutum*. The reservoir is used by aquatic birds, including migratory limicolous species. Although the area is well conserved, the Jamari National Park has seen several areas degraded by prospecting and illegal occupation. Occurrence of *Guaruba guarouba*.

DIAGNOSTIC ELEMENTS: *Species richness:* 4 • *Phylogenetic diversity:* 5 • *Endemism:* 4 • *Richness of rare/threatened species:* 4 • *Hotspots:* 4 • *Special biological features:* 5 • *Economically important species:* 5 • *Biological importance:* 5 • *Intrinsic fragility:* 2 • *Conservation level:* 3 • *Level of threat:* 4 • ACTION RECOMMENDED: *Restoration:* 5 • *Biological inventory:* 3 • *Creation of conservation area:* 2 • *Management:* 5.

AV 074 - Cuniã - PRIORITY LEVEL: C • LOCATION: *State:* Rondônia • *Main municipality:* Porto Velho • *Municipalities covered:* 1 • VEGETATION TYPES: Ab, Da, Pa, SO, Sp • COMMENTS: One of the largest floodplain areas of the Madeira, with an important system of lakes. Limited observations reveal a large number of aquatic birds using the area, apparently migrants from other regions of Amazonia. The biggest part of the area is in the process of becoming a Fishing Extractive Reserve. Includes large populations of the black Amazon caiman (*Melanosuchus niger*) and the manatee (*Trichechus inunguis*).

DIAGNOSTIC ELEMENTS: *Special biological features:* 5 • *Economically important species:* 5 • *Biological importance:* 5 • *Intrinsic fragility:* 5 • *Conservation level:* 4 • *Level of threat:* 3 • ACTION RECOMMENDED: *Biological inventory:* 5 • *Creation of conservation area:* 4 • *Management:* 5.

AV 075 - Serra dos Três Irmãos - PRIORITY LEVEL: A • LOCATION: *State:* Amazonas/Rondônia • *Main municipality:* Porto Velho • *Municipalities covered:* 3 • VEGETATION TYPES: Ab, As, Ds, SO • COMMENTS: Covers the transition between the Madeira floodplains, terra firme forests and the savanna enclave on the Amazonas-Rondônia boundary. Only area of occurrence of endemic species, such as *Xiphorhynchus jurianus, Gymnopithys salvini, Crypturellus erythropus, Pteroglossus flavirostris, Rhegmatorhina melanosticta* and *Pipra coronata exquisita* on the left bank of the Madeira in Rondônia. Threatened by the settlement of the savannas of southern Amazonas (highway under construction), and settlement of the left bank of the Madeira, near Porto Velho, by farms, including INCRA settlement schemes.

DIAGNOSTIC ELEMENTS: *Species richness:* 5 • *Phylogenetic diversity:* 5 • *Endemism:* 4 • *Richness of rare/threatened species:* 3 • *Hotspots:* 4 • *Special biological features:* 5 • *Economically important species:* 5 • *Biological importance:* 5 • *Intrinsic fragility:* 4 • *Conservation level:* 4 • *Level of threat:* 4 • ACTION RECOMMENDED: *Biological inventory:* 1 • *Creation of conservation area:* 1 • *Management:* 5.

AV 076 - Pacaás Novos - PRIORITY LEVEL: A • LOCATION: *State:* Rondônia • *Main municipality:* Nova Mamoré • *Municipalities covered:* 3 • VEGETATION TYPES: AA, Ab, As, Da, Ds, Sa, Sd, SO • COMMENTS: The area covers the Pacaás Novos massif and the associated ranges, the forests on their slopes and adjacent valleys. High species richness in the region (over 450 species), including rare endemic species such as *Psophia viridis, Selenidera gouldii, Rhegmatoshina hoffmannsi, Pyrrhura perlata, Aratinga weddellii, Pionopsitta barrabandi* and *Pipra nattereri*. The presence of rocky grasslands and Andean forest elements suggest the presence of endemic species at higher altitudes. The massif constitutes an ecologically highly unusual area of open formations surrounded by forest. Human impact is limited but is growing. The opening of the BR-421 highway will cut through the north of the Guajará-Mirim State Park, and will be a driver of uncontrolled settlement of the area. There is pressure from logging companies surrounding the area.

DIAGNOSTIC ELEMENTS: *Species richness:* 5 • *Phylogenetic diversity:* 5 • *Endemism:* 5 • *Richness of rare/threatened species:* 5 • *Hotspots:* 5 • *Special biological features:* 5 • *Economically important species:* 5 • *Biological importance:* 5 • *Intrinsic fragility:* 4 • *Conservation level:* 5 • *Level of threat:* 4 • ACTION RECOMMENDED: *Biological inventory:* 3 • *Management:* 5.

AV 077 - Cautário River - Serra da Cotia - PRIORITY LEVEL: B • LOCATION: *State:* Rondônia • *Main municipality:* Guajará-Mirim • *Municipalities covered:* 5 • VEGETATION TYPES: Ab, As, Da, Ds, Pa, Sa, Sd, SO, Sp • COMMENTS: The area covers the basins of important Madeira tributaries, including the slopes between the foothills of the Pacaás Novos and Cotia ranges and the floodplains and igapós of the Guaporé valley. Adjacent areas reveal high species richness, including most of the endemic species of the region between the Madeira and the Tapajós. The presence of species characteristic of savannas (*Rhynchotus rufescens*) has been reported. There is a proposal to create a National Park in an area of 400,000 hectares. Ceded by the army to INCRA.

DIAGNOSTIC ELEMENTS: *Species richness:* 5 • *Endemism:* 5 • *Richness of rare/threatened species:* 5 • *Hotspots:* 2 • *Economically important species:* 5 • *Biological importance:* 5 • *Intrinsic fragility:* 3 • *Conservation level:* 5 • *Level of threat:* 2 • ACTION RECOMMENDED: *Biological inventory:* 5 • *Creation of conservation area:* 5 • *Management:* 5.

AV 078 - Guaporé - PRIORITY LEVEL: A • LOCATION: *State:* Rondônia • *Main municipality:* São Francisco do Guaporé • *Municipalities covered:* 7 • VEGETATION TYPES: Ab, Da, Pa, Sa, Sd, SO, Sp • COMMENTS: Area of high habitat diversity, including terra firme forests, floodplains, flooded grasslands, savannas and hillocky grasslands, where forest, savanna and aquatic species occur. Presence of rare/threatened species, including *Anodorhynchus hyacinthinus* and a large proportion of the endemic species in the region between the Madeira and the Tapajós. Presence of communities of aquatic birds such as the American *Mycteria, Ajaja ajaja*, several types of heron, and some fluvial species (*Rynchops niger, Phaetusa simplex* and *Sterna superciliaris*). It seems to be a migration corridor for aquatic birds between the Pantanal of Mato Grosso and the Madeira floodplains. Area threatened by the degradation of the headwaters of Guaporé tributaries, predatory fishing and hunting and expansion of soybean growing in southern Rondônia
   DIAGNOSTIC ELEMENTS: *Species richness:* 5 • *Endemism:* 4 • *Richness of rare/threatened species:* 3 • *Hotspots:* 5 • *Special biological features:* 5 • *Economically important species:* 5 • *Biological importance:* 5 • *Intrinsic fragility:* 4 • *Conservation level:* 4 • *Level of threat:* 4 • ACTION RECOMMENDED: *Restoration:* 2 • *Biological inventory:* 2 • *Creation of conservation area:* 4 • *Management:* 5.

AV 079 - Abunã - PRIORITY LEVEL: D • LOCATION: *State:* Amazonas/Rondônia • *Main municipality:* Porto Velho • *Municipalities covered:* 2 • VEGETATION TYPES: AA, Ab, As, Ds, SO, Sp • COMMENTS: Region of complex relief with many rapids, considered an area of high species diversity. Surveys undertaken in the nearby area in Bolivia have revealed an outstanding species richness which may also be the case in Brazil. Includes the only area of small bee habitats in Rondônia and campinas.
   DIAGNOSTIC ELEMENTS: *Intrinsic fragility:* 3 • *Conservation level:* 3 • *Level of threat:* 4 • ACTION RECOMMENDED: *Biological inventory:* 5.

AV 080 - Vilhena - PRIORITY LEVEL: C • LOCATION: *State:* Rondônia • *Main municipality:* Vilhena • *Municipalities covered:* 5 • VEGETATION TYPES: AA, Fb, Fs, ON, Sa, SN, SO • COMMENTS: Peripheral savanna area with records of several species characteristic of the biome; unique occurrence of some species (e.g. *Cyanocorax cristatelus*) in Rondônia. Linked to semi-deciduous forests on the slopes of the Serra dos Parecis. Area intensively settled, threatening natural habitats, including the headwaters of the Guaporé tributaries.
   DIAGNOSTIC ELEMENTS: *Species richness:* 3 • *Endemism:* 2 • *Richness of rare/threatened species:* 2 • *Hotspots:* 2 • *Special biological features:* 5 • *Economically important species:* 5 • *Biological importance:* 3 • *Intrinsic fragility:* 5 • *Conservation level:* 1 • *Level of threat:* 5 • ACTION RECOMMENDED: *Restoration:* 5 • *Biological inventory:* 5 • *Creation of conservation area:* 5 • *Management:* 5.

AV 081 - Jaci-Paraná - PRIORITY LEVEL: D • LOCATION: *State:* Rondônia • *Main municipality:* Porto Velho • *Municipalities covered:* 2 • VEGETATION TYPES: As, Ds • COMMENTS: Surveys of nearby areas have revealed high species diversity, including the majority of the endemic species in the region between the Madeira and the Tapajós. There is the possibility of linking up with the area AV 076, to form part of the Guaporé ecological corridor. The fauna is unprotected and under great pressure from settlers. Area of potentially high biological diversity.
   DIAGNOSTIC ELEMENTS: *Endemism:* 4 • *Intrinsic fragility:* 2 • *Conservation level:* 4 • *Level of threat:* 3 • ACTION RECOMMENDED: *Biological inventory:* 5.

AV 082 - Autazes - PRIORITY LEVEL: A • LOCATION: *State:* Amazonas • *Main municipality:* Autazes • *Municipalities covered:* 6 • VEGETATION TYPES: AA, Da, Db, Pa • COMMENTS: Little information on the area.
   DIAGNOSTIC ELEMENTS: *Species richness:* 5 • *Phylogenetic diversity:* 5 • *Endemism:* 5 • *Richness of rare/threatened species:* 5 • *Special biological features:* 4 • *Economically important species:* 5 • *Biological importance:* 5 • *Intrinsic fragility:* 4 • *Conservation level:* 2 • *Level of threat:* 2 • ACTION RECOMMENDED: *Biological inventory:* 4 • *Creation of conservation area:* 5.

AV 083 - Lower Purus - PRIORITY LEVEL: C • LOCATION: *State:* Amazonas • *Main municipality:* Beruri • *Municipalities covered:* 6 • VEGETATION TYPES: Da, Db, Ds • COMMENTS: Existence of an Environmental Protection Area (Middle Purus). Species diversity.
   DIAGNOSTIC ELEMENTS: *Species richness:* 5 • *Phylogenetic diversity:* 5 • *Endemism:* 4 • *Richness of rare/threatened species:* 3 • *Hotspots:* 2 • *Special biological features:* 3 • *Economically important species:* 5 • *Biological importance:* 4 • *Intrinsic fragility:* 2 • *Conservation level:* 2 • *Level of threat:* 2.

AV 084 - Middle Purus - PRIORITY LEVEL: D • LOCATION: *State:* Amazonas • *Main municipality:* Tapauá • *Municipalities covered:* 2 • VEGETATION TYPES: Ab, Da, Db, Ds • COMMENTS: Lack of knowledge about the area.
   ACTION RECOMMENDED: *Biological inventory:* 5.

AV 085 - Ituxi River - PRIORITY LEVEL: A • LOCATION: *State:* Amazonas • *Main municipality:* Lábrea • *Municipalities covered:* 2 • VEGETATION TYPES: Ab, As, Da, Db, Pa, SO, Sp • COMMENTS: Encompasses an indigenous land of high biological diversity.
   DIAGNOSTIC ELEMENTS: *Species richness:* 5 • *Phylogenetic diversity:* 5 • *Endemism:* 3 • *Richness of rare/threatened species:* 5 • *Hotspots:* 3 • *Special biological features:* 5 • *Economically important species:* 1 • *Biological importance:* 5 • *Intrinsic fragility:* 3 • *Conservation level:* 2 • *Level of threat:* 2 • ACTION RECOMMENDED: *Biological inventory:* 4 • *Creation of conservation area:* 5.

AV 086 - Boca do Acre - PRIORITY LEVEL: D • LOCATION: *State:* Amazonas • *Main municipality:* Lábrea • *Municipalities covered:* 3 • VEGETATION TYPES: AA, Ab, Da, Db, Ds, Pa • COMMENTS: The area has a mosaic of vegetation including areas of alluvial influence, areas of anthropogenic pressure, and also a small patch of campina. This region probably contains high biological diversity, but has no data on bird richness.
   ACTION RECOMMENDED: *Biological inventory:* 5.

AV 087 - Manicoré - PRIORITY LEVEL: A • LOCATION: *State:* Amazonas • *Main municipality:* Manicoré • *Municipalities covered:* 2 • VEGETATION TYPES: Da, Db, Ds, Pa • COMMENTS: Area of high species richness. Bird species potentially threatened. Little information. Endemic species.
   DIAGNOSTIC ELEMENTS: *Species richness:* 5 • *Phylogenetic diversity:* 5 • *Endemism:* 3 • *Richness of rare/threatened species:* 2 • *Hotspots:* 1 • *Special biological features:* 5 • *Economically important species:* 5 • *Biological importance:* 5 • *Intrinsic fragility:* 4 • *Conservation level:* 2 • *Level of threat:* 1 • ACTION RECOMMENDED: *Biological inventory:* 4 • *Creation of conservation area:* 5.

AV 088 - Iaco - PRIORITY LEVEL: D • LOCATION: *State:* Acre • *Main municipality:* Sena Madureira • *Municipalities covered:* 5 • VEGETATION TYPES: Ab, Da, Db • COMMENTS: Alluvial dense rainforest with no bird records so far.
   ACTION RECOMMENDED: *Biological inventory:* 5.

AV 089 - Upper Purus - Envira - PRIORITY LEVEL: D • LOCATION: *State:* Acre • *Main municipality:* Feijó • *Municipalities covered:* 6 • VEGETATION TYPES: Ab, Da, Db • COMMENTS: An area of alluvial dense rainforest with patches of bamboos, probably containing a large number of species. This fact justifies the urgent need for a biological inventory in the region. Includes an area along Brazil-Peru frontier in southern Acre.
   ACTION RECOMMENDED: *Biological inventory:* 5.

AV 090 - Upper Juruá - PRIORITY LEVEL: A • LOCATION: *State:* Acre • *Main municipality:* Porto Walter • *Municipalities covered:* 5 • VEGETATION TYPES: Ab, Da, Db, Ds • COMMENTS: Area of high bird diversity. With twelve new species for Brazil in this region alone, and at least one endemic species. Various rare species or species with restricted geographic distribution recorded.
   DIAGNOSTIC ELEMENTS: *Species richness:* 5 • *Phylogenetic diversity:* 5 • *Endemism:* 5 • *Richness of rare/threatened species:* 5 • *Hotspots:* 1 • *Special biological features:* 1 • *Biological importance:* 5 • *Conservation level:* 5 • *Level of threat:* 3 • ACTION RECOMMENDED: *Management:* 5.

AV 091 - Acre - Bolivia Frontier - PRIORITY LEVEL: D • LOCATION: *State:* AC • *Main municipality:* Brasiléia • *Municipalities covered:* 8 • VEGETATION TYPES: AA, Ab, Da, Db • COMMENTS: Frontier Brazil-Bolivia and Brazil-Peru. Contains areas of probable high biological diversity.
   ACTION RECOMMENDED: *Biological inventory:* 5.

AV 092 - Tefé - Coari - PRIORITY LEVEL: D • LOCATION: *State:* Amazonas • *Main municipality:* Coari • *Municipalities covered:* 6 • VEGETATION

TYPES: AA, Da, Db, Ds, Pa • COMMENTS: Area with gaps in knowledge. ACTION RECOMMENDED: *Biological inventory:* 5.

AV 093 - Lower Jutaí - Juruá - PRIORITY LEVEL: A • LOCATION: *State:* Amazonas • *Main municipality:* Juruá • *Municipalities covered:* 8 • VEGETATION TYPES: Ab, Da, Db • COMMENTS: Important stretch of open and the lower Juruá dense rainforests and floodplains.

DIAGNOSTIC ELEMENTS: *Species richness:* 5 • *Phylogenetic diversity:* 4 • *Endemism:* 3 • *Richness of rare/threatened species:* 4 • *Hotspots:* 3 • *Special biological features:* 2 • *Biological importance:* 4 • *Intrinsic fragility:* 3 • *Conservation level:* 2 • *Level of threat:* 2 • ACTION RECOMMENDED: *Biological inventory:* 4 • *Creation of conservation area:* 5.

AV 094 - Middle Juruá - PRIORITY LEVEL: D • LOCATION: *State:* Amazonas • *Main municipality:* Carauari • *Municipalities covered:* 4 • VEGETATION TYPES: Ab, Da, Db • COMMENTS: In light of research carried out in nearby rainforest areas, this region is likely to contain a large number of species of restricted geographical distribution.

ACTION RECOMMENDED: *Biological inventory:* 5.

AV 095 - Jaquirana - Ipixuna Rivers - PRIORITY LEVEL: D • LOCATION: *State:* Acre/Amazonas • *Main municipality:* Atalaia do Norte • *Municipalities covered:* 3 • VEGETATION TYPES: AA, Ab, Da, Db, La, Ld • COMMENTS: Brazil-Peru frontier area as yet unstudied, but which probably contains high biological diversity.

ACTION RECOMMENDED: *Biological inventory:* 5.

AV 096 - Quixito River - PRIORITY LEVEL: D • LOCATION: *State:* Amazonas • *Main municipality:* Atalaia do Norte • *Municipalities covered:* 2 • VEGETATION TYPES: AA, Ab, Da, Db • COMMENTS: Frontier area with probably high biological diversity.

ACTION RECOMMENDED: *Biological inventory:* 5.

AV 097 - Mamirauá - PRIORITY LEVEL: B • LOCATION: *State:* Amazonas • *Main municipality:* Fonte Boa • *Municipalities covered:* 7 • VEGETATION TYPES: Da, Db, Pa • COMMENTS: The largest area of floodplain forest in central Amazonia, with important populations of macaws, horned screamers and parrots. The whole floodplain region is contained within the state-level Mamirauá Sustainable Development Reserve.

DIAGNOSTIC ELEMENTS: *Species richness:* 3 • *Special biological features:* 5 • *Intrinsic fragility:* 3 • *Conservation level:* 2 • *Level of threat:* 2 • ACTION RECOMMENDED: *Restoration:* 3 • *Biological inventory:* 3 • *Management:* 5.

AV 098 - Upper Içá - PRIORITY LEVEL: D • LOCATION: *State:* Amazonas • *Main municipality:* Santo Antônio do Içá • *Municipalities covered:* 3 • VEGETATION TYPES: Da, Db, Ld, LO • COMMENTS: Unknown area and unique in the ecoregion.

ACTION RECOMMENDED: *Biological inventory:* 5.

AV 099 - Eirunepé - PRIORITY LEVEL: B • LOCATION: *State:* Amazonas • *Main municipality:* Eirunepé • *Municipalities covered:* 5 • VEGETATION TYPES: AA, Ab, Da, Db • COMMENTS: Region of high bird diversity, including rare species or species of restricted geographical distribution.

DIAGNOSTIC ELEMENTS: *Species richness:* 5 • *Phylogenetic diversity:* 5 • *Endemism:* 5 • *Richness of rare/threatened species:* 5 • *Hotspots:* 1 • *Special biological features:* 5 • *Biological importance:* 5 • *Intrinsic fragility:* 1 • *Conservation level:* 1 • *Level of threat:* 1 • ACTION RECOMMENDED: *Creation of conservation area:* 5.

AV 100 - Maraã - PRIORITY LEVEL: C • LOCATION: *State:* Amazonas • *Main municipality:* Santa Isabel do Rio Negro • *Municipalities covered:* 4 • VEGETATION TYPES: Da, Db, La, Ld, LO • COMMENTS: Endemism in the region between the Japurá and the Rio Negro.

DIAGNOSTIC ELEMENTS: *Species richness:* 4 • *Phylogenetic diversity:* 4 • *Endemism:* 5 • *Richness of rare/threatened species:* 5 • *Hotspots:* 1 • *Economically important species:* 3 • *Biological importance:* 4 • *Intrinsic fragility:* 1 • *Conservation level:* 5 • *Level of threat:* 1 • ACTION RECOMMENDED: *Creation of conservation area:* 5.

AV 101 - Manacapuru - PRIORITY LEVEL: B • LOCATION: *State:* Amazonas • *Main municipality:* Manacapuru • *Municipalities covered:* 4 • VEGETATION TYPES: AA, Da, Db, Pa • COMMENTS: Distribution of endemic species of the Rio Negro basin. Occurrence of habitats with restricted distribution in Amazonia. Occurrence of highly restricted species (e.g. *Nonnula amaurocephala*).

DIAGNOSTIC ELEMENTS: *Phylogenetic diversity:* 4 • *Endemism:* 5 • *Richness of rare/threatened species:* 1 • *Hotspots:* 1 • *Special biological features:* 1 • *Economically important species:* 1 • *Biological importance:* 4 • *Intrinsic fragility:* 5 • *Conservation level:* 1 • *Level of threat:* 3 • ACTION RECOMMENDED: *Biological inventory:* 2 • *Creation of conservation area:* 5 • *Management:* 4.

AV 102 - Cachimbo - PRIORITY LEVEL: A • LOCATION: *State:* Pará • *Main municipality:* Novo Progresso • *Municipalities covered:* 4 • VEGETATION TYPES: As, Cs, Da, ON, Sa, Sd, Sg, SN, SO, Sp • COMMENTS: The Serra do Cachimbo is an extremely ecologically diverse area, with a mosaic of different type of forests, campinas and savannas. Rare species such as the *Rhytipterna immunda* occur in the region. Endemic species are likely to be found.

DIAGNOSTIC ELEMENTS: *Species richness:* 5 • *Phylogenetic diversity:* 5 • *Endemism:* 5 • *Richness of rare/threatened species:* 4 • *Hotspots:* 3 • *Special biological features:* 5 • *Biological importance:* 5 • *Intrinsic fragility:* 5 • *Conservation level:* 1 • *Level of threat:* 3 • ACTION RECOMMENDED: *Restoration:* 1 • *Biological inventory:* 4 • *Creation of conservation area:* 5 • *Management:* 4.

AV 103 - Humaitá - PRIORITY LEVEL: A • LOCATION: *State:* Amazonas/Rondônia • *Main municipality:* Canutama • *Municipalities covered:* 4 • VEGETATION TYPES: AA, Ab, Da, Db, Sa, Sg, SO, Sp • COMMENTS: Important island of isolated savanna along the Madeira. Contains isolated populations of cerrado bird species undergoing processes of differentiation. Several species of migratory birds from southern South America over-winter or use the locality. Characteristic species: *Rhynchotus rufescens, Lepidocolaptes angustirostris*.

DIAGNOSTIC ELEMENTS: *Species richness:* 3 • *Phylogenetic diversity:* 3 • *Endemism:* 3 • *Richness of rare/threatened species:* 3 • *Hotspots:* 3 • *Special biological features:* 4 • *Biological importance:* 3 • *Intrinsic fragility:* 5 • *Conservation level:* 3 • *Level of threat:* 5 • ACTION RECOMMENDED: *Restoration:* 3 • *Biological inventory:* 4 • *Creation of conservation area:* 5 • *Management:* 5.

AV 104 - Pacaás - Guaporé - PRIORITY LEVEL: C • LOCATION: *State:* Rondônia • *Main municipality:* Alvorada d'Oeste • *Municipalities covered:* 14 • VEGETATION TYPES: AA, As, Ds, Sa, Sd, SO, Sp • COMMENTS: Area included in the Savanna and Wetlands Workshop, corresponding to the Urupá grasslands region, one of the (originally) largest savanna enclaves in Rondônia. The greater part now occupied as a result of settlement along the BR-364 highway. Part of this system of savannas is included in area 77.

DIAGNOSTIC ELEMENTS: *Intrinsic fragility:* 5 • *Conservation level:* 5 • *Level of threat:* 5 • ACTION RECOMMENDED: *Restoration:* 4 • *Biological inventory:* 5.

AV 105 - Mucajaí - PRIORITY LEVEL: B • LOCATION: *State:* Roraima • *Main municipality:* Mucajaí • *Municipalities covered:* 6 • VEGETATION TYPES: Ds, Ld, LO, ON, Sg, SN • COMMENTS: Presence of threatened species, such as *Cercomacra carbonaria*, which is only found in gallery forest in Roraima.

DIAGNOSTIC ELEMENTS: *Species richness:* 4 • *Phylogenetic diversity:* 4 • *Endemism:* 3 • *Richness of rare/threatened species:* 3 • *Hotspots:* 3 • *Special biological features:* 3 • *Biological importance:* 4 • *Intrinsic fragility:* 3 • *Conservation level:* 4 • *Level of threat:* 5 • ACTION RECOMMENDED: *Restoration:* 2 • *Biological inventory:* 3 • *Creation of conservation area:* 5 • *Management:* 4.

AV 106 - Headwaters of the Marmelos - PRIORITY LEVEL: D • LOCATION: *State:* Amazonas/Mato Grosso/Rondônia • *Main municipality:* Manicoré • *Municipalities covered:* 5 • VEGETATION TYPES: As, Db, Ds, Pa, Sa, SO, Sp • COMMENTS: Area of savanna in the middle of dense rainforest.

ACTION RECOMMENDED: *Biological inventory:* 5.

AV 107 - Ribeirão Cascalheira and areas in the Araguaia, Tocantins and Maranhão cerrados - PRIORITY LEVEL: A • LOCATION: *State:* Maranhão/Mato Grosso/Pará/Tocantins • *Main municipality:* Cocalinho • *Municipalities covered:* 70 • VEGETATION TYPES: AA, As, Cs, Fa, Fs, ON, Sa, Sd, Sg, SN, SO, Sp • COMMENTS: Ten areas incorporated as a result of the 'Priority Actions for the Conservation of the Biodiversity of the Cerrado and the Pantanal' project, in accordance with the map published by Conservation International in 1999.

ACTION RECOMMENDED: *Creation of conservation area:* 5 • *Management:* 5.

AV 108 - Papagaio River - PRIORITY LEVEL: B • LOCATION: *State:* Mato Grosso • *Main municipality:* Tangará da Serra • *Municipalities covered:* 11 • VEGETATION TYPES: AA, Fa, Sa, Sd, SN, Sp • COMMENTS: incorporated as a result of the 'Priority Action for the Conservation of the Biodiversity of the Cerrado and the Pantanal' project, in accordance with the map published by Conservation International in 1999.

ACTION RECOMMENDED: *Biological inventory:* 5.

AV 109 - Headwaters of the Xingu, Alto Boa Vista and southern Tocantins - PRIORITY LEVEL: D • LOCATION: *State:* Mato Grosso/Tocantins • *Main municipality:* Paranatinga • *Municipalities covered:* 22 • VEGETATION TYPES: AA, Cs, Fa, Fs, ON, Pa, Sa, Sd, SN, Sp • COMMENTS: Three areas incorporated as a result of the 'Priority Action for the Conservation of the Biodiversity of the Cerrado and the Pantanal' project, in accordance with the map published by Conservation International in 1999.

ACTION RECOMMENDED: *Biological inventory:* 5

2
PRIORITY AREAS FOR AQUATIC BIOTA*

Aquatic, marine and inland water environments contain a great variety of living beings from different kingdoms, ranging from algae and bacteria, through macrophytes and arthropods (crustaceans and insects), and ending up with vertebrates. Of the fauna inhabiting aquatic environments, fish constitute a little more than half of the known vertebrate species in the world with 24,618 species, of which 9,966 species are permanent fresh water inhabitants (Nelson 1994).

The size of the Amazon basin and its great environmental heterogeneity are factors of fundamental importance for the maintenance of its high diversity. The characteristics of the basin and the landscapes it contains constitute the background to any consideration of its aquatic system.

The drainage area of the Amazon river, together with that of the Tocantins, amounts to 6,869,000 km^2, meaning it is one and a half times larger than the next largest basin, that of the Congo river in Africa (Marlier 1973). It occupies around one third of the area of South America. The discharge from the Amazon represents almost five times the discharge of the Congo, the second in the world in terms of discharge, and almost 20% of all the freshwater entering the planet's oceans from all rivers.

The Amazon landscape is basically formed by three geological structures: the Andean range to the west and the crystalline shields – the Guiana shield to the north, and the Brazilian shield to the south, as well as the sedimentary basin. These three geological structures are of fundamental importance for the chemical quality of the water and the composition and production of fish in Amazonian rivers, as the drainage area has a decisive influence on the chemical characteristics of its waters. The current classification of water types follows that of the geological structures and can be grouped into three types: white water, clear water and black water (Sioli 1967, 1975; Sioli and Klinge 1965).

White water rivers are those holding large quantities of material in suspension and, as a result, are highly turbid with a visibility of around 20 cm. Examples are the Juruá, Purus and Madeira rivers. Clear water rivers are highly transparent with a visibility of up to five meters, such as the Tapajós, Xingu and Trombetas. Black water rivers, such as the Rio Negro and the Urubu, contain a very high level of acidic colloidal humus, making their waters dark and with a low pH level of 4 to 5.5.

The number of fish species in Latin America is still unknown, but the greatest diversity is found in Amazonia (Menezes 1996). Roberts (1972) estimates the number of fish species within the basin to be greater than 1,300; a number larger than that found for any other basin in the world. Böhlke et al. (1978) consider that the present state of knowledge of fish fauna in South America is on a level with that of the United States and Canada a hundred years ago and that at least 40% of species have not yet been described. This would increase the total to around 1,800. Menezes (1996) estimates the number of fish species in South America to be around 3,000.

The Brazilian Amazon contains 68% of the total drainage area of the basin and assessments of its diversity have been made for different regions. Goulding et al. (1988) identified at least 450 fish species in the Rio Negro, but estimate that this total will pass 700 when the different biotypes are properly sampled. Santos (1986, 1987) found more than 260 species in the Jamari, Machado, Guaporé and Mamoré rivers in the state of Rondônia. Bayley (1982) found more than 220 species in the Solimões floodplain area near Manaus. Santos et al. (1984) inventoried more than 300 species just in the channel of the lower Tocantins. Ferreira et al. (1998) list more than 130 commercial fish species in the floodplain region of Santarém. Many of these species are widely distributed, including migratory species such as the tambaqui (Araújo-Lima and Goulding 1998) and the large catfish (Barthem and Goulding 1997). Others are restricted to specific regions as a result of environmental barriers, such as the Amazon river itself for species inhabiting the headwaters of its tributaries, or the chemical characteristics of the water.

Various factors have been proposed as the cause of this high diversity, such as the age and size of the drainage system; high environmental heterogeneity leading to a great diversity of niches; and, over geological time, a history of capture of rivers from neighboring basins allowing the interchange of fauna. These are some of the causes of the high alpha and beta diversity levels (Lowe-McConnell 1987).

However we know that the numbers given underestimate the real situation, since finding new species is very common and there are several groups whose description warrants more attention. An example of the backwardness of our knowledge of Amazon fish fauna, even in relation to the knowledge of species held by local fishers, is the case of Merodontotus tigrinum, a species of the family Pimelodidae (Siluriformes), large in size (around 55 cm) and which has recently been described (Britski 1981). It is not difficult to imagine that there is a high level of endemism in the headwaters (Menezes 1996) and that future review will separate out species that are currently thought of as being a single species, including some that are extremely well-known to all of us such as the filhote or the piraíba.

---

* Text drawn in part from 'Aquatic biota' by Ronaldo B. Barthem, the full version of which can be found on page 62 of this book.

There is no reliable information about threats, disappearances or extinctions of fish species in the Brazilian Amazon. What has frequently happened is the reduction or even the local disappearance of some species as a result of excessive capture or of some environmental change, such as the clearing of bank-side vegetation, mining on the river bed, or impoundment.

There are two Amazon species recorded by IUCN as 'data deficient', where more information is needed for a better assessment. The pirarucu (*Arapaima gigas*) is one of these and, despite being considered a species liable to suffer extinction as a result of human activity, its populations have so far survived even under the pressure of fishing and in highly altered environments, such as the lakes on Marajó island or the lower Amazon. The other species, *Phreatobius cisternatum*, inhabits the water table of a large area at the mouth of the Amazon. The extent of its distribution and whether or not it is threatened are both unknown.

The adoption of keystone (endemic or rare) species to define priority conservation areas runs into the problem of the lack of knowledge on the taxonomic composition and distribution patterns of its fish fauna (Menezes 1996). The lack of good collections in the region as a whole makes the identification of areas of endemism difficult. Because of this, the premise on which the definition of priority actions is based should be that, if the mechanisms controlling the aquatic ecological system are conserved, the greater the likelihood that the aquatic biodiversity will also be conserved.

Environments such as the rapids and small streams of the crystalline Guiana and Brazilian shields, the main river channels, and the different types of flooded areas (by river overflow, forests and savannas periodically flooded by rain, and tidally flooded coastal areas) house not just endemic species, but also a huge fish biomass that is exploited by commercial and subsistence fisheries. These environments can be regarded as keystone environments, which will assist in the definition of priority areas for conservation. One way of classifying these environments can be to consider the different sub-basins of the Amazon basin, the landscapes defined by their geological pasts, and the different types of flooded areas. In addition to these aspects, the study undertaken of migratory species reveals that conservation actions and biodiversity management should be brought together and should involve the countries that share the Amazon basin.

In this way priority actions for the conservation and sustainable use of the biological diversity of the aquatic system of the Brazilian Amazon should be concentrated on studies of the taxonomy, biogeography, biology and ecology of the endemic species of specific regions and of migratory species, and actions to protect and manage the following keystone environments: the flooded areas of the Amazon plain (floodplains and igapós); flooded areas, rapids and headwaters of the Guiana shield (the Rio Negro, Trombetas, Jari, Araguari and other rivers); flooded areas, rapids and headwaters of the Brazilian shield (the Tocantins, Xingu, Tapajós and tributaries of the Madeira rivers); and the Andean foothills (the Amazonas, Madeira, Purus, Juruá and Japurá rivers).

During the Macapá Workshop, 31 priority areas for the aquatic biota of the Amazon were identified (see the map on page 444 and the listing). Of these, 19 (61.3%) reveal high levels of phylogenetic diversity, 14 (45.2%) contain species diversity, and 13 (41.9%) contain economically important species and show high levels of threat of degradation (Table 2).

TABLE 2 - PRIORITY AREAS FOR AQUATIC BIOTA DIAGNOSTIC ELEMENTS THAT SCORE HIGHEST		
Diagnostic elements	Number of areas	%[1]
Species richness	14	45.2
Phylogenetic diversity	19	61.3
Endemism	6	19.4
Richness of rare or threatened species	4	12.9
Hotspots	10	32.3
Special biological features	11	35.5
Economically important species	13	41.9
Biological importance	13	41.9
Intrinsic fragility	15	48.4
Conservation level	0	-
Level of threat	13	41.9

1. Of the total proposed areas (31).

BA 001 - Aripuanã - Roosevelt - PRIORITY LEVEL: A • LOCATION: *State:* Amazonas/Mato Grosso/Rondônia • *Main municipality:* Aripuanã • *Municipalities covered:* 12 • VEGETATION TYPES: AA, As, Da, Db, Ds, Fs, ON, Pa, Sa, Sd, Sg, SN, SO, Sp • COMMENTS: Little studied area, with average anthropogenic impact. Area of known importance for endemic species (Menezes, Santos).

DIAGNOSTIC ELEMENTS: *Species richness:* 5 • *Phylogenetic diversity:* 5 • *Endemism:* 5 • *Richness of rare/threatened species:* 5 • *Hotspots:* 5 • *Special biological features:* 3 • *Economically important species:* 5 • *Biological importance:* 5 • *Intrinsic fragility:* 4 • *Conservation level:* 3 • *Level of threat:* 4 • ACTION RECOMMENDED: *Restoration:* 2 • *Biological inventory:* 5 • *Creation of conservation area:* 5 • *Management:* 4.

BA 002 - Guaporé - PRIORITY LEVEL: B • LOCATION: *State:* Rondônia • *Main municipality:* Guajará-Mirim • *Municipalities covered:* 19 • VEGETATION TYPES: AA, Ab, As, Da, Ds, Fa, Fb, Fs, ON, Pa, Sa, Sd, Sg, SN, SO, Sp • COMMENTS: Transition area from Andean fauna to that of the Guiana shields. A tributary of the Madeira which rises in an open landscape. High anthropogenic pressure.

DIAGNOSTIC ELEMENTS: *Species richness:* 3 • *Phylogenetic diversity:* 5 • *Endemism:* 3 • *Richness of rare/threatened species:* 3 • *Hotspots:* 4 • *Special biological features:* 3 • *Economically important species:* 3 • *Biological importance:* 4 • *Intrinsic fragility:* 2 • *Conservation level:* 2 • *Level of threat:* 4 • ACTION RECOMMENDED: *Biological inventory:* 5 • *Creation of conservation area:* 4 • *Management:* 1.

BA 003 - Tacutu basin (Negro) - PRIORITY LEVEL: A • LOCATION: *State:* Roraima • *Main municipality:* Uiramutã • *Municipalities covered:* 5 • VEGETATION TYPES: Dm, Ds, ON, Sg, SN, Sp, Td, Tp • COMMENTS: Headwater area of a Rio Branco tributary rising in an open landscape. Watershed suffering very high anthropogenic pressure.

DIAGNOSTIC ELEMENTS: *Species richness:* 3 • *Phylogenetic diversity:* 3 • *Endemism:* 2 • *Richness of rare/threatened species:* 4 • *Hotspots:* 3 • *Special biological features:* 1 • *Economically important species:* 2 • *Biological importance:* 3 • *Intrinsic fragility:* 5 • *Conservation level:* 3 • *Level of threat:* 5 • ACTION RECOMMENDED: *Restoration:* 3 • *Biological inventory:* 4 • *Creation of conservation area:* 4 • *Management:* 3.

BA 004 - Headwaters and rapids of the Jaú and Paru - PRIORITY LEVEL: B • LOCATION: *State:* Amapá/Pará • *Main municipality:* Almeirim • *Municipalities covered:* 5 • VEGETATION TYPES: AA, Da, Dm, Ds, SO, Sp • COMMENTS: Areas of high biological importance, of specific and characteristic composition and richness, revealing endemism linked to environmental heterogeneity.

DIAGNOSTIC ELEMENTS: *Species richness:* 5 • *Phylogenetic diversity:* 5 • *Endemism:* 5 • *Richness of rare/threatened species:* 3 • *Hotspots:* 1 • *Special biological features:* 4 • *Economically important species:* 3 • *Biological importance:* 5 • *Intrinsic fragility:* 5 • *Conservation level:* 1 • *Level of threat:* 1 • ACTION RECOMMENDED: *Biological inventory:* 5 • *Creation of conservation area:* 3 • *Management:* 2.

BA 005 - Headwaters of the Juruá - Acre - PRIORITY LEVEL: B • LOCATION: *State:* Acre/Amazonas • *Main municipality:* Marechal Thaumaturgo • *Municipalities covered:* 8 • VEGETATION TYPES: AA, Ab, Da, Db, Ds, La, Ld • COMMENTS: Located between two areas of high anthropogenic pressure, with endemic species.

DIAGNOSTIC ELEMENTS: *Species richness:* 3 • *Phylogenetic diversity:* 3 • *Endemism:* 2 • *Richness of rare/threatened species:* 2 • *Hotspots:* 2 • *Special biological features:* 1 • *Economically important species:* 2 • *Biological importance:* 3 • *Intrinsic fragility:* 1 • *Conservation level:* 1 • *Level of threat:* 4 • ACTION RECOMMENDED: *Biological inventory:* 5 • *Creation of conservation area:* 4.

BA 006 - Araguari - headwaters and rapids - PRIORITY LEVEL: B • LOCATION: *State:* Amapá • *Main municipality:* Pedra Branca do Amapari • *Municipalities covered:* 10 • VEGETATION TYPES: AA, Da, Db, Ds, Sd, SO, Sp • COMMENTS: Areas of high biological importance, of specific and characteristic composition and richness, revealing endemism linked related to environmental heterogeneity.

DIAGNOSTIC ELEMENTS: *Species richness:* 5 • *Phylogenetic diversity:* 5 • *Endemism:* 5 • *Richness of rare/threatened species:* 3 • *Hotspots:* 1 • *Special biological features:* 4 • *Economically important species:* 3 • *Biological importance:* 5 • *Intrinsic fragility:* 5 • *Conservation level:* 1 • *Level of threat:* 1 • ACTION RECOMMENDED: *Biological inventory:* 5 • *Creation of conservation area:* 3 • *Management:* 2.

BA 007 - Pará and Maranhão Mangroves - PRIORITY LEVEL: A • LOCATION: *State:* Maranhão/Pará • *Main municipality:* Turiaçu • *Municipalities covered:* 90 • VEGETATION TYPES: AA, Da, Pa, Pf • COMMENTS: High biological productivity. Breeding area for marine, inland water and transitional species.

DIAGNOSTIC ELEMENTS: *Species richness:* 2 • *Phylogenetic diversity:* 5 • *Endemism:* 1 • *Richness of rare/threatened species:* 1 • *Hotspots:* 3 • *Special biological features:* 5 • *Economically important species:* 5 • *Biological importance:* 5 • *Intrinsic fragility:* 5 • *Conservation level:* 3 • *Level of threat:* 5 • ACTION RECOMMENDED: *Biological inventory:* 3 • *Creation of conservation area:* 3 • *Management:* 5.

BA 008 - Flooded area in the Barcelos - Monte do Cordeiro region - PRIORITY LEVEL: B • LOCATION: *State:* Amazonas/Roraima • *Main municipality:* Barcelos • *Municipalities covered:* 3 • VEGETATION TYPES: Da, Db, La, Ld, Lg, LO • COMMENTS: Area of high diversity and endemism; capture of fish resources (ornamental fish).

DIAGNOSTIC ELEMENTS: *Species richness:* 5 • *Phylogenetic diversity:* 4 • *Endemism:* 4 • *Richness of rare/threatened species:* 2 • *Hotspots:* 1 • *Special biological features:* 3 • *Economically important species:* 4 • *Biological importance:* 4 • *Intrinsic fragility:* 4 • *Conservation level:* 2 • *Level of threat:* 1 • ACTION RECOMMENDED: *Biological inventory:* 4 • *Creation of conservation area:* 1 • *Management:* 3.

BA 009 - Purus Rapids - PRIORITY LEVEL: B • LOCATION: *State:* Acre/Amazonas • *Main municipality:* Sena Madureira • *Municipalities covered:* 16 • VEGETATION TYPES: AA, Ab, Da, Db • COMMENTS: Area of transition from the fauna from central Brazilian shields to that of the Purus valley.

DIAGNOSTIC ELEMENTS: *Species richness:* 3 • *Phylogenetic diversity:* 2 • *Endemism:* 2 • *Richness of rare/threatened species:* 2 • *Hotspots:* 1 • *Special biological features:* 1 • *Economically important species:* 3 • *Biological importance:* 3 • *Intrinsic fragility:* 2 • *Conservation level:* 2 • *Level of threat:* 1 • ACTION RECOMMENDED: *Biological inventory:* 4 • *Creation of conservation area:* 1 • *Management:* 1.

BA 010 - Teles Pires - Juruena headwaters - PRIORITY LEVEL: A • LOCATION: *State:* Amazonas/Mato Grosso/Pará/Rondônia • *Main municipality:* Juara • *Municipalities covered:* 52 • VEGETATION TYPES: AA, As, Cs, Da, Ds, Fa, Fs, ON, Pa, Sa, Sd, SN, SO, Sp • COMMENTS: Area where the Tapajós tributaries rise, with evidence of high anthropogenic pressure (ranches, etc.).

DIAGNOSTIC ELEMENTS: *Species richness:* 5 • *Phylogenetic diversity:* 5 • *Endemism:* 5 • *Richness of rare/threatened species:* 5 • *Hotspots:* 5 • *Special biological features:* 5 • *Economically important species:* 5 • *Biological importance:* 5 • *Intrinsic fragility:* 5 • *Conservation level:* 2 • *Level of threat:* 4 • ACTION RECOMMENDED: *Biological inventory:* 5 • *Creation of conservation area:* 5 • *Management:* 4.

BA 011 - Madeira Rapids - PRIORITY LEVEL: A • LOCATION: *State:* Amazonas/Rondônia • *Main municipality:* Porto Velho • *Municipalities covered:* 5 • VEGETATION TYPES: AA, Ab, As, Da, Db, SO, Sp • COMMENTS: Hydrologic barrier, with a clear separation of aquatic fauna. Maintenance of commercially important fish stocks. High anthropogenic pressure, caused mainly by prospecting and fishing.

DIAGNOSTIC ELEMENTS: *Species richness:* 4 • *Phylogenetic diversity:* 4 • *Endemism:* 4 • *Richness of rare/threatened species:* 3 • *Hotspots:* 5 • *Special biological features:* 4 • *Economically important species:* 4 • *Biological importance:* 5 • *Intrinsic fragility:* 3 • *Conservation level:* 3 • *Level of threat:* 5 • ACTION RECOMMENDED: *Restoration:* 4 • *Biological inventory:* 4 • *Creation of conservation area:* 5 • *Management:* 4.

BA 012 - Tapajós Rapids - PRIORITY LEVEL: B • LOCATION: *State:* Amazonas/Mato Grosso/Pará • *Main municipality:* Jacareacanga • *Municipalities covered:* 6 • VEGETATION TYPES: AA, As, Da, Ds, SO • COMMENTS: Area of high diversity and endemism, subject to the impacts of prospecting.

DIAGNOSTIC ELEMENTS: *Species richness:* 4 • *Phylogenetic diversity:* 4 • *Endemism:* 4 • *Richness of rare/threatened species:* 5 • *Hotspots:* 5 • *Special biological features:* 3 • *Economically important species:* 4 • *Biological importance:* 5 • *Intrinsic fragility:* 4 • *Conservation level:* 4 • *Level of threat:* 5 • ACTION RECOMMENDED: *Restoration:* 3 • *Biological inventory:* 5 • *Creation of conservation area:* 5 • *Management:* 2.

BA 013 - Flooded areas of the Araguaia and Tocantins rivers - PRIORITY LEVEL: A • LOCATION: *State:* Goiás/Mato Grosso/Pará/Tocantins • *Main municipality:* Formoso do Araguaia • *Municipalities covered:* 22 • VEGETATION TYPES: AA, As, Fa, Sa, Sd, Sg, SN, SO, Sp • COMMENTS: Flooded upper Araguaia environment. Breeding area for turtles; anthropogenic pressure; reasonably protected indigenous reserves; subject to impacts from sport fishing; threatened by waterway construction.

DIAGNOSTIC ELEMENTS: *Species richness:* 4 • *Phylogenetic diversity:* 5 • *Endemism:* 2 • *Richness of rare/threatened species:* 1 • *Hotspots:* 3 • *Special biological features:* 5 • *Economically important species:* 5 • *Biological importance:* 4 • *Intrinsic fragility:* 5 • *Conservation level:* 3 • *Level of threat:* 5 • ACTION RECOMMENDED: *Restoration:* 1 • *Biological inventory:* 5 • *Creation of conservation area:* 1 • *Management:* 5.

BA 014 - Middle Tocantins Rapids region - PRIORITY LEVEL: A • LOCATION: *State:* Maranhão/Tocantins • *Main municipality:* Tocantínia • *Municipalities covered:* 42 • VEGETATION TYPES: AA, As, Sa, Sd, Sg, SN, SO, Sp • COMMENTS: Tocantins rapids area subject to strong anthropogenic pressures (hydroelectric plant and waterway under construction). These impacts require greater attention.

DIAGNOSTIC ELEMENTS: *Species richness:* 3 • *Phylogenetic diversity:* 5 • *Endemism:* 2 • *Richness of rare/threatened species:* 1 • *Hotspots:* 3 • *Special biological features:* 2 • *Economically important species:* 2 • *Biological importance:* 2 • *Intrinsic fragility:* 1 • *Conservation level:* 4 • *Level of threat:* 5 • ACTION RECOMMENDED: *Biological inventory:* 5 • *Creation of conservation area:* 4.

BA 015 - Anavilhanas Archipelago and Flooded Areas of the Rio Branco - PRIORITY LEVEL: B • LOCATION: *State:* Amazonas/Roraima • *Main municipality:* Caracaraí • *Municipalities covered:* 6 • VEGETATION TYPES: Ab, As, Da, Db, Ds, La, Ld, Lg, LO • COMMENTS: The region of the lower Rio Branco/Anavilhanas represents an important biotype for feeding and growth of some commercial fish species, as well as housing a set of diverse fish fauna representative of the Rio Negro basin.

DIAGNOSTIC ELEMENTS: *Species richness:* 5 • *Phylogenetic diversity:* 4 • *Endemism:* 2 • *Richness of rare/threatened species:* 2 • *Hotspots:* 2 • *Special biological features:* 2 • *Economically important species:* 4 • *Biological importance:* 4 • *Intrinsic fragility:* 4 • *Conservation level:* 2 • ACTION RECOMMENDED: *Biological inventory:* 2 • *Creation of conservation area:* 1 • *Management:* 1.

BA 016 - Uraricoera Basin - PRIORITY LEVEL: B • LOCATION: *State:* Roraima • *Main municipality:* Amajari • *Municipalities covered:* 4 • VEGETATION TYPES: As, Dm, Ds, Fs, ON, rm, Sg, SN, Sp, Ta, Td, Tp • COMMENTS: Linkage to the Orinoco basin; species richness; high habitat diversity.

DIAGNOSTIC ELEMENTS: *Species richness:* 5 • *Phylogenetic diversity:* 5 • *Endemism:* 3 • *Richness of rare/threatened species:* 2 • *Hotspots:* 1 • *Special biological features:* 2 • *Economically important species:* 3 • *Biological importance:* 4 • *Intrinsic fragility:* 2 • *Conservation level:* 2 • *Level of threat:* 1 • ACTION RECOMMENDED: *Restoration:* 1 • *Biological inventory:* 5 • *Creation of conservation area:* 4 • *Management:* 1.

BA 017 - Amapá Mangroves - PRIORITY LEVEL: A • LOCATION: *State:* Amapá • *Main municipality:* Oiapoque • *Municipalities covered:* 5 • VEGETATION TYPES: Da, Db, Ds, Pa, Pf, Sa, SO, Sp • COMMENTS: High biological productivity. Breeding ground for marine, transitional and inland water species.

DIAGNOSTIC ELEMENTS: *Species richness:* 2 • *Phylogenetic diversity:* 5 • *Endemism:* 1 • *Richness of rare/threatened species:* 1 • *Hotspots:* 3 • *Special biological features:* 5 • *Economically important species:* 5 • *Biological importance:* 5 • *Intrinsic fragility:* 5 • *Conservation level:* 1 • *Level of threat:* 3 • ACTION RECOMMENDED: *Biological inventory:* 3 • *Creation of conservation area:* 5 • *Management:* 5.

BA 018 - Middle Madeira Floodplains - PRIORITY LEVEL: A • LOCATION: *State:* Amazonas/Rondônia • *Main municipality:* Humaitá • *Municipalities covered:* 5 • VEGETATION TYPES: Ab, Da, Db, Pa, SO, Sp • COMMENTS: Area of high importance for the composition and productivity of Amazon basin fish. Area of expansion of agricultural frontier. Suffering land use impacts.

DIAGNOSTIC ELEMENTS: *Species richness:* 4 • *Phylogenetic diversity:* 5 • *Endemism:* 4 • *Richness of rare/threatened species:* 2 • *Hotspots:* 5 • *Special biological features:* 5 • *Economically important species:* 5 • *Biological importance:* 4 • *Intrinsic fragility:* 5 • *Conservation level:* 2 • *Level of threat:* 3 • ACTION RECOMMENDED: *Restoration:* 2 • *Biological inventory:* 5 • *Creation of conservation area:* 3 • *Management:* 3.

BA 019 - Solimões and Amazonas Floodplains - PRIORITY LEVEL: A • LOCATION: *State:* Amazonas/Pará • *Main municipality:* Fonte Boa • *Municipalities covered:* 47 • VEGETATION TYPES: AA, Ab, As, Da, Db, Ds, La, LO, Pa, SO, Sp • COMMENTS: Extremely important area for composition and production of Amazon basin fish. Area of expansion of agricultural frontier. Suffering land use impacts (ranching, agriculture and prospecting).

DIAGNOSTIC ELEMENTS: *Species richness:* 4 • *Phylogenetic diversity:* 5 • *Endemism:* 4 • *Richness of rare/threatened species:* 2 • *Hotspots:* 5 • *Special biological features:* 5 • *Economically important species:* 5 • *Biological importance:* 4 • *Intrinsic fragility:* 5 • *Conservation level:* 4 • *Level of threat:* 5 • ACTION RECOMMENDED: *Restoration:* 3 • *Biological inventory:* 5 • *Creation of conservation area:* 3 • *Management:* 5.

BA 020 - Juruá and Amazonas Floodplains - PRIORITY LEVEL: B • LOCATION: *State:* Acre/Amazonas • *Main municipality:* Carauari • *Municipalities covered:* 16 • VEGETATION TYPES: AA, Ab, Da, Db, La, Ld • COMMENTS: Extremely important area for composition and production of Amazon basin fish.

DIAGNOSTIC ELEMENTS: *Species richness:* 4 • *Phylogenetic diversity:* 5 • *Endemism:* 4 • *Richness of rare/threatened species:* 2 • *Hotspots:* 5 • *Special biological features:* 5 • *Economically important species:* 5 • *Biological importance:* 4 • *Intrinsic fragility:* 5 • *Conservation level:* 1 • *Level of threat:* 5 • ACTION RECOMMENDED: *Biological inventory:* 5 • *Creation of conservation area:* 3 • *Management:* 5.

BA 021 - Purus Floodplains - PRIORITY LEVEL: B • LOCATION: *State:* Amazonas • *Main municipality:* Tapauá • *Municipalities covered:* 7 • VEGETATION TYPES: Ab, Da, Db, Ds, Pa, SO • COMMENTS: Extremely important area for composition and production of Amazon basin fish.

DIAGNOSTIC ELEMENTS: *Species richness:* 4 • *Phylogenetic diversity:* 5 • *Endemism:* 4 • *Richness of rare/threatened species:* 2 • *Hotspots:* 5 • *Special biological features:* 5 • *Economically important species:* 5 • *Biological importance:* 4 • *Intrinsic fragility:* 5 • *Conservation level:* 1 • *Level of threat:* 5 • ACTION RECOMMENDED: *Biological inventory:* 5 • *Creation of conservation area:* 3 • *Management:* 5.

BA 022 - Jutaí Floodplains - PRIORITY LEVEL: B • LOCATION: *State:* Amazonas • *Main municipality:* Jutaí • *Municipalities covered:* 1 • VEGETATION TYPES: Ab, Da, Db, Pa • COMMENTS: Extremely important area for composition and production of Amazon basin fish.

DIAGNOSTIC ELEMENTS: *Species richness:* 4 • *Phylogenetic diversity:* 5 • *Endemism:* 4 • *Richness of rare/threatened species:* 2 • *Hotspots:* 5 • *Special biological features:* 5 • *Economically important species:* 5 • *Biological importance:* 4 • *Intrinsic fragility:* 5 • *Conservation level:* 1 • *Level of threat:* 5 • ACTION RECOMMENDED: *Biological inventory:* 5 • *Creation of conservation area:* 3 • *Management:* 5.

BA 023 - Japurá Floodplains, above the Auati-Paraná - PRIORITY LEVEL: B • LOCATION: *State:* Amazonas • *Main municipality:* Japurá • *Municipalities covered:* 3 • VEGETATION TYPES: Ab, Da, Db, Ds, La, Ld, LO • COMMENTS: Extremely important area for composition and production of Amazon basin fish.

DIAGNOSTIC ELEMENTS: *Species richness:* 4 • *Phylogenetic diversity:* 5 • *Endemism:* 4 • *Richness of rare/threatened species:* 2 • *Hotspots:* 5 • *Special biological features:* 5 • *Economically important species:* 5 • *Biological importance:* 4 • *Intrinsic fragility:* 5 • *Conservation* level: 1 • Level of threat: 5 • ACTION RECOMMENDED: *Biological inventory:* 5 • *Creation of conservation area:* 3 • *Management:* 5.

BA 024 - Rio Javari Basin - PRIORITY LEVEL: B • LOCATION: *State:* Amazonas • *Main municipality:* Atalaia do Norte • *Municipalities covered:* 2 • VEGETATION TYPES: Ab, Da, Db • COMMENTS: Area of high species richness, with the presence of endemic species from the upper Solimões.

DIAGNOSTIC ELEMENTS: *Species richness:* 5 • *Phylogenetic diversity:* 5 • *Endemism:* 5 • *Richness of rare/threatened species:* 2 • *Hotspots:* 3 • *Special biological features:* 1 • *Economically important species:* 2 • *Biological importance:* 5 • *Intrinsic fragility:* 3 • *Conservation level:* 3 • *Level of threat:* 3 • ACTION RECOMMENDED: *Biological inventory:* 4 • *Creation of conservation area:* 1 • *Management:* 2.

BA 025 - Headwaters and Rapids of the Trombetas - PRIORITY LEVEL: A • LOCATION: *State:* Amazonas/Pará/Roraima • *Main municipality:* Oriximiná • *Municipalities covered:* 6 • VEGETATION TYPES: As, Da, Db, Dm, Ds, Pa, Sd, SO, Sp • COMMENTS: Area of high diversity and endemism.

DIAGNOSTIC ELEMENTS: *Species richness:* 5 • *Phylogenetic diversity:* 4 • *Endemism:* 4 • *Richness of rare/threatened species:* 2 • *Hotspots:* 1 • *Special biological features:* 2 • *Economically important species:* 2 • *Biological importance:* 5 • *Intrinsic fragility:* 3 • *Conservation level:* 2 • *Level of threat:* 1 • ACTION RECOMMENDED: *Biological inventory:* 3 • *Creation of conservation area:* 2 • *Management:* 1.

BA 026 - Jaú and Unini basins - PRIORITY LEVEL: A • LOCATION: *State:* Amazonas • *Main municipality:* Barcelos • *Municipalities covered:* 4 • VEGETATION TYPES: Ab, Da, Db, Ds, La, Ld, Lg, LO • COMMENTS: The Jaú basin is located within the Jaú National Park and is important for the size of the protected area and for the diversity of species of fish occurring (350 species or more). Important as frontier of aquatic mammal species.

DIAGNOSTIC ELEMENTS: *Species richness:* 5 • *Phylogenetic diversity:* 4 • *Endemism:* 2 • *Richness of rare/threatened species:* 2 • *Hotspots:* 1 • *Special biological features:* 1 • *Economically important species:* 3 • *Biological importance:* 5 • *Intrinsic fragility:* 4 • *Conservation level:* 2 • *Level of threat:* 1 • ACTION RECOMMENDED: *Biological inventory:* 2 • *Management:* 1.

BA 027 - Amazon delta, islands and estuary plains of Amapá - PRIORITY LEVEL: A • LOCATION: *State:* Amapá/Pará • *Main municipality:* Anajás • *Municipalities covered:* 29 • VEGETATION TYPES: AA, Da, Db, Pa, Pf, Sd, SO, Sp • COMMENTS: Area flooded by tides or rain, encompassing communities adapted to flooded landscape conditions with physiological stress and high biological productivity.

DIAGNOSTIC ELEMENTS: *Species richness:* 5 • *Phylogenetic diversity:* 5 • *Endemism:* 1 • *Richness of rare/threatened species:* 1 • *Hotspots:* 3 • *Special biological features:* 5 • *Economically important species:* 5 • *Biological importance:* 5 • *Intrinsic fragility:* 5 • *Conservation level:* 2 • *Level of threat:* 5 • ACTION RECOMMENDED: *Biological inventory:* 3 • *Creation of conservation area:* 5 • *Management:* 5.

BA 028 - Middle Xingu and rapids - PRIORITY LEVEL: B • LOCATION: *State:* Mato Grosso/Pará • *Main municipality:* São Félix do Xingu • *Municipalities covered:* 6 • VEGETATION TYPES: AA, As, Da, Ds, ON, Pa, Sa, Sd, Sg, SO, Sp • COMMENTS: Area of rapids under strong pressure from commercial fishing. Area reasonably conserved as a result of being located between conservation areas and indigenous lands.

DIAGNOSTIC ELEMENTS: *Species richness:* 5 • *Phylogenetic diversity:* 4 • *Endemism:* 5 • *Richness of rare/threatened species:* 5 • *Hotspots:* 2 • *Special biological features:* 2 • *Economically important species:* 5 • *Biological importance:* 4 • *Intrinsic fragility:* 1 • *Conservation level:* 2 • *Level of threat:* 2 • ACTION RECOMMENDED: *Restoration:* 1 • *Biological inventory:* 5 • *Creation of conservation area:* 2.

BA 029 - Xingu headwaters - PRIORITY LEVEL: A • LOCATION: *State:* Mato Grosso • *Main municipality:* Paranatinga • *Municipalities covered:* 15 • VEGETATION TYPES: AA, Da, Fa, ON, Pa, Sa, Sd, SN, Sp • COMMENTS: Headwaters of the Xingu located between areas of high anthropogenic pressure followed by an area of ecological tension. There is evidence of endemism and of high diversity, still unstudied. Occurrence of threatened species (giant river otter).

DIAGNOSTIC ELEMENTS: *Species richness:* 5 • *Phylogenetic diversity:* 5 • *Endemism:* 3 • *Hotspots:* 3 • *Economically important species:* 2 • *Biological importance:* 5 • *Intrinsic fragility:* 5 • *Conservation level:* 2 • *Level of threat:* 5 • ACTION RECOMMENDED: *Restoration:* 5 • *Biological inventory:* 5 • *Creation of conservation area:* 5.

BA 030 - Upper Rio Negro, upstream from Barcelos - PRIORITY LEVEL: B • LOCATION: *State:* Amazonas • *Main municipality:* São Gabriel da Cachoeira • *Municipalities covered:* 5 • VEGETATION TYPES: Ab, As, Da, Db, Dm, Ds, La, Ld, Lg, LO, rm • COMMENTS: Area of high diversity and endemism, fishing and anthropogenic pressure from indians.

DIAGNOSTIC ELEMENTS: *Species richness:* 5 • *Phylogenetic diversity:* 4 • *Endemism:* 4 • *Richness of rare/threatened species:* 2 • *Hotspots:* 1 • *Special biological features:* 3 • *Economically important species:* 4 • *Biological importance:* 4 • *Intrinsic fragility:* 4 • *Conservation level:* 2 • *Level of threat:* 1 • ACTION RECOMMENDED: *Biological inventory:* 4 • *Creation of conservation area:* 1 • *Management:* 3.

BA 031 - Legal Amazon - PRIORITY LEVEL: D • LOCATION: *State:* All • *Main municipality:* Various • *Municipalities covered:* 219 • VEGETATION TYPES: Several • COMMENTS: Eighteen areas with gaps of information, identified as priorities for biological inventories.

ACTION RECOMMENDED: *Biological inventory:* 5.

3
PRIORITY AREAS FOR MAMMALS*

The total number of existing mammal species in the world is estimated to be 4,650, with 502 represented in Brazil (Vivo 1998). In Amazonia there are currently 311 recorded species: 22 marsupials, 11 edentates, 124 bats, 57 primates, 16 carnivores, 2 cetaceans, 5 ungulates, 1 sirenian, 72 rodents and 1 lagomorph. However these numbers should be regarded as only approximate, as they will certainly need to be revised when taxonomic reviews are carried out.

Given its large size, high species richness and habitat diversity, the gaps in our scientific knowledge of Amazon mammal fauna continue to be enormous. The existing museum collections are incomplete, especially in respect of interfluve areas. In the great majority of localities inventoried only a few mammal groups were covered and the surveys undertaken have been insufficient to populate cumulative species graphs. Studies have shown that undertaking relatively full inventories requires not only long periods in the field (five months or more), but also the use of multiple sampling methods (Voss and Emmons 1996, Simmons and Voss 1998). Voss and Emmons (1996) found only two sites that had been the subject of relatively complete surveys of mammals in the five million square kilometers of the Brazilian Amazon. Full inventories are thus waiting to be carried out in practically the whole region.

This lack of taxonomic knowledge is especially critical in the case of marsupials, rodents and bats, which make up around 70.1% of the taxa but for which the total number of species is still not certain.

Generally speaking, mammal diversity is probably greater in western Amazonia where there are up to 200 sympatric species in some localities, making this one of the most diverse regions in the Americas and possibly the world. Mammal diversity is lower in the region of the Guianas and intermediate in southeastern Amazonia. However Roosmalen (personal communication) argues that in central Amazonia, within a radius of 10 km from the town of Novo Aripuanã at the confluence of the Madeira and Aripuanã rivers, there is a level of primate diversity amounting to more than 21 species (or 23+ taxa), without doubt the highest in the world.

Among the mammal species present in the Brazilian Amazon, six can be classified as rare and 44 are threatened, at risk or considered vulnerable.

Amazonia still has not been properly inventoried. A substantial survey effort is required to identify the patterns and processes that regulate the ecological structuring of sympatric communities, the geographical distribution of species, and biogeographical gradients, amongst other things. This effort needs to be followed by taxonomic reviews of the most problematic groups, using modern methods and analytical approaches. Even for the larger mammal fauna, widely distributed throughout the Amazon basin, we still do not understand the level of genetic and geographic structuring of these species.

Priority areas for inventories are: (i) interfluve regions throughout the entire Amazon basin; (ii) areas of transition vegetation, such as the transition forests between Amazonia and the outside region to the south, dry forests (the transition strip between the Araguaia and the Amazon forest) and semi-deciduous forests; (iii) bamboo forests (*Guadua* spp), campinaranas, cerrado enclaves on the edges of pre-Amazon closed canopy forests and the buriti palm forests (denominated *Mauritia flexuosa*) of eastern Amazonia; (iv) the western Amazon region to the south of the Solimões river, especially along the length of the Madeira and Purus; (v) the western Amazon region to the north of the Solimões river and west of the Rio Negro; (vi) the states of Amazonas, Pará and Amapá to the north of the Amazon river and east of the Rio Negro; (vii) southeastern Amazonia; (viii) areas along the Solimões-Amazonas axis and the lower and middle stretches of the rivers of this region, including the Rio Branco where there is a high degree of habitat heterogeneity in contact, including floodplains, terra firme, lakes and igapós.

Priority areas for conservation are: areas with high diversity and endemic species and regions suffering high anthropogenic pressure, such as the area in the zone of influence of the Transamazonica highway, the Arc of Deforestation, areas susceptible to understorey fires, settlements along the BR-369 highway, the north of Mato Grosso (Alta Floresta, Serra do Roncador, etc.) and the settlement frontier of the upper Jatapu.

During the Macapá Workshop 39 priority areas for mammals in Amazonia were identified (see the map on page 445 and the listing). Of these, 6 (15.4%) are of high biological importance; 4 (10.3%) show high levels of endemism, richness of rare and threatened species, special biological features; and 6 (15.4%) are suffering high levels of threats of degradation (Table 3).

TABLE 3 - PRIORITY AREAS FOR MAMMALS DIAGNOSTIC ELEMENTS THAT SCORE HIGHEST		
Diagnostic elements	Number of areas	%[1]
Species richness	5	12.8
Phylogenetic diversity	2	5.1
Endemism	4	10.3
Richness of rare or threatened species	4	10.3
Hotspots	4	10.3
Special biological features	4	10.3
Economically important species	1	2.6
Biological importance	6	15.4
Intrinsic fragility	4	10.3
Conservation level	3	7.7
Level of threat	6	15.4

1. Of the total proposed areas (39).

---

* Text drawn in part from 'Biogeography and conservation of mammals in the Brazilian Amazon Forest' by Maria Nazareth F. da Silva, Anthony B. Rylands and James L. Patton, the full version of which can be found on page 109 of this book.

MM 001 - Amapá Coast - PRIORITY LEVEL: B • LOCATION: *State:* Amapá • *Main municipality:* Oiapoque • *Municipalities covered:* 9 • VEGETATION TYPES: AA, Da, Db, Ds, Pa, Pf, Sa, Sd, SO, Sp • COMMENTS: Area classified as priority in the Savanna and Floodplain Workshop. Related to area 58 on the final map and to area 2 of mammals working group, both from 1990 Amazonia Workshop. Savanna area threatened by acquisitions for the purpose of transformation into area of monoculture. High importance as wilderness area. Presence of unique vegetation types (and topographies) and 'wilderness areas'. Needs protection of species typical of savannas, occurring only in the Guianas and in Suriname.

DIAGNOSTIC ELEMENTS: *Species richness:* 3 • *Endemism:* 4 • *Richness of rare/threatened species:* 3 • *Hotspots:* 4 • *Special biological features:* 5 • *Biological importance:* 4 • *Intrinsic fragility:* 5 • *Conservation level:* 3 • *Level of threat:* 4 • ACTION RECOMMENDED: *Biological inventory:* 5 • *Creation of conservation area:* 5 • *Management:* 5.

MM 002 - Southern Guianas and neighboring frontiers - PRIORITY LEVEL: D • LOCATION: *State:* Amapá/Pará/Roraima • *Main municipality:* Oriximiná • *Municipalities covered:* 10 • VEGETATION TYPES: As, Da, Dm, Ds, Sd, SO, Sp • COMMENTS: High importance in zoogeographical terms (transition areas and habitat mosaic). Encompasses part of the Paru savannas (411 = savanna working group) and region 57 of the 1990 Amazonia Workshop. High importance as wilderness area, contains populations of large mammals.

DIAGNOSTIC ELEMENTS: *Species richness:* 3 • *Hotspots:* 1 • *Biological importance:* 2 • *Conservation level:* 1 • *Level of threat:* 1 • ACTION RECOMMENDED: *Restoration:* 1 • *Biological inventory:* 5 • *Creation of conservation area:* 5 • *Management:* 4.

MM 003 - Neblina - PRIORITY LEVEL: A • LOCATION: *State:* Amazonas • *Main municipality:* Santa Isabel do Rio Negro • *Municipalities covered:* 3 • VEGETATION TYPES: As, Dm, Ds, La, Ld, LO, rm • COMMENTS: High importance for primate and for threatened and rare species. High importance as wilderness area. High importance in zoogeographical terms, for vegetation types, aquatic and topographic ecosystems. Northern limit of distribution of some species. 86 bats, 7 marsupials, 10 edentates, 10 primate species.

DIAGNOSTIC ELEMENTS: *Species richness:* 3 • *Endemism:* 5 • *Richness of rare/threatened species:* 3 • *Hotspots:* 5 • *Special biological features:* 5 • *Biological importance:* 5 • *Intrinsic fragility:* 5 • *Conservation level:* 2 • *Level of threat:* 4 • ACTION RECOMMENDED: *Biological inventory:* 5 • *Creation of conservation area:* 1 • *Management:* 5.

MM 004 - Caparú - PRIORITY LEVEL: B • LOCATION: *State:* Amazonas • *Main municipality:* Japurá • *Municipalities covered:* 2 • VEGETATION TYPES: Ds, Ld, LO • COMMENTS: Medium importance for diversity. Medium importance for primates. High importance for rare and threatened endemic species. Medium importance in zoogeographical terms. High importance for unique and diverse vegetation types. Threatened species: *Cacajao melanocephalus ouakary, Lagothrix lagotricha lagotricha* (IBAMA list); *Ateles belzebuth belzebuth* (IBAMA list and IUCN-vulnerable); *Ateles chamek* (IBAMA list); *Trichechus inunguis* (IBAMA and and IUCN). 10 primates, 90 bats, 6 marsupials and 10 edentate species.

DIAGNOSTIC ELEMENTS: *Species richness:* 3 • *Endemism:* 4 • *Richness of rare/threatened species:* 5 • ACTION RECOMMENDED: *Biological inventory:* 4.

MM 005 - Anacayacu - PRIORITY LEVEL: D • LOCATION: *State:* Amazonas • *Main municipality:* Santo Antônio do Içá • *Municipalities covered:* 7 • VEGETATION TYPES: Ab, Da, Db, LO, Pa • COMMENTS: High species diversity. High importance for primates and rare and threatened species. Medium importance in zoogeographical terms. High importance as wilderness area. High importance for vegetation types, aquatic and topographic ecosystems. 92 bats 92, 10 marsupials, 11 edentates and 14 primates species.

DIAGNOSTIC ELEMENTS: *Species richness:* 4 • *Richness of rare/threatened species:* 3 • ACTION RECOMMENDED: *Biological inventory:* 5.

MM 006 - Serra do Divisor - PRIORITY LEVEL: B • LOCATION: *State:* Acre • *Main municipality:* Cruzeiro do Sul • *Municipalities covered:* 5 • VEGETATION TYPES: Ab, Da, Db, Ds • COMMENTS: High species diversity. High importance for primates. Avarega importance for rare and threatened endemic species. High importance in zoogeographical terms (transition). High importance for unique and diverse vegetation types. 87 bats, 10 marsupials, 11 edentates and 17 primate species.

DIAGNOSTIC ELEMENTS: *Species richness:* 5 • *Endemism:* 3 • *Richness of rare/threatened species:* 3 • ACTION RECOMMENDED: *Biological inventory:* 3.

MM 007 - Cobija - tri-national region- PRIORITY LEVEL: B • LOCATION: *State:* Acre • *Main municipality:* Xapuri • *Municipalities covered:* 9 • VEGETATION TYPES: AA, Ab, Da, Db • COMMENTS: Medium species diversity. Medium importance for primates. High importance for threatened and rare species. Medium importance in zoogeographical terms. Low importance as wilderness area. Low importance for vegetation type, aquatic and topographic system. Southern limit of distribution of species. 86 bats, 9 marsupials, 11 edentates and 14 primate species.

DIAGNOSTIC ELEMENTS: *Species richness:* 4 • *Endemism:* 4 • *Richness of rare/threatened species:* 4 • ACTION RECOMMENDED: *Biological inventory:* 5 • *Creation of conservation area:* 3.

MM 008 - Upper Juruá - PRIORITY LEVEL: A • LOCATION: *State:* Acre/Amazonas • *Main municipality:* Tarauacá • *Municipalities covered:* 11 • VEGETATION TYPES: AA, Ab, Da, Db • COMMENTS: High species diversity. High importance for primates (largest primate diversity in the basin) and for endemic and rare species. High importance in zoogeographical terms (transition). Medium importance of unique and diverse vegetation types. 22 primates, 87 bats, 11 edentates and 11 marsupial species.

DIAGNOSTIC ELEMENTS: *Species richness:* 5 • *Endemism:* 4 • *Richness of rare/threatened species:* 4 • *Hotspots:* 3 • *Special biological features:* 3 • *Biological importance:* 4 • *Intrinsic fragility:* 1 • *Conservation level:* 2 • *Level of threat:* 3 • ACTION RECOMMENDED: *Biological inventory:* 3 • *Creation of conservation area:* 5.

MM 009 - Upper Purus - PRIORITY LEVEL: A • LOCATION: *State:* Acre/Amazonas • *Main municipality:* Pauini • *Municipalities covered:* 12 • VEGETATION TYPES: AA, Ab, Da, Db • COMMENTS: 1990 Amazonia Workshop. 19 primates, 10 marsupials, 86 bats and 11 edentate species. High species diversity. High importance in zoogeographical terms. High level of endemic and rare species. Medium to low importance as wilderness area. High diversity of vegetation systems.

DIAGNOSTIC ELEMENTS: *Species richness:* 5 • *Phylogenetic diversity:* 4 • *Endemism:* 4 • *Richness of rare/threatened species:* 4 • *Hotspots:* 5 • *Economically important species:* 3 • *Biological importance:* 4 • *Intrinsic fragility:* 3 • *Conservation level:* 1 • *Level of threat:* 3 • ACTION RECOMMENDED: *Biological inventory:* 5.

MM 010 - Upper Madeira - PRIORITY LEVEL: A • LOCATION: *State:* Amazonas/Rondônia • *Main municipality:* Guajará-Mirim • *Municipalities covered:* 4 • VEGETATION TYPES: AA, Ab, As, Da, Db, Ds, Pa, Sd, SO, Sp • COMMENTS: Located within area 11 (Workshop 90). High importance for endemic species. High primates diversity. Important for the presence of unique vegetation types. Importance in zoogeographical terms due to the fauna shared only with southern Amazonia. Area crossed by the BR-364 highway.

DIAGNOSTIC ELEMENTS: *Species richness:* 4 • *Phylogenetic diversity:* 3 • *Endemism:* 5 • *Richness of rare/threatened species:* 4 • *Hotspots:* 5 • *Special biological features:* 4 • *Biological importance:* 4 • *Intrinsic fragility:* 5 • *Conservation level:* 4 • *Level of threat:* 5 • ACTION RECOMMENDED: *Restoration:* 4 • *Biological inventory:* 3 • *Creation of conservation area:* 2 • *Management:* 5

MM 011 - Guaporé - Parecis - PRIORITY LEVEL: B • LOCATION: *State:* Mato Grosso/Tocantins • *Main municipality:* São Francisco do Guaporé • *Municipalities covered:* 36 • VEGETATION TYPES: AA, Ab, As, Da, Ds, Fa, Fb, Fs, ON, Pa, Sa, Sd, Sg, SN, SO, Sp • COMMENTS: Occurrence of an unique vegetation type and associated fauna (Pantanal and Pacaás Novos). Highly threatened by anthropogenic activities; conservation area with high level of human impact. Occurrence of threatened species (primates). Potentially un-described species. Occurrence of the maned wolf (*Chrysocyson brachiurus*).

DIAGNOSTIC ELEMENTS: *Species richness:* 3 • *Endemism:* 3 • *Richness of rare/threatened species:* 2 • *Hotspots:* 1 • *Special biological features:* 4 • *Biological importance:* 4 • *Intrinsic fragility:* 2 • *Conservation level:* 2 • *Level of threat:* 2 • ACTION RECOMMENDED: *Biological inventory:* 3 • *Management:* 4.

MM 012 - Jamari - Machado - PRIORITY LEVEL: A • LOCATION: *State:* Amazonas/Rondônia • *Main municipality:* Humaitá • *Municipalities covered:* 10 • VEGETATION TYPES: AA, Ab, As, Da, Db, Ds, Pa, Sa, SO, Sp • COMMENTS: Encompasses three interfluves where two new primate species have been described. High primate diversity. Encompasses part of the Humaitá grasslands, which are threatened by agricultural policy, and part of the wetland, whose vegetation type is unique and includes associated mammals. Located within area 70 ('Workshop 90'). Occurrence of isolated savannas with potentially un-described associated mammals. Importance in zoogeographical terms for fauna shared only with southern Amazonia.

DIAGNOSTIC ELEMENTS: *Endemism:* 5 • *Richness of rare/threatened species:* 4 • *Hotspots:* 1 • *Special biological features:* 5 • *Biological importance:* 5 • *Intrinsic fragility:* 1 • *Conservation level:* 2 • *Level of threat:* 3 • ACTION RECOMMENDED: *Biological inventory:* 5 • *Management:* 5.

MM 013 - Upper Aripuanã - PRIORITY LEVEL: B • LOCATION: *State:* Amazonas/Mato Grosso • *Main municipality:* Aripuanã • *Municipalities covered:* 3 • VEGETATION TYPES: AA, As, Da, Db, Ds, ON, Pa, Sd, Sg, SO, Sp • COMMENTS: Medium species diversity. High importance for primates. Medium importance for threatened, endemic and rare species. Medium importance in zoogeographical terms. Medium importance as wilderness area. High importance for vegetation type, aquatic ecosystem and topography. 88 bats, 8 marsupials, 11 edentates and 12 primate species.

DIAGNOSTIC ELEMENTS: *Species richness:* 4 • *Phylogenetic diversity:* 2 • *Endemism:* 3 • *Richness of rare/threatened species:* 2 • *Hotspots:* 2 • *Special biological features:* 3 • *Biological importance:* 4 • *Intrinsic fragility:* 1 • *Conservation level:* 3 • *Level of threat:* 2 • ACTION RECOMMENDED: *Restoration:* 1 • *Biological inventory:* 4 • *Creation of conservation area:* 4 • *Management:* 2.

MM 014 - Headwaters of the Tapajós - Xingu - PRIORITY LEVEL: A • LOCATION: *State:* Amazonas/Mato Grosso/Pará • *Main municipality:* Jacareacanga • *Municipalities covered:* 19 • VEGETATION TYPES: AA, As, Cs, Da, Ds, Fs, ON, Sa, Sd, Sg, SN, SO, Sp • COMMENTS: High species diversity. High importance for primates and for threatened, endemic and rare species. High importance in zoogeographical terms. Low but significant importance as wilderness area. High importance for vegetation type, aquatic ecosystem and topography. 13 primates, 9 marsupials, 83 bats and 10 edentate species.

DIAGNOSTIC ELEMENTS: *Species richness:* 3 • *Phylogenetic diversity:* 2 • *Endemism:* 2 • *Richness of rare/threatened species:* 3 • *Hotspots:* 3 • *Special biological features:* 4 • *Biological importance:* 4 • *Intrinsic fragility:* 3 • *Conservation level:* 3 • *Level of threat:* 3 • ACTION RECOMMENDED: *Restoration:* 1 • *Biological inventory:* 4 • *Creation of conservation area:* 4 • *Management:* 4

MM 015 - Bananal - PRIORITY LEVEL: C • LOCATION: *State:* Goiás/Tocantins • *Main municipality:* Formoso do Araguaia • *Municipalities covered:* 5 • VEGETATION TYPES: AA, As, Fa, Sa, Sd, Sg, SN, Sp • COMMENTS: High importance for threatened endemic fauna and fauna of restricted distribution. Medium species diversity. High importance in zoogeographical terms. High importance for unique vegetation types with associated fauna. Occurrence of aquatic ecosystems. Presence of *Blastocerus dichotomus* (IBAMA and IUCN lists). Three primate species. Occurrence of fauna associated with transition between central Brazilian savannas and Amazon rainforest.

DIAGNOSTIC ELEMENTS: *Species richness:* 2 • *Phylogenetic diversity:* 1 • *Endemism:* 1 • *Richness of rare/threatened species:* 1 • *Hotspots:* 3 • *Special biological features:* 2 • *Biological importance:* 2 • *Intrinsic fragility:* 3 • *Conservation level:* 3 • *Level of threat:* 3 • ACTION RECOMMENDED: *Biological inventory:* 2 • *Creation of conservation area:* 1 • *Management:* 3

MM 016 - Maranhão coast - PRIORITY LEVEL: C • LOCATION: *State:* Maranhão • *Main municipality:* Rosário • *Municipalities covered:* 11 • VEGETATION TYPES: AA, Pa, Pf, Sa • COMMENTS: Medium species diversity. Low importance for primates. High importance for threatened, endemic and rare species. Medium importance in zoogeographical terms. Low importance as wilderness area. High importance for vegetation type, aquatic ecosystem and topography. 5 primates, 88 bats, 8 marsupials and 10 edentate species.

DIAGNOSTIC ELEMENTS: *Species richness:* 2 • *Endemism:* 3 • *Richness of rare/threatened species:* 3 • *Hotspots:* 3 • *Special biological features:* 2 • *Economically important species:* 3 • *Biological importance:* 4 • ACTION RECOMMENDED: *Biological inventory:* 2 • *Creation of conservation area:* 4 • *Management:* 2.

MM 017 - Gurupi - Pindaré - PRIORITY LEVEL: A • LOCATION: *State:* Amapá • *Main municipality:* Centro Novo do Maranhão • *Municipalities covered:* 33 • VEGETATION TYPES: AA, Da, Db, Pa, Pf • COMMENTS: Medium species diversity. Low importance for primates. High importance for threatened, endemic and rare species. High importance in zoogeographical terms. Low importance as wilderness area. Medium importance for vegetation type, aquatic ecosystem and topography. Needs special consideration because of the deforestation of Eastern Amazonia. 7 primates, 88 bats, 7 marsupials and 10 edentate species.

DIAGNOSTIC ELEMENTS: *Species richness:* 3 • *Endemism:* 3 • *Richness of rare/threatened species:* 4 • *Hotspots:* 4 • *Special biological features:* 2 • *Biological importance:* 3 • *Intrinsic fragility:* 5 • *Conservation level:* 5 • *Level of threat:* 5 • ACTION RECOMMENDED: *Restoration:* 4 • *Biological inventory:* 3 • *Creation of conservation area:* 5 • *Management:* 4.

MM 018 - Lower Xingu - Tocantins - PRIORITY LEVEL: C • LOCATION: *State:* Pará • *Main municipality:* Portel • *Municipalities covered:* 15 • VEGETATION TYPES: AA, As, Da, Db, Ds, Pa • COMMENTS: Included within area 70 (Workshop 90). Occurrence of vulnerable species (primates). High importance due to heterogeneity of vegetation and associated species. High savage importance due to the existence of bat species restricted to cargrons and of primates whose distribution is restricted to these interfluves.

DIAGNOSTIC ELEMENTS: *Species richness:* 3 • *Phylogenetic diversity:* 2 • *Endemism:* 3 • *Richness of rare/threatened species:* 2 • *Hotspots:* 4 • *Special biological features:* 4 • *Biological importance:* 3 • *Intrinsic fragility:* 2 • *Conservation level:* 4 • *Level of threat:* 4 • ACTION RECOMMENDED: *Restoration:* 4 • *Biological inventory:* 3 • *Creation of conservation area:* 4 • *Management:* 2.

MM 019 - Marajó Archipelago - PRIORITY LEVEL: C • LOCATION: *State:* Amapá/Pará • *Main municipality:* Anajás • *Municipalities covered:* 11 • VEGETATION TYPES: AA, Da, Db, Pa, Sp • COMMENTS: Included within area 71-72 (Workshop 90). High importance for species of mammals endemic to savanna. High importance for the presence of endemic species (*Monodelphis, Echymis*). Presence of unique vegetation types. Estuary of high importance for aquatic species. First record of threatened (sprolhos) and other species. Highly threatened by the waterway program.

DIAGNOSTIC ELEMENTS: *Species richness:* 3 • *Endemism:* 2 • *Richness of rare/threatened species:* 3 • *Hotspots:* 4 • *Special biological features:* 4 • *Biological importance:* 4 • *Intrinsic fragility:* 4 • *Conservation level:* 5 • *Level of threat:* 5 • ACTION RECOMMENDED: *Restoration:* 4 • *Biological inventory:* 5 • *Management:* 5.

MM 020 - Lower Xingu - Tapajós - PRIORITY LEVEL: B • LOCATION: *State:* Pará • *Main municipality:* Porto de Moz • *Municipalities covered:* 7 • VEGETATION TYPES: AA, Da, Db, Ds, Pa, Sp • COMMENTS: Medium species diversity. High importance for threatened, endemic and rare species. Medium importance in zoogeographical terms. Medium importance as wilderness area. High importance for vegetation type, aquatic ecosystems and topography. 8 primates, 83 bats, 10 marsupials and 10 edentate species.

DIAGNOSTIC ELEMENTS: *Species richness:* 3 • *Endemism:* 3 • *Richness of rare/threatened species:* 2 • *Hotspots:* 4 • *Special biological features:* 3 • *Biological importance:* 3 • *Intrinsic fragility:* 3 • *Conservation level:* 3 • *Level of threat:* 4 • ACTION RECOMMENDED: *Biological inventory:* 4 • *Creation of conservation area:* 3 • *Management:* 2.

MM 021 - Xingu - Iriri - PRIORITY LEVEL: C • LOCATION: *State:* Pará • *Main municipality:* Altamira • *Municipalities covered:* 4 • VEGETATION TYPES: AA, As, Da, Ds, Sa, SO • COMMENTS: Medium importance for endemic, threatened and rare fauna. High importance as wilderness area. High importance for unique and diverse vegetation types. Biogeographical importance; three interfluves making up distinct biogeographical units. Aquatic ecosystems. 11 primates, 82 bats, 10 marsupials and 10 edentate species.

DIAGNOSTIC ELEMENTS: *Species richness:* 3 • *Phylogenetic diversity:* 2 • *Endemism:* 2 • *Richness of rare/threatened species:* 2 • *Hotspots:* 1 • *Special biological features:* 1 • *Biological importance:* 2 • *Intrinsic fragility:* 2 • *Conservation level:* 2 • *Level of threat:* 2 • ACTION RECOMMENDED: *Restoration:* 1 • *Biological inventory:* 3 • *Creation of conservation area:* 4 • *Management:* 2.

MM 022 - Monte Cristo - PRIORITY LEVEL: C • LOCATION: *State:* Pará • *Main municipality:* Trairão • *Municipalities covered:* 6 • VEGETATION TYPES: AA, As, Db, Ds • COMMENTS: High importance for threatened, endemic fauna and fauna of restricted distribution. Area of importance in zoogeographical terms, encompassing three interfluves with endemic fauna. High importance for unique vegetation types. 9 primates, 83 bats, 7 marsupials and 10 edentate species.

DIAGNOSTIC ELEMENTS: *Species richness:* 3 • *Endemism:* 2 • *Richness of rare/threatened species:* 2 • *Hotspots:* 2 • *Special biological features:* 1 • *Biological importance:* 2 • *Intrinsic fragility:* 2 • *Conservation level:* 2 • *Level of threat:* 2 • ACTION RECOMMENDED: *Restoration:* 1 • *Biological inventory:* 4 • *Creation of conservation area:* 5 • *Management:* 3

MM 023 - Lower Madeira and Tapajós - PRIORITY LEVEL: B • LOCATION: *State:* Amazonas/Pará • *Main municipality:* Maués • *Municipalities covered:* 12 • VEGETATION TYPES: AA, As, Da, Db, Ds, Pa, SO, Sp • COMMENTS: Medium species diversity. Medium importance for primates. High importance for threatened, endemic and rare species. 16 primates, 85 bats, 10 marsupials and 10 edentate species. High importance in zoogeographical terms. Medium importance as wilderness area. Medium importance for vegetation type, aquatic ecosystem and topography.

DIAGNOSTIC ELEMENTS: *Species richness:* 4 • *Endemism:* 4 • *Richness of rare/threatened species:* 3 • *Hotspots:* 3 • *Special biological features:* 3 • *Biological importance:* 4 • *Intrinsic fragility:* 1 • *Conservation level:* 2 • *Level of threat:* 1 • ACTION RECOMMENDED: *Biological inventory:* 4 • *Creation of conservation area:* 5 • *Management:* 2.

MM 024 - Uatumã - Trombetas Complex - PRIORITY LEVEL: C • LOCATION: *State:* Amazonas/Pará • *Main municipality:* São Sebastião do Uatumã • *Municipalities covered:* 18 • VEGETATION TYPES: AA, As, Da, Db, Ds, LO, Pa, Sp • COMMENTS: Medium species diversity. Medium importance for primates. High importance for threatened, endemic and rare species. High importance in zoogeographical terms. Medium importance as wilderness area. Medium importance for vegetation type, aquatic ecosystem and topography. 12 primates, 94 bats, 12 marsupials and 10 edentate species.

DIAGNOSTIC ELEMENTS: *Species richness:* 3 • *Endemism:* 4 • *Richness of rare/threatened species:* 4 • *Hotspots:* 3 • *Biological importance:* 4 • *Intrinsic fragility:* 4 • *Conservation level:* 2 • *Level of threat:* 4 • ACTION RECOMMENDED: *Biological inventory:* 4.

MM 025 - Negro - Japurá interfluve - PRIORITY LEVEL: B • LOCATION: *State:* Amazonas • *Main municipality:* Barcelos • *Municipalities covered:* 5 • VEGETATION TYPES: Ab, Da, Db, Ds, La, Ld, LO • COMMENTS: Largest population of *Trichecus inunguis*. Medium species diversity. Medium importance for primates. High importance for endemic, threatened and rare mammals. Large extent of conserved areas. Medium importance for vegetation types, aquatic ecosystems and topographic characteristics. High importance in zoogeographical terms (transition). 13 primate, 95 bats, 12 marsupials and 10 edentate species.

DIAGNOSTIC ELEMENTS: *Species richness:* 3 • *Phylogenetic diversity:* 3 • *Endemism:* 2 • *Richness of rare/threatened species:* 3 • *Hotspots:* 1 • *Special biological features:* 2 • *Biological importance:* 4 • *Intrinsic fragility:* 4 • *Conservation level:* 2 • *Level of threat:* 1 • ACTION RECOMMENDED: *Restoration:* 1 • *Biological inventory:* 2 • *Creation of conservation area:* 1 • *Management:* 4.

MM 026 - Parima - Pacaraima - Surumu - PRIORITY LEVEL: B • LOCATION: *State:* Roraima • *Main municipality:* Amajari • *Municipalities covered:* 13 • VEGETATION TYPES: As, Dm, Ds, Fs, LO, ON, rm, Sa, Sg, SN, SO, Sp, Ta, Td, Tp • COMMENTS: High importance for endemic and rare endemic savanna mammals (*Daptomys, Marmosa*). Medium importance as wilderness area. Included in the final map of the 1990 Amazonia Workshop. High importance in zoogeographical terms. Proposed expansion to include parts of the *surumu* formation with typical vegetation type and associated small mammal fauna. Occurrence of threatened species (*Cacajao m. melanoceplalus* and *Lagothrix lagotricha*). Conservation areas (except Maracá) showing high levels of human impacts and disturbance.

DIAGNOSTIC ELEMENTS: *Species richness:* 4 • *Endemism:* 4 • *Richness of rare/threatened species:* 4 • *Hotspots:* 2 • *Special biological features:* 4 • *Biological importance:* 4 • *Intrinsic fragility:* 3 • *Conservation level:* 5 • *Level of threat:* 4 • ACTION RECOMMENDED: *Restoration:* 4 • *Biological inventory:* 4 • *Creation of conservation area:* 4 • *Management:* 4.

MM 027 - Auati - Panauá - Mamirauá - PRIORITY LEVEL: A • LOCATION: *State:* Amazonas • *Main municipality:* Fonte Boa • *Municipalities covered:* 8 • VEGETATION TYPES: Da, Db, LO, Pa • COMMENTS: Low species diversity. High importance for primates and for rare, threatened and endemic species. High importance in zoogeographical terms. High importance as wilderness area. High importance for vegetation type, aquatic ecosytem and topography. The eastwards expansion of the terra firme area may increase the number of species. 14 primates, 95 bats, 10 marsupials and 10 edentate species.

DIAGNOSTIC ELEMENTS: *Species richness:* 3 • *Endemism:* 4 • *Richness of rare/threatened species:* 4 • *Hotspots:* 2 • *Special biological features:* 4 • *Biological importance:* 3 • *Intrinsic fragility:* 4 • *Conservation level:* 2 • *Level of threat:* 1 • ACTION RECOMMENDED: *Restoration:* 1 • *Biological inventory:* 3 • *Creation of conservation area:* 1 • *Management:* 2.

MM 028 - Tefé river and lake - PRIORITY LEVEL: B • LOCATION: *State:* Amazonas • *Main municipality:* Coari • *Municipalities covered:* 4 • VEGETATION TYPES: AA, Ab, Da, Db, Pa • COMMENTS: High species diversity. High importance for threatened, endemic and rare fauna. High biogeographical importance. Threatened species: *Pithecia albicans* (IBAMA and IUCN), *Lagothrix lagothrica cana* and *Lagothrix l. poeppigii* (IBAMA and IUCN). Sympatrical species. High importance as wilderness area. High importance for unique and diverse vegetation types. 14 primates, 92 bats, 10 marsupials and 10 edentate species.

DIAGNOSTIC ELEMENTS: *Species richness:* 4 • *Phylogenetic diversity:* 4 • *Endemism:* 4 • *Richness of rare/threatened species:* 4 • *Hotspots:* 4 • *Biological importance:* 4 • *Intrinsic fragility:* 3 • *Conservation level:* 2 • *Level of threat:* 5 • ACTION RECOMMENDED: *Biological inventory:* 3 • *Creation of conservation area:* 5.

MM 029 - Lower Juruá - PRIORITY LEVEL: B • LOCATION: *State:* Amazonas • *Main municipality:* Carauari • *Municipalities covered:* 8 • VEGETATION TYPES: Ab, Da, Db • COMMENTS: Not considered for the final areas. Collection of unique species separated by an importance geographical barrier. Some endemic species (e.g. *Pithecta albicans*). Composition of important habitats at the interface of floodplain and terra firme. 16 primates, 91 bats, 9 marsupials and 11 edentate species.

DIAGNOSTIC ELEMENTS: *Species richness:* 4 • *Phylogenetic diversity:* 4 • *Endemism:* 3 • *Richness of rare/threatened species:* 3 • *Hotspots:* 4 • *Special biological features:* 3 • *Biological importance:* 4 • *Intrinsic fragility:* 3 • *Conservation level:* 2 • *Level of threat:* 4 • ACTION RECOMMENDED: *Biological inventory:* 3 • *Creation of conservation area:* 5.

MM 030 - Middle Purus - PRIORITY LEVEL: B • LOCATION: *State:* Amazonas • *Main municipality:* Tapauá • *Municipalities covered:* 3 • VEGETATION TYPES: Ab, Da, Db, Ds, Pa, SO • COMMENTS: High species diversity. High importance for primates. High importance in zoogeographical terms. Medium importance as wilderness area. Low importance for vegetation type, aquatic ecosystem and topography. To be included in the Purus/Madeira savanna region. 20 primates, 88 bats, 9 marsupials and 10 edentate species.

DIAGNOSTIC ELEMENTS: *Species richness:* 4 • *Phylogenetic diversity:* 4 • *Endemism:* 3 • *Richness of rare/threatened species:* 4 • *Hotspots:* 3 • *Special biological features:* 3 • *Economically important species:* 3

• *Biological importance:* 4 • *Intrinsic fragility:* 3 • *Conservation level:* 1 • *Level of threat:* 2 • ACTION RECOMMENDED: *Biological inventory:* 5.

MM 031 - Lower Javari - PRIORITY LEVEL: B • LOCATION: *State:* Amazonas • *Main municipality:* Atalaia do Norte • *Municipalities covered:* 2 • VEGETATION TYPES: AA, Ab, Da, Db • COMMENTS: High species diversity. High importance for primates and for threatened, endemic and rare species. Medium importance in zoogeographical terms. High importance as wilderness area. Low importance for vegetation type, aquatic ecosystem and topography. 13 primates, 87 bats, 10 marsupials and 11 edentate species.

DIAGNOSTIC ELEMENTS: *Endemism:* 1 • *Richness of rare/threatened species:* 4 • *Special biological features:* 3 • ACTION RECOMMENDED: *Biological inventory:* 5.

MM 032 - Jari - Trombetas - Paredão do Pará - PRIORITY LEVEL: C • LOCATION: *State:* Amapá/Pará • *Main municipality:* Almeirim • *Municipalities covered:* 8 • VEGETATION TYPES: AA, As, Da, Db, Ds, Pa, Sd, SO • COMMENTS: Located within area 60 (Workshop 90). Bat endemism. Occurrence of vulnerable species (primates).

DIAGNOSTIC ELEMENTS: *Species richness:* 3 • *Endemism:* 3 • *Richness of rare/threatened species:* 3 • *Hotspots:* 3 • *Special biological features:* 4 • *Biological importance:* 3 • *Intrinsic fragility:* 3 • *Conservation level:* 3 • *Level of threat:* 4 • ACTION RECOMMENDED: *Biological inventory:* 4 • *Creation of conservation area:* 4 • *Management:* 4.

MM 033 - Upper Jutaí - PRIORITY LEVEL: A • LOCATION: *State:* Amazonas • *Main municipality:* Jutaí • *Municipalities covered:* 2 • VEGETATION TYPES: Ab, Da, Db • COMMENTS: Located within a basin of extremely high diversity, with confirmed occurrence of a new taxon of Lagothrix; high diversity of forest types. Black-water basin 'squeezed' between two large white-water rivers. There are no conservation areas.

DIAGNOSTIC ELEMENTS: *Species richness:* 5 • *Phylogenetic diversity:* 5 • *Endemism:* 4 • *Richness of rare/threatened species:* 5 • *Hotspots:* 1 • *Economically important species:* 3 • *Biological importance:* 4 • *Intrinsic fragility:* 4 • *Conservation level:* 1 • *Level of threat:* 1 • ACTION RECOMMENDED: *Restoration:* 1 • *Biological inventory:* 5 • *Creation of conservation area:* 5 • *Management:* 4.

MM 034 - Lower Purus - PRIORITY LEVEL: A • LOCATION: *State:* Amazonas • *Main municipality:* Beruri • *Municipalities covered:* 6 • VEGETATION TYPES: Da, Db, Ds • COMMENTS: Region of lower river, flowing with the middle Solimões, including high habitat diversity and viable populations of *Lagothrix* and *Pithecia albicans*. Black-water lakes located within floodplain spur; indications that area not used for hunting and offers good opportunities for conservation.

DIAGNOSTIC ELEMENTS: *Species richness:* 4 • *Phylogenetic diversity:* 4 • *Endemism:* 3 • *Richness of rare/threatened species:* 4 • *Hotspots:* 4 • *Special biological features:* 4 • *Economically important species:* 5 • *Biological importance:* 5 • *Intrinsic fragility:* 4 • *Conservation level:* 1 • *Level of threat:* 3 • ACTION RECOMMENDED: *Biological inventory:* 2.

MM 035 - Novo Aripuanã - PRIORITY LEVEL: A • LOCATION: *State:* Amazonas • *Main municipality:* Novo Aripuanã • *Municipalities covered:* 3 • VEGETATION TYPES: As, Da, Db, Ds, Pa • COMMENTS: Pocket of speciation containing several new primate and tree species (*Lecythis sp*), including epiphyte Cactaceae, previously only collected in the Guianas.

DIAGNOSTIC ELEMENTS: *Species richness:* 5 • *Phylogenetic diversity:* 5 • *Endemism:* 5 • *Richness of rare/threatened species:* 5 • *Hotspots:* 3 • *Biological importance:* 5 • *Intrinsic fragility:* 3 • *Conservation level:* 2 • *Level of threat:* 2 • ACTION RECOMMENDED: *Creation of conservation area:* 4 • *Management:* 5.

MM 036 - Pindaré - Mearim - PRIORITY LEVEL: B • LOCATION: *State:* Maranhão • *Main municipality:* Amarante do Maranhão • *Municipalities covered:* 25 • VEGETATION TYPES: AA, Cs, Da, Db, Sa, Sd, SN • COMMENTS: Eastern limit of several Amazon species. Habitat degradation status advancing towards peripheral areas. Vegetation type little represented in conservation areas.

DIAGNOSTIC ELEMENTS: *Species richness:* 2 • *Endemism:* 1 • *Richness of rare/threatened species:* 3 • *Hotspots:* 5 • *Special biological features:* 2 • *Biological importance:* 3 • *Intrinsic fragility:* 3 • *Conservation level:* 4 • *Level of threat:* 5 • ACTION RECOMMENDED: *Biological inventory:* 3 • *Creation of conservation area:* 4 • *Management:* 2.

MM 037 - Middle Iriri - PRIORITY LEVEL: B • LOCATION: *State:* Pará • *Main municipality:* Altamira • *Municipalities covered:* 1 • VEGETATION TYPES: As, Da, Ds, Sa, SO • COMMENTS: New species of primates and probably of other mammals suspected; lack of conservation areas in the basin; probable barrier of terrestrial mammal representation. Relatively near to the frontier; anthropogenic pressure from logging and ranching; presence of *Ateles marginatus*.

DIAGNOSTIC ELEMENTS: *Species richness:* 3 • *Phylogenetic diversity:* 3 • *Endemism:* 4 • *Richness of rare/threatened species:* 5 • *Hotspots:* 4 • *Economically important species:* 3 • *Biological importance:* 4 • *Intrinsic fragility:* 3 • *Conservation level:* 2 • *Level of threat:* 3 • ACTION RECOMMENDED: *Restoration:* 2 • *Biological inventory:* 5 • *Creation of conservation area:* 5.

MM 038 - Rio Branco Basin - PRIORITY LEVEL: A • LOCATION: *State:* Amazonas/Roraima • *Main municipality:* Caracaraí • *Municipalities covered:* 3 • VEGETATION TYPES: Ab, Da, Db, Ds, La, Ld, Lg, LO • COMMENTS: Absence of information on mammals. Large areas of campina and campinarana potentially different of those of the Rio Negro. Area of potential occurrence of different species in the Amazon ecological context. Presence of paleodunes and extremely floodable areas.

DIAGNOSTIC ELEMENTS: *Endemism:* 3 • *Richness of rare/threatened species:* 2 • *Hotspots:* 2 • *Special biological features:* 5 • *Biological importance:* 5 • *Intrinsic fragility:* 2 • *Conservation level:* 2 • *Level of threat:* 2 • ACTION RECOMMENDED: *Biological inventory:* 5 • *Creation of conservation area:* 4 • *Management:* 4.

MM 039 - Lower Araguaia - PRIORITY LEVEL: D • LOCATION: *State:* Maranhão/Pará/Tocantins • *Main municipality:* São Geraldo do Araguaia • *Municipalities covered:* 62 • VEGETATION TYPES: AA, As, Cs, Da, Dm, Ds, Sa, Sd, SO, Sp • COMMENTS: Important transition area encompassing species habitats and open formations. Area of high anthropogenic pressure. Potentially un-described fauna.

DIAGNOSTIC ELEMENTS: *Hotspots:* 3 • *Special biological features:* 3 • *Biological importance:* 5 • *Intrinsic fragility:* 4 • *Conservation level:* 4 • *Level of threat:* 5 • ACTION RECOMMENDED: *Restoration:* 1 • *Biological inventory:* 5 • *Creation of conservation area:* 5 • *Management:* 3.

4
PRIORITY AREAS FOR INVERTEBRATES*

Invertebrates make up more than 95% of all existing animal species and are classified into 20 to 30 phyla. In Amazonia these animals have diversified in an explosive fashion, with the tree canopy of the tropical forest representing the center of the greatest diversification.

Despite dominating the Amazon forest in terms of numbers of species, numbers of individuals and animal biomass, and notwithstanding their importance for the healthy functioning of ecosystems by means of their roles as pollinators, agents of seed dispersal, 'bodyguards' of certain plants, and natural biological pest control agents, and for human well-being, invertebrates still have not been given priority in the drawing up of biodiversity conservation projects and are only rarely regarded as important components of the biodiversity to be conserved. More than 70% of Amazonian species still have not received scientific names and, given current rates of survey and taxonomic work, this situation will persist for a long time.

Given these factors, the use of these animals for defining biological conservation priorities for the region is difficult and, out of all the invertebrates, only the butterflies can offer reliable indications. Other groups rich in species and locally abundant in several ecosystems, such as ants, bees, social wasps, some beetle families, termites, Oribatida mites, earthworms, some soil arthropods, dragonflies and aquatic groups offer a high potential for identifying conservation areas and actions, but need further study.

Prioritizing areas for biological conservation is normally undertaken by comparing the relative or absolute numbers of species. Given the limited information available, the criteria in the case of invertebrates should take the following into account: the use of species as biological indicators of biodiversity (surrogates) and of the healthy functioning of ecosystems (environmental quality); species with popular appeal (butterflies, dragonflies); keystone species; and rare species isolated as a result of evolutionary processes (relict species). On the other hand, invertebrates – like vertebrates – do not live in isolation and can only be conserved as an integral part of functioning ecosystems.

There are currently approximately 7,500 known butterfly species in the world, with 3,300 in Brazil and 1,800 in Amazonia (Legg 1978, Shields 1989, Brown 1996). For ants, which make up almost a third of animal biomass in the tree canopies of the Amazon forest (Fittkau and Klinge 1973, Adis et al. 1984), the estimate is of around 3,000 species (Overal, estimate derived from unpublished data). For bees, there are more than 30,000 described species worldwide, of which more than 7,000 in South America and more than 4,000 in Brazil (O'Toole and Raw 1991) and between 2,500 and 3,000 in the Amazon region.

Other invertebrate groups show similarly large numbers of species in Amazonia, such as: social wasps – 220, spiders – more than 500 known species and an expectation of 2,500, earthworms – more than 100, millipedes – more than 3,000 with 200 already described, Collembola – 80, pseudo-scorpions – an estimated 120.

Among the areas deserving priority attention for the conservation of Amazon invertebrate species, the following are prominent: igapó forests; floodplain forests; enclave areas, such as the Rio Negro campinas and the rocky grasslands of central Amazonia; and caves.

Environmental education campaigns are also needed to inform the public of the importance of invertebrates and to include these animals in biological conservation plans for Amazonia, together with greater collecting and research efforts.

During the Macapá Workshop, 28 priority areas for invertebrates in Amazonia were identified (see the map on page 445 and the listing). Of these, 25 (89.3%) show high richness of rare and threatened species; 19 (67.9%) contain high phylogenetic diversity and economically important species; and 11 (39.3%) suffer high levels of threat of degradation (Table 4).

TABLE 4 - PRIORITY AREAS FOR INVERTEBRATES DIAGNOSTIC ELEMENTS THAT SCORE HIGHEST		
Diagnostic elements	Number of areas	%[1]
Species richness	13	46.4
Phylogenetic diversity	19	67.9
Endemism	15	53.6
Richness of rare or threatened species	25	89.3
Hotspots	3	10.7
Special biological features	17	60.7
Economically important species	19	67.9
Biological importance	7	25.0
Intrinsic fragility	8	28.6
Conservation level	7	25.0
Level of threat	11	39.3

1. Of the total proposed areas (28).

---

* Text drawn in part from 'The importance of invertebrates for the conservation of Amazonian biodiversity' by William L. Overal, the full version of which can be found on page 52 of this book.

IV 001 - Adolfo Ducke Forest Reserve - Priority level: A • Location: *State:* Amazonas • *Main municipality:* Manaus • *Municipalities covered:* 2 • Vegetation types: Db, LO • Comments: Research tradition. Point of reference for invertebrate fauna in central Amazonia. High biological diversity.

Diagnostic elements: *Species richness:* 5 • *Phylogenetic diversity:* 5 • *Endemism:* 5 • *Hotspots:* 5 • *Conservation level:* 3 • *Level of threat:* 3 • Action recommended: *Restoration:* 3 • *Biological inventory:* 5 • *Creation of conservation area:* 4.

IV 002 - Mamirauá Sustainable Development Reserve - Priority level: A • Location: *State:* Amazonas • *Main municipality:* Maraã • *Municipalities covered:* 5 • Vegetation types: Da, Db, La, LO.

Diagnostic elements: *Phylogenetic diversity:* 5 • *Endemism:* 5 • *Richness of rare/threatened species:* 5 • *Economically important species:* 5 • *Conservation level:* 3 • Action recommended: *Restoration:* 5.

IV 003 - Anavilhanas archipelago - Priority level: A • Location: *State:* Amazonas • *Main municipality:* Novo Airão • *Municipalities covered:* 3 • Vegetation types: Da, Db, LO.

Diagnostic elements: *Species richness:* 5 • *Phylogenetic diversity:* 5 • *Endemism:* 5 • *Richness of rare/threatened species:* 5 • *Special biological features:* 5 • *Economically important species:* 5 • *Conservation level:* 4 • *Level of threat:* 3 • Action recommended: *Restoration:* 5 • *Creation of conservation area:* 5.

IV 004 - Caxiuanã National Forest - Priority level: A • Location: *State:* Pará • *Main municipality:* Portel • *Municipalities covered:* 3 • Vegetation types: Db.

Diagnostic elements: *Species richness:* 5 • *Phylogenetic diversity:* 5 • *Richness of rare/threatened species:* 5 • *Special biological features:* 5 • *Economically important species:* 5 • *Conservation level:* 4 • *Level of threat:* 1 • Action recommended: *Restoration:* 5 • *Creation of conservation area:* 2.

IV 005 - Carajás National Forest - Priority level: A • Location: *State:* Pará • *Main municipality:* Parauapebas • *Municipalities covered:* 4 • Vegetation types: AA, As, Dm, Ds.

Diagnostic elements: *Species richness:* 5 • *Endemism:* 5 • *Richness of rare/threatened species:* 5 • *Hotspots:* 5 • *Special biological features:* 5 • *Economically important species:* 5 • *Biological importance:* 5 • *Intrinsic fragility:* 5 • *Conservation level:* 1 • *Level of threat:* 4 • Action recommended: *Biological inventory:* 4 • *Creation of conservation area:* 4.

IV 006 - Santarém (floodplain, Alter do Chão, Taperinha) - Priority level: B • Location: *State:* Pará • *Main municipality:* Santarém • *Municipalities covered:* 3 • Vegetation types: AA, Db, Pa, Sp.

Diagnostic elements: *Species richness:* 5 • *Endemism:* 5 • *Richness of rare/threatened species:* 5 • *Economically important species:* 5 • *Biological importance:* 5 • *Conservation level:* 2 • *Level of threat:* 5 • Action recommended: *Restoration:* 4 • *Biological inventory:* 3 • *Creation of conservation area:* 5.

IV 007 - Belém (Apeg-Mocambo) - Priority level: B • Location: *State:* Pará • *Main municipality:* Santa Isabel do Pará • *Municipalities covered:* 8 • Vegetation types: AA, Da.

Diagnostic elements: *Species richness:* 5 • *Phylogenetic diversity:* 5 • *Endemism:* 5 • *Hotspots:* 5 • *Economically important species:* 5 • *Intrinsic fragility:* 5 • *Conservation level:* 2 • *Level of threat:* 3 • Action recommended: *Biological inventory:* 3 • *Creation of conservation area:* 5.

IV 008 - Pacaás Novos National Park and Serra dos Parecis (NW) - Priority level: D • Location: *State:* Rondônia • *Main municipality:* Guajará-Mirim • *Municipalities covered:* 10 • Vegetation types: AA, Ab, As, Da, Ds, Sa, Sd, SO, Sp.

Diagnostic elements: *Species richness:* 5 • *Phylogenetic diversity:* 5 • *Endemism:* 5 • *Richness of rare/threatened species:* 5 • *Special biological features:* 5 • *Economically important species:* 5 • *Biological importance:* 5 • *Conservation level:* 1 • *Level of threat:* 1 • Action recommended: *Restoration:* 5.

IV 009 - Marajó flooded grasslands - Priority level: D • Location: *State:* Pará • *Main municipality:* Anajás • *Municipalities covered:* 5 • Vegetation types: Da, Pa, Sp.

Diagnostic elements: *Richness of rare/threatened species:* 5 • *Special biological features:* 5 • *Conservation level:* 4 • *Level of threat:* 5 • Action recommended: *Restoration:* 5 • *Biological inventory:* 5.

IV 010 - Serra do Navio - Priority level: D • Location: *State:* Amapá • *Main municipality:* Pedra Branca do Amapari • *Municipalities covered:* 5 • Vegetation types: AA, Ds.

Diagnostic elements: *Species richness:* 5 • *Endemism:* 5 • *Richness of rare/threatened species:* 5 • *Special biological features:* 5 • *Intrinsic fragility:* 5 • *Conservation level:* 5 • *Level of threat:* 2 • Action recommended: *Restoration:* 4 • *Biological inventory:* 5 • *Creation of conservation area:* 3.

IV 011 - Northeastern coast of Pará and Maranhão - Priority level: D • Location: *State:* Maranhão/Pará • *Main municipality:* Viseu • *Municipalities covered:* 18 • Vegetation types: AA, Pa, Pf.

Diagnostic elements: *Phylogenetic diversity:* 5 • *Richness of rare/threatened species:* 5 • *Special biological features:* 5 • *Economically important species:* 5 • *Intrinsic fragility:* 5 • *Conservation level:* 2 • *Level of threat:* 4 • Action recommended: *Restoration:* 4 • *Creation of conservation area:* 3.

IV 012 - Gurupi Biological Reserve - Priority level: D • Location: *State:* Maranhão/Pará • *Main municipality:* Centro Novo do Maranhão • *Municipalities covered:* 6 • Vegetation types: AA, Db.

Diagnostic elements: *Phylogenetic diversity:* 5 • *Richness of rare/threatened species:* 5 • *Economically important species:* 5 • *Conservation level:* 3 • *Level of threat:* 5 • Action recommended: *Restoration:* 4 • *Creation of conservation area:* 5.

IV 013 - Kayapó Indigenous Land - Priority level: D • Location: *State:* Pará • *Main municipality:* São Félix do Xingu • *Municipalities covered:* 2 • Vegetation types: As, Ds, Sd, SO.

Diagnostic elements: *Phylogenetic diversity:* 5 • *Richness of rare/threatened species:* 5 • *Economically important species:* 5 • *Conservation level:* 2 • *Level of threat:* 5 • Action recommended: *Restoration:* 1 • *Creation of conservation area:* 5.

IV 014 - Querari (Upper Rio Negro) - Priority level: D • Location: *State:* Amazonas • *Main municipality:* São Gabriel da Cachoeira • *Municipalities covered:* 1 • Vegetation types: As, Ds, Ld, LO.

Diagnostic elements: *Endemism:* 5 • *Richness of rare/threatened species:* 5 • *Special biological features:* 5 • *Economically important species:* 5 • *Biological importance:* 5 • *Conservation level:* 4 • *Level of threat:* 1 • Action recommended: *Restoration:* 5 • *Biological inventory:* 4.

IV 015 - Serra do Tumucumaque - Priority level: D • Location: *State:* Pará • *Main municipality:* Oriximiná • *Municipalities covered:* 3 • Vegetation types: Da, Ds, Sd, SO, Sp.

Diagnostic elements: *Phylogenetic diversity:* 5 • *Richness of rare/threatened species:* 5 • *Special biological features:* 5 • *Economically important species:* 5 • *Conservation level:* 5 • *Level of threat:* 3 • Action recommended: *Restoration:* 5.

IV 016 - São Gabriel da Cachoeira and Pico da Neblina National Park - Priority level: D • Location: *State:* Amazonas • *Main municipality:* São Gabriel da Cachoeira • *Municipalities covered:* 1 • Vegetation types: Ds, La, Ld, LO.

Diagnostic elements: *Species richness:* 5 • *Phylogenetic diversity:* 5 • *Endemism:* 5 • *Richness of rare/threatened species:* 5 • *Special biological features:* 5 • *Economically important species:* 5 • *Biological importance:* 5 • *Intrinsic fragility:* 5 • *Conservation level:* 5 • *Level of threat:* 1 • Action recommended: *Restoration:* 5.

IV 017 - Tabatinga - Priority level: D • Location: *State:* Amazonas • *Main municipality:* São Paulo de Olivença • *Municipalities covered:* 4 • Vegetation types: AA, Ab, Da, Db, Pa.

Diagnostic elements: *Endemism:* 5 • *Richness of rare/threatened species:* 5 • *Special biological features:* 5 • *Economically important species:* 5 • *Conservation level:* 3 • *Level of threat:* 3 • Action recommended: *Restoration:* 5.

IV 018 - Aripuanã - Priority level: D • Location: *State:* Amazonas/Mato Grosso • *Main municipality:* Aripuanã • *Municipalities covered:* 3 • Vegetation types: As, Ds, SO.

Diagnostic elements: *Species richness:* 5 • *Phylogenetic diversity:* 5 • *Endemism:* 5 • *Richness of rare/threatened species:* 5 •

Economically important species: 5 • *Intrinsic fragility:* 5 • *Conservation level:* 4 • *Level of threat:* 5 • ACTION RECOMMENDED: *Restoration:* 4 • *Biological inventory:* 3 • *Creation of conservation area:* 5.

IV 019 - Serra do Divisor - PRIORITY LEVEL: D • LOCATION: *State:* Acre • *Main municipality:* Cruzeiro do Sul • *Municipalities covered:* 5 • VEGETATION TYPES: Ab, Da, Db, Ds.

DIAGNOSTIC ELEMENTS: *Phylogenetic diversity:* 5 • *Endemism:* 5 • *Richness of rare/threatened species:* 5 • *Special biological features:* 5 • *Conservation level:* 4 • *Level of threat:* 5 • ACTION RECOMMENDED: *Restoration:* 5 • *Creation of conservation area:* 4.

IV 020 - Serra de Pacaraima - PRIORITY LEVEL: D • LOCATION: *State:* Roraima • *Main municipality:* Uiramutã • *Municipalities covered:* 6 • VEGETATION TYPES: As, Dm, Ds, Fs, ON, Sg, SN, Sp, Ta, Td, Tp.

DIAGNOSTIC ELEMENTS: *Species richness:* 5 • *Phylogenetic diversity:* 5 • *Endemism:* 5 • *Richness of rare/threatened species:* 5 • *Special biological features:* 5 • *Economically important species:* 5 • *Biological importance:* 5 • *Intrinsic fragility:* 5 • *Conservation level:* 2 • *Level of threat:* 5 • ACTION RECOMMENDED: *Creation of conservation area:* 5.

IV 021 - Serra de Parima - PRIORITY LEVEL: D • LOCATION: *State:* Amazonas/Roraima • *Main municipality:* Alto Alegre • *Municipalities covered:* 5 • VEGETATION TYPES: As, Dm, Ds, ON, rm.

DIAGNOSTIC ELEMENTS: *Species richness:* 5 • *Phylogenetic diversity:* 5 • *Endemism:* 5 • *Richness of rare/threatened species:* 5 • *Special biological features:* 5 • *Economically important species:* 5 • *Biological importance:* 5 • *Intrinsic fragility:* 5 • *Conservation level:* 5 • *Level of threat:* 3 • ACTION RECOMMENDED: *Restoration:* 5.

IV 022 - Marajó (NE) - PRIORITY LEVEL: D • LOCATION: *State:* Pará • *Main municipality:* Soure • *Municipalities covered:* 3 • VEGETATION TYPES: AA, Da, Pa, Pf, Sp.

DIAGNOSTIC ELEMENTS: *Richness of rare/threatened species:* 5 • *Special biological features:* 5 • *Level of threat:* 5 • ACTION RECOMMENDED: *Creation of conservation area:* 5.

IV 023 - Curiaú Environmental Protection Area - PRIORITY LEVEL: D • LOCATION: *State:* Amapá • *Main municipality:* Macapá • *Municipalities covered:* 1 • VEGETATION TYPES: Da, Sp.

DIAGNOSTIC ELEMENTS: *Phylogenetic diversity:* 5 • *Richness of rare/threatened species:* 5 • *Economically important species:* 5 • *Conservation level:* 3 • *Level of threat:* 4 • ACTION RECOMMENDED: *Restoration:* 4 • *Biological inventory:* 3 • *Creation of conservation area:* 5.

IV 024 - Carauari - Rio Juruá - PRIORITY LEVEL: D • LOCATION: *State:* Amazonas • *Main municipality:* Carauari • *Municipalities covered:* 3 • VEGETATION TYPES: Ab, Da, Db.

DIAGNOSTIC ELEMENTS: *Species richness:* 5 • *Phylogenetic diversity:* 5 • *Richness of rare/threatened species:* 5 • *Conservation level:* 5 • *Level of threat:* 5 • ACTION RECOMMENDED: *Restoration:* 5.

IV 025 - Urucu - PRIORITY LEVEL: D • LOCATION: *State:* Amazonas • *Main municipality:* Coari • *Municipalities covered:* 2 • VEGETATION TYPES: Ab, Da, Db.

DIAGNOSTIC ELEMENTS: *Richness of rare/threatened species:* 5 • *Conservation level:* 5 • *Level of threat:* 5 • ACTION RECOMMENDED: *Restoration:* 4 • *Biological inventory:* 5.

IV 026 - Tapajós river - Amazonia National Park - PRIORITY LEVEL: D • LOCATION: *State:* Pará • *Main municipality:* Itaituba • *Municipalities covered:* 2 • VEGETATION TYPES: AA, As, Ds.

DIAGNOSTIC ELEMENTS: *Phylogenetic diversity:* 5 • *Richness of rare/threatened species:* 5 • *Special biological features:* 5 • *Conservation level:* 5 • *Level of threat:* 1 • ACTION RECOMMENDED: *Restoration:* 4 • *Biological inventory:* 5.

IV 027 - Araguaia National Park + transition area with savannas (Vale do Araguaia and Pantanal do Rio das Mortes) - PRIORITY LEVEL: D • LOCATION: *State:* Pará/Tocantins • *Main municipality:* Conceição do Araguaia • *Municipalities covered:* 13 • VEGETATION TYPES: AA, As, Ds, Fa, Sa, Sd, Sg, SN, SO, Sp.

DIAGNOSTIC ELEMENTS: *Phylogenetic diversity:* 5 • *Richness of rare/threatened species:* 5 • *Special biological features:* 5 • *Economically important species:* 5 • *Conservation level:* 2 • *Level of threat:* 5 • ACTION RECOMMENDED: *Restoration:* 5.

IV 028 - Legal Amazonia - PRIORITY LEVEL: D • LOCATION: *State:* All • *Main municipality:* Various • *Municipalities covered:* 169 • VEGETATION TYPES: Several • COMMENTS: Sixteen areas without information, identified as priorities for biological inventories.

DIAGNOSTIC ELEMENTS: *Hotspots:* 0 • ACTION RECOMMENDED: *Biological inventory:* 5.

5
PRIORITY AREAS FOR PLANTS*

The richness of the Amazonian flowering plant flora has been estimated at approximately 21,000 species (Gentry 1982). According to information obtained from research in herbaria, central Amazonia hosts a greater diversity than eastern Amazonia. Compared to other neotropical humid forests, the Amazon forest contains a greater number of widely distributed species.

It should be pointed out however that the data from herbaria do not yet allow us to adequately portray the geography of plant diversity or the concentration of non-edaphic endemism in the region. This problem is the result, on the one hand, of the fact that many species are rare and, on the other, that collecting efforts have been regionally unbalanced, resulting in incomplete local listings and biased results when comparisons are made. This is a persistent problem, notwithstanding the existence of approximately 300,000 different herbaria specimens of Brazilian Amazon angiosperms.

Floristic patterns in Amazonia are more reliable when inferred from surveys carried out in one-hectare plots. Analysis of several published inventories based on dried specimens, together with the research of Steege et al. (2000), shows that the species richness of trees in the plots is greater in the central and western regions of Amazonia as compared to the eastern part or the Guianas. There is a relation between plot richness and annual precipitation which reaches the asymptote at between 2,000 and 2,500 mm a year. On the basis of the abundance of trees by family, the axis of greatest floristic variation forms a southwest to northeast gradient passing through central Amazonia.

Taking abundance of trees by family and genera as a measure of similarity, multivariate analysis of plots reveals two indicators of floristic complementarity that greatly assist the identification of locations for the creation of new conservation areas: vegetation type and geographical distance.

Analysis of the current coverage of legal protection for the 21 vegetation types within the Brazilian Amazon regarded as floristically dissimilar, following the Radam project data (IBGE 1997) and the classification system proposed by Veloso et al. (1991), confirms that conservation areas are frequently poorly distributed, leading to gaps and to the absence of connectivity between them. As a result, locally endemic species, together with genetic diversity below the level of species, are vulnerable.

Using this methodology it is possible to confirm that 17 of the 21 vegetation types in the region have less than 10% of their area safeguarded by means of strict protection conservation areas. Seven vegetation types have less than 2% of their area under protection: seasonally deciduous montane forest (0% under full protection); open rainforest dominated by vines (0.9%); seasonally deciduous transition forests (1.3%) and deciduous forests below an altitude of 600 meters (0.4%); the ecotone between savanna and closed canopy forest (0.6%); savanna woodland (1.9%); and true savanna (1.1%). The situation is made worse by the fact that these vegetation types are concentrated in the proximity of deforested or degraded areas and are thus threatened.

When less restrictive conservation area categories (sustainable use areas) and indigenous lands are included in the analysis, all 21 vegetation types reveal more than 10% of their areas under protection.

Finally, the study classified the geographical distribution of the conservation areas as good, average or poor. Thirteen of the 21 vegetation types show a poor distribution of full protection conservation areas. When both levels of protection – full protection and sustainable use – are considered, four vegetation types remain classified as poor: evergreen montane forest; seasonally deciduous montane forest; woody primary succession in coastal environments of mangrove or shrubs; and the ecotone between savanna and closed canopy forest. These vegetation types are of limited extent and those furthest from conservation areas occur in regions where deforestation, logging and fires are observed. They should therefore be regarded as of high priority.

During the Macapá Workshop 61 priority areas in Amazonia for plants were identified (see the map on page 446 and the listing). Of these, 28 (45.9%) contain high species richness, 25 (41%) have high levels of (mainly edaphic) species endemism, and only two (3.3%) show a high level of conservation (Table 5).

TABLE 5 - PRIORITY AREAS FOR PLANTS DIAGNOSTIC ELEMENTS THAT SCORE HIGHEST		
Diagnostic elements	Number of areas	%[1]
Species richness	28	45.9
Phylogenetic diversity	13	21.3
Endemism	25	41.0
Richness of rare or threatened species	10	16.4
Hotspots	11	18.0
Special biological features	12	19.7
Economically important species	4	6.6
Biological importance	9	14.8
Intrinsic fragility	13	21.3
Conservation level	2	3.3
Level of threat	7	11.5

1. Of the total proposed areas (61).

---

* Text drawn in part from 'Quantitative floristic inventory and conservation status of vegetation types in the Brazilian Amazon' by Bruce W. Nelson and Alexandre A. de Oliveira, the full version of which can be found on page 131 of this book.

BT 001 - Peixe-Boi, Vila Anani - PRIORITY LEVEL: B • LOCATION: *State:* Pará • *Main municipality:* Capanema • *Municipalities covered:* 8 • VEGETATION TYPES: AA, Pf • COMMENTS: One of the last remaining dense forest areas of the Bragantina region. 96% of its original area has been altered, under high anthropogenic pressure. One of highest population densitis in Amazonia (IBGE). This are could be transformed into biological reserve and also into an *in situ* germplasm collection meeting the needs of programs of restoration of degraded areas.

DIAGNOSTIC ELEMENTS: *Species richness:* 5 • *Endemism:* 5 • *Richness of rare/threatened species:* 2 • *Hotspots:* 3 • *Economically important species:* 4 • *Biological importance:* 5 • *Intrinsic fragility:* 2 • *Conservation level:* 4 • *Level of threat:* 4 • ACTION RECOMMENDED: *Restoration:* 2 • *Biological inventory:* 5 • *Creation of conservation area:* 5 • *Management:* 4.

BT 002 - Forest- Savanna transition in Marajó - PRIORITY LEVEL: A • LOCATION: *State:* Pará • *Main municipality:* Muaná • *Municipalities covered:* 9 • VEGETATION TYPES: AA, Da, Pa, Sp • COMMENTS: The Afuá region is considered unusual as it is located within a low-lying area of the Marajó grasslands with extensive populations of assai palms (*Enterpederacea Mart.*) producing a concentration of during the rainy season (the period between regional harvests). With the creation of Marajó waterway, these populations will be highly threatened by the palm-heart canning industry. This area serves as breeding ground for the *muçuã*, a little known, but heavily hunted, aquatic chelonian. The remaining forest-savanna transition constitutes a large gap in the conservation of floodplain vegetation types.

DIAGNOSTIC ELEMENTS: *Species richness:* 2 • *Endemism:* 2 • *Richness of rare/threatened species:* 3 • *Hotspots:* 2 • *Special biological features:* 3 • *Economically important species:* 3 • *Biological importance:* 3 • *Intrinsic fragility:* 1 • *Conservation level:* 1 • *Level of threat:* 4 • ACTION RECOMMENDED: *Biological inventory:* 4 • *Creation of conservation area:* 5 • *Management:* 1.

BT 003 - Castanhais - PRIORITY LEVEL: A • LOCATION: *State:* Amapá/Pará • *Main municipality:* Vitória do Jari • *Municipalities covered:* 6 • VEGETATION TYPES: AA, As, Da, Db, Ds, Pa, SO • COMMENTS: Consolidation and expansion of the extractive potential of the Brazil nut areas (part of the area is protected).

DIAGNOSTIC ELEMENTS: *Species richness:* 3 • *Endemism:* 5 • *Hotspots:* 5 • *Special biological features:* 5 • *Economically important species:* 5 • *Biological importance:* 4 • *Intrinsic fragility:* 4 • *Conservation level:* 3 • ACTION RECOMMENDED: *Biological inventory:* 5 • *Management:* 5.

BT 004 - Cacaual Caciporé - Cunani - PRIORITY LEVEL: C • LOCATION: *State:* Amapá • *Main municipality:* Calçoene • *Municipalities covered:* 2 • VEGETATION TYPES: Ds • COMMENTS: Management and extractive activities. Existence of abandoned cocoa plantations, needing management for their economic recovery.

DIAGNOSTIC ELEMENTS: *Species richness:* 3 • *Economically important species:* 2 • *Intrinsic fragility:* 1 • *Conservation level:* 5 • *Level of threat:* 1 • ACTION RECOMMENDED: *Restoration:* 3 • *Biological inventory:* 5 • *Creation of conservation area:* 5 • *Management:* 5.

BT 005 - Maracá - Santa Clara Savanna - PRIORITY LEVEL: B • LOCATION: *State:* Amapá • *Main municipality:* Mazagão • *Municipalities covered:* 2 • VEGETATION TYPES: Db, Ds, Pa, SO • COMMENTS: Intact savanna, with areas of grasslands and middle to high woody vegetation, isolated representative of savanna type, already transformed by monoculture to the north.

DIAGNOSTIC ELEMENTS: *Species richness:* 5 • *Hotspots:* 5 • *Biological importance:* 5 • *Intrinsic fragility:* 5 • *Conservation level:* 1 • *Level of threat:* 5 • ACTION RECOMMENDED: *Biological inventory:* 5 • *Creation of conservation area:* 1 • *Management:* 5.

BT 006 - Amapá Grande Savanna - PRIORITY LEVEL: A • LOCATION: *State:* Amapá • *Main municipality:* Amapá • *Municipalities covered:* 3 • VEGETATION TYPES: Da, Ds, Pa, Sa, SO, Sp • COMMENTS: Transformation of the original vegetation into exotic monoculture of eucalyptus forest. Representative of the savanna of the extreme north of eastern Amazonia. Part of the priority area.

DIAGNOSTIC ELEMENTS: *Species richness:* 1 • *Hotspots:* 1 • *Biological importance:* 5 • *Intrinsic fragility:* 5 • *Conservation level:* 2 • *Level of threat:* 5 • ACTION RECOMMENDED: *Restoration:* 1 • *Biological inventory:* 1 • *Creation of conservation area:* 5 • *Management:* 5.

BT 007 - Santarém dry forest-savanna - PRIORITY LEVEL: C • LOCATION: *State:* Pará • *Main municipality:* Santarém • *Municipalities covered:* 2 • VEGETATION TYPES: AA, Db • COMMENTS: High richness of woody species. Presence of *murici*, an economical important species. Vegetation which ensures feeding source for migratory fauna. Threatened by fires and tourism.

DIAGNOSTIC ELEMENTS: *Species richness:* 5 • *Richness of rare/threatened species:* 2 • *Hotspots:* 5 • *Special biological features:* 2 • *Economically important species:* 1 • *Biological importance:* 5 • *Intrinsic fragility:* 5 • *Conservation level:* 2 • *Level of threat:* 5 • ACTION RECOMMENDED: *Creation of conservation area:* 5 • *Management:* 5.

BT 008 - Humaitá - Apuí forest-savanna transition - PRIORITY LEVEL: A • LOCATION: *State:* Amazonas/Pará/Rondônia • *Main municipality:* Humaitá • *Municipalities covered:* 5 • VEGETATION TYPES: AA, As, Ds, ON, Pa, Sa, Sd, Sg, SO, Sp • COMMENTS: Rare tree species, restricted to western Amazonia (e.g. *Octhocomus barrae*). Threats from Amazonas state government programs aiming at converting the grasslands of the region to soybean cultivation.

DIAGNOSTIC ELEMENTS: *Species richness:* 5 • *Endemism:* 2 • *Richness of rare/threatened species:* 2 • *Biological importance:* 3 • *Intrinsic fragility:* 1 • *Conservation level:* 2 • *Level of threat:* 3 • ACTION RECOMMENDED: *Biological inventory:* 2 • *Creation of conservation area:* 5 • *Management:* 4.

BT 009 - Xingu Savanna Forest - PRIORITY LEVEL: B • LOCATION: *State:* Mato Grosso/Pará • *Main municipality:* São Félix do Xingu • *Municipalities covered:* 7 • VEGETATION TYPES: Ab, Da, Ds • COMMENTS: Savanna area and transition forest with babaçu.

DIAGNOSTIC ELEMENTS: *Species richness:* 1 • *Richness of rare/threatened species:* 1 • *Economically important species:* 1 • *Biological importance:* 2 • *Intrinsic fragility:* 2 • *Conservation level:* 2 • *Level of threat:* 5 • ACTION RECOMMENDED: *Restoration:* 1 • *Biological inventory:* 4 • *Creation of conservation area:* 4 • *Management:* 4.

BT 010 - Upper Jari and Amapari - PRIORITY LEVEL: B • LOCATION: *State:* Amapá/Pará • *Main municipality:* Vitória do Jari • *Municipalities covered:* 2 • VEGETATION TYPES: Ds, Dm • COMMENTS: Forest vegetation type at the edge of its range and not found in protected areas (montane refugium).

DIAGNOSTIC ELEMENTS: *Species richness:* 5 • *Phylogenetic diversity:* 5 • *Endemism:* 5 • *Richness of rare/threatened species:* 3 • *Hotspots:* 5 • *Special biological features:* 5 • *Economically important species:* 5 • *Biological importance:* 4 • *Intrinsic fragility:* 2 • *Conservation level:* 1 • *Level of threat:* 3 • ACTION RECOMMENDED: *Biological inventory:* 5 • *Creation of conservation area:* 5.

BT 011 - Upper Jari and Amapari - PRIORITY LEVEL: B • LOCATION: *State:* Amapá • *Main municipality:* Pedra Branca do Amapari • *Municipalities covered:* 4 • VEGETATION TYPES: Ds • COMMENTS: Forest vegetation type at the edge of its range and not found in protected areas (montane refugium).

DIAGNOSTIC ELEMENTS: *Species richness:* 5 • *Phylogenetic diversity:* 5 • *Endemism:* 5 • *Richness of rare/threatened species:* 5 • *Hotspots:* 5 • *Special biological features:* 5 • *Economically important species:* 5 • *Biological importance:* 4 • *Intrinsic fragility:* 2 • *Conservation level:* 1 • *Level of threat:* 3 • ACTION RECOMMENDED: *Biological inventory:* 5 • *Creation of conservation area:* 5.

BT 012 - Rio Branco floodplains - PRIORITY LEVEL: D • LOCATION: *State:* Amazonas/Roraima • *Main municipality:* Caracaraí • *Municipalities covered:* 3 • VEGETATION TYPES: Da, Db, Ld, LO • COMMENTS: White-water floodplains isolated from the Andean, Solimões and Amazonas systems.

DIAGNOSTIC ELEMENTS: *Endemism:* 2 • *Intrinsic fragility:* 5 • *Conservation level:* 1 • *Level of threat:* 1 • ACTION RECOMMENDED: *Biological inventory:* 5 • *Creation of conservation area:* 5.

BT 013 - Maicuru mountain range - PRIORITY LEVEL: A • LOCATION: *State:* Pará • *Main municipality:* Almeirim • *Municipalities* *covered:* 2 • VEGETATION TYPES: Ds • COMMENTS: Area of high floristic importance.

> DIAGNOSTIC ELEMENTS: *Endemism:* 3 • *Richness of rare/threatened species:* 3 • *Hotspots:* 1 • *Special biological features:* 3 • *Biological importance:* 3 • *Intrinsic fragility:* 4 • *Conservation level:* 1 • *Level of threat:* 1 • ACTION RECOMMENDED: *Biological inventory:* 5 • *Creation of conservation area:* 5 • *Management:* 1.

BT 014 - Serra dos Carajás - PRIORITY LEVEL: A • LOCATION: *State:* Pará • *Main municipality:* Parauapebas • *Municipalities covered:* 4 • VEGETATION TYPES: AA, As, Dm, Ds • COMMENTS: High endemism of herbaceous flora.

> DIAGNOSTIC ELEMENTS: *Species richness:* 1 • *Phylogenetic diversity:* 3 • *Endemism:* 5 • *Richness of rare/threatened species:* 5 • *Hotspots:* 4 • *Special biological features:* 5 • *Economically important species:* 5 • *Biological importance:* 5 • *Intrinsic fragility:* 5 • *Conservation level:* 2 • *Level of threat:* 5 • ACTION RECOMMENDED: *Restoration:* 3 • *Biological inventory:* 2 • *Creation of conservation area:* 5 • *Management:* 5.

BT 015 - Pico da Neblina - PRIORITY LEVEL: A • LOCATION: *State:* Amazonas • *Main municipality:* São Gabriel da Cachoeira • *Municipalities covered:* 2 • VEGETATION TYPES: Dm, Ds, Ld, LO, rm • COMMENTS: The area consists of isolated mountain-tops with high altitudes grasslands and several other vegetation types.

> DIAGNOSTIC ELEMENTS: *Species richness:* 3 • *Phylogenetic diversity:* 5 • *Endemism:* 4 • *Richness of rare/threatened species:* 4 • *Hotspots:* 4 • *Special biological features:* 4 • *Economically important species:* 1 • *Biological importance:* 4 • *Intrinsic fragility:* 3 • *Conservation level:* 2 • *Level of threat:* 3 • ACTION RECOMMENDED: *Restoration:* 2 • *Biological inventory:* 4 • *Creation of conservation area:* 1 • *Management:* 2.

BT 016 - Içana River and the Igarapé Pégua mountains - PRIORITY LEVEL: A • LOCATION: *State:* Amazonas • *Main municipality:* São Gabriel da Cachoeira • *Municipalities covered:* 1 • VEGETATION TYPES: Ds, Ld, LO, rm • COMMENTS: The area includes large areas of campinarana as well as montane forests, a very rare Brazilian vegetation type. Area of transition to rainforest.

> DIAGNOSTIC ELEMENTS: *Species richness:* 3 • *Phylogenetic diversity:* 4 • *Endemism:* 5 • *Richness of rare/threatened species:* 4 • *Hotspots:* 3 • *Special biological features:* 1 • *Biological importance:* 4 • *Intrinsic fragility:* 5 • *Conservation level:* 1 • *Level of threat:* 1 • ACTION RECOMMENDED: *Restoration:* 1 • *Biological inventory:* 5 • *Creation of conservation area:* 4 • *Management:* 1.

BT 017 - Rio Amazonas flooded forests - PRIORITY LEVEL: D • LOCATION: *State:* Pará • *Main municipality:* Santarém • *Municipalities covered:* 2 • VEGETATION TYPES: Db, SO • COMMENTS: There are few flooded forests (igapó) in the lower Amazon region.

> DIAGNOSTIC ELEMENTS: *Endemism:* 3 • *Intrinsic fragility:* 5 • *Conservation level:* 1 • *Level of threat:* 1 • ACTION RECOMMENDED: *Biological inventory:* 5 • *Creation of conservation area:* 5.

BT 018 - Campinas of the middle Rio Madeira and upper Andirá - PRIORITY LEVEL: A • LOCATION: *State:* Amazonas/Pará • *Main municipality:* Borba • *Municipalities covered:* 7 • VEGETATION TYPES: Da, Db, Ds, Pa • COMMENTS: Probable endemism in sandy soil outliers. Campinas originating from two sources: river beds (18A) and podzolization of interfluves (18B and 18C).

> DIAGNOSTIC ELEMENTS: *Endemism:* 5 • *Richness of rare/threatened species:* 4 • *Special biological features:* 5 • *Biological importance:* 4 • *Intrinsic fragility:* 5 • *Conservation level:* 1 • *Level of threat:* 1 • ACTION RECOMMENDED: *Biological inventory:* 5 • *Creation of conservation area:* 4 • *Management:* 5.

BT 019 - Isolated bamboo forest - PRIORITY LEVEL: B • LOCATION: *State:* Mato Grosso • *Main municipality:* Brasnorte • *Municipalities covered:* 3 • VEGETATION TYPES: AA, As, Da, Fa, ON, SN, SO • COMMENTS: Bamboo-dominated forest, the only example identified by the RADAM project outside southwestern Amazonia.

> DIAGNOSTIC ELEMENTS: *Hotspots:* 2 • *Special biological features:* 5 • *Conservation level:* 5 • ACTION RECOMMENDED: *Biological inventory:* 5 • *Creation of conservation area:* 5.

BT 020 - Upper Juruá campinas - PRIORITY LEVEL: A • LOCATION: *State:* Acre/Amazonas • *Main municipality:* Guajará • *Municipalities covered:* 3 • VEGETATION TYPES: AA, Ab, Da, Db, La, Ld • COMMENTS: Extensive and continuous region of campinas, far from other areas of campinas.

> DIAGNOSTIC ELEMENTS: *Species richness:* 3 • *Phylogenetic diversity:* 3 • *Endemism:* 4 • *Richness of rare/threatened species:* 5 • *Hotspots:* 3 • *Biological importance:* 5 • *Intrinsic fragility:* 4 • *Conservation level:* 2 • *Level of threat:* 2 • ACTION RECOMMENDED: *Restoration:* 1 • *Biological inventory:* 5 • *Creation of conservation area:* 5 • *Management:* 2.

BT 021 - North of Manaus - PRIORITY LEVEL: B • LOCATION: *State:* Amazonas • *Main municipality:* Manaus • *Municipalities covered:* 4 • VEGETATION TYPES: As, Da, Db, Ds, LO • COMMENTS: Region of high tree diversity and risk of deforestation.

> DIAGNOSTIC ELEMENTS: *Species richness:* 5 • *Phylogenetic diversity:* 5 • *Endemism:* 4 • *Richness of rare/threatened species:* 5 • *Hotspots:* 4 • *Special biological features:* 4 • *Economically important species:* 3 • *Biological importance:* 5 • *Intrinsic fragility:* 2 • *Conservation level:* 2 • *Level of threat:* 5 • ACTION RECOMMENDED: *Restoration:* 2 • *Biological inventory:* 2 • *Creation of conservation area:* 2 • *Management:* 5.

BT 022 - Middle Rio Negro - Cuiuni river - PRIORITY LEVEL: A • LOCATION: *State:* Amazonas • *Main municipality:* Barcelos • *Municipalities covered:* 2 • VEGETATION TYPES: La, Ld, Lg, LO • COMMENTS: Gaps in conservation areas for this specific vegetation type (campina and campinarana); high levels of endemic species and genera.

> DIAGNOSTIC ELEMENTS: *Species richness:* 3 • *Phylogenetic diversity:* 4 • *Endemism:* 5 • *Richness of rare/threatened species:* 4 • *Hotspots:* 2 • *Special biological features:* 4 • *Economically important species:* 2 • *Biological importance:* 4 • *Intrinsic fragility:* 4 • *Conservation level:* 1 • *Level of threat:* 2 • ACTION RECOMMENDED: *Biological inventory:* 5 • *Creation of conservation area:* 5 • *Management:* 2.

BT 023 - Surucucus tepuis - PRIORITY LEVEL: C • LOCATION: *State:* Roraima • *Main municipality:* Alto Alegre • *Municipalities covered:* 1 • VEGETATION TYPES: Dm, rm • COMMENTS: Endemic vegetation poorly represented in conservation areas. Threatened by fires.

> DIAGNOSTIC ELEMENTS: *Species richness:* 2 • *Phylogenetic diversity:* 4 • *Endemism:* 5 • *Richness of rare/threatened species:* 5 • *Hotspots:* 5 • *Biological importance:* 4 • *Intrinsic fragility:* 4 • *Conservation level:* 4 • *Level of threat:* 4 • ACTION RECOMMENDED: *Biological inventory:* 5 • *Creation of conservation area:* 5 • *Management:* 4.

BT 024 - Serra de Ufaranda tepuis - PRIORITY LEVEL: C • LOCATION: *State:* Roraima • *Main municipality:* Alto Alegre • *Municipalities covered:* 1 • VEGETATION TYPES: As, Dm, rm • COMMENTS: Endemic vegetation from the Guiana shields region; high level of endemism.

> DIAGNOSTIC ELEMENTS: *Species richness:* 3 • *Phylogenetic diversity:* 4 • *Endemism:* 5 • *Richness of rare/threatened species:* 4 • *Hotspots:* 3 • *Special biological features:* 5 • *Biological importance:* 5 • *Intrinsic fragility:* 5 • *Conservation level:* 1 • *Level of threat:* 3 • ACTION RECOMMENDED: *Biological inventory:* 5 • *Creation of conservation area:* 5.

BT 025 - Andorinhas mountains, northern part - PRIORITY LEVEL: B • LOCATION: *State:* Pará/Tocantins • *Main municipality:* São Geraldo do Araguaia • *Municipalities covered:* 4 • VEGETATION TYPES: AA, As, Ds, SO • COMMENTS: Area of high floristic and landscape importance, region of limited endemism due to the occurrence of halogenous soils, with high levels of magnesium, potassium and sodium. Atypical open vegetation.

> DIAGNOSTIC ELEMENTS: *Species richness:* 2 • *Endemism:* 3 • *Richness of rare/threatened species:* 2 • *Economically important species:* 3 • *Biological importance:* 3 • *Intrinsic fragility:* 5 • *Conservation level:* 2 • ACTION RECOMMENDED: *Biological inventory:* 4 • *Creation of conservation area:* 5 • *Management:* 4.

BT 026 - Upper Juruá - PRIORITY LEVEL: A • LOCATION: *State:* Acre • *Main municipality:* Cruzeiro do Sul • *Municipalities covered:* 5 • VEGETATION TYPES: Ab, As, Da, Db, Ds, Pa, SO, Sp • COMMENTS: Relatively high levels of endemism. New rare species found in recent years. Affinity between the highest lands in the range and the Andes. Very high diversity of palms, with the presence of Amazon campinas. Species with single records in Brazil.

DIAGNOSTIC ELEMENTS: *Species richness:* 5 • *Phylogenetic diversity:* 4 • *Endemism:* 4 • *Richness of rare/threatened species:* 4 • *Hotspots:* 3 • *Economically important species:* 4 • *Biological importance:* 4 • *Conservation level:* 2 • *Level of threat:* 3 • ACTION RECOMMENDED: *Restoration:* 1 • *Biological inventory:* 5 • *Creation of conservation area:* 3 • *Management:* 4.

BT 027 - Middle and upper Tarauacá - PRIORITY LEVEL: A • LOCATION: *State:* Acre • *Main municipality:* Tarauacá • *Municipalities covered:* 3 • VEGETATION TYPES: Ab, Da, Db • COMMENTS: There is no strict use conservation area in the Tarauacá basin. The soils of this basin are distinct from the rest of the state; according to the study published by INPA, several rare species have been found in recent years. Rocky outcrops in the upper stretches near the Jordão river.

DIAGNOSTIC ELEMENTS: *Species richness:* 5 • *Phylogenetic diversity:* 4 • *Endemism:* 4 • *Richness of rare/threatened species:* 4 • *Hotspots:* 3 • *Economically important species:* 3 • *Biological importance:* 4 • *Conservation level:* 2 • *Level of threat:* 2 • ACTION RECOMMENDED: *Restoration:* 2 • *Biological inventory:* 5 • *Creation of conservation area:* 3 • *Management:* 3.

BT 028 - Upper Acre - PRIORITY LEVEL: A • LOCATION: *State:* Acre • *Main municipality:* Assis Brasil • *Municipalities covered:* 3 • VEGETATION TYPES: Ab, Db • COMMENTS: According to available data, relatively high levels of endemism. Very broken terrain near Assis Brasil. Presence of open bamboo forest. Growing anthropogenic pressure, including proposed construction of a highway to the Pacific in Assis Brasil. Open forest with floristic affinities with drier regions.

DIAGNOSTIC ELEMENTS: *Species richness:* 5 • *Phylogenetic diversity:* 3 • *Endemism:* 4 • *Richness of rare/threatened species:* 4 • *Hotspots:* 3 • *Economically important species:* 4 • *Biological importance:* 4 • *Conservation level:* 3 • *Level of threat:* 3 • ACTION RECOMMENDED: *Restoration:* 1 • *Biological inventory:* 5 • *Creation of conservation area:* 5 • *Management:* 4.

BT 029 - Iaco - Macauã rivers - PRIORITY LEVEL: B • LOCATION: *State:* Acre • *Main municipality:* Sena Madureira • *Municipalities covered:* 1 • VEGETATION TYPES: Ab, Da, Db • COMMENTS: Relatively high levels of endemism, open terra firme forest with affinities with drier regions. Region with large reserves hardwood (yellow mahogany) and, as a consequence, under threat.

DIAGNOSTIC ELEMENTS: *Species richness:* 5 • *Phylogenetic diversity:* 4 • *Endemism:* 4 • *Richness of rare/threatened species:* 4 • *Hotspots:* 3 • *Economically important species:* 4 • *Biological importance:* 4 • *Intrinsic fragility:* 3 • *Conservation level:* 2 • *Level of threat:* 3 • ACTION RECOMMENDED: *Restoration:* 2 • *Biological inventory:* 5 • *Creation of conservation area:* 4 • *Management:* 4.

BT 030 - River Acre microbasins - PRIORITY LEVEL: B • LOCATION: *State:* Acre • *Main municipality:* Porto Acre • *Municipalities covered:* 4 • VEGETATION TYPES: AA, Ab, Da, Db • COMMENTS: This region's floodplains are structurally very complex and their floristic composition is very different from the floodplains of the main rivers, including frontiers only known from here to Acre.

DIAGNOSTIC ELEMENTS: *Species richness:* 4 • *Phylogenetic diversity:* 3 • *Endemism:* 3 • *Richness of rare/threatened species:* 4 • *Hotspots:* 3 • *Economically important species:* 4 • *Biological importance:* 4 • *Intrinsic fragility:* 4 • *Conservation level:* 3 • *Level of threat:* 4 • ACTION RECOMMENDED: *Restoration:* 2 • *Biological inventory:* 5 • *Creation of conservation area:* 5 • *Management:* 4.

BT 031 - Mount Roraima - PRIORITY LEVEL: A • LOCATION: *State:* Roraima • *Main municipality:* Uiramutã • *Municipalities covered:* 1 • VEGETATION TYPES: Dm • COMMENTS: According to the experience of some botanists, and also to data obtained on the Venezuelan part, this area contains vegetation types poorly represented or unrepresented in Brazil. It is a high altitude area (up to 3,000 meters).

DIAGNOSTIC ELEMENTS: *Species richness:* 4 • *Phylogenetic diversity:* 5 • *Endemism:* 5 • *Richness of rare/threatened species:* 5 • *Hotspots:* 2 • *Special biological features:* 4 • *Economically important species:* 1 • *Biological importance:* 5 • *Intrinsic fragility:* 5 • *Conservation level:* 2 • *Level of threat:* 3 • ACTION RECOMMENDED: *Restoration:* 1 • *Biological inventory:* 4 • *Creation of conservation area:* 2 • *Management:* 3.

BT 032 - Serra do Aracá inselbergs - PRIORITY LEVEL: A • LOCATION: *State:* Amazonas • *Main municipality:* Barcelos • *Municipalities covered:* 1 • VEGETATION TYPES: Dm, Ds, Lg, rm • COMMENTS: As floristic islands the mountain tops have high levels of endemism. Mountain tops in areas of 900 to 1,000 meters, intermediate compared with others identified as priority. Mountain vegetation of the granite substrate also included. Igapó, campina and campinarana vegetations of the surrounding region also included.

DIAGNOSTIC ELEMENTS: *Species richness:* 2 • *Phylogenetic diversity:* 3 • *Endemism:* 5 • *Richness of rare/threatened species:* 4 • *Hotspots:* 1 • *Special biological features:* 5 • *Economically important species:* 1 • *Biological importance:* 4 • *Intrinsic fragility:* 5 • *Conservation level:* 1 • *Level of threat:* 1 • ACTION RECOMMENDED: *Biological inventory:* 2.

BT 033 - Dry forest-savanna transition in western Roraima - PRIORITY LEVEL: A • LOCATION: *State:* Roraima • *Main municipality:* Amajari • *Municipalities covered:* 2 • VEGETATION TYPES: As, Ds, Fs, ON, rm, Sp • COMMENTS: The semi-deciduous forests are among the least known, most fragile, most threatened and least protected (by conservation areas) environments in Amazonia, or in the neotropical region as a whole. This area also includes transition to savannas and more humid forests.

DIAGNOSTIC ELEMENTS: *Species richness:* 3 • *Endemism:* 3 • *Richness of rare/threatened species:* 3 • *Hotspots:* 4 • *Biological importance:* 4 • *Intrinsic fragility:* 5 • *Conservation level:* 3 • *Level of threat:* 5 • ACTION RECOMMENDED: *Restoration:* 3 • *Biological inventory:* 3 • *Creation of conservation area:* 5 • *Management:* 5.

BT 034 - Purus - Juruá interfluve - PRIORITY LEVEL: B • LOCATION: *State:* Amazonas • *Main municipality:* Tapauá • *Municipalities covered:* 4 • VEGETATION TYPES: Ab, Da, Db • COMMENTS: There is no conservation area, only indigenous lands. Large gap in conservation area system.

DIAGNOSTIC ELEMENTS: *Species richness:* 4 • *Phylogenetic diversity:* 3 • *Hotspots:* 3 • *Intrinsic fragility:* 3 • *Conservation level:* 1 • *Level of threat:* 1 • ACTION RECOMMENDED: *Biological inventory:* 5 • *Creation of conservation area:* 5 • *Management:* 2.

BT 035 - Areas of no botanical collecting - PRIORITY LEVEL: D • LOCATION: *State:* Amapá/Amazonas/Mato Grosso/Pará/Roraima • *Main municipality:* Various • *Municipalities covered:* 81 • VEGETATION TYPES: AA, Ab, As, Cs, Da, Db, Dm, Ds, Fa, Fs, ON, Pa, Sa, Sd, Sg, SN, SO • COMMENTS: Areas with no inventories and no information in herbaria. Recommended for future inventories.

DIAGNOSTIC ELEMENTS: *Conservation level:* 0 • ACTION RECOMMENDED: *Biological inventory:* 5.

BT 036 - Purus - Madeira Ecoregion - PRIORITY LEVEL: A • LOCATION: *State:* Amazonas/Rondônia • *Main municipality:* Lábrea • *Municipalities covered:* 3 • VEGETATION TYPES: Ab, As, Db, Ds, Sa, SO, Sp • COMMENTS: Vegetation type not protected within existing conservation areas.

DIAGNOSTIC ELEMENTS: *Species richness:* 5 • *Phylogenetic diversity:* 1 • *Endemism:* 5 • *Richness of rare/threatened species:* 3 • *Hotspots:* 3 • *Special biological features:* 5 • ACTION RECOMMENDED: *Restoration:* 5.

BT 037 - Purus - Madeira Ecoregion - PRIORITY LEVEL: A • LOCATION: *State:* Amazonas • *Main municipality:* Tapauá • *Municipalities covered:* 3 • VEGETATION TYPES: Ab, Da, Db • COMMENTS: Vegetation type not protected within existing conservation areas.

DIAGNOSTIC ELEMENTS: *Species richness:* 5 • *Phylogenetic diversity:* 3 • *Endemism:* 4 • *Richness of rare/threatened species:* 1 • *Hotspots:* 3 • *Special biological features:* 5 • ACTION RECOMMENDED: *Restoration:* 5.

BT 038 - Caquetá Ecoregion - PRIORITY LEVEL: A • LOCATION: *State:* Amazonas • *Main municipality:* Japurá • *Municipalities covered:* 1 • VEGETATION TYPES: Ab, Da, La, Ld, LO • COMMENTS: Vegetation type not protected within existing conservation areas.

DIAGNOSTIC ELEMENTS: *Species richness:* 5 • *Endemism:* 1 • *Richness of rare/threatened species:* 1 • *Hotspots:* 4 • *Special biological features:* 5 • ACTION RECOMMENDED: *Restoration:* 5.

BT 039 - Gurupá and Monte Alegre Floodplains Ecoregion - PRIORITY LEVEL: A • LOCATION: *State:* Pará • *Main municipality:* Prainha •

Municipalities covered: 3 • Vegetation types: AA, Da, Db, Ds, Pa • Comments: Vegetation type not protected within existing conservation areas.

Diagnostic elements: *Species richness:* 5 • *Phylogenetic diversity:* 3 • *Endemism:* 1 • *Richness of rare/threatened species:* 4 • *Hotspots:* 4 • *Special biological features:* 1 • Action recommended: *Restoration:* 5.

BT 040 - Monte Alegre Floodplains Ecoregion - Priority level: A • Location: *State:* Amazonas • *Main municipality:* Coari • *Municipalities covered:* 5 • Vegetation types: AA, Da, Db, Ds • Comments: Region of high biological importance and poorly protected by existing conservation areas.

Diagnostic elements: *Species richness:* 5 • *Phylogenetic diversity:* 3 • *Endemism:* 3 • *Richness of rare/threatened species:* 2 • *Hotspots:* 4 • *Special biological features:* 3 • Action recommended: *Restoration:* 5.

BT 041 - Xingu - Tocantins - Araguaia Ecoregion - Priority level: A • Location: *State:* Pará • *Main municipality:* Melgaço • *Municipalities covered:* 4 • Vegetation types: AA, Da, Db, Pa • Comments: Vegetation type not protected within existing conservation areas.

Diagnostic elements: *Species richness:* 5 • *Phylogenetic diversity:* 3 • *Endemism:* 5 • *Richness of rare/threatened species:* 3 • *Hotspots:* 5 • *Special biological features:* 2 • Action recommended: *Restoration:* 5.

BT 042 - Xingu - Tocantins - Araguaia Ecoregion (lower Xingu) - Priority level: A • Location: *State:* Amazonas/Pará • *Main municipality:* Senador José Porfírio • *Municipalities covered:* 3 • Vegetation types: As • Comments: Vegetation type not protected within existing conservation areas.

Diagnostic elements: *Species richness:* 5 • *Phylogenetic diversity:* 5 • *Endemism:* 5 • *Richness of rare/threatened species:* 4 • *Special biological features:* 2 • Action recommended: *Restoration:* 5.

BT 043 - Mato Grosso dry forests Ecoregion (upper Xingu) - Priority level: A • Location: *State:* Mato Grosso/Pará • *Main municipality:* São Félix do Xingu • *Municipalities covered:* 3 • Vegetation types: AA, As, ON, Pa, Sa, Sd, Sg, SO, Sp • Comments: Vegetation type not protected within existing conservation areas.

Diagnostic elements: *Species richness:* 5 • *Phylogenetic diversity:* 4 • *Endemism:* 5 • *Richness of rare/threatened species:* 4 • *Hotspots:* 3 • *Special biological features:* 3 • Action recommended: *Restoration:* 5.

BT 044 - Mato Grosso Dry Forests Ecoregion - Priority level: A • Location: *State:* Mato Grosso/Pará • *Main municipality:* Novo Progresso • *Municipalities covered:* 8 • Vegetation types: As, SO, Sp • Comments: Vegetation type not protected within existing conservation areas.

Diagnostic elements: *Species richness:* 5 • *Phylogenetic diversity:* 3 • *Endemism:* 5 • *Richness of rare/threatened species:* 2 • *Hotspots:* 4 • *Special biological features:* 3 • Action recommended: *Restoration:* 5.

BT 045 - Pantanal Ecoregion - Priority level: A • Location: *State:* Mato Grosso • *Main municipality:* Cáceres • *Municipalities covered:* 1 • Vegetation types: Fa, Sa, Sd, Sg, SN, Sp, ST, Tp.

Diagnostic elements: *Species richness:* 4 • *Phylogenetic diversity:* 3 • *Endemism:* 3 • *Richness of rare/threatened species:* 3 • *Special biological features:* 3 • Action recommended: *Restoration:* 5.

BT 046 - Uatumã - Trombetas ecoregion and Guiana savannas ecoregion - Priority level: A • Location: *State:* Pará • *Main municipality:* Alenquer • *Municipalities covered:* 2 • Vegetation types: Da, Ds • Comments: Small indigenous land with acess restricted. The proposed area is an enclave between indigenous lands.

Diagnostic elements: *Species richness:* 3 • *Phylogenetic diversity:* 2 • *Endemism:* 5 • *Richness of rare/threatened species:* 1 • *Hotspots:* 1 • Action recommended: *Restoration:* 5.

BT 047 - Uatumã - Trombetas Ecoregion and Guiana Forests Ecoregion - Priority level: A • Location: *State:* Amapá • *Main municipality:* Vitória do Jari • *Municipalities covered:* 3 • Vegetation types: Da, Pa, SO, Sp • Comments: Create buffer-zone around the indigenous land. Area proposed for INCRA resettlement project.

Diagnostic elements: *Species richness:* 4 • *Phylogenetic diversity:* 2 • *Endemism:* 5 • *Richness of rare/threatened species:* 3 • *Hotspots:* 5 • *Special biological features:* 3 • Action recommended: *Restoration:* 5.

BT 048 - Southwestern Amazonia Ecoregion - Priority level: A • Location: *State:* Amazonas • *Main municipality:* Guajará • *Municipalities covered:* 1 • Vegetation types: Ab, As, Db, Ds, La, Ld, Lg, LO • Comments: Only campinarana group to the south of the Solimões system.

Diagnostic elements: *Species richness:* 5 • *Phylogenetic diversity:* 5 • *Endemism:* 3 • *Richness of rare/threatened species:* 5 • *Hotspots:* 1 • *Special biological features:* 1 • Action recommended: *Restoration:* 5.

BT 049 - Guiana Savannas Ecoregion - Priority level: A • Location: *State:* Amapá • *Main municipality:* Tartarugalzinho • *Municipalities covered:* 3 • Vegetation types: AA, Da, Pa, Pf • Comments: Only ecosystem in the state not protected by conservation area.

Diagnostic elements: *Species richness:* 5 • *Phylogenetic diversity:* 5 • *Endemism:* 4 • *Richness of rare/threatened species:* 4 • *Hotspots:* 4 • *Special biological features:* 3 • Action recommended: *Restoration:* 5 • *Biological inventory:* 5 • *Creation of conservation area:* 5 • *Management:* 5.

BT 050 - Tapajós - Xingu interfluve Ecoregion - Priority level: A • Location: *State:* Pará • *Main municipality:* Altamira • *Municipalities covered:* 2 • Vegetation types: As, Cs, Ds, ON, Sa, Sd, SN, SO, Sp • Comments: Creation of a corridor to maximize protection of several vegetation types.

Diagnostic elements: *Species richness:* 4 • *Phylogenetic diversity:* 1 • *Endemism:* 5 • *Richness of rare/threatened species:* 2 • *Special biological features:* 4 • Action recommended: *Restoration:* 5.

BT 051 - Madeira - Tapajós Ecoregion - Priority level: A • Location: *State:* Rondônia • *Main municipality:* Guajará-Mirim • *Municipalities covered:* 1 • Vegetation types: Ab, As, Da, Pa, Sa, Sd, SO, Sp • Comments: Area important for the consolidation of the western corridor in Rondônia.

Diagnostic elements: *Species richness:* 3 • *Phylogenetic diversity:* 4 • *Endemism:* 5 • *Richness of rare/threatened species:* 2 • *Hotspots:* 4 • *Special biological features:* 4 • Action recommended: *Restoration:* 5.

BT 052 - Negro, Branco and Rio Negro Campinaranas Ecoregion - Priority level: A • Location: *State:* Amazonas • *Main municipality:* Santa Isabel do Rio Negro • *Municipalities covered:* 2 • Vegetation types: Da, Ds, Sd, SO • Comments: Conserves vegetation types not represented in conservation areas and important to guaranteeing the linkages between indigenous lands.

Diagnostic elements: *Species richness:* 5 • *Phylogenetic diversity:* 1 • *Endemism:* 5 • *Richness of rare/threatened species:* 1 • *Special biological features:* 4 • Action recommended: *Restoration:* 5.

BT 053 - Tocantins - Araguaia - Maranhão Ecoregion - Priority level: A • Location: *State:* Pará • *Main municipality:* Curuçá • *Municipalities covered:* 16 • Vegetation types: AA, As, Da, Ds, Sa, SO • Comments: Very important mangrove area.

Diagnostic elements: *Species richness:* 5 • *Phylogenetic diversity:* 5 • *Endemism:* 3 • *Richness of rare/threatened species:* 4 • *Special biological features:* 1 • Action recommended: *Restoration:* 5.

BT 054 - Tocantins - Araguaia - Maranhão Ecoregion - Priority level: A • Location: *State:* Pará • *Main municipality:* Tomé-Açu • *Municipalities covered:* 3 • Vegetation types: AA, Da, Db • Comments: Highly threatened area and there are no conservation areas in the ecoregion.

Diagnostic elements: *Species richness:* 5 • *Phylogenetic diversity:* 5 • *Endemism:* 1 • *Richness of rare/threatened species:* 5 • *Special biological features:* 1 • Action recommended: *Restoration:* 5.

BT 055 - Southwestern Amazônia Ecoregion - Priority level: A • Location: *State:* Acre • *Main municipality:* Manoel Urbano • *Municipalities covered:* 4 • Vegetation types: Ab, Da • Comments: Connects indigenous land and extractive reserves. Located within the western Amazonas corridor. Area considered as high priority for conservation in the 1990 Amazonia Workshop. Anthropogenic pressure still low.

Diagnostic elements: *Species richness:* 5 • *Phylogenetic diversity:* 1

• *Endemism:* 5 • *Richness of rare/threatened species:* 2 • *Hotspots:* 5 • *Special biological features:* 4 • ACTION RECOMMENDED: *Restoration:* 5.

BT 056 - Mato Grosso Savanna and Dry Forest Ecoregion - PRIORITY LEVEL: A • LOCATION: *State:* Maranhão/Tocantins • *Main municipality:* Babaçulândia • *Municipalities covered:* 12 • VEGETATION TYPES: AA, As, Sa, Sd, SO, Sp • COMMENTS: No conservation areas. Vegetation types poorly represented in the ecoregion. Highly threatened.

DIAGNOSTIC ELEMENTS: *Species richness:* 4 • *Phylogenetic diversity:* 5 • *Endemism:* 3 • *Richness of rare/threatened species:* 5 • *Special biological features:* 1 • ACTION RECOMMENDED: *Restoration:* 5.

BT 057 - Savanna Ecoregion - PRIORITY LEVEL: A • LOCATION: *State:* Tocantins • *Main municipality:* Goiatins • *Municipalities covered:* 5 • VEGETATION TYPES: AA, Sa, Sd, Sp • COMMENTS: Region unrepresented in conservation areas.

DIAGNOSTIC ELEMENTS: *Species richness:* 4 • *Phylogenetic diversity:* 5 • *Endemism:* 3 • *Richness of rare/threatened species:* 4 • *Special biological features:* 1 • ACTION RECOMMENDED: *Restoration:* 5.

BT 058 - Mato Grosso Dry Forests and Savanna Ecoregion - PRIORITY LEVEL: A • LOCATION: *State:* Pará/Tocantins • *Main municipality:* Caseara • *Municipalities covered:* 8 • VEGETATION TYPES: AA, As, Sa, Sd, SN, Sp • COMMENTS: There are no conservation areas. Vegetation types poorly represented in the ecoregion. Highly threatened.

DIAGNOSTIC ELEMENTS: *Species richness:* 4 • *Phylogenetic diversity:* 5 • *Endemism:* 4 • *Richness of rare/threatened species:* 5 • *Special biological features:* 1 • ACTION RECOMMENDED: *Restoration:* 5.

BT 059 - Juruá - Purus Ecoregion - PRIORITY LEVEL: A • LOCATION: *State:* Amazonas • *Main municipality:* Coari • *Municipalities covered:* 2 • VEGETATION TYPES: AA, Da, Db • COMMENTS: Unprotected vegetation type.

DIAGNOSTIC ELEMENTS: *Species richness:* 5 • *Phylogenetic diversity:* 1 • *Endemism:* 4 • *Hotspots:* 4 • ACTION RECOMMENDED: *Restoration:* 5.

BT 060 - Southwestern Amazonas Ecoregion - PRIORITY LEVEL: A • LOCATION: *State:* Acre/Amazonas • *Main municipality:* Guajará • *Municipalities covered:* 3 • VEGETATION TYPES: AA, Db, La • COMMENTS: High connectivity: connects the western Amazon corridor to the central corridor through the indigenous land in the state of Amazonas and in the area surrounding the Serra do Divisor National Park. Very low anthropogenic pressure.

DIAGNOSTIC ELEMENTS: *Species richness:* 4 • *Phylogenetic diversity:* 1 • *Endemism:* 5 • *Richness of rare/threatened species:* 1 • *Hotspots:* 5 • *Special biological features:* 5 • ACTION RECOMMENDED: *Restoration:* 5.

BT 061 - Madeira - Tapajós Ecoregion - PRIORITY LEVEL: A • LOCATION: *State:* Amazonas/Rondônia • *Main municipality:* Manicoré • *Municipalities covered:* 3 • VEGETATION TYPES: Da, Db • COMMENTS: Protects vegetation types not represented in conservation areas and allows connectivity between two indigenous lands.

DIAGNOSTIC ELEMENTS: *Species richness:* 5 • *Phylogenetic diversity:* 2 • *Endemism:* 5 • *Richness of rare/threatened species:* 2 • *Hotspots:* 5 • *Special biological features:* 3 • ACTION RECOMMENDED: *Restoration:* 5

6
PRIORITY AREAS FOR REPTILES AND AMPHIBIANS*

Reptiles

The total number of reptile species in the world is estimated at 6,000, of which 465 have been identified in Brazil (Marques 1998). Dixon (1979) states that there are 550 species of reptiles recorded for the Amazon basin, of which 62% are endemic.

Faunistic surveys for some reptile groups in Amazonia are very incomplete. Studies of caimans and turtles are the most complete in respect of their distribution, taxonomy, status, and species ecology. This may be related to the fact these groups contain a smaller number of species compared, for example, to snakes, as well as having a greater importance commercially. Historically, the financial returns from turtle and caiman species have led to a better understanding of their distribution and increased the interest in their conservation.

The majority of Amazon turtle species are better protected than in other parts of the world. There are 14 freshwater and two terrestrial species in Amazonia, of which five are endemic and one threatened. There are also three species of marine turtle that lay their eggs on the islands and beaches along the coastline of Amazonia, but which are not considered part of the regional fauna.

In Amazonia there are four species of caiman distributed throughout the basin, of which two are endemic and three threatened. These species have been affected by indiscriminate hunting and environmental change.

There are at least 89 species of lizard in the region, distributed among 9 families (Avila-Pires 1995), of which 26% to 29% also occur outside the region.

The distribution, abundance and population status of snakes are much less well known than is the case for other groups of Amazonian reptiles and such studies as exist do not allow us to make reliable recommendations as to their conservation. Dixon (1979) listed 63 genera and 284 species of tropical forest snakes in South America at altitudes below 1000 meters. This includes areas of Amazonia outside Brazil and the Atlantic Forest. Given the descriptions of many new species in the last twenty years, it is not unlikely that the total for Amazonia may be in excess of 300 species.

Priority areas in Amazonia for new inventories of reptile fauna are: the upper and middle Rio Negro basin; from the Rio Branco basin to the Jari; the Tapajós basin; the Xingu basin; the Tocantins basin; the Araguaia basin; the Amanã Sustainable Development Reserve; the Japurá basin; the Purus basin; the Juruá basin; and the Madeira basin.

Those areas where there is intense anthropogenic pressure and increasing degradation of natural habitats – such as the states of Rondônia and Acre, some regions of Pará, and the north of Mato Grosso – should be immediate candidates for surveying.

It is urgent and essential that stretches of the basins of all the large Amazon rivers be designated as conservation areas. Reserves created in aquatic ecosystems should have areas protected on both banks of the river, in contrast to what has so far been the case. This is a fundamental measure for the protection of aquatic animals.

With respect to the protection of turtles and caimans, the establishment of reserves in the following places is essential: the Guaporé river; the upper and middle Rio Negro; the Rio Branco; the Trombetas, by extending the existing reserve to cover both banks; the Purus, by extending the existing reserve to cover both banks; the Juruá; areas within the Amanã reserve, giving priority to the protection of the animal population rather than to the economic activities of the resident human population; the Tapajós; the Xingu; the Araguaia; the Rio das Mortes; the Japurá.

Despite their extreme importance for the maintenance of turtle populations, hatching beaches are only one part of the habitat utilized by these species. Not protecting these animals in their foraging habitats or during their migrations will not remove the risks to their populations. Conserving river corridors protects not just the turtles, but also many other forest animals that are not so prized economically.

Amphibians

There is a total of 163 recorded amphibian species in the Brazilian Amazon. This represents approximately 4% of the 4,000 species which are thought to exist worldwide, and 27% of the estimated total of 600 for Brazil (Haddad 1998). It should be pointed out however that this represents the lowest likely number, since undetermined species and recorded descriptions of isolated species have not been used in the analysis. In some locations this figure reaches 40% of collected species, which demonstrates the current difficulties of taxonomy and, as a result, of assessing amphibian diversity in the region.

The species richness of amphibians identified represents the minimum known number and is biased in favor of Anura (frogs and toads). Information on Gyminophiona (Caecilians) is rare. Although only one species of salamander (*Bolitoglossa*

---

* Text drawn in part from 'Technical report on the amphibian diversity of the Brazilian Amazon' by Claudia Azevedo-Ramos and Ulisses Galatti and from 'Reptile biodiversity of the Amazon Forest biome and priority action for its conservation' by Richard C. Vogt, Gláucia Maciel Moreira and Ana Cristina de Oliveira Cordeiro Duarte, the full versions of which can be found on pages 80 and 90 of this book.

altamazonica) has been recorded in Amazonia, little is known about its geographical distribution.

Since the 'Workshop Amazônia' held in 1990 there has been a considerable increase in the data on the distribution of amphibian species in the region. Such knowledge is however still very dispersed and poorly accessible through the specialist literature. The great majority of studies concentrate on areas along the banks of the main Amazon tributaries or in locations accessible by the road network. Twenty nine sites in the Brazilian Amazon were found to have been surveyed for amphibians. Only 13 (46%) of these inventories can be considered as long-term studies (a period of more than two months).

Apparently endemism does not constitute a reliable variable to guide the establishment of conservation areas for Amazon amphibians, since the number of endemic species found is very low. Neither are there any references to species considered as threatened. A total of 38 species have been identified as occurring in only one location. However the majority of these species are known to occur in other places in Brazil or in the wider Amazon region (Frost 1985, Duellman 1993). A comparison of these figures with those of Frost (1985) and Duellman (1993) suggests that probably only 12 species, equivalent to 7.4% of those present in the region, are endemic to the Brazilian Amazon, although new descriptions may reveal patterns of endemism still unknown.

The areas where the greatest species richness was found were: Manaus, Amazonas; Carajás, Pará; the Madeira in Amazonas; Costa Marques, Rondônia; Guajará-Mirim, Rondônia; and along the BR-364 highway in Rondônia.

Analyzing the research gaps, fifteen regions can be considered as priorities for new inventories. These are: the region between the Madeira and the Tapajós, as far as the southern edge of Amazonia; the Tapajós basin; the area between the Tapajós and the Xingu, as far as the southern edge of Amazonia; the Xingu basin; the area between the Xingu and the Tocantins, as far as the southern edge of Amazonia; the Tocantins and Araguaia basins, as far as the southern edge of Amazonia; the Gurupi river region in northeastern Pará; Marajó island; the area between the Rio Branco and the Jari, including the basins and micro-basins of the Jatapu, Mapuera, Trombetas, Paru and Ipitinga; the Rio Negro basin; the area between the Rio Negro and the Solimões, and the Japurá region; the area between the Solimões and Javari and the Juruá; the area between the Juruá and the Purus; the area between the Purus and the Madeira; and the region within and to the south of the Guaporé Biological Reserve, on the border with Bolivia.

Given that these areas constitute a large proportion of Amazonia, efforts should be concentrated on sites that are representative of the diversity of natural environments in such a way as to enable a representative collection of the diversity of the local fauna to be obtained. In addition, areas near the Arc of Deforestation (northeastern and southern Pará, northern Mato Grosso, northern Rondônia and Acre) should be given priority as they are experiencing intense anthropogenic activity that is altering natural habitats. Since inventories carried out on an east-west axis have identified a fauna that is typical of each locality, and not sub-samples of richer areas, it is strongly recommended that the survey design include localities along this axis in order to gain a better picture of Amazonian diversity. The region between the Rio Branco and the Jari should also be considered an equal priority for new inventories because of the high level of endemism found in the areas bordering Suriname and French Guiana, suggesting the possibility of finding a specific fauna in this area.

In terms of the conservation of amphibians, the following areas are priorities: the Juruá basin; the region between the Juruá and the Purus; the part of the Madeira basin within the state of Amazonas; the southern part of the area between the Tapajós and the Xingu; the Pará-Mato Grosso border region; Alter do Chão, Pará; the Tapajós National Forest; the region of the border with Suriname and French Guiana; the Serra do Navio, Amapá; northeastern Pará; and Marajó island.

During the Macapá Workshop, 46 priority areas for reptiles and amphibians in Amazonia were identified (see the map on page 446 and the listing). Of these, 20 (43.5%) are of high biological value; 14 (30.4%) have high phylogenetic diversity; and 11 (23.9%) are highly threatened by the risk of degradation (Table 6).

TABLE 6 - PRIORITY AREAS FOR REPTILES AND AMPHIBIANS DIAGNOSTIC ELEMENTS THAT SCORE HIGHEST		
Diagnostic elements	Number of areas	%[1]
Species richness	11	23.9
Phylogenetic diversity	14	30.4
Endemism	3	6.5
Richness of rare or threatened species	5	10.9
Hotspots	5	10.9
Special biological features	7	15.2
Economically important species	8	17.4
Biological importance	20	43.5
Intrinsic fragility	14	30.4
Conservation level	4	8.7
Level of threat	11	23.9

1. Of the total proposed areas (46).

RA 001 - São Gabriel da Cachoeira - Cabeça do Cachorro - Priority level: D • Location: *State:* Amazonas • *Main municipality:* São Gabriel da Cachoeira • *Municipalities covered:* 1 • Vegetation types: As, Ds, Ld, LO • Comments: Area of high biological importance, well conserved, and with probable endemic species, judging by assessments made in neighboring regions of Colombia.

Diagnostic elements: *Endemism:* 4 • *Richness of rare/threatened species:* 4 • *Hotspots:* 1 • *Economically important species:* 1 • *Biological importance:* 5 • *Intrinsic fragility:* 1 • *Conservation level:* 1 • *Level of threat:* 1 • Action recommended: *Biological inventory:* 5.

RA 002 - Japurá-Tiquié - Priority level: D • Location: *State:* Amazonas • *Main municipality:* Japurá • *Municipalities covered:* 2 • Vegetation types: Ab, Da, Db, Ds, La, Ld, LO • Comments: Area of probable endemism, given its proximity to higher areas in Colombia.

Diagnostic elements: *Endemism:* 3 • *Richness of rare/threatened species:* 3 • *Hotspots:* 1 • *Special biological features:* 1 • *Economically important species:* 1 • *Biological importance:* 4 • *Intrinsic fragility:* 4 • *Conservation level:* 1 • *Level of threat:* 1 • Action recommended: *Biological inventory:* 5 • *Creation of conservation area:* 1 • *Management:* 1.

RA 003 - Pico da Neblina - Priority level: D • Location: *State:* Amazonas • *Main municipality:* São Gabriel da Cachoeira • *Municipalities covered:* 2 • Vegetation types: As, Dm, Ds, La, Ld, LO, rm • Comments: Area of high biological importance, altitudinal gradient and endemism.

Diagnostic elements: *Richness of rare/threatened species:* 4 • *Hotspots:* 1 • *Economically important species:* 1 • *Biological importance:* 5 • *Intrinsic fragility:* 1 • *Conservation level:* 1 • *Level of threat:* 1 • Action recommended: *Biological inventory:* 5 • *Management:* 4.

RA 004 - Serra do Surucucus forests - Priority level: D • Location: *State:* Roraima • *Main municipality:* Alto Alegre • *Municipalities covered:* 5 • Vegetation types: As, Dm, Ds, ON, rm • Comments: Region almost unknown in terms of its fauna and, in particular, its herpetofauna. As an intact region (the Yanomami indigenous area, of difficult access), it should be studied and inventoried as a matter of urgency with a view to creating a permanent conservation area. High biological importance on the basis of endemism in adjacent areas.

Diagnostic elements: *Hotspots:* 1 • *Biological importance:* 5 • *Conservation level:* 1 • *Level of threat:* 1 • Action recommended: *Biological inventory:* 5 • *Creation of conservation area:* 2 • *Management:* 1.

RA 005 - Lavrado de Roraima - Priority level: A • Location: *State:* Roraima • *Main municipality:* Pacaraima • *Municipalities covered:* 6 • Vegetation types: As, Dm, Ds, Fs, ON, Sg, SN, Sp, Ta, Td, Tp • Comments: Encompasses open areas of the *Lavrado* (plains) of northeastern Roraima. A unique and differentiated ecosystem, highly ecological fragile. Currently suffering impacts from cattle ranching and the beginning of rice and soybean cultivation over relatively large areas.

Diagnostic elements: *Species richness:* 4 • *Phylogenetic diversity:* 5 • *Endemism:* 1 • *Hotspots:* 1 • *Biological importance:* 5 • *Intrinsic fragility:* 5 • *Conservation level:* 2 • *Level of threat:* 2 • Action recommended: *Restoration:* 1 • *Biological inventory:* 5 • *Creation of conservation area:* 5 • *Management:* 5.

RA 006 - Middle Rio Negro - Demini River - Priority level: B • Location: *State:* Amazonas • *Main municipality:* Barcelos • *Municipalities covered:* 1 • Vegetation types: Da, Db, La, Ld, Lg, LO • Comments: Need for a reserve to protect populations of the black-water species *Padocnemis erythrocephalo* and *Peltocephalus dumerilianus*. There are no reserves with representative populations of these species.

Diagnostic elements: *Species richness:* 2 • *Phylogenetic diversity:* 2 • *Richness of rare/threatened species:* 4 • *Special biological features:* 4 • *Economically important species:* 4 • *Biological importance:* 5 • *Intrinsic fragility:* 1 • *Conservation level:* 2 • *Level of threat:* 4 • Action recommended: *Restoration:* 2 • *Biological inventory:* 4 • *Creation of conservation area:* 4 • *Management:* 4.

RA 007 - Rio Branco - Priority level: A • Location: *State:* Roraima • *Main municipality:* Caracaraí • *Municipalities covered:* 2 • Vegetation types: Da, Db, Ld, Lg, LO • Comments: Hatching area for *Podocnemis expansa, P. unifilis* and *P. sextuberculata*; important because of the high density of these species in white-water communities.

Diagnostic elements: *Species richness:* 5 • *Phylogenetic diversity:* 5 • *Endemism:* 5 • *Richness of rare/threatened species:* 5 • *Hotspots:* 5 • *Special biological features:* 5 • *Economically important species:* 5 • *Biological importance:* 5 • *Intrinsic fragility:* 5 • *Conservation level:* 1 • *Level of threat:* 3 • Action recommended: *Restoration:* 1 • *Biological inventory:* 4 • *Creation of conservation area:* 5 • *Management:* 5.

RA 008 - Solimões-Negro interfluve - Priority level: D • Location: *State:* Amazonas • *Main municipality:* Novo Airão • *Municipalities covered:* 4 • Vegetation types: Ab, Da, Db, Ds, La, Ld, LO • Comments: An inventory of reptiles and amphibians is lacking for this region, including for the new Amaná Reserve as far as the Rio Negro.

Diagnostic elements: *Economically important species:* 4 • *Intrinsic fragility:* 1 • *Conservation level:* 2 • *Level of threat:* 2 • Action recommended: *Biological inventory:* 5.

RA 009 - Trombetas - Priority level: B • Location: *State:* Pará • *Main municipality:* Oriximiná • *Municipalities covered:* 2 • Vegetation types: Db, Ds • Comments: Hatching area for *Podocnemis expansa, P. unifilis, P. sextuberculata* and *Peltocephalus dumerilianus*; general lack of knowledge of herpetofauna.

Diagnostic elements: *Species richness:* 5 • *Phylogenetic diversity:* 2 • *Endemism:* 1 • *Richness of rare/threatened species:* 5 • *Special biological features:* 5 • *Economically important species:* 5 • *Biological importance:* 5 • *Intrinsic fragility:* 5 • *Conservation level:* 2 • *Level of threat:* 4 • Action recommended: *Biological inventory:* 3 • *Management:* 3.

RA 010 - Guiana shield - Priority level: A • Location: *State:* Amapá/Pará • *Main municipality:* Oriximiná • *Municipalities covered:* 8 • Vegetation types: Da, Dm, Ds, Sd, SO, Sp • Comments: Region included on the basis of knowledge about the Guianas, where there is high richness of endemic species of amphibians and reptiles.

Diagnostic elements: *Species richness:* 3 • *Phylogenetic diversity:* 3 • *Endemism:* 3 • *Hotspots:* 2 • *Biological importance:* 3 • *Intrinsic fragility:* 2 • *Conservation level:* 1 • *Level of threat:* 1 • Action recommended: *Biological inventory:* 5 • *Creation of conservation area:* 5.

RA 011 - Alter do Chão region - Foz do Tapajós - Priority level: B • Location: *State:* Pará • *Main municipality:* Santarém • *Municipalities covered:* 6 • Vegetation types: AA, Db, Pa, SO, Sp • Comments: Despite its low diversity, the area contains assemblages representative of savannas and floodplains, with low similarity to the neighboring forest areas.

Diagnostic elements: *Species richness:* 3 • *Phylogenetic diversity:* 4 • *Endemism:* 1 • *Richness of rare/threatened species:* 1 • *Hotspots:* 1 • *Special biological features:* 1 • *Economically important species:* 1 • *Biological importance:* 3 • *Intrinsic fragility:* 5 • *Conservation level:* 3 • *Level of threat:* 3 • Action recommended: *Restoration:* 2 • *Biological inventory:* 2 • *Creation of conservation area:* 5 • *Management:* 1.

RA 012 - Lower Amazonas - Priority level: D • Location: *State:* Pará • *Main municipality:* Prainha • *Municipalities covered:* 4 • Vegetation types: AA, As, Db, Ds, Pa, SO • Comments: There is lack of reserves along the Amazon river corridor, where it is possible to conserve the floodplain species between the Tapajós and Xingu rivers.

Diagnostic elements: *Economically important species:* 5 • *Biological importance:* 5 • *Intrinsic fragility:* 3 • *Conservation level:* 4 • *Level of threat:* 4 • Action recommended: *Biological inventory:* 4 • *Creation of conservation area:* 4.

RA 013 - Serra do Navio - Priority level: B • Location: *State:* Amapá • *Main municipality:* Porto Grande • *Municipalities covered:* 4 • Vegetation types: AA, Db, Ds, SO, Sp • Comments: Well conserved area, with significant rare species richness.

Diagnostic elements: *Species richness:* 5 • *Phylogenetic diversity:* 5 • *Endemism:* 3 • *Richness of rare/threatened species:* 4 • *Hotspots:* 2 • *Biological importance:* 5 • *Intrinsic fragility:* 5 • *Conservation level:* 2 • *Level of threat:* 1 • Action recommended: *Restoration:* 1 • *Biological inventory:* 5 • *Creation of conservation area:* 5 • *Management:* 1.

RA 014 - Amazon Delta - Marajó Island - PRIORITY LEVEL: B • LOCATION: *State:* Amapá/Pará • *Main municipality:* Anajás • *Municipalities covered:* 28 • VEGETATION TYPES: AA, Da, Db, Pa, Pf, Sp • COMMENTS: Extremely important region for an understanding of the history of the mouth of the Amazon. Sea level changes result in the isolation and consequent differentiation of some populations now found on the estuary islands. The waterway under construction will cause impacts. Occurrence of *Crotalus durissus marajoensis* (endemic).

DIAGNOSTIC ELEMENTS: *Species richness:* 3 • *Phylogenetic diversity:* 3 • *Endemism:* 3 • *Richness of rare/threatened species:* 2 • *Hotspots:* 2 • *Economically important species:* 2 • *Biological importance:* 3 • *Intrinsic fragility:* 3 • *Conservation level:* 3 • *Level of threat:* 4 • ACTION RECOMMENDED: *Biological inventory:* 5 • *Creation of conservation area:* 5.

RA 015 - Içá River - PRIORITY LEVEL: C • LOCATION: *State:* Amazonas • *Main municipality:* Santo Antônio do Içá • *Municipalities covered:* 2 • VEGETATION TYPES: Da, Db, LO • COMMENTS: Area of potentially high diversity due to the influence of fauna from higher regions of Peru and Colombia. Area of high potential endemism. Well conserved area and low anthropogenic pressure.

DIAGNOSTIC ELEMENTS: *Species richness:* 5 • *Phylogenetic diversity:* 5 • *Endemism:* 3 • *Richness of rare/threatened species:* 2 • *Hotspots:* 1 • *Special biological features:* 2 • *Economically important species:* 2 • *Biological importance:* 4 • *Intrinsic fragility:* 2 • *Conservation level:* 1 • *Level of threat:* 1 • ACTION RECOMMENDED: *Restoration:* 1 • *Biological inventory:* 5 • *Creation of conservation area:* 3 • *Management:* 1.

RA 016 - Lower Juruá - PRIORITY LEVEL: A • LOCATION: *State:* Amazonas • *Main municipality:* Carauari • *Municipalities covered:* 3 • VEGETATION TYPES: Ab, Da, Db • COMMENTS: Area of high species diversity; fauna representative of the western Amazon region; hatching area for turtles.

DIAGNOSTIC ELEMENTS: *Species richness:* 5 • *Phylogenetic diversity:* 5 • *Endemism:* 1 • *Richness of rare/threatened species:* 1 • *Hotspots:* 1 • *Special biological features:* 1 • *Economically important species:* 2 • *Biological importance:* 4 • *Intrinsic fragility:* 1 • *Conservation level:* 1 • *Level of threat:* 2 • ACTION RECOMMENDED: *Restoration:* 1 • *Biological inventory:* 3 • *Creation of conservation area:* 3 • *Management:* 1.

RA 017 - Urucu River Basin (Tefé-Coari interfluve) - PRIORITY LEVEL: A • LOCATION: *State:* Amazonas • *Main municipality:* Coari • *Municipalities covered:* 2 • VEGETATION TYPES: Ab, Da, Db • COMMENTS: High diversity and important for the creation of ecological corridors.

DIAGNOSTIC ELEMENTS: *Species richness:* 5 • *Phylogenetic diversity:* 5 • *Endemism:* 1 • *Richness of rare/threatened species:* 2 • *Hotspots:* 1 • *Special biological features:* 2 • *Economically important species:* 2 • *Biological importance:* 5 • *Intrinsic fragility:* 2 • *Conservation level:* 2 • *Level of threat:* 3 • ACTION RECOMMENDED: *Restoration:* 1 • *Biological inventory:* 3 • *Creation of conservation area:* 5 • *Management:* 2.

RA 018 - Purus River - Abufari Biological Reserve - PRIORITY LEVEL: B • LOCATION: *State:* Amazonas • *Main municipality:* Tapauá • *Municipalities covered:* 3 • VEGETATION TYPES: Ab, Da, Db, Ds • COMMENTS: There are populations of three species of *Podocnemis* (*expansa, sextubeculata, unifilis*) spawning in a white-water river. There is a reserve, but it lacks management and control.

DIAGNOSTIC ELEMENTS: *Species richness:* 3 • *Phylogenetic diversity:* 2 • *Richness of rare/threatened species:* 5 • *Special biological features:* 5 • *Economically important species:* 5 • *Biological importance:* 5 • *Intrinsic fragility:* 3 • *Conservation level:* 3 • *Level of threat:* 3 • ACTION RECOMMENDED: *Biological inventory:* 2 • *Management:* 4

RA 019 - Careiro - Castanho - PRIORITY LEVEL: D • LOCATION: *State:* Amazonas • *Main municipality:* Careiro • *Municipalities covered:* 9 • VEGETATION TYPES: AA, Da, Db, Pa • COMMENTS: Little known herpetofauna and at risk of strong anthropogenic pressure.

DIAGNOSTIC ELEMENTS: *Endemism:* 1 • *Richness of rare/threatened species:* 2 • *Hotspots:* 3 • *Economically important species:* 1 • *Biological importance:* 4 • *Intrinsic fragility:* 1 • *Conservation level:* 2 • *Level of threat:* 2 • ACTION RECOMMENDED: *Restoration:* 2 • *Biological inventory:* 5 • *Creation of conservation area:* 3 • *Management:* 1.

RA 020 - Abacaxis River - Priority level: D • Location: *State:* Amazonas • *Main municipality:* Borba • *Municipalities covered:* 3 • Vegetation types: Da, Db, Ds, Pa • Comments: Lacking inventories of reptiles and amphibians for the entire region; may contain high diversity and high differentiation between the Tapajós and the Madeira.

ACTION RECOMMENDED: *Biological inventory:* 4

RA 021 - Middle Tapajós-Tabuleiro de Monte Cristo - PRIORITY LEVEL: C • LOCATION: *State:* Pará • *Main municipality:* Aveiro • *Municipalities covered:* 3 • VEGETATION TYPES: AA, Db, Ds • COMMENTS: The Tabuleiro de Monte Cristo is a spawning ground for *Podocnemis expansa, P. unifilis* and *P. sextuberculata*. Important clear-water river for spawning.

DIAGNOSTIC ELEMENTS: *Species richness:* 1 • *Phylogenetic diversity:* 1 • *Richness of rare/threatened species:* 4 • *Special biological features:* 5 • *Economically important species:* 5 • *Biological importance:* 4 • *Intrinsic fragility:* 3 • *Conservation level:* 2 • *Level of threat:* 4 • ACTION RECOMMENDED: *Biological inventory:* 1 • *Creation of conservation area:* 5 • *Management:* 4.

RA 022 - Lower Xingu - PRIORITY LEVEL: A • LOCATION: *State:* Pará • *Main municipality:* Altamira • *Municipalities covered:* 6 • VEGETATION TYPES: AA, As, Da, Ds • COMMENTS: Need for protection of a region of eastern Pará still not severely impacted, but under increasing pressure, and with high diversity. Presence of the Xingu falls and rocky beds with species typical of open areas. Presence of sub-montane forest.

DIAGNOSTIC ELEMENTS: *Species richness:* 5 • *Phylogenetic diversity:* 5 • *Endemism:* 2 • *Hotspots:* 5 • *Economically important species:* 1 • *Biological importance:* 5 • *Intrinsic fragility:* 3 • *Conservation level:* 3 • *Level of threat:* 5 • ACTION RECOMMENDED: *Restoration:* 2 • *Biological inventory:* 3 • *Creation of conservation area:* 5 • *Management:* 3.

RA 023 - Lower Tocantins - PRIORITY LEVEL: A • LOCATION: *State:* Pará • *Main municipality:* Portel • *Municipalities covered:* 10 • VEGETATION TYPES: AA, As, Da, Db, Ds, Pa • COMMENTS: Represents a region already extremely altered and little protected. Includes elements of open and isolated areas.

DIAGNOSTIC ELEMENTS: *Species richness:* 3 • *Phylogenetic diversity:* 4 • *Endemism:* 1 • *Hotspots:* 3 • *Economically important species:* 1 • *Biological importance:* 3 • *Intrinsic fragility:* 4 • *Conservation level:* 3 • *Level of threat:* 5 • ACTION RECOMMENDED: *Restoration:* 3 • *Biological inventory:* 2 • *Creation of conservation area:* 5 • *Management:* 4.

RA 024 - Bragantina region - PRIORITY LEVEL: A • LOCATION: *State:* Pará • *Main municipality:* Bragança • *Municipalities covered:* 29 • VEGETATION TYPES: AA, Da, Pa, Pf • COMMENTS: Region highly threatened by anthropogenic activity, with few remaining natural habitats. Native local fauna highly threatened.

DIAGNOSTIC ELEMENTS: *Species richness:* 3 • *Phylogenetic diversity:* 3 • *Endemism:* 1 • *Richness of rare/threatened species:* 1 • *Hotspots:* 1 • *Special biological features:* 1 • *Economically important species:* 1 • *Biological importance:* 3 • *Intrinsic fragility:* 5 • *Conservation level:* 4 • *Level of threat:* 5 • ACTION RECOMMENDED: *Restoration:* 5 • *Biological inventory:* 5 • *Creation of conservation area:* 5 • *Management:* 5.

RA 025 - Tapirapé - Tuerê - PRIORITY LEVEL: A • LOCATION: *State:* Pará • *Main municipality:* Marabá • *Municipalities covered:* 2 • VEGETATION TYPES: AA, As, Ds • COMMENTS: Area of high species richness in eastern Amazonia, under threat due to land disputes and mining.

DIAGNOSTIC ELEMENTS: *Species richness:* 5 • *Phylogenetic diversity:* 5 • *Endemism:* 3 • *Hotspots:* 4 • *Biological importance:* 4 • *Intrinsic fragility:* 5 • *Conservation level:* 3 • *Level of threat:* 5 • ACTION RECOMMENDED: *Biological inventory:* 4 • *Creation of conservation area:* 4.

RA 026 - Serra do Divisor - PRIORITY LEVEL: B • LOCATION: *State:* Acre • *Main municipality:* Porto Walter • *Municipalities covered:* 5 • VEGETATION TYPES: Ab, Da, Db, Ds • COMMENTS: Area of high biological diversity, the ranges may contain endemic species. Two new species are being described for the area, in lowland forest outside the present limits of the reserve.

DIAGNOSTIC ELEMENTS: *Species richness:* 5 • *Phylogenetic diversity:* 5 • *Hotspots:* 1 • *Economically important species:* 3 • *Biological importance:* 5 • *Conservation level:* 1 • *Level of threat:* 1 • ACTION RECOMMENDED: *Biological inventory:* 5 • *Creation of conservation area:* 2 • *Management:* 2

RA 027 - Upper Juruá - PRIORITY LEVEL: A • LOCATION: *State:* Amazonas • *Main municipality:* Ipixuna • *Municipalities covered:* 7 • VEGETATION TYPES: AA, Ab, Da, Db • COMMENTS: Potential for high diversity and one of the last large populations of *Podocnemis expansa*. Unprotected hatching ground. High Squamata and Anura diversity.

DIAGNOSTIC ELEMENTS: *Species richness:* 2 • *Phylogenetic diversity:* 1 • *Endemism:* 1 • *Richness of rare/threatened species:* 2 • *Hotspots:* 5 • *Special biological features:* 5 • *Economically important species:* 5 • *Biological importance:* 5 • *Intrinsic fragility:* 3 • *Conservation level:* 5 • *Level of threat:* 3 • ACTION RECOMMENDED: *Biological inventory:* 2 • *Creation of conservation area:* 5 • *Management:* 5.

RA 028 - Upper Purus - PRIORITY LEVEL: B • LOCATION: *State:* Acre • *Main municipality:* Feijó • *Municipalities covered:* 4 • VEGETATION TYPES: AA, Ab, Da • COMMENTS: Presence of turtle hatching grounds. Region of high diversity of species representative of southwestern Amazonia.

DIAGNOSTIC ELEMENTS: *Species richness:* 4 • *Phylogenetic diversity:* 4 • *Hotspots:* 1 • *Special biological features:* 3 • *Economically important species:* 3 • *Biological importance:* 4 • *Conservation level:* 1 • *Level of threat:* 1 • ACTION RECOMMENDED: *Biological inventory:* 5 • *Management:* 3.

RA 029 - Pauini River region - PRIORITY LEVEL: B • LOCATION: *State:* Amazonas • *Main municipality:* Pauini • *Municipalities covered:* 4 • VEGETATION TYPES: Da, Db • COMMENTS: Region of potentially high diversity judging by surveys carried out on the Juruá and Purus rivers; encompasses the interfluve area between these two rivers, and may contain faunistic elements of both.

DIAGNOSTIC ELEMENTS: *Species richness:* 4 • *Phylogenetic diversity:* 4 • *Hotspots:* 2 • *Biological importance:* 1 • *Intrinsic fragility:* 1 • *Conservation level:* 1 • *Level of threat:* 1 • ACTION RECOMMENDED: *Biological inventory:* 5 • *Creation of conservation area:* 3 • *Management:* 1.

RA 030 - Headwaters of the Ituxi - PRIORITY LEVEL: C • LOCATION: *State:* Acre/Amazonas/Rondônia • *Main municipality:* Lábrea • *Municipalities covered:* 6 • VEGETATION TYPES: AA, Ab, As, Da, Db, Ds • COMMENTS: High diversity, lack of knowledge of the region, lack of conservation areas.

DIAGNOSTIC ELEMENTS: *Species richness:* 5 • *Phylogenetic diversity:* 5 • *Endemism:* 2 • *Richness of rare/threatened species:* 3 • *Hotspots:* 3 • *Special biological features:* 2 • *Economically important species:* 1 • *Biological importance:* 5 • *Intrinsic fragility:* 3 • *Conservation level:* 2 • *Level of threat:* 3 • ACTION RECOMMENDED: *Restoration:* 2 • *Biological inventory:* 5 • *Creation of conservation area:* 5 • *Management:* 2.

RA 031 - Cuniuá river and middle Purus interfluve - PRIORITY LEVEL: A • LOCATION: *State:* Amazonas • *Main municipality:* Tapauá • *Municipalities covered:* 3 • VEGETATION TYPES: Ab, Da, Db, Pa • COMMENTS: Region of high diversity; fauna representative of eastern Amazonia.

DIAGNOSTIC ELEMENTS: *Species richness:* 4 • *Phylogenetic diversity:* 4 • *Hotspots:* 1 • *Biological importance:* 4 • *Intrinsic fragility:* 1 • *Conservation level:* 1 • *Level of threat:* 1 • ACTION RECOMMENDED: *Biological inventory:* 5 • *Creation of conservation area:* 5 • *Management:* 1

RA 032 - Humaitá, Apuí and middle Madeira grasslands region - PRIORITY LEVEL: A • LOCATION: *State:* Amazonas/Rondônia • *Main municipality:* Humaitá • *Municipalities covered:* 9 • VEGETATION TYPES: AA, Ab, As, Da, Db, Pa, Sa, Sg, SO, Sp • COMMENTS: The region encompasses open areas of the Humaitá, Lábrea e Apuí grasslands, as well as the dense lowland alluvial rainforests of the middle Madeira. Among these main formations are transitional areas with the characteristics of ecotones. The region is threatened by the Arc of Deforestation and the arrival of rice and soybean. Occurrence of isolated populations of savanna species.

DIAGNOSTIC ELEMENTS: *Species richness:* 4 • *Phylogenetic diversity:* 5 • *Endemism:* 1 • *Hotspots:* 2 • *Biological importance:* 5 • *Intrinsic fragility:* 4 • *Conservation level:* 3 • *Level of threat:* 5 • ACTION RECOMMENDED: *Restoration:* 1 • *Biological inventory:* 5 • *Creation of conservation area:* 5 • *Management:* 2.

RA 033 - Lower Aripuanã - PRIORITY LEVEL: C • LOCATION: *State:* Amazonas • *Main municipality:* Novo Aripuanã • *Municipalities covered:* 3 • VEGETATION TYPES: As, Da, Db, Ds, Pa, Sa • COMMENTS: Region of the lower reaches of the Aripuanã and interfluves with no information on reptiles or amphibians. The falls on the upper reaches prevent the free passage of fresh-water fish fauna, suggesting that these may also act as a barrier to turtles and caimans.

DIAGNOSTIC ELEMENTS: *Biological importance:* 5 • *Intrinsic fragility:* 3 • *Conservation level:* 3 • *Level of threat:* 2 • ACTION RECOMMENDED: *Biological inventory:* 5 • *Creation of conservation area:* 2.

RA 034 - Aripuanã - Juruena - Apiacás - PRIORITY LEVEL: A • LOCATION: *State:* Amazonas/Mato Grosso • *Main municipality:* Apiacás • *Municipalities covered:* 5 • VEGETATION TYPES: As, Ds, Sa, SN, SO, Sp • COMMENTS: Area of high diversity confirmed by recent assessments, which found new and rare species, such as *Anolis phyllorhinus*, and several species of *Phyllomedusa* and *Phrynohyas*. Some of them, rare in other areas, are common in this region. Species occur in the forests that are usually found in open areas.

DIAGNOSTIC ELEMENTS: *Species richness:* 5 • *Phylogenetic diversity:* 5 • *Endemism:* 5 • *Hotspots:* 5 • *Biological importance:* 5 • *Intrinsic fragility:* 4 • *Conservation level:* 5 • *Level of threat:* 5 • ACTION RECOMMENDED: *Biological inventory:* 3 • *Creation of conservation area:* 5 • *Management:* 3.

RA 035 - Tapajós - Araguaia interfluve - PRIORITY LEVEL: D • LOCATION: *State:* Pará • *Main municipality:* Altamira • *Municipalities covered:* 16 • VEGETATION TYPES: DE • COMMENTS: Area with no information on amphibians and under grave threat from the expansion of the agricultural frontier and from the fire-arc.

DIAGNOSTIC ELEMENTS: *Conservation level:* 2 • *Level of threat:* 4 • ACTION RECOMMENDED: *Biological inventory:* 5 • *Creation of conservation area:* 5.

RA 036 - Apinajés - PRIORITY LEVEL: A • LOCATION: *State:* Maranhão/Tocantins • *Main municipality:* Tocantinópolis • *Municipalities covered:* 28 • VEGETATION TYPES: AA, As, Cs, Sa, Sd, SO, Sp • COMMENTS: Need to conserve the gallery forest. Area under strong anthropogenic pressure.

DIAGNOSTIC ELEMENTS: *Species richness:* 3 • *Phylogenetic diversity:* 3 • *Richness of rare/threatened species:* 3 • *Hotspots:* 1 • *Biological importance:* 3 • *Intrinsic fragility:* 5 • *Conservation level:* 3 • *Level of threat:* 5 • ACTION RECOMMENDED: *Restoration:* 2 • *Biological inventory:* 5 • *Creation of conservation area:* 4 • *Management:* 3.

RA 037 - São Luís do Maranhão - PRIORITY LEVEL: A • LOCATION: *State:* Maranhão • *Main municipality:* Alcântara • *Municipalities covered:* 21 • VEGETATION TYPES: AA, Pa, Pf • COMMENTS: Flat area, meeting place of freshwater turtle species endemic to the Brazilian Amazon and the threatened *Kinosternon scorpioides*.

DIAGNOSTIC ELEMENTS: *Endemism:* 5 • *Richness of rare/threatened species:* 4 • *Economically important species:* 4 • *Biological importance:* 3 • *Intrinsic fragility:* 3 • *Conservation level:* 5 • *Level of threat:* 5 • ACTION RECOMMENDED: *Restoration:* 2 • *Biological inventory:* 3 • *Creation of conservation area:* 3 • *Management:* 3.

RA 038 - Guajará-Mirim - Pacaás Novos - PRIORITY LEVEL: A • LOCATION: *State:* Rondônia • *Main municipality:* Guajará-Mirim • *Municipalities covered:* 10 • VEGETATION TYPES: AA, Ab, As, Da, Ds, Sa, Sd, SO, Sp • COMMENTS: One of the few remaining unaltered areas of Rondônia, with high richness of species representative of the region.

DIAGNOSTIC ELEMENTS: *Species richness:* 4 • *Phylogenetic diversity:* 4 • *Endemism:* 4 • *Conservation level:* 2 • *Level of threat:* 3 • ACTION RECOMMENDED: *Restoration:* 2 • *Biological inventory:* 3 • *Management:* 4.

RA 039 - Middle Guaporé region - PRIORITY LEVEL: A • LOCATION: *State:* Rondônia • *Main municipality:* São Francisco do Guaporé • *Municipalities covered:* 3 • VEGETATION TYPES: Ab, As, Da, Pa, Sa, Sd, SO, Sp • COMMENTS: Contains spawning grounds of threatened and economically prized turtle species.

DIAGNOSTIC ELEMENTS: *Species richness:* 2 • *Phylogenetic diversity:* 1 • *Endemism:* 1 • *Richness of rare/threatened species:* 5 • *Hotspots:* 1 • *Special biological features:* 5 • *Economically important species:* 5 • *Biological importance:* 4 • *Intrinsic fragility:* 5 • *Conservation level:* 3 • *Level of threat:* 5 • ACTION RECOMMENDED: *Creation of conservation area:* 3 • *Management:* 3.

RA 040 - Corumbiara river region - PRIORITY LEVEL: A • LOCATION: *State:* Rondônia • *Main municipality:* Pimenteiras do Oeste • *Municipalities covered:* 5 • VEGETATION TYPES: AA, Ab, Da, Fa, Fb, Pa, Sd, Sg, SO, Sp • COMMENTS: Forest-savanna transition area, with flooded areas similar to the Pantanal of Mato Grosso and floodplain/igapó-like flooded areas. Borders the Bolivia National Park, forming a biological corridor.

DIAGNOSTIC ELEMENTS: *Species richness:* 4 • *Phylogenetic diversity:* 5 • *Endemism:* 1 • *Richness of rare/threatened species:* 2 • *Hotspots:* 2 • *Special biological features:* 4 • *Economically important species:* 3 • *Biological importance:* 5 • *Intrinsic fragility:* 5 • *Conservation level:* 2 • *Level of threat:* 2 • ACTION RECOMMENDED: *Restoration:* 1 • *Biological inventory:* 4 • *Creation of conservation area:* 4 • *Management:* 2.

RA 041 - Cláudia - PRIORITY LEVEL: B • LOCATION: *State:* Mato Grosso • *Main municipality:* Marcelândia • *Municipalities covered:* 10 • VEGETATION TYPES: AA, As, Da, Ds, ON, Pa, SN • COMMENTS: Area includes species that are rare or only recently described in Amazonia (e.g. *Anops bilabialatus, Gonatodes sp.n*).

DIAGNOSTIC ELEMENTS: *Species richness:* 4 • *Phylogenetic diversity:* 4 • *Endemism:* 4 • *Hotspots:* 5 • *Economically important species:* 3 • *Biological importance:* 4 • *Intrinsic fragility:* 5 • *Conservation level:* 5 • *Level of threat:* 5 • ACTION RECOMMENDED: *Biological inventory:* 5 • *Creation of conservation area:* 4 • *Management:* 4.

RA 042 - Teles Pires - Xingu - PRIORITY LEVEL: A • LOCATION: *State:* Mato Grosso • *Main municipality:* Gaúcha do Norte • *Municipalities covered:* 7 • VEGETATION TYPES: AA, Fa, ON, Pa, Sa, Sd, SN, Sp • COMMENTS: Areas of ecological transition marked by abrupt contacts between transitional forests and savannas, and by several savanna enclaves. High species diversity resulting from ecotones between forests and open areas.

DIAGNOSTIC ELEMENTS: *Species richness:* 4 • *Phylogenetic diversity:* 5 • *Endemism:* 4 • *Richness of rare/threatened species:* 3 • *Hotspots:* 3 • *Special biological features:* 3 • *Biological importance:* 3 • *Intrinsic fragility:* 2 • *Conservation level:* 2 • *Level of threat:* 2 • ACTION RECOMMENDED: *Biological inventory:* 4 • *Creation of conservation area:* 3 • *Management:* 2.

RA 043 - Rio das Mortes - PRIORITY LEVEL: C • LOCATION: *State:* Mato Grosso • *Main municipality:* Água Boa • *Municipalities covered:* 4 • VEGETATION TYPES: Fs, Sa, SN, Sp • COMMENTS: Area suffering impacts due to the presence of rare turtle species of high economic value. Contains important spawning grounds for *Podocnemis expansa*.

DIAGNOSTIC ELEMENTS: *Species richness:* 1 • *Phylogenetic diversity:* 1 • *Richness of rare/threatened species:* 3 • *Special biological features:* 4 • *Economically important species:* 4 • *Biological importance:* 4 • *Intrinsic fragility:* 5 • *Conservation level:* 2 • *Level of threat:* 4 • ACTION RECOMMENDED: *Restoration:* 1 • *Creation of conservation area:* 4 • *Management:* 5.

RA 044 - Tabuleiros do Araguaia - PRIORITY LEVEL: B • LOCATION: *State:* Mato Grosso • *Main municipality:* Cocalinho • *Municipalities covered:* 1 • VEGETATION TYPES: Sa, Sd, SN, Sp • COMMENTS: Spawning ground for threatened and economically prized turtle species.

DIAGNOSTIC ELEMENTS: *Species richness:* 1 • *Phylogenetic diversity:* 1 • *Endemism:* 1 • *Richness of rare/threatened species:* 5 • *Hotspots:* 1 • *Special biological features:* 5 • *Economically important species:* 5 • *Biological importance:* 5 • *Intrinsic fragility:* 5 • *Conservation level:* 1 • *Level of threat:* 5 • ACTION RECOMMENDED: *Restoration:* 5 • *Creation of conservation area:* 5 • *Management:* 5.

RA 045 - Cachimbo - PRIORITY LEVEL: A • LOCATION: *State:* Mato Grosso/Pará • *Main municipality:* Novo Progresso • *Municipalities covered:* 6 • VEGETATION TYPES: AA, As, Cs, Ds, ON, Sd, SN, SO, Sp • COMMENTS: Area containing relict species of fauna from the residual southern highlands of Pará, which hosts endemic species and species of considerable diversity.

DIAGNOSTIC ELEMENTS: *Species richness:* 4 • *Phylogenetic diversity:* 4 • *Endemism:* 4 • *Richness of rare/threatened species:* 3 • *Hotspots:* 4 • *Biological importance:* 3 • *Intrinsic fragility:* 2 • *Conservation level:* 4 • *Level of threat:* 4 • ACTION RECOMMENDED: *Biological inventory:* 1 • *Creation of conservation area:* 2 • *Management:* 2.

RA 046 - São Félix do Xingu - PRIORITY LEVEL: A • LOCATION: *State:* Pará • *Main municipality:* São Félix do Xingu • *Municipalities covered:* 1 • VEGETATION TYPES: DRE • COMMENTS: Area of extremely high importance for turtle spawning habitats, especially *Padocnemis expansa*.

DIAGNOSTIC ELEMENTS: *Special biological features:* 4 • *Economically important species:* 4 • *Biological importance:* 4 • *Intrinsic fragility:* 5 • *Conservation level:* 2 • *Level of threat:* 4 • ACTION RECOMMENDED: *Biological inventory:* 4 • *Creation of conservation area:* 5 • *Management:* 4.

7
PRIORITY AREAS FOR CONSERVATION AREAS*

With almost one third of the world's remaining tropical forests, Brazil is clearly one of the most important countries in terms of biological diversity (Prance 1987). Despite this prominent position, only 2.03% of the continental area of the Brazilian territory is protected by means of federal strict protection conservation areas (Ibama 2001), a significantly lower proportion than the international average of 6% (Sales 1996). Recent studies have however shown that the true national picture is even worse, as many conservation areas are poorly distributed among the biomes and ecotones. Many have not been fully implemented, which leaves them moderately or very vulnerable and significantly reduces the number of effective protected areas.

The biological complexity of the natural environments has challenged those attempting a biogeographical classification and leads to a series of difficulties in defining strategies and methodologies for identifying priority areas for conservation. The Convention on Biological Diversity, opened for signature during the Earth Summit in Rio de Janeiro in 1992, recommends that in their conservation strategies, countries adopt an approach that encompasses all possible scales: ecosystems, protected areas, species, genetic resources, amongst others.

One of the most effective strategies for conserving biological diversity is the establishment of a coherent network of protected areas. This is because, as well conserving biodiversity *in situ* and accumulating environmental capital for the future, protected areas directly contribute to the maintenance of a balanced and healthy environment through the provision of a wide range of environmental services that benefit society. In order that the system can achieve its aims, however, the protected areas need to be distributed in a balanced way across the biogeographical categories present in a given region, in such a way as to conserve significant representative samples of species and landscape diversity.

Studies carried out in Amazonia aimed at selecting priority areas for biodiversity conservation on the basis of the distribution of species richness or the presence of endemic, rare or threatened species run into difficulties due to the lack of information or an unequal understanding of the different biological groups. This leads to an analytical bias where those areas with a high concentration of endemic species are, generally speaking, the localities where the greatest collecting efforts have taken place (Nelson 1990). Thus the main criticism of methodologies based on species distribution is that they require excellent datasets on systematics and the distribution of flora and fauna – a situation that does not apply to the principal tropical ecosystems, where there is a critical lack of basic information on the distribution of biodiversity.

Methodologies based on ecosystem distribution have been suggested by several authors as an alternative for identifying priority conservation areas in Amazonia, where knowledge of species distribution is unavailable or insufficient.

One of the ways of separating out the different ecosystems that make up a given region is to use the concept of the ecoregion. An ecoregion can be understood as 'a set of geographically distinct natural communities that share the majority of their species and ecological dynamics and processes, and which show similar environmental conditions by which ecological interactions are critical to their long term survival (Dinerstein et al. 1995).

The Amazon biome is composed of 23 ecoregions and comprises an area of 4,105,401 km2 (48.1% of the Brazilian territory). These ecoregions represent the most varied habitat types and contain different physiognomies, structures and vegetation types.

One of the main elements employed in the definition of the ecoregions of the Amazon biome is that of the large interfluve areas. The importance of the large rivers as biogeographical barriers has been stressed ever since the early naturalists began scientific exploration of the region. This fact was first recognized by Wallace (1853) and was supported in the work of Snethlage (1910) and Hellmayr (1910). Since then, the hypothesis of rivers as barriers has been continually supported in studies on the distribution and differentiation of plants and animals in Amazonia (Sick 1967; Haffer 1974, 1978; Ayres and Clutton-Brock 1992; Caparella 1991). On the basis of such studies, the use of interfluve regions, particularly in the middle and lower stretches of the rivers, has become well established as one of the criteria for separating out the ecoregions of the Amazon biome and as a biogeographical unit of study for conservation. Interfluves have well defined natural boundaries, implying differences in evolutionary history and thus in the distribution of natural communities.

The large interfluves of the Amazon biome are found mainly to the south of the Solimões-Amazonas river. In this region we

---

* Text drawn in part from 'Identifying priority areas for biodiversity conservation by means of the representativity of conservation areas and vegetation types in the ecoregions of Brazilian Amazonia' by Leando V. Ferreira, Rosa Lemos de Sá, Robert Buschbacher, Garo Batmanian, José Maria Cardoso da Silva, Moacyr B. Arruda, Edmar Moretti, Luís Fernando S. N. de Sá, Júlio Falcomer and Maria Iolita Bampi, the full version of which can be found on page 266 of this book.

find the ecoregions comprised by the interfluves of the main tributaries, such as the Juruá, Purus, Madeira, Tapajós, Xingu, Tocantins and Araguaia. The main tributaries to the north of the Solimões-Amazonas, such as the Branco and the Trombetas, are not regarded as barriers to species distribution. Other important factors for separating ecoregions are altitude levels (inselbergs and the Andes), soil types (the campinaranas of the Rio Negro), variable levels of rivers and tides (floodplains and flooded forests), and geological formations (southwestern Amazonia, floodplains), amongst others.

The proportion of the area occupied by each of the 23 ecoregions of the Amazon biome varies from 0.02% (inselbergs) to 16.7% (the Madeira-Tapajós interfluve). Only three ecoregions – the Madeira-Tapajós interfluve, the Uatumã-Trombetas interfluve and the dry forests of Mato Grosso – occupy more than 10% of the region, and the majority of the ecoregions – 15% or 65.2% – make up less than 5% of the biome.

This fact partially supports the concept proposed by Prance (1987) that Amazonia is made up of a large mosaic of environments with different evolutionary histories. This makes the selection of priority areas for biodiversity conservation, and of a representative set of the majority of the habitats present, an extremely difficult and delicate task.

Analysis of the distribution of the thirty federal strict protection conservation areas in Amazonia shows that these are not equally spread across the 23 ecoregions of the biome. Four (17.4%) are completely left out; twelve (52.2%) contain less than 5% of their area under this type of protection; five (21.7%) have between 5% and 20%; and only two ecoregions (8.7%) have more than 20% of their area under this type of protection.

When we consider the 70 vegetation types in Amazonia not altered by human impacts that exist, according to the IBGE (1997), in the 23 ecoregions, we find that 31 (44.28%) are not represented in any federal strict protection conservation area; sixteen (22.86%) have less than 1% of their area protected by means of this category of conservation area; eleven (15.71%) have between 1% and 4.9$ protected; seven (10%) have between 5% and 9.9%; and only five vegetation types (7.14%) have more than 10% of their area protected in this way.

Thus, in a way similar to that of ecoregions, the federal conservation area system is insufficient to protect the large diversity of vegetation types that exists in the 23 ecoregions that make up the Amazon biome.

From this it is clear that there is a need to significantly increase the number of strict protection conservation areas in each ecoregion in order to cover all the vegetation types found within them, paying particular attention to unique environments and to examples of restricted distribution, as these have the greatest likelihood of containing unusual biotic elements. When defining such areas, those which are unprotected or where the level of protection is less than 10% should be considered as priorities.

Conservation areas created within each of the ecoregions can and must be connected by means of corridors. These may include other types of conservation area categories and protected areas, such as sustainable use conservation areas and indigenous lands, provided that there is permanent monitoring of the environmental quality of these areas. Such corridors should preferably be aligned parallel to the main Solimões-Amazonas tributaries or located on the boundaries between ecoregions not divided by interfluves. This will maximize the possibilities of connecting the network of reserves by means of the narrowest stretches of rivers or other physical barriers, where the likelihood of gene flow between the populations of different ecoregions is greatest (Haffer 1992).

Another important aspect is the incorporation of socioeconomic processes into the analysis of the representativity of priority areas for the conservation of the biodiversity of the Amazon biome. The main processes to be analyzed include the location of the main towns, roads and waterways; land use types; the location of areas of deforestation; and the expanding agricultural frontier.

During the Macapá Workshop, the conservation area working group identified 51 priority areas, of which 25 refer to existing areas and 26 to localities suggested for the creation of new conservation areas identified on the basis of gaps in the protection of the ecoregions of the Amazon biome (see the map on page 447 and the listing).

Of the 25 areas that match to existing conservation areas, twelve (48%) show a high degree of representativity in terms of vegetation types and ecoregions, and ten (40%) contain a high degree of connectivity. On the other hand, only six (24%) enjoy a high degree of protection and none scores the highest mark in terms of full implementation (Table 7a).

TABLE 7A - PRIORITY AREAS FOR EXISTING CONSERVATION AREAS DIAGNOSTIC ELEMENTS THAT SCORE HIGHEST		
Diagnostic elements	Number of areas	%[1]
Landscape representativity	12	48.0
Level of threat	4	16.0
Connectivity	10	40.0
Human presence	6	24.0
Description of the natural resource base for sustainable use	6	24.0
Level of protection	6	24.0
Level of implementation	0	–

1. Of the total proposed areas (25).

Of the 26 areas considered to be priorities for the creation of new conservation areas, seventeen (65.4%) show a high degree of representativity in terms of vegetation types and ecoregions; thirteen (50%) a high degree of connectivity; and four (15.4%) score highest for human presence (Table 7b).

TABLE 7B - PRIORITY AREAS FOR NEW CONSERVATION AREAS DIAGNOSTIC ELEMENTS THAT SCORE HIGHEST		
Diagnostic elements	Number of areas	%[1]
Landscape representativity	17	65.4
Level of threat	8	30.8
Connectivity	13	50.0
Human presence	4	15.4
Description of the natural resource base for sustainable use	5	19.2
Level of protection	4	15.4

1. Of the total proposed areas (26).

UC 001 - Trombetas Biological Reserve - PRIORITY LEVEL: B • LOCATION: *State:* Pará • *Main municipality:* Oriximiná • *Municipalities covered:* 1 • VEGETATION TYPES: Db, Ds • COMMENTS: Area with good connectivity, low population pressure and relatively protected by the Rio do Norte mining operation.

DIAGNOSTIC ELEMENTS: *Representativity:* 4 • *Level of threat:* 1 • *Connectivity:* 4 • *Human presence:* 1 • *Sustainable use base:* 2 • *Protection level:* 5 • *Full implementation level:* 4 • ACTION RECOMMENDED: *Preparation of management plan:* 4 • *Full implementation of management plan:* 5 • *Integration with the surrounding area:* 4 • *Economic sustainability:* 4.

UC 002 - Lago Piratuba Biological Reserve, Cabo Orange National Park, Maracá Jipioca Ecological Station and Parazinho Biological Reserve - PRIORITY LEVEL: A • LOCATION: *State:* Amapá • *Main municipality:* Amapá • *Municipalities covered:* 4 • VEGETATION TYPES: Da, Db, Ds, Pa, Pf, SO • COMMENTS: Only set protecting the coastal areas of Amapá, with high landscape representativity.

DIAGNOSTIC ELEMENTS: *Representativity:* 5 • *Level of threat:* 3 • *Connectivity:* 4 • *Human presence:* 2 • *Sustainable use base:* 3 • *Protection level:* 4 • *Full implementation level:* 2 • ACTION RECOMMENDED: *Preparation of management plan:* 5 • *Full implementation of management plan:* 5 • *Integration with the surrounding area:* 4 • *Economic sustainability:* 4.

UC 003 - Amapá National Forest - PRIORITY LEVEL: B • LOCATION: *State:* Amapá • *Main municipality:* Pracuuba • *Municipalities covered:* 3 • VEGETATION TYPES: Ds • COMMENTS: Needs a management plan, high anthropogenic pressure.

DIAGNOSTIC ELEMENTS: *Representativity:* 4 • *Level of threat:* 5 • *Connectivity:* 1 • *Human presence:* 4 • *Sustainable use base:* 5 • *Protection level:* 2 • *Full implementation level:* 1 • ACTION RECOMMENDED: *Preparation of management plan:* 5 • *Full implementation of management plan:* 5 • *Integration with the surrounding area:* 2 • *Economic sustainability:* 2.

UC 004 - Cajari State Extractive Reserve - PRIORITY LEVEL: B • LOCATION: *State:* Amapá • *Main municipality:* Mazagão • *Municipalities covered:* 3 • VEGETATION TYPES: Da, Db, Ds, Pa, SO • COMMENTS: High level of landscape representativity, only reserve in the state.

DIAGNOSTIC ELEMENTS: *Representativity:* 4 • *Level of threat:* 4 • *Connectivity:* 2 • *Human presence:* 5 • *Sustainable use base:* 4 • *Protection level:* 3 • *Full implementation level:* 3 • ACTION RECOMMENDED: *Preparation of management plan:* 5 • *Full implementation of management plan:* 5 • *Integration with the surrounding area:* 2 • *Economic sustainability:* 3.

UC 005 - Amapá State Conservation Areas (Iratapuru Sustainable Development Reserve, Curiaú Environmental Protection Area and Fazendinha Biological Reserve) - PRIORITY LEVEL: A • LOCATION: *State:* Amapá • *Main municipality:* Vitória do Jari • *Municipalities covered:* 5 • VEGETATION TYPES: Da, Ds, Pa, Pf, Sp • COMMENTS: Direct use areas with good possibilities for sustainability, through ecotourism and the Brazil nut programs, with good levels of conservation.

DIAGNOSTIC ELEMENTS: *Representativity:* 5 • *Level of threat:* 5 • *Connectivity:* 4 • *Human presence:* 5 • *Sustainable use base:* 4 • *Protection level:* 2 • *Full implementation level:* 2 • ACTION RECOMMENDED: *Preparation of management plan:* 5 • *Full implementation of management plan:* 5 • *Integration with the surrounding area:* 1 • *Economic sustainability:* 3.

UC 006 - Samuel Ecological Station - PRIORITY LEVEL: B • LOCATION: *State:* Rondônia • *Main municipality:* Candeias do Jamari • *Municipalities covered:* 1 • VEGETATION TYPES: Ab, As • COMMENTS: Environmental compensation area, highly protected by good connectivity.

DIAGNOSTIC ELEMENTS: *Representativity:* 3 • *Level of threat:* 3 • *Connectivity:* 5 • *Human presence:* 1 • *Sustainable use base:* 1 • *Protection level:* 4 • *Full implementation level:* 1 • ACTION RECOMMENDED: *Preparation of management plan:* 5 • *Full implementation of management plan:* 5 • *Integration with the surrounding area:* 1

UC 007 - Jaú National Park - PRIORITY LEVEL: A • LOCATION: *State:* Amazonas • *Main municipality:* Barcelos • *Municipalities covered:* 2 • VEGETATION TYPES: Ab, Da, Db, Ds, La, Ld, LO • COMMENTS: This area, together with the Anavilhanas, Mamirauá and Amanã areas, comprises the heart of the central Amazon ecological corridor. Largest environmental protection area in the world.

DIAGNOSTIC ELEMENTS: *Representativity:* 5 • *Level of threat:* 1 • *Connectivity:* 5 • *Human presence:* 1 • *Sustainable use base:* 5 • *Protection level:* 5 • *Full implementation level:* 3 • ACTION RECOMMENDED: *Preparation of management plan:* 1 • *Full implementation of management plan:* 5 • *Integration with the surrounding area:* 5 • *Economic sustainability:* 5.

UC 008 - Juami-Japurá (Ecological Reserve and Ecological Station) and Jutaí-Solimões Ecological Reserve - PRIORITY LEVEL: D • LOCATION: *State:* Amazonas • *Main municipality:* Japurá • *Municipalities covered:* 3 • VEGETATION TYPES: Da, Db, Ld, LO • COMMENTS: Insufficiently known and of difficult access, with no threat to its biodiversity, landscape already protected within other conservation areas.

DIAGNOSTIC ELEMENTS: *Representativity:* 2 • *Level of threat:* 2 • *Connectivity:* 4 • *Human presence:* 1 • *Sustainable use base:* 1 • *Protection level:* 5 • *Full implementation level:* 1 • ACTION RECOMMENDED: *Preparation of management plan:* 5 • *Full implementation of management plan:* 5 • *Economic sustainability:* 5.

UC 009 - Rio Negro State Park (right and left banks) - PRIORITY LEVEL: C • LOCATION: *State:* Amazonas • *Main municipality:* Manaus • *Municipalities covered:* 5 • VEGETATION TYPES: Ab, Da, Db, Ds, LO • COMMENTS: Area very altered by human impacts and with no management plan. Conservation area unclear and partially overlapping other conservation areas. Landscape type already represented in other, better thought out, conservation areas.

DIAGNOSTIC ELEMENTS: *Representativity:* 2 • *Level of threat:* 3 • *Connectivity:* 5 • *Human presence:* 5 • *Sustainable use base:* 2 • *Protection level:* 3 • *Full implementation level:* 1 • ACTION RECOMMENDED: *Preparation of management plan:* 5 • *Full implementation of management plan:* 5 • *Integration with the surrounding area:* 4 • *Economic sustainability:* 5.

UC 010 - Anavilhanas Federal Ecological Station - PRIORITY LEVEL: A • LOCATION: *State:* Amazonas • *Main municipality:* Novo Airão • *Municipalities covered:* 5 • VEGETATION TYPES: Da, Db, Ds, LO • COMMENTS: This area, together with the Jaú, the Mamirauá and the Amanã areas, comprises the heart of the central Amazon ecological corridor. Largest continuous environmental protection area in the world.

DIAGNOSTIC ELEMENTS: *Representativity:* 5 • *Level of threat:* 3 • *Connectivity:* 5 • *Human presence:* 1 • *Sustainable use base:* 1 • *Protection level:* 4 • *Full implementation level:* 3 • ACTION RECOMMENDED: *Preparation of management plan:* 3 • *Full implementation of management plan:* 5 • *Integration with the surrounding area:* 5 • *Economic sustainability:* 5.

UC 011 - Chico Mendes Extractive Reserve - PRIORITY LEVEL: A • LOCATION: *State:* Acre • *Main municipality:* Rio Branco • *Municipalities covered:* 6 • VEGETATION TYPES: AA, Ab, Da, Db • COMMENTS: Highly representative, under great threat from the expansion of ranching. In addition, is little known biologically.

DIAGNOSTIC ELEMENTS: *Representativity:* 5 • *Level of threat:* 4 • *Connectivity:* 3 • *Human presence:* 3 • *Sustainable use base:* 2 • *Protection level:* 4 • *Full implementation level:* 3 • ACTION RECOMMENDED: *Full implementation of management plan:* 3 • *Integration with the surrounding area:* 2 • *Economic sustainability:* 3.

UC 012 - Amanã Sustainable Development Reserve - PRIORITY LEVEL: A • LOCATION: *State:* Amazonas • *Main municipality:* Barcelos • *Municipalities covered:* 4 • VEGETATION TYPES: Ab, Da, Db, La, Ld, LO • COMMENTS: This area, together with the Jaú, the Mamirauá and the Amanã areas, constitutes the heart of the central Amazon ecological corridor. Largest environmental protection area in the world.

DIAGNOSTIC ELEMENTS: *Representativity:* 3 • *Level of threat:* 1 • *Connectivity:* 5 • *Human presence:* 1 • *Protection level:* 5 • *Full implementation level:* 1 • ACTION RECOMMENDED: *Preparation of management plan:* 5 • *Integration with the surrounding area:* 5 • *Economic sustainability:* 5.

UC 013 - Mamirauá Sustainable Development Reserve - PRIORITY LEVEL: A • LOCATION: *State:* Amazonas • *Main municipality:* Fonte Boa • *Municipalities covered:* 4 • VEGETATION TYPES: Da, Db • COMMENTS:

This area, together with the Jaú, the Mamirauá and the Amanã areas, constitutes the heart of the central Amazon ecological corridor. Largest environmental protection area in the world.

DIAGNOSTIC ELEMENTS: *Representativity:* 5 • *Level of threat:* 2 • *Connectivity:* 5 • *Human presence:* 2 • *Sustainable use base:* 4 • *Protection level:* 4 • *Full implementation level:* 3 • ACTION RECOMMENDED: *Preparation of management plan:* 1 • *Full implementation of management plan:* 5 • *Integration with the surrounding area:* 5 • *Economic sustainability:* 5.

UC 014 - Middle Juruá Extractive Reserve - PRIORITY LEVEL: A • LOCATION: *State:* Amazonas • *Main municipality:* Carauari • *Municipalities covered:* 1 • VEGETATION TYPES: Ab, Da, Db • COMMENTS: High level of protection. Only extractive reserve in the state of Amazonas. Highly motivated extractivist association. Potential for high use.

DIAGNOSTIC ELEMENTS: *Representativity:* 3 • *Level of threat:* 2 • *Connectivity:* 2 • *Human presence:* 3 • *Sustainable use base:* 5 • *Protection level:* 5 • *Full implementation level:* 3 • ACTION RECOMMENDED: *Preparation of management plan:* 1 • *Full implementation of management plan:* 3 • *Integration with the surrounding area:* 5 • *Economic sustainability:* 5.

UC 015 - Tefé National Forest - PRIORITY LEVEL: D • LOCATION: *State:* Amazonas • *Main municipality:* Tefé • *Municipalities covered:* 4 • VEGETATION TYPES: Da, Db.

DIAGNOSTIC ELEMENTS: *Representativity:* 2 • *Level of threat:* 2 • *Connectivity:* 2 • *Human presence:* 2 • *Sustainable use base:* 5 • *Protection level:* 5 • *Full implementation level:* 1 • ACTION RECOMMENDED: *Preparation of management plan:* 5 • *Full implementation of management plan:* 5 • *Integration with the surrounding area:* 5 • *Economic sustainability:* 5.

UC 016 - Abufari Biological Reserve - PRIORITY LEVEL: A • LOCATION: *State:* Amazonas • *Main municipality:* Tapauá • *Municipalities covered:* 1 • VEGETATION TYPES: Ab, Da • COMMENTS: Protection of species threatened with extinction from pressure of use.

DIAGNOSTIC ELEMENTS: *Representativity:* 4 • *Level of threat:* 5 • *Connectivity:* 1 • *Human presence:* 2 • *Sustainable use base:* 5 • *Protection level:* 2 • *Full implementation level:* 1 • ACTION RECOMMENDED: *Preparation of management plan:* 1 • *Full implementation of management plan:* 3 • *Integration with the surrounding area:* 4 • *Economic sustainability:* 5.

UC 017 - Serra do Divisor National Park - PRIORITY LEVEL: A • LOCATION: *State:* Acre • *Main municipality:* Mâncio Lima • *Municipalities covered:* 5 • VEGETATION TYPES: Ab, Da, Db, Ds • COMMENTS: Highly representative. It is under great threat and allows connectivity with other conservation areas. Needs an urgent regularization of land titles (large number of families living within it). Many endemic species, high diversity, new species for science. Includes the only occurrence of submontane dense forest in the southwestern Amazon ecoregion. Located within the western Amazon corridor.

DIAGNOSTIC ELEMENTS: *Representativity:* 5 • *Level of threat:* 4 • *Connectivity:* 5 • *Human presence:* 5 • *Sustainable use base:* 2 • *Protection level:* 4 • *Full implementation level:* 3 • ACTION RECOMMENDED: *Full implementation of management plan:* 4 • *Integration with the surrounding area:* 4

UC 018 - Set of conservation areas and indigenous lands in the northwestern Amazon - PRIORITY LEVEL: A • LOCATION: *State:* Amazonas/Roraima • *Main municipality:* São Gabriel da Cachoeira • *Municipalities covered:* 5 • VEGETATION TYPES: Ab, As, Da, Dm, Ds, Fs, La, Ld, Lg, LO, ON, rm, Sp • COMMENTS: Large area covered by several types of conservation areas and indigenous lands and with high degree of overlap and needing action to regularize this situation. Annulment of the Caracaraí military area.

DIAGNOSTIC ELEMENTS: *Representativity:* 5 • *Level of threat:* 4 • *Connectivity:* 5 • *Human presence:* 3 • *Sustainable use base:* 5 • *Protection level:* 3 • *Full implementation level:* 3 • ACTION RECOMMENDED: *Preparation of management plan:* 5 • *Full implementation of management plan:* 5 • *Integration with the surrounding area:* 5 • *Economic sustainability:* 5.

UC 019 - Gurupi Biological Reserve - PRIORITY LEVEL: A • LOCATION: *State:* Maranhão • *Main municipality:* Centro Novo do Maranhão • *Municipalities covered:* 3 • VEGETATION TYPES: AA, Db • COMMENTS: Only conservation area in the Tocantins-Araguaia interfluve, in the eastern Amazon, in the center of a vulnerable implemented area with deforestation and land settlement.

DIAGNOSTIC ELEMENTS: *Representativity:* 5 • *Level of threat:* 5 • *Connectivity:* 5 • *Human presence:* 5 • *Sustainable use base:* 2 • *Protection level:* 1 • *Full implementation level:* 1 • ACTION RECOMMENDED: *Preparation of management plan:* 5 • *Integration with the surrounding area:* 5.

UC 020 - Corumbiara State Park - PRIORITY LEVEL: B • LOCATION: *State:* Rondônia • *Main municipality:* Pimenteiras do Oeste • *Municipalities covered:* 4 • VEGETATION TYPES: Ab, Da, Fa, Fb, Pa, Sd, Sg, SO, Sp • COMMENTS: High representativity, threatened by the expansion of logging activities and by the ranching in the south of the state. Important for the consolidation of the western corridor.

DIAGNOSTIC ELEMENTS: *Representativity:* 4 • *Level of threat:* 4 • *Connectivity:* 4 • *Human presence:* 2 • *Sustainable use base:* 3 • *Protection level:* 3 • *Full implementation level:* 1 • ACTION RECOMMENDED: *Preparation of management plan:* 5 • *Full implementation of management plan:* 5 • *Integration with the surrounding area:* 5 • *Economic sustainability:* 5.

UC 021 - Upper Juruá Extractive Reserve - PRIORITY LEVEL: B • LOCATION: *State:* Acre • *Main municipality:* Marechal Thaumaturgo • *Municipalities covered:* 1 • VEGETATION TYPES: Ab, Da, Db • COMMENTS: Very representative area, but not seriously threatened.

DIAGNOSTIC ELEMENTS: *Representativity:* 5 • *Level of threat:* 3 • *Connectivity:* 5 • *Human presence:* 3 • *Sustainable use base:* 3 • *Protection level:* 4 • *Full implementation level:* 3 • ACTION RECOMMENDED: *Full implementation of management plan:* 4 • *Integration with the surrounding area:* 4.

UC 022 - Guaporé Biological Reserve - PRIORITY LEVEL: A • LOCATION: *State:* Rondônia • *Main municipality:* São Francisco do Guaporé • *Municipalities covered:* 2 • VEGETATION TYPES: Ab, Da, Pa, Sa, Sd, Sp • COMMENTS: The biological reserve shows high biogeographical representativity and is strongly threatened by the presence of illegal ranching and logging activities.

DIAGNOSTIC ELEMENTS: *Representativity:* 5 • *Level of threat:* 4 • *Connectivity:* 4 • *Human presence:* 4 • *Sustainable use base:* 2 • *Protection level:* 2 • *Full implementation level:* 2 • ACTION RECOMMENDED: *Preparation of management plan:* 4 • *Full implementation of management plan:* 2 • *Integration with the surrounding area:* 2 • *Economic sustainability:* 5.

UC 023 - Ouro Preto State Extractive Reserve - PRIORITY LEVEL: B • LOCATION: *State:* Rondônia • *Main municipality:* Guajará-Mirim • *Municipalities covered:* 2 • VEGETATION TYPES: Ab, As, Da, Sd, SO • COMMENTS: The extractive reserve was created in the context of the threat of the area becoming a settlement project. Its consolidation will ensure biodiversity conservation, previously highly threatened.

DIAGNOSTIC ELEMENTS: *Representativity:* 3 • *Level of threat:* 3 • *Connectivity:* 4 • *Human presence:* 5 • *Sustainable use base:* 4 • *Protection level:* 4 • *Full implementation level:* 2 • ACTION RECOMMENDED: *Full implementation of management plan:* 3 • *Integration with the surrounding area:* 2 • *Economic sustainability:* 5.

UC 024 - Pacaás Novos National Park - PRIORITY LEVEL: A • LOCATION: *State:* Rondônia • *Main municipality:* São Miguel do Guaporé • *Municipalities covered:* 7 • VEGETATION TYPES: AA, Ab, As, Ds, Sa, Sd, SO, Sp • COMMENTS: The entire area overlaps the Uru Eu Wau Wau Indigenous Land, which reinforces its category A classification given the need to resolve this conflict.

DIAGNOSTIC ELEMENTS: *Representativity:* 5 • *Level of threat:* 4 • *Connectivity:* 4 • *Human presence:* 4 • *Sustainable use base:* 4 • *Protection level:* 3 • *Full implementation level:* 4 • ACTION RECOMMENDED: *Preparation of management plan:* 4 • *Full implementation of management plan:* 5 • *Integration with the surrounding area:* 5 • *Economic sustainability:* 5.

UC 025 - State extractive reserves (21) - PRIORITY LEVEL: B • LOCATION: *State:* Rondônia • *Main municipality:* Candeias do Jamari • *Municipalities covered:* 13 • VEGETATION TYPES: AA, Ab, As, Da, Db, Ds, Pa, Sa, SO • COMMENTS: These comprise almost one million hectares, mostly located within the Guaporé valley, western corridor. Encompasses most of the rubber and Brazil nut areas in Rondônia, and the non-consolidation of these areas will certainly result in their occupation by the conventional expanding frontier.

DIAGNOSTIC ELEMENTS: *Representativity:* 4 • *Level of threat:* 4 • *Connectivity:* 4 • *Human presence:* 3 • *Sustainable use base:* 3 • *Protection level:* 2 • *Full implementation level:* 2 • ACTION RECOMMENDED: *Full implementation of management plan:* 4 • *Integration with the surrounding area:* 4 • *Economic sustainability:* 5.

UC 026 - Purus - Madeira ecoregion - PRIORITY LEVEL: A • LOCATION: *State:* Amazonas/Rondônia • *Main municipality:* Lábrea • *Municipalities covered:* 3 • VEGETATION TYPES: Ab, As, Db, Ds, Sa, SO, Sp • COMMENTS: Vegetation type not protected within an existing conservation area.

DIAGNOSTIC ELEMENTS: *Representativity:* 5 • *Level of threat:* 1 • *Connectivity:* 5 • *Human presence:* 3 • *Sustainable use base:* 3 • *Protection level:* 5 • ACTION RECOMMENDED: *Creation of conservation area:* 5.

UC 027 - Purus - Madeira ecoregion - PRIORITY LEVEL: A • LOCATION: *State:* Amazonas • *Main municipality:* Tapauá • *Municipalities covered:* 3 • VEGETATION TYPES: Ab, Da, Db • COMMENTS: Vegetation type not protected within an existing conservation area.

DIAGNOSTIC ELEMENTS: *Representativity:* 5 • *Level of threat:* 3 • *Connectivity:* 4 • *Human presence:* 1 • *Sustainable use base:* 3 • *Protection level:* 5 • ACTION RECOMMENDED: *Creation of conservation area:* 5.

UC 028 - Caquetá ecoregion - PRIORITY LEVEL: A • LOCATION: *State:* Amazonas • *Main municipality:* Japurá • *Municipalities covered:* 1 • VEGETATION TYPES: Ab, Da, La, Ld, LO • COMMENTS: Vegetation type not protected within an existing conservation area.

DIAGNOSTIC ELEMENTS: *Representativity:* 5 • *Connectivity:* 1 • *Human presence:* 1 • *Sustainable use base:* 4 • *Protection level:* 5 • ACTION RECOMMENDED: *Creation of conservation area:* 5

UC 029 - Gurupá floodplains and Monte Alegre ecoregion - PRIORITY LEVEL: A • LOCATION: *State:* Pará • *Main municipality:* Prainha • *Municipalities covered:* 3 • VEGETATION TYPES: AA, Da, Db, Ds, Pa • COMMENTS: Vegetation type not protected within an existing conservation area.

DIAGNOSTIC ELEMENTS: *Representativity:* 5 • *Level of threat:* 3 • *Connectivity:* 1 • *Human presence:* 4 • *Sustainable use base:* 4 • *Protection level:* 1 • ACTION RECOMMENDED: *Creation of conservation area:* 5.

UC 030 - Monte Alegre floodplains ecoregion - PRIORITY LEVEL: A • LOCATION: *State:* Amazonas • *Main municipality:* Anori • *Municipalities covered:* 5 • VEGETATION TYPES: AA, Da, Db, Ds • COMMENTS: Region of high biological importance and poorly protected within existing conservation areas.

DIAGNOSTIC ELEMENTS: *Representativity:* 5 • *Level of threat:* 3 • *Connectivity:* 3 • *Human presence:* 2 • *Sustainable use base:* 4 • *Protection level:* 3 • ACTION RECOMMENDED: *Creation of conservation area:* 5.

UC 031 - Xingu - Tocantins - Araguaia ecoregion - PRIORITY LEVEL: A • LOCATION: *State:* Pará • *Main municipality:* Melgaço • *Municipalities covered:* 4 • VEGETATION TYPES: AA, Da, Db, Pa • COMMENTS: Vegetation type not protected within an existing conservation area.

DIAGNOSTIC ELEMENTS: *Representativity:* 5 • *Level of threat:* 3 • *Connectivity:* 5 • *Human presence:* 3 • *Sustainable use base:* 5 • *Protection level:* 2 • ACTION RECOMMENDED: *Creation of conservation area:* 5.

UC 032 - Xingu - Tocantins - Araguaia (lower Xingu) ecoregion - PRIORITY LEVEL: A • LOCATION: *State:* Amazonas/Pará • *Main municipality:* Borba • *Municipalities covered:* 3 • VEGETATION TYPES: As • COMMENTS: Vegetation type not protected within an existing conservation area.

DIAGNOSTIC ELEMENTS: *Representativity:* 5 • *Level of threat:* 5 • *Connectivity:* 5 • *Human presence:* 4 • *Protection level:* 2 • ACTION RECOMMENDED: *Creation of conservation area:* 5.

UC 033 - Mato Grosso dry forests (upper Xingu) ecoregion - PRIORITY LEVEL: A • LOCATION: *State:* Mato Grosso/Pará • *Main municipality:* São Félix do Xingu • *Municipalities covered:* 3 • VEGETATION TYPES: AA, As, ON, Pa, Sa, Sd, Sg, SO, Sp • COMMENTS: Vegetation type not protected within an existing conservation area.

DIAGNOSTIC ELEMENTS: *Representativity:* 5 • *Level of threat:* 4 • *Connectivity:* 5 • *Human presence:* 4 • *Sustainable use base:* 3 • *Protection level:* 3 • ACTION RECOMMENDED: *Creation of conservation area:* 5.

UC 034 - Mato Grosso dry forests ecoregion - PRIORITY LEVEL: A • LOCATION: *State:* Mato Grosso/Pará • *Main municipality:* Novo Progresso • *Municipalities covered:* 8 • VEGETATION TYPES: As, SO, Sp • COMMENTS: Vegetation type not protected within an existing conservation area.

DIAGNOSTIC ELEMENTS: *Representativity:* 5 • *Level of threat:* 3 • *Connectivity:* 5 • *Human presence:* 2 • *Sustainable use base:* 4 • *Protection level:* 3 • ACTION RECOMMENDED: *Creation of conservation area:* 5

UC 035 - Pantanal ecoregion - PRIORITY LEVEL: A • LOCATION: *State:* Mato Grosso • *Main municipality:* Cáceres • *Municipalities covered:* 1 • VEGETATION TYPES: Fa, Sa, Sd, Sg, SN, Sp, ST, Tp.

DIAGNOSTIC ELEMENTS: *Representativity:* 4 • *Level of threat:* 3 • *Connectivity:* 3 • *Human presence:* 3 • *Protection level:* 3 • ACTION RECOMMENDED: *Creation of conservation area:* 5.

UC 036 - Uatumã - Trombetas and Guiana savannas ecoregion - PRIORITY LEVEL: A • LOCATION: *State:* Pará • *Main municipality:* Alenquer • *Municipalities covered:* 2 • VEGETATION TYPES: Da, Ds • COMMENTS: Small indigenous land with access restricted. This area is an enclave between indigenous lands.

DIAGNOSTIC ELEMENTS: *Representativity:* 3 • *Level of threat:* 2 • *Connectivity:* 5 • *Human presence:* 1 • *Sustainable use base:* 1 • ACTION RECOMMENDED: *Creation of conservation area:* 5.

UC 037 - Uatumã - Trombetas and Guiana forests ecoregion - PRIORITY LEVEL: A • LOCATION: *State:* Amapá • *Main municipality:* Vitória do Jari • *Municipalities covered:* 3 • VEGETATION TYPES: Da, Pa, SO, Sp • COMMENTS: Create a buffer-zone around the indigenous land. Area of proposed INCRA settlement project.

DIAGNOSTIC ELEMENTS: *Representativity:* 4 • *Level of threat:* 2 • *Connectivity:* 5 • *Human presence:* 3 • *Sustainable use base:* 5 • *Protection level:* 3 • ACTION RECOMMENDED: *Creation of conservation area:* 5.

UC 038 - Southwestern Amazonia ecoregion - PRIORITY LEVEL: A • LOCATION: *State:* Amazonas • *Main municipality:* Guajará • *Municipalities covered:* 1 • VEGETATION TYPES: Ab, As, Db, Ds, La, Ld, Lg, LO • COMMENTS: Only campinarana group on the southern bank of the Solimões system.

DIAGNOSTIC ELEMENTS: *Representativity:* 5 • *Level of threat:* 5 • *Connectivity:* 3 • *Human presence:* 5 • *Sustainable use base:* 1 • *Protection level:* 1 • ACTION RECOMMENDED: *Creation of conservation area:* 5.

UC 039 - Guiana savannas ecoregion - PRIORITY LEVEL: A • LOCATION: *State:* Amapá • *Main municipality:* Tartarugalzinho • *Municipalities covered:* 3 • VEGETATION TYPES: AA, Da, Pa, Pf • COMMENTS: Only ecosystem in the state not protected by conservation area.

DIAGNOSTIC ELEMENTS: *Representativity:* 5 • *Level of threat:* 5 • *Connectivity:* 4 • *Human presence:* 4 • *Sustainable use base:* 4 • *Protection level:* 3 • ACTION RECOMMENDED: *Creation of conservation area:* 5 • *Preparation of management plan:* 5 • *Full implementation of management plan:* 5 • *Integration with the surrounding area:* 5 • *Economic sustainability:* 5.

UC 040 - Tapajós-Xingu interfluve ecoregion - PRIORITY LEVEL: A • LOCATION: *State:* Pará • *Main municipality:* Altamira • *Municipalities covered:* 2 • VEGETATION TYPES: As, Cs, Ds, ON, Sa, Sd, SN, SO, Sp • COMMENTS: Creation of a corridor increasing the protection for several vegetation types.

DIAGNOSTIC ELEMENTS: *Representativity:* 4 • *Level of threat:* 1 • *Connectivity:* 5 • *Human presence:* 2 • *Protection level:* 4 • ACTION RECOMMENDED: *Creation of conservation area:* 5.

UC 041 - Madeira-Tapajós ecoregion - PRIORITY LEVEL: A • LOCATION: *State:* Rondônia • *Main municipality:* Guajará-Mirim • *Municipalities covered:* 2 • VEGETATION TYPES: Ab, As, Da, Pa, Sa, Sd, SO, Sp • COMMENTS: Consolidation of the western corridor in Rondônia.

DIAGNOSTIC ELEMENTS: *Representativity:* 3 • *Level of threat:* 4 • *Connectivity:* 5 • *Human presence:* 2 • *Sustainable use base:* 4 • *Protection level:* 4 • ACTION RECOMMENDED: *Creation of conservation area:* 5.

UC 042 - Negro, Branco and Rio Negro campinaranas ecoregion - PRIORITY LEVEL: A • LOCATION: *State:* Amazonas • *Main municipality:* Santa Isabel do Rio Negro • *Municipalities covered:* 2 • VEGETATION TYPES: Da, Ds, Sd, SO • COMMENTS: Conserve physiognomies not represented in conservation areas and increase the connectivity between indigenous lands.

> DIAGNOSTIC ELEMENTS: *Representativity:* 5 • *Level of threat:* 1 • *Connectivity:* 5 • *Human presence:* 1 • *Protection level:* 4 • ACTION RECOMMENDED: *Creation of conservation area:* 5.

UC 043 - Tocantins-Araguaia-Maranhão ecoregion - PRIORITY LEVEL: A • LOCATION: *State:* Pará • *Main municipality:* Curuçá • *Municipalities covered:* 16 • VEGETATION TYPES: AA, As, Da, Ds, Sa, SO • COMMENTS: Very important mangrove area.

> DIAGNOSTIC ELEMENTS: *Representativity:* 5 • *Level of threat:* 5 • *Connectivity:* 3 • *Human presence:* 4 • *Protection level:* 1 • ACTION RECOMMENDED: *Creation of conservation area:* 5.

UC 044 - Tocantins-Araguaia-Maranhão ecoregion - PRIORITY LEVEL: A • LOCATION: *State:* Pará • *Main municipality:* Tomé-Açu • *Municipalities covered:* 3 • VEGETATION TYPES: AA, Da, Db • COMMENTS: Highly threatened area and no conservation areas in the ecoregion.

> DIAGNOSTIC ELEMENTS: *Representativity:* 5 • *Level of threat:* 5 • *Connectivity:* 1 • *Human presence:* 5 • *Protection level:* 1 • ACTION RECOMMENDED: *Creation of conservation area:* 5

UC 045 - Southwestern Amazonia ecoregion - PRIORITY LEVEL: A • LOCATION: *State:* Acre • *Main municipality:* Manoel Urbano • *Municipalities covered:* 4 • VEGETATION TYPES: Ab, Da • COMMENTS: Connects indigenous lands and extractive reserves. Located within the western Amazon corridor. A single area of very high conservation priority for the 1990 Workshop. Anthropogenic pressure still low.

> DIAGNOSTIC ELEMENTS: *Representativity:* 5 • *Level of threat:* 1 • *Connectivity:* 5 • *Human presence:* 2 • *Sustainable use base:* 5 • *Protection level:* 4 • ACTION RECOMMENDED: *Creation of conservation area:* 5.

UC 046 • Mato Grosso savanna and dry forests ecoregion - PRIORITY LEVEL: A • LOCATION: *State:* Maranhão/Tocantins • *Main municipality:* Babaçulândia • *Municipalities covered:* 12 • VEGETATION TYPES: AA, As, Sa, Sd, SO, Sp • COMMENTS: No existing conservation areas. Vegetation types poorly represented in the ecoregion. Highly threatened.

> DIAGNOSTIC ELEMENTS: *Representativity:* 4 • *Level of threat:* 5 • *Connectivity:* 3 • *Human presence:* 5 • *Protection level:* 1 • ACTION RECOMMENDED: *Creation of conservation area:* 5.

UC 047 - Savanna Ecoregion - PRIORITY LEVEL: A • LOCATION: *State:* Tocantins • *Main municipality:* Goiatins • *Municipalities covered:* 5 • VEGETATION TYPES: AA, Sa, Sd, Sp • COMMENTS: Region not represented in conservation areas.

> DIAGNOSTIC ELEMENTS: *Representativity:* 4 • *Level of threat:* 5 • *Connectivity:* 3 • *Human presence:* 4 • *Protection level:* 1 • ACTION RECOMMENDED: *Creation of conservation area:* 5.

UC 048 - Mato Grosso dry forests and savanna ecoregion - PRIORITY LEVEL: A • LOCATION: *State:* Pará/Tocantins • *Main municipality:* Caseara • *Municipalities covered:* 8 • VEGETATION TYPES: AA, As, Sa, Sd, SN, Sp • COMMENTS: No existing conservation areas. Vegetation types poorly represented in the ecoregion. Highly threatened.

> DIAGNOSTIC ELEMENTS: *Representativity:* 4 • *Level of threat:* 5 • *Connectivity:* 4 • *Human presence:* 5 • *Protection level:* 1 • ACTION RECOMMENDED: *Creation of conservation area:* 5

UC 049 - Juruá-Purus ecoregion - PRIORITY LEVEL: A • LOCATION: *State:* Amazonas • *Main municipality:* Coari • *Municipalities covered:* 2 • VEGETATION TYPES: AA, Da, Db • COMMENTS: Unprotected vegetation type.

> DIAGNOSTIC ELEMENTS: *Representativity:* 5 • *Level of threat:* 1 • *Connectivity:* 4 • *Sustainable use base:* 4 • ACTION RECOMMENDED: *Creation of conservation area:* 5

UC 050 - Southwestern Amazonas ecoregion - PRIORITY LEVEL: A • LOCATION: *State:* Acre/Amazonas • *Main municipality:* Guajará • *Municipalities covered:* 3 • VEGETATION TYPES: AA, Db, La • COMMENTS: High connectivity: connects the western Amazon corridor to the central corridor through the indigenous land in the state of Amazonas and around the Serra do Divisor National Park buffer zone. Very low anthropogenic pressure.

> DIAGNOSTIC ELEMENTS: *Representativity:* 4 • *Level of threat:* 1 • *Connectivity:* 5 • *Human presence:* 1 • *Sustainable use base:* 5 • *Protection level:* 5 • ACTION RECOMMENDED: *Creation of conservation area:* 5

UC 051 - Madeira-Tapajós Ecoregion - PRIORITY LEVEL: A • LOCATION: *State:* Amazonas/Rondônia • *Main municipality:* Manicoré • *Municipalities covered:* 3 • VEGETATION TYPES: Da, Db • COMMENTS: Protects a vegetation type not represented in conservation areas and allows connectivity between two indigenous lands.

> DIAGNOSTIC ELEMENTS: *Representativity:* 5 • *Level of threat:* 2 • *Connectivity:* 5 • *Human presence:* 2 • *Sustainable use base:* 5 • *Protection level:* 3 • ACTION RECOMMENDED: *Creation of conservation area:* 5

8
PRIORITY AREAS FOR ENVIRONMENTAL GOODS AND SERVICES*

What is the value of a cubic meter of water released by the Amazon forest through evaporation and which returns in the form of rain, keeping the climate of the region humid? What is the value of the accumulated nutrients in the trunks and barks of old-growth trees? What would be the damage caused by forest fires in Amazonia, if these did not burn out at the forest edge? How much is a kilo of carbon worth when it is not released into the atmosphere because it is stored in forests?

Such questions relate to the value of what can be called the 'ecological services' provided by Amazonian forests. The importance of such services becomes clear when we consider a 'deforested Amazon' scenario. If the greater part of the vast expansion of the forest in existence today were removed, not only would an enormous number of species disappear, but the planet's atmosphere would come to contain much more carbon gas, aggravating the greenhouse effect and the global warming that resulted. Regional rainfall would be reduced by 20% to 30% and temperatures would rise. There would also be greater surface runoff during heavy rains, carrying nutrients from the highlands to the rivers and stream, causing silting and flooding. The drier and hotter climate would help the outbreak of fires and the burning of large areas, affecting protected forests in conservation areas and indigenous lands.

Amazonia acts as a gigantic stable carbon storehouse. A typical regional forest contains an average of 460 tons of biomass per hectare, corresponding to 230 tons of carbon fixed in plant tissue (Fearnside 1997). When the forest is cleared and burned however, this carbon is released into the atmosphere in the form of CO_2 and the ecological service of carbon storage is disrupted.

Considering only the figures from INPE, deforestation in the Brazilian Amazon releases around 0.3 billion tons of carbon a year. This is an amount equal to 5% of total human emissions (Fearnside 1997) and reduces still further the amount of carbon withdrawn from the atmosphere by forests.

When we add in carbon released by logging activity and by fires in the understorey which is not included in the INPE figures, emissions from the Brazilian Amazon may make up 10% of global emissions resulting from human activities in extremely dry years, when many fires occur (Nepstad et al. 1999a).

As well as relasing CO_2 into the atmosphere, deforestation causes hydrological and climate change in Amazonia by reducing the evapotranspiration that cools the air and makes rain possible, increasing soil and air temperatures, and altering drainage and surface water runoff, thereby causing flooding by increasing the volume of water in the rivers. In addition, the vegetation which substitutes the primary forest has a lower capacity for rooting, and thus lower potential for evapotranspiration.

The Amazon forest releases about seven trillion tons of water a year into the atmosphere via evapotranspiration. This process is extremely important for the climate of Amazonia as it generates the water vapor needed to form the cumulus clouds responsible for the greater part of the rainfall. In addition, the conversion of water into vapor cools the air, allowing the forests to function as truly gigantic air conditioners.

Various experiments using climate modeling have shown that Amazon deforestation may result in a reduction of 20% to 30% in rainfall by volume and an increase in air temperatures (Land and Warrilow 1989; Shukla et al. 1990; Nobre et al. 1991; Henderson-Sellars et al. 1993). In a drier climate, even those intact forests in conservation areas or indigenous lands would be threatened with disappearance, or at least with suffering drastic alteration to their structure and species diversity. They would also be vulnerable to the risk of fire. Strategies for the conservation of the biological wealth of Amazonia should therefore take account of the fact that it is very likely that in the future the region will be drier. The extent to which it is drier will be closely connected to the size of the remaining forest area.

As well as supplying the climate with enormous quantities of water vapor, forests provide another extremely important ecological service, particularly in regions with pronounced dry seasons: that of a firebreak. Because their root systems can draw up water from the soil from a depth of up to 10 meters, trees of these forests are able to retain their leaves throughout the dry season. They thus prevent sunlight penetrating the canopy and reducing the humidity of the interior of the forest.

Constanza et al. (1997) calculated the economic value of planetary ecosystem services to be around 33 trillion dollars, or 1.8 times global GDP. The service which provides the greatest part of this value is that of nutrient recycling, which corresponds to 17 trillion dollars or more than half the total. Genetic resources are estimated at 78 billion dollars, or 0.2% of the total. Around 38% of the total value of the services is supplied by terrestrial ecosystems. The services provided by forests amount to 4.7 trillion dollars and include nutrient recycling, raw materials, climate regulation, and erosion control. Forest genetic resources, on the other hand, only make up 2% of the total (80 billion dollars).

---

* Text drawn in part from 'The ecological functions of forest ecosystems: implications for the conservation and use of Amazonian biodiversity' by Paulo Moutinho and Daniel Nepstad, the full version of which can be found on page 175 of this book.

The ecological services of the secondary forests of the Amazon region, generally growing over abandoned pasture, may also be very important, depending on the region. A secondary forest in eastern Amazonia that is less than twenty years old, for example, can release the same quantity of water into the atmosphere as a primary forest (Jipp et al. 1998). It can reconstitute the nutrient cycle (Nepstad et al. forthcoming). Such forests may also house a significant number of native animal and plant species (Gascon and Moutinho 1998; Nepstad et al. 1996). However, areas of secondary forest in their growth phase should also be considered important within conservation strategies, above all in areas where the original vegetation cover is absent.

Conserving the ecological services of the Amazon forest should be a priority within the biodiversity conservation and use strategies for the region. Such strategies should consider ecosystems and/or landscapes as the units to be conserved, and not just species. In this way, we will be conserving the basic functions that keeps the biosphere alive, and, as a result, its existing species known and unknown.

During the Macapá Workshop, 31 priority areas for environmental goods and services in Amazonia were identified (see the map on page 447 and the listing). Of these, fifteen (48.4%) contain a high number of dense high forests (high biomass), and thirteen (41.9%) contain hydrographic sub-basins of high importance for the rate of flow of rivers or which experience fires and burning during 'El Niño' years (Table 8).

TABLE 8 - PRIORITY AREAS FOR ENVIRONMENTAL GOODS AND SERVICES (DIAGNOSTIC ELEMENTS THAT SCORE HIGHEST)

Diagnostic elements	Number of areas	%[1]
Fires and burning during 'El Niño' years	13	41.9
Sandy soils susceptible to erosion	10	32.3
Hydrographic sub-basins of high importance for river flow rates	13	41.9
Presence of dense high forests (high biomass)	15	48.4

1. Of the total proposed areas (31).

AS 001 - Upper Tapajós - Xingu - PRIORITY LEVEL: A • LOCATION: *State:* Pará • *Main municipality:* Altamira • *Municipalities covered:* 7 • VEGETATION TYPES: AA, As, Da, Ds, Sa, SN, SO.
  DIAGNOSTIC ELEMENTS: *Risk of fire and burning in 'El Niño' years:* 4 • *Sandy soils susceptible to erosion:* 3 • *Hydrographic sub-basins important for the maintenance of river flow rates:* 5 • *Presence of dense high forests (high biomass):* 5 • ACTION RECOMMENDED: *Forest canopy protection:* 5 • *Investments to prevent forest fires:* 3 • *Land use restriction* • *Forest use in at least 80% of the forest area:* 5.

AS 002 - Eastern Pará (Pará-15°) - PRIORITY LEVEL: A • LOCATION: *State:* Pará/Maranhão/Tocantins/Mato Grosso • *Main municipality:* São Félix do Xingu • *Municipalities covered:* 79 • VEGETATION TYPES: AA, As, Da, Db, Dm, Ds, Sa, Sd, Sg, SO, Sp.
  DIAGNOSTIC ELEMENTS: *Risk of fire and burning in 'El Niño' years:* 5 • *Sandy soils susceptible to erosion:* 5 • *Hydrographic sub-basins important for the maintenance of river flow rates:* 4 • *Presence of dense high forests (high biomass):* 4 • ACTION RECOMMENDED: *Forest canopy protection:* 5 • *Investments to prevent forest fires:* 5 • *Land use restriction* • *Forest use in at least 80% of the forest area:* 5.

AS 003 - Northwestern Mato Grosso - PRIORITY LEVEL: A • LOCATION: *State:* Mato Grosso/Amazonas/Rondônia/Pará • *Main municipality:* Apiacás • *Municipalities covered:* 19 • VEGETATION TYPES: AA, As, Cs, Da, Ds, ON, Sa, Sd, Sg, SN, SO, Sp.
  DIAGNOSTIC ELEMENTS: *Risk of fire and burning in 'El Niño' years:* 5 • *Sandy soils susceptible to erosion:* 4 • *Hydrographic sub-basins important for the maintenance of river flow rates:* 4 • *Presence of dense high forests (high biomass):* 3 • ACTION RECOMMENDED: *Forest canopy protection:* 5 • *Investments to prevent forest fires:* 5 • *Land use restriction* • *Forest use in at least 80% of the forest area:* 4.

AS 004 - Upper Xingu - PRIORITY LEVEL: A • LOCATION: *State:* Mato Grosso • *Main municipality:* Nova Ubiratã • *Municipalities covered:* 5 • VEGETATION TYPES: Fa, ON, Sa, Sd, SN, Sp.
  DIAGNOSTIC ELEMENTS: *Risk of fire and burning in 'El Niño' years:* 5 • *Sandy soils susceptible to erosion:* 5 • *Hydrographic sub-basins important for the maintenance of river flow rates:* 1 • *Presence of dense high forests (high biomass):* 1 • ACTION RECOMMENDED: *Forest canopy protection:* 5 • *Investments to prevent forest fires:* 5 • *Land use restriction* • *Forest use in at least 80% of the forest area:* 5.

AS 005 - Trombetas - PRIORITY LEVEL: A • LOCATION: *State:* Roraima/Pará/Amazonas • *Main municipality:* Oriximiná • *Municipalities covered:* 8 • VEGETATION TYPES: As, Da, Db, Dm, Ds.
  DIAGNOSTIC ELEMENTS: *Risk of fire and burning in 'El Niño' years:* 4 • *Sandy soils susceptible to erosion:* 2 • *Hydrographic sub-basins important for the maintenance of river flow rates:* 4 • *Presence of dense high forests (high biomass):* 5 • ACTION RECOMMENDED: *Forest canopy protection:* 5 • *Investments to prevent forest fires:* 2 • *Land use restriction* • *Forest use in at least 80% of the forest area:* 5.

AS 006 - Almeirim - PRIORITY LEVEL: A • LOCATION: *State:* Pará/Amapá • *Main municipality:* Almeirim • *Municipalities covered:* 9 • VEGETATION TYPES: AA, As, Da, Db, Dm, Ds, Pa, Sd, SO.
  DIAGNOSTIC ELEMENTS: *Risk of fire and burning in 'El Niño' years:* 4 • *Sandy soils susceptible to erosion:* 2 • *Hydrographic sub-basins important for the maintenance of river flow rates:* 4 • *Presence of dense high forests (high biomass):* 5 • ACTION RECOMMENDED: *Forest canopy protection:* 5 • *Investments to prevent forest fires:* 2 • *Land use restriction* • *Forest use in at least 80% of the forest area:* 5.

AS 007 - Upper Jamari - PRIORITY LEVEL: A • LOCATION: *State:* Rondônia • *Main municipality:* Governador Jorge Teixeira • *Municipalities covered:* 13 • VEGETATION TYPES: AA, Ab, As, Ds, Sa, Sd, SO, Sp.
  DIAGNOSTIC ELEMENTS: *Risk of fire and burning in 'El Niño' years:* 5 • *Sandy soils susceptible to erosion:* 5 • *Hydrographic sub-basins important for the maintenance of river flow rates:* 3 • *Presence of dense high forests (high biomass):* 5 • ACTION RECOMMENDED: *Forest canopy protection:* 5 • *Investments to prevent forest fires:* 5 • *Land use restriction* • *Forest use in at least 80% of the forest area:* 5.

AS 008 - Southwestern Roraima - PRIORITY LEVEL: A • LOCATION: *State:* Roraima/Amazonas • *Main municipality:* Barcelos • *Municipalities covered:* 3 • VEGETATION TYPES: As, Dm, Ds, Lg.
  DIAGNOSTIC ELEMENTS: *Risk of fire and burning in 'El Niño' years:* 4 • *Sandy soils susceptible to erosion:* 4 • *Hydrographic sub-basins important for the maintenance of river flow rates:* 1 • *Presence of dense high forests (high biomass):* 5 • ACTION RECOMMENDED: *Forest canopy protection:* 5 • *Investments to prevent forest fires:* 4 • *Land use restriction* • *Forest use in at least 80% of the forest area:* 4.

AS 009 - Northern Roraima - PRIORITY LEVEL: A • LOCATION: *State:* Roraima • *Main municipality:* Amajari • *Municipalities covered:* 5 • VEGETATION TYPES: As, Dm, Ds, ON, rm, Sp, Td, Tp.
  DIAGNOSTIC ELEMENTS: *Risk of fire and burning in 'El Niño' years:* 4 • *Sandy soils susceptible to erosion:* 5 • *Hydrographic sub-basins important for the maintenance of river flow rates:* 5 • *Presence of dense high forests (high biomass):* 5 • ACTION RECOMMENDED: *Forest canopy protection:* 4 • *Investments to prevent forest fires:* 5 • *Land use restriction* • *Forest use in at least 80% of the forest area:* 5.

AS 010 - Upper Ji-Paraná river - PRIORITY LEVEL: A • LOCATION: *State:* Rondônia/Mato Grosso • *Main municipality:* Aripuanã • *Municipalities covered:* 7 • VEGETATION TYPES: AA, As, Da, Ds.
  DIAGNOSTIC ELEMENTS: *Risk of fire and burning in 'El Niño' years:* 5 • *Sandy soils susceptible to erosion:* 2 • *Hydrographic sub-basins important for the maintenance of river flow rates:* 4 • *Presence of dense high forests (high biomass):* 3 • ACTION RECOMMENDED: *Forest canopy protection:* 5 • *Investments to prevent forest fires:* 5 • *Land use restriction* • *Forest use in at least 80% of the forest area:* 5.

AS 011 - Lower Coari - PRIORITY LEVEL: A • LOCATION: *State:* Amazonas • *Main municipality:* Coari • *Municipalities covered:* 6 • VEGETATION TYPES: AA, Ab, Da, Db, Ds, Pa.
  DIAGNOSTIC ELEMENTS: *Risk of fire and burning in 'El Niño' years:* 3 • *Sandy soils susceptible to erosion:* 2 • *Hydrographic sub-basins important for the maintenance of river flow rates:* 2 • *Presence of dense high forests (high biomass):* 5 • ACTION RECOMMENDED: *Forest canopy protection:* 3 • *Investments to prevent forest fires:* 4 • *Land use restriction* • *Forest use in at least 80% of the forest area:* 4.

AS 012 - Upper Xingu - PRIORITY LEVEL: B • LOCATION: *State:* Mato Grosso • *Main municipality:* Sorriso • *Municipalities covered:* 10 • VEGETATION TYPES: AA, Da, Fa, Fs, ON, Pa, Sa, Sd, SN, Sp.
  DIAGNOSTIC ELEMENTS: *Risk of fire and burning in 'El Niño' years:* 4 • *Sandy soils susceptible to erosion:* 2 • *Hydrographic sub-basins important for the maintenance of river flow rates:* 4 • *Presence of dense high forests (high biomass):* 2 • ACTION RECOMMENDED: *Forest canopy protection:* 4 • *Investments to prevent forest fires:* 5 • *Land use restriction* • *Forest use in at least 80% of the forest area:* 5.

AS 013 - Lower Tapajós - PRIORITY LEVEL: B • LOCATION: *State:* Pará/Amazonas/Amapá • *Main municipality:* Maués • *Municipalities covered:* 28 • VEGETATION TYPES: AA, As, Da, Db, Ds, Pa, Sd, SO, Sp.
  DIAGNOSTIC ELEMENTS: *Risk of fire and burning in 'El Niño' years:* 5 • *Sandy soils susceptible to erosion:* 2 • *Hydrographic sub-basins important for the maintenance of river flow rates:* 2 • *Presence of dense high forests (high biomass):* 5 • ACTION RECOMMENDED: *Forest canopy protection:* 3 • *Investments to prevent forest fires:* 5 • *Land use restriction* • *Forest use in at least 80% of the forest area:* 5.

AS 014 - Rio Negro - PRIORITY LEVEL: B • LOCATION: *State:* Amazonas/Pará/Roraima • *Main municipality:* Novo Airão • *Municipalities covered:* 19 • VEGETATION TYPES: AA, Ab, As, Da, Db, Ds, La, Ld, Lg, LO, Pa.
  DIAGNOSTIC ELEMENTS: *Risk of fire and burning in 'El Niño' years:* 5 • *Sandy soils susceptible to erosion:* 2 • *Hydrographic sub-basins*

important for the maintenance of river flow rates: 5 • *Presence of dense high forests (high biomass):* 5 • ACTION RECOMMENDED: *Forest canopy protection:* 5 • *Investments to prevent forest fires:* 5 • *Land use restriction* • *Forest use in at least 80% of the forest area:* 5.

AS 015 - Northwestern Amazonas - PRIORITY LEVEL: B • LOCATION: *State:* Amazonas/Roraima • *Main municipality:* Santa Isabel do Rio Negro • *Municipalities covered:* 4 • VEGETATION TYPES: As, Dm, Ds, Ld, Lg, LO, rm.

DIAGNOSTIC ELEMENTS: *Risk of fire and burning in 'El Niño' years:* 4 • *Sandy soils susceptible to erosion:* 3 • *Hydrographic sub-basins important for the maintenance of river flow rates:* 2 • *Presence of dense high forests (high biomass):* 5 • ACTION RECOMMENDED: *Forest canopy protection:* 3 • *Investments to prevent forest fires:* 5 • *Land use restriction* • *Forest use in at least 80% of the forest area:* 5.

AS 016 - Eastern upper Xingu - PRIORITY LEVEL: B • LOCATION: *State:* Mato Grosso • *Main municipality:* Querência • *Municipalities covered:* 7 • VEGETATION TYPES: AA, Fa, ON, Pa, Sa, SN.

DIAGNOSTIC ELEMENTS: *Risk of fire and burning in 'El Niño' years:* 5 • *Sandy soils susceptible to erosion:* 3 • *Hydrographic sub-basins important for the maintenance of river flow rates:* 5 • *Presence of dense high forests (high biomass):* 3 • ACTION RECOMMENDED: *Forest canopy protection:* 5 • *Investments to prevent forest fires:* 5 • *Land use restriction* • *Forest use in at least 80% of the forest area:* 5.

AS 017 - Porto Velho - PRIORITY LEVEL: B • LOCATION: *State:* Rondônia • *Main municipality:* Candeias do Jamari • *Municipalities covered:* 3 • VEGETATION TYPES: AA, Ab, As, Da, SO.

DIAGNOSTIC ELEMENTS: *Risk of fire and burning in 'El Niño' years:* 5 • *Sandy soils susceptible to erosion:* 2 • *Hydrographic sub-basins important for the maintenance of river flow rates:* 2 • *Presence of dense high forests (high biomass):* 5 • ACTION RECOMMENDED: *Forest canopy protection:* 4 • *Investments to prevent forest fires:* 5 • *Land use restriction* • *Forest use in at least 80% of the forest area:* 5.

AS 018 - Northeastern Mato Grosso - PRIORITY LEVEL: B • LOCATION: *State:* Mato Grosso/Pará • *Main municipality:* São José do Xingu • *Municipalities covered:* 11 • VEGETATION TYPES: AA, As, ON, Sa, Sd, SO, Sp.

DIAGNOSTIC ELEMENTS: *Risk of fire and burning in 'El Niño' years:* 5 • *Sandy soils susceptible to erosion:* 5 • *Hydrographic sub-basins important for the maintenance of river flow rates:* 4 • *Presence of dense high forests (high biomass):* 3 • ACTION RECOMMENDED: *Forest canopy protection:* 5 • *Investments to prevent forest fires:* 5 • *Land use restriction* • *Forest use in at least 80% of the forest area:* 5.

AS 019 - Tucuruí - PRIORITY LEVEL: B • LOCATION: *State:* Pará • *Main municipality:* Novo Repartimento • *Municipalities covered:* 12 • VEGETATION TYPES: AA, As, Da, Db, Ds.

DIAGNOSTIC ELEMENTS: *Risk of fire and burning in 'El Niño' years:* 5 • *Sandy soils susceptible to erosion:* 2 • *Hydrographic sub-basins important for the maintenance of river flow rates:* 2 • *Presence of dense high forests (high biomass):* 5 • ACTION RECOMMENDED: *Forest canopy protection:* 3 • *Investments to prevent forest fires:* 5 • *Land use restriction* • *Forest use in at least 80% of the forest area:* 5.

AS 020 - Upper Pindaré - PRIORITY LEVEL: B • LOCATION: *State:* Maranhão/Tocantins • *Main municipality:* Amarante do Maranhão • *Municipalities covered:* 33 • VEGETATION TYPES: AA, As, Cs, Da, Db, Sa, Sd, SO, Sp.

DIAGNOSTIC ELEMENTS: *Risk of fire and burning in 'El Niño' years:* 5 • *Sandy soils susceptible to erosion:* 2 • *Hydrographic sub-basins important for the maintenance of river flow rates:* 2 • *Presence of dense high forests (high biomass):* 3 • ACTION RECOMMENDED: *Forest canopy protection:* 3 • *Investments to prevent forest fires:* 5 • *Land use restriction* • *Forest use in at least 80% of the forest area:* 5.

AS 021 - Western Mato Grosso - Juruena river - PRIORITY LEVEL: C • LOCATION: *State:* Mato Grosso/Rondônia • *Main municipality:* Comodoro • *Municipalities covered:* 27 • VEGETATION TYPES: AA, As, Da, Ds, Fa, Fs, ON, Pa, Sa, Sd, SN, SO, Sp.

DIAGNOSTIC ELEMENTS: *Risk of fire and burning in 'El Niño' years:* 2 • *Sandy soils susceptible to erosion:* 5 • *Hydrographic sub-basins important for the maintenance of river flow rates:* 5 • *Presence of dense high forests (high biomass):* 2 • ACTION RECOMMENDED: *Forest canopy protection:* 5 • *Investments to prevent forest fires:* 4 • *Land use restriction* • *Forest use in at least 80% of the forest area:* 4.

AS 022 - Cuiabá - PRIORITY LEVEL: C • LOCATION: *State:* Mato Grosso • *Main municipality:* Novo São Joaquim • *Municipalities covered:* 21 • VEGETATION TYPES: AA, Cs, Fs, Pa, Sa, Sd, Sg, SN, Sp.

DIAGNOSTIC ELEMENTS: *Risk of fire and burning in 'El Niño' years:* 3 • *Sandy soils susceptible to erosion:* 5 • *Hydrographic sub-basins important for the maintenance of river flow rates:* 5 • *Presence of dense high forests (high biomass):* 3 • ACTION RECOMMENDED: *Forest canopy protection:* 5 • *Investments to prevent forest fires:* 3 • *Land use restriction* • *Forest use in at least 80% of the forest area:* 3.

AS 023 - Roosevelt river - PRIORITY LEVEL: C • LOCATION: *State:* Mato Grosso/Rondônia/Amazonas • *Main municipality:* Aripuanã • *Municipalities covered:* 19 • VEGETATION TYPES: AA, As, Da, Db, Ds, Pa, Sa, Sd, Sg, SO, Sp.

DIAGNOSTIC ELEMENTS: *Risk of fire and burning in 'El Niño' years:* 2 • *Sandy soils susceptible to erosion:* 2 • *Hydrographic sub-basins important for the maintenance of river flow rates:* 5 • *Presence of dense high forests (high biomass):* 3 • ACTION RECOMMENDED: *Forest canopy protection:* 5 • *Investments to prevent forest fires:* 3 • *Land use restriction* • *Forest use in at least 80% of the forest area:* 3.

AS 024 - Southwestern Rondônia - PRIORITY LEVEL: C • LOCATION: *State:* Rondônia • *Main municipality:* São Miguel do Guaporé • *Municipalities covered:* 10 • VEGETATION TYPES: AA, Ab, As, Da, Ds, Fs, Pa, Sa, Sd, SO, Sp.

DIAGNOSTIC ELEMENTS: *Risk of fire and burning in 'El Niño' years:* 5 • *Sandy soils susceptible to erosion:* 2 • *Hydrographic sub-basins important for the maintenance of river flow rates:* 5 • *Presence of dense high forests (high biomass):* 4 • ACTION RECOMMENDED: *Forest canopy protection:* 5 • *Investments to prevent forest fires:* 5 • *Land use restriction* • *Forest use in at least 80% of the forest area:* 5.

AS 025 - Arinos river - PRIORITY LEVEL: C • LOCATION: *State:* Mato Grosso • *Main municipality:* Nova Mutum • *Municipalities covered:* 5 • VEGETATION TYPES: AA, Fa, Fs, ON, Sa, SN.

DIAGNOSTIC ELEMENTS: *Risk of fire and burning in 'El Niño' years:* 2 • *Sandy soils susceptible to erosion:* 5 • *Hydrographic sub-basins important for the maintenance of river flow rates:* 2 • *Presence of dense high forests (high biomass):* 3 • ACTION RECOMMENDED: *Forest canopy protection:* 5 • *Investments to prevent forest fires:* 3 • *Land use restriction* • *Forest use in at least 80% of the forest area:* 3.

AS 026 - Eastern Tocantins - PRIORITY LEVEL: C • LOCATION: *State:* Tocantins/Maranhão • *Main municipality:* Ponte Alta do Tocantins • *Municipalities covered:* 17 • VEGETATION TYPES: AA, Sa, Sd, Sg, SN, Sp.

DIAGNOSTIC ELEMENTS: *Risk of fire and burning in 'El Niño' years:* 4 • *Sandy soils susceptible to erosion:* 5 • *Hydrographic sub-basins important for the maintenance of river flow rates:* 5 • *Presence of dense high forests (high biomass):* 2 • ACTION RECOMMENDED: *Forest canopy protection:* 5 • *Investments to prevent forest fires:* 4 • *Land use restriction* • *Forest use in at least 80% of the forest area:* 4.

AS 027 - Western Tocantins - PRIORITY LEVEL: C • LOCATION: *State:* Tocantins • *Main municipality:* Dois Irmãos do Tocantins • *Municipalities covered:* 20 • VEGETATION TYPES: AA, Fa, Sa, Sg, SO, Sp.

DIAGNOSTIC ELEMENTS: *Risk of fire and burning in 'El Niño' years:* 3 • *Sandy soils susceptible to erosion:* 5 • *Hydrographic sub-basins important for the maintenance of river flow rates:* 5 • *Presence of dense high forests (high biomass):* 2 • ACTION RECOMMENDED:

Forest canopy protection: 5 • *Investments to prevent forest fires:* 3 • *Land use restriction* • *Forest use in at least 80% of the forest area:* 3.

AS 028 - Madeira river - Priority level: C • Location: *State:* Amazonas • *Main municipality:* Manicoré • *Municipalities covered:* 6 • Vegetation types: Da, Db, Ds, Pa.

Diagnostic elements: *Risk of fire and burning in 'El Niño' years:* 4 • *Sandy soils susceptible to erosion:* 2 • *Hydrographic sub-basins important for the maintenance of river flow rates:* 2 • *Presence of dense high forests (high biomass):* 5 • Action recommended: *Forest canopy protection:* 3 • *Investments to prevent forest fires:* 4 • *Land use restriction* • *Forest use in at least 80% of the forest area:* 4.

AS 029 - Rio Branco - Boca do Acre • Priority level: C • Location: *State:* Amazonas/Acre • *Main municipality:* Lábrea • *Municipalities covered:* 5 • Vegetation types: AA, Ab, As, Da, Db, Ds.

Diagnostic elements: *Risk of fire and burning in 'El Niño' years:* 2 • *Sandy soils susceptible to erosion:* 2 • *Hydrographic sub-basins important for the maintenance of river flow rates:* 5 • *Presence of dense high forests (high biomass):* 5 • Action recommended: *Forest canopy protection:* 5 • *Investments to prevent forest fires:* 3 • *Land use restriction* • *Forest use in at least 80% of the forest area:* 3.

AS 030 - Northern Amapá - Priority level: C • Location: *State:* Amapá • *Main municipality:* Serra do Navio • *Municipalities covered:* 9 • Vegetation types: AA, Da, Db, Ds, Sd, SO, Sp.

Diagnostic elements: *Risk of fire and burning in 'El Niño' years:* 3 • *Sandy soils susceptible to erosion:* 2 • *Hydrographic sub-basins important for the maintenance of river flow rates:* 5 • *Presence of dense high forests (high biomass):* 5 • Action recommended: *Forest canopy protection:* 5 • *Investments to prevent forest fires:* 3 • *Land use restriction* • *Forest use in at least 80% of the forest area:* 3.

AS 031 - Southwestern Pará - Priority level: C • Location: *State:* Pará/Amazonas/Mato Grosso • *Main municipality:* Altamira • *Municipalities covered:* 12 • Vegetation types: AA, As, Cs, Da, Ds, Fs, ON, Sa, Sd, Sg, SN, SO, Sp.

Diagnostic elements: *Risk of fire and burning in 'El Niño' years:* 4 • *Sandy soils susceptible to erosion:* 2 • *Hydrographic sub-basins important for the maintenance of river flow rates:* 5 • *Presence of dense high forests (high biomass):* 4 • Action recommended: *Forest canopy protection:* 5 • *Investments to prevent forest fires:* 4 • *Land use restriction* • *Forest use in at least 80% of the forest area:* 4.

9
PRIORITY AREAS FOR NEW ECONOMIC OPPORTUNITIES*

Development policies for the Brazilian Amazon have always been based on subsidies, tax incentives and other benefits for entrepreneurs disposed to operate in the region. This model has given rise to grave distortions in the economic, social, political and environmental fields and has led to agricultural, mining and infrastructural enterprises that are incompatible with the socio-environmental characteristics of the region.

From an economic point of view, the substitution of 464 tons of biomass and the hundreds of plant and animal species present in a hectare of native forest by pasture that generates 11 tons of biomass (Fearnside 1997) and involves only two species – cows and grass – does not make much sense when the possibilities of generating income from managed forests are properly analyzed. In addition, intensive resource use practices, such as diversified agriculture, permit higher levels of return than extensive production systems (Almeida and Uhl 1998). In social terms, a large landholding, whether it is a ranch or not, creates far fewer employment opportunities than a small property with more intensive use of means of production (Almeida and Uhl 1998). From an environmental perspective, the numbers relating to the loss of biodiversity speak for themselves.

The distortions caused by the excess of incentives and their misuse have ended up encouraging the adoption of a productive model for Amazonia that is barely sustainable, as well as being socially unjust and environmentally destructive.

Local, national and international pressure for the sustainable use of Amazonian natural resources has however grown steadily over recent years. This has led public bodies to increase monitoring. Fines, or the prospect of receiving them, have increased the risk for those enterprises that fail to comply with environmental protection legislation. To a certain extent, this has encouraged those who comply with the current rules of the game and acted as a disincentive to illegal exploitation. Much remains to be done, particularly as regards monitoring, but acting illegally in Amazonia is beginning to be expensive.

On the other hand, a number of financial institutions and investors in general are beginning to organize themselves to offer financial resources for investments in Amazonia, provided these are sustainable and involve conservation of the environment. Resources from private funds and international donations from governments, foundations and large non-governmental organizations are starting to acquire importance in the region. In addition, federal agencies such as BNDES and the Banco da Amazônia are now much more rigorous in their prior assessment of the social and environmental impacts of the financing they give.

In this way, we can see that the basic ingredients of laws, policies, financial resources, and, in particular, the market are slowly moving towards supporting the sustainable use of forests, rather than predatory behavior.

In order that this favorable scenario can lead to a new cycle of economic development in Amazonia however, there is a need to adopt a set of measures that include, amongst other things: improving the capacity of organizations operating in the region to access financial resources by preparing sound projects, carrying out market research, and adopting appropriate financial and accounting procedures; training for cooperatives, small individual producers and extractive workers in business management, including familiarity with accounting, payment of taxes, programming investments, efficient distribution of dividends, improvement in product quality, and the search for good suppliers and distributors; training of local leaders who can exercise a positive influence on the direction of state investments, through an economic and social cost-benefit analysis of infrastructural investments and analysis of alternative models that are better suited to regional realities; promotion of commercial partnerships between productive initiatives in the countryside and distribution companies and/or consumers of their products, such as the creation of investment funds for joint enterprises involving producers and intermediaries or programs for producer groups that clarify the workings of the market; and support to banks and financial institutions for the adaptation of their lines of credit to the realities facing enterprises in Amazonia.

TABLE 9 - PRIORITY AREAS FOR NEW ECONOMIC OPPORTUNITIES DIAGNOSTIC ELEMENTS THAT SCORE HIGHEST		
Diagnostic elements	Number of areas	%[1]
Capacity for income generation	18	23.7
Improvement of income distribution	33	43.4
Environmental impact	0	–
Impact on traditional populations	13	17.1
Favorable local capacity for the development of the activity	50	65.8
Diversification and the integrated use of different resources	46	60.5
Level of infrastructural needs	2	2.6

1. Of the total proposed areas (76).

---

* Text drawn in part from 'Business opportunities in Amazonia: sustainable alternatives' by André Guimarães, the full version of which can be found on page 345 of this book.

During the Macapá Workshop, 76 priority areas for new economic opportunities in Amazonia were identified, addressing extractive activities, the breeding of wild animals, handicrafts, forest management, small scale production, fishing, reforestation, and tourism (see the map on page 448 and the listing).

Of these, 50 (65.8%) already show a highly favorable local capacity for the development of the activity, 46 (60.5%) have a high capacity for diversification and the integrated use of different resources, and only 2 (2.6%) show a high level of infrastructural needs (Table 9).

OE 001 - Upper Juruá Extractive Reserve - PRIORITY LEVEL: ? • LOCATION: *State:* Acre • *Main municipality:* Marechal Thaumaturgo • *Municipalities covered:* 1 • VEGETATION TYPES: Ab, Da, Db • COMMENTS: Prior mapping carried out for the whole reserve, identifying suitable natural resources. Presence of communities organized in associations. Resolution of issues relating to land ownership.

DIAGNOSTIC ELEMENTS: *Capacity for income generation:* 4 • *Improvement of income distribution:* 5 • *Environmental impact:* 4 • *Impact on traditional populations:* 4 • *Local capacity for development of the activity:* 5 • *Diversification and integrated resource use:* 5 • *Level of infrastructural needs:* 1 • ACTION RECOMMENDED: *Infrastructure:* 4 • *Capacity building/training:* 5 • *Economic instruments:* 5 • *Marketing (commercial, certification, added product value):* 5 • *Research/product development:* 4.

OE 002 - Chico Mendes Extractive Reserve - PRIORITY LEVEL: ? • LOCATION: *State:* Acre • *Main municipality:* Xapuri • *Municipalities covered:* 6 • VEGETATION TYPES: AA, Ab, Da, Db • COMMENTS: Prior mapping carried out for the whole reserve, identifying suitable natural resources. Presence of communities organized in associations. Resolution of issues relating to land ownership.

DIAGNOSTIC ELEMENTS: *Capacity for income generation:* 4 • *Improvement of income distribution:* 5 • *Environmental impact:* 4 • *Impact on traditional populations:* 4 • *Local capacity for development of the activity:* 5 • *Diversification and integrated resource use:* 5 • *Level of infrastructural needs:* 3 • ACTION RECOMMENDED: *Infrastructure:* 4 • *Capacity building/training:* 5 • *Economic instruments:* 5 • *Marketing (commercial, certification, added product value):* 5 • *Research/product development:* 4.

OE 003 - Middle Juruá Extractive Reserve - PRIORITY LEVEL: ? • LOCATION: *State:* Amazonas • *Main municipality:* Caruari • *Municipalities covered:* 1 • VEGETATION TYPES: Ab, Da, Db • COMMENTS: Prior mapping carried out for the whole reserve, identifying suitable natural resources. Presence of communities organized in associations. Resolution of issues relating to land ownership.

DIAGNOSTIC ELEMENTS: *Capacity for income generation:* 4 • *Improvement of income distribution:* 5 • *Environmental impact:* 4 • *Impact on traditional populations:* 4 • *Diversification and integrated resource use:* 5 • *Level of infrastructural needs:* 1 • ACTION RECOMMENDED: *Infrastructure:* 4 • *Capacity building/training:* 5 • *Economic instruments:* 5 • *Marketing (commercial, certification, added product value):* 5 • *Research/product development:* 4.

OE 004 - Rio Liberdade Extractive Reserve - PRIORITY LEVEL: ? • LOCATION: *State:* Acre/Amazonas • *Main municipality:* Tarauacá • *Municipalities covered:* 4 • VEGETATION TYPES: Ab, Da, Db • COMMENTS: Prior mapping carried out for the whole reserve, identifying suitable natural resources. Presence of communities organized in associations. Resolution of issues relating to land ownership.

DIAGNOSTIC ELEMENTS: *Capacity for income generation:* 4 • *Improvement of income distribution:* 5 • *Environmental impact:* 4 • *Impact on traditional populations:* 4 • *Local capacity for development of the activity:* 5 • *Diversification and integrated resource use:* 5 • *Level of infrastructural needs:* 1 • ACTION RECOMMENDED: *Infrastructure:* 4 • *Capacity building/training:* 5 • *Economic instruments:* 5 • *Marketing (commercial, certification, added product value):* 5 • *Research/product development:* 4.

OE 005 - Rio Ouro Preto Extractive Reserve - PRIORITY LEVEL: ? • LOCATION: *State:* Rondônia • *Main municipality:* Guajará-Mirim • *Municipalities covered:* 2 • VEGETATION TYPES: Ab, As, Da, Sd, SO • COMMENTS: Prior mapping carried out for the whole reserve, identifying suitable natural resources. Presence of communities organized in associations. Resolution of issues relating to land ownership.

DIAGNOSTIC ELEMENTS: *Capacity for income generation:* 4 • *Improvement of income distribution:* 5 • *Environmental impact:* 4 • *Impact on traditional populations:* 4 • *Local capacity for development of the activity:* 4 • *Diversification and integrated resource use:* 5 • *Level of infrastructural needs:* 2 • ACTION RECOMMENDED: *Infrastructure:* 4 • *Capacity building/training:* 5 • *Economic instruments:* 5 • *Marketing (commercial, certification, added product value):* 5 • *Research/product development:* 4.

OE 006 - Rio Cautário Extractive Reserve - PRIORITY LEVEL: ? • LOCATION: *State:* Rondônia • *Main municipality:* Costa Marques • *Municipalities covered:* 2 • VEGETATION TYPES: Ab, As, Da • COMMENTS: Prior mapping carried out for the whole reserve, identifying suitable natural resources. Presence of communities organized in associations. Resolution of issues relating to land ownership.

DIAGNOSTIC ELEMENTS: *Capacity for income generation:* 4 • *Improvement of income distribution:* 5 • *Environmental impact:* 4 • *Impact on traditional populations:* 4 • *Local capacity for development of the activity:* 4 • *Diversification and integrated resource use:* 5 • *Level of infrastructural needs:* 2 • ACTION RECOMMENDED: *Infrastructure:* 4 • *Capacity building/training:* 5 • *Economic instruments:* 5 • *Marketing (commercial, certification, added product value):* 5 • *Research/product development:* 4.

OE 007 - Pedras Negras Extractive Reserve - PRIORITY LEVEL: ? • LOCATION: *State:* Rondônia • *Main municipality:* São Francisco do Guaporé • *Municipalities covered:* 2 • VEGETATION TYPES: Ab, Da, Pa, Sa • COMMENTS: Prior mapping carried out for the whole reserve, identifying suitable natural resources. Presence of communities organized in associations. Resolution of issues relating to land ownership.

DIAGNOSTIC ELEMENTS: *Capacity for income generation:* 4 • *Improvement of income distribution:* 5 • *Environmental impact:* 4 • *Impact on traditional populations:* 4 • *Local capacity for development of the activity:* 4 • *Diversification and integrated resource use:* 5 • *Level of infrastructural needs:* 2 • ACTION RECOMMENDED: *Infrastructure:* 4 • *Capacity building/training:* 5 • *Economic instruments:* 5 • *Marketing (commercial, certification, added product value):* 5 • *Research/product development:* 4.

OE 008 - Rio Jaci-Paraná Extractive Reserve - PRIORITY LEVEL: ? • LOCATION: *State:* Rondônia • *Main municipality:* Porto Velho • *Municipalities covered:* 3 • VEGETATION TYPES: As • COMMENTS: Prior mapping carried out for the whole reserve, identifying suitable natural resources. Presence of communities organized in associations. Resolution of issues relating to land ownership.

DIAGNOSTIC ELEMENTS: *Capacity for income generation:* 4 • *Improvement of income distribution:* 5 • *Environmental impact:* 4 • *Impact on traditional populations:* 4 • *Local capacity for development of the activity:* 4 • *Diversification and integrated resource use:* 5 • *Level of infrastructural needs:* 2 • ACTION RECOMMENDED: *Infrastructure:* 4 • *Capacity building/training:* 5 • *Economic instruments:* 5 • *Marketing (commercial, certification, added product value):* 5 • *Research/product development:* 4.

OE 009 - Guariba-Roosevelt Extractive Reserve - PRIORITY LEVEL: ? • LOCATION: *State:* Mato Grosso • *Main municipality:* Aripuanã • *Municipalities covered:* 1 • VEGETATION TYPES: As, Ds • COMMENTS: Prior mapping carried out for the whole reserve, identifying suitable natural resources. Presence of communities organized in associations. Resolution of issues relating to land ownership.

DIAGNOSTIC ELEMENTS: *Capacity for income generation:* 4 • *Improvement of income distribution:* 5 • *Environmental impact:* 4 • *Impact on traditional populations:* 4 • *Local capacity for development of the activity:* 4 • *Diversification and integrated resource use:* 5 • *Level of infrastructural needs:* 1 • ACTION RECOMMENDED: *Infrastructure:* 4 • *Capacity building/training:* 5 • *Economic instruments:* 5 • *Marketing (commercial, certification, added product value):* 5 • *Research/product development:* 4.

OE 010 - Tapajós-Arapiuns Extractive Reserve - PRIORITY LEVEL: ? • LOCATION: *State:* Pará • *Main municipality:* Santarém • *Municipalities covered:* 2 • VEGETATION TYPES: Db, SO • COMMENTS: Prior mapping carried out for the whole reserve, identifying suitable natural resources. Presence of communities organized in associations. Resolution of issues relating to land ownership.

DIAGNOSTIC ELEMENTS: *Capacity for income generation:* 4 • *Improvement of income distribution:* 5 • *Environmental impact:* 4 • *Impact on traditional populations:* 4 • *Local capacity for development of the activity:* 4 • *Diversification and integrated resource use:* 5 • *Level of infrastructural needs:* 2 • ACTION RECOMMENDED: *Infrastructure:* 4 • *Capacity building/training:* 5 • *Economic instruments:* 5 •

Marketing (commercial, certification, added product value): 5 • *Research/product development:* 4.

OE 011 - Rio Iratapuru Sustainable Development Reserve - PRIORITY LEVEL: ? • LOCATION: *State:* Amapá • *Main municipality:* Vitória do Jari • *Municipalities covered:* 3 • VEGETATION TYPES: Da, Ds • COMMENTS: Prior mapping carried out for the whole reserve, identifying suitable natural resources. Presence of communities organized in associations. Resolution of issues relating to land ownership.

> DIAGNOSTIC ELEMENTS: *Capacity for income generation:* 4 • *Improvement of income distribution:* 5 • *Environmental impact:* 4 • *Impact on traditional populations:* 4 • *Local capacity for development of the activity:* 5 • *Diversification and integrated resource use:* 5 • *Level of infrastructural needs:* 3 • ACTION RECOMMENDED: *Infrastructure:* 4 • *Capacity building/training:* 5 • *Economic instruments:* 5 • *Marketing (commercial, certification, added product value):* 5 • *Research/product development:* 4.

OE 012 - Cajari Extractive Reserve - PRIORITY LEVEL: ? • LOCATION: *State:* Amapá • *Main municipality:* Mazagão • *Municipalities covered:* 3 • VEGETATION TYPES: Da, Db, Ds, Pa, SO • COMMENTS: Prior mapping carried out for the whole reserve, identifying suitable natural resources. Presence of communities organized in associations. Resolution of issues relating to land ownership.

> DIAGNOSTIC ELEMENTS: *Capacity for income generation:* 4 • *Improvement of income distribution:* 5 • *Environmental impact:* 4 • *Impact on traditional populations:* 4 • *Local capacity for development of the activity:* 5 • *Diversification and integrated resource use:* 5 • *Level of infrastructural needs:* 3 • ACTION RECOMMENDED: *Infrastructure:* 4 • *Capacity building/training:* 5 • *Economic instruments:* 5 • *Marketing (commercial, certification, added product value):* 5 • *Research/product development:* 4.

OE 013 - Sucuriju Marine Extractive Reserve - PRIORITY LEVEL: ? • LOCATION: *State:* Amapá • *Main municipality:* Amapá • *Municipalities covered:* 1 • VEGETATION TYPES: Pa, Pf • COMMENTS: Prior mapping carried out for the whole reserve, identifying suitable natural resources. Presence of communities organized in associations. Resolution of issues relating to land ownership.

> DIAGNOSTIC ELEMENTS: *Capacity for income generation:* 4 • *Improvement of income distribution:* 5 • *Environmental impact:* 4 • *Impact on traditional populations:* 4 • *Local capacity for development of the activity:* 5 • *Diversification and integrated resource use:* 5 • *Level of infrastructural needs:* 1 • ACTION RECOMMENDED: *Infrastructure:* 4 • *Capacity building/training:* 5 • *Economic instruments:* 5 • *Marketing (commercial, certification, added product value):* 5 • *Research/product development:* 4.

OE 014 - Maracá region - PRIORITY LEVEL: ? • LOCATION: *State:* Amapá • *Main municipality:* Mazagão • *Municipalities covered:* 3 • VEGETATION TYPES: AA, Da, Db, Ds, Pa, SO, Sp • COMMENTS: Prior mapping carried out for the whole reserve, identifying suitable natural resources. Presence of communities organized in associations. Resolution of issues relating to land ownership.

> DIAGNOSTIC ELEMENTS: *Capacity for income generation:* 4 • *Improvement of income distribution:* 5 • *Environmental impact:* 4 • *Impact on traditional populations:* 4 • *Local capacity for development of the activity:* 5 • *Diversification and integrated resource use:* 5 • *Level of infrastructural needs:* 1 • ACTION RECOMMENDED: *Infrastructure:* 4 • *Capacity building/training:* 5 • *Economic instruments:* 5 • *Marketing (commercial, certification, added product value):* 5 • *Research/product development:* 4.

OE 015 - Pedra Branca do Amapari region - PRIORITY LEVEL: ? • LOCATION: *State:* Amapá • *Main municipality:* Serra do Navio • *Municipalities covered:* 2 • VEGETATION TYPES: Ds • COMMENTS: Prior mapping carried out for the whole reserve, identifying suitable natural resources. Presence of communities organized in associations. Resolution of issues relating to land ownership.

> DIAGNOSTIC ELEMENTS: *Capacity for income generation:* 4 • *Improvement of income distribution:* 5 • *Environmental impact:* 4 • *Impact on traditional populations:* 4 • *Local capacity for development of the activity:* 5 • *Diversification and integrated resource use:* 5 • *Level of infrastructural needs:* 3 • ACTION RECOMMENDED: *Infrastructure:* 4 • *Capacity building/training:* 5 • *Economic instruments:* 5 • *Marketing (commercial, certification, added product value):* 5 • *Research/product development:* 4.

OE 016 - Amazon estuary floodplain region - PRIORITY LEVEL: ? • LOCATION: *State:* Amapá/Pará • *Main municipality:* Breves • *Municipalities covered:* 20 • VEGETATION TYPES: AA, Da, Db, Pa, Pf, SO, Sp • COMMENTS: Prior mapping carried out for the whole reserve, identifying suitable natural resources. Presence of communities organized in associations. Resolution of issues relating to land ownership.

> DIAGNOSTIC ELEMENTS: *Capacity for income generation:* 4 • *Improvement of income distribution:* 5 • *Environmental impact:* 4 • *Impact on traditional populations:* 4 • *Local capacity for development of the activity:* 5 • *Diversification and integrated resource use:* 5 • *Level of infrastructural needs:* 2 • ACTION RECOMMENDED: *Infrastructure:* 4 • *Capacity building/training:* 5 • *Economic instruments:* 5 • *Marketing (commercial, certification, added product value):* 5 • *Research/product development:* 4.

OE 017 - Arc of Deforestation - PRIORITY LEVEL: ? • LOCATION: *State:* Acre/Amazonas/Goiás/Maranhão/Mato Grosso/Pará/Rondônia/Tocantins • *Main municipality:* Guajará-Mirim • *Municipalities covered:* 415 • VEGETATION TYPES: AA, Ab, As, Cs, Da, Db, Dm, Ds, Fa, Fb, Fs, ON, Pa, Pf, Sa, Sd, Sg • COMMENTS: Degraded areas, importance for protection of areas still conserved (avoidance of fragmentation of continuous areas).

> DIAGNOSTIC ELEMENTS: *Capacity for income generation:* 4 • *Improvement of income distribution:* 2 • *Environmental impact:* 4 • *Impact on traditional populations:* 4 • *Local capacity for development of the activity:* 4 • *Diversification and integrated resource use:* 4 • *Level of infrastructural needs:* 3 • ACTION RECOMMENDED: *Infrastructure:* 2 • *Capacity building/training:* 5 • *Economic instruments:* 5 • *Marketing (commercial, certification, added product value):* 3 • *Research/product development:* 4.

OE 018 - Macauã National Forest - PRIORITY LEVEL: ? • LOCATION: *State:* Acre • *Main municipality:* Sena Madureira • *Municipalities covered:* 1 • VEGETATION TYPES: Ab, Da • COMMENTS: Legal potential (tendering).

> DIAGNOSTIC ELEMENTS: *Capacity for income generation:* 4 • *Improvement of income distribution:* 2 • *Environmental impact:* 3 • *Impact on traditional populations:* 2 • *Local capacity for development of the activity:* 4 • *Diversification and integrated resource use:* 4 • *Level of infrastructural needs:* 3 • ACTION RECOMMENDED: *Infrastructure:* 3 • *Capacity building/training:* 4 • *Economic instruments:* 4 • *Marketing (commercial, certification, added product value):* 5 • *Research/product development:* 4.

OE 019 - Mapiá-Inauini and Purus National Forests - PRIORITY LEVEL: ? • LOCATION: *State:* Amazonas • *Main municipality:* Boca do Acre • *Municipalities covered:* 2 • VEGETATION TYPES: Ab, Da, Db • COMMENTS: Legal potential (tendering).

> DIAGNOSTIC ELEMENTS: *Capacity for income generation:* 4 • *Improvement of income distribution:* 2 • *Environmental impact:* 3 • *Impact on traditional populations:* 2 • *Local capacity for development of the activity:* 3 • *Diversification and integrated resource use:* 4 • *Level of infrastructural needs:* 2 • ACTION RECOMMENDED: *Infrastructure:* 3 • *Capacity building/training:* 4 • *Economic instruments:* 4 • *Marketing (commercial, certification, added product value):* 5 • *Research/product development:* 4.

OE 020 - Tefé National Forest - PRIORITY LEVEL: ? • LOCATION: *State:* Amazonas • *Main municipality:* Tefé • *Municipalities covered:* 4 • VEGETATION TYPES: Da, Db • COMMENTS: Public tendering.

> DIAGNOSTIC ELEMENTS: *Capacity for income generation:* 4 • *Improvement of income distribution:* 2 • *Environmental impact:* 3 • *Impact on traditional populations:* 2 • *Local capacity for development of the activity:* 3 • *Diversification and integrated resource use:* 4 • *Level of infrastructural needs:* 4 • ACTION RECOMMENDED: *Infrastructure:* 3 • *Capacity building/training:* 4 • *Economic instruments:* 4 • *Marketing (commercial, certification, added product value):* 5 • *Research/product development:* 4.

OE 021 - Bom Futuro National Forest - PRIORITY LEVEL: ? • LOCATION: *State:* Rondônia • *Main municipality:* Porto Velho • *Municipalities covered:* 2 • VEGETATION TYPES: As, Ds • COMMENTS: Public tendering.

DIAGNOSTIC ELEMENTS: *Capacity for income generation:* 4 • *Improvement of income distribution:* 2 • *Environmental impact:* 3 • *Impact on traditional populations:* 2 • *Local capacity for development of the activity:* 5 • *Diversification and integrated resource use:* 4 • *Level of infrastructural needs:* 4 • ACTION RECOMMENDED: *Infrastructure:* 3 • *Capacity building/training:* 4 • *Economic instruments:* 4 • *Marketing (commercial, certification, added product value):* 5 • *Research/product development:* 4.

OE 022 - Jamari National Forest - PRIORITY LEVEL: ? • LOCATION: *State:* Rondônia • *Main municipality:* Jamari • *Municipalities covered:* 2 • VEGETATION TYPES: Ab, As • COMMENTS: Public tendering.

DIAGNOSTIC ELEMENTS: *Capacity for income generation:* 4 • *Improvement of income distribution:* 2 • *Environmental impact:* 3 • *Impact on traditional populations:* 2 • *Local capacity for development of the activity:* 5 • *Diversification and integrated resource use:* 4 • *Level of infrastructural needs:* 4 • ACTION RECOMMENDED: *Infrastructure:* 3 • *Capacity building/training:* 4 • *Economic instruments:* 4 • *Marketing (commercial, certification, added product value):* 5 • *Research/product development:* 4.

OE 023 - Humaitá National Forest - PRIORITY LEVEL: ? • LOCATION: *State:* Amazonas/Rondônia • *Main municipality:* Humaitá • *Municipalities covered:* 3 • VEGETATION TYPES: As, Db, Pa, SO, Sp • COMMENTS: Public tendering.

DIAGNOSTIC ELEMENTS: *Capacity for income generation:* 4 • *Improvement of income distribution:* 2 • *Environmental impact:* 3 • *Impact on traditional populations:* 2 • *Local capacity for development of the activity:* 4 • *Diversification and integrated resource use:* 4 • *Level of infrastructural needs:* 2 • ACTION RECOMMENDED: *Infrastructure:* 3 • *Capacity building/training:* 4 • *Economic instruments:* 4 • *Marketing (commercial, certification, added product value):* 5 • *Research/product development:* 4.

OE 024 - Saracataquera National Forest - PRIORITY LEVEL: ? • LOCATION: *State:* Pará • *Main municipality:* Oriximiná • *Municipalities covered:* 3 • VEGETATION TYPES: AA, Db, Pa • COMMENTS: Public tendering.

DIAGNOSTIC ELEMENTS: *Capacity for income generation:* 4 • *Improvement of income distribution:* 2 • *Environmental impact:* 3 • *Impact on traditional populations:* 2 • *Local capacity for development of the activity:* 5 • *Diversification and integrated resource use:* 4 • *Level of infrastructural needs:* 3 • ACTION RECOMMENDED: *Infrastructure:* 3 • *Capacity building/training:* 4 • *Economic instruments:* 4 • *Marketing (commercial, certification, added product value):* 5 • *Research/product development:* 4.

OE 025 - Amapá National Forest - PRIORITY LEVEL: ? • LOCATION: *State:* Amapá • *Main municipality:* Pracuúba • *Municipalities covered:* 5 • VEGETATION TYPES: Ds • COMMENTS: Public tendering.

DIAGNOSTIC ELEMENTS: *Capacity for income generation:* 4 • *Improvement of income distribution:* 2 • *Environmental impact:* 3 • *Impact on traditional populations:* 2 • *Local capacity for development of the activity:* 4 • *Diversification and integrated resource use:* 4 • *Level of infrastructural needs:* 4 • ACTION RECOMMENDED: *Infrastructure:* 3 • *Capacity building/training:* 4 • *Economic instruments:* 4 • *Marketing (commercial, certification, added product value):* 5 • *Research/product development:* 4.

OE 026 - Cuxiuanã National Forest - PRIORITY LEVEL: ? • LOCATION: *State:* Pará • *Main municipality:* Portel • *Municipalities covered:* 2 • VEGETATION TYPES: Db, Pa • COMMENTS: Public tendering.

DIAGNOSTIC ELEMENTS: *Capacity for income generation:* 4 • *Improvement of income distribution:* 2 • *Environmental impact:* 3 • *Impact on traditional populations:* 2 • *Local capacity for development of the activity:* 5 • *Diversification and integrated resource use:* 4 • *Level of infrastructural needs:* 4 • ACTION RECOMMENDED: *Infrastructure:* 3 • *Capacity building/training:* 4 • *Economic instruments:* 4 • *Marketing (commercial, certification, added product value):* 5 • *Research/product development:* 4.

OE 027 - Tapajós National Forest - PRIORITY LEVEL: ? • LOCATION: *State:* Pará • *Main municipality:* Santarém • *Municipalities covered:* 5 • VEGETATION TYPES: AA, Db, Ds • COMMENTS: Public tendering.

DIAGNOSTIC ELEMENTS: *Capacity for income generation:* 4 • *Improvement of income distribution:* 2 • *Environmental impact:* 3 • *Impact on traditional populations:* 2 • *Local capacity for development of the activity:* 5 • *Diversification and integrated resource use:* 4 • *Level of infrastructural needs:* 4 • ACTION RECOMMENDED: *Infrastructure:* 3 • *Capacity building/training:* 4 • *Economic instruments:* 4 • *Marketing (commercial, certification, added product value):* 5 • *Research/product development:* 4.

OE 028 - Itaituba National Forest - PRIORITY LEVEL: ? • LOCATION: *State:* Pará • *Main municipality:* Trairão • *Municipalities covered:* 2 • VEGETATION TYPES: As, Ds • COMMENTS: Public tendering.

DIAGNOSTIC ELEMENTS: *Capacity for income generation:* 4 • *Improvement of income distribution:* 2 • *Environmental impact:* 3 • *Impact on traditional populations:* 2 • *Local capacity for development of the activity:* 5 • *Diversification and integrated resource use:* 4 • *Level of infrastructural needs:* 3 • ACTION RECOMMENDED: *Infrastructure:* 3 • *Capacity building/training:* 4 • *Economic instruments:* 4 • *Marketing (commercial, certification, added product value):* 5 • *Research/product development:* 4.

OE 029 - Altamira National Forest - PRIORITY LEVEL: ? • LOCATION: *State:* Pará • *Main municipality:* Altamira • *Municipalities covered:* 3 • VEGETATION TYPES: As, Ds • COMMENTS: Public tendering.

DIAGNOSTIC ELEMENTS: *Capacity for income generation:* 4 • *Improvement of income distribution:* 2 • *Environmental impact:* 3 • *Impact on traditional populations:* 2 • *Local capacity for development of the activity:* 5 • *Diversification and integrated resource use:* 4 • *Level of infrastructural needs:* 2 • ACTION RECOMMENDED: *Infrastructure:* 3 • *Capacity building/training:* 4 • *Economic instruments:* 4 • *Marketing (commercial, certification, added product value):* 5 • *Research/product development:* 4.

OE 030 - Tapirapé-Aquiri and Carajás National Forests and Xikrin do Cateté Indigenous Land - PRIORITY LEVEL: ? • LOCATION: *State:* Pará • *Main municipality:* Parauapebas • *Municipalities covered:* 5 • VEGETATION TYPES: AA, As, Dm, Ds.

DIAGNOSTIC ELEMENTS: *Capacity for income generation:* 4 • *Improvement of income distribution:* 2 • *Environmental impact:* 3 • *Impact on traditional populations:* 2 • *Local capacity for development of the activity:* 5 • *Diversification and integrated resource use:* 4 • *Level of infrastructural needs:* 3 • ACTION RECOMMENDED: *Capacity building/training:* 3 • *Economic instruments:* 4 • *Marketing (commercial, certification, added product value):* 4 • *Research/product development:* 5.

OE 031 - Arc of Deforestation - PRIORITY LEVEL: ? • LOCATION: *State:* Several • *Main municipality:* Guajará-Mirim • *Municipalities covered:* 415 • VEGETATION TYPES: AA, Ab, As, Cs, Da, Db, Dm, Ds, Fa, Fb, Fs, ON, Pa, Pf, Sa, Sd, Sg • COMMENTS: Forest remnants with potential for logging about to be discovered.

DIAGNOSTIC ELEMENTS: *Capacity for income generation:* 4 • *Improvement of income distribution:* 2 • *Environmental impact:* 3 • *Impact on traditional populations:* 2 • *Local capacity for development of the activity:* 5 • *Diversification and integrated resource use:* 4 • *Level of infrastructural needs:* 3 • ACTION RECOMMENDED: *Infrastructure:* 3 • *Capacity building/training:* 4 • *Economic instruments:* 4 • *Marketing (commercial, certification, added product value):* 5 • *Research/product development:* 4.

OE 032 - Itacoatiara - PRIORITY LEVEL: ? • LOCATION: *State:* Amazonas • *Main municipality:* Autazes • *Municipalities covered:* 4 • VEGETATION TYPES: AA, Da, Db, Pa • COMMENTS: Important timber processing center.

DIAGNOSTIC ELEMENTS: *Capacity for income generation:* 4 • *Improvement of income distribution:* 2 • *Environmental impact:* 3 • *Impact on traditional populations:* 2 • *Local capacity for development of the activity:* 5 • *Diversification and integrated resource use:* 4 • *Level of infrastructural needs:* 4 • ACTION RECOMMENDED: *Infrastructure:* 3 • *Capacity building/training:* 4 • *Economic instruments:* 4 • *Marketing (commercial, certification, added product value):* 5 • *Research/product development:* 4.

OE 033 - Southern Acre - PRIORITY LEVEL: ? • LOCATION: *State:* Acre/Amazonas • *Main municipality:* Rio Branco • *Municipalities covered:* 13 • VEGETATION TYPES: AA, Ab, Da, Db • COMMENTS: Presence of small producers. Highway for product export. Proximity of large centers.

DIAGNOSTIC ELEMENTS: *Capacity for income generation:* 3 • *Improvement of income distribution:* 4 • *Environmental impact:* 3 • *Impact on traditional populations:* 2 • *Local capacity for development of the activity:* 4 • *Diversification and integrated resource use:* 4 • *Level of infrastructural needs:* 3 • ACTION RECOMMENDED: *Infrastructure:* 3 • *Capacity building/training:* 5 • *Economic instruments:* 5 • *Marketing (commercial, certification, added product value):* 5 • *Research/product development:* 4.

OE 034 - Rondônia - PRIORITY LEVEL: ? • LOCATION: *State:* Amazonas/Mato Grosso/Rondônia • *Main municipality:* Porto Velho • *Municipalities covered:* 52 • VEGETATION TYPES: AA, Ab, As, Da, Db, Ds, Fa, Fb, Fs, ON, Pa, Sa, SN, SO, Sp • COMMENTS: Access to markets. Good infrastructure. Presence of small producers. Tradition of small farms (migrants from southern Brazil).

DIAGNOSTIC ELEMENTS: *Capacity for income generation:* 3 • *Improvement of income distribution:* 4 • *Environmental impact:* 3 • *Impact on traditional populations:* 3 • *Local capacity for development of the activity:* 5 • *Diversification and integrated resource use:* 4 • *Level of infrastructural needs:* 4 • ACTION RECOMMENDED: *Infrastructure:* 3 • *Capacity building/training:* 5 • *Economic instruments:* 5 • *Marketing (commercial, certification, added product value):* 5 • *Research/product development:* 4.

OE 035 - Eastern Xingu - PRIORITY LEVEL: ? • LOCATION: *State:* Mato Grosso/Pará • *Main municipality:* São Félix do Araguaia • *Municipalities covered:* 13 • VEGETATION TYPES: AA, As, ON, Pa, Sa, SN, SO, Sp • COMMENTS: Presence of settlements. Concentration of small properties (relative).

DIAGNOSTIC ELEMENTS: *Capacity for income generation:* 3 • *Improvement of income distribution:* 4 • *Environmental impact:* 3 • *Impact on traditional populations:* 3 • *Local capacity for development of the activity:* 4 • *Diversification and integrated resource use:* 4 • *Level of infrastructural needs:* 3 • ACTION RECOMMENDED: *Infrastructure:* 3 • *Capacity building/training:* 5 • *Economic instruments:* 5 • *Marketing (commercial, certification, added product value):* 5 • *Research/product development:* 4.

OE 036 - Marabá - PRIORITY LEVEL: ? • LOCATION: *State:* Maranhão/Pará/Rondônia/Tocantins • *Main municipality:* Marabá • *Municipalities covered:* 58 • VEGETATION TYPES: AA, As, Da, Db, Ds, Fa, Sa, Sd, Sg, SN • COMMENTS: High concentration of small producers. Settlements. Infrastructure. Market.

DIAGNOSTIC ELEMENTS: *Capacity for income generation:* 3 • *Improvement of income distribution:* 4 • *Environmental impact:* 3 • *Impact on traditional populations:* 3 • *Local capacity for development of the activity:* 5 • *Diversification and integrated resource use:* 4 • *Level of infrastructural needs:* 4 • ACTION RECOMMENDED: *Infrastructure:* 3 • *Capacity building/training:* 5 • *Economic instruments:* 5 • *Marketing (commercial, certification, added product value):* 5 • *Research/product development:* 4.

OE 037 - Transamazonica highway - PRIORITY LEVEL: ? • LOCATION: *State:* Pará • *Main municipality:* Pacajá • *Municipalities covered:* 22 • VEGETATION TYPES: AA, As, Da, Db, Ds, Pa, Sp • COMMENTS: Good land. Settlements.

DIAGNOSTIC ELEMENTS: *Capacity for income generation:* 3 • *Improvement of income distribution:* 4 • *Environmental impact:* 3 • *Impact on traditional populations:* 3 • *Local capacity for development of the activity:* 4 • *Diversification and integrated resource use:* 4 • *Level of infrastructural needs:* 2 • ACTION RECOMMENDED: *Infrastructure:* 3 • *Capacity building/training:* 5 • *Economic instruments:* 5 • *Marketing (commercial, certification, added product value):* 5 • *Research/product development:* 4.

OE 038 - Western Maranhão - PRIORITY LEVEL: ? • LOCATION: *State:* Maranhão/Pará • *Main municipality:* Amarante do Maranhão • *Municipalities covered:* 74 • VEGETATION TYPES: AA, Cs, Db, Pa, Sa, SN • COMMENTS: Settlements. Infrastructure. Market.

DIAGNOSTIC ELEMENTS: *Capacity for income generation:* 3 • *Improvement of income distribution:* 4 • *Environmental impact:* 3 • *Impact on traditional populations:* 3 • *Local capacity for development of the activity:* 4 • *Diversification and integrated resource use:* 4 • *Level of infrastructural needs:* 4 • ACTION RECOMMENDED: *Infrastructure:* 3 • *Capacity building/training:* 5 • *Economic instruments:* 5 • *Marketing (commercial, certification, added product value):* 5 • *Research/product development:* 4.

OE 039 - Bragantina region - PRIORITY LEVEL: ? • LOCATION: *State:* Pará/MA • *Main municipality:* Viseu • *Municipalities covered:* 76 • VEGETATION TYPES: AA, Da, Db, Pf • COMMENTS: Infrastructure. Market. Settlements. Agricultural tradition.

DIAGNOSTIC ELEMENTS: *Capacity for income generation:* 3 • *Improvement of income distribution:* 4 • *Environmental impact:* 3 • *Impact on traditional populations:* 3 • *Local capacity for development of the activity:* 5 • *Diversification and integrated resource use:* 4 • *Level of infrastructural needs:* 4 • ACTION RECOMMENDED: *Infrastructure:* 3 • *Capacity building/training:* 5 • *Economic instruments:* 5 • *Marketing (commercial, certification, added product value):* 5 • *Research/product development:* 4.

OE 040 - BR-156 Highway/Amapá Corridor - PRIORITY LEVEL: ? • LOCATION: *State:* Amapá/Pará • *Main municipality:* Mazagão • *Municipalities covered:* 13 • VEGETATION TYPES: AA, Da, Db, Ds, Pa, SO, Sp • COMMENTS: Settlements. Infrastructure.

DIAGNOSTIC ELEMENTS: *Capacity for income generation:* 3 • *Improvement of income distribution:* 4 • *Environmental impact:* 3 • *Impact on traditional populations:* 3 • *Local capacity for development of the activity:* 4 • *Diversification and integrated resource use:* 4 • *Level of infrastructural needs:* 3 • ACTION RECOMMENDED: *Infrastructure:* 3 • *Capacity building/training:* 5 • *Economic instruments:* 5 • *Marketing (commercial, certification, added product value):* 5 • *Research/product development:* 4.

OE 041 - Cruzeiro do Sul - PRIORITY LEVEL: ? • LOCATION: *State:* Acre/Amazonas • *Main municipality:* Guajará • *Municipalities covered:* 9 • VEGETATION TYPES: Ab, Da, Db • COMMENTS: Natural capacity. Serra do Divisor National Park.

DIAGNOSTIC ELEMENTS: *Capacity for income generation:* 5 • *Improvement of income distribution:* 5 • *Environmental impact:* 3 • *Impact on traditional populations:* 3 • *Local capacity for development of the activity:* 5 • *Diversification and integrated resource use:* 5 • *Level of infrastructural needs:* 2 • ACTION RECOMMENDED: *Infrastructure:* 5 • *Capacity building/training:* 5 • *Economic instruments:* 5 • *Marketing (commercial, certification, added product value):* 5 • *Research/product development:* 3.

OE 042 - São Gabriel da Cachoeira - PRIORITY LEVEL: ? • LOCATION: *State:* Amazonas • *Main municipality:* São Gabriel do Rio Negro • *Municipalities covered:* 2 • VEGETATION TYPES: La, Ld, LO • COMMENTS: Socio-diversity (largest demarcated indigenous land in Brazil). Natural beauty. Energy infrastructure.

DIAGNOSTIC ELEMENTS: *Capacity for income generation:* 5 • *Improvement of income distribution:* 5 • *Environmental impact:* 3 • *Impact on traditional populations:* 3 • *Local capacity for development of the activity:* 5 • *Diversification and integrated resource use:* 5 • *Level of infrastructural needs:* 3

OE 043 - Mamirauá - PRIORITY LEVEL: ? • LOCATION: *State:* Amazonas • *Main municipality:* Maraã • *Municipalities covered:* 8 • VEGETATION TYPES: Da, Db, La, LO • COMMENTS: Scientific ecotourism.

DIAGNOSTIC ELEMENTS: *Capacity for income generation:* 5 • *Improvement of income distribution:* 5 • *Environmental impact:* 3 • *Impact on traditional populations:* 3 • *Local capacity for development of the activity:* 4 • *Diversification and integrated resource use:* 5 • *Level of infrastructural needs:* 3.

OE 044 - Middle and lower Rio Negro - PRIORITY LEVEL: ? • LOCATION: *State:* Amazonas/Roraima • *Main municipality:* Barcelos • *Municipalities covered:* 19 • VEGETATION TYPES: AA, Ab, Da, Db, Ds, La, Ld, Lg, LO, Pa • COMMENTS: Sport fishing. Ornamental fishing. Ecotourism.

DIAGNOSTIC ELEMENTS: *Capacity for income generation:* 5 • *Improvement of income distribution:* 5 • *Environmental impact:* 3 • *Impact on traditional populations:* 3 • *Local capacity for development of the activity:* 5 • *Diversification and integrated resource use:* 5 • *Level of infrastructural needs:* 1.

OE 045 - Boa Vista - Cotingo River - PRIORITY LEVEL: ? • LOCATION: *State:* Roraima • *Main municipality:* Uiramutã • *Municipalities covered:* 10 • VEGETATION TYPES: As, Ds, Fs, ON, Sg, SN, SO, Sp • COMMENTS: Monte Roraima National Park. Bio-tourism.

DIAGNOSTIC ELEMENTS: *Capacity for income generation:* 5 • *Improvement of income distribution:* 5 • *Environmental impact:* 3 • *Impact on traditional populations:* 3 • *Local capacity for development of the activity:* 5 • *Diversification and integrated resource use:* 5 • *Level of infrastructural needs:* 3.

OE 046 - Santarém - Mouth of the Tapajós - PRIORITY LEVEL: ? • LOCATION: *State:* Amazonas/Pará • *Main municipality:* Santarém • *Municipalities covered:* 16 • VEGETATION TYPES: AA, As, Da, Db, Ds, Pa, SO, Sp • COMMENTS: Natural potential. Tapajós river. Arapiuns. Alter do Chão. Rapids. Çairé festival. Caves and rock carvings. Sport fishing.

DIAGNOSTIC ELEMENTS: *Capacity for income generation:* 5 • *Improvement of income distribution:* 5 • *Environmental impact:* 3 • *Impact on traditional populations:* 3 • *Local capacity for development of the activity:* 4 • *Diversification and integrated resource use:* 5 • *Level of infrastructural needs:* 4.

OE 047 - Amapá coast - PRIORITY LEVEL: ? • LOCATION: *State:* Amapá/Pará • *Main municipality:* Amapá • *Municipalities covered:* 18 • VEGETATION TYPES: AA, Da, Db, Ds, Pa, Pf, Sa, SO, Sp • COMMENTS: Natural features. Scenic beauty. Sport fishing. Cultural tourism.

DIAGNOSTIC ELEMENTS: *Capacity for income generation:* 5 • *Improvement of income distribution:* 5 • *Environmental impact:* 3 • *Impact on traditional populations:* 3 • *Local capacity for development of the activity:* 4 • *Diversification and integrated resource use:* 5 • *Level of infrastructural needs:* 2

OE 048 - Belém - Eastern Marajó island - PRIORITY LEVEL: ? • LOCATION: *State:* Pará • *Main municipality:* Soure • *Municipalities covered:* 52 • VEGETATION TYPES: AA, Da, Db, Pa, Pf, Sp • COMMENTS: Natural beauty. Ocean and river beaches. Cultural tourism.

DIAGNOSTIC ELEMENTS: *Capacity for income generation:* 5 • *Improvement of income distribution:* 5 • *Environmental impact:* 3 • *Impact on traditional populations:* 3 • *Local capacity for development of the activity:* 4 • *Diversification and integrated resource use:* 5 • *Level of infrastructural needs:* 3

OE 049 - Pará and Maranhão coast - PRIORITY LEVEL: ? • LOCATION: *State:* Pará/Maranhão • *Main municipality:* Viseu • *Municipalities covered:* 25 • VEGETATION TYPES: AA, Pf • COMMENTS: Beaches. Natural potential.

DIAGNOSTIC ELEMENTS: *Capacity for income generation:* 5 • *Improvement of income distribution:* 5 • *Environmental impact:* 3 • *Impact on traditional populations:* 3 • *Local capacity for development of the activity:* 5 • *Diversification and integrated resource use:* 5 • *Level of infrastructural needs:* 4.

OE 050 - São Luís and Maranhão coast - PRIORITY LEVEL: ? • LOCATION: *State:* Maranhão • *Main municipality:* Alcântara • *Municipalities covered:* 38 • VEGETATION TYPES: AA, Pa, Pf, Sa.

DIAGNOSTIC ELEMENTS: *Capacity for income generation:* 5 • *Improvement of income distribution:* 5 • *Environmental impact:* 3 • *Impact on traditional populations:* 3 • *Local capacity for development of the activity:* 5 • *Diversification and integrated resource use:* 5 • *Level of infrastructural needs:* 4.

OE 051 - Carajás - PRIORITY LEVEL: ? • LOCATION: *State:* Maranhão/Pará • *Main municipality:* Açailândia • *Municipalities covered:* 19 • VEGETATION TYPES: AA, Da, Db • COMMENTS: Educational tourism (mine visits, indigenous community and ecotourism etc.). Infrastructure.

DIAGNOSTIC ELEMENTS: *Capacity for income generation:* 5 • *Improvement of income distribution:* 5 • *Environmental impact:* 3 • *Impact on traditional populations:* 3 • *Local capacity for development of the activity:* 3 • *Diversification and integrated resource use:* 5 • *Level of infrastructural needs:* 1.

OE 052 - Carolina - PRIORITY LEVEL: ? • LOCATION: *State:* Maranhão/Tocantins • *Main municipality:* Carolina • *Municipalities covered:* 34 • VEGETATION TYPES: AA, As, Ds, Sa, Sd, SO, Sp • COMMENTS: Scenic beauty (waterfalls). Socio-diversity. Archaeological site.

DIAGNOSTIC ELEMENTS: *Capacity for income generation:* 5 • *Improvement of income distribution:* 5 • *Environmental impact:* 3 • *Impact on traditional populations:* 3 • *Local capacity for development of the activity:* 5 • *Diversification and integrated resource use:* 5 • *Level of infrastructural needs:* 1.

OE 053 - Ilha do Bananal - Araguaia river - PRIORITY LEVEL: ? • LOCATION: *State:* Goiás/Mato Grosso/Pará/Tocantins • *Main municipality:* Cocalinho • *Municipalities covered:* 37 • VEGETATION TYPES: AA, As, Ds, Fa, ON, Sa, Sg, SN, SO, Sp • COMMENTS: Socio-diversity. Ecotourism. Fishing.

DIAGNOSTIC ELEMENTS: *Capacity for income generation:* 5 • *Improvement of income distribution:* 5 • *Environmental impact:* 3 • *Impact on traditional populations:* 3 • *Local capacity for development of the activity:* 4 • *Diversification and integrated resource use:* 5 • *Level of infrastructural needs:* 3.

OE 054 - Xingu headwaters - PRIORITY LEVEL: ? • LOCATION: *State:* Mato Grosso • *Main municipality:* Paranatinga • *Municipalities covered:* 8 • VEGETATION TYPES: Da, Fa, ON, Pa, Sa, Sd, SN, Sp • COMMENTS: Indigenous people. Cultural festivals. Sport fishing.

DIAGNOSTIC ELEMENTS: *Capacity for income generation:* 5 • *Improvement of income distribution:* 3 • *Environmental impact:* 3 • *Impact on traditional populations:* 5 • *Local capacity for development of the activity:* 5 • *Diversification and integrated resource use:* 5 • *Level of infrastructural needs:* 2.

OE 055 - Cuiabá - Chapada dos Guimarães - PRIORITY LEVEL: ? • LOCATION: *State:* Mato Grosso • *Main municipality:* Chapada dos Guimarães • *Municipalities covered:* 23 • VEGETATION TYPES: AA, Fs, Pa, Sa, Sd, SN, Sp, ST • COMMENTS: Scenic beauty. Infrastructure. Ecotourism.

DIAGNOSTIC ELEMENTS: *Capacity for income generation:* 5 • *Improvement of income distribution:* 5 • *Environmental impact:* 3 • *Impact on traditional populations:* 3 • *Local capacity for development of the activity:* 5 • *Diversification and integrated resource use:* 5 • *Level of infrastructural needs:* 3.

OE 056 - Pantanal Mato-grossense - PRIORITY LEVEL: ? • LOCATION: *State:* Mato Grosso • *Main municipality:* Cáceres • *Municipalities covered:* 15 • VEGETATION TYPES: AA, Cs, Fa, Fs, Sa, Sd, Sg, SN, Sp, ST • COMMENTS: Ecotourism. Fishing. Scenic beauty. Infrastructure.

DIAGNOSTIC ELEMENTS: *Capacity for income generation:* 5 • *Improvement of income distribution:* 5 • *Environmental impact:* 3 • *Impact on traditional populations:* 3 • *Local capacity for development of the activity:* 5 • *Diversification and integrated resource use:* 5 • *Level of infrastructural needs:* 3.

OE 057 - Rio Guaporé Valley - PRIORITY LEVEL: ? • LOCATION: *State:* Rondônia • *Main municipality:* Pimenteiras do Oeste • *Municipalities covered:* 8 • VEGETATION TYPES: AA, Ab, As, Da, Fa, Fb, Fs, ON, Pa, Sa, SN, SO • COMMENTS: Ecotourism. Sport fishing. Scenic beauty.

DIAGNOSTIC ELEMENTS: *Capacity for income generation:* 5 • *Improvement of income distribution:* 5 • *Environmental impact:* 3 • *Impact on traditional populations:* 3 • *Local capacity for development of the activity:* 5 • *Diversification and integrated resource use:* 5 • *Level of infrastructural needs:* 1.

OE 058 - Rio Branco - Chico Mendes Extractive Reserve - PRIORITY LEVEL: ? • LOCATION: *State:* Acre • *Main municipality:* Rio Branco • *Municipalities covered:* 10 • VEGETATION TYPES: AA, Ab, Da, Db • COMMENTS: Cultural tourism.

DIAGNOSTIC ELEMENTS: *Capacity for income generation:* 5 • *Improvement of income distribution:* 5 • *Environmental impact:* 3 • *Impact on traditional populations:* 3 • *Local capacity for development of the activity:* 3 • *Diversification and integrated resource use:* 5 • *Level of infrastructural needs:* 3.

OE 059 - Kampa do Rio Amônea Indigenous Land - PRIORITY LEVEL: ? • LOCATION: *State:* Acre • *Main municipality:* Marechal Thaumaturgo • *Municipalities covered:* 1 • VEGETATION TYPES: Ab, Da • COMMENTS: Indigenous handicrafts.

DIAGNOSTIC ELEMENTS: *Capacity for income generation:* 3 • *Improvement of income distribution:* 4 • *Environmental impact:* 4 • *Impact on traditional populations:* 5 • *Local capacity for development of the activity:* 5 • *Diversification and integrated resource use:* 5 • *Level of infrastructural needs:* 4 • ACTION RECOMMENDED: *Infrastructure:* 3 • *Capacity building/training:* 4 • *Economic instruments:* 5 • *Marketing (commercial, certification, added product value):* 5 • *Research/product development:* 3.

OE 060 - Kaxinauá do Rio Jordão Indigenous Land - PRIORITY LEVEL: ? • LOCATION: *State:* Acre • *Main municipality:* Feijó • *Municipalities* *covered:* 3 • VEGETATION TYPES: Ab, Da, Db • COMMENTS: Indigenous handicrafts.

> DIAGNOSTIC ELEMENTS: *Capacity for income generation:* 3 • *Improvement of income distribution:* 4 • *Environmental impact:* 4 • *Impact on traditional populations:* 5 • *Local capacity for development of the activity:* 5 • *Diversification and integrated resource use:* 5 • *Level of infrastructural needs:* 4 • ACTION RECOMMENDED: *Infrastructure:* 3 • *Capacity building/training:* 4 • *Economic instruments:* 5 • *Marketing (commercial, certification, added product value):* 5 • *Research/product development:* 3.

OE 061 - Panará Indigenous Land - PRIORITY LEVEL: ? • LOCATION: *State:* Mato Grosso/Pará • *Main municipality:* Altamira • *Municipalities covered:* 3 • VEGETATION TYPES: As, Sd, Sg, SN • COMMENTS: Indigenous handicrafts.

> DIAGNOSTIC ELEMENTS: *Capacity for income generation:* 3 • *Improvement of income distribution:* 4 • *Environmental impact:* 4 • *Impact on traditional populations:* 5 • *Local capacity for development of the activity:* 5 • *Diversification and integrated resource use:* 5 • *Level of infrastructural needs:* 4 • ACTION RECOMMENDED: *Infrastructure:* 3 • *Capacity building/training:* 4 • *Economic instruments:* 5 • *Marketing (commercial, certification, added product value):* 5 • *Research/product development:* 3.

OE 062 - Xingu Indigenous Park - PRIORITY LEVEL: ? • LOCATION: *State:* Mato Grosso • *Main municipality:* Gaúcha do Norte • *Municipalities covered:* 10 • VEGETATION TYPES: AA, Da, Fa, ON, Pa, SN • COMMENTS: Indigenous handicrafts.

> DIAGNOSTIC ELEMENTS: *Capacity for income generation:* 3 • *Improvement of income distribution:* 4 • *Environmental impact:* 4 • *Impact on traditional populations:* 5 • *Local capacity for development of the activity:* 5 • *Diversification and integrated resource use:* 5 • *Level of infrastructural needs:* 4 • ACTION RECOMMENDED: *Infrastructure:* 3 • *Capacity building/training:* 4 • *Economic instruments:* 5 • *Marketing (commercial, certification, added product value):* 5 • *Research/product development:* 3.

OE 063 - Upper Rio Negro - Içana - PRIORITY LEVEL: ? • LOCATION: *State:* Amazonas • *Main municipality:* São Gabriel da Cachoeira • *Municipalities covered:* 3 • VEGETATION TYPES: Dm, Ds, La, Ld, LO, rm • COMMENTS: Indigenous handicrafts.

> DIAGNOSTIC ELEMENTS: *Capacity for income generation:* 3 • *Improvement of income distribution:* 4 • *Environmental impact:* 4 • *Impact on traditional populations:* 5 • *Local capacity for development of the activity:* 5 • *Diversification and integrated resource use:* 5 • *Level of infrastructural needs:* 5 • ACTION RECOMMENDED: *Infrastructure:* 3 • *Capacity building/training:* 4 • *Economic instruments:* 5 • *Marketing (commercial, certification, added product value):* 5 • *Research/product development:* 3.

OE 064 - Boca do Tapajós - PRIORITY LEVEL: ? • LOCATION: *State:* Pará • *Main municipality:* Santarém • *Municipalities covered:* 7 • VEGETATION TYPES: AA, As, Db, Ds, Pa, SO, Sp • COMMENTS: Indigenous handicrafts.

> DIAGNOSTIC ELEMENTS: *Capacity for income generation:* 3 • *Improvement of income distribution:* 4 • *Environmental impact:* 4 • *Impact on traditional populations:* 5 • *Local capacity for development of the activity:* 5 • *Diversification and integrated resource use:* 5 • *Level of infrastructural needs:* 5 • ACTION RECOMMENDED: *Infrastructure:* 3 • *Capacity building/training:* 4 • *Economic instruments:* 5 • *Marketing (commercial, certification, added product value):* 5 • *Research/product development:* 3.

OE 065 - Boca do Jaú - Waimiri-Atroari Indigenous Land - PRIORITY LEVEL: ? • LOCATION: *State:* Amazonas/Roraima • *Main municipality:* Novo Airão • *Municipalities covered:* 4 • VEGETATION TYPES: Ab, As, Da, Db, Ds, LO • COMMENTS: Indigenous handicrafts.

> DIAGNOSTIC ELEMENTS: *Capacity for income generation:* 3 • *Improvement of income distribution:* 4 • *Environmental impact:* 4 • *Impact on traditional populations:* 5 • *Local capacity for development of the activity:* 5 • *Diversification and integrated resource use:* 5 • *Level of infrastructural needs:* 3 • ACTION RECOMMENDED: *Infrastructure:* 3 • *Capacity building/training:* 4 • *Economic instruments:* 5 • *Marketing (commercial, certification, added product value):* 5 • *Research/product development:* 3.

OE 066 - Marubo - PRIORITY LEVEL: ? • LOCATION: *State:* Amazonas • *Main municipality:* Atalaia • *Municipalities covered:* 6 • VEGETATION TYPES: AA, Ab, Da, Db • COMMENTS: Indigenous handicrafts.

> DIAGNOSTIC ELEMENTS: *Capacity for income generation:* 3 • *Improvement of income distribution:* 4 • *Environmental impact:* 4 • *Impact on traditional populations:* 5 • *Local capacity for development of the activity:* 5 • *Diversification and integrated resource use:* 5 • *Level of infrastructural needs:* 3 • ACTION RECOMMENDED: *Infrastructure:* 3 • *Capacity building/training:* 4 • *Economic instruments:* 5 • *Marketing (commercial, certification, added product value):* 5 • *Research/product development:* 3.

OE 067 - Waiãpi - PRIORITY LEVEL: ? • LOCATION: *State:* Amapá • *Main municipality:* Vitória do Jari • *Municipalities covered:* 4 • VEGETATION TYPES: Ds • COMMENTS: Indigenous handicrafts.

> DIAGNOSTIC ELEMENTS: *Capacity for income generation:* 3 • *Improvement of income distribution:* 4 • *Environmental impact:* 4 • *Impact on traditional populations:* 5 • *Local capacity for development of the activity:* 5 • *Diversification and integrated resource use:* 5 • *Level of infrastructural needs:* 3 • ACTION RECOMMENDED: *Infrastructure:* 3 • *Capacity building/training:* 4 • *Economic instruments:* 5 • *Marketing (commercial, certification, added product value):* 5 • *Research/product development:* 3.

OE 068 - Tumucumaque - PRIORITY LEVEL: ? • LOCATION: *State:* Amapá • *Main municipality:* Oiapoque • *Municipalities covered:* 1 • VEGETATION TYPES: Da, Db, Ds, Pa, SO • COMMENTS: Indigenous handicrafts.

> DIAGNOSTIC ELEMENTS: *Capacity for income generation:* 3 • *Improvement of income distribution:* 4 • *Environmental impact:* 4 • *Impact on traditional populations:* 5 • *Local capacity for development of the activity:* 5 • *Diversification and integrated resource use:* 5 • *Level of infrastructural needs:* 3 • ACTION RECOMMENDED: *Infrastructure:* 3 • *Capacity building/training:* 4 • *Economic instruments:* 5 • *Marketing (commercial, certification, added product value):* 5 • *Research/product development:* 3.

OE 069 - Tumucumaque - Paru river - PRIORITY LEVEL: ? • LOCATION: *State:* Amapá/Pará • *Main municipality:* Almeirim • *Municipalities covered:* 2 • VEGETATION TYPES: Ds, Dm • COMMENTS: Indigenous handicrafts.

> DIAGNOSTIC ELEMENTS: *Capacity for income generation:* 3 • *Improvement of income distribution:* 4 • *Environmental impact:* 4 • *Impact on traditional populations:* 5 • *Local capacity for development of the activity:* 5 • *Diversification and integrated resource use:* 5 • *Level of infrastructural needs:* 3 • ACTION RECOMMENDED: *Infrastructure:* 3 • *Capacity building/training:* 4 • *Economic instruments:* 5 • *Marketing (commercial, certification, added product value):* 5 • *Research/product development:* 3.

OE 070 - Tikuna - PRIORITY LEVEL: ? • LOCATION: *State:* Amazonas • *Main municipality:* Codajás • *Municipalities covered:* 8 • VEGETATION TYPES: AA, Ab, Da, Db, LO • COMMENTS: Indigenous handicrafts.

> DIAGNOSTIC ELEMENTS: *Capacity for income generation:* 3 • *Improvement of income distribution:* 4 • *Environmental impact:* 4 • *Impact on traditional populations:* 5 • *Local capacity for development of the activity:* 5 • *Diversification and integrated resource use:* 5 • *Level of infrastructural needs:* 3 • ACTION RECOMMENDED: *Infrastructure:* 3 • *Capacity building/training:* 4 • *Economic instruments:* 5 • *Marketing (commercial, certification, added product value):* 5 • *Research/product development:* 3.

OE 071 - Amapá coastal zone and adjacent oceanic region, mouth of the Amazon - PRIORITY LEVEL: ? • LOCATION: *State:* Amapá/Pará • *Main municipality:* Calçoene • *Municipalities covered:* 53 • VEGETATION TYPES: AA, Da, Db, Ds, Pa, Pf, SO • COMMENTS: High productivity.

> DIAGNOSTIC ELEMENTS: *Capacity for income generation:* 4 • *Improvement of income distribution:* 4 • *Environmental impact:* 3 • *Impact on traditional populations:* 4 • *Local capacity for development of the activity:* 5 • *Diversification and integrated resource use:* 4 • *Level of infrastructural needs:* 1 • ACTION RECOMMENDED: *Infrastructure:* 4 • *Capacity building/training:* 5 • *Economic instruments:* 4 • *Marketing (commercial, certification, added product value):* 3 • *Research/product development:* 2.

OE 072 - Middle-lower Amazonas - PRIORITY LEVEL: ? • LOCATION: *State:* Amapá/Amazonas/Pará • *Main municipality:* Santarém •

Municipalities covered: 30 • Vegetation types: AA, As, Da, Db, Ds, Pa, SO, Sp • Comments: High productivity.

Diagnostic elements: *Capacity for income generation: 4 • Improvement of income distribution: 4 • Environmental impact: 3 • Impact on traditional populations: 4 • Local capacity for development of the activity: 5 • Diversification and integrated resource use: 4 • Level of infrastructural needs: 2* • Action recommended: *Infrastructure: 4 • Capacity building/training: 5 • Economic instruments: 4 • Marketing (commercial, certification, added product value): 2 • Research/product development: 3.*

OE 073 - Upper Amazonas - Priority level: ? • Location: *State:* Amazonas • *Main municipality:* Jutaí • *Municipalities covered:* 16 • Vegetation types: AA, Ab, Da, Db, La, LO • Comments: High productivity.

Diagnostic elements: *Capacity for income generation: 4 • Improvement of income distribution: 4 • Environmental impact: 3 • Impact on traditional populations: 4 • Local capacity for development of the activity: 5 • Diversification and integrated resource use: 4 • Level of infrastructural needs: 1* • Action recommended: *Infrastructure: 4 • Capacity building/training: 5 • Economic instruments: 4 • Marketing (commercial, certification, added product value): 2 • Research/product development: 3.*

OE 074 - Juruá river valley - Priority level: ? • Location: *State:* Amazonas • *Main municipality:* Carauari • *Municipalities covered:* 15 • Vegetation types: Ab, Da, Db • Comments: High productivity.

Diagnostic elements: *Capacity for income generation: 4 • Improvement of income distribution: 4 • Environmental impact: 3 • Impact on traditional populations: 4 • Local capacity for development of the activity: 5 • Diversification and integrated resource use: 4 • Level of infrastructural needs: 1.*

OE 075 - Boca do Acre - Priority level: ? • Location: *State:* Amazonas • *Main municipality:* Boca do Acre • *Municipalities covered:* 3 • Vegetation types: AA, Ab, As, Da, Db • Comments: High productivity.

Diagnostic elements: *Capacity for income generation: 4 • Improvement of income distribution: 4 • Environmental impact: 3 • Impact on traditional populations: 4 • Local capacity for development of the activity: 5 • Diversification and integrated resource use: 4 • Level of infrastructural needs: 1* • Action recommended: *Infrastructure: 4 • Capacity building/training: 5 • Economic instruments: 4 • Marketing (commercial, certification, added product value): 2 • Research/product development: 3.*

OE 076 - Atlantic coast of Pará - Priority level: ? • Location: *State:* Maranhão/Pará • *Main municipality:* Bragança • *Municipalities covered:* 20 • Vegetation types: AA, Pf • Comments: High productivity.

Diagnostic elements: *Capacity for income generation: 4 • Improvement of income distribution: 4 • Environmental impact: 3 • Impact on traditional populations: 4 • Diversification and integrated resource use: 4* • Action recommended: *Infrastructure: 4 • Capacity building/training: 5 • Economic instruments: 4 • Marketing (commercial, certification, added product value): 2 • Research/product development: 3.*

10

PRIORITY AREAS FOR TRADITIONAL POPULATIONS AND INDIGENOUS PEOPLES*

Traditional populations are groups that have achieved, or are fighting to achieve, by practical or symbolic means, a public identity that includes some, but not necessarily all, of the following characteristics: the use of low impact environmental techniques; equitable forms of social organization; the presence of institutions with the legitimacy to ensure compliance with their laws; local leadership; and, finally, cultural traits that are selectively reaffirmed and reworked.

At the moment the term 'traditional populations' is still in its early phase of life. It is a thinly populated category, but it already numbers a few members and has candidates at the door. To begin with, it has administrative existence: the Centro Nacional de Populações Tradicionais (CNPT – National Center for Traditional Populations), a unit within Ibama. At the beginning, the category consisted of rubber tappers and brazil-nut gatherers from the Amazon region. It then expanded to include other groups, ranging from cockle collectors in Santa Catarina to babassu nut gatherers in southern Maranhão and quilombolas in Tocantins. What all these groups have in common is the fact that they have, at least to some extent, a history of low environmental impact, and that they currently have an interest in maintaining or recovering control over the territory they exploit. And, above all, they are willing to negotiate: in exchange for control over their territory, they commit themselves to supplying environmental services

Although traditional populations have followed the example of indigenous populations, the category 'traditional populations' does not include indigenous populations. The separation rests on a fundamental legal distinction: indigenous territorial rights are not defined in terms of conservation, even when we see that indigenous lands act as 'islands' of environmental conservation in a context of accelerating devastation. Indigenous rights gained their own chapter in the Constitution of 1988. The definition of indigenous land in its article 231 explicitly included not only inhabited spaces and areas of cultivation, but also the territory required for the 'preservation of the environmental resources necessary for the well-being of the indigenous populations, as well as the land necessary for their physical and cultural reproduction, in conformity with their habits, customs and traditions'.

The rights to indigenous land were declared to be 'originários', a legal term implying over-riding precedence, and which limits the role of the state to recognizing such rights, but not to granting them. This formulation has the virtue of linking territorial rights to their historical roots (and not to cultural status or a situation of tutelage). The legal personality of indigenous groups and associations was recognized and, in particular, their ability to start legal proceedings in their own name, independently of the opinion of the legal guardian, with the Prosecutor-General's office having responsibility for assisting them before a court of law. All these procedures constitute basic instruments for guaranteeing their rights (Cunha 1989).

Throughout this process the success of indigenous claims to land gained visibility and had the unexpected and paradoxical result that other dispossessed sectors of society, such as quilombolas and, as we will see, seringueiros (rubber-tappers) began to copy them.

Seringueiros, who a few years previously had constituted a category believed to be destined for rapid disappearance, had by the end of the 1980s taken on a leadership role in terms of environmental mobilization. At the end of 1988 an alliance for the defense of the forests and its inhabitants emerged in Acre under the name of the Alliance of Forest Peoples, made up of seringueiro and indigenous groups in the form of the two national organizations recently created: the Conselho Nacional dos Seringueiros and the União das Nações Indígenas. The meeting at Altamira (February 1989) organized by the Kayapó against the Xingu dam project, had an explicit environmental connotation. By the end of the 1980s, the environmental connection had become explicit. In contrast to the Yellowstone model, which sought to create an 'untouched' North American environment with no human population, it was argued that local communities, who had protected the environment on which their way of life was based, should be the partners and not the victims of environmental conservation.

On the contrary, in order to protect the environment, local communities should take on the responsibility for the management and control of the natural resources in the environments in which they lived. The new factor was the active role attributed to local communities. At the beginning of 1992 the explicit link between indigenous populations and conservation gained international prominence with the creation of the International Alliance of Tribal and Indigenous Populations of Tropical Forests, of which one of the founder organizations was COICA (Confederação das Organizações Indígenas da Bacia Amazônica – Confederation of Indigenous Organizations of the Amazon

---

* Text drawn in part from 'Traditional populations and environmental conservation' by Manuela Carneiro da Cunha and Mauro W. B. Almeida; 'Contemporary native sociodiversity in Brazil and biodiversity in the Amazon' by Beto Ricardo; and 'Traditional populations and biodiversity in Amazonia: a GIS-based bibliographical survey' by Antonio Carlos Diegues, Geraldo Andrello and Márcia Nunes, the full versions of which can be found on pages 182, 192 and 203 of this book.

Basin). The Convention on Biological Diversity and Agenda 21, approved in 1992, explicitly recognized the important role played by indigenous and local communities. In 1996, Colombia put into practice on a large scale the idea of making indigenous populations officially responsible for large areas of tropical forest. In Brazil, as we will see below, the same idea was applied six years earlier than in Colombia, on a smaller yet no less important scale, in the form of extractive reserves. The first protagonists of this experiment were the seringueiros, rather than indigenous groups.

In the region making up Legal Amazonia there are currently twelve extractive reserves established by the federal government, which amount to approximately 3.3 million hectares and contain 22,300 inhabitants (Ibama 2001). There area also seven state extractive reserves, one in Mato Gross and the remainder in Rondônia, comprising a total area of around 960,000 hectares (ISA 2001).

As regards quilombolas, Anjos (1999) has recorded the occurrence of 357 communities of descendents of former quilombos in the Amazon region, with 196 in Pará, 12 in Amapá, 4 in Tocantins and 145 in that part of Maranhão falling with Legal Amazonia.

It is calculated that the indigenous population of Brazil amounts to approximately 310,000 individuals, of whom 280,000 live on indian lands. Although this population is relatively small, its social diversity is extremely rich. There are 206 indigenous societies, 160 of them in the Amazon region, and approximately 195 different languages. It is estimated that there are 50 isolated indigenous groups with no regular contact with the outside world.

With the exception of the brief and violent rubber boom, which lasted from 1870 to 1910, the major part of Amazonia, away from the main channel of the Amazon river, remained a relative stranger to the process of human occupation. As a consequence, the majority of the surviving indigenous groups and the major part of the lands they succeeded in preserving are found within Amazonia, where almost 99% of the total area of indigenous lands in Brazil is concentrated.

Although dispersed, the extent of indigenous lands as a whole is impressive. Indians have a constitutional right to almost 12% of the Brazilian territory, made up of 574 different areas and encompassing 20.6% of the Brazilian Amazon. Conservation areas where human presence is permitted, sustainable use conservation areas, cover another 7.9% (ISA 2001) of the Amazon region.

In the 1980s, the extent of indian lands in Brazil seemed an exaggeration: 'too much land for too few Indians'. This focus has changed. The cover story of Veja magazine of June 20th, 1999, told of the 3,600 indians of the Xingu who 'preserved an ecological paradise' of the size of Belgium. The point was that a small number of Indians could take good care of a vast territory. The idea that the people who are most qualified to care for the conservation of an area are those who live off it in a sustainable way is also the premise for the creation of extractive reserves.

The results of the project 'Biodiversity and Traditional Communities in Brazil', carried out by Nupaub-USP in 1999 with the objective of compiling an inventory of studies on traditional knowledge related to the natural world showed that, over the course of generations, the traditional peoples of Amazonia have built up a considerable body of knowledge and practices concerning the natural world and biodiversity, and that this is fundamental to their survival in the forest and on the riverbanks and lakeshores.

Various studies analyzed during the course of the survey carried out by Nupaub (Balée 1993; Balick and Cox 1996; Anderson, May and Balick 1991; Descola 1997) suggest that species, ecosystem, and genetic diversity is not just a natural phenomenon, but is also a cultural phenomenon, in other words it is also the result of human action. According to these studies, human populations not only co-exist with the forest and know its inhabitants, but they also manage it, that is to say they manipulate its organic and non-organic components. Consequently, as Ribeiro (1990) emphasizes, the management of natural species by Amazonian peoples results in the increase of plant communities and their integration with animal species and with humans.

Thus, what natural scientists (botanists, biologists, ichthyologists) call biodiversity, translated into long lists of plant and animal species and viewed out of its cultural context, is different from the concept of biodiversity that is, to a large extent, materially and symbolically constructed and adopted by traditional peoples.

The selection of priority areas for biodiversity conservation in Amazonia should not start from the premise that human activities in this biome always pose a threat to biodiversity. While this may be true in the case of some categories of human populations and their technologies, it is not the case for many traditional populations.

Although they are not 'ecologists by nature', indians deserve historic credit for having managed their natural resources gently, causing little environmental disturbance prior to the arrival of the European conquistadors. Faced with the real, constant and usually unpunished, albeit illegal, pressures of the predatory forms of natural resource use prevailing in Amazonia today, it is also true that some indigenous populations have actively bought into such models, in the form of junior partners. This was recently and notoriously the case with the involvement of the Kayapó in Pará in the illegal extraction of gold and mahogany on their lands. On the other side of the coin are the emerging links between the resources found on indigenous lands and so-called green capitalism.

Either way, amongst the various alternatives on the table, bringing together indigenous projects and non-indigenous strategies for the sustainable use of natural resources, whether public or private, would in theory increase indians' chances of favorably reconciling in the future their possession of extensive lands with their low demography, and would contribute enormously to the conservation and sustainable use of biodiversity, particularly in Amazonia. In the same way, it is absolutely necessary to have a clear State compensation policy which would give practical effect to constitutional rights and would strategically value native socio-diversity and its connection to biodiversity.

Clearly not all conservation areas can be administered by their pre-existing populations. But it is similarly clear that a solid and viable environmental policy for Brazil has to include local populations. In addition, to expel people from conservation areas without offering them alternative means of survival is a course for certain disaster.

During the Macapá Workshop, seventeen priority areas for traditional populations were identified (see the map on page 448 and the listing). Of these areas, fifteen (71.4%) show a high degree of local social demands, and twelve (57.1%) possess representative organizations of the local actors. On the other hand, six (28.6%) already show high levels of impact resulting from natural resource use, although there was only one identified case of a high level of external anthropogenic pressure (Table 10).

As far as indigenous peoples are concerned, participants in the Macapá Workshop grouped the status of all the indigenous lands into four categories:

a) Areas of indigenous occupation, or of evidence of the existence of uncontacted indians, where there are no overlaps with conservation areas and where the processes of identification, demarcation and protection need speeding up. These areas were assigned the highest priority level (A) with the recommendation that the procedures for recognizing and demarcating the areas, and measures for their urgent protection, be started or accelerated.

b) Areas of indigenous occupation, or of evidence of the existence of uncontacted indians, in places where there are overlaps with conservation areas and where the processes of identification and demarcation and protection need speeding up. These areas were also assigned the highest priority level (A) with the recommendation that the procedures for recognizing and demarcating the areas, and measures for their urgent protection, be started or continued.

c) Officially recognized indigenous lands, where there are no overlaps with conservation areas and where action is required to support conservation and the sustainable use of natural resources, were assigned priority level B and the recommendation that protection measures be adopted.

d) Officially recognized indigenous lands overlapping conservation areas were assigned priority level C. The recommendation for these areas is for support to the conservation and sustainable use of natural resources and the adoption of measures aimed at resolving the use conflicts arising from the overlap with the conservation areas, taking into account the constitutional usufruct rights over such areas enjoyed by the indigenous populations.

As far as the diagnostic elements are concerned, all the areas relating to indigenous peoples received the highest score possible for cultural and biological importance.

TABLE 10 - PRIORITY AREAS FOR TRADITIONAL POPULATIONS
DIAGNOSTIC ELEMENTS THAT SCORE HIGHEST

Diagnostic elements	Number of areas	%[1]
Local social demands for the area	15	71.4
Legal/political status of the area	2	9.5
Existence of representative organizations of local actors	12	57.1
Existence of collaborative partnerships	15	71.4
Sustainable development projects	11	52.4
Traditional knowledge	7	33.3
Interface with protected areas	7	33.3
External anthropogenic pressures	1	4.8
Current capacity for sustainability		–
Level of impact of natural resource use	6	28.6
Trading levels		–

1. Of the total proposed areas (21).

PP 001 - Centro Novo - PRIORITY LEVEL: A • LOCATION: *State:* Amapá • *Main municipality:* Vitória do Jari • *Municipalities covered:* 1 • VEGETATION TYPES: Ds • COMMENTS: Area of high potential (andiroba, liana, copaiba, Brazil nut) in the region between the Cajari Reserve, the State Multiple Use Reserve and the Maracá Extractive Settlement project. Historically the area has been inhabited and worked by 42 families. There is a constant threat of illegal occupation by loggers and prospectors.

PP 002 - Lago Piratuba Biological Reserve - Sucuriju - PRIORITY LEVEL: A • LOCATION: *State:* Amapá • *Main municipality:* Amapá • *Municipalities covered:* 1 • VEGETATION TYPES: Pa, Pf • COMMENTS: Presence of an important traditional fishing community within a biological reserve.

PP 003 - Pará estuary and coastline - PRIORITY LEVEL: A • LOCATION: *State:* Pará • *Main municipality:* Curralinho • *Municipalities covered:* 36 • VEGETATION TYPES: AA, Da, Db, Pa, Pf, Sp • COMMENTS: Traditional fishers. Social demand for support to sustainable 'traditional fishery', as they call their activity. High level of organization. High level of external pressure caused by unsustainable commercial fishery.

PP 004 - Gurupá - Porto de Moz - PRIORITY LEVEL: B • LOCATION: *State:* Pará • *Main municipality:* Porto de Moz • *Municipalities covered:* 8 • VEGETATION TYPES: AA, Da, Db, Pa • COMMENTS: Population density of riverside fishing community, subject to high pressure from loggers and demanding sustainable use regulations for the area.

PP 005 - Lower Amazonas - Tapajós - PRIORITY LEVEL: A • LOCATION: *State:* Amazonas/Pará • *Main municipality:* Santarém • *Municipalities covered:* 16 • VEGETATION TYPES: AA, As, Da, Db, Ds, Pa, SO, Sp • COMMENTS: An area of traditional populations (ribeirinhos, extrativistas) of longstanding occupation, under heavy pressure mainly from 'commercial fishers', in other words fishers from outside the area.

PP 006 - Babaçuais - Quilombos - PRIORITY LEVEL: A • LOCATION: *State:* Maranhão/Tocantins • *Main municipality:* Amarante do Maranhão • *Municipalities covered:* 103 • VEGETATION TYPES: AA, Cs, Da, Db, Pa, Sa, Sd, SN, SO, Sp • COMMENTS: Social demand, conservation of the babaçuais stands, high levels of political and economic organization, conservation of Brazilian quilombo areas.

PP 007 - Middle Amazonas - PRIORITY LEVEL: B • LOCATION: *State:* Amazonas • *Main municipality:* Itacoatiara • *Municipalities covered:* 15 • VEGETATION TYPES: AA, Da, Db, Pa, SO, Sp • COMMENTS: Presence of traditional population (ribeirinhos), with demands for an ecotourism program and the management and conservation of fishing resources (lakes).

PP 008 - Lower Solimões - PRIORITY LEVEL: C • LOCATION: *State:* Amazonas • *Main municipality:* Coari • *Municipalities covered:* 8 • VEGETATION TYPES: AA, Ab, Da, Db, Ds, LO • COMMENTS: Area occupied by traditional population, demanding assistance with its environmental problems, but getting little help from community support institutions. Could benefit more from activities being carried out on the middle Solimões.

PP 009 - Middle Solimões - PRIORITY LEVEL: C • LOCATION: *State:* Amazonas • *Main municipality:* Maraã • *Municipalities covered:* 10 • VEGETATION TYPES: Da, Db, La, LO, Pa • COMMENTS: Ribeirinho populations engaged in social movements for environmental conservation, with high potential for disseminating experiences and influencing adjacent areas. Problems of illegal occupation and pressure on natural resources. Area of high conservation activity, so its priority classification reflects more the need for replication than implementation.

PP 010 - Upper Solimões - PRIORITY LEVEL: C • LOCATION: *State:* Amazonas • *Main municipality:* Jutaí • *Municipalities covered:* 8 • VEGETATION TYPES: Ab, Da, Db, LO • COMMENTS: Traditional ribeirinho populations, with long history of low environmental impact occupancy. Located in the region between the Ticuna indigenous lands and needing to be linked into the process of implementing sustainable management which have been set up in these areas. Receiving little attention from conservation support institutions.

PP 011 - Regional - Carajás - PRIORITY LEVEL: A • LOCATION: *State:* Pará • *Main municipality:* Marabá • *Municipalities covered:* 16 • VEGETATION TYPES: AA, As, Db, Dm, Ds • COMMENTS: Presence of traditional populations with social demands. These are organized but need political and administrative support for trading and resource management.

PP 012 - Upper Purus - PRIORITY LEVEL: A • LOCATION: *State:* Acre • *Main municipality:* Sena Madureira • *Municipalities covered:* 14 • VEGETATION TYPES: AA, Ab, Da, Db • COMMENTS: Population spread throughout the entire area. They are extrativistas and small producers, with a tradition of very low impact natural resource use. In this area there are national parks and forests, extractive reserve and indigenous lands, which risk degradation from unprotected inter-lying areas through which destructive forces can reach the protected areas.

PP 013 - Middle Rio Negro - PRIORITY LEVEL: D • LOCATION: *State:* Amazonas • *Main municipality:* Barcelos • *Municipalities covered:* 2 • VEGETATION TYPES: Da, Db, Ds, La, Ld, Lg, LO • COMMENTS: Many resident ribeirinho communities, between which there are very isolated indigenous groups. There is a demand for FOIRN to survey the communities in the area because of the setting up of the Special Rio Negro Indigenous Health District.

PP 014 - Regional - Tocantins - PRIORITY LEVEL: C • LOCATION: *State:* Tocantins • *Main municipality:* Porto Nacional • *Municipalities covered:* 41 • VEGETATION TYPES: AA, Sa, Sd, Sg, SN, SO, Sp • COMMENTS: Savanna area, threatened biome, one of the few areas with management that includes traditional populations.

PP 015 - Quilombos (several) - PRIORITY LEVEL: A • LOCATION: *State:* Amapá/Maranhão/Mato Grosso/Pará • *Main municipality:* Vários • *Municipalities covered:* 25 • VEGETATION TYPES: AA, As, Da, Db, Pf, Sa, SO, Sp • COMMENTS: Conservation of black *quilombola* culture.

PP 016 - Middle Purus and middle Juruá - PRIORITY LEVEL: B • LOCATION: *State:* AC/Amazonas • *Main municipality:* Lábrea • *Municipalities covered:* 13 • VEGETATION TYPES: AA, Ab, As, Da, Db, Pa, Sa, SO, Sp • COMMENTS: Area inhabited by extractive populations, small farmers and fishers, connecting indigenous lands and protected areas, revealing sustainable development initiatives.

PP 017 - Jaciparaná - Guaporé - Corumbiara - Madeira Rivers - PRIORITY LEVEL: A • LOCATION: *State:* Rondônia • *Main municipality:* Guajará-Mirim • *Municipalities covered:* 28 • VEGETATION TYPES: AA, Ab, As, Da, Db, Ds, Fa, Fb, Fs, ON, Pa, Sa, Sd, SN, SO, Sp • COMMENTS: Area inhabited by extractive populations and small farmers in areas adjacent to indigenous lands.

PP 018 - Indigenous lands not officially recognized and not overlapping conservation areas - PRIORITY LEVEL: A • LOCATION: *State:* Several • *Main municipality:* Several • *Municipalities covered:* 85 • VEGETATION TYPES: Several • COMMENTS: Areas of indigenous occupation or with evidence of the existence of uncontacted indians, which need studies for their identification, demarcation and protection speeded up.

PP 019 - Indigenous lands not officially recognized and overlapping conservation areas - PRIORITY LEVEL: A • LOCATION: *State:* Amazonas/Rondônia • *Main municipality:* Several • *Municipalities covered:* 8 • VEGETATION TYPES: Diversas • COMMENTS: Areas of indigenous occupation or with evidence of the existence of uncontacted indians, which need the identification and demarcation studies speeded up.

PP 020 - Officially recognized indigenous lands not overlapping conservation areas - PRIORITY LEVEL: B • LOCATION: *State:* Vários • *Main municipality:* Vários • *Municipalities covered:* 247 • VEGETATION TYPES: Several • COMMENTS: Several o COMMENTS: Recognized indigenous lands, the majority of which of extremely high biological importance, where action in support of conservation and for sustainable natural resource use are needed, taking into account the constitutional usufruct rights over such areas enjoyed by the indigenous populations.

PP 021 - Officially recognized indigenous lands overlapping conservation areas - PRIORITY LEVEL: C • LOCATION: *State:* Amapá/Amazonas/Maranhão/Mato Grosso/Rondônia/Roraima/Tocantins • *Main municipality:* Several • *Municipalities covered:* 46 • VEGETATION TYPES: Several • COMMENTS: Recognized indigenous lands, the majority of which of extremely high biological importance, where action in support of conservation and for sustainable natural resource use are needed, as well as the adoption of measures aimed at resolving the use conflicts arising from the overlap with the conservation areas, taking into account the constitutional usufruct rights over such areas enjoyed by the indigenous populations.

11
PRIORITY AREAS FOR ANTHROPOGENIC PRESSURE*

According to the 2000 population census figures from the IBGE, the region that makes up Legal Amazonia comprised a total of approximately 20.1 million inhabitants, corresponding to about 11.8% of the total population of Brazil. The states of the Federation with the largest proportions of the regional population were Pará with 6.18 million inhabitants; Maranhão, 4.78 million, Amazonas, 2.81 million, and Mato Grosso with 2.5 million. Together, these four states account for approximately 80% the total regional population.

The demographic portrait of the Legal Amazon Region is one of a region largely made up of municipalities with total populations of fewer than 100,000 inhabitants. There is a higher concentration of population in the eastern part of the region, in a north-south line along the eastern border of Pará and the western border of Maranhão, an area made up of a large number of municipalities with total populations of more than 40,000 inhabitants. There was an increase of 75% in the number of municipalities with populations greater than 100,000 during the period 1980 to 1996: in 1980 there were only 13, by 1991 there were 19, and by 1996 this number had reached 23.

The demographic density of the total population of the Amazon region is around 3.9 inhabitants per square kilometer according to data for 2000. Virtually all states showed indices equivalent to or less than six inhabitants per square kilometer, with the exception of Maranhão, which recorded the highest levels in the region for this year – around 14.4 inhabitants per square kilometer. Spatial analysis of the indicator reveals the existence, from 1980 onwards, of a sub-region of higher population densities, with a significant concentration of municipalities with levels greater than fifteen inhabitants per square kilometer, in an area extending from the centre-north of Maranhão to northeastern Pará. In the period 1980 to 1996 we can see not only a higher density for municipalities in this sub-region in 1991, but also the formation of sub-regions with demographic densities of more than five inhabitants per square kilometer such as: the Rondônia-Acre corridor; the area surrounding Manaus; eastern Amazonas and western Pará; the central-northern Tocantins corridor; and the central part of Mato Grosso.

Analysis of urban population data indicates that the population size doubled during the period 1980 to 2000, reaching a total of approximately 13.9 million inhabitants by 1996. The Amazon states which showed the highest indices of urbanization levels in 2000 are: Amapá (89.0%), Mato Grosso (79.3%) and Roraima (76.1%). Analysis of levels of urbanization reveals that, generally speaking, there was a tendency in the period 1980 to 1996 towards the concentration of municipalities with high levels of urbanization (more than 80%) across Rondônia, southern Mato Grosso and along the corridor linking the central and northern parts of Tocantins.

The tendency towards increasing levels of urbanization in the region has led to the same problems as those which affect the populations of large Brazilian cities and which result from a combination of different factors. Amongst these are high growth rates, the poverty of the migrating population, the lack of resources on the part of municipal and state governments, and tropical environmental factors, which consequently lead to more serious problems of environmental degradation than those found in the more developed urban areas, since a large part of the regional population has to make do with precarious infrastructural conditions, principally as regards sanitation (GTA/Amigos da Terra 1998).

As regards rural population, the percentage of the population living in rural areas varies between 77% and 87% in those regional municipalities with populations of fewer than 20,000.

Comparing the 1980-1991 and 1991-1996 periods it can be seen that the yearly average rate of population growth fell from 3.5% to 2%. The reduction in the rate of population growth was observed in almost all states, with Amapá and Tocantins as the only exceptions. Rondônia and Roraima show significant reductions, in the order of 6 to 7 percentage points, whilst the remaining states show gradual reductions, consistent with the regional average. As in the case of total population, urban population showed significant growth during recent years.

One of the methodologies available to analyze the pressure exerted by human communities over the natural resources of a given area is the adoption of the Anthropogenic Pressure Index (API). This is an indicator that synthesizes the economic and demographic pressures and is made up of secondary data. The principal data sources are derived from the following IBGE publications: population censuses, agriculture and livestock censuses, and municipal agricultural and livestock production data. The methodological basis for developing the API consists of combining the stock (size or density) and the flow (speed or growth) sizes (Sawyer 1997). It is assumed that pressure is greater when the stock and the flow are higher, and less when both are lower.

Anthropogenic Pressure Index (API) analysis applied to the Amazon region shows that levels of anthropogenic pressure for the region as a whole can, generally speaking, be considered to

---

* Text drawn in part from 'An analysis of the demography, socioeconomics and anthropogenic pressures in the Legal Amazon region' by Maurício Pontes Monteiro and Donald Sawyer, the full version of which can be found on page 306 of this book.

be medium, the category that accounts for approximately 48% of regional municipalities. In the eastern part of the region higher levels of pressure were found, normally medium or high, above all in southern Mato Grosso, northwestern Maranhão and northeastern Pará. On the basis of analysis of components of the API, the strong influence of urban anthropogenic pressures and of farming and ranching was observed in eastern and northeastern Pará and in Maranhão and Tocantins. This can be linked to the development corridors implanted in the region, such as the Carajás railway and the Belém-Brasília highway. In Mato Grosso the main cause of anthropogenic pressure is farming and ranching, mainly in the eastern and southern regions. The areas of lowest anthropogenic pressures are located in northern Para and part of Amapá. There are also a few isolated nuclei of low anthropogenic pressure, mainly in municipalities in Mato Grosso where there are biodiversity conservation areas, such as the Chapada dos Guimarães national park, the northern part of the Pantanal Matogrossense and environmental protection areas along the Araguaia river.

The western part of the region reveals fewer anthropogenic impacts than the eastern part. Areas of low or very low pressure are found in the southern and the northern parts of Amazonas and in central Acre, while those with higher levels of anthropogenic pressure are confined to central Rondônia, eastern Acre and the area surrounding Manaus. In Rondônia there are two distinct situations concerning anthropogenic pressure in the northwestern and southeastern parts of the state. In the northwest the pressure is mainly demographic, whereas in the southeast the anthropogenic pressure mainly takes the form of agriculture and cattle raising. In the area around Manaus, as well as in a number of municipalities located along the Amazon river, anthropogenic pressure is above all urban, probably resulting from the migration of riverbank populations into urban centers in search of better living standards.

From the analysis of the results obtained, we can offer some considerations on demographic, socio-economic and anthropogenic trends in the Legal Amazon region.

The demographic summary of the Amazon region shows a marked concentration of population in its eastern part, principally in eastern and northeastern Pará and in Maranhão, where population densities are higher than 15 inhabitants per square kilometer. In the western part the highest population pressures are to be found in areas surrounding the principal cities, such as Manaus and Porto Velho. Rates of population growth, although falling over recent years, continue at levels above 2% per year.

In the case of the distribution of urban and rural population in the region, a trend towards urbanization can be observed. Over 69% of the population currently lives in urban areas, a fact which tends to aggravate environmental and social problems on the outskirts of large urban centers, compounding pre-existing local environmental problems. Some states which showed high urban population growth rates in the period 1980-1991, such as Rondônia and Roraima, have stabilized their rates and have been overtaken by other states such as Maranhão, Amapá and Tocantins. Notwithstanding the implementation of agricultural settlement projects, rural demographic trends have been stable over recent years, revealing a certain decline.

For extractive activities, principally timber, we can observe a correlation with areas of higher concentrations of population, indicating that the activity in question is related to issues of infrastructure and market. Areas of higher regional demographic concentration imply better availability of energy and as a consequence offer more favorable conditions that enable distribution, because of proximity to the principal development corridors.

Anthropogenic pressure in the Amazon region is shown to be strongly influenced by the factors of urban anthropogenic pressure, of farming and of stock raising, and is less the result of rural anthropogenic pressure. Given the concentration of population, economic activities and the major development corridors, the situation is more critical in the eastern part of the region where the areas of higher anthropogenic pressure are more intense and concentrated than in the western part where the areas of higher anthropogenic pressure are sparsely distributed.

We should also note that some places in the region, such as Maranhão and eastern Pará, as well as showing higher levels of anthropogenic pressure, are also areas of low levels of human development, with an HDI of generally less than 0.40. From a socio-environmental viewpoint, these areas thus represent less sustainable conditions; leading, in other words, to the exhaustion of resources with no corresponding improvements in living standards. This is not seen in states such as Tocantins, Rondônia and Mato Grosso which, despite high levels of anthropogenic pressure, also reveal better levels of human development, with HDIs of over 0.60. On the other hand, from a social and environmental point of view, there are some scattered centers characterized by better social and environmental sustainability, such as northwestern Mato Grosso and southern Roraima, where levels of anthropogenic pressure are low and those of human development are comparatively high.

During the Macapá Workshop, 49 priority areas in Amazonia for anthropogenic pressure were identified (see the map on page 449 and the listing). Of these areas, twenty (40.8%) show a high degree of alteration of vegetation cover, sixteen (32.7%) are suffering severe impacts from logging and eleven (22.4%) are regions subject to high pressure from infrastructural investments of the expansion of the agricultural frontier (Table 11).

TABLE 11 - PRIORITY AREAS FOR ANTHROPOGENIC PRESSURE DIAGNOSTIC ELEMENTS THAT SCORE HIGHEST		
Diagnostic elements	Number of areas	%[1]
Alteration of forest cover	20	40.8
Infrastructure	11	22.4
Agricultural frontier	11	22.4
Urban dynamics	6	12.2
Logging	16	32.7
Mining	8	16.3
Fishing	3	6.1

1. Of the total proposed areas (49).

PA 001 - BR-364 Highway, Rondônia - Priority level: A • Location: *State:* Mato Grosso/Rondônia • *Main municipality:* Chupinguaia • *Municipalities covered:* 47 • Vegetation types: AA, Ab, As, Ds, Fa, Fb, Fs, ON, Pa, Sa, Sd, SN, SO, Sp • Comments: Region of innumerable settlements projects since the seventies, whose developments have led to high fragmentation. 20% remaining as extensive areas (mainly between Cacoal and Ariquem). Predominance of ranching, with possible degradation of pastures in large number of areas.
Diagnostic elements: *Alteration of forest cover:* 5 • *Infrastructure:* 5 • *Agricultural frontier:* 4 • *Urban dynamics:* 4 • *Logging:* 4 • *Mining:* 2 • Action recommended: *Conservation:* 5 • *Sustainable use:* 1 • *Sustainable production:* 5 • *Public policies:* 4 • *Research and development of pilot projects:* 3.

PA 002 - BR-429 Highway - Priority level: B • Location: *State:* Rondônia • *Main municipality:* São Francisco do Guaporé • *Municipalities covered:* 5 • Vegetation types: AA, Ab, As, Da, Ds, Pa • Comments: High rates of deforestation in the last ten years. Presence of areas of high vulnerability. Possible growth of ranching and fragmentation of habitats.
Diagnostic elements: *Alteration of forest cover:* 4 • *Infrastructure:* 4 • *Agricultural frontier:* 3 • *Urban dynamics:* 2 • *Logging:* 3 • *Mining:* 5 • Action recommended: *Conservation:* 4 • *Sustainable use:* 4 • *Sustainable production:* 4 • *Public policies:* 4 • *Research and development of pilot projects:* 3.

PA 003 - Machadinho d'Oeste - Priority level: B • Location: *State:* Rondônia • *Main municipality:* Machadinho d'Oeste • *Municipalities covered:* 6 • Vegetation types: AA, As, Da, Ds • Comments: Area of INCRA settlement (failing) and corn. Family-based subsistence cultivation of coffee, cocoa, rice and beans. Soil erosion. Family members occupying lands outside the boundaries of the settlement project in the buffer area. Small scale forest production (freijó wood).
Diagnostic elements: *Alteration of forest cover:* 3 • *Agricultural frontier:* 4 • Action recommended: *Conservation:* 4 • *Sustainable use:* 4 • *Sustainable production:* 4.

PA 004 - Guajará-Mirim - Priority level: B • Location: *State:* Rondônia • *Main municipality:* Guajará-Mirim • *Municipalities covered:* 2 • Vegetation types: AA, Ab, As, Da, Sd, SO • Comments: Presence of important settlement areas. Possible growth of ranching in the area.
Diagnostic elements: *Alteration of forest cover:* 4 • *Infrastructure:* 4 • *Agricultural frontier:* 3 • *Urban dynamics:* 3 • *Logging:* 3 • *Mining:* 5 • Action recommended: *Conservation:* 4 • *Sustainable use:* 4 • *Sustainable production:* 4 • *Public policies:* 4 • *Research and development of pilot projects:* 3.

PA 005 - BR-364 Highway from Porto Velho to Rio Branco • Priority level: B • Location: *State:* Acre/Amazonas/Rondônia • *Main municipality:* Porto Velho • *Municipalities covered:* 5 • Vegetation types: AA, Ab, As, Da, Db, Ds, SO, Sp • Comments: High deforestation levels in the last five years.
Diagnostic elements: *Alteration of forest cover:* 4 • *Infrastructure:* 4 • *Agricultural frontier:* 3 • *Urban dynamics:* 3 • *Logging:* 5 • *Mining:* 5 • Action recommended: *Conservation:* 4 • *Sustainable use:* 3 • *Sustainable production:* 4 • *Public policies:* 4 • *Research and development of pilot projects:* 3.

PA 006 - Acre valley - Priority level: B • Location: *State:* Acre/Amazonas • *Main municipality:* Rio Branco • *Municipalities covered:* 13 • Vegetation types: AA, Ab, Da, Db • Comments: Ranching, degraded pasture. Logging activities. Paved highway. Possible outlet to the Pacific. Arrival of soybean. Urban growth. Chico Mendes Extractive Reserve. Government of Jorge Viana.
Diagnostic elements: *Alteration of forest cover:* 4 • *Infrastructure:* 3 • *Agricultural frontier:* 4 • *Urban dynamics:* 4 • *Logging:* 4 • *Mining:* 1 • *Pesca:* 1 • Action recommended: *Conservation:* 3 • *Sustainable use:* 5 • *Sustainable production:* 4 • *Public policies:* 5 • *Research and development of pilot projects:* 4.

PA 007 - BR-364 Highway, Acre - Priority level: C • Location: *State:* Acre/Amazonas • *Main municipality:* Feijó • *Municipalities covered:* 12 • Vegetation types: AA, Ab, Da, Db • Comments: Logging activities. Possible outlet to the Pacific. Agricultural and ranching frontier. Recently paved highway.
Diagnostic elements: *Alteration of forest cover:* 3 • *Infrastructure:* 3 • *Agricultural frontier:* 2 • *Urban dynamics:* 2 • *Logging:* 4 • *Mining:* 1 • Action recommended: *Conservation:* 3 • *Sustainable use:* 4 • *Sustainable production:* 3 • *Public policies:* 5 • *Research and development of pilot projects:* 3.

PA 008 - Cruzeiro do Sul - Priority level: C • Location: *State:* Acre/Amazonas • *Main municipality:* Cruzeiro do Sul • *Municipalities covered:* 6 • Vegetation types: AA, Ab, Da, Db, La, Ld • Comments: Possible outlet to the Pacific. Road connection with Rio Branco and the southeast. Upper Juruá Extractive Reserve. Serra do Divisor National Park. Indigenous lands. Logging activities.
Diagnostic elements: *Alteration of forest cover:* 2 • *Infrastructure:* 2 • *Agricultural frontier:* 3 • *Urban dynamics:* 4 • *Logging:* 4 • *Mining:* 1 • *Pesca:* 1 • Action recommended: *Conservation:* 3 • *Sustainable use:* 4 • *Sustainable production:* 3 • *Public policies:* 5 • *Research and development of pilot projects:* 3.

PA 009 - BR-317 Highway - Priority level: B • Location: *State:* Amazonas/Rondônia • *Main municipality:* Manicoré • *Municipalities covered:* 10 • Vegetation types: Ab, Da, Db, Ds, Pa, Sa, SO, Sp • Comments: As an area under extreme pressure, facing widespread deforestation. Due to the predominance of ranching in the municipality, and the precarious state of the Rio Branco to Boca do Acre Highway. Many fires during the summer, confirmed *in loco*. Boca do Acre and Paumari indigenous lands located on the border between Boca do Acre and Lábrea. The region is considered a large producer of cattle, with large ranches in the municipality. Raising and production of tambaqui and other fishes. River transportation via Manaus. Vary small agricultural production with very high returns.
Diagnostic elements: *Alteration of forest cover:* 1 • *Infrastructure:* 2 • *Logging:* 5 • Action recommended: *Conservation:* 1 • *Sustainable use:* 5 • *Sustainable production:* 0.

PA 010 - Upper Juruá - Cruzeiro do Sul - Priority level: C • Location: *State:* Amazonas • *Main municipality:* Eirunepé • *Municipalities covered:* 7 • Vegetation types: AA, Ab, Da, Db, La • Comments: Along the Eirunepé–Cruzeiro stretch there is deforestation of both local origin and related to urban dynamics. An area of seringueiro and ribeirinho populations. The paving of the BR-364 Highway will lead to the increase of settlement along its course.
Diagnostic elements: *Alteration of forest cover:* 4 • *Infrastructure:* 4 • *Agricultural frontier:* 3 • *Urban dynamics:* 4 • *Logging:* 4 • Action recommended: *Conservation:* 2 • *Sustainable use:* 4 • *Sustainable production:* 4 • *Public policies:* 3 • *Research and development of pilot projects:* 4.

PA 011 - Atalaia do Norte - Priority level: D • Location: *State:* Amazonas • *Main municipality:* Tabatinga • *Municipalities covered:* 5 • Vegetation types: AA, Ab, Da, Db, Pa • Comments: Area of low current anthropogenic pressure. However it is an important area, on account of its biodiversity associated with the socio-diversity represented by the presence of several ethnic groups, vulnerable to the expansion of logging activities and to increasing anthropogenic pressure.
Diagnostic elements: *Alteration of forest cover:* 1 • *Infrastructure:* 1 • *Agricultural frontier:* 1 • *Urban dynamics:* 1 • *Logging:* 5 • *Mining:* 1 • *Pesca:* 3 • Action recommended: *Conservation:* 1 • *Sustainable use:* 1 • *Sustainable production:* 4 • *Public policies:* 5 • *Research and development of pilot projects:* 1.

PA 012 - São Gabriel region - Cucuí and outskirts of São Gabriel - Priority level: D • Location: *State:* Amazonas • *Main municipality:* São Gabriel da Cachoeira • *Municipalities covered:* 1 • Vegetation types: Ds, Ld, LO • Comments: In a region of mainly indigenous inhabitants, the highway and its predicted function. With the Northern Perimeter highway, there is the risk of fragmentation of a cultural and ecologically well conserved area. The creation of an indigenous land was requested in 1996.
Diagnostic elements: *Alteration of forest cover:* 1 • *Infrastructure:* 3 • *Agricultural frontier:* 1 • *Urban dynamics:* 3 • *Logging:* 2 • *Mining:* 3 • *Pesca:* 5 • Action recommended: *Conservation:* 1 • *Sustainable use:* 2 • *Sustainable production:* 5 • *Public policies:* 5 • *Research and development of pilot projects:* 4.

PA 013 - Middle Solimões - PRIORITY LEVEL: C • LOCATION: *State:* Amazonas • *Main municipality:* Coari • *Municipalities covered:* 5 • VEGETATION TYPES: AA, Da, Db, Ds, Pa • COMMENTS: Unregulated commercial fishery. Logging. Concentrated population growth. Lack of urban planning. High environmental impact.

DIAGNOSTIC ELEMENTS: *Alteration of forest cover:* 1 • *Infrastructure:* 3 • *Agricultural frontier:* 1 • *Urban dynamics:* 4 • *Logging:* 5 • *Mining:* 1 • *Pesca:* 5 • ACTION RECOMMENDED: *Conservation:* 5 • *Sustainable use:* 5 • *Sustainable production:* 5 • *Public policies:* 5 • *Research and development of pilot projects:* 4.

PA 014 - Manaus - PRIORITY LEVEL: B • LOCATION: *State:* Amazonas • *Main municipality:* Itacoatiara • *Municipalities covered:* 20 • VEGETATION TYPES: AA, Ab, Da, Db, LO, Pa, SO, Sp • COMMENTS: Urban nucleus in expansion. Pressure on water resources. Uncontrolled urban growth. Demand for foodstuffs (fish, vegetables, fresh milk). Electric production (termal and hydro). Solid wastes and untreated effluents.

DIAGNOSTIC ELEMENTS: *Alteration of forest cover:* 5 • *Infrastructure:* 5 • *Agricultural frontier:* 1 • *Urban dynamics:* 5 • *Logging:* 4 • *Pesca:* 3 • ACTION RECOMMENDED: *Conservation:* 5 • *Sustainable use:* 4 • *Sustainable production:* 4 • *Public policies:* 5 • *Research and development of pilot projects:* 2.

PA 015 - BR-174 Highway - PRIORITY LEVEL: C • LOCATION: *State:* Amazonas • *Main municipality:* Presidente Figueiredo • *Municipalities covered:* 4 • VEGETATION TYPES: As, Da, Db, Ds, LO • COMMENTS: International economic linkage corridor. Recent paving transformed it into a new center for settlement. Traverses two important indigenous lands, with impact on indigenous communities.

DIAGNOSTIC ELEMENTS: *Alteration of forest cover:* 1 • *Infrastructure:* 3 • *Agricultural frontier:* 3 • *Urban dynamics:* 1 • *Logging:* 1 • *Mining:* 4 • *Pesca:* 1 • ACTION RECOMMENDED: *Conservation:* 2 • *Sustainable use:* 5 • *Sustainable production:* 5 • *Public policies:* 5 • *Research and development of pilot projects:* 4.

PA 016 - Parintins - PRIORITY LEVEL: C • LOCATION: *State:* Amazonas/Pará • *Main municipality:* Juruti • *Municipalities covered:* 13 • VEGETATION TYPES: AA, Da, Db, Pa, SO, Sp • COMMENTS: Subsistence cultivation: manioc. Low productivity of Brazil nut and rubber collecting. Buffalo raising on the floodplain. Second largest population in the state. Selective logging of rosewood.

DIAGNOSTIC ELEMENTS: *Alteration of forest cover:* 2 • *Infrastructure:* 1 • *Agricultural frontier:* 3 • *Urban dynamics:* 2 • *Logging:* 3 • *Mining:* 1 • *Pesca:* 2 • ACTION RECOMMENDED: *Conservation:* 2 • *Sustainable use:* 5 • *Sustainable production:* 5 • *Public policies:* 3 • *Research and development of pilot projects:* 2.

PA 017 - Apuí - PRIORITY LEVEL: C • LOCATION: *State:* Amazonas/Pará • *Main municipality:* Apuí • *Municipalities covered:* 6 • VEGETATION TYPES: As, Da, Db, Ds, Pa, Sa, SO, Sp • COMMENTS: Possible expansion of the agricultural settlement following the repair of the BR-320 Highway. Current agricultural settlement along the BR-320 Highway.

DIAGNOSTIC ELEMENTS: *Alteration of forest cover:* 5 • *Infrastructure:* 5 • *Agricultural frontier:* 5 • *Urban dynamics:* 2 • *Logging:* 2 • *Mining:* 2 • ACTION RECOMMENDED: *Conservation:* 1 • *Sustainable use:* 4 • *Sustainable production:* 4 • *Public policies:* 4 • *Research and development of pilot projects:* 4.

PA 018 - Boa Vista - PRIORITY LEVEL: B • LOCATION: *State:* Roraima • *Main municipality:* Cantá • *Municipalities covered:* 6 • VEGETATION TYPES: As, Ds, Fs, ON, Sg, SN, Sp • COMMENTS: Strong urban dynamics with creation of a poverty belt and environmental degradation. Possible expansion of these along the highway network.

DIAGNOSTIC ELEMENTS: *Alteration of forest cover:* 5 • *Infrastructure:* 5 • *Agricultural frontier:* 4 • *Urban dynamics:* 5 • *Logging:* 3 • *Mining:* 2 • *Pesca:* 5 • ACTION RECOMMENDED: *Conservation:* 1 • *Sustainable use:* 2 • *Sustainable production:* 4 • *Public policies:* 5 • *Research and development of pilot projects:* 4.

PA 019 - Northern Perimeter Highway in Roraima - PRIORITY LEVEL: B • LOCATION: *State:* Roraima • *Main municipality:* Caracaraí • *Municipalities covered:* 7 • VEGETATION TYPES: As, Da, Ds, Ld, Lg, LO, ON, SO • COMMENTS: Degradation of the biodiversity of the ecotones by the intensification of agricultural settlements (fires).

DIAGNOSTIC ELEMENTS: *Alteration of forest cover:* 5 • *Infrastructure:* 5 • *Agricultural frontier:* 5 • *Urban dynamics:* 2 • *Logging:* 2 • *Mining:* 1 • ACTION RECOMMENDED: *Conservation:* 3 • *Sustainable use:* 2 • *Sustainable production:* 4 • *Public policies:* 4 • *Research and development of pilot projects:* 4.

PA 020 - Cuiabá-Santarém Highway - Pará - PRIORITY LEVEL: C • LOCATION: *State:* Pará • *Main municipality:* Novo Progresso • *Municipalities covered:* 3 • VEGETATION TYPES: AA, As, Cs, Ds, Sd, SN, Sp • COMMENTS: Highway being paved, of increasing importance in linking centers of production, with the port infrastructure of Santarém currently being upgraded. Encompasses important expanding logging centers and allows access to a region of low levels of occupation. Corridor of increasing importance due to its impacts on the area surrounding an important set of indigenous lands along the Xingu river.

DIAGNOSTIC ELEMENTS: *Alteration of forest cover:* 2 • *Infrastructure:* 3 • *Agricultural frontier:* 2 • *Urban dynamics:* 1 • *Logging:* 5 • *Mining:* 3 • ACTION RECOMMENDED: *Conservation:* 1 • *Sustainable use:* 5 • *Sustainable production:* 5 • *Public policies:* 5 • *Research and development of pilot projects:* 4.

PA 021 - Tapajós prospecting region - PRIORITY LEVEL: D • LOCATION: *State:* Pará • *Main municipality:* Itaituba • *Municipalities covered:* 2 • VEGETATION TYPES: AA, As, Da, Ds, SO • COMMENTS: Very intensive gold prospecting. Mercury pollution of water resources, affecting local food safety. Public health problems and endemic diseases. Local deforestation also leading to the pollution of water resources, such as the leaching of soil mercury.

DIAGNOSTIC ELEMENTS: *Alteration of forest cover:* 3 • *Infrastructure:* 1 • *Urban dynamics:* 1 • *Logging:* 2 • *Mining:* 5 • ACTION RECOMMENDED: *Conservation:* 5 • *Sustainable use:* 3 • *Sustainable production:* 3 • *Public policies:* 5 • *Research and development of pilot projects:* 5.

PA 022 - Itaituba - Maués - PRIORITY LEVEL: C • LOCATION: *State:* Amazonas/Pará • *Main municipality:* Aveiro • *Municipalities covered:* 6 • VEGETATION TYPES: AA, As, Da, Db, Ds, Pa • COMMENTS: Selective logging (rosewood, itaúba). Sandy soil areas conductive to understorey fires. Impacts on fauna, forest offers poor food suplly for local fauna. Agricultural cooperatives, manioc for subsistence, Brazil nut/rubber. River with poor fishing. Itaituba Maués Program in planning phase. Decree issued establishing the Tapajós Arapiuns Extractive Reserve (contiguous with the Parintins reserve). The highway may traverse the Sateré Maués Indigenous Reserve. Oil prospecting under discussion. Unfragmented understorey impact of fires.

DIAGNOSTIC ELEMENTS: *Alteration of forest cover:* 0 • *Logging:* 3 • ACTION RECOMMENDED: *Sustainable use:* 5 • *Sustainable production:* 5.

PA 023 - Transamazonica Highway - PRIORITY LEVEL: C • LOCATION: *State:* Pará • *Main municipality:* Uruará • *Municipalities covered:* 10 • VEGETATION TYPES: AA, As, Da, Db, Ds • COMMENTS: Area of intensive human settlement, with low levels of technological capacity and resources, high levels of abandonment of areas.

DIAGNOSTIC ELEMENTS: *Alteration of forest cover:* 5 • *Infrastructure:* 2 • *Agricultural frontier:* 4 • *Urban dynamics:* 5 • *Logging:* 5 • ACTION RECOMMENDED: *Conservation:* 4 • *Sustainable use:* 4 • *Sustainable production:* 5 • *Public policies:* 4 • *Research and development of pilot projects:* 4.

PA 024 - Santarém - Rurópolis - PRIORITY LEVEL: A • LOCATION: *State:* Pará • *Main municipality:* Santarém • *Municipalities covered:* 8 • VEGETATION TYPES: AA, Db, Ds, Pa, SO, Sp • COMMENTS: Area proposed for the creation of a center of soybean cultivation under Pará's economic plan (according to the Secretary for Agriculture). Regional development - construction and entry into operation of waterway carrying grain from Brazil's mid-west.

DIAGNOSTIC ELEMENTS: *Alteration of forest cover:* 5 • *Infrastructure:* 4 • *Agricultural frontier:* 4 • *Urban dynamics:* 4 • *Logging:* 4 • ACTION RECOMMENDED: *Conservation:* 4 • *Sustainable use:* 5 • *Sustainable production:* 5 • *Public policies:* 5 • *Research and development of pilot projects:* 5.

PA 025 - Monte Alegre - PRIORITY LEVEL: A • LOCATION: *State:* Pará • *Main municipality:* Monte Alegre • *Municipalities covered:* 5 • VEGETATION TYPES: AA, As, Da, Db, Ds, Pa, SO, Sp • COMMENTS: Intensive deforestation for the planting of new areas of manioc cultivation. Setting up of manioc flour mills. Activity carried out by traditional populations and by new migrants (from the northeast people). Lumber-mills (logging).

> DIAGNOSTIC ELEMENTS: *Alteration of forest cover:* 4 • *Infrastructure:* 3 • *Agricultural frontier:* 3 • *Urban dynamics:* 2 • *Logging:* 3 • ACTION RECOMMENDED: *Conservation:* 1 • *Sustainable use:* 4 • *Sustainable production:* 4 • *Public policies:* 4 • *Research and development of pilot projects:* 3.

PA 026 - Jari - PRIORITY LEVEL: B • LOCATION: *State:* Amapá/Pará • *Main municipality:* Almeirim • *Municipalities covered:* 5 • VEGETATION TYPES: AA, As, Da, Db, Ds, Pa, SO • COMMENTS: Area strongly affected by Jari project, started at the end of the sixties with guelina, pine and eucalyptus plantations and kaolin and bauxite mining. On a smaller scale, rice plantations. Area rich in forests products, including Brazil nut, and products of the floodplains. There is a patch of red earth. Shifting agriculture has increased in Amapá, with strong population pressure along the highway corridor to Macapá. Special areas: Jari Ecological Station, Cajari Extractive Reserve and the Rio Iratapuru Cachoeira de Santo Antônio Sustainable Development Reserve).

> DIAGNOSTIC ELEMENTS: *Agricultural frontier:* 2 • *Logging:* 5 • *Mining:* 4 • ACTION RECOMMENDED: *Sustainable production:* 5 • *Public policies:* 5 • *Research and development of pilot projects:* 5.

PA 027 - Western Marajó - PRIORITY LEVEL: C • LOCATION: *State:* Pará • *Main municipality:* Breves • *Municipalities covered:* 8 • VEGETATION TYPES: AA, Da, Db, Pa, Sp • COMMENTS: This area has suffered intensive logging of premium woods for export as well as being deforested to supply local markets. It is also suffering a heavy loss of assai palms for palm heart extraction and to supply small canneries. This area may suffer significant impacts from the expected dredging for the waterway, proposed under the Avança Brasil Program (Belém-Macapá waterway).

> DIAGNOSTIC ELEMENTS: *Alteration of forest cover:* 5 • *Infrastructure:* 1 • *Urban dynamics:* 1 • *Logging:* 5 • *Pesca:* 1 • ACTION RECOMMENDED: *Conservation:* 5 • *Sustainable use:* 5 • *Sustainable production:* 1 • *Public policies:* 5 • *Research and development of pilot projects:* 5.

PA 028 - Belém - Bragantina - PRIORITY LEVEL: A • LOCATION: *State:* Maranhão/Pará • *Main municipality:* Viseu • *Municipalities covered:* 53 • VEGETATION TYPES: AA, Da, Db, Pa, Pf • COMMENTS: The population density has historically exerted pressure on the region as forests were replaced by pastures, especially in Castanhal which today has important agricultural and ranching sectors. Touristic potential in the coastal region encourages real estate especulation, which is having strong impacts on the mangroves through uncontrolled development. Road construction that ignores appropriate safeguards, traversing large stretches of mangroves, has caused significant alterations to this ecosystem.

> DIAGNOSTIC ELEMENTS: *Alteration of forest cover:* 5 • *Infrastructure:* 4 • *Agricultural frontier:* 4 • *Urban dynamics:* 4 • ACTION RECOMMENDED: *Conservation:* 4 • *Sustainable use:* 5 • *Sustainable production:* 4 • *Public policies:* 5 • *Research and development of pilot projects:* 5.

PA 029 - Lower Tocantins - PRIORITY LEVEL: B • LOCATION: *State:* Pará • *Main municipality:* Moju • *Municipalities covered:* 14 • VEGETATION TYPES: AA, Da, Db, Pa • COMMENTS: The lower Tocantins region, encompassing Cametá, Limoeiro do Ajuri, Mocajuba, Baião, Oeiras do Pará. Considered an area of very high pressure, due to relentless deforestation, with a predominance of ranches. Destruction of Brazil nut and andiroba trees leading to the disappearance of these species, causing the impoverishment of forests. Game animals and fish have disappeared from these regions.

> DIAGNOSTIC ELEMENTS: *Alteration of forest cover:* 5 • *Infrastructure:* 2 • *Agricultural frontier:* 1 • *Urban dynamics:* 3 • *Logging:* 2 • ACTION RECOMMENDED: *Conservation:* 4 • *Sustainable use:* 2 • *Sustainable production:* 2 • *Public policies:* 3 • *Research and development of pilot projects:* 1.

PA 030 - Paragominas - PRIORITY LEVEL: A • LOCATION: *State:* Pará • *Main municipality:* Paragominas • *Municipalities covered:* 5 • VEGETATION TYPES: AA, Da, Db • COMMENTS: Area of high concentration of logging industries. Plans for developing extensive monoculture (soybean). Establishment of a large meatpacking plant.

> DIAGNOSTIC ELEMENTS: *Alteration of forest cover:* 5 • *Infrastructure:* 5 • *Agricultural frontier:* 5 • *Urban dynamics:* 5 • *Logging:* 5 • *Mining:* 5 • ACTION RECOMMENDED: *Conservation:* 4 • *Sustainable use:* 1 • *Sustainable production:* 4 • *Public policies:* 4 • *Research and development of pilot projects:* 4.

PA 031 - Tucuruí - PRIORITY LEVEL: A • LOCATION: *State:* Pará • *Main municipality:* Itupiranga • *Municipalities covered:* 10 • VEGETATION TYPES: AA, As, Db, Ds • COMMENTS: PA-150 highway paved, Transamazonica Highway. Logging. Ranching. Connection to Belém. Settlements and resettlements. Extractive reserve in the reservoir of the Tucuruí hydro plant.

> DIAGNOSTIC ELEMENTS: *Alteration of forest cover:* 5 • *Infrastructure:* 5 • *Agricultural frontier:* 5 • *Urban dynamics:* 5 • *Logging:* 5 • *Mining:* 2 • *Pesca:* 3 • ACTION RECOMMENDED: *Conservation:* 4 • *Sustainable use:* 4 • *Sustainable production:* 4 • *Public policies:* 5.

PA 032 - Altamira - Novo Repartimento - PRIORITY LEVEL: A • LOCATION: *State:* Pará • *Main municipality:* Pacajá • *Municipalities covered:* 7 • VEGETATION TYPES: AA, As, Db, Ds • COMMENTS: Agricultural expansion, the creation and existence of human settlement, and the occurrence of high value forest wood species (ipê and mahogany). The building of roads at right angles to the south side of the Transamazonica Highway allowing extraction in areas where this species is found.

> DIAGNOSTIC ELEMENTS: *Alteration of forest cover:* 5 • *Infrastructure:* 4 • *Agricultural frontier:* 4 • *Urban dynamics:* 3 • *Logging:* 5 • ACTION RECOMMENDED: *Conservation:* 5 • *Sustainable use:* 5 • *Sustainable production:* 5 • *Public policies:* 4.

PA 033 - Marabá - Redenção - PRIORITY LEVEL: A • LOCATION: *State:* Pará/Tocantins • *Main municipality:* Santana do Araguaia • *Municipalities covered:* 28 • VEGETATION TYPES: AA, As, Dm, Ds, Fa, Sa, Sd, Sg, SN, SO, Sp • COMMENTS: Ranching, soil impoverishment. Area fragmentation.

> DIAGNOSTIC ELEMENTS: *Alteration of forest cover:* 5 • *Infrastructure:* 5 • *Agricultural frontier:* 5 • *Urban dynamics:* 4 • ACTION RECOMMENDED: *Conservation:* 5 • *Sustainable use:* 5 • *Sustainable production:* 5 • *Public policies:* 5 • *Research and development of pilot projects:* 5.

PA 034 - Pará-279 Highway - Kaiapó - PRIORITY LEVEL: B • LOCATION: *State:* Pará • *Main municipality:* São Félix do Xingu • *Municipalities covered:* 6 • VEGETATION TYPES: AA, As, Ds, Sa, Sd, SO • COMMENTS: Former prospecting areas (protection of degraded areas). Logging. Hunting and fishing. Extensive ranching in the surrounding areas. Rivers beginning to silt up. Impacts from selective logging.

> DIAGNOSTIC ELEMENTS: *Alteration of forest cover:* 4 • *Agricultural frontier:* 4 • *Logging:* 4 • *Mining:* 3 • ACTION RECOMMENDED: *Conservation:* 5 • *Sustainable use:* 4 • *Sustainable production:* 4 • *Public policies:* 3.

PA 035 - Macapá, Santana, Northern Perimeter Highway - PRIORITY LEVEL: C • LOCATION: *State:* Amapá/Pará • *Main municipality:* Mazagão • *Municipalities covered:* 11 • VEGETATION TYPES: AA, Da, Db, Ds, Pa, Sd, SO, Sp • COMMENTS: Pacuí: high concentration of producers, although it is a transition area. Northern Perimeter Highway: opening of highway and occupation of settlement areas, implementation of SCOMI, search for valuable minerals. Bailique: degradation of extractive (palm heart) by collectors. Santana: construction of the SCOMI port, construction of industrial area and migration of people from other states.

> DIAGNOSTIC ELEMENTS: *Alteration of forest cover:* 2 • *Infrastructure:* 2 • *Agricultural frontier:* 1 • *Urban dynamics:* 5 • *Logging:* 5 • *Mining:* 2 • *Pesca:* 2 • ACTION RECOMMENDED: *Conservation:* 1 • *Sustainable use:* 5 • *Sustainable production:* 0.

PA 036 - Amapá coastal - PRIORITY LEVEL: B • LOCATION: *State:* Amapá • *Main municipality:* Calçoene • *Municipalities covered:* 7 • VEGETATION TYPES: Da, Db, Ds, Pa, Pf, Sa, SO, Sp • COMMENTS: Region of predominant deforestation, subject to fires. Improper clandestine logging. Mining.

DIAGNOSTIC ELEMENTS: *Alteration of forest cover:* 3 • *Agricultural frontier:* 2 • *Urban dynamics:* 3 • *Logging:* 5 • *Mining:* 5 • *Pesca:* 2 • ACTION RECOMMENDED: *Conservation:* 2 • *Sustainable use:* 2 • *Sustainable production:* 3 • *Public policies:* 4 • *Research and development of pilot projects:* 4.

PA 037 - Pre-Amazon region of Maranhão - PRIORITY LEVEL: A • LOCATION: *State:* Maranhão/Pará • *Main municipality:* Santa Luzia • *Municipalities covered:* 142 • VEGETATION TYPES: AA, Cs, Da, Db, Pa, Pf, Sa, Sd, SN, Sp • COMMENTS: Existing pressures, given logging activities and creation of extensive ranching, as well as settlement projects for small farmers for food production. Degradation of pastures and soil. Deforestation of native forest for charcoal production to supply the steelmaking industries located along the Carajás railway. The areas where babassu palms occur, despite minor loss from ranching activities, are still used for extractive activities.

DIAGNOSTIC ELEMENTS: *Alteration of forest cover:* 5 • *Infrastructure:* 5 • *Agricultural frontier:* 5 • *Urban dynamics:* 1 • *Logging:* 5 • ACTION RECOMMENDED: *Conservation:* 5 • *Sustainable use:* 1 • *Sustainable production:* 1 • *Public policies:* 5 • *Research and development of pilot projects:* 5.

PA 038 - Imperatriz - PRIORITY LEVEL: A • LOCATION: *State:* Maranhão/Pará/Tocantins • *Main municipality:* Açailândia • *Municipalities covered:* 30 • VEGETATION TYPES: AA, Cs, Da, Db, Sa, Sd, SN, Sp • COMMENTS: Area of high population density, clearly affected by the Belém-Brasília Highway and classified as deforested (anthropogenic pressure level: medium to high). Area of intensive grain cultivation, logging and ranching.

DIAGNOSTIC ELEMENTS: *Alteration of forest cover:* 5 • *Infrastructure:* 3 • *Agricultural frontier:* 5 • *Urban dynamics:* 4 • *Logging:* 5 • ACTION RECOMMENDED: *Conservation:* 5 • *Sustainable use:* 5 • *Sustainable production:* 5 • *Public policies:* 5 • *Research and development of pilot projects:* 5.

PA 039 - Balsas - PRIORITY LEVEL: B • LOCATION: *State:* Maranhão/Tocantins • *Main municipality:* Balsas • *Municipalities covered:* 11 • VEGETATION TYPES: Sa, Sd, SN, Sp • COMMENTS: Anthropogenic pressure level: low to medium. Dominance of savannas, which area under pressured from grain cultivation and extensive ranching.

DIAGNOSTIC ELEMENTS: *Alteration of forest cover:* 4 • *Infrastructure:* 3 • *Agricultural frontier:* 4 • *Urban dynamics:* 3 • *Logging:* 4 • ACTION RECOMMENDED: *Conservation:* 3 • *Sustainable use:* 3 • *Sustainable production:* 3 • *Public policies:* 3 • *Research and development of pilot projects:* 3.

PA 040 - Bico do Papagaio - PRIORITY LEVEL: A • LOCATION: *State:* Maranhão/Pará/Tocantins • *Main municipality:* Araguatins • *Municipalities covered:* 39 • VEGETATION TYPES: AA, As, Cs, Da, Ds, Sa, Sd, SO, Sp • COMMENTS: Ranching, soil impoverishment. Area fragmentation.

DIAGNOSTIC ELEMENTS: *Alteration of forest cover:* 5 • *Infrastructure:* 5 • *Agricultural frontier:* 4 • *Urban dynamics:* 2 • ACTION RECOMMENDED: *Conservation:* 5 • *Sustainable use:* 5 • *Sustainable production:* 5 • *Public policies:* 5 • *Research and development of pilot projects:* 5.

PA 041 - Belém-Brasília Highway - PRIORITY LEVEL: A • LOCATION: *State:* Pará/Tocantins • *Main municipality:* Dois Irmãos do Tocantins • *Municipalities covered:* 52 • VEGETATION TYPES: AA, As, Ds, Fa, Sa, Sd, Sg, SN, SO, Sp • COMMENTS: Deforestation. Ranching.

DIAGNOSTIC ELEMENTS: *Alteration of forest cover:* 5 • *Infrastructure:* 5 • *Agricultural frontier:* 2 • *Urban dynamics:* 4 • ACTION RECOMMENDED: *Conservation:* 5 • *Sustainable use:* 5 • *Sustainable production:* 5 • *Public policies:* 5 • *Research and development of pilot projects:* 5.

PA 042 - Gurupi - PRIORITY LEVEL: A • LOCATION: *State:* Goiás/Tocantins • *Main municipality:* Araguaçu • *Municipalities covered:* 18 • VEGETATION TYPES: AA, Sa, Sg, SN, Sp • COMMENTS: Region of population growth caused by the Belém-Brasília Highway. Trends of future threats from the Tocantins-Araguaia waterway; lack of conservation areas.

DIAGNOSTIC ELEMENTS: *Alteration of forest cover:* 3 • *Infrastructure:* 3 • *Agricultural frontier:* 4 • *Urban dynamics:* 3 • *Mining:* 1 • ACTION RECOMMENDED: *Conservation:* 3 • *Sustainable use:* 4 • *Sustainable production:* 4 • *Public policies:* 4 • *Research and development of pilot projects:* 2.

PA 043 - Aurora do Tocantins - PRIORITY LEVEL: C • LOCATION: *State:* Goiás/Tocantins • *Main municipality:* Arraias • *Municipalities covered:* 7 • VEGETATION TYPES: AA, Cs, Fs, Sa, SN • COMMENTS: Region of intensive agriculture and ranching activities (crops and cattle). Lack of conservation areas.

DIAGNOSTIC ELEMENTS: *Alteration of forest cover:* 3 • *Infrastructure:* 2 • *Agricultural frontier:* 3 • *Urban dynamics:* 2 • ACTION RECOMMENDED: *Conservation:* 3 • *Sustainable use:* 3 • *Sustainable production:* 4 • *Public policies:* 3 • *Research and development of pilot projects:* 3.

PA 044 - BR-070 and BR-364 Highways (western Mato Grosso) - PRIORITY LEVEL: B • LOCATION: *State:* Mato Grosso • *Main municipality:* Tangará da Serra • *Municipalities covered:* 47 • VEGETATION TYPES: AA, Cs, Fa, Fb, Fs, ON, Pa, Sa, Sd, Sg, SN, Sp, ST, TN • COMMENTS: The area is characterized by the presence of ranches of more than 1,000 hectares, with significant deforestation. Some settlements in the Cáceres and Comodoro region have increased anthropogenic pressure and may potentially increase habitat fragmentation.

DIAGNOSTIC ELEMENTS: *Alteration of forest cover:* 5 • *Infrastructure:* 4 • *Agricultural frontier:* 5 • *Urban dynamics:* 3 • *Logging:* 4 • *Mining:* 5 • ACTION RECOMMENDED: *Conservation:* 4 • *Sustainable use:* 4 • *Sustainable production:* 4 • *Public policies:* 4 • *Research and development of pilot projects:* 3.

PA 045 - Juína - Apiacás - PRIORITY LEVEL: B • LOCATION: *State:* Mato Grosso • *Main municipality:* Juara • *Municipalities covered:* 15 • VEGETATION TYPES: AA, As, Da, Ds, Fa, ON, Sa, Sd, SN, SO, Sp • COMMENTS: High levels of deforestation. Growth of ranching with possible degradation of pastures.

DIAGNOSTIC ELEMENTS: *Alteration of forest cover:* 4 • *Infrastructure:* 4 • *Agricultural frontier:* 5 • *Urban dynamics:* 3 • *Logging:* 4 • *Mining:* 5 • ACTION RECOMMENDED: *Conservation:* 4 • *Sustainable use:* 4 • *Sustainable production:* 4 • *Public policies:* 4 • *Research and development of pilot projects:* 3.

PA 046 - Cuiabá - Santarém Highway - Mato Grosso - PRIORITY LEVEL: A • LOCATION: *State:* Mato Grosso/Pará • *Main municipality:* Marcelândia • *Municipalities covered:* 30 • VEGETATION TYPES: AA, As, Cs, Da, Ds, Fa, Fs, ON, Pa, Sa, Sd, Sg, SN, SO, Sp • COMMENTS: Important Amazon occupation corridor which encompasses important centers of activity: ranching, agriculture and selective logging. Recent paving has accelerated deforestation and uncontrolled processes of land occupation and natural resource uses. The region contains the headwaters of important tributaries of the Xingu and the Teles Pires. Occupation corridor is causing a growing impact on the biodiversity associated to with the socio-diversity of the Xingu Indigenous Park.

DIAGNOSTIC ELEMENTS: *Alteration of forest cover:* 5 • *Infrastructure:* 4 • *Agricultural frontier:* 4 • *Urban dynamics:* 4 • *Logging:* 5 • *Mining:* 3 • ACTION RECOMMENDED: *Conservation:* 4 • *Sustainable use:* 5 • *Sustainable production:* 5 • *Public policies:* 5 • *Research and development of pilot projects:* 4.

PA 047 - Barra do Garças - Vila Rica - PRIORITY LEVEL: B • LOCATION: *State:* Mato Grosso/Pará/Tocantins • *Main municipality:* Querência • *Municipalities covered:* 24 • VEGETATION TYPES: AA, As, Fa, Fs, ON, Pa, Sa, Sd, SN, SO, Sp • COMMENTS: The area is suffering intensive anthropogenic pressure since the fifties with government tax incentives for the establishment of agricultural and ranching projects. There is currently a market trend towards soybean cultivation, and deforestation continues. The region already contains a good road network increasing anthropogenic pressure.

DIAGNOSTIC ELEMENTS: *Infrastructure:* 4 • *Agricultural frontier:* 5 • ACTION RECOMMENDED: *Sustainable production:* 0 • *Public policies:* 4 • *Research and development of pilot projects:* 5.

PA 048 - Canarana - Paranatinga - PRIORITY LEVEL: B • LOCATION: *State:* Mato Grosso • *Main municipality:* Paranatinga • *Municipalities covered:* 6 • VEGETATION TYPES: AA, Fa, ON, Pa, Sa, Sd, SN, Sp • COMMENTS: Region containing main Xingu tributaries, importance for the conservation of the basin, whose degradation is increasingly affecting the sustainability of biodiversity and socio-diversity of the

Xingu Indigenous Park. Region with increasing levels of deforestation and a growing road network. The increasing growth of anthropogenic activity requires action to regulate the process of land occupation, so as to protect the river and the Xingu Park.

DIAGNOSTIC ELEMENTS: *Alteration of forest cover:* 4 • *Infrastructure:* 3 • *Agricultural frontier:* 5 • *Urban dynamics:* 4 • *Logging:* 1 • *Mining:* 1 • ACTION RECOMMENDED: *Conservation:* 4 • *Sustainable use:* 4 • *Sustainable production:* 4 • *Public policies:* 5 • *Research and development of pilot projects:* 4.

PA 049 - Rondonópolis - PRIORITY LEVEL: A • LOCATION: *State:* Mato Grosso • *Main municipality:* Poxoréo • *Municipalities covered:* 28 • VEGETATION TYPES: AA, Fa, Fs, Pa, Sa, Sd, Sg, SN, Sp • COMMENTS: Population pressure (area with municipalities with population density above 10 inhabitants per square kilometer). Region of expanding soybean cultivation and ranching, with high cattle population density.

DIAGNOSTIC ELEMENTS: *Alteration of forest cover:* 4 • *Infrastructure:* 4 • *Agricultural frontier:* 4 • *Urban dynamics:* 3 • *Mining:* 2 • ACTION RECOMMENDED: *Conservation:* 5 • *Sustainable use:* 4 • *Sustainable production:* 4 • *Public policies:* 4 • *Research and development of pilot projects:* 3.

12
PRIORITY AREAS FOR DEVELOPMENT CORRIDORS*

An established goal of the Brazilian government has been to restructure or create national transportation and development corridors. The main purpose of this is to stimulate domestic production and the internal and international integration of Brazil, expanding the frontiers of development. Highways, waterways and railroads will open the way for industry, agriculture, stock raising and commerce, which will now be able to reach remote locations.

These transportation and production corridors will link the Brazilian Amazon region to markets in Peru, Bolivia, Venezuela, Guyana and French Guiana, thereby shortening the distance to American and European export markets, as well as enabling communication with the Pacific.

The corridors have also been created to stimulate centers of production. Large scale cultivation of soybean and maize, cattle raising, timber production and agriculture will be encouraged by a reduction in transportation and production costs. In addition, there will be greater and easier access to natural resources.

There are currently four main integration and development corridors with an impact on the Amazon region: the northern arc corridor; the Madeira-Amazonas corridor; the Araguaia-Tocantins corridor; and the western corridor.

The northern arc corridor comprises the states of Roraima and Amapá and currently includes four planned or completed infrastructure projects: the paving of the BR-174 highway allowing the linking of Manaus to Caracas by a 2,331 kilometer highway, connecting the Brazilian market to those of the Caribbean, Central America and the east coasts of the Nafta member countries; the Guri (Venezuela) to Boa Vista power line of around 780 kilometers (560 kilometers in Venezuela and 220 kilometers in Brazil), ensuring power supplies for twenty years by meeting demands of up to 200,000 Kw; paving 90 kilometers of the BR-401 highway between Boa Vista and Bonfim, thereby repairing the highway through to Georgetown, Guyana; and paving 460 kilometers of the BR-156 highway between Tracajuba, Amapá and Oiapoque, Amapá with the aim of the economic integration of Amapá and linking Brazil and French Guiana.

The Madeira-Amazonas corridor has the largest number of planned or completed projects. There are seven projects designed to integrate the Amazon region into the rest of the country: the Madeira waterway designed to improve the navigability of 1,056 kilometers of the Madeira river; the Tapajós-Teles Pires waterway with a length of 1,043 kilometers; the Marajó waterway intended to inter-connect the Atuá (67 kilometers) and Anajás (207 kilometers) river basins on the island of Marajó, thereby forming a corridor which will shorten the sailing distance between the cities of Belém, Pará and Macapá, Amapá by more than 140 kilometers; the paving of the BR-163 highway between Santarém, Pará and the state border with Mato Grosso; paving 200 kilometers of the BR-317 highway between the Fazenda Vaca Branca and Assis Brasil, Acre, and by repairing the 140 kilometer stretch between Rio Branco and the Fazenda Vaca Branca; construction of the 1,007 kilometer Tucuruí power line, connecting Tucuri, Altamira, Rurópolis, Santarém and Itaituba; and the exploitation of the Urucu-Juruá gas fields in Amazonas, with the capacity to produce 4 million cubic meters of natural gas a day.

The Araguaia-Tocantins corridor comprises the states of Goiás and Tocantins, parts of Maranhão, Pará and Mato Grosso, and the Federal District and will permit important economic links between Brazilian regions. Its area of influence includes some of the most important grain producing and livestock areas, thereby allowing transport and distribution to internal and external markets at reduced distances and costs. The following projects constitute this corridor: the Araguaia Tocantins waterway made up of the das Mortes, Araguaia, and Tocantins rivers with a length of 1,516 kilometers; the North-South Railroad with two lines and a total length of 963 kilometers connecting the region of Colinas do Tocantins, Tocantins to the Carajás Railroad at Açailândia, Maranhão, and Porongatu, Goiás to Senador Canedo, Goiás; the BR-153 highway between Marabá, Pará and São Geraldo, Pará; paving of 132 kilometers of the Transamazonica highway (BR-230) between Marabá and Altamira, in Pará; the Rio Capim Waterway; and the construction of a 1,276 kilometer 500 Kw power line connecting the northern/northeastern electricity grid to the southern/southeastern/midwestern grid.

The western corridor, comprising Mato Grosso, Mato Grosso do Sul, part of Rondônia and one city in Pará, is regarded as the new frontier of the country's economic and agricultural development. The program includes the repair of 520 kilometers of the BR-364, 070 and 163 highways and the setting up of the Ferronorte railroad. This is a railroad transportation network comprising two lines (Santa Fé do Sul, São Paulo via Alto Taquari, Mato Grosso to Cuiabá, Mato Grosso and Uberlândia, Minas Gerais to Alto Araguaia, Mato Grosso, 1,728 kilometers) and two long sections towards the north (Cuiabá to Porto Velho,

---

* Text drawn in part from 'Amazon integration and development corridors – projects and plans' by Marky Brito and 'Overview of land use in Amazonia: timber, agriculture and livestock' by Adalberto Veríssimo, Eugênio Arima and Eirivelthon Lima, the full versions of which can be found on pages 318 and 324 of this book.

a distance of 1,500 kilometers; and Cuiabá to Santarém, a distance of 2,000 kilometers).

Current data show that agriculture and livestock activities are concentrated in the south of the Amazon Basin within an arc which that extends from northeastern and southern Pará through northern Mato Grosso to Rondônia. Logging occurs mainly in terra firme forests found in the north of the 'arc of deforestation'. This 'logging belt' can extend further into northern Mato Grosso and western Pará because of the presence of mahogany, a species of high commercial value. Logging also occurs along the main rivers of the Amazon Basin. The areas where intensive logging is taking place are those which are most likely to be deforested in the near future.

The geography of agricultural usage and of logging may change if the new infrastructure projects planned by the federal government and the projects in support of the proposed 'development hubs' are implemented. For instance, paving highways will reduce timber transportation costs and will increase the economic reach of logging (Souza Jr. et al. 1999). In the same way, incentives for large scale agriculture such as soybean will lead to changes in the geography of land use. It will be possible to plant soybean in forest areas or in areas that are currently used for grazing, thereby moving cattle-raising to even more marginal forest areas (Arima & Uhl 1997).

During the Macapá Workshop, eighteen priority areas in Amazonia for development corridors and hubs were identified (see the map on page 449 and the listing). Of these, five (27.8%) show the highest levels of impacts from roads and four (22.2%) are at high risk from deforestation and fires (Table 12).

TABLE 12 - PRIORITY AREAS FOR DEVELOPMENT CORRIDORS AND HUBS DIAGNOSTIC ELEMENTS THAT SCORE HIGHEST		
Diagnostic elements	Number of areas	%[1]
Deforestation	4	22.2
Impacts of roads	5	27.8
Risk of fires	4	22.2
Logging	1	5.6
Lack of conservation areas	2	11.1
Human settlements	0	–

1. Of the total proposed areas (18).

ED 001 - Amapá - PRIORITY LEVEL: C • LOCATION: *State:* Amapá • *Main municipality:* Calçoene • *Municipalities covered:* 12 • VEGETATION TYPES: AA, Da, Db, Ds, Pa, Pf, Sa, Sd, SO, Sp • COMMENTS: High level of conservation of primary forest, expected risks from paving of the BR-156 highway and its socio-environmental impacts. Presence of indigenous areas.

DIAGNOSTIC ELEMENTS: *Deforestation:* 1 • *Impact of roads:* 4 • *Risk of fires:* 2 • *Logging:* 1 • *Lack of conservation areas:* 3 • *Human settlements:* 2.

ED 002 - Marabá - Paragominas - PRIORITY LEVEL: A • LOCATION: *State:* Maranhão/Pará/Tocantins • *Main municipality:* Paragominas • *Municipalities covered:* 147 • VEGETATION TYPES: AA, As, Cs, Da, Db, Dm, Ds, Fa, Sa, Sd, Sg, SO, Sp • COMMENTS: Area of high deforestation, very high risk of fires, important centers of anthropogenic impacts (settlements, important road network, significant logging activities, and small conservation areas of insignificant sizes).

DIAGNOSTIC ELEMENTS: *Deforestation:* 5 • *Impact of roads:* 5 • *Risk of fires:* 5 • *Logging:* 5 • *Lack of conservation areas:* 3 • *Human settlements:* 4.

ED 003 - Palmas - Bananal - Rio das Mortes - PRIORITY LEVEL: B • LOCATION: *State:* Goiás/Maranhão/Mato Grosso/Pará/Tocantins • *Main municipality:* Santana do Araguaia • *Municipalities covered:* 100 • VEGETATION TYPES: AA, As, Ds, Fa, Fs, ON, Pa, Sa, Sd, Sg, SN, SO, Sp • COMMENTS: Area of high deforestation, with patches at middle and high risk of forest fires. Long-standing intensive logging. A former economic frontier whose potential should be made use of through investments in roads, waterways and soybean. The area contains a few protected areas fragments which merit a special conservation attention.

DIAGNOSTIC ELEMENTS: *Deforestation:* 4 • *Impact of roads:* 5 • *Risk of fires:* 5 • *Logging:* 4 • *Lack of conservation areas:* 2 • *Human settlements:* 3.

ED 004 - Savannas - Mato Grosso/Pará - PRIORITY LEVEL: C • LOCATION: *State:* Mato Grosso • *Main municipality:* Poxoréo • *Municipalities covered:* 42 • VEGETATION TYPES: AA, Fa, Fs, ON, Pa, Sa, Sd, Sg, SN, SO, Sp • COMMENTS: Former frontier area, with deforestation, logging, and moderate risk of forest fires (level 4). Soybean cultivation in the savanna threatens the region, and does the concentration of settlement projects.

DIAGNOSTIC ELEMENTS: *Deforestation:* 4 • *Impact of roads:* 5 • *Risk of fires:* 4 • *Logging:* 2 • *Lack of conservation areas:* 5 • *Human settlements:* 3.

ED 005 - Lower Amazonas - PRIORITY LEVEL: C • LOCATION: *State:* Pará • *Main municipality:* Almeirim • *Municipalities covered:* 10 • VEGETATION TYPES: AA, As, Da, Db, Ds, Pa, SO, Sp • COMMENTS: High deforestation, medium sized highway network, lack of protected areas and low number of settlements.

DIAGNOSTIC ELEMENTS: *Deforestation:* 4 • *Impact of roads:* 3 • *Risk of fires:* 4 • *Logging:* 2 • *Lack of conservation areas:* 3 • *Human settlements:* 2.

ED 006 - Transamazonica Highway - PRIORITY LEVEL: A • LOCATION: *State:* Pará • *Main municipality:* Uruará • *Municipalities covered:* 10 • VEGETATION TYPES: AA, As, Da, Db, Ds • COMMENTS: The Transamazonica corridor is experiencing increasing deforestation, with no effective monitoring or control. On the one hand, there is uncontrolled deforestation from rapidly expanding logging, leaving the area more susceptible to forest fires. On the other, there is very small environmental protection area.

DIAGNOSTIC ELEMENTS: *Deforestation:* 5 • *Impact of roads:* 5 • *Risk of fires:* 3 • *Logging:* 3 • *Lack of conservation areas:* 4 • *Human settlements:* 4.

ED 007 - BR-163 Highway - Pará - PRIORITY LEVEL: B • LOCATION: *State:* Amazonas/Mato Grosso/Pará • *Main municipality:* Itaituba • *Municipalities covered:* 16 • VEGETATION TYPES: AA, As, Cs, Da, Db, Ds, Fs, ON, Pa, Sa, Sd, Sg, SN, SO, Sp • COMMENTS: Agricultural frontier in expansion with the creation of centers of soybean cultivation and logging. There is also the region's vulnerability to forest fires because of its degree of inflammability as a result of the degradation of water resources.

DIAGNOSTIC ELEMENTS: *Deforestation:* 2 • *Impact of roads:* 2 • *Risk of fires:* 5 • *Logging:* 3 • *Lack of conservation areas:* 1 • *Human settlements:* 2.

ED 008 - Teles Pires - Juruena - PRIORITY LEVEL: A • LOCATION: *State:* Mato Grosso/Pará • *Main municipality:* Juara • *Municipalities covered:* 57 • VEGETATION TYPES: AA, As, Cs, Da, Ds, Fa, Fs, ON, Pa, Sa, Sd, SN, SO, Sp • COMMENTS: The southernmost of area 8 has been being settled since the 1970s with land use directed towards soybean and cotton monocultures. From the 1990s, this land use has crossed the 12ºS parallel moving northwards. The main actors of this process have been lobbying for the continued expansion of their businesses in the area. Existing and planned investments in communications, together with increasing fires and the settlement of migrants, represents a risk for the area of ecological transition between savanna and forest with significant impacts not only for biodiversity but also for the status of the Juruena, Teles Pires and Tapajós rivers.

DIAGNOSTIC ELEMENTS: *Deforestation:* 5 • *Impact of roads:* 3 • *Risk of fires:* 5 • *Logging:* 3 • *Lack of conservation areas:* 2 • *Human settlements:* 3.

ED 009 - Boa Vista - PRIORITY LEVEL: B • LOCATION: *State:* Roraima • *Main municipality:* Caracaraí • *Municipalities covered:* 11 • VEGETATION TYPES: As, Da, Ds, Fs, Ld, Lg, LO, ON, Sg, SN, SO, Sp • COMMENTS: Critical area due to risk of fires and to the BR-174 highway. Expanding settlements.

DIAGNOSTIC ELEMENTS: *Deforestation:* 2 • *Impact of roads:* 4 • *Risk of fires:* 3 • *Logging:* 2 • *Lack of conservation areas:* 2 • *Human settlements:* 3.

ED 010 - Manaus - PRIORITY LEVEL: A • LOCATION: *State:* Amazonas • *Main municipality:* Itacoatiara • *Municipalities covered:* 13 • VEGETATION TYPES: AA, As, Da, Db, Ds, LO, Pa, SO, Sp • COMMENTS: Area of influence of the Manaus-Boa Vista (BR-174) highway and deforestation in the area surrounding Manaus. Expanding logging in the outlying areas of the municipality.

DIAGNOSTIC ELEMENTS: *Deforestation:* 2 • *Impact of roads:* 4 • *Risk of fires:* 4 • *Logging:* 4 • *Lack of conservation areas:* 2 • *Human settlements:* 2.

ED 011 - Madeira - PRIORITY LEVEL: C • LOCATION: *State:* Amazonas • *Main municipality:* Manicoré • *Municipalities covered:* 4 • VEGETATION TYPES: Ab, Da, Db, Pa, SO, Sp • COMMENTS: Means of making the Madeira-Amazonas corridor sustainable. Development potential despite the sparse population. Patches of savanna (Humaitá).

DIAGNOSTIC ELEMENTS: *Deforestation:* 1 • *Impact of roads:* 3 • *Risk of fires:* 1 • *Logging:* 1 • *Lack of conservation areas:* 3 • *Human settlements:* 1.

ED 012 - Polonoroeste - PRIORITY LEVEL: A • LOCATION: *State:* Mato Grosso/Rondônia • *Main municipality:* Comodoro • *Municipalities covered:* 70 • VEGETATION TYPES: AA, Ab, As, Cs, Da, Db, Ds, Fa, Fb, Fs, ON, Pa, Sa, Sd, SN, SO, Sp • COMMENTS: Area of very high pressure from human occupation and deforestation, BR-364 highway corridor, priority area for monitoring and control. There is a high concentration of settlements and colonization projects, near a network of conservation areas located around the area (or within it). There is a strong pressure from mining interests.

DIAGNOSTIC ELEMENTS: *Deforestation:* 5 • *Impact of roads:* 5 • *Risk of fires:* 3 • *Logging:* 4 • *Lack of conservation areas:* 4 • *Human settlements:* 4.

ED 013 - Urucu natural gas fields - PRIORITY LEVEL: C • LOCATION: *State:* Amazonas • *Main municipality:* Coari • *Municipalities covered:* 4 • VEGETATION TYPES: Ab, Da, Db • COMMENTS: This area is proposed because of the high level of natural gas exploitation by Petrobras. There is currently uncontrolled deforestation, as well as pollution (domestic and chemical waste), creating ecological imbalance.

DIAGNOSTIC ELEMENTS: *Deforestation:* 2 • *Impact of roads:* 1 • *Risk of fires:* 1 • *Logging:* 1 • *Lack of conservation areas:* 2 • *Human settlements:* 1.

ED 014 - Rio Branco - PRIORITY LEVEL: A • LOCATION: *State:* Acre/Amazonas/Rondônia • *Main municipality:* Rio Branco • *Municipalities covered:* 13 • VEGETATION TYPES: AA, Ab, Da, Db • COMMENTS:

Area of influence of the capital of Acre, possible international integration (Assis Brasil-Puerto Maldonado, Peru). Good extractive community organization (Xapuri).

DIAGNOSTIC ELEMENTS: *Deforestation:* 4 • *Impact of roads:* 4 • *Risk of fires:* 2 • *Logging:* 2 • *Lack of conservation areas:* 3 • *Human settlements:* 4.

ED 015 - BR-364 Highway - Acre - PRIORITY LEVEL: C • LOCATION: *State:* Acre/Amazonas • *Main municipality:* Sena Madureira • *Municipalities covered:* 5 • VEGETATION TYPES: AA, Ab, Da, Db • COMMENTS: State corridor with potential for international integration. Agricultural and ranching potential on good soil.

DIAGNOSTIC ELEMENTS: *Deforestation:* 2 • *Impact of roads:* 3 • *Risk of fires:* 1 • *Logging:* 1 • *Lack of conservation areas:* 2 • *Human settlements:* 3.

ED 016 - BR-364 Highway - Acre - PRIORITY LEVEL: C • LOCATION: *State:* Acre/Amazonas • *Main municipality:* Feijó • *Municipalities covered:* 6 • VEGETATION TYPES: AA, Ab, Da, Db • COMMENTS: State corridor with potential for international integration. Agricultural and ranching potential on good soil.

DIAGNOSTIC ELEMENTS: *Deforestation:* 2 • *Impact of roads:* 3 • *Risk of fires:* 1 • *Logging:* 1 • *Lack of conservation areas:* 2 • *Human settlements:* 3.

ED 017 - BR-364 Highway - Acre - PRIORITY LEVEL: C • LOCATION: *State:* Acre/Amazonas • *Main municipality:* Cruzeiro do Sul • *Municipalities covered:* 5 • VEGETATION TYPES: AA, Ab, Da, Db, La • COMMENTS: State corridor with potential for international integration. Agricultural and ranching potential on good soil.

DIAGNOSTIC ELEMENTS: *Deforestation:* 2 • *Impact of roads:* 3 • *Risk of fires:* 1 • *Logging:* 1 • *Lack of conservation areas:* 2 • *Human settlements:* 3.

ED 018 - Amapá savannas - PRIORITY LEVEL: B • LOCATION: *State:* Amapá • *Main municipality:* Tartarugalzinho • *Municipalities covered:* 6 • VEGETATION TYPES: AA, Da, Ds, Pa, Pf, Sa, Sd, SO, Sp • COMMENTS: Unusual example of savanna in the Amazon region and its fragility in the face of anthropogenic pressure from economic activity and from the presence of the BR-156 highway. High risk of fire. Eucalyptus plantation for production of wooden roof tiles.

DIAGNOSTIC ELEMENTS: *Deforestation:* 3 • *Impact of roads:* 4 • *Risk of fires:* 4 • *Logging:* 1 • *Lack of conservation areas:* 5 • *Human settlements:* 1.

General recommendations

WG1 – STRICT PROTECTION CONSERVATION AREAS

Basic principles

- Brazilian sectoral policies should include an environmental component and the country should invest in public policies for biodiversity conservation;
- The system of conservation for the region should be conceived in such a way as to include indigenous lands; federal, state and municipal conservation areas, both strict protection and sustainable use; and strategies for the sustainable use of natural resources;
- Bearing in mind the enormous gaps in our knowledge of the distribution, conservation and use of biodiversity, research in the Legal Amazon region needs to be given priority.

Critical activities

- Full implementation of existing conservation areas;
- Regularization of the land titles of conservation areas;
- Resolution of conflicts involving indigenous lands and traditional populations;
- Increase in the human resources available for conservation area management;
- Institutional cooperation;
- Development of scientific research;
- Zoning, management and administration of conservation areas;
- Systematization and dissemination of information;
- Ecological viability (buffer zones, connectivity, critical areas minimum viable area, etc.);
- Financial stability;
- Use of conservation areas and buffer zones;
- Illegal occupation and outside interference in conservation areas;
- Creation of conservation areas

Action proposed

Full implementation of existing conservation areas
- Regularization of the land titles of all conservation areas: look for alternative mechanisms to generate resources for regularizing titles (environmental compensation, writing off public debts, etc.) and for legal instruments that will allow the fairest forms of compensation for occupancy or the use of natural resources by traditional populations;
- Resolution of conflicts involving indigenous lands: creation of task forces to resolve specific cases and comprising the social actors involved, include Funai, Ibama, and indigenous groups;
- Resolution of conflicts involving traditional populations: carry out an overall assessment of conflicts between conservation areas and traditional peoples, and convene a workshop to discuss the issue;
- Reinforce governmental and non-governmental cooperation with a view to fully implementing conservation areas;
- Study the creation of a trust fund or other equivalent mechanisms capable of ensuring the financial stability needed for the implementation and maintenance of conservation areas;
- Encourage and promote environmental education and sustainable development practices among local populations;
- Create low impact economic opportunities for local populations linked to the existence of conservation areas so as to minimize impacts and illegal occupations;
- Provide financial incentives for municipalities and states hosting strict protection conservation areas, such as the existing tax on environmental goods and services.

Creation of conservation areas
- Use the outcomes of the 1999 Macapá Workshop to guide the creation of conservation areas in Amazonia;
- Encourage and regulate the different means of cooperation for the management and administration of conservation areas;
- Strengthen technical procedures for evaluating the real potential of areas in order to identify the appropriate category and ensure ecological viability (buffer zones, connectivity, critical areas, minimum viable area), taking into consideration all social actors involved;
- Increase the size of the area of the Brazilian Legal Amazon region under protection so as to ensure, as a first step (over the next five years), a minimum of 10% as strict protection conservation areas.

Institutional strenghtening and cooperation
- Reinforce institutional coalitions for the creation and viability of conservation areas;
- Strengthen the public bodies responsible for conservation area management, including the hiring and training of human resources;
- Strengthen non-governmental organizations operating in conservation areas;
- Encourage, regulate and establish cooperation mechanisms for conservation area management and administration.

Scientific research and dissemination of information

- Support to programs of integrated research on knowledge and monitoring of biodiversity in conservation areas;
- Development of programs of research on conservation areas;
- Creation of specific lines of finance by research funding bodies aimed at implementation of programs of research on conservation areas;
- Development of programs for building capacity among local populations for data collection and biodiversity monitoring in conservation areas;
- Use the outcomes of the Macapá Workshop to prioritize research within each conservation area and between areas;
- Creation of a minimum protocol for the collection and systematization of data on conservation areas (biotic, abiotic, social and institutional);
- Dissemination of information about conservation areas in language accessible to different audiences (local, regional, national and international) and development of initiatives to value protected areas.

WG2 – ECONOMIC USE OF ALTERED AREAS

General principles and the strategic orientation that should guide the economic use of altered areas

- Recognition of the importance of restoring altered areas as part of reestablishing the ecosystem functions of forests; recognition of the important role such areas play as buffer zones for protecting forest stands through the development of economic activities;
- Economic use and restoration of altered areas by means of forest management, agroforestry systems and reforestation. For example, 'green belts' can be created to contain the expansion of the agricultural frontier, which is unsustainable in its present form;
- Future human settlements should occupy areas already cleared which, in many cases, already offer good infrastructure; always bearing in mind basic social and environmental criteria;
- The Brazilian government should engage in the discussions on the operating rules for the Clean Development Mechanism as this is currently one of the most promising new financial mechanisms for supporting economic activities in altered areas;
- Inter-institutional collaboration between federal, state and municipal bodies, financial agencies and institutions engaged in training and capacity building is essential for ensuring that economic activities in altered areas achieves economic, social and environmental sustainability;
- Areas created as areas of permanent protection and which suffer alteration (e.g. riverbanks and headwaters, mountain peaks, and others), should be restored;
- Urban areas in Amazonia were considered to be altered areas by the working group; however they were not addressed, given the complexities of addressing them;
- The basic elements that should guide the economic use of altered areas are: adding value to their products; more equitable distribution of income; increased status of local action; diversification of the local productive base; and improvement in living standards for local populations.

Action proposed

Economic activities proposed by altered area type				
Activities	Secondary growth	Exploited forest	Flooded grasslands and floodplains	Deforested areas
Agroforestry systems	■			■
Extractive activities and handicrafts	■	■	■	
Family agriculture	■		■	■
Forest management (timber)		■		
Reforestation	■			■
Intensive agriculture			■	■
Livestock management				■
Ecotourism	■	■	■	■
Aquaculture			■	

Agroforestry systems

- Provide private community institutions with technical assistance;
- Incorporate agroforestry systems into municipal and state level agricultural policies;
- Involve farmers and producers in the design of programs of support (policies and credit);
- Strengthen the community association movement;
- Undertake in a participative fashion pilot demonstration projects for the diffusion of agroforestry system technologies;
- Regularize land titles;
- Training of local research and development agents (administration, commerce, product processing);
- Differentiated lines of credit (risks/activities).

Extractive activities

- Strengthen the community association movement;
- Support technical research for adding value to extractive products;
- Expand access to lines of credit (FNO-Prodex) to populations outside extractive reserves;
- Set up training workshops to build technical capacity of communities, promote exchange of experiences between projects, communities and activities;
- Set up and/or publicize clearing houses for extractive products with the involvement of financial institutions;
- Diversify the basket of extractive products;
- Improve participation and representation of extractive workers in decision making related to extractive activities;
- Ensure sustainable use by means of management plans;
- Strengthen certification initiatives.

Family agriculture

- Guarantee access to land and regularization of land titles;
- Credit: adjust calendar of payments to the maturing of the investment, release credit on a schedule compatible with the agricultural calendar (i.e. release credit for land preparation before the start of the rainy season) and harmonize interest rates with the capacity for a return on the investment;
- Support family schools;
- Disseminate models of semi-intensive agriculture;
- Strengthen the community association and cooperative movements.

Forest management

- Guarantee titling of areas for forest management (especially areas containing communities);
- Support the certification of forest management and campaigns to stimulate trade in certified timber;
- Establish training centers for forest management techniques;
- Encourage the development of community forest management: disseminate experiences, interchange between projects, etc.;
- Improve inter-institutional collaboration in order to encourage forest management in indigenous areas, where appropriate;
- Set the rules for forest management in conservation areas and indigenous lands.

Reforestation

- Guarantee access and title over areas in order to reduce the risk of future loss of the investment (reforestation);
- Set up forest replanting associations in the region;
- Structure financial support such that they meet the needs for long term investments;
- Prioritize native species and multiple use species (oils, firewood, timber);
- Encourage partnerships between small farmers (for the planting of forest essential oils) and the timber industry;
- Encourage the financing of reforestation in cleared areas by the Clean Development Mechanism (Kyoto Protocol).

Intensive agriculture

- Prioritize infrastructural improvements in already occupied (deforested) areas and not in still forested areas;
- Encourage programs of improvement of animal and plant species for small family farmers;
- Strengthen technical assistance to associations and cooperatives;
- Encourage partnerships between associations and local NGOs;
- Encourage captive breeding of wild animals.

Livestock management in flooded grassland and floodplains

- Set up stockbreeding systems compatible with the socio-environmental characteristics of the region (support capacity, selection of areas);
- Technical assistance and research on appropriate management techniques (animal health);
- Regularize land titles.

Ecotourism

- Create training programs to improve the skills of the local labor force;
- Provide training to populations in the buffer zones in order that ecotourism can become an opportunity for local income generation;
- Put in place the planning and participative management (by means of a management committee) of ecotourism projects in order to reduce negative impacts on local populations;
- Ensure infrastructure is appropriate to the local situation;
- Establish specific credit lines for the sector and support the creation of projects in communities where there is tourist potential and where there is a demand for this.

Aquaculture

- Encourage research on native species;
- Regional inter-institutional collaboration that aims to share experience and disseminate results;
- Establish a center for specific regional research.

WG3 – INDIGENOUS LANDS

Given the fundamental importance of indigenous lands for the conservation of the biodiversity of the Brazilian Amazon (making up more than 20% of the overall extent of the region, with the existence of forests and other associated ecosystems in a relatively better state of conservation, and also by containing the social and cultural diversity represented by the indigenous peoples living in the region), the working group charged with proposing strategic actions for the conservation of the biodiversity of these areas and seeking to bring together, better understand and systematize the information on this theme observed in the different thematic and regional working groups, proposes the following measures:

- Conclude the process of identification and demarcation of indigenous lands;
- Create a specific legal regime for the protection of biodiversity in indigenous lands compatible with the exclusive usufruct rights of the inhabitant population, applicable to especially important biological and landscape areas located within these lands;
- Extend the application of the legal protection regime to areas surrounding conservation areas and indigenous lands;
- Establish task forces made up of representatives of Ibama or the Ministry of the Environment and of the resident indigenous communities to work out negotiated solutions on a case by case basis for overlaps between indigenous lands and strict protection conservation areas;
- Review (by law or by decree) the instruments establishing those national forests superimposed on indigenous lands, so as to remove all existing overlaps;
- Assist indigenous populations inhabiting lands identified as priority areas for biodiversity conservation to carry out ethno-zoning;
- Provide technical and financial support to indigenous community projects aiming at economic sustainability, sustainable management and conservation of the natural resources present on their lands;
- Develop and carry out programs of biodiversity research involving indigenous communities and scientific research institutions or centers;
- Establish, under the aegis of the Ministry of the Environment, a permanent multilateral body bringing together governments, indigenous representatives and civil society of the Amazonian countries to consider joint policies or policies compatible with the protection of the biodiversity of indigenous lands located in national border regions;
- Develop and establish, under the aegis of the Ministry of the Environment, a national program for monitoring the environmental status of indigenous lands;
- Design and establish a joint program involving the federal agencies responsible for monitoring the conservation areas and indigenous lands located in the Legal Amazon region;
- Prioritize within restoration programs those environmentally degraded areas located within indigenous lands;
- Identify areas, located within indigenous lands and considered priorities for biodiversity conservation, which can be used as test cases for integrated socio-environmental planning, especially cases where there are superimpositions or juxtapositions with conservation areas;
- Respect the exclusive usufruct rights of indigenous communities in the procedures for regulating third party access to genetic resources found on their lands and associated traditional knowledge.

WG4 – SUSTAINABLE USE CONSERVATION AREAS AND TRADITIONAL POPULATIONS

Traditional populations are understood to be those whose systems of production and use of natural resources are of low environmental impact, allowing ecosystem reproduction. These populations, totaling approximately two million people in the Amazon region, and the sustainable use conservation areas, which currently cover 7.2% of the Amazon region, perform an important role in biodiversity conservation by bringing together social demands and the sustainable use of ecosystems and of biological resources.

As means for optimizing the role of these factors in the conservation and sustainable use of biodiversity and the equitable sharing of its benefits, the group proposes:

With respect to traditional populations:

- Acknowledge that traditional populations form part of a global strategy for biodiversity conservation;
- Acknowledge collective intellectual rights as an instrument for the protection of the knowledge held by traditional populations and as recompense for the use of their genetic resources and associated knowledge, within the framework of the draft law on access to genetic resources, whose approval by the National Congress is a priority;
- The striking out of paragraph XV of article 2 of draft law 2.892-B of 1992, dealing with the national system of conservation areas, which defines the term traditional population, given that the proposed definition does not satisfactorily address the situation of innumerable populations employing low environmental impact use and production systems;
- Increase understanding of traditional populations as regards their distribution (mapping), socioeconomic and cultural characteristics, organization, production systems and associated resources, and sustainable development projects, as well as their land tenure status and ecosystem conservation services (wild and domesticated biodiversity);
- Establish compensatory mechanisms, in the form of adequate remuneration, for the costs to extractive populations or associations of environmental conservation or conservation area management;
- Create appropriate incentive and support policies for the transport, export and commercialization of agro-extractive products both inside and outside sustainable use conservation areas;
- Set up initiatives for the support, conservation and improvement of traditional production systems, across all sectoral policies, emphasizing technical assistance, agricultural training and rural extension services;
- The national program for agricultural research should take account of the diversity of local production systems, assisting the development of technologies appropriate to the needs of traditional communities;
- Establish regular lines of credit and finance that meet the needs of traditional communities;
- Revise and adapt the Prodex program along the lines of the Procera program;
- Undertake studies of production alternatives that better meet the needs of traditional populations;
- Public authorities should give priority to regularizing land titles of the areas occupied by traditional populations, recognizing their tenure or ownership rights over the land and respecting their forms of social organization;
- Implement an ecological agrarian reform taking into account the forest potential of the Amazon region and the socio-cultural diversity of its local populations;
- Institutionally strengthen the Centro Nacional de Desenvolvimento das Populações Tradicionais (CNPT) transforming it into a national sustainable development agency for traditional populations, under the aegis of the Ministry of the Environment.

With respect to sustainable use conservation areas:

- Consolidate existing conservation areas and apply the legal protection regime to their surrounding areas: obtain the financial resources needed to regularize the legal titles of existing conservation areas; establish tasks forces made up of the appropriate government bodies (Ibama, Incra, Funai, etc.) and the local communities involved in order to resolve the conflicts in cases of overlapping conservation areas; speed up the concession contracts and conclude the process of demarcation of the conservation areas; and implement management, utilization, master and development plans for extractive reserves and other conservation areas;
- Implement sustainable development projects ensuring the participation of local populations;
- Strengthen the institutional capacity of social organizations, training human resources in economic, environmental, social and cultural management and developing institutional partnerships;
- Simplify and speed up procedures for releasing financial resources and the approval of plans and projects for the development of conservation areas;
- Identify and acknowledge local demands for the creation of conservation areas;
- Create and consolidate conservation areas in accordance with local demands;
- Establish a management group that brings together research institutions, local populations, and civil society organizations for the preparation, concession and monitoring of plans for exploiting the natural resources of national forests;
- Ensure compliance with the proposals emerging from the state ecological-economic zoning processes relating to conservation areas;
- Establish programs for the processing and vertical linkage of local level agro-extractive production, finding appropriate energy options for this purpose.

WG5 – RESEARCH ON BIOLOGICAL AND CULTURAL DIVERSITY

Training of human resources

- Preserve and strengthen the public universities of Amazonia as a strategic means for expanding teaching and research in the region;
- Reestablish the commitment of the funding agencies (Capes, CNPq and Finep) to the Northern Research and Postgraduate Training Program;
- Create mechanisms to oblige environmental use projects to invest in human resource training at all levels in Amazonia;
- Increase the number of postgraduate course on priority subjects for Amazonia; establish inter-institutional and inter-regional

programs by making use of existing holders of masters and doctoral degrees;
- Increase funding for human resource training in Amazonia at a rate not less than the direct proportion of its population or gross domestic product;
- Increase support for national and international exchanges of teachers and researchers on Amazonia;
- Improve the training of primary and secondary level teachers in the region by means of agreements between local state governments and universities, research institutes and the Ministry of Education;
- Expand the process of undergraduate training in Amazonian universities through Pibic, RHAE, PET and other instruments such as voluntary internships;
- Increase human resource training in specific areas by means of short term specialist courses;
- Create and implement systems of accessing bibliographic information (electronic databases and online journals) in support of teaching and research.

Retaining human resources

- Establish differentiated mechanisms for immediate hiring by Amazon teaching and research institutions;
- Offer competitive salaries in order to attract new well-qualified human resources to Amazon institutions;
- Encourage the creation and continuity of research groups committed to the training of human resources in and for Amazonia;
- Promote the move to the interior by professionals engaged in training by means of increased allowances for those working in rural areas.

General policies for strengthening research in the region

Financial support to research

- Create state research support foundations in all the states of Legal Amazonia, with a priority focus on the identification, use and management of biodiversity;
- Establish environmental compensation funds, to be administered by these foundations, with the resources directed towards research;
- Create a requirement for partnerships between consultancy firms and Amazon institutions for the preparation of environmental impact assessments;
- Make regional representation obligatory on bodies with decision-making powers over research projects in the region (Capes, CNPq and Finep);
- Create lines of financial support under the Pronabio for special long term programs: inventories, biodiversity monitoring, support to collections, databases, training of human resources at all levels for research on biodiversity;
- Strengthen existing lines of finance for biodiversity research, such as the Northern Research and Postgraduate Training Program, the Integrated Ecology Program and the FNMA;
- Establish partnerships between research institutes and the Probem to undertake a program in support of biological collections and the training and retention of human resources specialized in systematics.

Strengthening infrastructure and institutional interaction

- Creation of a permanent forum of regional research institutions to promote thematic discussion on the identification, use and management of biodiversity;
- Creation of special program of support to the improvement of the infrastructure of governmental and non-governmental scientific research institutes carrying out research on biological and cultural diversity in the Amazon region;
- Creation of permanent field research stations in strict protection conservation areas in each of the ecoregions of Amazonia;
- Digitation and availability of the information currently existing in the archives of regional botanical and ethnological collections, together with efforts to repatriate the information existing in overseas institutions;
- Long term investment in the creation of high speed connectivity for the exchange of electronic data between institutions;
- Support to the creation of thematic laboratories and the adaptation of existing laboratories.

Access to biological resources

- Legal distinction between access to biological resources for scientific research undertaken by research institutions and biodiversity prospecting by commercial companies;
- Guarantee and facilitation of inter-institutional exchanges of collected materials;
- Cutting red tape surrounding scientific visits by foreign researchers.

Dissemination of information

- Availability of resources for the publication of regional scientific journals;
- Setting up of thematic groups to study new ways of analyzing data on biological and cultural diversity;
- Production of teaching materials on Amazonia for use in primary and secondary schools in Brazil;
- Production of support materials for regional primary and secondary school teachers;
- Training courses for journalists on basic concepts of Amazonian biological and cultural diversity;
- Production of thematic books on Amazonia, such as taxonomic and environmental guides;
- Development of museological and environmental education research with a view to informing the general public about research carried out on the biological and cultural diversity of Amazonia;
- Support to radio and television programs of dissemination of scientific research on and in Amazonia;
- Establishment of a large scale information system on biological and cultural diversity in Amazonia, covering everything from regional library holdings to successful sustainable development experiments.

Priority research themes

- Need to include primary data in environmental impact assessments of proposed large scale development investments, especially those under the federal government multi-year investment plan;

- Creation of a national committee to develop strategies and procedures for multidisciplinary research programs on Amazon biodiversity;
- Creation of a national program of integrated biological inventories, supported by a special credit line from funding bodies, for the areas identified by the biome workshops as priorities for inventories;
- Creation of a forum, to include representation of the scientific community, for discussion on regulations for the transport and collection of wild organisms;
- Strengthening of the molecular biology laboratories existing in the region to carry out research on the genetic diversity of species;
- Creation and expansion (in the case of those already existing) of regional collections of Amazon tissue cultures;
- Creation of programs of support to scientific research aimed at improving techniques for monitoring, management and assessment of environmental impacts appropriate to the Amazon region, and development of standard protocols;
- Creation of special research programs intended to develop strategies for the sustainable use of Amazon biological diversity;
- Creation of a special training program for researchers and incentives for research on ethno-biology;
- Creation of a research program to develop techniques for the mitigation of impacts of specific anthropogenic activities on the Amazon environment and involving those generating the impacts (for example, mining and logging enterprises) in the financing of the research;
- Creation of an Amazon cultural diversity program aimed at mapping cultural diversity and environmental use strategies existing in the region;
- Incentives for research on the connection between environmental change and the spread of tropical diseases in Amazonia;
- Strengthening laboratories undertaking research on biotechnology and the chemistry of regional natural products;
- Socio-economic-environmental review of the productive and commercial chains involved in hunting, fishing, extraction of forest plant products, mining, ecotourism and ecological volunteering.

WG6 – ANTHROPOGENIC PRESSURES AND DEVELOPMENT CORRIDORS

The recommendations of the discussion group took into account deforested areas (15% of Legal Amazonia) and areas of forest cover (75% of the territory). Intact areas with no forest cover (10%) – natural grasslands and savannas – were not discussed as these areas were the subject of another event: the Savanna and Wetland Workshop.

Recommendations for altered areas

General objective: support the intensification of agriculture in areas already deforested. This will lead to an increase in productivity, raise the economic rate of return and fix farmers to these areas. In this way there would be little incentive to expand the agricultural frontier into forested areas.

Specific action recommended:
- Infrastructure: increase and improve local roads, the power transmission network, and communication within the deforested areas. This intensification of infrastructure will help reduce the costs of transportation, improve access to services (health, education), improve communications, and generate an increase in agricultural productivity;
- Credit: redirect credit provided by public banks (Basa, Banco do Brasil, BNDES) in support of sustainable resource use and the intensification of the use of altered areas, in order to fix populations in these areas and, as a result, hold back the advance of the agricultural frontier onto forested lands and helping, in particular, small producers;
- Extension services: provide technical assistance and training, particularly to small producers, in order to improve productivity in deforested areas;
- Economic-ecological zoning: tie the provision of public resources (credit, infrastructure, services) and agricultural credit to the zoning recommendations;
- Social democracy: ensure the participation of traditional populations in the decision-making process, especially in the processes of preparing, undertaking and evaluating development projects and programs;
- Community interchange: encourage the creation of a network for the exchange of experiences of sustainable natural resource use projects;
- Participative research: participative research in local development projects;
- Prevention of fires: implement partnerships between local communities, non-governmental organizations and government agencies for action to prevent accidental fires and to restrict or alter the terms of credit to farmers and ranchers who do not prepare and implement plans and measures for the prevention of accidental fires;
- Dissemination of agroforestry systems: encourage the adoption of agroforestry systems in light of the social, economic and (above all) environmental benefits they bring;
- Clean Development Mechanism: support the obtaining of international resources for carbon fixing by means of reforestation of degraded areas;
- Commercialization: encourage the commercialization of agricultural, agroforestry and extractive products through the intensification of their production in deforested areas (secondary growth);
- Inventory of opportunities: inventory the socio-economic uses of natural resources in deforested areas taking into account the potential for generating jobs and indicators of environmental, social and economic sustainability;
- Protection of the Legal Reserve: ensure the maintenance of the legal forest reserve established in law (80% of the property) in deforested areas. In cases of non-compliance, require the replanting of such areas with forest species (especially native species);
- Support fund for sustainable practices: creation of a financial fund for sustainable development in deforested areas of Amazonia, with public funds (Finam, Finor);

Recommendations for forested areas

General objective: ensure the forest potential of Amazonia by means of the maintenance of its native vegetation given its economic value (timber and non-timber forest products), environmental services (fire prevention, watershed protection, climate regulation), biological value, social and anthropological importance, tourism potential and hydroelectric potential.

Specific action recommended
- Forest use: encourage activities which maintain the forest cover (managed forest, planted forest, and mature secondary forest), agroforestry systems, perennial crops (palm oil, coffee, cocoa), extractive activities (rubber, assai);
- Forest management: promote sustainable forest management emphasizing multiple use (timber and non-timber forest products);
- Ecotourism: support ecotourism which promotes regional culture and offers employment opportunities to local communities;
- Management and protection of floodplains: study the viability of sustainable development reserves in floodplain regions for forest and fish resources management;
- Forest certification: support and encourage certification initiatives for forest products produced sustainably;
- Fire prevention: encourage productive activities that retain forest cover in areas of high risk of forest fires;
- 'Positive Agenda': support environmental management by means of cutting bureaucratic procedures and deadlines for approval of management plans, especially those prepared by local communities and, at the same time, increase the legal obstacles for the authorization of logging in forested areas;
- Environmental education: prepare and implement a program of environmental education in order to increase the public perception of forests as a source of ecological resources and services that are important for improving the standard of living and for the culture of the local inhabitants.

BIBLIOGRAPHY

ALMEIDA, O. T. de; UHL, C. F. *Planejamento do uso do solo do município de Paragominas utilizando dados econômicos e ecológicos*. Belém: Imazon, 1998. (Série Amazônia, 9.)

ANJOS, R. S. A. dos. *Territórios das comunidades remanescentes de antigos quilombos no Brasil*: primeira configuração espacial. Brasilia: Edição do Autor, 1999.

ARAÚJO-LIMA; GOULDING, M. *So fruitful a fish*: ecology, conservation, and aquaculture of the Amazon's Tambaqui. New York: Columbia Univ. Press, 1998. 191 p. (Biology and Resource Management in the Tropics Series.)

ARIMA, E. Y.; UHL, C. Ranching in the Brazilian Amazon in a national context: economics, policy and practices. *Society and Natural Resources*, n. 10, p. 433-51, 1997.

ARNT, R. O tesouro verde. *Revista Exame*, São Paulo: Abril, n. 739, 02/5/2001.

AVILA-PIRES, T. C. S. Lizards of Brazilian Amazonia (Reptilaia: Squamata). *Zool. Verh. Leiden*, 1995. 706 p.

AYRES, J. M.; CLUTTON-BRondôniaCK, T. H. River boundaries and species range size in Amazonian primates. *American Naturalist*, n. 140, p.531-7, 1992.

BALÉE, W. *Footprints of the forest*: Ka'Apor ethnobotany - The historical ecology of plant utilization by Amazonian People. New York: Columbia University Press, 1993

BALICK, M.; COX, P. *Plants, people and culture*: the science of ethnobotany. New York: Scientific American Library, 1996.

BARTHEM, R. B.; GOULDING, M. *The catfish connection*: ecology, migration, and conservation of Amazon predators. New York: Columbia University Press, 1997. 184 p. (Biology and Resource Management in the Tropics Series.)

BAYLEY, P. B. *Central Amazon fish populations*: biomass, production and some dynamic characteristics. Canada: Dalhousie University, 1982. 308 p. (Doctoral thesis in Philosophy, PhD)

BÖHLKE, J. E.; WEITZMAN, S. H.; MENEZES, N. A. Estado atual da sistemática dos peixes de água doce da América do Sul. *Acta Amazônica*. Manaus: Inpa, v. 8, n. 4, p.657-77, dez. 1978.

BRITSKI, E. A. Sobre um novo gênero e espécie de *Sorubiminae* da Amazônia (Pisces, Siluriformes). *Papéis Avulsos de Zoologia*, São Paulo, v. 34, n. 7, p.109-14, 1981.

CAPRELLA, A. P. Neotropical avian diversity and riverine barriers. *Acta Congressus Internationalis Ornithologici*, v. 20, p. 307-16, 1991.

COCHRANE, M. A. O significado das queimadas na Amazônia. *Ciência Hoje*, Rio de Janeiro: SBPC, v.26, n. 157, p.26-31, jan./feb. 2000.

COSTANZA, R. et al. The value of the world's ecosystem services and natural capital. *Nature*, n. 387, p. 253-9, 1997.

CUNHA, O. R. da; NASCIMENTO, F. P. do. Ofídios da Amazônia: as cobras da região do Pará. *Bol. Mus. Paraense Emílio Goeldi: Série Zoologia*, Belém: Museu Paraense Emílio Goeldi, v.9, 191 p., 1993.

DESCOLA, P. Ecologia e cosmologia. In: CASTRO, E.; PINTON, F. (Eds.) *Faces do trópico úmido*: conceitos e questões sobre desenvolvimento e meio ambiente. Belém: Cejup, 1997.

DINERSTEIN, E. et al. *A conservation assessment of the terrestrial ecoregions of Latin America and the Caribbean*. Washington: World Bank, 1995. 156 p.

DIXON, J. R. Origin and distribution of reptiles in lowland tropical rainforests of South America. In: DUELLMAN, W. E. (Ed.) *The South American herpetofauna*: its origin, evolution, and dispersal. Mus. Nat. Hist. Univ. Kansas, 1979. p.217-40. (Monogr., 7).

DUELLMAN, W. E. *Amphibian species of the world*: additions and corrections. Univ. Kansas Mus. Nat. Hist, 1993. 372 p. (Univ. Kansas Mus. Nat. Hist. Spec. Publ., 21).

FEARNSIDE, P. M. Greenhouse gases from deforestation in Brazilian Amazonia: net committed emissions. *Climatic Change*, n. 35, p. 321-60, 1997.

FERREIRA, E.; ZUANON, J. A. S.; SANTOS, G. M dos. *Peixes comerciais do Médio Amazonas*: Região de Santarém, Pará. Brasilia: Ibama, 1998. 211 p.

FERREIRA, L. V. et al. *Análise do grau de vulnerabilidade e implementação das Unidades de Conservação federais de uso indireto no Brasil*: Uma proposta de criação do ranking das unidades brasileiras. Technical report. Brasilia: WWF, 1999.

FROST, D. R. (Ed.) *Amphibian species of the World*. Lawrence: Allen Press, 1985. 732 p.

FUNBIO. *Financiando o uso sustentável da biodiversidade*. Rio de Janeiro: Funbio, 1998. (Estudos Funbio, 1)

GASCON, C.; MOUTINHO, P. *Floresta amazônica*: Dinâmica, regeneração e manejo. Manaus: Inpa, 1998.

GENTRY, A. H. Patterns of neotropical plant species diversity. *Evol. Biol.*, n. 15, 84 p., 1982.

GOULDING, M. Ecology and manegement of migratory food fishes of the Amazon Basin. In: ALMEIDA, F.; PRINGLE, C. M. (Eds.) *Tropical rainforests, diversity and conservation*. San Francisco: California Academy of Sciences, 1988. p.71-85.

GOULDING, M. SMITH, N.; MAHAR, D. J. *Floods of fortune*: ecology & economy along the Amazon. New York: Columbia University Press, 1996. 193 p.

GTA; AMIGOS DA TERRA INTERNACIONAL. Programa Amazônia. *Políticas públicas coerentes*: Para uma Amazônia sustentável, o desafio da inovação e o programa piloto. São Paulo: Amigos da Terra Internacional; Brasília: GTA, 1998. 189 p.

HADDAD, C. F. B. Biodiversidade de anfíbios no estado de São Paulo. In: JOLY, C. A. BICUDO, C. E. de M. (Eds.) *Biodiversidade do estado de São Paulo*: síntese do conhecimento ao final do século XX. v. 6: vertebrados. São Paulo: Fapesp, 1998. p.15-26.

HAFFER, J. *Avian Speciation in South America*. s.l.: Nuttall Ornithological Club, 1974. 390 p. (Publications of the Nuttall Ornithological Club 14)

―――. Distribution of Amazon Avians. *Bonner Zoologischen Beiträgen*, n. 29, p. 38-78, 1978.

―――. On the 'river effect' in some forest Avians of southern Amazonia. *Bol. Mus. Paraense Emílio Goeldi: Série Zoologia*, Belém: Museu Paraense Emílio Goeldi, v. 8, p. 217-45, 1992.

HELLMAYR, C. E. The Avians of the Rio Madeira. *Novitates Zoologicae*, v. 17, p. 257-428, 1910.

HENDERSON-SELLERS, A. et al. Tropical deforestation: modelling local to regional-scale climate change. *Journal Geophysics Research*, n. 98, p. 7289-315, 1993.

IBAMA. http://www.ibama.gov.br/.

IBGE. *Diagnóstico ambiental da Amazônia Legal*. Rio de Janeiro: IBGE, 1997. (CD-Rom)

IBGE; IBDF. *Mapa da vegetação do Brasil*. Brasília: IBGE; IBDF, 1988. (Mapa físico, Escala 1:5.000.000).

INPE. *Relatório desflorestamento na Amazônia*. São José dos Campos: Inpe, 1999.

―――. *Relatório do monitoramento da floresta amazônica brasileira por satélite – 1999-2000*. São José dos Campos: Inpe, 2001.

JIPP, P.; NEPSTAD, D.; CASSLE, K. Deep soil moisture storage and transpiration in forests and pastures of seasonally-dry Amazonia. *Climatic Change*, v. 39, n. 2/3, p.395-412, 1998.

KRUG, T. O quadro de desflorestamento da Amazônia. In: MINISTÉRIO DO MEIO AMBIENTE. Brasil. *Causas e dinâmicas do desmatamento na Amazônia*. Brasilia: MMA, 2001.

LEAN, J.; WARRILOW, D. A. Simulation of the regional climatic impact of Amazon deforestation. *Nature*, v. 342, p. 411-3, 1989.

MARLIER, G. Limnology of the Congo and Amazon Rivers. In: MEGGERS, B. J.; AYENSI, E. S.; DUCKWORTH, W. B. (Eds.) *Tropical forests ecosystem in Africa and South American*: a comparative review. Washington: Smithsoniam Inst. Press, 1973.

MARQUES, O. A. V.; ABE, A. S.; MARTINS, M. Estudo diagnóstico da diversidade de répteis do estado de São Paulo. In: JOLY, Carlos A.; BICUDO, C. E. de M. (Eds.) *Biodiversidade do estado de São Paulo:* síntese do conhecimento ao final do século XX. v. 6: Vertebrados. São Paulo: Fapesp, 1998. p.27-38.

McCONNELL, R. H. Lowe. *Ecological studies in tropical fish communities*. Cambridge: Cambridge University Press, 1987. 382 p.

MENEZES, M. A. O controle qualificado do desmatamento e o ordenamento territorial na região Amazônica. In: MINISTÉRIO DO MEIO AMBIENTE. Brasil. *Causas e dinâmicas do desmatamento na Amazônia*. Brasília: MMA, 2001.

MENEZES, N. A. Methods for assessing freshwater fish diversity. In: BICUDO, Carlos Eduardo de Mattos; MENEZES, N. A., (eds.) *Biodiversity in Brazil*: a first aproach. Proceedings of the Workshop Methods for the Assessment of Biodiversity in Plants and Animals held at Campos do Jordão, SP, Brazil, 26-30 May 1996. s.l.: s.ed., 1996. p.289-96.

MINISTÉRIO DO MEIO AMBIENTE. Brasil. *Primeiro relatório nacional para a Convenção sobre Diversidade Biológica*. Brasilia: MMA, 1998.

MÜLLER, F. de M. Sistema de Fiscalização, licenciamento e monitoramento de propriedades rurais de Mato Grosso do Sul. In: MINISTÉRIO DO MEIO AMBIENTE. Brasil. *Causas e dinâmicas do desmatamento na Amazônia*. Brasilia: MMA, 2001.

NELSON, B. W.; F., C. A. C.; SILVA, M. F., KAWASAKI, M. L. Endemism centres, refugia and botanical collection density in Brazilian Amazonia. *Nature*, n. 345, p. 714-6, 1990.

NELSON, J. S. *Fishes of the world*. n.l.: John Wiley & Sons, 1994. 600 p.

NEPSTAD, D. C. et al. The ecological importance of forest remnants in an eastern Amazonian frontier landscape. In: SCHELLAS, J.; GREENBERG, E. (Ed.) *Forest Patches in Tropical Forest Landscapes*. Washington: Island Press, 1996. p.133-50.

NEPSTAD, D. C. et al. Large-scale impoverishment of Amazonian forests by logging and fire. *Nature*, n. 398, p. 505-8, 1999.

NEPSTAD, D.; MOUTINHO, P.; MARKEWITZ, D. The recovery of biomass, nutrient stocks, and deep soil function in secondary forests. In: McCLAIN, M.; VICTORIA, R.; RICHEY, J. (Eds.) *Biogeochemistry of the Amazon*. Oxford University Press. forthcoming.

NOBRE, C. A.; SELLERS, P. J.; SHUKLA, J. Amazonian deforestation and regional climate change. *J. Climate*, n. 4, p.957-88, 1991.

PRANCE, G. T. Vegetation. In: WHITMORE, T. C.; PRANCE, G. T. (Eds.) *Biogeography and quaternary history in Tropical America*. Oxford: Clarendon Press, 1987. 214 p. (Oxford Monographs on Biogeography nº 3)

RADAM BRASIL. *Levantamento de Recursos Naturais*. vols 1-18. Rio de Janeiro: Ministério de Minas e Energia/Departamento Nacional de Produção Mineral, 1968-1978.

RIBEIRO, B. *Amazônia urgente. Cinco século de história e ecologia*. Belo Horizonte: Itatiaia, 1990.

ROBERTS, T. R. Ecology of fish in the Amazon and Congo basins. *Bulletin of the Museum of Comparative Zoology*, Harvard, n.143, p.117-47, 1972.

SALES, G. O sistema nacional de unidades de *Conservation:* o estado atual. SEMINÁRIO INTERNACIONAL SOBRE PRESENÇA HUMANA EM UNIDADES DE CONSERVAÇÃO (1996: Brasília, DF). *Anais*. Brasília: Câmara dos Deputados; ISA; Ipam; PPG-7; WWF, 1996. p.14-20.

SANTOS, M. dos. Composição dos pescado e situação da pesca no Estado de Rondônia. *Acta Amazônica*, Manaus: Inpa, v.16/17, p.43-84, 1986/1987.

SANTOS, M. dos; JEGU, M.; MERondôniaNA, B. de. *Catálogo de peixes comerciais do baixo rio Tocantins. Projeto Tucuruí*. Manaus: Eletronorte/CNPq/Inpa, 1984. 83 p.

SAWYER, D. *Índice de pressão antrópica*: uma proposta metodológica. Brasília: ISPN, 1997.

SHIMABUKURO, Y. E. et al. *Roraima*: o incêndio visto do espaço. *Ciência Hoje*, Rio de Janeiro: SBPC, v.26, n. 157, p.32-4, jan./fev. 2000.

SHUKLA, J.; NOBRE, C. A.; SELLERS, P. Amazon deforestation and climate change. *Science*, n. 247, p.1322-5, 1990.

SICK, H. Rios e enchentes na Amazônia como obstáculo para a avifauna. *Atas do Simpósio sobre a Biota Amazônica*. Rio de Janeiro: CNP, v. 5 (Zoologia), p. 495-520, 1967.

SILVA, W. R. Bases para o diagnóstico e o monitoramento da biodiversidade de aves no estado de São Paulo. In: JOLY, C. A.; BICUDO, C. E. de M., (Eds.) *Biodiversidade do estado de São Paulo:* síntese do conhecimento ao final do século XX. v. 6: Vertebrados. São Paulo: Fapesp, 1998. p.41-50.

SIMMONS, N. B.; VOSS, R. S. The mammals of Paracou, French Guiana: a neotropical lowland rainforest fauna part I. bats. *Bul. Am. Mus. Nat. Hist.*, v. 237, 219 p., 1998.

SIOLI, H.; KLINGE, H. Sobre águas e solo da Amazônia brasileira. *Boletim Geográfico*, v.185, p.195-205, 1965.

SIOLI, H. Studies in Amazonian waters. *Atas do Simpósio sobre a Biota Amazônica*, Rio de Janeiro: CNP, v. 3 (Limnologia), p. 9-50, 1967.

—————. Amazon tributaries and drainage basins. In: HASLER, A. D. (Ed.) *Coupling of land and water systems*. Berlim: Springer Verlaz, 1975. p. 199-213.

SNETHLAGE, E. Sobre a distribuição da avifauna campestre na Amazônia. *Bol. Mus. Paraense Emílio Goeldi*, Belém: Museu Paraense Emílio Goeldi, v. 6, p. 226-35, 1910.

SOUZA JÚNIOR, C.; VERISSIMO, A.; AMARAL, P. *Identificação de áreas com potencial para a criação de florestas nacionais no Estado do Pará*. Brasília: MMA; FAO, 1999. 33 p.

STEEGE, H. T. et al. An analysis of the floristic composition and diversity of Amazonian forests including those of the Guiana Shield. *Journal of Tropical Ecology*, v. 16, p.801-27, 2000.

UNEP. An assessment of the status of the World's Remanining Closed Forests. n.l.: UNEP/DEWA/TR, 01/02/2001.

VELOSO, H. P.; RANGEL FILHO, A. L. R.; LIMA, J. C. A. *Classificação da vegetação brasileira, adaptada a um sistema universal*. Rio de Janeiro: IBGE, 1991.

VIVO, M. de. Diversidade de mamíferos do estado de São Paulo. In: JOLY, C. A.; BICUDO, C. E. de M. (Eds.) *Biodiversidade do estado de São Paulo:* síntese do conhecimento ao final do século XX. v. 6: vertebrados. São Paulo: Fapesp, 1998. p.51-66.

VOSS, R. S.; EMMONS, L. H. Mammalian diversity in neotropical lowland rainforests: a preliminary assessment. *Bul. Am. Mus. Nat. Hist.*, v.230, 115 p., 1996.

WALLACE, A. R. *Viagens pelos rios Amazonas e Negro*. São Paulo: Edusp; Belo Horizonte: Itatiaia, 1979. 318 p.

List of participants in the Macapá Workshop (September 1999)

Adalberto Luís Val
Instituto Nacional de Pesquisas da Amazônia
- Aquatic Biota Thematic Working Group
- Rio Negro/Rio Branco Regional Working Group

Adalberto Veríssimo
Instituto do Homem e Meio Ambiente da Amazônia
- Development Corridors Thematic Working Group
- Upper Xingu/Tapajós/Rondônia/Mato Grosso Regional Working Group

Admilson Moreira Torres
Instituto de Pesquisas Científicas e Tecnológicas do Estado do Amapá
- Environmental Goods and Services Thematic Working Group
- Solimões/Amazonas Floodplains Regional Working Group

Adriana Gonçalves Moreira
Instituto de Pesquisa Ambiental da Amazônia
- Environmental Goods and Services Thematic Working Group

Adriana Ramos
Instituto Socioambiental
- Coordination

Alandy Patrícia do Socorro Cavalcante
Instituto de Pesquisas Científicas e Tecnológicas do Estado do Amapá
- New Economic Opportunities Thematic Working Group
- Guiana Shields Regional Working Group

Alexandre Adalardo de Oliveira
Universidade Paulista
- Plants Thematic Working Group
- Rio Negro/Rio Branco Regional Working Group

Alexandre Aleixo
Louisiana State University
- Birds Thematic Working Group
- Lower Xingu/Tapajós/Madeira Regional Working Group

Alicia Rolla
Instituto Socioambiental
- Support

Allen Arthur Jensen
Summer Institute of Linguistics
- Traditional Populations Thematic Working Group

Ana Cristina Araújo Bellini
Departamento Estadual de Turismo do Amapá
- New Economic Opportunities Thematic Working Group
- Guiana Shields Regional Working Group

Ana Cristina Barros
Instituto de Pesquisa Ambiental da Amazônia
- Development Corridors Thematic Working Group

Ana Cristina de Oliveira Cordeiro Duarte
Instituto Nacional de Pesquisas da Amazônia
- Reptiles and Amphibians Thematic Working Group
- Solimões/Amazonas Floodplains Regional Working Group

Ana Yoshi Harada
Museu Paraense Emílio Goeldi
- Invertebrates Thematic Working Group
- Juruá/Purus/Acre Regional Working Group

Analzita Muller e Muller
Secretaria de Coordenação da Amazônia, Ministério do Meio Ambiente
- Development Corridors Thematic Working Group
- Upper Xingu/Tapajós/Rondônia/Mato Grosso Regional Working Group

André Loubet Guimarães
Banco Mundial
- New Economic Opportunities Thematic Working Group

André Villas Boas
Instituto Socioambiental
- Anthropogenic Pressures Thematic Working Group
- Upper Xingu/Tapajós/Rondônia/Mato Grosso Regional Working Group

Andrea Nunes
Museu Paraense Emílio Goeldi
- Mammals Thematic Working Group
- Guiana Shields Regional Working Group

Anthony Brome Rylands
Universidade Federal do Maranhão
- Mammals Thematic Working Group

Antônia de Nazaré Vaz Vidal Pacheco
- Aquatic Biota Thematic Working Group
- Guiana Shields Regional Working Group

Antônio Augusto Ferreira Rodrigues
Universidade Federal do Maranhão
- Birds Thematic Working Group
- Solimões/Amazonas Floodplains Regional Working Group

Antonio Cláudio Almeida Carvalho
Instituto de Pesquisas Científicas e Tecnológicas do Estado do Amapá
- Development Corridors Thematic Working Group
- Guiana Shields Regional Working Group

Antônio Francisco Araújo Almeida
Instituto de Desenvolvimento Rural do Amapá
- Development Corridors Thematic Working Group

Antônio José da Silva Colares
Secretaria de Estado da Agricultura, Pesca, Floresta e do Abastecimento do Amapá
- Development Corridors Thematic Working Group

Antônio Nunes da Silva
Instituto de Desenvolvimento Rural do Amapá
- Traditional Populations Thematic Working Group

Antônio Tebaldi Tardin
Instituto de Pesquisas Científicas e Tecnológicas do Estado do Amapá
- Anthropogenic Pressures Thematic Working Group
- Upper Xingu/Tapajós/Rondônia/Mato Grosso Regional Working Group

Aristóteles Viana Fernandes
Instituto de Pesquisas Científicas e Tecnológicas do Estado do Amapá
- Traditional Populations Thematic Working Group
- Guiana Shields Regional Working Group

Arnaldo Bianchetti
Empresa Brasileira de Pesquisa Agropecuária
- Anthropogenic Pressures Thematic Working Group

Arnaldo de O. da Silva
- Guiana Shields Regional Working Group

Arnaldo Queiroz
Secretaria Estadual de Meio Ambiente
- Aquatic Biota Thematic Working Group

Benedito Vitor Rabelo
Instituto de Pesquisas Científicas e Tecnológicas do Estado do Amapá
- Plants Thematic Working Group

Biraci Brasil
Organização de Agricultores Extrativistas Yawanawá do Rio Gregório
- New Economic Opportunities Thematic Working Group
- Juruá/Purus/Acre Regional Working Group

Braulio Ferreira de Souza Dias
Ministério do Meio Ambiente
- Environmental Goods and Services Thematic Working Group

Bruce Albert
L'Institut de recherche pour le développement and *Instituto Socioambiental*
- Traditional Populations Thematic Working Group
- Rio Negro/Rio Branco Regional Working Group

Bruce Walker Nelson
Instituto Nacional de Pesquisas da Amazônia
- Plants Thematic Working Group
- Juruá/Purus/Acre Regional Working Group

Bruno Veras Nascimento
Instituto de Desenvolvimento Rural do Amapá
• Araguaia/Tocantins/Maranhão Regional Working Group

Carlos Alberto Ricardo
Instituto Socioambiental
• Traditional Populations Thematic Working Group
• Rio Negro/Rio Branco Regional Working Group

Carlos Magno Barbosa Sotão
Secretaria de Estado da Agricultura, Pesca, Floresta e do Abastecimento do Amapá
• New Economic Opportunities Thematic Working Group

Carlos Peres
University of East Anglia
• Mammals Thematic Working Group
• Juruá/Purus/Acre Regional Working Group

Carlos Ros Filho
Banco Mundial
• Development Corridors Thematic Working Group

Carlos Yamashita
Instituto Brasileiro do Meio Ambiente e dos Recursos Naturais Renováveis
• Birds Thematic Working Group
• Juruá/Purus/Acre Regional Working Group

Célio Magalhães Filho
Instituto Nacional de Pesquisas da Amazônia
• Aquatic Biota Thematic Working Group
• Lower Xingu/Tapajós/Madeira Regional Working Group

César Bernardo de Souza
Instituto de Pesquisas Científicas e Tecnológicas do Estado do Amapá
• New Economic Opportunities Thematic Working Group
• Guiana Shields Regional Working Group

Cheyl Joyce Jensen
Summer Institute of Linguistics
• Traditional Populations Thematic Working Group

Claudia Azevedo Ramos
Instituto Federal do Pará
• Reptiles and Amphibians Thematic Working Group

Dafran Gomes Macário
Núcleo de História Indígena Indigenismo, Universidade de São Paulo
• Traditional Populations Thematic Working Group
• Guiana Shields Regional Working Group

Daguinete Maria Chaves B. Gonçalves
Secretaria Estadual de Meio Ambiente
• Conservation Areas Thematic Working Group
• Guiana Shields Regional Working Group

Daniel Joseph Hogan
Universidade Estadual de Campinas
• Anthropogenic Pressures Thematic Working Group
• Araguaia/Tocantins/Maranhão Regional Working Group

Daniel Nepstad
Instituto de Pesquisa Ambiental da Amazônia
• Environmental Goods and Services Thematic Working Group
• Upper Xingu/Tapajós/Rondônia/Mato Grosso Regional Working Group

Daniela A. S. de Oliveira
• Conservation Areas Thematic Working Group
• Guiana Shields Regional Working Group

David C. Oren
Museu Paraense Emílio Goeldi
• Birds Thematic Working Group
• Upper Xingu/Tapajós/Rondônia/Mato Grosso Regional Working Group

Deborah de Magalhães Lima
Universidade Federal do Pará
• Traditional Populations Thematic Working Group
• Solimões/Amazonas Floodplains Regional Working Group

Diliam Pastana Monteiro
Instituto de Desenvolvimento Rural do Amapá
• Development Corridors Thematic Working Group

Diogenes Alves
Instituto Nacional de Pesquisas Espaciais
• Anthropogenic Pressures Thematic Working Group
• Lower Xingu/Tapajós/Madeira Regional Working Group

Dirck Byler
Conservation International
• Consultor

Djalma Dias dos Santos
Instituto Nacional de Colonização e Reforma Agrária/Amapá
• Anthropogenic Pressures Thematic Working Group
• Juruá/Purus/Acre Regional Working Group

Domingos S. Macedo
• Development Corridors Thematic Working Group
• Solimões/Amazonas Floodplains Regional Working Group

Donald R. Sawyer
Instituto Sociedade, População e Natureza
• Anthropogenic Pressures Thematic Working Group

Douglas Daly
New York Botanical Garden
• Plants Thematic Working Group
• Juruá/Purus/Acre Regional Working Group

Edmar Lima Oliveira
Universidade Federal do Amapá
• Invertebrates Thematic Working Group
• Guiana Shields Regional Working Group

Edmar Moretti
Instituto Brasileiro do Meio Ambiente e dos Recursos Naturais Renováveis
• Conservation Areas Thematic Working Group
• Upper Xingu/Tapajós/Rondônia/Mato Grosso Regional Working Group

Edson Cardoso Monteiro
• Guiana Shields Regional Working Group

Edson Guilherme da Silva
Universidade Federal do Acre
• Birds Thematic Working Group
• Juruá/Purus/Acre Regional Working Group

Efrem Jorge Gondim Ferreira
Instituto Nacional de Pesquisas da Amazônia
• Aquatic Biota Thematic Working Group
• Guiana Shields Regional Working Group

Eleneide Doff Sotta
Instituto do Homem e Meio Ambiente da Amazônia
• Anthropogenic Pressures Thematic Working Group
• Upper Xingu/Tapajós/Rondônia/Mato Grosso Regional Working Group

Elenilza Maria Pimentel Bentes Monteiro
Instituto de Pesquisas Científicas e Tecnológicas do Estado do Amapá
• Conservation Areas Thematic Working Group
• Guiana Shields Regional Working Group

Eneida de Almeida Melo
Fundação Tocaia, Universidade Federal do Pará
• Development Corridors Thematic Working Group
• Lower Xingu/Tapajós/Madeira Regional Working Group

Enrique Svirsky
Programa Estadual de Apoio às ONGs, Secretaria de Estado do Meio Ambiente de São Paulo
• New Economic Opportunities Thematic Working Group
• Rio Negro/Rio Branco Regional Working Group

Ernani Pilla
US Agency for International Development
• Environmental Goods and Services Thematic Working Group
• Upper Xingu/Tapajós/Rondônia/Mato Grosso Regional Working Group

Eugênio Arima
Instituto do Homem e Meio Ambiente da Amazônia
• Consultor
• Araguaia/Tocantins/Maranhão Regional Working Group

Fabio de Andrade Abdalla
Secretaria de Estado do Planejamento
• Development Corridors Thematic Working Group
• Rio Negro/Rio Branco Regional Working Group

Fabio Olmos
Universidade Estadual Paulista/Rio Claro
• Birds Thematic Working Group
• Upper Xingu/Tapajós/Rondônia/Mato Grosso Regional Working Group

Francineide Pereira S. Pena
Instituto de Pesquisas Científicas e Tecnológicas do Estado do Amapá
• Development Corridors Thematic Working Group
• Guiana Shields Regional Working Group

Francinete da Silva Facundes
Instituto de Pesquisas Científicas e Tecnológicas do Estado do Amapá
• Anthropogenic Pressures Thematic Working Group
• Guiana Shields Regional Working Group

Geraldo Andrello
Instituto Socioambiental
• Traditional Populations Thematic Working Group
• Rio Negro/Rio Branco Regional Working Group

Geraldo Mosimann da Silva
Instituto Socioambiental
• New Economic Opportunities Thematic Working Group
• Lower Xingu/Tapajós/Madeira Regional Working Group

Gilberto K. Yokomia
• Guiana Shields Regional Working Group

Gilmar Costa de Souza
Secretaria de Estado da Agricultura, Pesca, Floresta e do Abastecimento do Amapá
• Anthropogenic Pressures Thematic Working Group

Giseldo Cardoso
• Aquatic Biota Thematic Working Group

Gláucia Camarão Martins
Secretaria de Estado da Educação
• Conservation Areas Thematic Working Group/Répteis e Anfíbios

Gláucia Moreira Drummond
IEF
- Reptiles and Amphibians Thematic Working Group
- Araguaia/Tocantins/Maranhão Regional Working Group

Guarino Rinaldi Colli
Universidade de Brasília
- Reptiles and Amphibians Thematic Working Group
- Upper Xingu/Tapajós/Rondônia/Mato Grosso Regional Working Group

Hélcio Souza
- Traditional Populations Thematic Working Group
- Lower Xingu/Tapajós/Madeira Regional Working Group

Helder Lima de Queiroz
- Aquatic Biota Thematic Working Group
- Solimões/Amazonas Floodplains Regional Working Group

Helena Fany Pantaleoni Ricardo
Instituto Socioambiental
- Conservation Areas Thematic Working Group
- Rio Negro/Rio Branco Regional Working Group

Hermínio Morales Sandiford
Instituto de Estudos Sócio Ambiental
- Birds Thematic Working Group

Idelberto Conceição do Carmo Pinto
Agência de Desenvolvimento do Amapá
- New Economic Opportunities Thematic Working Group

Inácia Maria Vieira
Instituto de Pesquisas Científicas e Tecnológicas do Estado do Amapá
- Aquatic Biota Thematic Working Group
- Guiana Shields Regional Working Group

Ivanildo Brito
- Solimões/Amazonas Floodplains Regional Working Group

Iza Maria Castro dos Santos
Grupo de Trabalho Amazônico
- Development Corridors Thematic Working Group
- Lower Xingu/Tapajós/Madeira Regional Working Group

Jader Marinho–Filho
Universidade de Brasília
- Guiana Shields Regional Working Group

Janete Moro
- Guiana Shields Regional Working Group

Jansen Alfredo Sampaio Zuanon
Instituto Nacional de Pesquisas da Amazônia
- Aquatic Biota Thematic Working Group
- Lower Xingu/Tapajós/Madeira Regional Working Group

Jesus Manuel Delgado
Cooperativa Mista dos Pequenos Produtores de Bom Jesus da Lapa
- Conservation Areas Thematic Working Group
- Guiana Shields Regional Working Group

Joachim Adis
Max-Planck-Institute for Limnology
- Invertebrates Thematic Working Group
- Rio Negro/Rio Branco Regional Working Group

João Claudio Tupimanbá Arroyo
Instituto Universidade Popular and *Fórum da Amazônia Oriental*
- Development Corridors Thematic Working Group
- Araguaia/Tocantins/Maranhão Regional Working Group

João da Luz Freitas
Instituto de Pesquisas Científicas e Tecnológicas do Estado do Amapá
- Plants Thematic Working Group

João Paulo R. Capobianco
Instituto Socioambiental
- Coordination

José Elias de Souza Ávila
Instituto de Pesquisas Científicas e Tecnológicas do Estado do Amapá
- Development Corridors Thematic Working Group

José Fernando Pacheco
Universidade Federal do Rio de Janeiro
- Birds Thematic Working Group
- Guiana Shields Regional Working Group

José Freire Cordeiro
Departamento Estudual de Turismo do Amapá
- Environmental Goods and Services Thematic Working Group
- Lower Xingu/Tapajós/Madeira and Solimões/Amazonas Floodplains Regional Working Groups

José Heder Benatti
Instituto de Pesquisa Ambiental da Amazônia/Universidade Federal do Pará
- Conservation Areas Thematic Working Group
- Araguaia/Tocantins/Maranhão Regional Working Group

José Hilton Brandão
Secretaria de Estado da Agricultura, Pesca, Floresta e do Abastecimento do Amapá
- Environmental Goods and Services Thematic Working Group

José Maria Cardoso da Silva
Universidade Federal de Pernambuco
- Birds Thematic Working Group
- Araguaia/Tocantins/Maranhão Regional Working Group

José Pedro de Oliveira Costa
Secretaria de Florestas e Biodiversidade/Ministério do Meio Ambiente

José Reinaldo Alves Picanço
Instituto de Estudos Sócio Ambiental
- Development Corridors Thematic Working Group

Júlio Antônio Poubel Pedro
Secretaria de Estado do Planejamento
- Anthropogenic Pressures Thematic Working Group

Laure Emperaire
L'Institut de recherche pour le développement and Instituto Socioambiental
- Anthropogenic Pressures Thematic Working Group
- Rio Negro/Rio Branco Regional Working Group

Leandro O. Salles
Museu Nacional/Universidade Federal do Rio de Janeiro
- Mammals Thematic Working Group
- Rio Negro/Rio Branco Regional Working Group

Leandro Valle Ferreira
WWF
- Aquatic Biota Thematic Working Group
- Solimões/Amazonas Floodplains Regional Working Group

Lúcia Rapp Py–Daniel
Instituto Nacional de Pesquisas da Amazônia
- Aquatic Biota Thematic Working Group
- Upper Xingu/Tapajós/Rondônia/Mato Grosso Regional Working Group

Luciana Sonnewend Blondízio
Centro de Formação e Desenvolvimento de Recursos Humanos
- New Economic Opportunities Thematic Working Group
- Guiana Shields Regional Working Group

Luis Eustorgio Pinheiro Borges
Secretaria de Estado da Educação
- Traditional Populations Thematic Working Group
- Guiana Shields Regional Working Group

Luís Fernando S. Nogueira de Sá
Instituto Brasileiro do Meio Ambiente e dos Recursos Naturais Renováveis
- Conservation Areas Thematic Working Group
- Upper Xingu/Tapajós/Rondônia/Mato Grosso Regional Working Group

Luís Isamu Barros Kansaki
Universidade Federal do Amapá
- Traditional Populations Thematic Working Group
- Guiana Shields Regional Working Group

Luíz Alberto Costa Guedes
Instituto de Pesquisas Científicas e Tecnológicas do Estado do Amapá
- Anthropogenic Pressures Thematic Working Group

Luiz Carlos Castro de Aquino
Secretaria de Estado da Agricultura, Pesca, Floresta e do Abastecimento do Amapá
- Anthropogenic Pressures Thematic Working Group
- Guiana Shields and Alto Xingu/Tapajós/Rondônia/Mato Grosso Regional Working Groups

Luiz Carlos Ros Filho
- Anthropogenic Pressures Thematic Working Group
- Upper Xingu/Tapajós/Rondônia/Mato Grosso Regional Working Group

Luiz Flamarion Barbosa de Oliveira
Museu Nacional/Universidade Federal do Rio de Janeiro
- Mammals Thematic Working Group
- Rio Negro/Rio Branco Regional Working Group

Luíz Paulo de Souza Pinto
Instituto Conservation do Brasil S/C
- Consultant

Makin Menetes
- Conservation Areas Thematic Working Group

Manoel Reinaldo Costa Ferreira
Secretaria Estadual de Meio Ambiente
- Environmental Goods and Services Thematic Working Group
- Guiana Shields Regional Working Group

Marcelo Gordo
Fundação Universidade do Amazonas
- Reptiles and Amphibians Thematic Working Group
- Upper Xingu/Tapajós/Rondônia/Mato Grosso Regional Working Group

Marcelo Leite
Folha de São Paulo
- Press

Márcia Gonçalves Rodrigues
Fundação Aplicações de Tecnologias Críticas
- New Economic Opportunities Thematic Working Group
- Rio Negro/Rio Branco Regional Working Group

Márcio José Brando Santilli
Instituto Socioambiental
- Development Corridors Thematic Working Group
- Lower Xingu/Tapajós/Madeira Regional Working Group

Márcio Sousa da Silva
Instituto de Pesquisas Científicas e Tecnológicas do Estado do Amapá
• Aquatic Biota Thematic Working Group
• Guiana Shields Regional Working Group

Marco Antônio Chagas
• Conservation Areas Thematic Working Group

Marcos Aurélio Bezerra Araújo
Secretaria de Estado da Agricultura, Pesca, Floresta e do Abastecimento do Amapá
• Development Corridors Thematic Working Group

Marcos Reis Rosa
ArcPlan S/C Ltda.

Maria do Socorro Padilha de Oliveira
Empresa Brasileira de Pesquisa Agropecuária/Amazônia Oriental
• Plants Thematic Working Group
• Solimões/Amazonas Floodplains Regional Working Group

Maria Izabel da Silva Alves Coutinho
Secretaria Estadual de Meio Ambiente
• Environmental Goods and Services Thematic Working Group
• Guiana Shields Regional Working Group

Maria Luiza de Araújo Gastal
Ministério do Meio Ambiente
• Conservation Areas Thematic Working Group
• Araguaia/Tocantins/Maranhão Regional Working Group

Maria Nazareth F. Da Silva
Instituto Nacional de Pesquisas da Amazônia
• Mammals Thematic Working Group
• Juruá/Purus/Acre Regional Working Group

Mariluce Messias
• Mammals Thematic Working Group
• Upper Xingu/Tapajós/Rondônia/Mato Grosso Regional Working Group

Mario A. Menezes
Ministério do Meio Ambiente
• Traditional Populations Thematic Working Group
• Upper Xingu/Tapajós/Rondônia/Mato Grosso Regional Working Group

Mario Martins
Secretaria de Estado da Agricultura, Pesca, Floresta e do Abastecimento do Amapá
• Traditional Populations Thematic Working Group

Marky Lowell Rodrigues de Brito
Instituto do Homem e Meio Ambiente da Amazônia
• Development Corridors Thematic Working Group

Marlucia Bonifacio Martins
Museu Paraense Emílio Goeldi
• Invertebrates Thematic Working Group
• Araguaia/Tocantins/Maranhão Regional Working Group

Maurício Pontes Monteiro
Instituto Sociedade, População e Natureza
• Anthropogenic Pressures Thematic Working Group
• Araguaia/Tocantins/Maranhão Regional Working Group

Mauro Henrique Montoril Santiago
Secretaria de Estado da Agricultura, Pesca, Floresta e do Abastecimento do Amapá
• Plants Thematic Working Group
• Guiana Shields Regional Working Group

Mauro Luis Ruffino
Projeto IARA
• Aquatic Biota Thematic Working Group
• Solimões/Amazonas Floodplains Regional Working Group

Mauro William Barbosa de Almeida
Universidade Estadual de Campinas
• Traditional Populations Thematic Working Group
• Juruá/Purus/Acre Regional Working Group

Miguel Ângelo Rôla
Instituto de Pesquisas Científicas e Tecnológicas do Estado do Amapá
• Aquatic Biota Thematic Working Group

Miguel Treffaut Rodrigues
Museu de Zoologia, Universidade de São Paulo
• Reptiles and Amphibians Thematic Working Group
• Lower Xingu/Tapajós/Madeira Regional Working Group

Mike Hopkins
Instituto Nacional de Pesquisas da Amazônia
• Plants Thematic Working Group
• Rio Negro/Rio Branco Regional Working Group

Moacir Bueno Arruda
Instituto Brasileiro do Meio Ambiente e dos Recursos Naturais Renováveis
• Environmental Goods and Services Thematic Working Group
• Araguaia/Tocantins/Maranhão Regional Working Group

Mônica Tavares da Fonseca
Conservation International Brasil
• Mammals Thematic Working Group
• Araguaia/Tocantins/Maranhão Regional Working Group

Mucio Nobre da Costa Ribeiro
Fundação Nacional do Índio
• Anthropogenic Pressures Thematic Working Group

Muriel Saragoussi
Fundação Vitória Amazônica
• Conservation Areas Thematic Working Group
• Rio Negro/Rio Branco Regional Working Group

Neide Esterci
Universidade Federal do Rio de Janeiro
• Traditional Populations Thematic Working Group
• Juruá/Purus/Acre Regional Working Group

Newton Marcelo Nascimento dos Santos
Instituto de Estudos Sócio Ambiental
• Conservation Areas Thematic Working Group
• Guiana Shields Regional Working Group

Nurit Bensusan
Independent Consultant
• Conservation Areas Thematic Working Group
• Araguaia/Tocantins/Maranhão Regional Working Group

Oberdan Mascarenhas
• Conservation Areas Thematic Working Group

Odete Fátima Machado da Silva
Instituto de Pesquisas Científicas e Tecnológicas do Estado do Amapá
• Environmental Goods and Services Thematic Working Group
• Guiana Shields Regional Working Group

Odete Silveira
• Guiana Shields Regional Working Group

Olanise Ferreira dos Santos
Centro de Formação e Desenvolvimento de Recursos Humanos
• Development Corridors Thematic Working Group
• Guiana Shields Regional Working Group

Orlando Assunção Filho
• Anthropogenic Pressures Thematic Working Group
• Lower Xingu/Tapajós/Madeira Regional Working Group

Oswaldo de Carvalho Júnior
Instituto de Pesquisa Ambiental da Amazônia
• Araguaia/Tocantins/Maranhão Regional Working Group

Otizete Amador de Alencar da Penha
Instituto de Pesquisas Científicas e Tecnológicas do Estado do Amapá
• Conservation Areas Thematic Working Group
• Guiana Shields Regional Working Group

Paulo Andreas Buckup
Museu Nacional, Universidade Federal do Rio de Janeiro
• Aquatic Biota Thematic Working Group
• Araguaia/Tocantins/Maranhão Regional Working Group e Alto Xingu/Tapajós/Rondônia/Mato Grosso

Paulo Gustavo do Prado Pereira
Conservation International
• Anthropogenic Pressures Thematic Working Group
• Araguaia/Tocantins/Maranhão Regional Working Group

Paulo Leite de Mendonça
Secretaria de Estado da Agricultura, Pesca, Floresta e do Abastecimento do Amapá
• Anthropogenic Pressures Thematic Working Group
• Guiana Shields Regional Working Group

Paulo Maurício Teixeira da Costa
• Conservation Areas Thematic Working Group

Paulo Moutinho
Instituto de Pesquisa Ambiental da Amazônia
• Environmental Goods and Services Thematic Working Group
• Lower Xingu/Tapajós/Madeira Regional Working Group

Paulo Oliveira
Fase
• New Economic Opportunities Thematic Working Group
• Solimões/Amazonas Floodplains Regional Working Group

Paulo Roberto Spósito de Oliveira
Centro de Formação e Desenvolvimento de Recursos Humanos
• New Economic Opportunities Thematic Working Group
• Guiana Shields Regional Working Group

Pedro Bara Neto
Fundação Aplicação de Tecnologias Críticas
• Development Corridors Thematic Working Group
• Juruá/Purus/Acre Regional Working Group

Pedro Garcia Tariano
Federação das Organizações Indígenas do Rio Negro
• Traditional Populations Thematic Working Group
• Rio Negro/Rio Branco Regional Working Group

Pedro Kann
• Traditional Populations Thematic Working Group

Pedro Martinelli
• Freelance photographer

Pedro Ramos de Sousa
• Traditional Populations Thematic Working Group
• Solimões/Amazonas Floodplains Regional Working Group

Rafael de Paiva Salomão
Museu Paraense Emílio Goeldi
- Environmental Goods and Services Thematic Working Group
- Araguaia/Tocantins/Maranhão Regional Working Group

Raimundo Sérgio Barros Leitão
Instituto Socioambiental
- Traditional Populations Thematic Working Group
- Upper Xingu/Tapajós/Rondônia/Mato Grosso Regional Working Group

Regina Oliveira da Silva
Museu Paraense Emílio Goeldi
- Traditional Populations Thematic Working Group
- Solimões/Amazonas Floodplains Regional Working Group

Richard Carl Vogt
Universidad Autonoma de Mexico
- Reptiles and Amphibians Thematic Working Group
- Juruá/Purus/Acre Regional Working Group

Richard Pasquis
Núcleo de Apoio de Políticas Integradas da Amazônia
- Development Corridors Thematic Working Group
- Araguaia/Tocantins/Maranhão Regional Working Group

Roberto Cavalcanti
Conservation International
- Consultor
- Guiana Shields Regional Working Group

Ronaldo Barthem
Museu Paraense Emílio Goeldi
- Aquatic Biota Thematic Working Group
- Juruá/Purus/Acre Regional Working Group

Rosa de Belém das N. Alves
Centro Nacional de Pesquisa de Recursos Genéticos e Biotecnologia
- Traditional Populations Thematic Working Group
- Araguaia/Tocantins/Maranhão Regional Working Group

Rosa M. Lemos de Sá
WWF
- Conservation Areas Thematic Working Group
- Juruá/Purus/Acre Regional Working Group

Rosa Maria de Souza Melo
Instituto de Pesquisas Científicas e Tecnológicas do Estado do Amapá
- Anthropogenic Pressures Thematic Working Group

Rosângela do Socorro F. Rodrigues
Instituto de Pesquisas Científicas e Tecnológicas do Estado do Amapá
- Plants Thematic Working Group
- Guiana Shields Regional Working Group

Ruy de Goes Leite de Barros
Greenpeace
- New Economic Opportunities Thematic Working Group
- Juruá/Purus/Acre Regional Working Group

Samuel Soares Almeida
- Plants Thematic Working Group
- Araguaia/Tocantins/Maranhão Regional Working Group

Sérgio Henrique Borges
Fundação Vitória Amazônica
- Birds Thematic Working Group
- Rio Negro/Rio Branco Regional Working Group

Silvia Maria Lopes Braga Meireles
Secretaria de Estado da Agricultura, Pesca, Floresta e do Abastecimento do Amapá
- Environmental Goods and Services Thematic Working Group
- Guiana Shields Regional Working Group

Soter Sarquis Jr.
- Guiana Shields Regional Working Group

Stephen Francis Ferrari
Universidade Federal do Pará
- Mammals Thematic Working Group
- Upper Xingu/Tapajós/Rondônia/Mato Grosso Regional Working Group e Baixo Xingu/Tapajós/Madeira

Sueli Gomes Pontes dos Santos
Secretaria de Estado da Agricultura, Pesca, Floresta e do Abastecimento do Amapá
- New Economic Opportunities Thematic Working Group
- Guiana Shields Regional Working Group

Suely Aparecida Marques–Aguiar
Museu Paraense Emílio Goeldi
- Mammals Thematic Working Group

Tania Margarete Sanaiotti
Instituto Nacional de Pesquisas da Amazônia
- Plants Thematic Working Group
- Lower Xingu/Tapajós/Madeira Regional Working Group

Teresa Cristina Sauer de Avila Pires
Nationaal Natuurhistorisch Museum
- Reptiles and Amphibians Thematic Working Group
- Guiana Shields Regional Working Group

Terezinha de Jesus Soares dos Santos
Instituto de Pesquisas Científicas e Tecnológicas do Estado do Amapá
- New Economic Opportunities Thematic Working Group

Ulisses Caramaschi
Museu Nacional, Universidade Federal do Rio de Janeiro
- Reptiles and Amphibians Thematic Working Group
- Rio Negro/Rio Branco Regional Working Group

Ulisses Galatti
Museu Paraense Emílio Goeldi
- Reptiles and Amphibians Thematic Working Group
- Juruá/Purus/Acre Regional Working Group

Urbano Lopes da Silva Jr.
Instituto de Pesquisa Ambiental da Amazônia
- Environmental Goods and Services Thematic Working Group
- Guiana Shields Regional Working Group

Valdenira Ferreira dos Santos
Instituto de Pesquisas Científicas e Tecnológicas do Estado do Amapá
- New Economic Opportunities Thematic Working Group
- Solimões/Amazonas Floodplains Regional Working Group

Valdo de Freitas Felinto
Instituto de Tecnologia Intuitiva e Bio-Arquitetura
- New Economic Opportunities Thematic Working Group
- Solimões/Amazonas Floodplains Regional Working Group

Vera Maria F. Da Silva
Instituto Nacional de Pesquisas da Amazônia
- Aquatic Biota Thematic Working Group
- Solimões/Amazonas Floodplains Regional Working Group

Veronica Passos
Secretaria de Ciência, Tecnologia e Meio Ambiente do Acre
- Conservation Areas Thematic Working Group
- Juruá/Purus/Acre Regional Working Group

Vicent Brackelaire
European Commission
- Traditional Populations Thematic Working Group
- Rio Negro/Rio Branco Regional Working Group

Victor Py–Daniel
Instituto Nacional de Pesquisas da Amazônia
- Aquatic Biota Thematic Working Group
- Rio Negro/Rio Branco Regional Working Group

Waldeci Marques Gibson
Instituto de Pesquisas Científicas e Tecnológicas do Estado do Amapá
- Conservation Areas Thematic Working Group

Wildma Mota de Moraes
Secretaria de Estado da Educação
- Development Corridors Thematic Working Group

William Leslie Overal
Museu Paraense Emílio Goeldi
- Invertebrates Thematic Working Group
- Solimões/Amazonas Floodplains Regional Working Group

Wilson da Silva Moraes
Instituto de Pesquisas Científicas e Tecnológicas do Estado do Amapá
- Plants Thematic Working Group
- Guiana Shields Regional Working Group

Yucatan Teixeira da Silva
Independent consultant
- Development Corridors Thematic Working Group
- Lower Xingu/Tapajós/Madeira Regional Working Group

Photographic credits

Front cover *A Waiãpi indian holding a medicinal plant, Amapá*
Michel Pellanders (1996)

Back cover *Xingu river, Xingu Indigenous Park, Mato Grosso*
Pedro Martinelli (1999)

Spine *Orchid*
Araquém Alcântara (n.d.)

17 *Juruá river, Acre*
Araquém Alcântara (2000)

18/19 *Xingu river, Xingu Indigenous Park, Mato Grosso*
Pedro Martinelli (1999)

20 (top and center) *Flora of the Amazonia National Park, Pará*
Araquém Alcântara (1997)

20 (bottom) *Periquitambóia (Boa canina) on the upper Trombetas river, Pará*
Araquém Alcântara (1999)

21 (top) *Lower Amazon floodplain, Monte Alegre, Pará*
Araquém Alcântara (1999)

21 (bottom) *Children on the Araçá river, Barcelos Amazonas*
Araquém Alcântara (1999)

22 (top) *Rubber tapper, Moa river, Serra do Divisor National Park, Acre*
Araquém Alcântara (2000)

22 (bottom) *Riverbank resident, Juruá river, Acre*
Araquém Alcântara (2000)

23 *Erepecuru river, Oriximiná, Pará*
Araquém Alcântara (2000)

24/25 *Lençóis river, Reentrâncias Maranhenses, Maranhão*
Araquém Alcântara (1997)

26 (top) *Ingariko indian, Raposa Indigenous Land, Serra do Sol, Roraima*
Araquém Alcântara (1996)

26 (bottom) *Festival of Saint Benedict in a community of descendents of escaped slaves, Trombetas river, Pará*
Araquém Alcântara (2000)

27 (top) *Port of Manaus, Amazonas*
Araquém Alcântara (2001)

27 (bottom) *Rio Negro, São Gabriel da Cachoeira, Amazonas*
Beto Ricardo (1997)

28 (top) *Riverbank residents, Araçá river, Amazonas*
Araquém Alcântara (1999)

28 (center) *Ararajuba (Aratinga guarouba) on the Curuá river, northern Pará*
Araquém Alcântara (1998)

28 (bottom left) *Youth from a Brazil nut collecting community, Trombetas river, Pará*
Araquém Alcântara (1999)

28 (bottom right) *Jaguatirica (Felis pardalis), Amazonia National Park, Pará*
Araquém Alcântara (1998)

29 (top) *Riverbank vegetation, Rio Negro, Amazonas*
Araquém Alcântara (1997)

29 (bottom) *Porto Alegre, Reentrâncias Maranhenses, Maranhão*
Araquém Alcântara (2001)

30/31 *Floodplain near the Quilombo Silêncio do Mata-Mata, Óbidos, Pará*
Araquém Alcântara (1999)

32 (top left) *Biguá (Phalacrocorax ssp), Mamirauá Sustainable Development Reserve, Amazonas*
Araquém Alcântara (2000)

32 (center) *Caterpillars, Araguaia National Park, Tocantins*
Araquém Alcântara (1996)

32 (top right) *Riverbank resident, Moa river, Acre*
Araquém Alcântara (2000)

32 (bottom) *Vila Moura, Rio Negro, Amazonas*
Araquém Alcântara (1998)

33 (top) *Mariuá archipelago, Rio Negro, Barcelos, Amazonas*
Araquém Alcântara (2000)

33 (bottom) *Riverboat transporting bundles of piassava palm, Araçá river, Barcelos, Amazonas*
Araquém Alcântara (2000)

34 (top) *Felling and transporting timber, Rio Negro, Amazonas*
Araquém Alcântara (1997)

34 (bottom) *Fisherman and fig tree, Mamirauá Sustainable Development Reserve, Amazonas*
Araquém Alcântara (2000)

35 *Pau-mulato (*Calycophyllum spruceanum*), Amazonia National Park, Pará*
Araquém Alcântara (1995)

36 *Pink porpoise leaping, Mamirauá, Amazonas*
Paulo Santos (n.d.)

37 *City of Belém, Pará*
Paulo Santos (n.d.)

38 (top) *Cutting timber submerged by the reservoir of the Tucuruí hydroelectric plant, Pará*
Paulo Santos (s/ano)

38 (bottom) *Cattle raising in degraded forest, Pará*
Araquém Alcântara (1997)

39 (top left) *Boundary between cleared forest and the Xingu Indigenous Park, which remains one of the last conserved areas in northern Mato Grosso*
Pedro Martinelli (1999)

39 (top right) *Gold prospecting raft, Madeira river, Rondônia*
Araquém Alcântara (1996)

39 (bottom) *Sawmill, Ariquemes, Rondônia*
Araquém Alcântara (1996)

40 (top) *Fishing, Juruá river, Acre*
Araquém Alcântara (2000)

40 (center) *Fishing, Marajó island, Pará*
Araquém Alcântara (1997)

40 (bottom) *Collecting piassava palm, Araçá river, Barcelos, Amazonas*
Araquém Alcântara (2000)

40/41 *Rio Negro, Amazonas*
Araquém Alcântara (1998)

42 (top) *Forest, Xingu National Park, Mato Grosso*
Pedro Martinelli (1999)

42 (center) *Burning, Roraima*
Araquém Alcântara (1998)

42 (bottom) *Burning and deforestation on the boundaries of the Xingu Indigenous Park, Mato Grosso*
Pedro Martinelli (1999)

43 *Burning, Amazonas National Park, Pará*
Araquém Alcântara (1997)

44 (top) *Oriximiná, Amazonas river, Pará*
Araquém Alcântara (1999)

44 (bottom) *Fishing, Marajó island, Pará*
Araquém Alcântara (1997)

45 (top left) *Riverbank resident, Araçá river, Barcelos, Amazonas*
Araquém Alcântara (2000)

45 (top right) *Girl at school, Juruá river community, Acre*
Araquém Alcântara (2000)

45 (center) *Boy from a fishing community, Soure, Marajó island, Pará*
Araquém Alcântara (1997)

45 (bottom) *Coripaco indian village on the upper Içana, São Gabriel da Cachoeira, Amazonas*
Beto Ricardo (1997)

46 (top) *Ground-growing bromeliad, top of Mount Roraima, Roraima*
Araquém Alcântara (1997)

46 (bottom left) *Galo-da-serra (*Rupicola rupicola*), Presidente Figueiredo, Amazonas*
Araquém Alcântara (2001)

46 (bottom right) *Epiphyte, Amazonas river, Amazonas*
Araquém Alcântara (1997)

47 *Pupunha (spiny peachpalm) tree (*Guilielma speciosa*), Pico da Neblina National Park, Amazonas*
Araquém Alcântara (1997)

48 (top left) *Makuxi indian infant girl, Roraima*
Araquém Alcântara (1998)

48 (top right) *Assai palm (*Euterpe oleracea*), Amazonia National Park, Pará*
Araquém Alcântara (1998)

48 (bottom) *Panará indian village, Mato Grosso*
Pedro Martinelli (1999)

THIS BOOK WAS SET IN GATINEAU AND FUTURA LIGHT AND PRINTED IN SÃO PAULO, BRAZIL, IN JUNE 2004 BY LIS GRAFICA ON COATED PAPER IMAGE MATE 90 g/m^2, PRODUCED BY RIPASA S/A PULP AND PAPER IN HARMONY WITH THE ENVIRONMENT

IMAGE MATE